THE SCOTTISH PSALTER 1929

AND SCRIPTURE PARAPHRASES

THE

SCOTTISH PSALTER

1929

METRICAL VERSION AND
SCRIPTURE PARAPHRASES

With Tunes

GEOFFREY CUMBERLEGE
OXFORD UNIVERSITY PRESS
London Glasgow New York

14 *R. Crown* 8vo *Sol-fa*

Oxford University Press, Amen House, London E.C.4
GLASGOW NEW YORK TORONTO MELBOURNE WELLINGTON
BOMBAY CALCUTTA MADRAS KARACHI CAPE TOWN IBADAN
Geoffrey Cumberlege, Publisher to the University

THE SCOTTISH PSALTER 1929

METRICAL VERSION AND SCRIPTURE PARAPHRASES, WITH AUTHORIZED VERSION, POINTED, WITH CHANTS. *Sol-fa.* In one volume.

METRICAL VERSION AND SCRIPTURE PARAPHRASES. Separately. *Staff* or *Sol-fa.*

AUTHORIZED VERSION, POINTED, WITH CHANTS. Separately. *Staff* or *Sol-fa.*

METRICAL PSALMS WITH AUTHORIZED VERSION. WORDS ONLY, POINTED FOR CHANTING. In one volume.

METRICAL PSALMS. WORDS ONLY. Separately.

AUTHORIZED VERSION, WORDS ONLY, POINTED FOR CHANTING. Separately.

PRINTED IN GREAT BRITAIN

PREFACE

THE publication of the *Scottish Psalter, 1929*, was authorized in 1928 by the General Assemblies of the Church of Scotland and the United Free Church of Scotland, and its appearance coincides with the union of the two Churches.

With a view to promoting a more general use of the Metrical Psalter and likewise to securing some measure of uniformity in the association of tunes with particular Psalms, the Committee entrusted with the work of revision have prepared a List of selected portions of the Psalms and Paraphrases most suitable for use in public worship, with references to appropriate tunes. The Psalms and Paraphrases from which selections have been made are marked with an asterisk. An index has been compiled of the selected portions classified according to subjects.

A compelling motive for the preparation of the present Psalter was the desire to make such tunes as were common to the Psalter and the *Revised Church Hymnary* correspond in respect both of form and harmony. The compilers of the *Revised Church Hymnary* sought not only to bring back to use in our churches a large number of the tunes of the original Scottish Psalters which had not been included in the Psalters published in the latter half of the nineteenth century, but also to restore the original forms and rhythms, which in the later Psalters had been conformed to one common type and thereby robbed of their most distinctive features. In this Psalter likewise the older tunes have been restored to the original forms, which have more character and beauty than the arrangements familiar to recent generations. With a little use our congregations will become familiar with the change, and they will find that, if properly rendered, the original forms are calculated to brighten and improve congregational singing. Those who prefer the forms to which they are accustomed can still use them by making the notes of these tunes of equal length. The tunes which also appear in the *Revised Church Hymnary* are here reproduced without change with the following exceptions: in 'Kilmarnock', the more familiar harmony of previous books has been retained; in two other cases slight changes in the progressions of a part have been made, and in 'St. Anne' the first note of each line has been lengthened.

In the early Scottish Psalters the melody or people's part was given to the tenor, while the other parts supplied the harmony. This ancient practice of weaving parts round the tune in the tenor has been revived in recent times in what is commonly known as

'Faux-bourdon', wherein the congregation sings one or more verses to the melody while the choir supplies the harmony. 'Descant' is another old and beautiful variation in the use of tunes. In this form one or more verses of a Psalm are sung in unison by the congregation and choir, while a second melody over that of the tune—the top part of the Descant setting—is supplied by a few sopranos, the lower harmonies being reserved for the organ. Several Faux-bourdons and Descants are introduced into this Psalter in the hope that they may prove serviceable. They are, however, recommended for use only where there is a strong body of congregational singing in unison, and where the spirit of the words is vigorous and confident. In most cases it will be advisable to announce to the congregation the verses to which they will be sung. In rendering them it must always be borne in mind that these special treatments are but an embellishment of the melody of the tune, which is the main centre of interest. It is of the utmost importance that in the Faux-bourdon the choir should supply an unobtrusive background of harmony, and that in the Descant the upper part reserved for a few sopranos should be no more than audible. Otherwise the purpose of these varied settings will be defeated.

Another feature of interest in the present Psalter is the provision in the Staff notation editions of a number of varied organ accompaniments for unison singing. The Faux-bourdon and Descant settings, instead of being sung by the choir, may also be used as instrumental accompaniments.

G. Wauchope Stewart, *Convener of Committee.*
T. C. L. Pritchard, *Musical Editor.*

.625.

CONTENTS

ACKNOWLEDGEMENTS

PERMISSION to use copyright tunes has been granted as stated below. *An asterisk denotes that permission has been obtained on payment of a fee.*

COMPOSER	OWNER OF COPYRIGHT	NO. OF TUNE
Anderson, J. S.	*Oxford University Press	149.
Grace, Harvey	*The Faith Press, Ltd.	92 (Faux-bourdon from the 'Tenor Tune Book').
Gray, Alan	*Cambridge University Press	12, 13, 51, 61, 82, 85, 105, 114, 115, 144, 164 (from 'A Book of Descants').
Poole, C. W.	*Miss M. Morley Horder	156.
Pritchard, T. C. L.	*Oxford University Press	9, 42, 143, 181, 183, 185 (Descants and Faux-bourdons). App. to Staff notation editions 13, 27, 73, 120, 134, 144 (Varied Accompaniments).
Raymond-Barker, Mrs. E.	Rev. C. Raymond-Barker	44.
Shaw, Geoffrey T.	*The Faith Press, Ltd.	122 (Faux-bourdon from the 'Tenor Tune Book').
Shaw, Martin	*Messrs. J. Curwen & Sons, Ltd.	52, 100 (Faux-bourdons from Curwen Edition No. 6300).
Stewart, C. Hylton	*Messrs. J. Curwen & Sons, Ltd.	98 (from Curwen Edition No. 80632).
Strong, Right Rev. T. B., D.D.	*Oxford University Press	67.

Thanks are also due to the following:

Cockburn, R. W.		38, 128, 182.
,,	*Oxford University Press	App. to Staff notation editions 13.
Miss Stanford		102.

The following tunes have been harmonized or adapted by the Musical Editor:

Nos. 22, 41, 43, 47, 49, 65, 69, 88, 90, 93, 94, 99, 108, 119, 151, 153, 160, 174, 184, 188, 191, 192.

The following tunes have been harmonized or adapted by the Musical Editor of the Revised Church Hymnary:

Nos. 1, 4, 6, 8, 9, 12, 14, 17, 20, 24, 28, 36, 51, 52, 57, 58, 64, 74, 78, 86, App. 86, 112, 120, 124, 127, 133, 140, 152, 155, 158, 165, 170, 177.

1

FIRST (ORIGINAL) FORM

(SONG 34). (L.M.)

ORLANDO GIBBONS, 1583–1625.

d :d | r :— | m :— | f :r | s :— || d :m :f | s :—:r | s :—:fe | s :—:— ||
| s_1:d | t_1:— | d :— | l_1:t_1 | d :— || s_1:d :d | r :—:t_1 | d :r :— | t_1:—:— ||
— | m :m | s :— | s :— | f :f | m :— || m :s :f | r :—:s | s :l :— | s :—:— ||
:— | d :d | s :— | m :— | r :r | d :— || d :d :l_1 | t_1:—:s_1 | m :r :— | s_1:—:— ||

m :f :s | l :—:s | f :—:m | r :—:— || s :f :m | r :— :d | m :r :— | d :—:— || d | d ||
d :d :r.m | f :m :r | d :r :d | t_1:—:— || d :d :d | d :t_1 :l_1 | d :d :t_1 | d :—:— || l_1 | s_1 ||
s :d^1:ta | l :—:t | d^1:s :s | s :—:— || s :l :s | s :-.f:m | s :s :— | m :—:— || f | m ||
d :l_1:s_1 | f_1:—:s_1 | l_1:t_1 :d | s_1:—:— || m_1:f_1:d | s_1:— :l_1 | m_1:s_1:— | d :—:— || f_1 | d ||

A-men.

THE PSALMS OF DAVID

IN METRE

1*

THAT man hath perfect blessedness
who walketh not astray
In counsel of ungodly men,
nor stands in sinners' way,
Nor sitteth in the scorner's chair:
2 But placeth his delight
Upon God's law, and meditates
on his law day and night.

3 He shall be like a tree that grows
near planted by a river,
Which in his season yields his fruit,
and his leaf fadeth never:
And all he doth shall prosper well.
4 The wicked are not so;
But like they are unto the chaff,
which wind drives to and fro.

5 In judgment therefore shall not stand
such as ungodly are;
Nor in th' assembly of the just
shall wicked men appear.

6 For why? the way of godly men
unto the Lord is known:
Whereas the way of wicked men
shall quite be overthrown.

2

WHY rage the heathen? and vain things
why do the people mind?
2 Kings of the earth do set themselves,
and princes are combin'd,
To plot against the Lord, and his
Anointed, saying thus,
3 Let us asunder break their bands,
and cast their cords from us.

4 He that in heaven sits shall laugh;
the Lord shall scorn them all.
5 Then shall he speak to them in wrath,
in rage he vex them shall.

2

SECOND FORM

ANGELS' SONG. (L.M.)

Doh = F. Adapted from Orlando Gibbon[s]

:d	d :— :d	r :— :m	f :— :r	s
:s_1	s_1 :— :d	t_1 :— :d	l_1 :— :t_1	d
:m	m :— :m	s :— :s	f :— :f	m :
:d	d :— :d	s :— :m	r :— :r	d :—

:d	m :— :f	s :— :r	s :— :fe	s :— ‖
:s_1	d :— :d	r :— :t_1	d :r :—	t_1 :— ‖
:m	s :— :f	r :— :s	s :l :—	s :— ‖
:d	d :— :l_1	t_1 :— :s_1	m :r :—	s_1 :— ‖

PSALMS II, III, IV.

6 Yet, notwithstanding, I have him
to be my King appointed;
And over Sion, my holy hill,
I have him King anointed.

7 The sure decree I will declare;
the Lord hath said to me,
Thou art mine only Son; this day
I have begotten thee.

8 Ask of me, and for heritage
the heathen I'll make thine;
And, for possession, I to thee
will give earth's utmost line.

9 Thou shalt, as with a weighty rod
of iron, break them all;
And, as a potter's sherd, thou shalt
them dash in pieces small.

10 Now, therefore, kings, be wise; be
ye judges of the earth: [taught,
11 Serve God in fear, and see that ye
join trembling with your mirth.

12 Kiss ye the Son, lest in his ire
ye perish from the way,
If once his wrath begin to burn:
bless'd all that on him stay.

3

O LORD, how are my foes increas'd?
against me many rise.

2 Many say of my soul, For him
in God no succour lies.

3 Yet thou my shield and glory art,
th' uplifter of mine head.

4 I cry'd, and, from his holy hill,
the Lord me answer made.

5 I laid me down and slept, I wak'd;
for God sustained me.

6 I will not fear though thousands ten
set round against me be.

7 Arise, O Lord; save me, my God;
for thou my foes hast stroke
All on the cheek-bone, and the teeth
of wicked men hast broke.

8 Salvation doth appertain
unto the Lord alone:
Thy blessing, Lord, for evermore
thy people is upon.

4*

GIVE ear unto me when I call,
God of my righteousness:
Have mercy, hear my pray'r; thou
enlarg'd me in distress. [hast

2 O ye the sons of men! how long
will ye love vanities?
How long my glory turn to shame,
and will ye follow lies?

:m	f :— :s	l :— :s	f :— :m	r :—
:d	d :— :r.m	f :m :r	d :r :d	t_1 :—
:s	d^1 :— :ta	l :— :t	d^1 :s :s	s :—
:d	l_1 :— :s_1	f_1 :— :s_1	l_1 :t_1 :d	s_1 :—

:s	f :— :m	r :— :d	m :r :—	d :—	d	d
:d	d :— :d	d :t_1 :l_1	d :d :t_1	d :—	l_1	s_1
:s	l :— :s	s :—.f :m	s :s :—	m :—	f	m
:m_1	f_1 :— :d	s_1 :— :l_1	m_1 :s_1 :—	d :—	f_1	d

A - men.

PSALMS IV, V.

3 But know, that for himself the Lord
the godly man doth chuse:
The Lord, when I on him do call,
to hear will not refuse.
4 Fear, and sin not; talk with your
on bed, and silent be. [heart
5 Off'rings present of righteousness,
and in the Lord trust ye.

6 O who will shew us any good?
is that which many say:
But of thy countenance the light,
Lord, lift on us alway.
7 Upon my heart, bestow'd by thee,
more gladness I have found
Than they, ev'n then, when corn and
wine
did most with them abound.

8 I will both lay me down in peace,
and quiet sleep will take;
Because thou only me to dwell
in safety, Lord, dost make.

5*

GIVE ear unto my words, O Lord,
my meditation weigh.
2 Hear my loud cry, my King, my God;
for I to thee will pray.

3 Lord, thou shalt early hear my
I early will direct [voice:
My pray'r to thee; and, looking up,
an answer will expect.

4 For thou art not a God that doth
in wickedness delight;
Neither shall evil dwell with thee,
5 Nor fools stand in thy sight.
All that ill-doers are thou hat'st;
6 Cutt'st off that liars be:
The bloody and deceitful man
abhorred is by thee.

7 But I into thy house will come
in thine abundant grace;
And I will worship in thy fear
toward thy holy place.
8 Because of those mine enemies,
Lord, in thy righteousness
Do thou me lead; do thou thy way
make straight before my face.

9 For in their mouth there is no truth,
their inward part is ill;
Their throat 's an open sepulchre,
their tongue doth flatter still.
10 O God, destroy them; let them be
by their own counsel quell'd:
Them for their many sins cast out,
for they 'gainst thee rebell'd.

BRESLAU. (L.M.)

As Hymnodus Sacer, Leipsic, 1625.
Arranged by Felix Mendelssohn Bartholdy, 1809–47.

Doh = G.

```
:d     |d     :d      |l,  :d   |r      :t,      |l,  || l,  |t,  :d   |r   :s,.l, |t,  :l,   |s,  ||
:m,.f, |s,.l, :ta,.s, |f,  :s,  |f,     :r,.m,   |d,  || f,  |s,  :s,  |s,  :s,    |s,  :fe,  |s,  ||
:d     |d     :m      |f   :d   |d .t,  :l,.se,  |l,  || d   |r   :m   |f   :m     |r   :-.d  |t,  ||
:l,    |m,    :d,     |f,  :m,  |r,     :m,      |l,  || f,  |f,  :m,  |t,, :d,    |r,  :r,   |s,  ||

:s,    |d  :r  |m  :d  |f    :m     |r  || r     |m  :s  |f     :m    |r  :r  |d  || d  |d  ||
:s,    |s, :f, |m, :l, |l,   :s,    |s, || l,    |s, :s, |l,    :s,.d |d  :t, |d  || l, |s, ||
:s,    |l, :t, |d  :d  |d.t, :d     |t, || l,.t, |d  :m  |d .r  :m    |f  :r  |m  || f  |m  ||
:s,.f, |m, :r, |d, :f, |r,   :m,.f, |s, || f,    |m, :d, |l,.t, :d    |s, :s, |d, || f, |d, ||
                                                                                     A-men.
```

PSALMS V, VI.

11 But let all joy that trust in thee,
and still make shouting noise;
For them thou sav'st: let all that
thy name in thee rejoice. [love
12 For, Lord, unto the righteous man
thou wilt thy blessing yield:
With favour thou wilt compass him
about, as with a shield.

6

LORD, in thy wrath rebuke me not;
Nor in thy hot rage chasten me.
2 Lord, pity me, for I am weak:
Heal me, for my bones vexed be.
3 My soul is also vexed sore;
But, Lord, how long stay wilt thou
make?
4 Return, O Lord, my soul set free;
O save me, for thy mercies' sake.

5 Because those that deceased are
Of thee shall no remembrance have;
And who is he that will to thee
Give praises lying in the grave?
6 I with my groaning weary am,
I also all the night my bed
Have caused for to swim; and I
With tears my couch have watered.

7 Mine eye, consum'd with grief,
grows old,
Because of all mine enemies.
8 Hence from me, wicked workers all;
For God hath heard my weeping
cries.
9 God hath my supplication heard,
My pray'r received graciously. [foes,
10 Sham'd and sore vex'd be all my
Sham'd and back turned suddenly.

6 (2)

ANOTHER OF THE SAME.

IN thy great indignation,
O Lord, rebuke me not;
Nor on me lay thy chast'ning hand
in thy displeasure hot.
2 Lord, I am weak, therefore on me
have mercy, and me spare:
Heal me, O Lord, because thou
know'st
my bones much vexed are.

3 My soul is vexed sore: but, Lord,
how long stay wilt thou make?
4 Return, Lord, free my soul; and
me, for thy mercies' sake. [save
5 Because of thee in death there shall
no more remembrance be:

4

BROCKHAM (CONFIDENCE). (L.M.) JEREMIAH CLARK, *c.* 1659–1707.

Doh = G.

:s_1 |d :r |m :t_1 |d :r |t_1 ‖ r |f :-.f |m :d |m :fe |s ‖
:s_1 |s_1 :s_1 |s_1 :-.f_1 |m_1 :l_1 |s_1 ‖ t_1 |l_1 :-.l_1 |s_1 :s_1 |s_1 :d |t_1 ‖
:s_1 |d :t_1 |d :r |d :f |r ‖ s |d :-.r |m :s |m.r :d |r ‖
:s_1 |m_1 :s_1 |d :s_1 |l_1 :f_1 |s_1 ‖ s_1 |l_1 :-.t_1 |d :m |d.t_1 :l_1 |s_1 ‖

:s |m :d |l_1 :m |f :r |t_1 ‖ s_1 |d :-.r |m :s |m :r.d |d ‖ d |d ‖
:r |d :s_1 |l_1 :s_1 |f_1 :l_1 |s_1 ‖ s_1 |s_1 :-.t_1 |d :s_1 |d :t_1.d |s_1 ‖ l_1 |s_1 ‖
:s |s :d |d :de |r :r |r ‖ s_1 |s :-.f |m :d |s :f |m ‖ f |m ‖
:t_1 |d :m_1 |f_1 :m_1 |r_1 :f_1 |s_1 ‖ s_1.f_1 |m_1 :-.r_1 |d_1 :m_1 |s_1 :s_1 |d_1 ‖ f_1 |d_1 ‖

A-men.

PSALMS VI, VII.

Of those that in the grave do lie,
who shall give thanks to thee?
6 I with my groaning weary am,
and all the night my bed
I caused for to swim; with tears
my couch I watered.
7 By reason of my vexing grief
mine eye consumed is;
It waxeth old, because of all
that be mine enemies.
8 But now, depart from me all ye
that work iniquity: [voice,
For why? the Lord hath heard my
when I did mourn and cry.
9 Unto my supplication
the Lord did hearing give:
When I to him my prayer make,
the Lord will it receive.
10 Let all be sham'd and troubled sore,
that en'mies are to me;
Let them turn back, and suddenly
ashamed let them be.

7

O LORD my God, in thee do I
my confidence repose:
Save and deliver me from all
my persecuting foes;

2 Lest that the enemy my soul
should, like a lion, tear,
In pieces rending it, while there
is no deliverer.

3 O Lord my God, if it be so
that I committed this;
If it be so that in my hands
iniquity there is:
4 If I rewarded ill to him
that was at peace with me;
(Yea, ev'n the man that without
cause
my foe was I did free;)

5 Then let the foe pursue and take
my soul, and my life thrust
Down to the earth, and let him lay
mine honour in the dust.
6 Rise in thy wrath, Lord, raise thyself,
for my foes raging be;
And, to the judgment which thou
hast
commanded, wake for me.

7 So shall th' assembly of thy folk
about encompass thee:
Thou, therefore, for their sakes, return
unto thy place on high.

CANNONS. (L.M.) GEORGE FREDERICK HANDEL, 1685-1759.

Lah = F. Doh = A♭.

l_1 :m_1.,se_1	l_1 :t_1	d :-.r	t_1 :—	d :s_1.,t_1	d :r	m :-.f	r (fermata)
m_1 :m_1.,r_1	m_1 :m_1	l_1 :l_1	se_1 :—	l_1 :s_1.,f_1	s_1 :s_1	s_1 :l_1	s_1
d :d.,r	d :m	m :f	m :—	m :d.,r	m :r	d :d	t_1
l_1 :d.,t_1	l_1 :se_1	l_1 :r_1	m_1 :—	l_1 :m_1.,r_1	d_1 :t_2	d_1 :f_1	s_1

:m	f :-.m	r :-.d	t_1:l_1	se_1 (fermata)	t_1	m :l_1	r.m:d.t_1	t_1:-.l_1	l_1:— (fermata)	l_1	l_1
:s_1	f_1:s_1	l_1:s_1	f_1:r_1	m_1	se_1	l_1:l_1	se_1 :l_1	l_1:se_1	l_1:—	f_1	m_1
:t_1	d :t_1	l_1:d	r :l_1	t_1	m	m :f.m	r :m	m :r	d :—	r	de
:s_1	l_1:s_1	f_1:m_1	r_1:f_1	m_1	r_1	d_1:r_1.d_1	t_2 :l_2	m_1:m_1	l_2:—	r_1	l_2

A-men.

PSALMS VII, VIII.

8 The Lord he shall the people judge:
my judge, JEHOVAH, be,
After my righteousness, and mine
integrity in me.

9 O let the wicked's malice end;
but stablish stedfastly [God
The righteous: for the righteous
the hearts and reins doth try.

10 In God, who saves th' upright in
is my defence and stay. [heart,

11 God just men judgeth, God is wroth
with ill men ev'ry day.

12 If he do not return again,
then he his sword will whet;
His bow he hath already bent,
and hath it ready set:

13 He also hath for him prepar'd
the instruments of death;
Against the persecutors he
his shafts ordained hath.

14 Behold, he with iniquity
doth travail, as in birth;
A mischief he conceived hath,
and falsehood shall bring forth.

15 He made a pit, and digg'd it deep,
another there to take;
But he is fall'n into the ditch
which he himself did make.

16 Upon his own head his mischief
shall be returned home;
His vi'lent dealing also down
on his own pate shall come.

17 According to his righteousness
the Lord I'll magnify;
And will sing praise unto the name
of God that is most high.

8*

HOW excellent in all the earth,
Lord, our Lord, is thy name!
Who hast thy glory far advanc'd
above the starry frame.

2 From infants' and from sucklings' mouth
thou didest strength ordain,
For thy foes' cause, that so thou might'st
th' avenging foe restrain.

3 When I look up into the heav'ns,
which thine own fingers fram'd,
Unto the moon, and to the stars,
which were by thee ordain'd;

4 Then say I, What is man, that he
remember'd is by thee?
Or what the son of man, that thou
so kind to him should'st be?

COMMANDMENTS. (L.M.) *French Psalter*, 1549.

Doh = G.

```
:d  |d  :r  |m  :m  |f  :m  |r  ||m  |f    :m    |r  :d  |t,  :d  |r  ||
:s, |l, :t, |d  :d  |d  :d  |t, ||s, |d    :d    |t, :l, |se, :m, |s, ||
:m  |m  :s  |s  :d  |l  :s  |s  ||d  |d.r  :m.f  |s  :m  |m   :d  |t, ||
:d  |l, :s, |d  :l, |f, :d, |s, ||d  |l,   :d    |s, :l, |m,  :l, |s, ||

:s  |f  :m    |r  :t, |d  :l,   |s, ||m  |f    :m    |r  :d  |m      :r    |d  ||d  |d  ||
:t, |r  :d.t, |l, :s, |s, :fe,  |s, ||s, |d    :d    |t, :l, |s,     :-.f, |m, ||f, |m, ||
:r  |l  :s    |f  :r  |m  :r.d  |t, ||d  |d.r  :m.f  |s  :m  |d      :t,   |d  ||l, |s, ||
:s, |r, :m,   |f, :s, |d, :r,   |s, ||d  |l,   :d    |s, :l, |m,.f,  :s,   |d, ||f, |d, ||
                                                                                 A-men.
```

PSALMS VIII, IX.

5 For thou a little lower hast
him than the angels made;
With glory and with dignity
thou crowned hast his head.

6 Of thy hands' works thou mad'st him lord,
all under 's feet didst lay;

7 All sheep and oxen, yea, and beasts
that in the field do stray;

8 Fowls of the air, fish of the sea,
All that pass through the same.

9 How excellent in all the earth,
Lord, our Lord, is thy name!

9*

LORD, thee I'll praise with all my [heart,
thy wonders all proclaim.

2 In thee, most High, I'll greatly joy,
and sing unto thy name.

3 When back my foes were turn'd, they fell,
and perish'd at thy sight: [cause;

4 For thou maintain'dst my right and
on throne sat'st judging right.

5 The heathen thou rebuked hast,
the wicked overthrown;
Thou hast put out their names, that [they
may never more be known.

6 O en'my! now destructions have
an end perpetual:
Thou cities raz'd, perish'd with them
is their memorial.

7 God shall endure for aye; he doth
for judgment set his throne;

8 In righteousness to judge the world,
justice to give each one.

9 God also will a refuge be
for those that are oppress'd;
A refuge will he be in times
of trouble to distress'd.

10 And they that know thy name, in [thee
their confidence will place:
For thou hast not forsaken them
that truly seek thy face.

11 O sing ye praises to the Lord
that dwells in Sion hill;
And all the nations among
his deeds record ye still.

12 When he enquireth after blood,
he then rememb'reth them:
The humble folk he not forgets
that call upon his name.

13 Lord, pity me; behold the grief
which I from foes sustain;
Ev'n thou, who from the gates of [death
dost raise me up again;

7

CRASSELIUS. (L.M.)

Doh = B♭.

Musikalisch Hand-Buch, Hamburg, 1690.

:s_1	d :s_1	l_1 :l_1	s_1 :f_1	m_1 ‖
:m_1	s_1 :m_1	f_1 :f_1 .m_1	r_1 :t_2	d_1 ‖
:d	d :d	d :f_1	s_1 :s_1	s_1 ‖
:d_1	m_1 :d_1	f_1 :r_1 .d_1	t_2 :s_2	d_1 ‖

:m_1	f_1 :m_1	r_1 :s_1	s_1 :fe_1	𝄐 s_1 ‖
:d_1	d_1 :d_1	r_1 :m_1	m_1 :r_1	r_1 ‖
:s_1	l_1 :s_1 .l_1	t_1 :t_1	d .t_1 :l_1	t_1 ‖
:d_1	l_2 :d_1	s_2 :m_1	d_1 :r_1	s_2 ‖

PSALMS IX, X.

14 That I, in Sion's daughters' gates,
may all thy praise advance;
And that I may rejoice always
in thy deliverance.
15 The heathen are sunk in the pit
which they themselves prepar'd;
And in the net which they have hid
their own feet fast are snar'd.

16 The Lord is by the judgment known
which he himself hath wrought:
The sinners' hands do make the snares
wherewith themselves are caught.
17 They who are wicked into hell
each one shall turned be;
And all the nations that forget
to seek the Lord most high.

18 For they that needy are shall not
forgotten be alway;
The expectation of the poor
shall not be lost for aye.
19 Arise, Lord, let not man prevail;
judge heathen in thy sight:
20 That they may know themselves but men,
the nations, Lord, affright.

10

WHEREFORE is it that thou, O Lord,
dost stand from us afar?
And wherefore hidest thou thyself
when times so troublous are?
2 The wicked in his loftiness
doth persecute the poor:
In these devices they have fram'd
let them be taken sure.

3 The wicked of his heart's desire
doth talk with boasting great;
He blesseth him that 's covetous,
whom yet the Lord doth hate.
4 The wicked, through his pride of face,
on God he doth not call;
And in the counsels of his heart
the Lord is not at all.

5 His ways they always grievous are;
thy judgments from his sight
Removed are: at all his foes
he puffeth with despight.
6 Within his heart he thus hath said,
I shall not moved be;
And no adversity at all
shall ever come to me.

:s_1	d	:r	m	:d	f	:m	r		
:s_1	s_1	:f_1	m_1	:l_1 .s_1	f_1	:s_1	s_1		
:t_1	d	:l_1 .t_1	d	:d	d .t_1	:d	t_1		
:s_1 .f_1	m_1	:r_1	d_1	:f_1 .m_1	r_1	:m_1 .f_1	s_1		

:m	d	:l_1	s_1	:d	d	:t_1	d (fermata)	d	d
:s_1	s_1	:f_1	s_1	:m_1	l_1	:s_1	s_1	l_1	s_1
:d	d	:d	d	:d	r	:r	m	f	m
:d_1	m_1	:f_1	m_1	:l_1	f_1	:s_1	d_1	f_1	d_1

A-men.

PSALM X.

7 His mouth with cursing, fraud, deceit,
is fill'd abundantly;
And underneath his tongue there is
mischief and vanity.
8 He closely sits in villages;
he slays the innocent:
Against the poor that pass him by
his cruel eyes are bent.

9 He, lion-like, lurks in his den;
he waits the poor to take;
And when he draws him in his net,
his prey he doth him make.
10 Himself he humbleth very low,
he croucheth down withal,
That so a multitude of poor
may by his strong ones fall.

11 He thus hath said within his heart,
The Lord hath quite forgot;
He hides his countenance, and he
for ever sees it not.
12 O Lord, do thou arise; O God,
lift up thine hand on high:
Put not the meek afflicted ones
out of thy memory.

13 Why is it that the wicked man
thus doth the Lord despise?
Because that God will it require
he in his heart denies.
14 Thou hast it seen; for their mischief
and spite thou wilt repay:
The poor commits himself to thee;
thou art the orphan's stay.

15 The arm break of the wicked man,
and of the evil one;
Do thou seek out his wickedness,
until thou findest none.
16 The Lord is king through ages all,
ev'n to eternity;
The heathen people from his land
are perish'd utterly.

17 O Lord, of those that humble are
thou the desire didst hear;
Thou wilt prepare their heart, and thou
to hear wilt bend thine ear;
18 To judge the fatherless, and those
that are oppressed sore;
That man, that is but sprung of earth,
may them oppress no more.

DOVERSDALE. (L.M.)

Doh = D.

Samuel Stanley, 1767–1822.

:d	s .,f :m :r	d :— :s	s :l :t	d^1 :—	‖
:d	d .,r :d :t_1	d :— :r	d :— :f	m :—	‖
:d	s .,l :s :s	m :— :r	m :f :f	s :—	‖
:d	m .,f :s :s_1	l_1 :— :t_1	d :f :r	d :—	‖

A.t.

:$^{d^1}$f	f :— :f	m :- .r :d	r :d :t_1	d :—	‖
:$^{m}l_1$	l_1 :— :s_1	s_1 :— :m_1	l_1 :s_1 :s_1	s_1 :—	‖
:^{s}d	f :- .m :r	d :t_1 :d	f :m :r	m :—	‖
:$^{d}f_1$	r :- .d :t_1	d :s_1 :l_1	f_1 :s_1 :s_1	d_1 :—	‖

PSALMS XI, XII.

11

I IN the Lord do put my trust:
how is it then that ye
Say to my soul, Flee, as a bird,
unto your mountain high?
2 For, lo, the wicked bend their bow,
their shafts on string they fit,
That those who upright are in heart
they privily may hit.

3 If the foundations be destroy'd,
what hath the righteous done?
4 God in his holy temple is,
in heaven is his throne:
His eyes do see, his eyelids try
5 men's sons. The just he proves:
But his soul hates the wicked man,
and him that vi'lence loves.

6 Snares, fire and brimstone, furious storms,
on sinners he shall rain:
7 This, as the portion of their cup,
doth unto them pertain.
Because the Lord most righteous doth
in righteousness delight;
And with a pleasant countenance
beholdeth the upright.

12

HELP, Lord, because the godly man
doth daily fade away;
And from among the sons of men
the faithful do decay.
2 Unto his neighbour ev'ry one
doth utter vanity:
They with a double heart do speak,
and lips of flattery.

3 God shall cut off all flatt'ring lips,
tongues that speak proudly thus,
4 We'll with our tongue prevail, our lips
are ours: who 's lord o'er us?
5 For poor oppress'd, and for the sighs
of needy, rise will I,
Saith God, and him in safety set
from such as him defy.

6 The words of God are words most pure;
they be like silver try'd
In earthen furnace, seven times
that hath been purify'd.
7 Lord, thou shalt them preserve and keep
for ever from this race.
8 On each side walk the wicked, when
vile men are high in place.

f.D.

:^{d}s	s :l .s :f .m	f :— :f	f :s .f :m .r	m :—
:^{m}t$_{1}$	m :— :r .de	r :— :r	r :t$_{1}$:d .r	d :—
:^{d}s	l :— :l	l :— :l	s :— :s	s :—
:^{l}m	de :— :l$_{1}$	r :— :d	t$_{1}$:s$_{1}$:l$_{1}$.t$_{1}$	d :—

:s	s :l :t	d' :— :s	s .f:m :r	d :— :—	d	d
:t$_{1}$	d :— :f	m :— :d .m	m .r:d :t$_{1}$	d :— :—	l$_{1}$	s$_{1}$
:f	s :f :f	l :— :s	l :s :s	m :— :—	f	m
:r	m :f :r	l$_{1}$:— :m	f :s :s$_{1}$	d :— :—	f$_{1}$	d

A-men.

PSALMS XIII, XIV.

13

HOW long wilt thou forget me, Lord?
shall it for ever be?
O how long shall it be that thou
wilt hide thy face from me?
2 How long take counsel in my soul,
still sad in heart, shall I?
How long exalted over me
shall be mine enemy?

3 O Lord my God, consider well,
and answer to me make:
Mine eyes enlighten, lest the sleep
of death me overtake:
4 Lest that mine enemy should say,
Against him I prevail'd;
And those that trouble me rejoice,
when I am mov'd and fail'd.

5 But I have all my confidence
thy mercy set upon;
My heart within me shall rejoice
in thy salvation.
6 I will unto the Lord my God
sing praises cheerfully,
Because he hath his bounty shown
to me abundantly.

14

THAT there is not a God, the fool
doth in his heart conclude:
They are corrupt, their works are vile;
not one of them doth good.
2 Upon men's sons the Lord from heav'n
did cast his eyes abroad,
To see if any understood,
and did seek after God.

3 They altogether filthy are,
they all aside are gone;
And there is none that doeth good,
yea, sure there is not one.
4 These workers of iniquity
do they not know at all,
That they my people eat as bread,
and on God do not call?

5 There fear'd they much; for God is with
the whole race of the just.
6 You shame the counsel of the poor,
because God is his trust.
7 Let Isr'el's help from Sion come:
when back the Lord shall bring
His captives, Jacob shall rejoice,
and Israel shall sing.

DUKE STREET. (L.M.)

Doh = E♭. JOHN HATTON, ? –1793.

| d :m.f | s :l.t | d' :t.l | s :— ‖ s :s .s | l :s | f :m | r :— ‖
| s, :d.t, | d :d.r | m :r.d | t, :— ‖ d :t,.d | d :d.s, | l,.t, :d | t, :— ‖
| m :s.s | s :f | s :s.fe | s :— ‖ m :f .s | f :s | r :m.f | s :— ‖
| d :d.r | m :f.r | d :r | s, :— ‖ d :r .m | f :m | r :d | s, :— ‖

| m :m.r | d.m :s .d' | l.s :f .m | r :— ‖ s :l.t | d' :-.f | m :r | d :— ‖ f | m ‖
| d :d.t, | d :m .d | d :t,.d | t, :— ‖ d :d.f | m :-.r | d :t, | d :— ‖ d | d ‖
| s :s.f | m.s :d'.s | l.m :f .s | s :— ‖ s :f.f | s :-.l | s :s.f | m :— ‖ l | s ‖
| d :d.r | m :d .m | f.m :r .d | s, :— ‖ m :f.r | d.,r :m.f | s :s, | d :— ‖ f, | d ‖

A-men.

PSALMS XV, XVI.

15*

WITHIN thy tabernacle, Lord,
who shall abide with thee?
And in thy high and holy hill
who shall a dweller be?
2 The man that walketh uprightly,
and worketh righteousness,
And as he thinketh in his heart,
so doth he truth express.

3 Who doth not slander with his tongue,
nor to his friend doth hurt;
Nor yet against his neighbour doth
take up an ill report.
4 In whose eyes vile men are despis'd;
but those that God do fear
He honoureth; and changeth not,
though to his hurt he swear.
5 His coin puts not to usury,
nor take reward will he
Against the guiltless. Who doth thus
shall never moved be.

16*

LORD, keep me; for I trust in thee.
2 To God thus was my speech,
Thou art my Lord; and unto thee
my goodness doth not reach:
3 To saints on earth, to th' excellent,
where my delight 's all plac'd.
4 Their sorrows shall be multiply'd
to other gods that haste:

Of their drink-offerings of blood
I will no off'ring make;
Yea, neither I their very names
up in my lips will take.
5 God is of mine inheritance
and cup the portion;
The lot that fallen is to me
thou dost maintain alone.

6 Unto me happily the lines
in pleasant places fell;
Yea, the inheritance I got
in beauty doth excel.
7 I bless the Lord, because he doth
by counsel me conduct;
And in the seasons of the night
my reins do me instruct.

8 Before me still the Lord I set:
sith it is so that he
Doth ever stand at my right hand,
I shall not moved be.
9 Because of this my heart is glad,
and joy shall be exprest
Ev'n by my glory; and my flesh
in confidence shall rest.

DESCANT.

DUKE STREET, (L.M.)
Doh = E♭.

THOMAS CUTHBERTSON LEITHEAD PRITCHARD, 1885- .

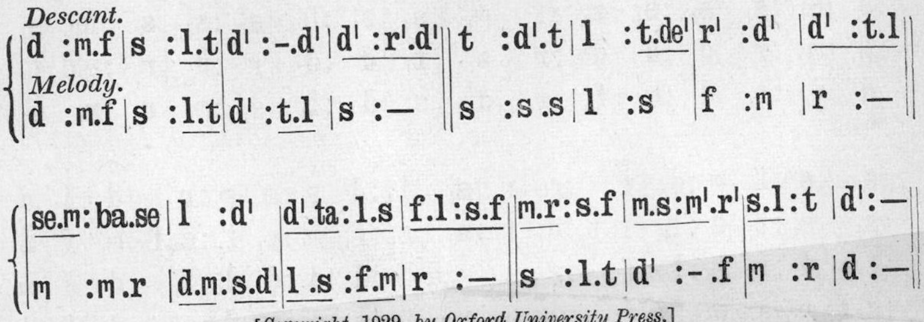

Descant.
d :m.f |s :l.t |d' :-.d' |d' :r'.d' || t :d'.t |l :t.de' |r' :d' |d' :t.l ||
Melody.
d :m.f |s :l.t |d' :t.l |s :— || s :s.s |l :s |f :m |r :— ||

se.m :ba.se |l :d' |d'.ta :l.s |f.l :s.f || m.r :s.f |m.s :m'.r' |s.l :t |d' :— ||
m :m.r |d.m :s.d' |l.s :f.m |r :— || s :l.t |d' :-.f |m :r |d :— ||

[*Copyright*, 1929, *by Oxford University Press.*]

PSALMS XVI, XVII.

10 Because my soul in grave to dwell
shall not be left by thee;
Nor wilt thou give thine Holy One
corruption to see.
11 Thou wilt me shew the path of life:
of joys there is full store
Before thy face; at thy right hand
are pleasures evermore.

17

LORD, hear the right, attend my
unto my pray'r give heed, [cry,
That doth not in hypocrisy
from feigned lips proceed.
2 And from before thy presence forth
my sentence do thou send:
Toward these things that equal are
do thou thine eyes intend.

3 Thou prov'dst mine heart, thou
visit'dst me
by night, thou didst me try,
Yet nothing found'st; for that my
mouth
shall not sin, purpos'd I.
4 As for men's works, I, by the word
that from thy lips doth flow,
Did me preserve out of the paths
wherein destroyers go.

5 Hold up my goings, Lord, me guide
in those thy paths divine,
So that my footsteps may not slide
out of those ways of thine.
6 I called have on thee, O God,
because thou wilt me hear:
That thou may'st hearken to my
speech,
to me incline thine ear.

7 Thy wondrous loving-kindness
shew,
thou that, by thy right hand,
Sav'st them that trust in thee from
those
that up against them stand.
8 As th' apple of the eye me keep;
in thy wings shade me close
9 From lewd oppressors, compassing
me round, as deadly foes.

10 In their own fat they are inclos'd;
their mouth speaks loftily.
11 Our steps they compass'd; and to
ground
down bowing set their eye.
12 He like unto a lion is
that 's greedy of his prey,
Or lion young, which lurking doth
in secret places stay.

ELY. (L.M.)

Doh = A.

THOMAS TURTON, 1780–1864.

```
:d  |d  :r  |m  :d  |l, :t, |d  ||r  |m  :d   |t, :d  |t, :l,  |s, ||
:s, |s, :s, |s, :s, |s, :f, |m, ||s, |s, :fe, |s, :s, |s, :fe, |s, ||
:m  |m  :r  |d  :d  |d  :r  |s, ||t, |d  :d   |r  :d  |r  :-.d |t, ||
:d  |d  :t, |d  :m, |f, :r, |d, ||s, |d  :l,  |s, :m, |r, :r,  |s, ||

:s,    |s  :f  |m :d   |f     :m |r  ||s,   |l, :d  |s, :m  |r  :r     |d  ||l, |d  ||
:s,    |s, :t, |d :l,  |l,.t, :d |t, ||s,   |s, :f, |m, :s, |l, :s,.f, |m, ||f, |s, ||
:t,    |d  :r  |m :l.s |f     :s |s  ||s,.d |d  :d  |d  :d  |d  :t,    |d  ||d  |m  ||
:s,.f, |m, :s, |d :f.m |r     :d |s, ||m,   |f, :l, |d  :m, |f, :s,    |d, ||f, |d, ||
```

A-men.

PSALMS XVII, XVIII.

13 Arise, and disappoint my foe,
and cast him down, O Lord:
My soul save from the wicked man,
the man which is thy sword.
14 From men, which are thy hand, O Lord,
from worldly men me save,
Which only in this present life
their part and portion have.

Whose belly with thy treasure hid
thou fill'st: they children have
In plenty; of their goods the rest
they to their children leave.
15 But as for me, I thine own face
in righteousness will see;
And with thy likeness, when I wake,
I satisfy'd shall be.

18

THEE will I love, O Lord, my strength.
2 My fortress is the Lord,
My rock, and he that doth to me
deliverance afford:
My God, my strength, whom I will [trust,
a buckler unto me,
The horn of my salvation,
and my high tow'r, is he.

3 Upon the Lord, who worthy is
of praises, will I cry;
And then shall I preserved be
safe from mine enemy.
4 Floods of ill men affrighted me,
death's pangs about me went;
5 Hell's sorrows me environed;
death's snares did me prevent.

6 In my distress I call'd on God,
cry to my God did I;
He from his temple heard my voice,
to his ears came my cry.
7 Th' earth, as affrighted, then did shake,
trembling upon it seiz'd:
The hills' foundations moved were,
because he was displeas'd.

8 Up from his nostrils came a smoke,
and from his mouth there came
Devouring fire, and coals by it
were turned into flame.
9 He also bowed down the heav'ns,
and thence he did descend;
And thickest clouds of darkness did
under his feet attend.

10 And he upon a cherub rode,
and thereon he did fly;

MAINZER. (L.M.) JOSEPH MAINZER, 1801–51.

Doh = C.

```
:s  |s  :s  |d' :t  |l  :l   |s  || l  |f  :s  |m  :d' |t  :l  |s  ||
:m  |d  :r  |m  :s  |f  :f   |m  || m  |r  :r  |m  :l  |s  :fe |s  ||
:d' |m' :r' |d' :d' |d' :l.t |d' || l  |l  :s  |s  :m' |r' :d' |t  ||
:d  |d' :t  |l  :m  |f  :f   |d  || de |r  :t, |d  :l, |r  :r  |s, ||
```

```
:s |s  :s |d' :t  |l  :l   |s  || s  |l   :t  |d' :m'.r' |d' :t  |d' || d' |d' ||
:r |m  :f |m  :s  |s  :f   |m  || m  |f   :f  |m  :f     |m  :r  |m  || f  |m  ||
:t |d' :t |d' :d' |d' :l.t |d' || d' |d'  :r' |d' :l     |s  :s  |s  || l  |s  ||
:f |m  :r |d  :m  |f  :f   |d  || d  |f.m :r  |l  :f     |s  :s, |d  || f  |d  ||
                                                                          A-men.
```

PSALM XVIII.

Yea, on the swift wings of the wind
his flight was from on high.
11 He darkness made his secret place:
about him, for his tent,
Dark waters were, and thickest clouds
of th' airy firmament.

12 And at the brightness of that light,
which was before his eye,
His thick clouds pass'd away, hailstones
and coals of fire did fly.
13 The Lord God also in the heav'ns
did thunder in his ire;
And there the Highest gave his voice,
hailstones and coals of fire.

14 Yea, he his arrows sent abroad,
and them he scattered;
His lightnings also he shot out,
and them discomfited.
15 The waters' channels then were seen,
the world's foundations vast
At thy rebuke discover'd were,
and at thy nostrils' blast.

16 And from above the Lord sent down,
and took me from below;
From many waters he me drew,
which would me overflow.
17 He me reliev'd from my strong foes,
and such as did me hate;
Because he saw that they for me
too strong were, and too great.

18 They me prevented in the day
of my calamity;
But even then the Lord himself
a stay was unto me.
19 He to a place where liberty
and room was hath me brought;
Because he took delight in me,
he my deliv'rance wrought.

20 According to my righteousness
he did me recompense,
He me repaid according to
my hands' pure innocence.
21 For I God's ways kept, from my God
did not turn wickedly.
22 His judgments were before me, I
his laws put not from me.

23 Sincere before him was my heart;
with him upright was I;
And watchfully I kept myself
from mine iniquity.

MELCOMBE. (L.M.) SAMUEL WEBBE, 1740-1816.

Doh = E♭.

```
:s |s  :f     |m  :r    |d  :l   |s  || s  |d'  :t     |l  :s  |s  :fe   |s
:d |s, :l,.t, |d  :t,   |l, :d   |d  || r  |d   :r     |r  :t, |m  :r.d  |t,
:m |m  :f     |s  :s.f  |m  :f   |m  || s  |fe  :s     |fe :s  |l  :l    |s
:d |m  :r     |d  :s,   |l, :f,  |d  || t, |l,  :t,.d  |r  :m  |d  :r    |s,

:m |m  :f     |s  :m  |r  :-.m  |f || f  |m  :r     |s  :f  |m  :r   |d || d  |d
:d |d  :t,.l, |s, :d  |t, :-.de |r || r  |d  :t,    |d  :d  |d  :t,  |d || l, |s,
:s |s  :f     |m  :s  |s  :-.s  |l || s  |s  :s     |s  :l  |s  :s.f |m || f  |m
:d |d  :r     |m  :d  |s  :-.m  |r || t, |d  :s,.f, |m, :f, |s, :s,  |d || f, |d
                                                                        A-men.
```

PSALM XVIII.

24 After my righteousness the Lord
hath recompensed me,
After the cleanness of my hands
appearing in his eye.

25 Thou gracious to the gracious art,
to upright men upright:
26 Pure to the pure, froward thou
kyth'st
unto the froward wight.
27 For thou wilt the afflicted save
in grief that low do lie:
But wilt bring down the countenance
of them whose looks are high.

28 The Lord will light my candle so,
that it shall shine full bright:
The Lord my God will also make
my darkness to be light.
29 By thee through troops of men I
break,
and them discomfit all;
And, by my God assisting me,
I overleap a wall.

30 As for God, perfect is his way:
the Lord his word is try'd;
He is a buckler to all those
who do in him confide.

31 Who but the Lord is God? but he
who is a rock and stay?
32 'Tis God that girdeth me with
strength,
and perfect makes my way.

33 He made my feet swift as the hinds,
set me on my high places.
34 Mine hands to war he taught, mine
arms
brake bows of steel in pieces.
35 The shield of thy salvation
thou didst on me bestow:
Thy right hand held me up, and
great
thy kindness made me grow.

36 And in my way my steps thou hast
enlarged under me,
That I go safely, and my feet
are kept from sliding free.
37 Mine en'mies I pursued have,
and did them overtake;
Nor did I turn again till I
an end of them did make.

38 I wounded them, they could not
they at my feet did fall. [rise;
39 Thou girdedst me with strength for
war;
my foes thou brought'st down all:

[12 *continued*]

MELCOMBE. (L.M.)

Doh = E♭. DESCANT. ALAN GRAY, 1855-

Descant.

```
:s  |s  :l.t |d' :t  |l  :d'   |d' ||r' |d' :r'  |d' :t  |m' :r'.d' |t  ||
:s  |s  :f   |m  :r  |d  :l    |s  ||s  |d' :t   |l  :s  |s  :fe    |s  ||
```

Melody.

```
:d' |d' :t.l |s  :d' |t  :-.d' |r' ||r' |d' :t.l |s  :d' |d' :t     |d' ||
:m  |m  :f   |s  :m  |r  :-.m  |f  ||f  |m  :r   |s  :f  |m  :r     |d  ||
```

PSALMS XVIII, XIX.

40 And thou hast giv'n to me the necks
of all mine enemies;
That I might them destroy and slay,
who did against me rise.

41 They cried out, but there was none
that would or could them save;
Yea, they did cry unto the Lord,
but he no answer gave.
42 Then did I beat them small as dust
before the wind that flies;
And I did cast them out like dirt
upon the street that lies.

43 Thou mad'st me free from people's
strife,
and heathen's head to be:
A people whom I have not known
shall service do to me.
44 At hearing they shall me obey,
to me they shall submit.
45 Strangers for fear shall fade away,
who in close places sit.

46 God lives, bless'd be my Rock; the
God
of my health praised be.
47 God doth avenge me, and subdues
the people under me.

48 He saves me from mine enemies;
yea, thou hast lifted me
Above my foes; and from the man
of vi'lence set me free.

49 Therefore to thee will I give thanks
the heathen folk among;
And to thy name, O Lord, I will
sing praises in a song.
50 He great deliv'rance gives his king:
he mercy doth extend
To David, his anointed one,
and his seed without end.

19*

THE heav'ns God's glory do
declare,
the skies his hand-works preach:
2 Day utters speech to-day, and night
to night doth knowledge teach.
3 There is no speech nor tongue to
which
their voice doth not extend:
4 Their line is gone through all the
earth,
their words to the world's end.

In them he set the sun a tent;
5 Who, bridegroom-like, forth goes

OLD 100TH: (L.M.) *French Psalter*, 1551.

Doh = G.

| d :— | d :t_1 | l_1:s_1 | d :— | r :— | m :— ‖ m :— | m :m | r :d | f :— | m :— | r :— ‖
| s_1:— | s_1:s_1 | m_1:m_1 | m_1:— | s_1:— | s_1:— ‖ s_1:— | s_1:d | t_1:d | d :— | d :— | t_1:— ‖
| m :— | m :r | d :t_1 | d :— | t_1:— | d :— ‖ d :— | m :s | s :m | l :— | s :— | s :— ‖
| d :— | d :s_1 | l_1:m_1 | l_1:— | s_1:— | d_1:— ‖ d :— | d :d | s_1:l_1 | f_1:— | d_1:— | s_1:— ‖

| d :— | r :m | r :d | l_1:— | t_1:— | d :— | s :— | m :d | r :f | m :— | r :— | d :— ‖ d | d ‖
| d :— | s_1:s_1 | s_1:s_1 | l_1:— | f_1:— | s_1:— | s_1:— | s_1:d | t_1:l_1.t_1 | d :— | t_1:— | s_1:— ‖ l_1 | s_1 ‖
| m :— | r :d | t_1:d | d :— | r :— | m :— | r :— | d :m.fe | s :l | s :— | s :f | m :— ‖ f | m ‖
| l_1:— | t_1:d | s_1:m_1 | f_1:— | r_1:— | d_1:— | t_1:— | d :l_1 | s_1:r_1 | m_1:f_1 | s_1:— | d_1:— ‖ f_1 | d_1 ‖

[*There is a Faux-bourdon setting in the Revised Church Hymnary, No.* 229.] A-men.

PSALMS XIX, XX.

From 's chamber, as a strong man doth
to run his race rejoice.
6 From heav'n's end is his going forth,
circling to th' end again;
And there is nothing from his heat
that hidden doth remain.

7 God's law is perfect, and converts
the soul in sin that lies:
God's testimony is most sure,
and makes the simple wise.
8 The statutes of the Lord are right,
and do rejoice the heart:
The Lord's command is pure, and doth
light to the eyes impart.

9 Unspotted is the fear of God,
and doth endure for ever:
The judgments of the Lord are true
and righteous altogether.
10 They more than gold, yea, much fine gold,
to be desired are:
Than honey, honey from the comb
that droppeth, sweeter far.

11 Moreover, they thy servant warn
how he his life should frame:
A great reward provided is
for them that keep the same.
12 Who can his errors understand?
O cleanse thou me within
13 From secret faults. Thy servant keep
from all presumptuous sin:

And do not suffer them to have
dominion over me:
Then, righteous and innocent,
I from much sin shall be.
14 The words which from my mouth proceed,
the thoughts sent from my heart,
Accept, O Lord, for thou my strength
and my Redeemer art.

20*

JEHOVAH hear thee in the day
when trouble he doth send:
And let the name of Jacob's God
thee from all ill defend.
2 O let him help send from above,
out of his sanctuary:
From Sion, his own holy hill,
let him give strength to thee.

OLD 100TH. (L.M.)

Doh = G. DESCANT. ALAN GRAY, 1855-

Descant.

|s :— |s :s |m :m |m :— |s :— |s :— ||s :— |d^{1} :s |t :l |l :— |s :— |s :— ||

Melody

|d :— |d :t_{1} |l_{1} :s_{1} |d :— |r :— |m :— ||m :— |m :m |r :d |f :— |m :— |r :— ||

|m :— |r :d |s :m |f :— |f :— |m :— ||s :— |l :d^{1} |l :t |s :— |— :f |m :— ||

|d :— |r :m |r :d |l_{1} :— |t_{1} :— |d :— ||s :— |m :d |r :f |m :— |r :— |d :— ||

PSALMS XX, XXI.

3 Let him remember all thy gifts,
accept thy sacrifice: [fulfil
4 Grant thee thine heart's wish, and
thy thoughts and counsel wise.
5 In thy salvation we will joy;
in our God's name we will
Display our banners: and the Lord
thy prayers all fulfil.

6 Now know I God his king doth save:
he from his holy heav'n
Will hear him, with the saving
strength
by his own right hand giv'n.
7 In chariots some put confidence,
some horses trust upon:
But we remember will the name
of our Lord God alone.

8 We rise, and upright stand, when
are bowed down, and fall. [they
9 Deliver, Lord; and let the King
us hear, when we do call.

21

THE king in thy great strength,
O Lord,
shall very joyful be:
In thy salvation rejoice
how veh'mently shall he!

2 Thou hast bestowed upon him
all that his heart would have;
And thou from him didst not withhold
whate'er his lips did crave.

3 For thou with blessings him prevent'st
of goodness manifold;
And thou hast set upon his head
a crown of purest gold.
4 When he desired life of thee,
thou life to him didst give;
Ev'n such a length of days, that he
for evermore should live.

5 In that salvation wrought by thee
his glory is made great;
Honour and comely majesty
thou hast upon him set.
6 Because that thou for evermore
most blessed hast him made;
And thou hast with thy countenance
made him exceeding glad.

7 Because the king upon the Lord
his confidence doth lay;
And through the grace of the most
High
shall not be mov'd away.

14

ROCKINGHAM (COMMUNION). (L.M.)

Doh = E♭.

Adapted by EDWARD MILLER, 1731–1807.

:d	|	m	:f	:r	|	d	:—	:m	|	s	:—	:l	|	s	:—	‖
:d	|	d	:—	:t,	|	d	:—	:d	|	d	:—	:d	|	d	:—	‖
:m	|	s	:l	:s .f	|	m	:—	:s	|	s	:—	:f	|	m	:—	‖
:d	|	d	:f,	:s,	|	d	:—	:d	|	m	:—	:f	|	d	:—	‖

:s	|	d'	:—	:t	|	l	:—	:s	|	s	:f	:m	|	m	:r	‖
:r	|	d	:—	:d	|	d	:r	:m	|	m	:r	:d	|	d	:t,	‖
:s	|	m	:f	:s	|	l	:t	:d'	|	d'	:s	:s	|	s	:—	‖
:t,	|	l,	:—	:s,	|	f,	:f	:m	|	l,	:t,	:d	|	s,	:—	‖

PSALMS XXI, XXII.

8 Thine hand shall all those men find out
that en'mies are to thee;
Ev'n thy right hand shall find out those
of thee that haters be.

9 Like fiery ov'n thou shalt them make,
when kindled is thine ire;
God shall them swallow in his wrath,
devour them shall the fire.

10 Their fruit from earth thou shalt destroy,
their seed men from among:

11 For they beyond their might 'gainst thee
did plot mischief and wrong.

12 Thou therefore shalt make them turn back,
when thou thy shafts shalt place
Upon thy strings, made ready all
to fly against their face.

13 In thy great pow'r and strength, O Lord,
be thou exalted high;
So shall we sing with joyful hearts,
thy power praise shall we.

22*

MY God, my God, why hast thou me
forsaken? why so far
Art thou from helping me, and from
my words that roaring are?

2 All day, my God, to thee I cry,
yet am not heard by thee;
And in the season of the night
I cannot silent be.

3 But thou art holy, thou that dost
inhabit Isr'el's praise.

4 Our fathers hop'd in thee, they hop'd,
and thou didst them release.

5 When unto thee they sent their cry,
to them deliv'rance came:
Because they put their trust in thee,
they were not put to shame.

6 But as for me, a worm I am,
and as no man am priz'd:
Reproach of men I am, and by
the people am despis'd.

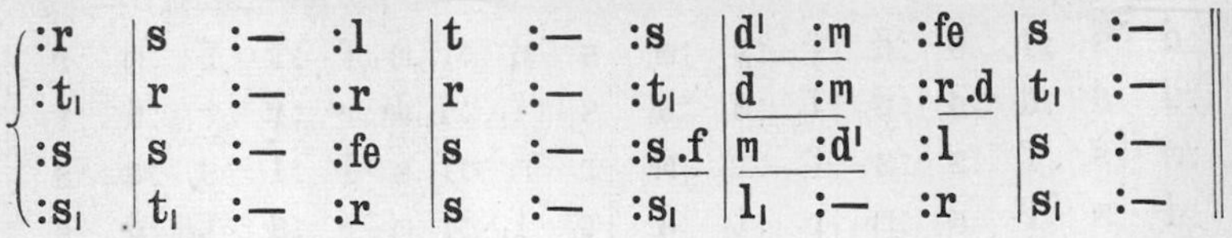

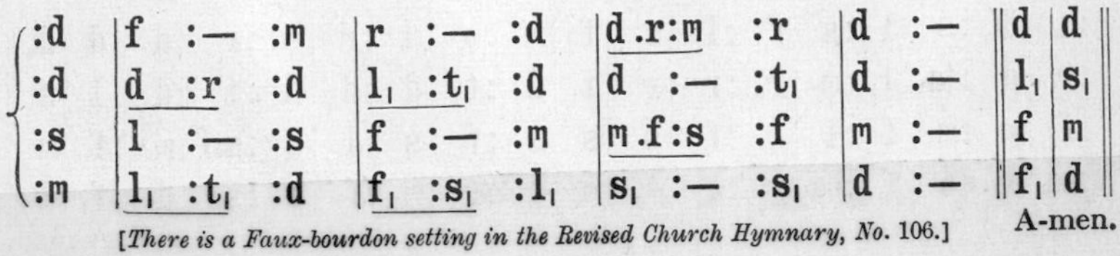

```
:r  | s  :—  :l  | t  :—  :s   | d'   :m  :fe  | s  :—  ||
:t, | r  :—  :r  | r  :—  :t,  | d    :m  :r.d | t, :—  ||
:s  | s  :—  :fe | s  :—  :s.f | m    :d' :l   | s  :—  ||
:s, | t, :—  :r  | s  :—  :s,  | l,   :—  :r   | s, :—  ||

:d  | f  :—  :m  | r  :—  :d   | d.r:m   :r    | d  :—  || d  | d  ||
:d  | d  :r  :d  | l, :t, :d   | d   :—  :t,   | d  :—  || l, | s, ||
:s  | l  :—  :s  | f  :—  :m   | m.f:s   :f    | m  :—  || f  | m  ||
:m  | l, :t, :d  | f, :s, :l,  | s,  :—  :s,   | d  :—  || f, | d  ||
                                                          A-men.
```

[*There is a Faux-bourdon setting in the Revised Church Hymnary, No.* 106.]

PSALM XXII.

7 All that me see laugh me to scorn;
shoot out the lip do they;
They nod and shake their heads at me,
and, mocking, thus do say,

8 This man did trust in God, that he
would free him by his might:
Let him deliver him, sith he
had in him such delight.
9 But thou art he out of the womb
that didst me safely take;
When I was on my mother's breasts
thou me to hope didst make.

10 And I was cast upon thy care,
ev'n from the womb till now;
And from my mother's belly, Lord,
my God and guide art thou.
11 Be not far off, for grief is near,
and none to help is found.
12 Bulls many compass me, strong bulls
of Bashan me surround.

13 Their mouths they open'd wide on me,
upon me gape did they,
Like to a lion ravening
and roaring for his prey.

14 Like water I'm pour'd out, my bones
all out of joint do part:
Amidst my bowels, as the wax,
so melted is my heart.

15 My strength is like a potsherd dry'd;
my tongue it cleaveth fast
Unto my jaws; and to the dust
of death thou brought me hast.
16 For dogs have compass'd me about:
the wicked, that did meet
In their assembly, me inclos'd;
they pierc'd my hands and feet.

17 I all my bones may tell; they do
upon me look and stare.
18 Upon my vesture lots they cast,
and clothes among them share.
19 But be not far, O Lord, my strength;
haste to give help to me.
20 From sword my soul, from pow'r of dogs
my darling set thou free.

21 Out of the roaring lion's mouth
do thou me shield and save:
For from the horns of unicorns
an ear to me thou gave.

15

ST. SEPULCHRE. (L.M.) GEORGE COOPER, 1820–76.

Doh = E♭.

:d |s :l |s :d |f :s |m ||s |d :r.m |f :f |f :m |r ||
:d |d :d |d :d |l, :s, |s, ||s, |l, :l,.de |r :r |r :d |t, ||
:m |s :f |s :s |f :r |m ||r |m :f.s |l :l |s :s |s ||
:d |m :f |m :m |r :t, |d ||t, |l, :f.m |r :d |t, :d |s, ||

:t |d' :s |l :s |f :l |s ||f |m :s |d :r |m :r |d ||d |d ||
:r |d :ta, |l, :m |r :r |r ||t, |d :t, |d :d |d :t, |d ||l, |s, ||
:f |m :m |f :l |l :f |s ||s |s :f |s :l |s :s.f |m ||f |m ||
:se, |l, :d |f :de |r :d |t, ||s, |d :r |m :f |s :s, |d ||f, |d ||

A-men.

PSALMS XXII, XXIII.

22 I will shew forth thy name unto
those that my brethren are;
Amidst the congregation
thy praise I will declare.

23 Praise ye the Lord, who do him fear;
him glorify all ye
The seed of Jacob: fear him all
that Isr'el's children be.
24 For he despis'd not nor abhorr'd
th' afflicted's misery;
Nor from him hid his face, but heard
when he to him did cry.

25 Within the congregation great
my praise shall be of thee;
My vows before them that him fear
shall be perform'd by me.
26 The meek shall eat, and shall be fill'd;
they also praise shall give
Unto the Lord that do him seek:
your heart shall ever live.

27 All ends of th' earth remember shall,
and turn the Lord unto;
All kindreds of the nations
to him shall homage do:
28 Because the kingdom to the Lord
doth appertain as his;
Likewise among the nations
the Governor he is.

29 Earth's fat ones eat, and worship shall:
all who to dust descend
Shall bow to him; none of them can
his soul from death defend.
30 A seed shall service do to him;
unto the Lord it shall
Be for a generation
reckon'd in ages all.

31 They shall come, and they shall declare
his truth and righteousness
Unto a people yet unborn,
and that he hath done this.

23*

THE Lord's my shepherd, I'll not want.
2 He makes me down to lie
In pastures green: he leadeth me
the quiet waters by.
3 My soul he doth restore again;
and me to walk doth make
Within the paths of righteousness,
ev'n for his own name's sake.

16

SAXONY. (L.M.) Adapted from *Spangenberg's Gesangbuch*, 1568.

Lah = E. Doh = G.

```
:l,  |l,  :l,  |d   :l,  |d   :r   |m   ||m   |m   :m   |s   :m   |r   :r   |d   ||
:m,  |f,  :f,  |m,  :m,  |l,  :l,  |se, ||l,  |t,  :l,  |t,  :s,  |l,  :s,  |m,  ||
:d   |d   :r   |d   :d   |l,  :l,  |t,  ||d   |t,  :d   |r   :d   |d   :t,  |d   ||
:l,  |f,  :r,  |l,  :l,  |f,  :f,  |m,  ||l,  |se, :l,  |s,  :d   |f,  :s,  |d   ||

:m   |m   :l,  |d   :t,  |l,  :l,  |s,  ||t,  |d   :m   |r   :d   |t,  :t,  |l,  ||l,  |l,  ||
:l,  |m,  :l,  |l,  :s,  |s,  :fe, |s,  ||s,  |m,  :s,  |l,  :l,  |l,  :se, |l,  ||f,  |m,  ||
:d   |t,  :d   |f   :r   |m   :r   |t,  ||r   |d   :d   |f   :m   |f   :m   |d   ||r   |de  ||
:l,  |se, :l,  |f,  :s,  |d,  :r,  |s,  ||s,  |l,  :m,  |f,  :l,  |r,  :m,  |l,  ||r,  |l,  ||
                                                                               A-men.
```


4 Yea, though I walk in death's dark vale,
yet will I fear none ill:
For thou art with me; and thy rod
and staff me comfort still.
5 My table thou hast furnished
in presence of my foes;
My head thou dost with oil anoint,
and my cup overflows.

6 Goodness and mercy all my life
shall surely follow me:
And in God's house for evermore
my dwelling-place shall be.

24*

THE earth belongs unto the Lord,
and all that it contains;
The world that is inhabited,
and all that there remains.
2 For the foundations thereof
he on the seas did lay,
And he hath it established
upon the floods to stay.

3 Who is the man that shall ascend
into the hill of God?
Or who within his holy place
shall have a firm abode?

4 Whose hands are clean, whose heart [is pure,
and unto vanity
Who hath not lifted up his soul,
nor sworn deceitfully.

5 He from th' Eternal shall receive
the blessing him upon,
And righteousness, ev'n from the [God
of his salvation.
6 This is the generation
that after him enquire,
O Jacob, who do seek thy face
with their whole heart's desire.

7 Ye gates, lift up your heads on high;
ye doors that last for aye,
Be lifted up, that so the King
of glory enter may.
8 But who of glory is the King?
The mighty Lord is this;
Ev'n that same Lord, that great in [might
and strong in battle is.

9 Ye gates, lift up your heads; ye [doors,
doors that do last for aye,
Be lifted up, that so the King
of glory enter may.
10 But who is he that is the King
of glory? who is this?
The Lord of hosts, and none but he,
the King of glory is.

17

SOLDAU. (L.M.) Adapted from *Wittenberg Gesangbuch*, 1524.

Doh = G.

:d |r :r |d :l, |s, :l, |d ||m |s :l |s :m |d :l, |d ||
:m, |l, :s, |m, :f, |s, :f, |m, ||d |t, :r |r :t, |l, :l, |s, ||
:d |d :t, |d :d |d :d |d ||s |m :fe |s :s |m :f |m ||
:d |f, :s, |l, :f, |m, :f, |d, ||d |m :r.d |t, :s, |l, :f, |d, ||

:m |m :r |m :d |r :r |m ||d |l, :s, |l, :-.t, |d :d |d ||t, |d ||
:d |d :t, |t, :d |d :t, |d ||s, |f, :r, |f, :-.f, |s, :l, |s, ||s, |s, ||
:s |s :s |s :m |l :s |s ||d |d :t, |d :-.r |m :f |m ||r |m ||
:d |d :s, |m, :l, |f, :s, |d, ||m, |f, :s, |f, :-.r, |d, :f, |d, ||s, |d, ||

A-men.

PSALM XXV.

25*

TO thee I lift my soul:
2 O Lord, I trust in thee:
My God, let me not be asham'd,
nor foes triumph o'er me.
3 Let none that wait on thee
be put to shame at all; [gress,
But those that without cause trans-
let shame upon them fall.

4 Shew me thy ways, O Lord;
thy paths, O teach thou me:
5 And do thou lead me in thy truth,
therein my teacher be:
For thou art God that dost
to me salvation send,
And I upon thee all the day
expecting do attend.

6 Thy tender mercies, Lord,
I pray thee to remember,
And loving-kindnesses; for they
have been of old for ever.
7 My sins and faults of youth
do thou, O Lord, forget:
After thy mercy think on me,
and for thy goodness great.

8 God good and upright is:
the way he'll sinners show.
9 The meek in judgment he will guide,
and make his path to know.
10 The whole paths of the Lord
are truth and mercy sure,
To those that do his cov'nant keep,
and testimonies pure.

11 Now, for thine own name's sake,
O Lord, I thee entreat
To pardon mine iniquity;
for it is very great.
12 What man is he that fears
the Lord, and doth him serve?
Him shall he teach the way that he
shall chuse, and still observe.

13 His soul shall dwell at ease;
and his posterity
Shall flourish still, and of the earth
inheritors shall be.
14 With those that fear him is
the secret of the Lord;
The knowledge of his covenant
he will to them afford.

15 Mine eyes upon the Lord
continually are set;
For he it is that shall bring forth
my feet out of the net.

18

UFFINGHAM. (L.M.) JEREMIAH CLARK, *c.* 1659–1707.

Lah=F. Doh=A♭.

```
l,:l,.s,:f, | m,:—:t, | d :t,:l,   | se,:—:— || m :m :m   | r :—:d   | r :t,:— | d :—:— ||
m,:m,  :r,  | d,:—:m, | m,:—:m,.r, | m, :—:— || m,:s,:s,  | s,:f,:m, | f,:r,:— | m,:—:— ||
d :l,  :l,  | d :—:t, | l,:t,:d .l,| t, :—:— || d :d :d   | t,:—:d   | l,:s,:— | s,:—:— ||
l,:d,  :r,  | l,:—:se,| l,:s,:f,   | m, :—:— || d,:m,:d,  | s,:—:l,  | f,:s,:— | d,:—:— ||

s :s :f  | m:—:m  | m :r :d       | t,:— | t,  | d :t,:l,    | se,:—:m  | d :—:t, .l,  | l,:—:— || l, | l, ||
d :d :t, | d:—:s, | s,:—:s,.fe,   | s,:— | se, | l,:m,:-.r,  | m, :—:m, | m,:—:se,.l,  | m,:—:— || f, | m, ||
m :d :r  | m:—:m  | d :r :m .d    | r :— | m   | m :—:l,    | t, :—:l, | l,:—:t,      | d :—:— || r  | de ||
d
d, :m,:s,| d:—:d  | d :t,:l,      | s,:— | m,  | l,:s,:f,   | m, :—:d, | m,:—:m,      | l, l,2 :—:— || r, | l,2 ||
                                                                                              A-men.
```

PSALM XXV.

16 Turn unto me thy face,
and to me mercy show;
Because that I am desolate,
and am brought very low.

17 My heart's griefs are increas'd:
me from distress relieve.
18 See mine affliction and my pain,
and all my sins forgive.
19 Consider thou my foes,
because they many are;
And it a cruel hatred is
which they against me bear.

20 O do thou keep my soul,
do thou deliver me:
And let me never be asham'd,
because I trust in thee.
21 Let uprightness and truth
keep me, who thee attend.
22 Redemption, Lord, to Israel
from all his troubles send.

25 (2)

ANOTHER OF THE SAME.

TO thee I lift my soul, O Lord:
2 My God, I trust in thee:
Let me not be asham'd; let not
my foes triumph o'er me.

3 Yea, let thou none ashamed be
that do on thee attend:
Ashamed let them be, O Lord,
who without cause offend.

4 Thy ways, Lord, shew; teach me
thy paths:
5 Lead me in truth, teach me:
For of my safety thou art God;
all day I wait on thee.
6 Thy mercies, that most tender are,
do thou, O Lord, remember,
And loving-kindnesses; for they
have been of old for ever.

7 Let not the errors of my youth
nor sins, remember'd be:
In mercy, for thy goodness' sake,
O Lord, remember me.
8 The Lord is good and gracious,
he upright is also:
He therefore sinners will instruct
in ways that they should go.

9 The meek and lowly he will guide
in judgment just alway:
To meek and poor afflicted ones
he'll clearly teach his way.

19

WALTON. (L.M.)

Doh = B♭.

William Gardiner's Sacred Melodies, 1815.

:s,	d :— :t,	d :— :r	s, :l, :t,	d :— ‖
:s,	s, :— :s,	s, :— :l,	s, :— :f,	m, :— ‖
:m	m :— :f	m :— :r	m :— :r	d :— ‖
:d,	d, :— :r,	m, :— :f,	s, :— :s,	d, :— ‖

F.t.

:[d]f	f :m :r	s :— :m	m.r :d :t,	d :— ‖
:[m]l,	t, :— :t,	d :— :d.t,	l, :s, :f,	m, :— ‖
:[d]f	s :— :s	s :— :d	f :m :r	d :— ‖
:[l,]r	s, :— :f,	m, :— :l,	f, :s, :s,	d :— ‖

PSALMS XXV, XXVI.

10 The whole paths of the Lord our God
are truth and mercy sure,
To such as keep his covenant,
and testimonies pure.

11 Now, for thine own name's sake, O Lord,
I humbly thee entreat
To pardon mine iniquity;
for it is very great.
12 What man fears God? him shall he teach
the way that he shall chuse.
13 His soul shall dwell at ease; his seed
the earth, as heirs, shall use.

14 The secret of the Lord is with
such as do fear his name;
And he his holy covenant
will manifest to them.
15 Towards the Lord my waiting eyes
continually are set;
For he it is that shall bring forth
my feet out of the net.

16 O turn thee unto me, O God,
have mercy me upon;
Because I solitary am,
and in affliction.

17 Enlarg'd the griefs are of mine heart;
me from distress relieve.
18 See mine affliction and my pain,
and all my sins forgive.

19 Consider thou mine enemies,
because they many are;
And it a cruel hatred is
which they against me bear.
20 O do thou keep my soul; O God,
do thou deliver me:
Let me not be asham'd; for I
do put my trust in thee.

21 O let integrity and truth
keep me, who thee attend.
22 Redemption, Lord, to Israel
from all his troubles send.

26*

JUDGE me, O Lord, for I have walk'd
in mine integrity:
I trusted also in the Lord;
slide therefore shall not I.
2 Examine me, and do me prove;
try heart and reins, O God:
3 For thy love is before mine eyes,
thy truth's paths I have trode.

f.B♭.

```
:ᵈs,  | s,  :—  :d   | d   :t,  :l,    | s,  :—  :m   | m   :r   ||
:ˢr,  | m,  :—  :m,  | f,  :—   :f,    | s,  :—  :s,  | l,  :—   ||
:ᵐt,  | d   :—  :s,  | s,  :—   :l,.t, | d   :—  :d   | l,  :—   ||
:ᵈs,  | d,  :—  :d,  | r,  :—   :r,    | m,  :—  :m,  | f,  :—   ||

:d    | t,  :—  :f   | f   :m   :r     | d   :r  :t,  | d   :—   || d  | d  ||
:l,   | s,  :—  :t,  | d   :—   :l,    | s,  :—  :f,  | m,  :—   || f, | m, ||
:r    | r   :—  :r   | d   :—   :r     | m   :f  :r   | d   :—   || l, | s, ||
:f,   | s,  :—  :s,  | l,  :—   :f,    | s,  :—  :s,  | d,  :—   || f, | d, ||
                                                                    A-men.
```

PSALMS XXVI, XXVII.

4 With persons vain I have not sat,
nor with dissemblers gone:
5 Th' assembly of ill men I hate;
to sit with such I shun.
6 Mine hands in innocence, O Lord,
I'll wash and purify;
So to thine holy altar go,
and compass it will I:

7 That I, with voice of thanksgiving,
may publish and declare,
And tell of all thy mighty works,
that great and wondrous are.
8 The habitation of thy house,
Lord, I have loved well;
Yea, in that place I do delight
where doth thine honour dwell.

9 With sinners gather not my soul,
and such as blood would spill:
10 Whose hands mischievous plots, right hand
corrupting bribes do fill.
11 But as for me, I will walk on
in mine integrity:
Do thou redeem me, and, O Lord,
be merciful to me.

12 My foot upon an even place
doth stand with stedfastness:
Within the congregations
th' Eternal I will bless.

27*

THE Lord's my light and saving health,
who shall make me dismay'd?
My life's strength is the Lord, of whom
then shall I be afraid?
2 When as mine enemies and foes,
most wicked persons all,
To eat my flesh against me rose,
they stumbled and did fall.

3 Against me though an host encamp,
my heart yet fearless is:
Though war against me rise, I will
be confident in this.
4 One thing I of the Lord desir'd,
and will seek to obtain,
That all days of my life I may
within God's house remain;

That I the beauty of the Lord
behold may and admire,
And that I in his holy place
may rev'rently enquire.

WAREHAM. (L.M.)

Doh = B♭.

William Knapp, 1698–1768.

:d | d :t_1 :l_1 | s_1 :— :d | r :d :t_1 | d :— ||

:m_1 | m_1 :— :f_1 | s_1 :— :m_1 | l_1 :s_1 :s_1 | s_1 :— ||

:s_1 | d :— :d | d :— :d | f :m :r | m :— ||

:d_1 | d_1 :— :f_1 | m_1 :— :l_1 | f_1 :s_1 :s_1 | d_1 :— ||

:r | m :r :d | t_1 :d :r | d :t_1 :l_1 | s_1 :— ||

:s_1 | s_1 :— :s_1.fe_1 | s_1 :— :s_1 | l_1 :s_1 :fe_1 | s_1 :— ||

:t_1 | d :r :m.d | r :d :t_1 | m :r :d | t_1 :— ||

:s_1 | d :t_1 :l_1 | s_1 :m_1 :t_2 | d_1 :r_1 :r_1 | s_1 :— ||

PSALMS XXVII, XXVIII.

5 For he in his pavilion shall
me hide in evil days;
In secret of his tent me hide,
and on a rock me raise.

6 And now, ev'n at this present time,
mine head shall lifted be
Above all those that are my foes,
and round encompass me:
Therefore unto his tabernacle
I'll sacrifices bring
Of joyfulness; I'll sing, yea, I
to God will praises sing.

7 O Lord, give ear unto my voice,
when I do cry to thee;
Upon me also mercy have,
and do thou answer me.

8 When thou didst say, Seek ye my face,
then unto thee reply
Thus did my heart, Above all things
thy face, Lord, seek will I.

9 Far from me hide not thou thy face;
put not away from thee
Thy servant in thy wrath: thou hast
an helper been to me.
O God of my salvation,
leave me not, nor forsake:

10 Though me my parents both should leave,
the Lord will me up take.

11 O Lord, instruct me in thy way,
to me a leader be
In a plain path, because of those
that hatred bear to me.

12 Give me not to mine en'mies' will;
for witnesses that lie
Against me risen are, and such
as breathe out cruelty.

13 I fainted had, unless that I
believed had to see
The Lord's own goodness in the land
of them that living be.

14 Wait on the Lord, and be thou strong,
and he shall strength afford
Unto thine heart; yea, do thou wait,
I say, upon the Lord.

28*

To thee I'll cry, O Lord, my rock;
hold not thy peace to me;
Lest like those that to pit descend
I by thy silence be.

:s,	l, :s, :l,.t,	d :— :t,	d :— :r	m :—
:s,	f, :s, :f,	s, :— :s,	m, :— :l,	se, :—
:d	d :— :f	m :d :r	d :t, :l,	t, :—
:m,	f, :m, :r,	d, :m, :s,	l, :s, :f,	m, :—

:r.m	f :m :r	d :t, :d	r :d :t,	d :—	d	d
:l,.s,	f, :s, :l,	s, :f, :m,	l, :s, :s,	s, :—	f,	m,
:l,	t, :d :f	m :r :d	f :m :r	m :—	l,	s,
:f,.m,	r, :m, :f,	s, :— :l,	f, :s, :s,	d, :—	f,	d,
					A-	men.

PSALMS XXVIII, XXIX.

2 The voice hear of my humble pray'rs,
when unto thee I cry;
When to thine holy oracle
I lift mine hands on high.

3 With ill men draw me not away
that work iniquity;
That speak peace to their friends, while in
their hearts doth mischief lie.
4 Give them according to their deeds
and ills endeavoured:
And as their handy-works deserve,
to them be rendered.

5 God shall not build, but them destroy,
who would not understand
The Lord's own works, nor did regard
the doing of his hand.
6 For ever blessed be the Lord,
for graciously he heard
The voice of my petitions,
and prayers did regard.

7 The Lord's my strength and shield; my heart
upon him did rely;
And I am helped: hence my heart
doth joy exceedingly.
And with my song I will him praise.
8 Their strength is God alone:
He also is the saving strength
of his anointed one.

9 O thine own people do thou save,
bless thine inheritance;
Them also do thou feed, and them
for evermore advance.

29

GIVE ye unto the Lord, ye sons
that of the mighty be,
All strength and glory to the Lord
with cheerfulness give ye.
2 Unto the Lord the glory give
that to his name is due;
And in the beauty of holiness
unto JEHOVAH bow.

3 The Lord's voice on the waters is;
the God of majesty
Doth thunder, and on multitudes
of waters sitteth he.
4 A pow'rful voice it is that comes
out from the Lord most high;
The voice of that great Lord is full
of glorious majesty.

21

WHITEHALL. (L.M.)

Doh = A.

HENRY LAWES, 1596–1662.

```
d  :—  |t, :l, |d  :m, |f, :l, |s, :— || s, :— |l, :t, |d  :t, |l, :m  |r  :— ||
s, :—  |s, :f, |m, :d, |d, :f, |d, :— || m, :— |f, :f, |s, :s, |f, :s, |s, :— ||
m  :—  |m  :d  |d  :t, |l, :t, |d  :— || d  :— |d  :r  |d  :d  |d  :d  |t, :— ||
d, :—  |m, :f, |l, :s, |f, :r, |m, :— || d, :— |f, :r, |m, :m, |f, :d, |s, :— ||

r  :—  |f  :m  |l, :t, |d  :r  |m  :— || m  :— |s  :r   |f  :m     |r  :r  |d  :— || d  |d  ||
s, :—  |l, :s, |s, :f, |m, :l, |s, :— || l, :— |t, :ta, |l, :l,.s, |f, :s, |m, :— || f, |m, ||
ta,:—  |l, :d  |d  :s  |s  :f  |m  :— || d  :— |r  :r   |d  :d     |d  :t, |d  :— || l, |s, ||
s, :—  |r, :m, |f, :s, |l, :t, |d  :— || l, :— |s, :ta, |f, :l,    |r, :s, |d, :— || f, |d, ||
                                                                                      A-men.
```

PSALMS XXIX, XXX.

5 The voice of the Eternal doth
asunder cedars tear;
Yea, God the Lord doth cedars break
that Lebanon doth bear.
6 He makes them like a calf to skip,
ev'n that great Lebanon,
And, like to a young unicorn,
the mountain Sirion.

7 God's voice divides the flames of fire;
8 The desert it doth shake:
The Lord doth make the wilderness
of Kadesh all to quake.
9 God's voice doth make the hinds to calve,
it makes the forest bare:
And in his temple ev'ry one
his glory doth declare.

10 The Lord sits on the floods; the Lord
sits King, and ever shall.
11 The Lord will give his people strength,
and with peace bless them all.

30*

LORD, I will thee extol, for thou
hast lifted me on high,
And over me thou to rejoice
mad'st not mine enemy.
2 O thou who art the Lord my God,
I in distress to thee,
With loud cries lifted up my voice,
and thou hast healed me.

3 O Lord, my soul thou hast brought up,
and rescu'd from the grave;
That I to pit should not go down,
alive thou didst me save.
4 O ye that are his holy ones,
sing praise unto the Lord;
And give unto him thanks, when ye
his holiness record.

5 For but a moment lasts his wrath;
life in his favour lies:
Weeping may for a night endure,
at morn doth joy arise.
6 In my prosperity I said,
that nothing shall me move.
7 O Lord, thou hast my mountain made
to stand strong by thy love:

22

WITTENBERG. (L.M.) *Geistliche Lieder*, 1543.

Lah = E. Doh = G.

```
:l, |d  :l, |s, :l, |d  :t, |l, ||d  |r  :r  |m  :d  |r  :r  |m  ||
:m, |m, :f, |m, :m, |s, :s, |m, ||l, |l, :t, |d  :d  |l, :s, |s, ||
:d  |l, :d  |d  :d  |d  :r  |d  ||d  |f  :s  |m  :m  |r  :t, |t, ||
:l, |l, :f, |d  :l, |m, :s, |l, ||f, |r, :s, |d, :l, |f, :s, |m, ||

:m  |f  :m  |s  :m  |r  :r  |d  ||m  |d  :r  |d  :t, |l, :s, |l, ||l, |l, ||
:l, |l, :l, |s, :s, |l, :t, |d  ||t, |l, :l, |s, :s, |m, :m, |m, ||f, |m, ||
:d  |r  :m  |r  :m  |f  :r  |m  ||m  |m  :r  |m  :r  |d  :t, |d  ||r  |de ||
:l, |r  :d  |t, :d  |f, :s, |d  ||s, |l, :f, |m, :s, |d, :m, |l, ||r, |l, ||
                                                               A-men.
```


But when that thou, O gracious [God,
didst hide thy face from me,
Then quickly was my prosp'rous [state
turn'd into misery.
8 Wherefore unto the Lord my cry
I caused to ascend:
My humble supplication
I to the Lord did send.

9 What profit is there in my blood,
when I go down to pit?
Shall unto thee the dust give praise?
thy truth declare shall it?
10 Hear, Lord, have mercy; help me, Lord:
11 Thou turned hast my sadness
To dancing; yea, my sackcloth loos'd,
and girded me with gladness;

12 That sing thy praise my glory may,
and never silent be.
O Lord my God, for evermore
I will give thanks to thee.

31*

IN thee, O Lord, I put my trust,
sham'd let me never be;
According to thy righteousness
do thou deliver me.

2 Bow down thine ear to me, with speed
send me deliverance:
To save me, my strong rock be thou,
and my house of defence.

3 Because thou art my rock, and thee
I for my fortress take;
Therefore do thou me lead and guide,
ev'n for thine own name's sake.
4 And sith thou art my strength, therefore
pull me out of the net,
Which they in subtilty for me
so privily have set.

5 Into thine hands I do commit
my sp'rit: for thou art he,
O thou, JEHOVAH, God of truth,
that hast redeemed me.
6 Those that do lying vanities
regard, I have abhorr'd:
But as for me, my confidence
is fixed on the Lord.

7 I'll in thy mercy gladly joy:
for thou my miseries
Consider'd hast; thou hast my soul
known in adversities:

23

PETERBOROUGH. (D.L.M.)

Doh = C. JOHN GOSS, 1800-80.

```
:s  |s  :s  |d' :-.s |l  :l   |s  ||s  |d' :r'   |m' :d' |r' :d'.t |d' ||
:m  |m  :m  |m  :-.m |f  :d.r |m  ||m  |s  :s    |s  :s  |f  :m.r  |m  ||
:d' |d' :d' |s  :-.d'|d' :l.t |d' ||d' |d' :t    |d' :d' |l  :s    |s  ||
:d  |d  :d  |d  :-.d |f  :f   |d  ||d  |m  :s    |d' :m  |f  :s    |d  ||

                                       G.t.                          f.C.
:s  |s  :s  |d' :-.s |l  :l   |s  ||s  |d'f  :m.r   |s  :d  |f  :m.r  |ds  ||
:m  |m  :m  |m  :-.m |f  :d.r |m  ||m  |lr   :d.t,  |d  :d  |r  :d.t, |ds  ||
:d' |d' :d' |s  :-.d'|d' :l.t |d' ||d' |m'l  :s     |s  :m  |l  :s.f  |mt  ||
:d  |d  :d  |d  :-.d |f  :f   |d  ||d  |l,r, :s,.f, |m, :l, |r, :s,  |ds, ||
```

PSALM XXXI.

8 And thou hast not inclosed me
within the en'my's hand;
And by thee have my feet been made
in a large room to stand.

9 O Lord, upon me mercy have,
for trouble is on me:
Mine eye, my belly, and my soul,
with grief consumed be.

10 Because my life with grief is spent,
my years with sighs and groans:
My strength doth fail; and for my sin
consumed are my bones.

11 I was a scorn to all my foes,
and to my friends a fear;
And specially reproach'd of those
that were my neighbours near:
When they me saw they from me fled.

12 Ev'n so I am forgot,
As men are out of mind when dead:
I'm like a broken pot.

13 For slanders I of many heard;
fear compass'd me, while they
Against me did consult, and plot
to take my life away.

14 But as for me, O Lord, my trust
upon thee I did lay;
And I to thee, Thou art my God,
did confidently say.

15 My times are wholly in thine hand:
do thou deliver me
From their hands that mine enemies
and persecutors be.

16 Thy countenance to shine do thou
upon thy servant make:
Unto me give salvation,
for thy great mercies' sake.

17 Let me not be asham'd, O Lord,
for on thee call'd I have:
Let wicked men be sham'd, let them
be silent in the grave.

18 To silence put the lying lips,
that grievous things do say,
And hard reports, in pride and scorn,
on righteous men do lay.

19 How great's the goodness thou for them
that fear thee keep'st in store,

:s |s :s |s :l.t |d' :d' |d' ‖d' |d' :d' |f' :m' |r' :d' |t ‖
:s |s :s |s :l.t |d' :d' |d' ‖s |s :s |f :s |l :m.fe |s ‖
:s |s :s |s :l.t |d' :d' |d' ‖m' |m' :m' |d' :d' |f' :d' |r' ‖
:s |s :s |s :l.t |d' :d' |d' ‖d |d' :ta |l :s |f :l |s ‖

:s |d' :ta |l :-.l |r' :d' |t ‖s |m' :d' |l :d'.r' |m' :r' |d' ‖d' |d' ‖
:s |s :m |f :-.f |l :fe |s ‖s |s :s |f :l |s :-.f |m ‖f |m ‖
:t |d' :d' |d' :-.d' |r' :r' |r' ‖t |d' :d' |d' :d' |d' :t |d' ‖l |s ‖
:s |m :d |f :-.f |fe :r |s ‖s |d :m |f :f |s :s, |d ‖f |d ‖

A-men.

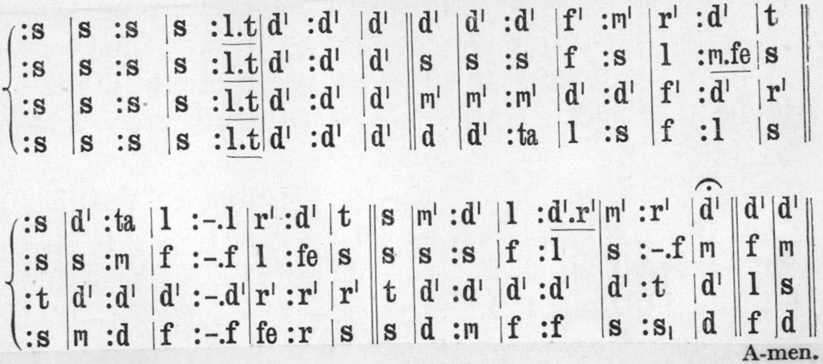

And wrought'st for them that trust in thee
the sons of men before!
20 In secret of thy presence thou
shalt hide them from man's pride:
From strife of tongues thou closely shalt,
as in a tent, them hide.

21 All praise and thanks be to the Lord;
for he hath magnify'd
His wondrous love to me within
a city fortify'd.
22 For from thine eyes cut off I am,
I in my haste had said;
My voice yet heard'st thou, when to thee
with cries my moan I made.

23 O love the Lord, all ye his saints;
because the Lord doth guard
The faithful, and he plenteously
proud doers doth reward.
24 Be of good courage, and he strength
unto your heart shall send,
All ye whose hope and confidence
doth on the Lord depend.

32*

O BLESSED is the man to whom
is freely pardoned
All the transgression he hath done,
whose sin is covered.
2 Bless'd is the man to whom the Lord
imputeth not his sin,
And in whose sp'rit there is no guile,
nor fraud is found therein.

3 When as I did refrain my speech,
and silent was my tongue,
My bones then waxed old, because
I roared all day long.
4 For upon me both day and night
thine hand did heavy lie,
So that my moisture turned is
in summer's drought thereby.

5 I thereupon have unto thee
my sin acknowledged,
And likewise mine iniquity
I have not covered:
I will confess unto the Lord
my trespasses, said I;
And of my sin thou freely didst
forgive th' iniquity.

ABBEY. (C.M.)

Doh = G. f.C. *Scottish Psalter*, 1615.

d :—	d :m	r :d	d :t,	d :—		fd' :—	t :l	l :se	l :—	
s, :—	s, :d	t, :l,	l, :s,	s, :—		ds :—	f :d.r	m :m	m :—	
m :—	s :s	s :m	f :r	m :—		fd' :—	r' :l	t :t	d' :—	
d :—	m :d	s, :l,	f, :s,	d :—		lm :—	r :f	m :m	l :—	

G.t.

r's :—	m :d	f :m	r :d	t, :—		s, :—	l, :d	d :t,	d :—		d	d	
rs, :—	s, :s,	d :—.t,	l, :m,.f,	s, :—		s, :—	f, :s,	l, :s,	s, :—		l,	s,	
lr :—	m :m	f :s	l :d	r :—		d :—	d :d	f.m :r	m :—		f	m	
fet, :—	d :d.t,	l, :s,	f, :l,	s, :—		m, :—	f, :m,	r, :s,	d, :—		f,	d,	

A-men.

6 For this shall ev'ry godly one
his prayer make to thee;
In such a time he shall thee seek,
as found thou mayest be.
Surely, when floods of waters great
do swell up to the brim,
They shall not overwhelm his soul,
nor once come near to him.

7 Thou art my hiding-place, thou shalt
from trouble keep me free;
Thou with songs of deliverance
about shalt compass me.
8 I will instruct thee, and thee teach
the way that thou shalt go;
And, with mine eye upon thee set,
I will direction show.

9 Then be not like the horse or mule,
which do not understand;
Whose mouth, lest they come near to thee,
a bridle must command.
10 Unto the man that wicked is
his sorrows shall abound;
But him that trusteth in the Lord
mercy shall compass round.

11 Ye righteous, in the Lord be glad,
in him do ye rejoice:
All ye that upright are in heart,
for joy lift up your voice.

33*

YE righteous, in the Lord rejoice;
it comely is and right,
That upright men, with thankful voice,
should praise the Lord of might.
2 Praise God with harp, and unto him
sing with the psaltery;
Upon a ten-string'd instrument
make ye sweet melody.

3 A new song to him sing, and play
with loud noise skilfully;
4 For right is God's word, all his works
are done in verity.
5 To judgment and to righteousness
a love he beareth still;
The loving-kindness of the Lord
the earth throughout doth fill.

6 The heavens by the word of God
did their beginning take;
And by the breathing of his mouth
he all their hosts did make.
7 The waters of the seas he brings
together as an heap;

on, 1735.

m :— ‖
se$_1$:— ‖
m :— ‖
m$_1$:— ‖

‖ r | de ‖
‖ l$_1$ | l$_1$ ‖
‖ f | m ‖
‖ r$_1$ | l$_1$ ‖
A-men.

ARNOLD. (C.M.) SAMUEL ARNOLD, 1740–1802.

Doh = E♭.

:s |s :m :s |f :r :f |m :f :m |r :— ‖ r |m :f :s |l.,s:f :m |r :— ‖
:d |d :— :d |t$_1$:— :r |d :r :d |t$_1$:— ‖ t$_1$ |d :— :d |d :— :d |t$_1$:— ‖
:m |m :s :m |r :s :s |s :— :s |s :— ‖ s |s :f :m |f.,s:l :s |s :— ‖
:d |d :— :d |s$_1$:— :t$_1$ |d :t$_1$:d |s$_1$:— ‖ s$_1$ |d :l$_1$:s$_1$ |f$_1$:— :d |s$_1$:— ‖

:s |l.,t:d':l |s :m :s |l.,t:d':l |s :— ‖ s |l :t :d'.s |f :m :r |d :— ‖ d |d ‖
:d |d :— :d |d :— :d |d :— :d |d :— ‖ d |d :f :m |r :d :t$_1$ |d :— ‖ l$_1$ |s$_1$ ‖
:s |f.,s:l :f |s :— :s |f.,s:l :f |m :— ‖ s |f :— :s |l :s :s.f |m :— ‖ f |m ‖
:m |f :— :f |m :d :m |f :— :f$_1$ |d :— ‖ m |f :r :m |f :s :s$_1$ |d :— ‖ f$_1$ |d ‖

A-men.

PSALM XXXIII.

And in storehouses, as it were,
he layeth up the deep.

8 Let earth, and all that live therein,
with rev'rence fear the Lord;
Let all the world's inhabitants
dread him with one accord.
9 For he did speak the word, and done
it was without delay;
Established it firmly stood,
whatever he did say.

10 God doth the counsel bring to nought
which heathen folk do take;
And what the people do devise
of none effect doth make.
11 O but the counsel of the Lord
doth stand for ever sure;
And of his heart the purposes
from age to age endure.

12 That nation blessed is, whose God
JEHOVAH is, and those
A blessed people are, whom for
his heritage he chose.
13 The Lord from heav'n sees and beholds
all sons of men full well:
14 He views all from his dwelling-place
that in the earth do dwell.

15 He forms their hearts alike, and all
their doings he observes.
16 Great hosts save not a king, much strength
no mighty man preserves.
17 An horse for preservation
is a deceitful thing;
And by the greatness of his strength
can no deliv'rance bring.

18 Behold, on those that do him fear
the Lord doth set his eye;
Ev'n those who on his mercy do
with confidence rely.
19 From death to free their soul, in dearth
life unto them to yield.
20 Our soul doth wait upon the Lord;
he is our help and shield.

21 Sith in his holy name we trust,
our heart shall joyful be.
22 Lord, let thy mercy be on us,
as we do hope in thee.

ASPURG. (C.M.)

Doh = D.

JOHANN GEORG FRECH, 1790–1864.

```
:s  |d' :s  |m :l   |s  :s.f |m  ||r   |d :m.fe |s  :l   |s  :— |— ||
:d  |m  :r  |d :d   |d  :t,  |d  ||t,  |d :d    |t, :r.d |t, :— |— ||
:m  |s  :s  |s :f.m |r  :s   |s  ||s.f |m :l    |s  :fe  |s  :— |— ||
:d  |d  :t, |d :f,  |s, :s,  |d  ||s,  |l, :l,  |m  :r   |s, :— |— ||

:s  |t :s   |d' :m |f     :m |r  ||m.f |s :d'  |d' :t  |d' :— |— ||d' |d' ||
:t, |r :t,  |d  :d |d.r   :d |t, ||d   |d :d.r |m  :r  |m  :— |— ||f  |m  ||
:s  |s :r'  |s  :s |l     :s |s  ||s.f |m :m.f |s  :s  |s  :— |— ||l  |s  ||
:s, |s :s.f |m  :d |l,.t, :d |s, ||d.r |m :l,  |s, :s, |d  :— |— ||f  |d  ||
                                                                  A-men.
```

PSALM XXXIV.

34*

GOD will I bless all times; his praise
my mouth shall still express.
2 My soul shall boast in God: the meek
shall hear with joyfulness.
3 Extol the Lord with me, let us
exalt his name together.
4 I sought the Lord, he heard, and did
me from all fears deliver.

5 They look'd to him, and lighten'd were:
not shamed were their faces.
6 This poor man cry'd, God heard, and sav'd
him from all his distresses.
7 The angel of the Lord encamps,
and round encompasseth
All those about that do him fear,
and them delivereth.

8 O taste and see that God is good:
who trusts in him is bless'd.
9 Fear God his saints: none that him fear
shall be with want oppress'd.
10 The lions young may hungry be,
and they may lack their food:
But they that truly seek the Lord
shall not lack any good.

11 O children, hither do ye come,
and unto me give ear;
I shall you teach to understand
how ye the Lord should fear.
12 What man is he that life desires,
to see good would live long?
13 Thy lips refrain from speaking guile,
and from ill words thy tongue.

14 Depart from ill, do good, seek peace,
pursue it earnestly.
15 God's eyes are on the just; his ears
are open to their cry.
16 The face of God is set against
those that do wickedly,
That he may quite out from the earth
cut off their memory.

17 The righteous cry unto the Lord,
he unto them gives ear;
And they out of their troubles all
by him deliver'd are.
18 The Lord is ever nigh to them
that be of broken sp'rit;
To them he safety doth afford
that are in heart contrite.

ARNOLD. (C.M.) SAMUEL ARNOLD, 1740-1802.

Doh = E♭.

:s	s :m :s	f :r :f	m :f :m	r :— ‖	r	m :f :s	l.,s:f :m	r :— ‖
:d	d :— :d	t_1 :— :r	d :r :d	t_1 :— ‖	t_1	d :— :d	d :— :d	t_1 :— ‖
:m	m :s :m	r :s :s	s :— :s	s :— ‖	s	s :f :m	f.,s:l :s	s :— ‖
:d	d :— :d	s_1 :— :t_1	d :t_1 :d	s_1 :— ‖	s_1	d :l_1 :s_1	f_1 :— :d	s_1 :— ‖

:s	l.,t:d^1:l	s :m :s	l.,t:d^1:l	s :— ‖	s	l :t :d^1.s	f :m :r	d :— ‖	d	d ‖
:d	d :— :d	d :— :d	d :— :d	d :— ‖	d	d :f :m	r :d :t_1	d :— ‖	l_1	s_1 ‖
:s	f.,s:l :f	s :— :s	f.,s:l :f	m :— ‖	s	f :— :s	l :s :s.f	m :— ‖	f	m ‖
:m	f :— :f	m :d :m	f :— :f_1	d :— ‖	m	f :r :m	f :s :s_1	d :— ‖	f_1	d ‖

A-men.

PSALM XXXIII.

And in storehouses, as it were,
he layeth up the deep.

8 Let earth, and all that live therein,
with rev'rence fear the Lord;
Let all the world's inhabitants
dread him with one accord.
9 For he did speak the word, and done
it was without delay;
Established it firmly stood,
whatever he did say.

10 God doth the counsel bring to nought
which heathen folk do take;
And what the people do devise
of none effect doth make.
11 O but the counsel of the Lord
doth stand for ever sure;
And of his heart the purposes
from age to age endure.

12 That nation blessed is, whose God
JEHOVAH is, and those
A blessed people are, whom for
his heritage he chose.
13 The Lord from heav'n sees and beholds
all sons of men full well:

14 He views all from his dwelling-place
that in the earth do dwell.

15 He forms their hearts alike, and all
their doings he observes.
16 Great hosts save not a king, much strength
no mighty man preserves.
17 An horse for preservation
is a deceitful thing;
And by the greatness of his strength
can no deliv'rance bring.

18 Behold, on those that do him fear
the Lord doth set his eye;
Ev'n those who on his mercy do
with confidence rely.
19 From death to free their soul, in dearth
life unto them to yield.
20 Our soul doth wait upon the Lord;
he is our help and shield.

21 Sith in his holy name we trust,
our heart shall joyful be.
22 Lord, let thy mercy be on us,
as we do hope in thee.

ASPURG. (C.M.)

Doh = D.

JOHANN GEORG FRECH, 1790–1864.

:s | d^1 :s | m :l | s :s.f | m ‖ r | d :m.fe | s :l | s :— | — ‖
:d | m :r | d :d | d :t_1 | d ‖ t_1 | d :d | t_1 :r.d | t_1 :— | — ‖
:m | s :s | s :f.m | r :s | s ‖ s.f | m :l | s :fe | s :— | — ‖
:d | d :t_1 | d :f_1 | s_1 :s_1 | d ‖ s_1 | l_1 :l_1 | m :r | s_1 :— | — ‖

:s | t :s | d^1 :m | f :m | r ‖ m.f | s :d^1 | d^1 :t | d^1 :— | — ‖ d^1 | d^1 ‖
:t_1 | r :t_1 | d :d | d.r :d | t_1 ‖ d | d :d.r | m :r | m :— | — ‖ f | m ‖
:s | s :r^1 | s :s | l :s | s ‖ s.f | m :m.f | s :s | s :— | — ‖ l | s ‖
:s_1 | s :s.f | m :d | l_1.t_1 :d | s_1 ‖ d.r | m :l_1 | s_1 :s_1 | d :— | — ‖ f | d ‖

A-men.

PSALM XXXIV.

34*

GOD will I bless all times; his praise
my mouth shall still express.
2 My soul shall boast in God: the meek
shall hear with joyfulness.
3 Extol the Lord with me, let us
exalt his name together.
4 I sought the Lord, he heard, and did
me from all fears deliver.

5 They look'd to him, and lighten'd were:
not shamed were their faces.
6 This poor man cry'd, God heard, and sav'd
him from all his distresses.
7 The angel of the Lord encamps,
and round encompasseth
All those about that do him fear,
and them delivereth.

8 O taste and see that God is good:
who trusts in him is bless'd.
9 Fear God his saints: none that him fear
shall be with want oppress'd.
10 The lions young may hungry be,
and they may lack their food:
But they that truly seek the Lord
shall not lack any good.

11 O children, hither do ye come,
and unto me give ear;
I shall you teach to understand
how ye the Lord should fear.
12 What man is he that life desires,
to see good would live long?
13 Thy lips refrain from speaking guile,
and from ill words thy tongue.

14 Depart from ill, do good, seek peace,
pursue it earnestly.
15 God's eyes are on the just; his ears
are open to their cry.
16 The face of God is set against
those that do wickedly,
That he may quite out from the earth
cut off their memory.

17 The righteous cry unto the Lord,
he unto them gives ear;
And they out of their troubles all
by him deliver'd are.
18 The Lord is ever nigh to them
that be of broken sp'rit;
To them he safety doth afford
that are in heart contrite.

BALLERMA. (C.M.) Adapted by ROBERT SIMPSON, 1790-1832.

Doh = Ab.

```
:d  | m :—:r  | d :—:l,   | s, :—:l, | d :—  || d  | m :—:r     | m :s :m   | r :—  ||
:m, | s, :—:f,| m, :—:f,  | d, :—:d, | m, :— || m, | s, :—:s,   | s, :—:s,  | s, :— ||
:d  | d :—:t, | d :—:d    | d :—:l,  | s, :— || s, | d :—:t,    | d :m :d   | t, :— ||
:d, | d :—:s, | l, :s, :f,| m, :—:f, | d, :— || d, | d, :m, :s, | d :—:d,   | s, :— ||
```

```
:d  | m :—:r  | d :—:l,   | s, :—:m, | s, :— || d  | m :s :m    | r :m :r     | d :—  || d  | d  ||
:m, | s, :—:f,| m, :—:f,  | d, :—:d, | r, :— || s, | s, :—:s,   | l, :s, :f,  | m, :— || f, | m, ||
:d  | d :—:t, | d :—:d    | d :—:d   | t, :— || d  | d :m :d    | d :—:t,     | d :—  || l, | s, ||
:d, | d :—:s, | l, :s, :f,| m, :—:l, | s, :— || m, | d, :—:d,   | f, :s, :s,  | d, :— || f, | d, ||
                                                                                        A-men.
```

PSALMS XXXIV, XXXV.

19 The troubles that afflict the just
in number many be;
But yet at length out of them all
the Lord doth set him free.
20 He carefully his bones doth keep,
whatever can befall;
That not so much as one of them
can broken be at all.

21 Ill shall the wicked slay; laid waste
shall be who hate the just.
22 The Lord redeems his servants' souls;
none perish that him trust.

35

PLEAD, Lord, with those that plead; and fight
with those that fight with me.
2 Of shield and buckler take thou hold,
stand up mine help to be.
3 Draw also out the spear, and do
against them stop the way
That me pursue: unto my soul,
I'm thy salvation, say.

4 Let them confounded be and sham'd
that for my soul have sought:
Who plot my hurt turn'd back be they,
and to confusion brought.
5 Let them be like unto the chaff
that flies before the wind;
And let the angel of the Lord
pursue them hard behind.

6 With darkness cover thou their way,
and let it slipp'ry prove;
And let the angel of the Lord
pursue them from above.
7 For without cause have they for me
their net hid in a pit,
They also have without a cause
for my soul digged it.

8 Let ruin seize him unawares;
his net he hid withal
Himself let catch; and in the same
destruction let him fall.
9 My soul in God shall joy; and glad
in his salvation be:
10 And all my bones shall say, O Lord,
who is like unto thee,

Which dost the poor set free from him
that is for him too strong;

28

BANGOR. (C.M.)

Lah = C. Doh = E♭. *Tans'ur's Harmony of Zion*, 1735.

```
|m  :—  |d  :t, |l,  :m      |l  :s.f |m  ||m   |m  :s.fe |m  :re   |m   :— ||
|se,:—  |l, :se,|l,  :d      |d  :r   |d  ||t,  |l, :t,.d |t, :-.l, |se, :— ||
|t, :—  |d  :r  |m   :m      |f  :l   |l  ||r'  |d' :t.l  |s  :fe   |m   :— ||
|m, :—  |l, :t, |d.t,:l,.s,  |f, :r,  |l, ||se, |l, :s,.l,|t, :t,   |m,  :— ||

|m :—    |l :se |l :d'.t |l   :s.f |m ||m    |l    :m.r |d :t,   |l,:— ||r  |de ||
|t,:—    |m :r  |d :d    |d   :t,  |d ||m.r  |d    :l,  |l,:se,  |l,:— ||l, |l, ||
|se:—    |l :t  |m :s    |f.m :r.s |s ||m    |m    :m.f |m :-.r  |d :— ||f  |m  ||
|m :-.r  |d :t, |l,:m,   |f,  :s,  |d ||d.t, |l,.t,:d.r |m :m,   |l,:— ||r, |l, ||
                                                                     A-me-en.
```

PSALM XXXV.

The poor and needy from the man
that spoils and does him wrong?
11 False witnesses rose; to my charge
things I not knew they laid.
12 They, to the spoiling of my soul,
me ill for good repaid.

13 But as for me, when they were sick,
in sackcloth sad I mourn'd:
My humbled soul did fast, my pray'r
into my bosom turn'd.
14 Myself I did behave as he
had been my friend or brother;
I heavily bow'd down, as one
that mourneth for his mother.

15 But in my trouble they rejoic'd,
gath'ring themselves together;
Yea, abjects vile together did
themselves against me gather:
I knew it not; they did me tear,
and quiet would not be.
16 With mocking hypocrites, at feasts
they gnash'd their teeth at me.

17 How long, Lord, look'st thou on? from those
destructions they intend
Rescue my soul, from lions young
my darling do defend.

18 I will give thanks to thee, O Lord,
within th' assembly great;
And where much people gather'd are
thy praises forth will set.

19 Let not my wrongful enemies
proudly rejoice o'er me;
Nor who me hate without a cause,
let them wink with the eye.
20 For peace they do not speak at all;
but crafty plots prepare
Against all those within the land
that meek and quiet are.

21 With mouths set wide, they 'gainst me said,
Ha, ha! our eye doth see.
22 Lord, thou hast seen, hold not thy peace;
Lord, be not far from me.
23 Stir up thyself; wake, that thou may'st
judgment to me afford,
Ev'n to my cause, O thou that art
my only God and Lord.

24 O Lord my God, do thou me judge
after thy righteousness;

BEDFORD. (C.M.) WILLIAM WEALE, ? -1727.

Doh = E♭.

```
:s | m :—:d | l :—:s  | f :m :— | r :— || s  | d' :—:t   | l :l :—   | s :—  ||
:m | d :—:d | d :—:d  | t1:d :— | t1:— || r  | d  :—:r   | m :r :—   | t1:—  ||
:s | s :—:s | l :—:d' | f :s :— | s :— || r  | m  :fe:s   | s :—:fe   | s :—  ||
:d | d :—:m | f :—:m  | r :d :— | s1:— || t1 | l1 :—:t1   | d :r :—   | s1:—  ||

:m | f :—:s  | l :—:s   | f :m :— | r :— || s  | d':—:m  | f :r :—   | d :—      || d  | d  ||
:d | d :—:m  | f :—:r   | d :d :— | r :— || t1 | d :—:d  | d :—:t1   | d :—      || l1 | s1 ||
:s | f :—:d' | d':—:ta  | l :s :l | t :— || s  | s :—:m  | l :s :—   | m :—      || f  | m  ||
:d | l1:—:d  | f1:—:s1  | l1:d :— | s1:— || s1 | m1:—:l1 | f1:s1:—   | d/d1 :—   || f1 | d  ||
```

[*This tune may be sung in duple time.*] A-men.

PSALMS XXXV, XXXVI.

And let them not their joy 'gainst me
triumphantly express:
25 Nor let them say within their hearts,
Ah, we would have it thus;
Nor suffer them to say, that he
is swallow'd up by us.

26 Sham'd and confounded be they all
that at my hurt are glad;
Let those against me that do boast
with shame and scorn be clad.
27 Let them that love my righteous cause
be glad, shout, and not cease
To say, The Lord be magnify'd,
who loves his servant's peace.

28 Thy righteousness shall also be
declared by my tongue;
The praises that belong to thee
speak shall it all day long.

36*

THE wicked man's transgression
within my heart thus says,
Undoubtedly the fear of God
is not before his eyes.

2 Because himself he flattereth
in his own blinded eye,
Until the hatefulness be found
of his iniquity.

3 Words from his mouth proceeding are,
fraud and iniquity:
He to be wise, and to do good,
hath left off utterly.
4 He mischief, lying on his bed,
most cunningly doth plot:
He sets himself in ways not good,
ill he abhorreth not.

5 Thy mercy, Lord, is in the heav'ns;
thy truth doth reach the clouds:
6 Thy justice is like mountains great;
thy judgments deep as floods:
Lord, thou preservest man and beast.
7 How precious is thy grace!
Therefore in shadow of thy wings
men's sons their trust shall place.

8 They with the fatness of thy house
shall be well satisfy'd;
From rivers of thy pleasures thou
wilt drink to them provide.
9 Because of life the fountain pure
remains alone with thee;

BELGRAVE. (C.M.) WILLIAM HORSLEY, 1774-1858.

Doh = E♭.

:s	m :— :s	d^1 :— :m	f :s :l	r :—	s.,f	m :fe :s .,l	t :— :l	s :—
:d	d :— :r	d :— :d	d :— :d	t_1 :—	r	d :— :r .,m	r :— :r.d	t_1 :—
:m	s :— :r	m :— :s	f :m :r	s :—	s	s :l :s	s :— :fe	s :—
:d	d :— :t_1	l_1 :— :ta_1	l_1 :s_1 :f_1	s_1 :—	t_1	d :l_1 :t_1.,d	r :— :r	s_1 :—

:d^1	m :— :l	r :— :s	d :r :m	m :r	s	s :f :m	m.,r:d :t_1	d :—	d	d
:d	d :— :d	t_1 :— :d	l_1 :t_1:d	d :t_1	t_1	d :r :d	l_1 :s_1:s_1	s_1 :—	l_1	s_1
:s	d^1:t :l	s :— :s	l.,s:f :m	s :—	r	s :— :s	f :m :r	m :—	f	m
:m	l :s :f	s :f_1 :m	f.,m:r :d	s_1 :—	s_1	l_1:t_1:d	f_1 :s_1:s_1	d :—	f_1	d

A-men.

PSALMS XXXVI, XXXVII.

And in that purest light of thine
we clearly light shall see.

10 Thy loving-kindness unto them
continue that thee know;
And still on men upright in heart
thy righteousness bestow.
11 Let not the foot of cruel pride
come, and against me stand;
And let me not removed be,
Lord, by the wicked's hand.

12 There fallen are they, and ruined,
that work iniquities:
Cast down they are, and never shall
be able to arise.

37*

FOR evil doers fret thou not
thyself unquietly;
Nor do thou envy bear to those
that work iniquity.
2 For, even like unto the grass,
soon be cut down shall they;
And, like the green and tender herb,
they wither shall away.

3 Set thou thy trust upon the Lord,
and be thou doing good;
And so thou in the land shalt dwell,
and verily have food.
4 Delight thyself in God; he'll give
thine heart's desire to thee.
5 Thy way to God commit, him trust,
it bring to pass shall he.

6 And, like unto the light, he shall
thy righteousness display;
And he thy judgment shall bring
forth
like noon-tide of the day.
7 Rest in the Lord, and patiently
wait for him: do not fret
For him who, prosp'ring in his way,
success in sin doth get.

8 Do thou from anger cease, and
wrath
see thou forsake also:
Fret not thyself in any wise,
that evil thou should'st do.
9 For those that evil doers are
shall be cut off and fall:
But those that wait upon the Lord
the earth inherit shall.

10 For yet a little while, and then
the wicked shall not be;
His place thou shalt consider well,
but it thou shalt not see.

31

BELMONT. (C.M.) *William Gardiner's Sacred Melodies*, 1812.

Doh = A♭.

```
:s, | m :—:r  | d :—:t,  | t,:l, :d  | s, :— || s  | s :f :m   | m :r :d    | d :t, ||
:m, | s,:—:f, | m,:—:s,  | s,:f, :f, | m, :— || s, | s,:—:s,   | l,:—:l,    | s,:—  ||
:d  | d :—:t, | d :—:m   | d :—:d    | d :—  || m  | r :—:s    | s :f :m    | m :r  ||
:d, | d :—:s, | l,:—:m,  | f,:—:l,   | d :—  || d  | t,:—:d    | f,:—:fe,   | s,:—  ||

:s, | m :—:r  | d :—:t,  | t,:l, :d  | s,:—  || s  | s :f :r   | d :m :r    | d :—  || d  | d  ||
:s, | s,:—:f, | m,:—:s,  | s,:f, :f, | m,:—  || s, | l,:—:l,   | s,:—:f,    | m,:—  || f, | m, ||
:r  | d :—:t, | d :—:m   | d :—:d    | d :—  || d  | d :—:f    | m :d :t,   | d :—  || l, | s, ||
:t, | d :—:s, | l,:—:m,  | f,:—:l,   | d :—  || m, | f,:—:f,   | s,:—:s,    | d,:—  || f, | d, ||
                                                                                        A-men.
```

PSALM XXXVII.

11 But by inheritance the earth
the meek ones shall possess:
They also shall delight themselves
in an abundant peace.

12 The wicked plots against the just,
and at him whets his teeth:
13 The Lord shall laugh at him, because
his day he coming seeth.
14 The wicked have drawn out the sword,
and bent their bow, to slay
The poor and needy, and to kill
men of an upright way.

15 But their own sword, which they have drawn,
shall enter their own heart:
Their bows which they have bent shall break,
and into pieces part.
16 A little that a just man hath
is more and better far
Than is the wealth of many such
as lewd and wicked are.

17 For sinners' arms shall broken be;
but God the just sustains.
18 God knows the just man's days, and still
their heritage remains.
19 They shall not be asham'd when they
the evil time do see;
And when the days of famine are,
they satisfy'd shall be.

20 But wicked men, and foes of God,
as fat of lambs, decay;
They shall consume, yea, into smoke
they shall consume away.
21 The wicked borrows, but the same
again he doth not pay;
Whereas the righteous mercy shews,
and gives his own away.

22 For such as blessed be of him
the earth inherit shall;
And they that cursed are of him
shall be destroyed all.
23 A good man's footsteps by the Lord
are ordered aright;
And in the way wherein he walks
he greatly doth delight.

24 Although he fall, yet shall he not
be cast down utterly;
Because the Lord with his own hand
upholds him mightily.

32

BISHOPTHORPE. (C.M.) — Jeremiah Clark, *c.* 1659–1707.

Doh = G.

```
:s.,f |m :-.r:d |t,:l,:f |m :d :t, |d :—  ||r  |m :-.f:s |s :f :m |m :r  ||
:d    |s,:— :s, |f,:—:f, |s,:—:s,  |s,:—  ||t, |d :-.r:m |m :r :d |d :t, ||
:m.,r |d :— :d  |d :—:d  |d :m :r  |d :—  ||f  |m :— :d  |d :s :s |s :—  ||
:d    |d :— :m, |f,:—:l, |s,:—:f,  |m,:—  ||r, |d,:— :d  |l,:t,:d |s,:—  ||
```

```
:s   |s :f :m  |f :—:f  |f :m :r  |m :—  ||s.,f |m :-.r:d |l,.,r:d :t, |d :—  ||d  |d  ||
:r   |de:r :l, |l,:—:l, |t,:d :s, |s,:—  ||r    |d :— :s, |l,   :s,:s, |s,:—  ||l, |s, ||
:s   |m :r :de |r :—:r  |r :d :t, |d :—  ||r    |s :— :s  |f    :m :r  |m :—  ||f  |m  ||
:ta, |l,:—:l,  |r,:—:r, |s,:—:s,  |d :—  ||t,   |d :— :m, |f,   :s,:s, |d,:—  ||f, |d, ||
                                                                             A-men.
```

PSALM XXXVII.

25 I have been young, and now am old,
yet have I never seen
The just man left, nor that his seed
for bread have beggars been.

26 He 's ever merciful, and lends:
his seed is bless'd therefore.
27 Depart from evil, and do good,
and dwell for evermore.
28 For God loves judgment, and his saints
leaves not in any case;
They are kept ever: but cut off
shall be the sinner's race.

29 The just inherit shall the land,
and ever in it dwell:
30 The just man's mouth doth wisdom speak;
his tongue doth judgment tell.
31 In 's heart the law is of his God,
his steps slide not away.
32 The wicked man doth watch the just,
and seeketh him to slay.

33 Yet him the Lord will not forsake,
nor leave him in his hands:
The righteous will he not condemn,
when he in judgment stands.

34 Wait on the Lord, and keep his way,
and thee exalt shall he
Th' earth to inherit; when cut off
the wicked thou shalt see.

35 I saw the wicked great in pow'r,
spread like a green bay-tree:
36 He pass'd, yea, was not; him I sought,
but found he could not be.
37 Mark thou the perfect, and behold
the man of uprightness;
Because that surely of this man
the latter end is peace.

38 But those men that transgressors are
shall be destroy'd together;
The latter end of wicked men
shall be cut off for ever.
39 But the salvation of the just
is from the Lord above;
He in the time of their distress
their stay and strength doth prove.

40 The Lord shall help, and them deliver:
he shall them free and save
From wicked men; because in him
their confidence they have.

33

BLOXHAM. (C.M.) *Williams's Psalmody*, 1770.

Doh = B♭. F.t. f.B♭.

```
:d  |d :t, :l, |s, :— :t, |d .r :m :r     |d :—  ||(m)l   |s :f :m    |r :d :t,   |(d)s, :—  ||
:m, |m, :— :f, |s, :— :f, |s,.l, :s, :s,.f, |m, :— ||(s,)d  |d :t, :d   |l, :s, :s, |(s,)r, :— ||
:d  |d :— :d   |d :— :r   |d :— :t,       |d :—  ||(d)f   |m :r :d    |f :m :r    |(m)t, :—  ||
:d, |d, :— :f, |m, :— :r, |m,.f, :s, :s,  |d, :— ||(d,)f, |s, :— :l,  |f, :s, :s, |(d)s, :—  ||

:d  |d :— :t,    |l, :— :s,  |d :r :m      |r :—  ||f   |m :r :d     |s, :l, :t, |d :—  ||d  |d  ||
:m, |m, :f, :s,  |f, :m, :r, |s, :— :s,    |s, :— ||r,  |m, :f, :s,  |s, :— :f,  |m, :— ||f, |m, ||
:d  |d :— :d     |d :— :t,   |d :t, :d     |t, :— ||r   |s, :t, :d   |m :— :r    |d :—  ||l, |s, ||
:d, |d, :r, :m,  |f, :— :f,  |m, :r, :d,   |s, :— ||t,, |d, :r, :m,  |s, :— :s,  |d, :— ||f, |d, ||
                                                                                          A-men.
```

PSALM XXXVIII.

38

IN thy great indignation,
  O Lord, rebuke me not;
Nor on me lay thy chast'ning hand,
  in thy displeasure hot.
2 For in me fast thine arrows stick,
  thine hand doth press me sore:
3 And in my flesh there is no health,
  nor soundness any more.

This grief I have, because thy wrath
  is forth against me gone;
And in my bones there is no rest,
  for sin that I have done.
4 Because gone up above mine head
  my great transgressions be;
And, as a weighty burden, they
  too heavy are for me.

5 My wounds do stink, and are corrupt;
  my folly makes it so.
6 I troubled am, and much bow'd down;
  all day I mourning go.
7 For a disease that loathsome is
  so fills my loins with pain,
That in my weak and weary flesh
  no soundness doth remain.

8 So feeble and infirm am I,
  and broken am so sore,
That, through disquiet of my heart,
  I have been made to roar.
9 O Lord, all that I do desire
  is still before thine eye;
And of my heart the secret groans
  not hidden are from thee.

10 My heart doth pant incessantly,
  my strength doth quite decay;
As for mine eyes, their wonted light
  is from me gone away.
11 My lovers and my friends do stand
  at distance from my sore;
And those do stand aloof that were
  kinsmen and kind before.

12 Yea, they that seek my life lay snares:
  who seek to do me wrong
Speak things mischievous, and deceits
  imagine all day long.
13 But, as one deaf, that heareth not,
  I suffer'd all to pass;
I as a dumb man did become,
  whose mouth not open'd was:

34

BRISTOL. (C.M.)

Doh = G. *Ravenscroft's Psalter*, 1621.

f.C.

s :—	f :r	m :d	r :-.r	d :—		[f]d' :—	t :l	l :se	l :—	
s, :—	l, :s,	s, :s,	l, :t,	d :—		[l]m :—	m :d.r	m :-.r	de :—	
m :—	r :t,	d :s	f :r	m :—		[r]l :—	se :l	t :t	l :—	
d :—	f, :s,	d, :m,	f, :s,	d, :—		[r]l, :—	m :f	m :m	l, :—	

G.t.

[l]r :—	m :f	m :d	r :d	t, :—		s :—	m :f	r :r	d :—		d	d	
[r]s, :—	s, :f,	s, :s,	f, :m,.f,	s, :—		r :—	d :d	d :t,	d :—		l,	s,	
[fe]t, :—	d :d	d :d	l, :d	r :—		s :—	s :l	r :s.f	m :—		f	m	
[r]s, :—	d :l,	d :m,	f, :l,	s, :—		t, :—	d :f,	s, :s,	d, :—		f,	d,	

A-men.

[*There is a Faux-bourdon setting in the Revised Church Hymnary, No.* 260.]

14 As one that hears not, in whose mouth
are no reproofs at all.
15 For, Lord, I hope in thee; my God,
thou'lt hear me when I call.
16 For I said, Hear me, lest they should
rejoice o'er me with pride;
And o'er me magnify themselves,
when as my foot doth slide.

17 For I am near to halt, my grief
is still before mine eye:
18 For I'll declare my sin, and grieve
for mine iniquity.
19 But yet mine en'mies lively are,
and strong are they beside;
And they that hate me wrongfully
are greatly multiply'd.

20 And they for good that render ill,
as en'mies me withstood;
Yea, ev'n for this, because that I
do follow what is good.
21 Forsake me not, O Lord; my God,
far from me never be.
22 O Lord, thou my salvation art,
haste to give help to me.

39

I SAID, I will look to my ways,
lest with my tongue I sin:
In sight of wicked men my mouth
with bridle I'll keep in.
2 With silence I as dumb became,
I did myself restrain
From speaking good; but then the more
increased was my pain.

3 My heart within me waxed hot;
and, while I musing was,
The fire did burn; and from my tongue
these words I did let pass:
4 Mine end, and measure of my days,
O Lord, unto me show
What is the same; that I thereby
my frailty well may know.

5 Lo, thou my days an handbreadth mad'st;
mine age is in thine eye
As nothing: sure each man at best
is wholly vanity.
6 Sure each man walks in a vain show;
they vex themselves in vain:

BUDE. (C.M.) SAMUEL SEBASTIAN WESLEY, 1810–76.

Doh = G.

:d	m :—:r	d :—:d	f :—:m	m :r	s_1	d :r :f	m :—:r	d :—
:d	d :—:t_1	d :—:d	d :r :d	d :t_1	s_1	s_1:l_1:f_1	s_1:—:f_1	m_1:—
:m	s :—:f	m :—:m	l :s :s	s :—	t_1	d :—:d	d :—:t_1	d :—
:d	d :—:s_1	l_1 :—:l_1	l_1:t_1 :d	s_1:—	f_1	m_1:f_1 :l_1	s_1:—:s_1	d_1:—

:l	s :—:f	m :—:d	d :t_1 :l_1	s_1:—	s_1	d :—:d	f :m :r	d :—	d	d
:l_1	r :—:t_1	d :—:l_1	l_1:s_1 :fe_1	s_1:—	r_1	s_1:—:m_1	l_1:s_1 :s_1	s_1 :—	l_1	s_1
:m	s :—:s	s :—:m	r :—:d	t_1:—	t_1	d :—:d	d :— :f	m :—	f	m
:d	t_1:—:s_1	d :—:d_1	r_1:—:r_1	s_1:—	f_1	m_1:—:l_1	f_1:s_1 {:t_1 / :s_1}	{d / d_1} :—	f_1	d_1

A-men.

PSALMS XXXIX, XL.

He heaps up wealth, and doth not know
to whom it shall pertain.

7 And now, O Lord, what wait I for?
my hope is fix'd on thee.
8 Free me from all my trespasses,
the fool's scorn make not me.
9 Dumb was I, op'ning not my mouth,
because this work was thine.
10 Thy stroke take from me; by the blow
of thine hand I do pine.

11 When with rebukes thou dost correct
man for iniquity,
Thou wastes his beauty like a moth:
sure each man's vanity.
12 Attend my cry, Lord, at my tears
and pray'rs not silent be:
I sojourn as my fathers all,
and stranger am with thee.

13 O spare thou me, that I my strength
recover may again,
Before from hence I do depart,
and here no more remain.

40*

I WAITED for the Lord my God,
and patiently did bear;
At length to me he did incline
my voice and cry to hear.
2 He took me from a fearful pit,
and from the miry clay,
And on a rock he set my feet,
establishing my way.

3 He put a new song in my mouth,
our God to magnify:
Many shall see it, and shall fear,
and on the Lord rely.
4 O blessed is the man whose trust
upon the Lord relies;
Respecting not the proud, nor such
as turn aside to lies.

5 O Lord my God, full many are
the wonders thou hast done;
Thy gracious thoughts to us-ward far
above all thoughts are gone:
In order none can reckon them
to thee: if them declare,
And speak of them I would, they more
than can be number'd are.

BURFORD. (C.M.) *Chetham's Psalmody*, 1718.

Lah = G. Doh = B♭.

:l, | l, :— :t, | d :— :r | m :r :d | t, :— || se, | l, :— :t, | d :— :r | m :— ||
:m, | m, :— :m, | m, :— :se, | l, :se, :l, | se, :— || m, | m, :— :m, | m, :— :l, | se, :— ||
:d | l, :— :se, | l, :m :r | d :r :m | m :— || t, | l, :— :se, | l, :— :l, | t, :— ||
:l,, | d, :— :m, | l, :— :t, | d :t, :l, | m, :— || r, | d, :— :m, | l, :s, :f, | m, :— ||

:m | r :d :t, | d :— :r | m :r :d | t, :— || se, | l, :— :d | t, :l, :se, | l, :— || l, | l, ||
:s, | l, :— :s, | s, :— :s, | s, :— :m, | m, :— || m, | d, :— :l, | f, :— :m, | m, :— || f, | m, ||
:m | f :m :r | d :— :t, | d :t, :l, | se, :— || t, | l, :— :m | r :d :t, | d :— || r | de ||
:d, | f, :— :s, | m, :— :s, | d :s, :l, | m, :— || m, | f, :— :d, | r, :— :m, | l,, :— || r, | l,, ||

A-men.

PSALM XL.

6 No sacrifice nor offering
didst thou at all desire;
Mine ears thou bor'd: sin-off'ring thou
and burnt didst not require:
7 Then to the Lord these were my words,
I come, behold and see;
Within the volume of the book
it written is of me:

8 To do thy will I take delight,
O thou my God that art;
Yea, that most holy law of thine
I have within my heart.
9 Within the congregation great
I righteousness did preach:
Lo, thou dost know, O Lord, that I
refrained not my speech.

10 I never did within my heart
conceal thy righteousness;
I thy salvation have declar'd,
and shown thy faithfulness:
Thy kindness, which most loving is,
concealed have not I,
Nor from the congregation great
have hid thy verity.

11 Thy tender mercies, Lord, from me
O do thou not restrain;
Thy loving-kindness, and thy truth,
let them me still maintain.
12 For ills past reck'ning compass me,
and mine iniquities
Such hold upon me taken have,
I cannot lift mine eyes:

They more than hairs are on mine head,
thence is my heart dismay'd.
13 Be pleased, Lord, to rescue me;
Lord, hasten to mine aid.
14 Sham'd and confounded be they all
that seek my soul to kill;
Yea, let them backward driven be,
and sham'd, that wish me ill.

15 For a reward of this their shame
confounded let them be,
That in this manner scoffing say,
Aha, aha! to me.
16 In thee let all be glad, and joy,
who seeking thee abide;
Who thy salvation love, say still,
The Lord be magnify'd.

37

CAITHNESS. (C.M.)

Doh = E♭. *Scottish Psalter*, 1635.

```
|d  :—  |m :f  |s  :d  |t, :d     |r  :— ||m  :— |f  :s  |l  :l     |s :— ||
|s, :—  |d :d  |t, :s, |f, :s,.l, |t, :— ||d  :— |d  :ta,|l, :l,.t, |d :— ||
|m  :—  |s :f  |r  :m  |f  :m     |s  :— ||s  :— |f  :m  |f  :d.r   |m :— ||
|d  :—  |d :l, |s, :m  |r  :d     |s, :— ||d  :— |l, :s, |f, :f,    |d :— ||

|s  :—  |l :t  |d' :m  |f  :s  |l  :— ||s  :— |f  :m  |r  :r   |d :— ||f  |m ||
|m  :—  |m :r  |d  :t, |d  :d  |d  :— ||t, :— |d  :d  |d  :t,  |d :— ||d  |d ||
|m  :—  |m :s  |l  :m  |l  :s  |f  :— ||r  :— |f  :s  |l  :s.f |m :— ||l  |s ||
|d  :—  |d :t, |l, :s, |f, :m, |f, :— ||s, :— |l, :d  |f, :s,  |d :— ||f, |d ||
                                                                      A - men.
```

PSALMS XL, XLI.

17 I'm poor and needy, yet the Lord
of me a care doth take:
Thou art my help and saviour,
my God, no tarrying make.

41

BLESSED is he that wisely doth
the poor man's case consider;
For when the time of trouble is,
the Lord will him deliver.
2 God will him keep, yea, save alive;
on earth he bless'd shall live;
And to his enemies' desire
thou wilt him not up give.

3 God will give strength when he on bed
of languishing doth mourn;
And in his sickness sore, O Lord,
thou all his bed wilt turn.
4 I said, O Lord, do thou extend
thy mercy unto me;
O do thou heal my soul; for why?
I have offended thee.

5 Those that to me are enemies,
of me do evil say,
When shall he die, that so his name
may perish quite away?

6 To see me if he comes, he speaks
vain words: but then his heart
Heaps mischief to it, which he tells,
when forth he doth depart.

7 My haters jointly whispering,
'gainst me my hurt devise.
8 Mischief, say they, cleaves fast to him;
he li'th, and shall not rise.
9 Yea, ev'n mine own familiar friend,
on whom I did rely,
Who ate my bread, ev'n he his heel
against me lifted high.

10 But, Lord, be merciful to me,
and up again me raise,
That I may justly them requite
according to their ways.
11 By this I know that certainly
I favour'd am by thee;
Because my hateful enemy
triumphs not over me.

12 But as for me, thou me uphold'st
in mine integrity;
And me before thy countenance
thou sett'st continually.

CAROLINE. (C.M.)

Lah = G. Doh = B♭. Arranged from Hugh Wilson, 1766-1824.

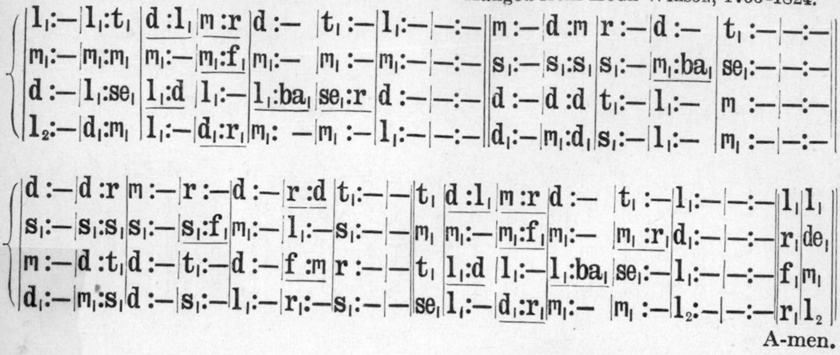

```
|l1:— |l1:t1 |d :l1 |m :r  |d :—  |t1 :—  |l1:— |— :— ||m :—  |d :m  |r :—  |d :—   |t1 :—  |— :—
|m1:— |m1:m1 |m1:—  |m1:f1 |m1:—  |m1 :—  |m1:— |— :— ||s1:— |s1:s1 |s1:— |m1:ba1 |se1:— |— :—
|d :— |l1:se1|l1:d  |l1:—  |l1:ba1|se1:r  |d :—  |— :— ||d :—  |d :d  |t1:—  |l1:—   |m :—   |— :—
|l2:— |d1:m1 |l1:—  |d1:r1 |m1: — |m1 :—  |l1:— |— :— ||d1:— |m1:d1 |s1:— |l1:—   |m1 :—  |— :—

|d :— |d :r  |m :—  |r :—  |d :—  |r :d   |t1:— |— t1 |d :l1 |m :r  |d :—    |t1 :—  |l1:— |— :— ||l1 |l1
|s1:— |s1:s1 |s1:— |s1:f1 |m1:— |l1:—  |s1:— |— m1 |m1:— |m1:f1 |m1:—   |m1 :r1 |d1:— |— :— ||r1 |de1
|m :— |d :t1 |d :—  |t1:— |d :—  |f :m   |r :—  |— t1 |l1:d |l1:— |l1:ba1 |se1:—  |l1:— |— :— ||f1 |m1
|d1:— |m1:s1 |d :—  |s1:— |l1:— |r1:—  |s1:— |— se1|l1:— |d1:r1 |m1:—  |m1 :—  |l2:— |— :— ||r1 |l2
                                                                                              A-men.
```

PSALMS XLI, XLII.

13 The Lord, the God of Israel,
be bless'd for ever then,
From age to age eternally.
Amen, yea, and amen.

42*

LIKE as the hart for water-brooks
in thirst doth pant and bray;
So pants my longing soul, O God,
that come to thee I may.
2 My soul for God, the living God,
doth thirst: when shall I near
Unto thy countenance approach,
and in God's sight appear?

3 My tears have unto me been meat,
both in the night and day,
While unto me continually,
Where is thy God? they say.
4 My soul is poured out in me,
when this I think upon;
Because that with the multitude
I heretofore had gone:

With them into God's house I went,
with voice of joy and praise;
Yea, with the multitude that kept
the solemn holy days.

5 O why art thou cast down, my soul?
why in me so dismay'd?
Trust God, for I shall praise him yet,
his count'nance is mine aid.

6 My God, my soul's cast down in me;
thee therefore mind I will
From Jordan's land, the Hermonites,
and ev'n from Mizar hill.
7 At the noise of thy water-spouts
deep unto deep doth call;
Thy breaking waves pass over me,
yea, and thy billows all.

8 His loving-kindness yet the Lord
command will in the day,
His song's with me by night; to God,
by whom I live, I'll pray:
9 And I will say to God my rock,
Why me forgett'st thou so?
Why, for my foes' oppression,
thus mourning do I go?

10 'Tis as a sword within my bones,
when my foes me upbraid;
Ev'n when by them, Where is thy God?
'tis daily to me said.

CHESHIRE. (C.M.)
Lah = E. Doh = G. *Este's Psalter*, 1592.

```
l, :— |l, :t, |d :d |t, :-.t, |l, :— |— || l, |d :-.d |r :s |m :— |— ||
m, :— |m, :m, |m, :l, |l, :se, |l, :— |— || f, |m, :m, |s, :s, |s, :— |— ||
d :— |d :t, |l, :m |m :-.r |d :— |— || l, |l,.t, :d |d :t, |d :— |— ||
l, :— |l, :se, |l, :d, |m, :m, |l, :— |— || r, |l, :-.l, |s, :s, |d, :— |— ||

:m |m :-.m |r :t, |d :r |m :— |— || m |r :d |r :t, |l, :— |— :— || l, |l, ||
:d |d :-.d |t, :s, |d :l, |se, :— |— || s, |t, :l, |l, :se, |l, :— |— :— || f, |m, ||
:s |s :-.s |s :s |m :r |t, :— |— || s |s :m |f :m.r |d :— |— :— || r |de ||
:d, |d :-.d |s, :s, |l, :f, |m, :— |— || d, |s, :l, |r, :m, |l, (l2) :— |— :— || r, |l, ||
```

A-men.

PSALMS XLII, XLIII, XLIV.

11 O why art thou cast down, my soul?
why, thus with grief opprest,
Art thou disquieted in me?
in God still hope and rest:

For yet I know I shall him praise,
who graciously to me
The health is of my countenance,
yea, mine own God is he.

43*

JUDGE me, O God, and plead my cause
against th' ungodly nation;
From the unjust and crafty man,
O be thou my salvation.
2 For thou the God art of my strength;
why thrusts thou me thee fro'?
For th' enemy's oppression
why do I mourning go?

3 O send thy light forth and thy truth;
let them be guides to me,
And bring me to thine holy hill,
ev'n where thy dwellings be.
4 Then will I to God's altar go,
to God my chiefest joy:
Yea, God, my God, thy name to praise
my harp I will employ.

5 Why art thou then cast down, my soul?
what should discourage thee?
And why with vexing thoughts art thou
disquieted in me?
Still trust in God; for him to praise
good cause I yet shall have:
He of my count'nance is the health,
my God that doth me save.

44

O GOD, we with our ears have heard,
our fathers have us told,
What works thou in their days hadst done,
ev'n in the days of old.
2 Thy hand did drive the heathen out,
and plant them in their place;
Thou didst afflict the nations,
but them thou didst increase.

3 For neither got their sword the land,
nor did their arm them save;
But thy right hand, arm, countenance;
for thou them favour gave.

40

CHICHESTER. (C.M.)

Doh = F. *Ravenscroft's Psalter*, 1621.

```
|d  :—  |m  :r  |f  :m  |l     :l    |s  :—  ||m  :—  |l  :s  |m  :fe |s  :—  ||
|s, :—  |d  :t, |d  :d  |l,.t, :d.r  |m  :—  ||d  :—  |d  :t, |d  :l, |t, :—  ||
|m  :—  |s  :s  |f  :s  |f .s  :l.t  |d' :—  ||s  :—  |f  :r  |d  :r  |r  :—  ||
|d  :—  |d  :s, |l, :d  |f,    :f    |d  :—  ||d  :—  |f, :s, |l, :r, |s, :—  ||

|s  :—  |m  :l  |s  :m     |f  :s  |l  :—  ||s  :—  |m  :d  |f  :r   |d  :—  ||f  |m    ||
|r  :—  |d  :d  |d  :d     |d  :d  |d  :—  ||t, :—  |d  :s, |l, :t,  |d  :—  ||l, |s,   ||
|s  :—  |s  :f  |s  :s     |f  :m  |f  :—  ||r  :—  |d  :m  |f  :s.f |m  :—  ||d  |d    ||
|t, :—  |d  :f  |m  :d.ta, |l, :d  |f, :—  ||s, :—  |l, :m, |r, :s,  |d  :—  ||f, |d/d, ||
                                                                                  A-men.
```

PSALM XLIV.

4 Thou art my King: for Jacob, Lord,
deliv'rances command.
5 Through thee we shall push down our foes,
that do against us stand:

We, through thy name, shall tread down those
that ris'n against us have.
6 For in my bow I shall not trust,
nor shall my sword me save.
7 But from our foes thou hast us sav'd,
our haters put to shame.
8 In God we all the day do boast,
and ever praise thy name.

9 But now we are cast off by thee,
and us thou putt'st to shame;
And when our armies do go forth,
thou go'st not with the same.
10 Thou mak'st us from the enemy,
faint-hearted, to turn back;
And they who hate us for themselves
our spoils away do take.

11 Like sheep for meat thou gavest us;
'mong heathen cast we be.
12 Thou didst for nought thy people sell;
their price enrich'd not thee.
13 Thou mak'st us a reproach to be
unto our neighbours near;
Derision and a scorn to them
that round about us are.

14 A by-word also thou dost us
among the heathen make;
The people, in contempt and spite,
at us their heads do shake.
15 Before me my confusion
continually abides;
And of my bashful countenance
the shame me ever hides:

16 For voice of him that doth reproach,
and speaketh blasphemy;
By reason of th' avenging foe,
and cruel enemy.
17 All this is come on us, yet we
have not forgotten thee;
Nor falsely in thy covenant
behav'd ourselves have we.

18 Back from thy way our heart not turn'd;
our steps no straying made;

COLCHESTER. (C.M.) *Tans'ur's Harmony of Zion*, 1735.

Doh = C.

:d' | d' :t :l | s :— :f | m :r :d | s :— || s | l :t :d' | r' :d' :t | d' :— ||
:m | d :— :d.r | s, :— :l,.t, | d :s, :l, | t, :— || d | d :r :m | f :m :r | m :— ||
:s | s :— :l.t | d' :— :s | s :— :s.fe | s :— || s | f :— :s | l :s :s | s :— ||
:d | m :— :f | m :— :r | d :t, :l, | s, :— || m | f :r :d | f :s :s, | d :— ||

:s | f :m :r | d :— :s | d' :t :l | s :— || t | d' :r' :m' | r' :d' :t | d' :— || d' | d' ||
:d | d :— :t, | d :— :r | m :r :r.d | t, :— || s | s :—.f :m | f :m :r | m :— || f | m ||
:s | l :s :—.f | m :l :s | s :—.m :fe | s :— || r' | d' :t :d' | l :s :s | s :— || l | s ||
:m | f :s :s, | l, :— :t, | d :r :r | s, :— || s.f | m :r :d | f :s :s, | d :— || f | d ||

A-men.

PSALMS XLIV, XLV.

19 Though us thou brak'st in dragons' place,
and cover'dst with death's shade.
20 If we God's name forgot, or stretch'd
to a strange god our hands,
21 Shall not God search this out? for he
heart's secrets understands.

22 Yea, for thy sake we're kill'd all day,
counted as slaughter-sheep.
23 Rise, Lord, cast us not ever off;
awake, why dost thou sleep?
24 O wherefore hidest thou thy face?
forgett'st our cause distress'd,
25 And our oppression? For our soul
is to the dust down press'd:

Our belly also on the earth
fast cleaving, hold doth take.
26 Rise for our help, and us redeem,
ev'n for thy mercies' sake.

45

MY heart brings forth a goodly thing;
my words that I indite
Concern the King: my tongue 's a pen
of one that swift doth write.

2 Thou fairer art than sons of men:
into thy lips is store
Of grace infus'd; God therefore thee
hath bless'd for evermore.

3 O thou that art the mighty One,
thy sword gird on thy thigh;
Ev'n with thy glory excellent,
and with thy majesty.
4 For meekness, truth, and righteousness,
in state ride prosp'rously;
And thy right hand shall thee instruct
in things that fearful be.

5 Thine arrows sharply pierce the heart
of th' en'mies of the King;
And under thy subjection
the people down do bring.
6 For ever and for ever is,
O God, thy throne of might;
The sceptre of thy kingdom is
a sceptre that is right.

7 Thou lovest right, and hatest ill;
for God, thy God, most high,
Above thy fellows hath with th' oil
of joy anointed thee.

42

COLESHILL. (C.M.)

Lah = A. Doh = C. *Barton's Psalms*, 1706.

```
|l  :—  |l  :s  |d' :s  |l  :l  |m  ||d' |m' :r' |d' :s  |d' :— |— ||
|m  :—  |f  :r  |s  :m  |d  :d  |d  ||m  |s  :f  |m  :r  |m  :— |— ||
|d' :—  |d' :t  |d' :d' |l  :f  |s  ||s  |d' :l  |s  :t  |d' :— |— ||
|l  :—  |f  :s  |m  :d  |f  :f  |d  ||d  |d  :r  |m  :s  |d  :— |— ||

:d' |m' :r' |d' :s  |l  :l  |m  ||d' |s   :l  |r'.d':t  |l  :— ||l |l  ||
:s  |s  :s  |m  :d  |d  :d  |d  ||m  |m.r :d  |f .m :r  |d  :— ||r |de ||
:m' |d' :t  |d' :d' |l  :f  |s  ||d' |t   :l  |l    :se |l  :— ||f |m  ||
:d  |d' :s  |l  :m  |f  :f  |d  ||d  |m   :f  |r    :m  |l, :— ||r |l, ||
                                                                   A-men.
```

PSALM XLV.

8 Of aloes, myrrh, and cassia,
a smell thy garments had,
Out of the iv'ry palaces,
whereby they made thee glad.

9 Among thy women honourable
kings' daughters were at hand:
Upon thy right hand did the queen
in gold of Ophir stand.

10 O daughter, hearken and regard,
and do thine ear incline;
Likewise forget thy father's house,
and people that are thine.

11 Then of the King desir'd shall be
thy beauty veh'mently:
Because he is thy Lord, do thou
him worship rev'rently.

12 The daughter there of Tyre shall be
with gifts and off'rings great:
Those of the people that are rich
thy favour shall entreat.

13 Behold, the daughter of the King
all glorious is within;
And with embroideries of gold
her garments wrought have been.

14 She shall be brought unto the King
in robes with needle wrought;
Her fellow-virgins following
shall unto thee be brought.

15 They shall be brought with gladness great,
and mirth on ev'ry side,
Into the palace of the King,
and there they shall abide.

16 Instead of those thy fathers dear,
thy children thou may'st take,
And in all places of the earth
them noble princes make.

17 Thy name remember'd I will make
through ages all to be:
The people therefore evermore
shall praises give to thee.

45 (2)*

ANOTHER OF THE SAME.

MY heart inditing is
good matter in a song:
I speak the things that I have made,
which to the King belong:
My tongue shall be as quick,
his honour to indite,
As is the pen of any scribe
that useth fast to write.

2 Thou'rt fairest of all men;
grace in thy lips doth flow:

FAUX-BOURDON SETTING.

COLESHILL. (C.M.) THOMAS CUTHBERTSON LEITHEAD PRITCHARD, 1885-

Lah = A. Doh = C.

:l	d' :-.t	l.t:d'	r' :d'	t		d'	s :l.t	d' :r'	m' :d'.r'	m'	
d :—	m.f :s	f :s	f :m.ba	se		l	s :s	s :f	m :-.f	s	
l :—	l :s	d' :s	l :l	m		d'	m' :r'	d' :s	d' :—	—	
l_1 :—	l :m	f :m	r :l_1	m		l_1	d :f	m :r	d :d'	t	

:fe'	s' :-.f'	m' :-.r'	d' :r'	t		d'	t :l	l :se	l :—	
:l	d' :t	d' :m	f.m:r.l	se		m	m.r:d	f :m.r	d :—	
:d'	m' :r'	d' :s	l :l	m		d'	s :l	r'.d':t	l :—	
:l	s :s_1	l_1 :ta_1	l_1 :f	m		l_1	m :f	r :m	l_1 :—	

[*Copyright*, 1929, *by Oxford University Press.*]

PSALM XLV.

And therefore blessings evermore
on thee doth God bestow.
3 Thy sword gird on thy thigh,
thou that art most of might:
Appear in dreadful majesty,
and in thy glory bright.

4 For meekness, truth, and right,
ride prosp'rously in state;
And thy right hand shall teach to thee
things terrible and great.
5 Thy shafts shall pierce their hearts
that foes are to the King;
Whereby into subjection
the people thou shalt bring.

6 Thy royal seat, O Lord,
for ever shall remain:
The sceptre of thy kingdom doth
all righteousness maintain.
7 Thou lov'st right, and hat'st ill;
for God, thy God, most high,
Above thy fellows hath with th' oil
of joy anointed thee.

8 Of myrrh and spices sweet
a smell thy garments had,
Out of the iv'ry palaces,
whereby they made thee glad.
9 And in thy glorious train
kings' daughters waiting stand;
And thy fair queen, in Ophir gold,
doth stand at thy right hand.

10 O daughter, take good heed,
incline, and give good ear;
Thou must forget thy kindred all,
and father's house most dear.
11 Thy beauty to the King
shall then delightful be:
And do thou humbly worship him,
because thy Lord is he.

12 The daughter then of Tyre
there with a gift shall be,
And all the wealthy of the land
shall make their suit to thee.
13 The daughter of the King
all glorious is within;
And with embroideries of gold
her garments wrought have been.

14 She cometh to the King
in robes with needle wrought;
The virgins that do follow her
shall unto thee be brought.
15 They shall be brought with joy,
and mirth on ev'ry side,
Into the palace of the King,
and there they shall abide.

43

CONSOLATION. (C.M.)

Doh = G.

Adapted from LUDWIG VAN BEETHOVEN, 1770–1827.

```
:s, |d  :d  |d  :d  |m  :r  |d  ||s, |r  :r  |f  :m |r  :— |— ||
:m, |m, :f, |s, :l, |s, :f, |m, ||s, |s, :t, |t, :d |t, :— |— ||
:d  |d  :d  |d  :d  |d  :t, |d  ||m  |r  :s  |s  :s |s  :— |— ||
:d, |d, :r, |m, :f, |s, :s, |d, ||d  |t, :s, |r  :d |s, :— |— ||
```

```
:s, |m  :m   |m  :m   |f   :s   |l  ||f.r|d  :d  |m  :r  |d  :— |— ||d  |d  ||
:s, |s, :se, |l, :s,  |d   :ta, |l, ||l, |s, :s, |t, :t, |s, :— |— ||l, |s, ||
:r  |m  :m   |m  :d   |d.r :m   |f  ||r.f|m  :m  |s  :f  |m  :— |— ||f  |m  ||
:t, |d  :r   |d  :ta, |l,  :s,  |f, ||f, |s, :s, |s, :s, |d, :— |— ||f, |d, ||
```

A-men.

PSALMS XLV, XLVI.

16 And in thy fathers' stead,
thy children thou may'st take,
And in all places of the earth
them noble princes make.
17 I will shew forth thy name
to generations all:
Therefore the people evermore
to thee give praises shall.

46*

GOD is our refuge and our strength,
in straits a present aid;
2 Therefore, although the earth remove,
we will not be afraid:
Though hills amidst the seas be cast;
3 Though waters roaring make,
And troubled be; yea, though the hills
by swelling seas do shake.

4 A river is, whose streams do glad
the city of our God;
The holy place, wherein the Lord
most high hath his abode.

5 God in the midst of her doth dwell;
nothing shall her remove:
The Lord to her an helper will,
and that right early, prove.

6 The heathen rag'd tumultuously,
the kingdoms moved were:
The Lord God uttered his voice,
the earth did melt for fear.
7 The Lord of hosts upon our side
doth constantly remain:
The God of Jacob 's our refuge,
us safely to maintain.

8 Come, and behold what wondrous works
have by the Lord been wrought;
Come, see what desolations
he on the earth hath brought.
9 Unto the ends of all the earth
wars into peace he turns:
The bow he breaks, the spear he cuts,
in fire the chariot burns.

10 Be still, and know that I am God;
among the heathen I
Will be exalted; I on earth
will be exalted high.

44

CORONA. (C.M.)

Lah = A. Doh = C. ELIZABETH RAYMOND-BARKER, 1829–1916.

```
:m  |d' :l  |se :t  |l  :f  |m  ||m  |m  :d' |t  :m  |l  :—  |—  ||
:m  |m  :m  |m  :m  |m  :r  |t, ||t, |m  :m  |re :r  |d  :—  |—  ||
:d' |d' :d' |r' :se |l  :l  |se ||se |l  :l  |fe :se |l  :—  |—  ||
:l  |l  :l  |t  :t, |d  :r  |m  ||r  |d  :l, |t, :m  |l, :—  |—  ||
```

```
:l  |r' :-.d'|t  :l  |l  :s  |s  ||d' |d' :-.d'|m' :r' |d' :—  |—  ||d' |d' ||
:m  |s  :-.s |s  :f  |f  :f  |m  ||fe |s  :-.s |s  :f  |m  :—  |—  ||f  |m  ||
:d' |t  :-.m'|r' :d' |t  :r' |d' ||r' |m' :-.m'|d' :t  |d' :—  |—  ||l  |s  ||
:l  |s  :-.s |s  :s  |s  :t  |d' ||l  |s  :-.s |s  :s  |d  :—  |—  ||f  |d  ||
                                                                   A-men.
```

PSALMS XLVI, XLVII, XLVIII.

11 Our God, who is the Lord of hosts,
is still upon our side;
The God of Jacob our refuge
for ever will abide.

47

ALL people, clap your hands; to God
with voice of triumph shout:
2 For dreadful is the Lord most high,
great King the earth throughout.
3 The heathen people under us
he surely shall subdue;
And he shall make the nations
under our feet to bow.

4 The lot of our inheritance
chuse out for us shall he,
Of Jacob, whom he loved well,
ev'n the excellency.
5 God is with shouts gone up, the Lord
with trumpets sounding high.
6 Sing praise to God, sing praise, sing praise,
praise to our King sing ye.

7 For God is King of all the earth;
with knowledge praise express.
8 God rules the nations: God sits on
his throne of holiness.
9 The princes of the people are
assembled willingly;
Ev'n of the God of Abraham
they who the people be.

For why? the shields that do defend
the earth are only his:
They to the Lord belong; yea, he
exalted greatly is.

48*

GREAT is the Lord, and greatly he
is to be praised still,
Within the city of our God,
upon his holy hill.
2 Mount Sion stands most beautiful,
the joy of all the land;
The city of the mighty King
on her north side doth stand.

3 The Lord within her palaces
is for a refuge known.
4 For, lo, the kings that gather'd were
together, by have gone.

45

COVENTRY. (C.M.)

Lah = F. Doh = A♭. SAMUEL HOWARD, 1710–82.

S	l_1 :—	m :t_1	d :r	d :t_1	l_1 :— ‖	d :—	r :m	f :m.r	m :— ‖
A	m_1 :—	m_1 :se_1	l_1 :l_1	l_1 :se_1	l_1 :— ‖	m_1 :—	l_1 :s_1	f_1 :s_1	s_1 :— ‖
T	d :—	t_1 :m	m :f	m :m.r	d :— ‖	d :—	d :d	d :t_1	d :— ‖
B	l_1 :—	se_1 :m_1	l_1 :r_1	m_1 :m_1	l_2 :— ‖	l_1 :—	f_1 :m_1	r_1 :s_1	d_1 :— ‖

S	m :—	s :d	t_1 :d	r :m	f :— ‖	r :—	m :l_1.t_1	d :t_1	l_1 :— ‖	l_1	l_1 ‖
A	s_1 :—	s_1 :l_1	s_1 :s_1	l_1 :s_1	f_1 :— ‖	s_1 :—	s_1 :l_1	l_1 :se_1	l_1 :— ‖	f_1	m_1 ‖
T	d :—	d :f.m	r :d	l_1 :t_1.de	r :— ‖	t_1 :—	d :d.r	m :m.r	d :— ‖	r	de ‖
B	d :—	m_1 :f_1	s_1 :m_1	f_1 :m_1	r_1 :— ‖	s_1 :—	d_1 :f_1	m_1 :m_1	l_2 :— ‖	r_1	l_1 l_2 ‖

A-men.

5 But when they did behold the same,
they, wond'ring, would not stay;
But, being troubled at the sight,
they thence did haste away.

6 Great terror there took hold on them;
they were possess'd with fear;
Their grief came like a woman's pain,
when she a child doth bear.
7 Thou Tarshish ships with east wind break'st:
8 As we have heard it told,
So, in the city of the Lord,
our eyes did it behold;

In our God's city, which his hand
for ever stablish will.
9 We of thy loving-kindness thought,
Lord, in thy temple still.
10 O Lord according to thy name,
through all the earth 's thy praise;
And tny right hand, O Lord, is full
of righteousness always.

11 Because thy judgments are made known,
let Sion mount rejoice;
Of Judah let the daughters all
send forth a cheerful voice.
12 Walk about Sion, and go round;
the high tow'rs thereof tell:
13 Consider ye her palaces,
and mark her bulwarks well;

That ye may tell posterity.
14 For this God doth abide
Our God for evermore; he will
ev'n unto death us guide.

49

HEAR this, all people, and give ear,
all in the world that dwell;
2 Both low and high, both rich and poor.
3 My mouth shall wisdom tell.
My heart shall knowledge meditate.
4 I will incline mine ear
To parables, and on the harp
my sayings dark declare.

5 Amidst those days that evil be,
why should I, fearing, doubt?
When of my heels th' iniquity
shall compass me about.

CREDITON. (C.M.)

Doh = C. THOMAS CLARK, 1775–1859.

:s |d' :t |d' :s |l :s.f |m ||s |l.t :d' |f :m |r :— |— ||
:m |m :f |s :m |f :m.r |d ||d |d :d |t, :d |t, :— |— ||
:s |s :s |s :d' |d' :t |d' ||d'.t |l :s |s :s |s :— |— ||
:d |d :r |m :d |f :s |d ||m |f :m |r :d |s, :— |— ||

:s |s :l.t |d' :m' |r' :d' |t ||s |l.t :d' |m'.r' :d'.t |d' :— |— ||d' |d' ||
:r |s :f |m :s |s.r :m.fe |s ||s |f :s |f :m :r |m :— |— ||f |m ||
:t |d' :f |s :d' |r' :l |r' ||d' |d'.r' :d' |l :s |s :— |— ||l |s ||
:s.f |m :r |d :d' |t :l |s ||m |f :m |f :s |d :— |— ||f |d ||

A-men.

PSALM XLIX.

6 Whoe'er they be that in their wealth
their confidence do pitch,
And boast themselves, because they are
become exceeding rich:

7 Yet none of these his brother can
redeem by any way;
Nor can he unto God for him
sufficient ransom pay,
8 (Their soul's redemption precious is,
and it can never be,)
9 That still he should for ever live,
and not corruption see.

10 For why? he seeth that wise men die,
and brutish fools also
Do perish; and their wealth, when dead,
to others they let go.
11 Their inward thought is, that their house
and dwelling-places shall
Stand through all ages; they their lands
by their own names do call.

12 But yet in honour shall not man
abide continually;
But passing hence, may be compar'd
unto the beasts that die.
13 Thus brutish folly plainly is
their wisdom and their way;
Yet their posterity approve
what they do fondly say.

14 Like sheep they in the grave are laid,
and death shall them devour;
And in the morning upright men
shall over them have pow'r:
Their beauty from their dwelling shall
consume within the grave.
15 But from hell's hand God will me free,
for he shall me receive.

16 Be thou not then afraid when one
enriched thou dost see,
Nor when the glory of his house
advanced is on high:
17 For he shall carry nothing hence
when death his days doth end;
Nor shall his glory after him
into the grave descend.

CRIMOND. (C.M.) DAVID GRANT, 1833-1893.

Doh = F.

:s, |m :— :f.,r |s :— :f .r |d :— :t, |d :— || m |m :r :r |fe :— :fe |s :— ||
:s, |d :— :t, |d :—.t, :l, |s, :l, :s, |s, :— || d |s, :— :t, |l, :t, :d |t, :— ||
:s |s :— :s |s :— :r .f |m :f :r |m :— || s |d :r :r |r :— :l |s :— ||
:s |d :— :r.,f |m :m, :f, |s, :— :s, |d :— || d |d :t, :s, |r, :— :r, |s, :— ||

:m |m :f :m |r :— :m |f :s :f |m :— || m |r :f :l |d :— :t, |d :— || d |d ||
:d |d :r :d |t, :— :d |d :t, :r |d :— || d.t, |l, :— :l, |s, :— :s, |s, :— || l, |s, ||
:s |s :— :s |s :— :s |l :s :s |s :— || s |f :r :f |m :— :r |m :— || f |m ||
:d |d :t, :d.m |s :f :m |r :s, :l,.t, |d :— || m, |f, :— :r, |s, :— :s, |d :— || f, |d ||

A-men.

PSALMS XLIX, L.

18 Although he his own soul did bless
whilst he on earth did live;
(And when thou to thyself dost well,
men will thee praises give;)
19 He to his fathers' race shall go,
they never shall see light.
20 Man honour'd wanting knowledge is
like beasts that perish quite.

50*

THE mighty God, the Lord,
hath spoken, and did call
The earth, from rising of the sun,
to where he hath his fall.
2 From out of Sion hill,
which of excellency
And beauty the perfection is,
God shined gloriously.

3 Our God shall surely come,
keep silence shall not he:
Before him fire shall waste, great storms
shall round about him be.
4 Unto the heavens clear
he from above shall call,
And to the earth likewise, that he
may judge his people all.

5 Together let my saints
unto me gather'd be,
Those that by sacrifice have made
a covenant with me.
6 And then the heavens shall
his righteousness declare:
Because the Lord himself is he
by whom men judged are.

7 My people Isr'el hear,
speak will I from on high,
Against thee I will testify;
God, ev'n thy God, am I.
8 I for thy sacrifice
no blame will on thee lay,
Nor for burnt-off'rings, which to me
thou offer'dst ev'ry day.

9 I'll take no calf nor goats
from house or fold of thine:
10 For beasts of forest, cattle all
on thousand hills, are mine.
11 The fowls on mountains high
are all to me well known;
Wild beasts which in the fields do lie
ev'n they are all mine own.

12 Then, if I hungry were,
I would not tell it thee;

CULROSS. (C.M.) *Scottish Psalter*, 1634.

Lah = A. Doh = C.

m :—	l :d'	t :l	se :l	t :—		m :—	l :se	l :t	d' :—	
d :—	m :m	m :m	m.r :d	m :—		t, :—	m :m	m :s	s :—	
l :—	l :l	se :l	m :l	se :—		se :—	l :t	d' :r'	m' :—	
l, :—	d :l,	m :d	t, :l,	m :—		m :—	d :m	l :s	d :—	

s :—	d' :m'	r' :d'	t :l	se :—		m :—	l :d'	t :t	l :—		l	l	
m :—	s :s	s :m	f :r	m :—		m :—	m :m	f :m.r	d :—		r	de	
d' :—	d' :d'	t :d'	r' :l	t :—		se :—	l :l	l :se	l :—		f	m	
d :—	m :d	s :l	r :f	m :—		m :-.r	d :l,	r :m	l, :—		r	l,	

A-men.

PSALM L.

Because the world, and fulness all
thereof, belongs to me.
13 Will I eat flesh of bulls?
or goats' blood drink will I?
14 Thanks offer thou to God, and pay
thy vows to the most High.

15 And call upon me when
in trouble thou shalt be;
I will deliver thee, and thou
my name shalt glorify.
16 But to the wicked man
God saith, My laws and truth
Should'st thou declare? how dar'st thou take
my cov'nant in thy mouth?

17 Sith thou instruction hat'st,
which should thy ways direct;
And sith my words behind thy back
thou cast'st, and dost reject.
18 When thou a thief didst see,
with him thou didst consent;
And with the vile adulterers
partaker on thou went.

19 Thou giv'st thy mouth to ill,
thy tongue deceit doth frame;
20 Thou sitt'st, and 'gainst thy brother speak'st,
thy mother's son dost shame.

21 Because I silence kept,
while thou these things hast wrought;
That I was altogether like
thyself, hath been thy thought;

Yet I will thee reprove,
and set before thine eyes,
In order ranked, thy misdeeds
and thine iniquities.
22 Now, ye that God forget,
this carefully consider;
Lest I in pieces tear you all,
and none can you deliver.

23 Whoso doth offer praise
me glorifies; and I
Will shew him God's salvation,
that orders right his way.

50 (2)

ANOTHER OF THE SAME.

THE mighty God, the Lord, hath spoke,
and call'd the earth upon,
Ev'n from the rising of the sun
unto his going down.

49

DRUMCLOG. (C.M.)

Doh = E♭.

MATTHEW WILSON, c. 1812-56.

```
:d |m  :l   |s.m:r .d |d' :l  |s  ||l    |s  :d .r |m  :r   |d :— |— ||
:d |d  :d   |d  :t,.d |d  :d  |d  ||l,.t,|d  :d    |d  :t,  |d :— |— ||
:m |s  :f   |m.s:f .s |f  :f  |m  ||f    |s  :m .f |s  :-.f |m :— |— ||
:d |d  :f,  |d  :r .m |l, :f, |d  ||f    |m  :l,   |s, :s,  |d :— |— ||
```

```
:s |m :d'.l |s  :f  |m.s:l .f |r  ||m |s :d'.l  |s  :r   |d :— |— ||d  |d  ||
:d |d :d .r |m  :r  |d  :d    |t, ||d |d :d     |d  :t,  |d :— |— ||l, |s, ||
:m |s :l .t |d' :s  |s.m:f .l |s  ||s |m :f     |m  :s .f|m :— |— ||f  |m  ||
:d |d :f    |m  :t, |d  :f,   |s, ||d |d :l,.f, |s, :s,  |d :— |— ||f, |d  ||
```

A-men.

PSALM L.

2 From out of Sion, his own hill,
where the perfection high
Of beauty is, from thence the Lord
hath shined gloriously.

3 Our God shall come, and shall no more
be silent, but speak out:
Before him fire shall waste, great storms
shall compass him about.
4 He to the heavens from above,
and to the earth below,
Shall call, that he his judgments may
before his people shew.

5 Let all my saints together be
unto me gathered;
Those that by sacrifice with me
a covenant have made.
6 And then the heavens shall declare
his righteousness abroad:
Because the Lord himself doth come;
none else is judge but God.

7 Hear, O my people, and I'll speak;
O Israel by name,
Against thee I will testify;
God, ev'n thy God, I am.
8 I for thy sacrifices few
reprove thee never will,
Nor for burnt-off'rings to have been
before me offer'd still.

9 I'll take no bullock nor he-goats
from house nor folds of thine:
10 For beasts of forests, cattle all
on thousand hills, are mine.
11 The fowls are all to me well known
that mountains high do yield;
And I do challenge as mine own
the wild beasts of the field.

12 If I were hungry, I would not
to thee for need complain;
For earth, and all its fulness, doth
to me of right pertain.
13 That I to eat the flesh of bulls
take pleasure dost thou think?
Or that I need, to quench my thirst,
the blood of goats to drink?

14 Nay, rather unto me, thy God,
thanksgiving offer thou:
To the most High perform thy word,
and fully pay thy vow:

DUKE'S TUNE. (C.M.)

Doh = F. *Scottish Psalter*, 1615.

d :—	m :f	s :s	f :f	m :—	m :—	r :s	s :fe	s :—
d :—	d :d	t, :d	d :d	d :—	d :—	t, :t,	l, :l,	t, :—
m :—	s :d	r :m	f :l	s :—	s :—	s :s	m :r	r :—
d :—	d :l,	s, :d	l, :f,	d :—	d :—	s, :m	d :r	s, :—

s :—	l :s	f :m	r :d	t, :—	m :—	r :d	d :t,	d :—	d	d
d :—	d :t,	l, :s,	l, :m,.f,	s, :—	s, :—	t, :d	l, :s,	s, :—	l,	s,
m :—	f :r	d.r :m	f :d	r :—	m :—	s :s	f :r	m :—	f	m
d :—	f, :s,	l,.t, :d	f, :l,	s, :—	d :—	s, :m,	f, :s,	d :—	f,	d

A-men.

15 And in the day of trouble great
see that thou call on me;
I will deliver thee, and thou
my name shalt glorify.

16 But God unto the wicked saith,
Why should'st thou mention make
Of my commands? how dar'st thou in
thy mouth my cov'nant take?
17 Sith it is so that thou dost hate
all good instruction;
And sith thou cast'st behind thy back,
and slight'st my words each one.

18 When thou a thief didst see, then straight
thou join'dst with him in sin,
And with the vile adulterers
thou hast partaker been.
19 Thy mouth to evil thou dost give,
thy tongue deceit doth frame.
20 Thou sitt'st, and 'gainst thy brother speak'st,
thy mother's son to shame.

21 These things thou wickedly hast done,
and I have silent been:
Thou thought'st that I was like thyself,
and did approve thy sin:
But I will sharply thee reprove,
and I will order right
Thy sins and thy transgressions
in presence of thy sight.

22 Consider this, and be afraid,
ye that forget the Lord,
Lest I in pieces tear you all,
when none can help afford.
23 Who off'reth praise me glorifies:
I will shew God's salvation
To him that ordereth aright
his life and conversation.

51*

AFTER thy loving-kindness, Lord,
have mercy upon me:
For thy compassions great, blot out
all mine iniquity.
2 Me cleanse from sin, and throughly wash
from mine iniquity:
3 For my transgressions I confess;
my sin I ever see.

DUNDEE (WINDSOR). (C.M.) *Damon's Psalmes*, 1591.

Lah = G. Doh = B♭.

l_1 :— | l_1 :t_1 | d :t_1 | l_1 :l_1 | se_1 :— || d :— | m :r | d :t_1 | d :— ||
m_1 :— | m_1 :m_1 | m_1 :m_1 | m_1 :m_1 | m_1 :— || m_1 :— | s_1 :l_1 | s_1 :-.f_1 | m_1 :— ||
d :— | d :t_1 | l_1 :se_1 | l_1 :d | t_1 :— || d :— | d :f | m :r | d :— ||
l_1 :— | l_1 :se_1 | l_1 :m_1 | d_1 :l_2 | m_1 :— || l_1 :— | m_1 :f_1 | s_1 :s_1 | d_1 :— ||

d :— | m :r | d :t_1 | l_1 :l_1 | se_1 :— || d :— | t_1 :l_1 | l_1 :se_1 | l_1 :— || l_1 | l_1 ||
s_1 :— | s_1 :s_1 | m_1 :s_1 | f_1 :f_1 | m_1 :— || s_1 :— | s_1 :m_1 | f_1 :m_1 | m_1 :— || f_1 | m_1 ||
m :— | d :t_1 | d :m | d :r | t_1 :— || m :— | r :d | r :t_1 | d :— || r | de ||
d_1 :— | d :s_1 | l_1 :m_1 | f_1 :r_1 | m_1 :— || d_1 :— | s_1 :l_1 | r_1 :m_1 | l_1 :— || r_1 | l_2 ||

A-men.

PSALM LI.

4 'Gainst thee, thee only, have I sinn'd,
in thy sight done this ill;
That when thou speak'st thou may'st be just,
and clear in judging still.
5 Behold, I in iniquity
was form'd the womb within;
My mother also me conceiv'd
in guiltiness and sin.

6 Behold, thou in the inward parts
with truth delighted art;
And wisdom thou shalt make me know
within the hidden part.
7 Do thou with hyssop sprinkle me,
I shall be cleansed so;
Yea, wash thou me, and then I shall
be whiter than the snow.

8 Of gladness and of joyfulness
make me to hear the voice;
That so these very bones which thou
hast broken may rejoice.
9 All mine iniquities blot out,
thy face hide from my sin.
10 Create a clean heart, Lord, renew
a right sp'rit me within.

11 Cast me not from thy sight, nor take
thy Holy Sp'rit away.
12 Restore me thy salvation's joy;
with thy free Sp'rit me stay.
13 Then will I teach thy ways unto
those that transgressors be;
And those that sinners are shall then
be turned unto thee.

14 O God, of my salvation God,
me from blood-guiltiness
Set free; then shall my tongue aloud
sing of thy righteousness.
15 My closed lips, O Lord, by thee
let them be opened;
Then shall thy praises by my mouth
abroad be published.

16 For thou desir'st not sacrifice,
else would I give it thee;
Nor wilt thou with burnt-offering
at all delighted be.
17 A broken spirit is to God
a pleasing sacrifice:
A broken and a contrite heart,
Lord, thou wilt not despise.

DUNDEE (WINDSOR). (C.M.) DESCANT. ALAN GRAY, 1855-

Lah = G. Doh = B♭.

Descant.
d :— |d :r |m :s |m :r |m :— ||m :— |s :l |m :r |d :— ||
Melody.
l, :— |l, :t, |d :t, |l, :l, |se, :— ||d :— |m :r |d :t, |d :— ||

m :— |s :s |m :m |d :r |t, :— ||l, :— |f :r |m :-.r |d :— ||
d :— |m :r |d :t, |l, :l, |se, :— ||d :— |t, :l, |l, :se, |l, :— ||

PSALMS LI, LII, LIII.

18 Shew kindness, and do good, O Lord,
to Sion, thine own hill:
The walls of thy Jerusalem
build up of thy good will.
19 Then righteous off'rings shall thee please,
and off'rings burnt, which they
With whole burnt-off'rings, and with calves,
shall on thine altar lay.

52

WHY dost thou boast, O mighty man,
of mischief and of ill?
The goodness of Almighty God
endureth ever still.
2 Thy tongue mischievous calumnies
deviseth subtilely,
Like to a razor sharp to cut,
working deceitfully.

3 Ill more than good, and more than truth
thou lovest to speak wrong:
4 Thou lovest all-devouring words,
O thou deceitful tongue.
5 So God shall thee destroy for aye,
remove thee, pluck thee out
Quite from thy house, out of the land
of life he shall thee root.
6 The righteous shall it see, and fear,
and laugh at him they shall:
7 Lo, this the man is that did not
make God his strength at all:
But he in his abundant wealth
his confidence did place;
And he took strength unto himself
from his own wickedness.
8 But I am in the house of God
like to an olive green:
My confidence for ever hath
upon God's mercy been.
9 And I for ever will thee praise,
because thou hast done this:
I on thy name will wait; for good
before thy saints it is.

53

THAT there is not a God, the fool
doth in his heart conclude:
They are corrupt, their works are vile,
not one of them doth good.

52

DUNFERMLINE. (C.M.)

Doh=F.

Scottish Psalter, 1615.

|d :— |d :r |m :f |s :s |m :— ||m :— |l :s |s :fe |s :— ||

|s$_1$:— |s$_1$:l$_1$.t$_1$ |d :d |d :t$_1$ |d :— ||d :— |l$_1$.t$_1$:d |r :r.d |t$_1$:— ||

|m :— |m :f |s :d |r :s |s :— ||s :— |f :s |l :l |s :— ||

|d :— |m :r |d :l$_1$ |s$_1$:s$_1$ |d :— ||d :— |f :m |r :r |s$_1$:— ||

|s :— |m :s |l :s |f :m |r :— ||m :— |r :d |d :t$_1$ |d :— ||d |d ||

|r :— |d :d.t$_1$ |l$_1$:t$_1$ |d.r :d |t$_1$:— ||d :— |t$_1$:d |l$_1$:s$_1$ |s$_1$:— ||l$_1$ |s$_1$ ||

|s :— |s :d |f.m :r |l :s |s :— ||s :— |s.f :m |f.m :r |m :— ||f |m ||

|t$_1$:— |d :m$_1$ |f$_1$:s$_1$ |l$_1$.t$_1$:d |s$_1$:— ||d :— |s$_1$:l$_1$ |f$_1$:s$_1$ |d / d$_1$:— ||f$_1$ |d$_1$ ||

A-men.

2 The Lord upon the sons of men
from heav'n did cast his eyes,
To see if any one there was
that sought God, and was wise.

3 They altogether filthy are,
they all are backward gone;
And there is none that doeth good,
no, not so much as one.

4 These workers of iniquity,
do they not know at all,
That they my people eat as bread,
and on God do not call?

5 Ev'n there they were afraid, and stood
with trembling, all dismay'd,
Whereas there was no cause at all
why they should be afraid:
For God his bones that thee besieg'd
hath scatter'd all abroad;
Thou hast confounded them, for they
despised are of God.

6 Let Isr'el's help from Sion come:
when back the Lord shall bring
His captives, Jacob shall rejoice,
and Israel shall sing.

54

SAVE me, O God, by thy great name,
and judge me by thy strength:
2 My prayer hear, O God; give ear
unto my words at length.
3 For they that strangers are to me
do up against me rise;
Oppressors seek my soul, and God
set not before their eyes.

4 The Lord my God my helper is,
lo, therefore I am bold:
He taketh part with ev'ry one
that doth my soul uphold.
5 Unto mine enemies he shall
mischief and ill repay:
O for thy truth's sake cut them off,
and sweep them clean away.

6 I will a sacrifice to thee
give with free willingness;
Thy name, O Lord, because 'tis good,
with praise I will confess.
7 For he hath me delivered
from all adversities;
And his desire mine eye hath seen
upon mine enemies.

FAUX-BOURDON SETTING.

DUNFERMLINE. (C.M.) MARTIN SHAW, 1876–

Doh = F.

```
m  :—  |m  :r  |d  :f  |r  :r  |m  :— ‖d  :—  |f  :m  |r  :r  |r  :— ‖
s, :—  |s, :s, |s, :d  |d  :t, |d  :— ‖s, :—  |d  :d  |l, :l, |t, :— ‖
d  :—  |d  :r  |m  :f  |s  :s  |m  :— ‖m  :—  |l  :s  |s  :fe |s  :— ‖
d  :—  |d  :t, |d  :l, |s, :s, |d  :— ‖d  :—  |f, :d  |r  :r  |s, :— ‖

m  :—  |m  :r  |f  :m  |r  :-.d |l, :— ‖d  :—  |t, :l, |l, :s, |s, :— ‖l, |s, ‖
d  :—  |d  :t, |d  :d  |l, :l,  |f, :— ‖s, :—  |s, :m, |f, :r, |m, :— ‖f, |m, ‖
s  :—  |m  :s  |l  :s  |f  :m   |r  :— ‖m  :—  |r  :d  |d  :t, |d  :— ‖d  |d  ‖
d  :—  |d  :s, |f, :d  |r  :l,  |r, :— ‖d, :—  |s, :l, |f, :s, |d, :— ‖f, |d, ‖
```

A-men.

* *For use only when the Faux-bourdon setting is sung to the closing verse.*

[*Copyright*, 1915, *by J. Curwen & Sons, Ltd.*]

PSALM LV.

55

LORD, hear my pray'r, hide not thyself
from my entreating voice:
2 Attend and hear me; in my plaint
I mourn and make a noise.
3 Because of th' en'my's voice, and for
lewd men's oppression great:
On me they cast iniquity,
and they in wrath me hate.

4 Sore pain'd within me is my heart:
death's terrors on me fall.
5 On me comes trembling, fear and dread
o'erwhelmed me withal.
6 O that I, like a dove, had wings,
said I, then would I flee
Far hence, that I might find a place
where I in rest might be.

7 Lo, then far off I wander would,
and in the desert stay;
8 From windy storm and tempest I
would haste to 'scape away.
9 O Lord, on them destruction bring,
and do their tongues divide;
For in the city violence
and strife I have espy'd.

10 They day and night upon the walls
do go about it round:
There mischief is, and sorrow there
in midst of it is found.
11 Abundant wickedness there is
within her inward part;
And from her streets deceitfulness
and guile do not depart.

12 He was no foe that me reproach'd,
then that endure I could;
Nor hater that did 'gainst me boast,
from him me hide I would.
13 But thou, man, who mine equal, guide,
and mine acquaintance wast:
14 We join'd sweet counsels, to God's house
in company we past.

15 Let death upon them seize, and down
let them go quick to hell;
For wickedness doth much abound
among them where they dwell.
16 I'll call on God: God will me save.
17 I'll pray, and make a noise
At ev'ning, morning, and at noon;
and he shall hear my voice.

53

DURHAM. (C.M.)

Doh = F. *Ravenscroft's Psalter*, 1621.

d :—	s :m	l :s	m :d	r :—		f :—	m :s	l :l	s :—	
s, :—	s, :s,	l, :t,	d :d	t, :—		d :—	d :t,	r :r.d	t, :—	
m :—	r :d	f :r	d :s	s :—		l :—	s :s	s :fe	s :—	
d :—	t, :d	f, :s,	l, :m,	s, :—		f, :—	d :m	r :r	s, :—	

s :—	f :m	s :d	t, :d	r :—		m :—	r :f	m :r	d :—		d	d	
s, :—	l,.t, :d	r :s,	s, :s,	s, :—		d :—	l, :r	d :t,	d :—		l,	s,	
m :—	f :s	s :m	r :d	t, :—		s :—	f :l	s :s.f	m :—		f	m	
m :—	r :d	t, :d	s,.f, :m,	s, :—		d, :—	f, :r,	m,.f, :s,	d, :—		f,	d,	

A-men.

PSALMS LV, LVI.

18 He hath my soul delivered,
that it in peace might be
From battle that against me was;
for many were with me.
19 The Lord shall hear, and them afflict,
of old who hath abode:
Because they never changes have,
therefore they fear not God.

20 'Gainst those that were at peace with him
he hath put forth his hand:
The covenant that he had made,
by breaking he profan'd.
21 More smooth than butter were his words,
while in his heart was war;
His speeches were more soft than oil,
and yet drawn swords they are.

22 Cast thou thy burden on the Lord,
and he shall thee sustain;
Yea, he shall cause the righteous man
unmoved to remain. [men
23 But thou, O Lord my God, those
in justice shalt o'erthrow,
And in destruction's dungeon dark
at last shalt lay them low:

The bloody and deceitful men
shall not live half their days:
But upon thee with confidence
I will depend always.

56

SHEW mercy, Lord, to me, for man
would swallow me outright;
He me oppresseth, while he doth
against me daily fight.
2 They daily would me swallow up
that hate me spitefully;
For they be many that do fight
against me, O most High.

3 When I'm afraid I'll trust in thee:
4 In God I'll praise his word;
I will not fear what flesh can do,
my trust is in the Lord.
5 Each day they wrest my words; their thoughts
'gainst me are all for ill.
6 They meet, they lurk, they mark my steps,
waiting my soul to kill.

7 But shall they by iniquity
escape thy judgments so?

EATINGTON. (C.M.)

Doh = G. WILLIAM CROFT, 1678–1727.

```
:d  |m  :-.f |r  :t, |d  :r  |m  ||r  |d    :t, |l, :-.r |t, :— |— ||
:s, |d  :-.d |t, :s, |s, :f, |m, ||s, |l,   :s, |s, :fe, |s, :— |— ||
:m  |s  :-.l |s  :r  |d  :t, |d  ||r  |m.fe :s  |m  :r   |r  :— |— ||
:d, |d  :-.f,|s, :f, |m, :s, |d  ||t, |l,   :t, |d  :r   |s, :— |— ||

:r  |s  :m  |f    :m  |l, :r  |t, ||s  |m  :d  |d   :-.t,|d  :— |— ||d  |d  ||
:s, |s, :l, |f,   :s, |s, :f, |s, ||s, |s, :s, |l,  :s,  |s, :— |— ||l, |s, ||
:t, |d  :d  |d.t, :d  |d  :r  |r  ||r  |d  :s  |f.m :r   |m  :— |— ||f  |m  ||
:f, |m, :l, |r,   :m, |f, :r, |s, ||t, |d  :m, |f,  :s,  |d, :— |— ||f, |d, ||
```

A-men.

PSALMS LVI, LVII.

O God, with indignation down
do thou the people throw.
8 My wand'rings all what they have been
thou know'st, their number took;
Into thy bottle put my tears:
are they not in thy book?

9 My foes shall, when I cry, turn back;
I know 't, God is for me.
10 In God his word I'll praise; his word
in God shall praised be.
11 In God I trust; I will not fear
what man can do to me.
12 Thy vows upon me are, O God:
I'll render praise to thee.

13 Wilt thou not, who from death me sav'd,
my feet from falls keep free,
To walk before God in the light
of those that living be?

57*

BE merciful to me, O God;
thy mercy unto me
Do thou extend; because my soul
doth put her trust in thee:
Yea, in the shadow of thy wings
my refuge I will place,
Until these sad calamities
do wholly overpass.

2 My cry I will cause to ascend
unto the Lord most high;
To God, who doth all things for me
perform most perfectly.
3 From heav'n he shall send down, and me
from his reproach defend
That would devour me: God his truth
and mercy forth shall send.

4 My soul among fierce lions is,
I firebrands live among,
Men's sons, whose teeth are spears and darts,
a sharp sword is their tongue.
5 Be thou exalted very high
above the heav'ns, O God;
Let thou thy glory be advanc'd
o'er all the earth abroad.

6 My soul 's bowed down; for they a net
have laid, my steps to snare:

55

EDEN. (C.M.

Doh = A.

WILLIAM HENRY HAVERGAL, 1793–1870.

```
:d  |m  :r  |d  :t,  |d  :l, |s, ‖ l, |d  :t, |l, :se, |l, :— |— ‖
:m, |s, :f, |m, :f,  |s, :f, |r, ‖ f, |s, :f, |m, :m,  |m, :— |— ‖
:s, |s, :s, |s, :r   |d  :d  |t, ‖ d  |m  :r  |d  :t,  |d  :— |— ‖
:d, |d, :t,,|d, :r,  |m, :f, |s, ‖ f, |d, :r, |m, :m,  |l, :— |— ‖

:d  |d  :t, |d  :r   |m  :f  |s  ‖ d  |m  :r  |d  :t,  |d  :— |— ‖ d  |d  ‖
:s, |l, :f, |s, :s,  |s, :d  |t, ‖ m, |s, :l, |s, :s,  |s, :— |— ‖ l, |s, ‖
:d  |d  :r  |m  :r   |d  :d  |r  ‖ d  |d  :f  |m  :r   |m  :— |— ‖ f  |m  ‖
:m, |f, :r, |d, :t,, |d, :l, |s, ‖ l, |m, :f, |s, :s,  |d, :— |— ‖ f, |d, ‖
```

A-men.

PSALMS LVII, LVIII.

Into the pit which they have digg'd
  for me, they fallen are.
7 My heart is fix'd, my heart is fix'd,
  O God; I'll sing and praise.
8 My glory wake; wake psalt'ry, harp;
  myself I'll early raise.

9 I'll praise thee 'mong the people, Lord;
  'mong nations sing will I:
10 For great to heav'n thy mercy is,
  thy truth is to the sky.
11 O Lord, exalted be thy name
  above the heav'ns to stand:
Do thou thy glory far advance
  above both sea and land.

58

DO ye, O congregation,
  indeed speak righteousness?
O ye that are the sons of men,
  judge ye with uprightness?
2 Yea, ev'n within your very hearts
  ye wickedness have done;
And ye the vi'lence of your hands
  do weigh the earth upon.

3 The wicked men estranged are,
  ev'n from the very womb;
They, speaking lies, do stray as soon
  as to the world they come.
4 Unto a serpent's poison like
  their poison doth appear;
Yea, they are like the adder deaf,
  that closely stops her ear;

5 That so she may not hear the voice
  of one that charm her would,
No, not though he most cunning were,
  and charm most wisely could.
6 Their teeth, O God, within their mouth
  break thou in pieces small;
The great teeth break thou out, O Lord,
  of these young lions all.

7 Let them like waters melt away,
  which downward still do flow:
In pieces cut his arrows all,
  when he shall bend his bow.
8 Like to a snail that melts away,
  let each of them be gone;
Like woman's birth untimely, that
  they never see the sun.

56

EFFINGHAM. (C.M.) Adapted from *Musikalisch Hand-Buch*, Hamburg, 1690.

Doh = B♭.

```
:s,  |d :— :s, |l, :— :l, |s, :— :f, |m, :— || m, |r, :— :s, |l, :s, :fe, |s, :— ||
:m,  |s, :— :m, |f, :— :f, |m, :— :r, |d, :— || d, |r, :— :m, |m, :r, :r, |r, :— ||
:d   |d :— :d |d :— :d |d :— :t, |d :— || s, |t, :— :t, |d :t, :l, |t, :— ||
:d,  |m, :— :d, |f, :— :f, |s, :— :s,, |d, :— || d, |s, :— :m, |d, :r, :r, |s,/s,, :— ||

:s,  |d :— :r |m :— :d |f :— :m |r :— || d |s, :— :d |m :— :r |d :— || d |d ||
:r,  |s, :— :s, |s, :— :m, |f, :s, :s, |s, :— || m, |s, :— :m, |s, :— :f, |m, :— || f, |m, ||
:t,  |d :— :t, |d :— :d |d :r :d |t, :— || d |d :— :d |d :— :t, |d :— || l, |s, ||
:s,.f, |m, :— :s, |d :— :ta, |l, :t, :d |s, :— || d, |m, :— :l, |s, :— :s,, |d, :— || f, |d, ||
```

A-men.

PSALMS LVIII, LIX.

9 He shall them take away before
your pots the thorns can find,
Both living, and in fury great,
as with a stormy wind.
10 The righteous, when he vengeance sees,
he shall be joyful then;
The righteous one shall wash his feet
in blood of wicked men.

11 So men shall say, The righteous man
reward shall never miss:
And verily upon the earth
a God to judge there is.

59

MY God, deliver me from those
that are mine enemies;
And do thou me defend from those
that up against me rise.
2 Do thou deliver me from them
that work iniquity;
And give me safety from the men
of bloody cruelty.

3 For, lo, they for my soul lay wait:
the mighty do combine
Against me, Lord; not for my fault,
nor any sin of mine.
4 They run, and, without fault in me,
themselves do ready make:
Awake to meet me with thy help;
and do thou notice take.

5 Awake therefore, Lord God of hosts,
thou God of Israel,
To visit heathen all: spare none
that wickedly rebel.
6 At ev'ning they go to and fro;
they make great noise and sound,
Like to a dog, and often walk
about the city round.

7 Behold, they belch out with their mouth,
and in their lips are swords:
For they do say thus, Who is he
that now doth hear our words?
8 But thou, O Lord, shalt laugh at them,
and all the heathen mock.
9 While he's in pow'r I'll wait on thee;
for God is my high rock.

10 He of my mercy that is God
betimes shall me prevent;
Upon mine en'mies God shall let
me see mine heart's content.

ELGIN. (C.M.)

Lah = G. Doh = B♭. *Scottish Psalter*, 1625.

d :—	t_1 :l_1	t_1 :—	m :—	r :d	t_1 :—		l_1:—	r :d	t_1:l_1	t_1 :—	
m_1:—	m_1 :m_1	m_1 :—	m_1:—	se_1:l_1	se_1:—		l_1:—	r_1 :m_1	f_1:m_1	m_1 :—	
l_1:—	t_1 :d	se_1:—	l_1:—	t_1 :d.r	m :—		d :—	$l_1.t_1$:d	r :d.l_1	se_1:—	
l_1:—	se_1:l_1	m_1 :—	d_1:—	t_2 :l_2	m_1 :—		l_1:—	f_1 :m_1	r_1:l_2	m_1 :—	

m :—	d :m	r :t_1	d :r	t_1 :—		l_1:—	r :d	t_1:t_1	l_1:—	—:—		l_1	l_1	
m_1:—	s_1:s_1	l_1:s_1	m_1:f_1	m_1 :—		m_1:—	r_1 :m_1	m_1:-.r_1	d_1:—	—:—		r_1	de_1	
s_1:—	s_1:d	l_1:r	d :$t_1.l_1$	se_1:—		l_1:—	se_1:l_1	l_1:se_1	l_1:—	—:—		f_1	m_1	
d_1:—	m_1:d_1	f_1:s_1	l_1:r_1	m_1 :—		d_1:—	t_2 :l_2	m_1:m_1	l_2:—	—:—		r_1	l_2	

A-men.

PSALMS LIX, LX.

11 Them slay not, lest my folk forget;
but scatter them abroad
By thy strong pow'r; and bring them down,
O thou our shield and God.

12 For their mouth's sin, and for the words
that from their lips do fly,
Let them be taken in their pride;
because they curse and lie.
13 In wrath consume them, them consume,
that so they may not be:
And that in Jacob God doth rule
to th' earth's ends let them see.

14 At ev'ning let thou them return,
making great noise and sound,
Like to a dog, and often walk
about the city round.
15 And let them wander up and down,
in seeking food to eat;
And let them grudge when they shall not
be satisfy'd with meat.

16 But of thy pow'r I'll sing aloud;
at morn thy mercy praise:
For thou to me my refuge wast,
and tow'r, in troublous days.
17 O God, thou art my strength, I will
sing praises unto thee;
For God is my defence, a God
of mercy unto me.

60

O LORD, thou hast rejected us,
and scatter'd us abroad;
Thou justly hast displeased been;
return to us, O God.
2 The earth to tremble thou hast made;
therein didst breaches make:
Do thou thereof the breaches heal,
because the land doth shake.

3 Unto thy people thou hard things
hast shew'd, and on them sent;
And thou hast caused us to drink
wine of astonishment.
4 And yet a banner thou hast giv'n
to them who thee do fear;
That it by them, because of truth,
displayed may appear.

EVAN. (C.M.)

Doh=A♭. WILLIAM HENRY HAVERGAL, 1793–1870.

```
:s, |s, :d  |m  :r  |d  :l, |s, ||s, |s, :d  |m  :d  |r  :— |— ||
:m, |s, :s, |s, :f, |m, :f, |m, ||m, |s, :s, |s, :l, |t, :— |— ||
:s, |d  :m  |d  :t, |d  :d  |d  ||s, |d  :m  |d  :m  |s  :— |— ||
:d, |m, :d, |d  :s, |l, :f, |d, ||d, |m, :d, |d  :l, |s, :— |— ||
```

```
:f  |m  :r  |d  :r  |m  :d  |l, ||s, |s, :d  |m  :r   |d  :— |— ||d  |d  ||
:d  |d  :t, |l, :t, |d  :s, |f, ||r, |s, :l, |d  :t,  |d  :— |— ||l, |s, ||
:l  |s  :s  |m  :s  |s  :d  |d  ||t, |d  :m  |s  :s.f |m  :— |— ||f  |m  ||
:f, |d  :s, |l, :s, |d, :m, |f, ||s, |m, :l, |s, :s,  |d, :— |— ||f, |d, ||
```

A-men.

PSALMS LX, LXI.

5 That thy beloved people may
deliver'd be from thrall,
Save with the pow'r of thy right hand,
and hear me when I call.
6 God in his holiness hath spoke;
herein I will take pleasure:
Shechem I will divide, and forth
will Succoth's valley measure.

7 Gilead I claim as mine by right;
Manasseh mine shall be;
Ephraim is of mine head the strength;
Judah gives laws for me;
8 Moab 's my washing-pot; my shoe
I'll over Edom throw;
And over Palestina's land
I will in triumph go.

9 O who is he will bring me to
the city fortify'd?
O who is he that to the land
of Edom will me guide?
10 O God, which hadest us cast off,
this thing wilt thou not do?
Ev'n thou, O God, which didest not
forth with our armies go?

11 Help us from trouble; for the help
is vain which man supplies.
12 Through God we'll do great acts; he shall
tread down our enemies.

61*

O GOD, give ear unto my cry;
unto my pray'r attend.
2 From th' utmost corner of the land
my cry to thee I'll send.
What time my heart is overwhelm'd
and in perplexity,
Do thou me lead unto the Rock
that higher is than I.

3 For thou hast for my refuge been
a shelter by thy pow'r;
And for defence against my foes
thou hast been a strong tow'r.
4 Within thy tabernacle I
for ever will abide;
And under covert of thy wings
with confidence me hide.

5 For thou the vows that I did make,
O Lord my God, didst hear:
Thou hast giv'n me the heritage
of those thy name that fear.
6 A life prolong'd for many days
thou to the king shalt give;

59

FARRANT. (C.M.)

Doh = G.

Adapted from a Melody attributed to Richard Farrant, c. 1530–80.

|d :— |d :-.r |m :r |d :f |r ||r |m.fe:s |s :fe |s :— ||

|s, :— |l, :-.t, |d :t, |l, :d |t, ||t, |d :t,.d |r :r.d |t, :— ||

|m :— |m :-.s |s :s |m :l |s ||s |s :s |l :l |s :— ||

|d :— |l, :-.s, |d :s, |l, :f, |s, ||s, |d :m |r :r |s, :— ||

|d :— |f :f |m :r |d :r |t, ||m |l,.t, :d |d :t, |d :— ||d |d ||

|d :— |r :r |d :t, |l, :l, |s, ||s, |f, :m,.f, |s, :s, |s, :— ||l, |s, ||

|m :— |l :s |s :s |m :f |r ||d |d :d |r :r |m :— ||f |m ||

|d :— |d :t, |d :s, |l, :r, |s, ||d, |f, :l, |s, :s, |d, :— ||f, |d, ||

A-men.

PSALMS LXI, LXII.

Like many generations be
the years which he shall live.

7 He in God's presence his abode
for evermore shall have:
O do thou truth and mercy both
prepare, that may him save.

8 And so will I perpetually
sing praise unto thy name;
That having made my vows, I may
each day perform the same.

62*

My soul with expectation
depends on God indeed;
My strength and my salvation doth
from him alone proceed.

2 He only my salvation is,
and my strong rock is he:
He only is my sure defence;
much mov'd I shall not be.

3 How long will ye against a man
plot mischief? ye shall all
Be slain; ye as a tott'ring fence
shall be, and bowing wall.

4 They only plot to cast him down
from his excellency:
They joy in lies; with mouth they bless,
but they curse inwardly.

5 My soul, wait thou with patience
upon thy God alone;
On him dependeth all my hope
and expectation.

6 He only my salvation is,
and my strong rock is he;
He only is my sure defence:
I shall not moved be.

7 In God my glory placed is,
and my salvation sure;
In God the rock is of my strength,
my refuge most secure.

8 Ye people, place your confidence
in him continually;
Before him pour ye out your heart:
God is our refuge high.

9 Surely mean men are vanity,
and great men are a lie;
In balance laid, they wholly are
more light than vanity.

10 Trust ye not in oppression,
in robb'ry be not vain;
On wealth set not your hearts, when as
increased is your gain.

FELIX. (C.M.)

Lah = B. Doh = D. Adapted from FELIX MENDELSSOHN-BARTHOLDY, 1809-47.

:d.r	m :l	s :m	d :r	m	l.t	d^1 :l	s :f	m :—	—
:d.r	m :l	s :m	d :r	m	d.r	m :d	r :t_1	d :—	—
:d.r	m :l	s :m	d :r	m	m	m :m	r :s	s :—	—
:d.r	m :l	s :m	d :r	m	l_1	l_1 :l_1	t_1 :s_1	d :—	—

:m.f	s :d^1	t :s	m :fe	s	r.f	m :l	l :se	l :—	—	l	l
:d	d :d	r :r	d :d	r	t_1	d :m	m :m.r	d :—	—	r	de
:d.r	m :s	s :s	s :l	s	s	s :d^1	t :t	l :—	—	f	m
:d	d :m	s :t_1	d :l_1	t_1	s_1	d :l_1	m :m	l_1 :—	—	r	l_1

A-men.

PSALMS LXII, LXIII, LXIV.

11 God hath it spoken once to me,
yea, this I heard again,
That power to Almighty God
alone doth appertain.
12 Yea, mercy also unto thee
belongs, O Lord, alone:
For thou according to his work
rewardest ev'ry one.

63*

LORD, thee my God, I'll early seek:
my soul doth thirst for thee;
My flesh longs in a dry parch'd land,
wherein no waters be:
2 That I thy power may behold,
and brightness of thy face,
As I have seen thee heretofore
within thy holy place.

3 Since better is thy love than life,
my lips thee praise shall give.
4 I in thy name will lift my hands,
and bless thee while I live.
5 Ev'n as with marrow and with fat
my soul shall filled be;
Then shall my mouth with joyful lips
sing praises unto thee:

6 When I do thee upon my bed
remember with delight,
And when on thee I meditate
in watches of the night.
7 In shadow of thy wings I'll joy,
for thou mine help hast been.
8 My soul thee follows hard; and me
thy right hand doth sustain.

9 Who seek my soul to spill shall sink
down to earth's lowest room.
10 They by the sword shall be cut off,
and foxes' prey become.
11 Yet shall the king in God rejoice,
and each one glory shall
That swear by him; but stopp'd shall be
the mouth of liars all.

64

WHEN I to thee my prayer make,
Lord, to my voice give ear;
My life save from the enemy,
of whom I stand in fear.
2 Me from their secret counsel hide
who do live wickedly;
From insurrection of those men
that work iniquity:

61

FRENCH. (C.M.)

Doh = E♭. *Scottish Psalter*, 1615.

```
|d  :— |m  :f  |s  :d  |r  :m  |f  :— ||m  :— |r  :d  |d  :t, |d  :— ||
|s, :— |d  :d  |d  :l, |t, :d  |d  :— ||d  :— |t, :l, |l, :s, |s, :— ||
|m  :— |s  :l  |s  :m  |s  :s  |l  :— ||s  :— |s  :m  |f  :r  |m  :— ||
|d  :— |d  :f, |m, :l, |s, :d  |f, :— ||d  :— |s, :l, |f, :s, |d  :— ||

|s  :— |d' :t  |l  :s  |s  :fe |s  :— ||m  :— |r  :d     |d  :t, |d  :— ||d  |d  ||
|d  :— |m  :r  |d  :t, |l, :l, |t, :— ||s, :— |l, :m,.f, |s, :s, |s, :— ||l, |s, ||
|m  :— |s  :s  |m  :r  |m  :r  |r  :— ||m  :— |f  :d     |r  :r  |m  :— ||f  |m  ||
|d  :— |d  :s, |l, :t, |d  :r  |s, :— ||d  :— |f, :l,    |s, :s, |d  :— ||f, |d  ||
```

[*There is a Faux-bourdon setting in the Revised Church Hymnary, No.* 227.] **A-men.**

PSALMS LXIV, LXV.

3 Who do their tongues with malice whet,
and make them cut like swords;
In whose bent bows are arrows set,
ev'n sharp and bitter words:
4 That they may at the perfect man
in secret aim their shot;
Yea, suddenly they dare at him
to shoot, and fear it not.

5 In ill encourage they themselves,
and their snares close do lay:
Together conference they have;
Who shall them see? they say.
6 They have search'd out iniquities,
a perfect search they keep:
Of each of them the inward thought,
and very heart, is deep.

7 God shall an arrow shoot at them,
and wound them suddenly:
8 So their own tongue shall them confound;
all who them see shall fly.
9 And on all men a fear shall fall,
God's works they shall declare;
For they shall wisely notice take
what these his doings are.

10 In God the righteous shall rejoice,
and trust upon his might;
Yea, they shall greatly glory all
in heart that are upright.

65*

PRAISE waits for thee in Sion, Lord:
to thee vows paid shall be.
2 O thou that hearer art of pray'r,
all flesh shall come to thee.
3 Iniquities, I must confess,
prevail against me do:
But as for our transgressions,
them purge away shalt thou.

4 Bless'd is the man whom thou dost chuse,
and mak'st approach to thee,
That he within thy courts, O Lord,
may still a dweller be:
We surely shall be satisfy'd
with thy abundant grace,
And with the goodness of thy house,
ev'n of thy holy place.

5 O God of our salvation,
thou, in thy righteousness,
By fearful works unto our pray'rs
thine answer dost express:

FRENCH. (C.M.)

Doh = E♭.

DESCANT.

ALAN GRAY, 1855-

Descant.
|d' :— |d' :d' |t :s |r' :ta |l :— ||s :— |s :m |l :s |s :— ||
Melody.
|d :— |m :f |s :d |r :m |f :— ||m :— |r :d |d :t, |d :— ||

|s :— |m' :r' |d' :t |l :l |t :— ||s :— |l :m.f |s :s |s :— ||f* |m ||
|s :— |d' :t |l :s |s :fe |s :— ||m :— |r :d |d :t, |d :— ||d |d ||
A-men.

* *For use only when the Descant is sung to the closing verse.*

PSALMS LXV, LXVI.

Therefore the ends of all the earth,
and those afar that be
Upon the sea, their confidence,
O Lord, will place in thee.

6 Who, being girt with pow'r, sets fast
by his great strength the hills.
7 Who noise of seas, noise of their waves,
and people's tumult, stills.
8 Those in the utmost parts that dwell
are at thy signs afraid:
Th' outgoings of the morn and ev'n
by thee are joyful made.

9 The earth thou visit'st, wat'ring it;
thou mak'st it rich to grow
With God's full flood; thou corn prepar'st,
when thou provid'st it so.
10 Her rigs thou wat'rest plenteously,
her furrows settelest:
With show'rs thou dost her mollify,
her spring by thee is blest.

11 So thou the year most lib'rally
dost with thy goodness crown;
And all thy paths abundantly
on us drop fatness down.

12 They drop upon the pastures wide,
that do in deserts lie;
The little hills on ev'ry side
rejoice right pleasantly.

13 With flocks the pastures clothed be,
the vales with corn are clad;
And now they shout and sing to thee,
for thou hast made them glad.

66*

ALL lands to God, in joyful sounds,
aloft your voices raise.
2 Sing forth the honour of his name,
and glorious make his praise.
3 Say unto God, How terrible
in all thy works art thou!
Through thy great pow'r thy foes to thee
shall be constrain'd to bow.

4 All on the earth shall worship thee,
they shall thy praise proclaim
In songs: they shall sing cheerfully
unto thy holy name.

GLASGOW. (C.M.) *Moore's Psalm-Singer's Pocket Companion*, 1756.

Doh = G.

:s, | d :—:r | m.,r :d:m | s.,l:s :f | m :— || m | r :—:f | m.,r :d :t, | d :— || s | s :—
:m, | s,:—:t, | d.,t,:d:d | d :—:t, | d :— || d | l,:—:r | d.,l,:s,:s, | s,:— || d | r :d
:d | s :—:s | s.,f :m:s | m.,f:m :r | d :— || s | f :—:l | s.,f :m :r | m :— || m | s.,f:m
:d, | m,:—:s, | d.,r :m:d | s, :—:s, | d,:— || d | f,:—:r, | m,.,f,:s,:s, | d,:— || d | t, :d

:m | f :—:l | s :f :m | r :— || s | d :r :m | f :m :r | d :— || d | d
:d | d.,ta,:l,:d | s,.,l,:t,:d | t,:— || t, | d :s,:d | d :—:t, | d :— || l, | s,
:s | f :—:d | d :r :m.fe | s :— || s.f | m :s :s | l :s :s.f | m :— || f | m
:ta, | l,.,s, :f,:f, | m, :r,:d, | s,:— || s, | l,:t,:d | f,:s,:s, | d,:— || f, | d,

A-men.

PSALM LXVI.

5 Come, and the works that God hath wrought
with admiration see:
In 's working to the sons of men
most terrible is he.

6 Into dry land the sea he turn'd,
and they a passage had;
Ev'n marching through the flood on foot,
there we in him were glad.
7 He ruleth ever by his pow'r;
his eyes the nations see:
O let not the rebellious ones
lift up themselves on high.

8 Ye people, bless our God; aloud
the voice speak of his praise:
9 Our soul in life who safe preserves,
our foot from sliding stays.
10 For thou didst prove and try us, Lord,
as men do silver try;
11 Brought'st us into the net, and mad'st
bands on our loins to lie.

12 Thou hast caus'd men ride o'er our heads;
and though that we did pass
Through fire and water, yet thou brought'st
us to a wealthy place.
13 I'll bring burnt-off'rings to thy house;
to thee my vows I'll pay,
14 Which my lips utter'd, my mouth spake,
when trouble on me lay.

15 Burnt-sacrifices of fat rams
with incense I will bring;
Of bullocks and of goats I will
present an offering.
16 All that fear God, come, hear, I'll tell
what he did for my soul.
17 I with my mouth unto him cry'd,
my tongue did him extol.

18 If in my heart I sin regard,
the Lord me will not hear:
19 But surely God me heard, and to
my prayer's voice gave ear.
20 O let the Lord, our gracious God,
for ever blessed be,
Who turned not my pray'r from him,
nor yet his grace from me.

63

GLENLUCE. (C.M.)

Doh = F.

Scottish Psalter, 1635.

m :—	m :f	s :l	s :—	f :—	m :—		r :—	m :s	s :fe	s :—	
d :—	d :d	t, :l,	d :—	— :t,	d :—		t, :—	d :r	r :r	r :—	
s :—	l :l	m :f	s :—	r :—	m :—		s :—	s :s	l :l	t :—	
d :—	l, :l,	s, :f,	m, :—	s, :—	d :—		s, :—	d :t,	r :r	s, :—	

r :—	r :s	f :m	r :—	d :—	t, :—		d :—	r :d	d :t,	d :—		d	d	
t, :—	l, :s,	d :d	l, :—	m, :f,	s, :—		s, :—	ta, :l,	s, :s,	s, :—		l,	s,	
s :—	l :d'	l :s	f :—	d :—	r :—		m :—	f :f	r :r	m :—		f	m	
s :—	f :m	l, :d	f, :—	l, :—	s, :—		d :—	ta, :f,	s, :s,	d :—		f,	d	

A-men.

67*

LORD, bless and pity us,
shine on us with thy face:
2 That th' earth thy way, and nations all
may know thy saving grace.
3 Let people praise thee, Lord;
let people all thee praise.
4 O let the nations be glad,
in songs their voices raise:
Thou 'lt justly people judge,
on earth rule nations all.
5 Let people praise thee, Lord; let them
praise thee, both great and small.
6 The earth her fruit shall yield,
our God shall blessing send.
7 God shall us bless; men shall him fear
unto earth's utmost end.

67 (2)

ANOTHER OF THE SAME.

LORD, unto us be merciful,
do thou us also bless;
And graciously cause shine on us
the brightness of thy face:

2 That so thy way upon the earth
to all men may be known;
Also among the nations all
thy saving health be shewn.

3 O let the people praise thee, Lord;
let people all thee praise.
4 O let the nations be glad,
and sing for joy always:
For rightly thou shalt people judge,
and nations rule on earth.
5 Let people praise thee, Lord; let all
the folk praise thee with mirth.

6 Then shall the earth yield her increase;
God, our God, bless us shall.
7 God shall us bless; and of the earth
the ends shall fear him all.

68*

LET God arise, and scattered
let all his en'mies be;
And let all those that do him hate
before his presence flee.

GLOUCESTER. (C.M.)

Doh = F. *Ravenscroft's Psalter*, 1621.

```
|d  :—  |s  :m  |r  :d    |f  :s     |l  :—  ‖m  :—  |r  :m  |f  :s   |m  :—  ‖
|s, :—  |s, :d  |t, :s,   |d  :—.ta, |l, :—  ‖d  :—  |t, :d  |r  :t,  |d  :—  ‖
|m  :—  |r  :s  |s  :m    |f  :m     |f  :—  ‖s  :—  |s  :s  |l  :s   |s  :—  ‖
|d  :—  |t, :d  |s, :d.ta,|l, :s,    |f, :—  ‖d  :—  |s  :m  |r  :s,  |d  :—  ‖
```

```
|s  :—  |m  :l      |s  :m  |r  :d    |r  :—  ‖f  :—   |m  :s   |r  :r    |d  :—  ‖d   |d   ‖
|r  :—  |s, :l,.t,  |d  :s, |s, :d    |t, :—  ‖r  :—   |s, :d   |d  :t,   |d  :—  ‖l,  |s,  ‖
|r  :—  |m  :f      |s  :d  |r  :m.fe |s  :—  ‖l  :—.t |d' :s   |l  :s.f  |m  :—  ‖f   |m   ‖
|t, :—  |d  :f,     |m, :d  |t, :l,   |s, :—  ‖r  :—   |m  :m,  |f, :s,   |d  :—  ‖f,  |d,  ‖
                                                                                  A-men.
```

PSALM LXVIII.

2 As smoke is driv'n, so drive thou them;
as fire melts wax away,
Before God's face let wicked men
so perish and decay.

3 But let the righteous be glad:
let them before God's sight
Be very joyful; yea, let them
rejoice with all their might.
4 To God sing, to his name sing praise;
extol him with your voice,
That rides on heav'n, by his name JAH,
before his face rejoice.

5 Because the Lord a father is
unto the fatherless;
God is the widow's judge, within
his place of holiness.
6 God doth the solitary set
in fam'lies: and from bands
The chain'd doth free; but rebels do
inhabit parched lands.

7 O God, what time thou didst go forth
before thy people's face;
And when through the great wilderness
thy glorious marching was;
8 Then at God's presence shook the earth,
then drops from heaven fell;
This Sinai shook before the Lord,
the God of Israel.

9 O God, thou to thine heritage
didst send a plenteous rain,
Whereby thou, when it weary was,
didst it refresh again.
10 Thy congregation then did make
their habitation there:
Of thine own goodness for the poor,
O God, thou didst prepare.

11 The Lord himself did give the word,
the word abroad did spread;
Great was the company of them
the same who published.
12 Kings of great armies foiled were,
and forc'd to flee away;
And women, who remain'd at home,
did distribute the prey.

13 Though ye have lien among the pots,
like doves ye shall appear,

65

GRÄFENBERG. (C.M.) JOHANN CRÜGER, 1598-1662.

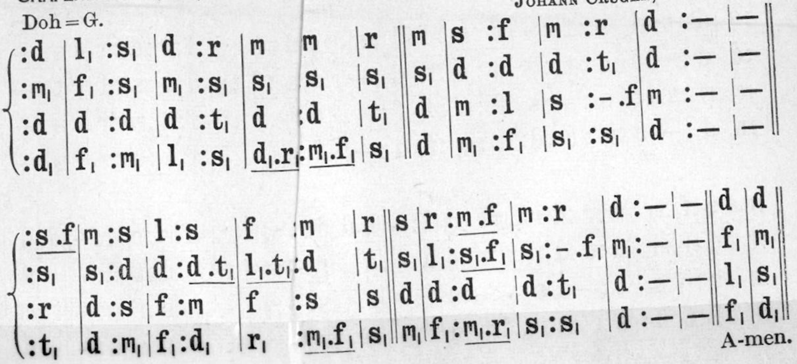

Doh = G.

```
:d  | l, :s,  | d :r   | m   m      | r  || m  | s :f      | m :r     | d :— | — ||
:m, | f, :s,  | m, :s, | s,  s,     | s, || s, | d :d      | d :t,    | d :— | — ||
:d  | d :d    | d :t,  | d   :d     | t, || d  | m :l      | s :-.f   | m :— | — ||
:d, | f, :m,  | l, :s, | d,.r, :m,.f, | s, || d | m, :f,    | s, :s,   | d :— | — ||

:s.f | m :s   | l :s     | f :m        | r  || s  | r :m.f       | m :r     | d :— | — || d  | d  ||
:s,  | s, :d  | d :d.t,  | l,.t, :d    | t, || s, | l, :s,.f,    | s, :-.f, | m, :— | — || f, | m, ||
:r   | d :s   | f :m     | f :s        | s  || d  | d :d         | d :t,    | d :— | — || l, | s, ||
:t,  | d :m,  | f, :d,   | r, :m,.f,   | s, || m, | f, :m,.r,    | s, :s,   | d :— | — || f, | d, ||
                                                                                         A-men.
```

PSALM LXVIII.

Whose wings with silver, and with gold
whose feathers cover'd are.

14 When there th' Almighty scatter'd kings,
like Salmon's snow 'twas white.

15 God's hill is like to Bashan hill,
like Bashan hill for height.

16 Why do ye leap, ye mountains high?
this is the hill where God
Desires to dwell; yea, God in it
for aye will make abode.

17 God's chariots twenty thousand are,
thousands of angels strong;
In 's holy place God is, as in
mount Sinai, them among.

18 Thou hast, O Lord, most glorious,
ascended up on high;
And in triumph victorious led
captive captivity:
Thou hast received gifts for men,
for such as did rebel;
Yea, ev'n for them, that God the Lord
in midst of them might dwell.

19 Bless'd be the Lord, who is to us
of our salvation God;
Who daily with his benefits
us plenteously doth load.

20 He of salvation is the God,
who is our God most strong;
And unto God the Lord from death
the issues do belong.

21 But surely God shall wound the head
of those that are his foes;
The hairy scalp of him that still
on in his trespass goes.

22 God said, My people I will bring
again from Bashan hill;
Yea, from the sea's devouring depths
them bring again I will;

23 That in the blood of enemies
thy foot imbru'd may be,
And of thy dogs dipp'd in the same
the tongues thou mayest see.

24 Thy goings they have seen, O God;
the steps of majesty
Of my God, and my mighty King,
within the sanctuary.

25 Before went singers, players next
on instruments took way;

HARINGTON. (C.M.) **66**

Doh = E♭. HENRY HARINGTON, 1727–1816.

						B♭.		f.E♭.
:s	d' :t :l	s :f :m	f :s :l	l :s	ˢd	d :t_1 :d	l_1.r :d :t_1	ᵈs :—
:d	d :— :d	d :t_1 :d	d :— :d	d :—	ᵐl_1	s_1 :f_1 :m_1	l_1 :s_1 :f_1	ᵐt_1 :—
:m	m :s :f	s :— :s	f :m :f	f :m	ˢd	m :r :d	f :m :r	ᵈs :—
:d	d :— :d	m :r :d	l_1 :s_1 :f_1	d :—	ᵈf_1	s_1 :— :l_1	f_1 :s_1 :s_1	ᵈs_1 :—

:r.s	s :f :m	m :r :d	r .,m :f :m	l :—	s.d'	d' :t :d'	r.m,f :m :r	d :—	d	d
:t_1	d :r :d	d :t_1 :d	t_1.,d :r :d	d :—	d	f :— :m.d	r :d :t_1	d :—	l_1	s_1
:s	s :— :s	s :— :s	s :— :s	f :—	s	s :— :s	l :s :f	m :—	f	m
:s_1	l_1 :t_1 :d.m	s :f :m	r .,d :t_1 :d	f :—	m	r :— :d	f_1 :s_1 :s_1	d :—	f_1	d

A-men.

PSALM LXVIII.

And them among the damsels were
that did on timbrels play.
26 Within the congregations
bless God with one accord:
From Isr'el's fountain do ye bless
and praise the mighty Lord.

27 With their prince, little Benjamin,
princes and council there
Of Judah were, there Zabulon's
and Napht'li's princes were.
28 Thy God commands thy strength; make strong
what thou wrought'st for us, Lord.
29 For thy house at Jerusalem
kings shall thee gifts afford.

30 The spearmen's host, the multitude
of bulls, which fiercely look,
Those calves which people have forth sent,
O Lord our God, rebuke,
Till ev'ry one submit himself,
and silver pieces bring:
The people that delight in war
disperse, O God and King.

31 Those that be princes great shall then
come out of Egypt lands;
And Ethiopia to God
shall soon stretch out her hands.
32 O all ye kingdoms of the earth,
sing praises to this King;
For he is Lord that ruleth all,
unto him praises sing.

33 To him that rides on heav'ns of heav'ns,
which he of old did found;
Lo, he sends out his voice, a voice
in might that doth abound.
34 Strength unto God do ye ascribe;
for his excellency
Is over Israel, his strength
is in the clouds most high.

35 Thou'rt from thy temple dreadful, Lord;
Isr'el's own God is he,
Who gives his people strength and pow'r:
O let God blessed be.

HEBDOMADAL. (C.M.)

Doh = D. THOMAS BANKS STRONG, 1861-

d' :—	s :m	d :—	— :d	l :—	— :l	s :—	—	s	d' :—	t :s	l :—	— :l	s :—	— :—	
m :—	r :t,	l, :—	t, :l,	d :—.t,	d :r	m :—	—	m	d :—	r :t,	m :—	r :d	t, :—	— :—	
s :—	s :s	m :—	— :f	l :—.s	l :t	d' :—	—	t	l :—	s :s	m :—	fe :fe	s :—	— :—	
d :—	t, :s,	l, :—	s, :f,	f :—	— :f	d :—	—	m	l, :—	t, :m	d :—	r :r	s, :—	— :—	

f.G. D.t.

(m)t, :—	l, :s,	m :—	s :—	(s)d' :—	— :r	r :—	l :—	s :—	d :—	d :—	r :—	d :—	— :—		d	d	
(d)s, :—	f, :f,	s, :—	l, :—	(l)r :—	— :d	t, :—	d :r	m :—	d :—	s, :—	t, :—	d :—	— :—		l,	s,	
(s)r :—	d :r	m :—	d :—	(m)l :—	— :l	s :—	l :t	d' :—	m :f	m :—	f :—	m :—	— :—		f	m	
(d)s, :—	l, :t,	d :—	l, :—	(d)f, :—	— :f,	s, :—	f :—	m :—	l, :—	s, :—	s, :—	d :—	— :—		f,	d	

A-men.

PSALM LXIX.

69

SAVE me, O God, because the floods
do so environ me,
That ev'n unto my very soul
come in the waters be.
2 I downward in deep mire do sink,
where standing there is none:
I am into deep waters come,
where floods have o'er me gone.

3 I weary with my crying am,
my throat is also dry'd;
Mine eyes do fail, while for my God
I waiting do abide.
4 Those men that do without a cause
bear hatred unto me,
Than are the hairs upon my head
in number more they be:

They that would me destroy, and are
mine en'mies wrongfully,
Are mighty: so what I took not,
to render forc'd was I.
5 Lord, thou my folly know'st, my sins
not cover'd are from thee.

6 Let none that wait on thee be sham'd,
Lord God of hosts, for me.

O Lord, the God of Israel,
let none, who search do make,
And seek thee, be at any time
confounded for my sake.
7 For I have borne reproach for thee,
my face is hid with shame.
8 To brethren strange, to mother's sons
an alien I became.

9 Because the zeal did eat me up,
which to thine house I bear;
And the reproaches cast at thee,
upon me fallen are.
10 My tears and fasts, t'afflict my soul,
were turned to my shame.
11 When sackcloth I did wear, to them
a proverb I became.

12 The men that in the gate do sit
against me evil spake;
They also that vile drunkards were
of me their song did make.

68

HERIOT'S TUNE. (C.M.)

Doh = G. *Alexander McDonald's Collection*, 1807.

```
:d  | r  :t,  | d  :f  | m  :r     | d  ‖ d | l  :s  | d  :r  | m :— | — ‖
:s, | l, :s,  | m, :l, | s, :s,.f, | m, ‖ d | d  :d  | l, :t, | d :— | — ‖
:m  | f  :r   | d  :d  | d  :t,    | d  ‖ m | f  :s  | m  :s  | s :— | — ‖
:d  | f, :s,  | l, :f, | s, :s,    | d, ‖ d | f, :m, | l, :s, | d :— | — ‖

:r  | m :f  | s  :f  | m  :d  | r  ‖ t,    | d  :f  | m  :r     | d  :— | — ‖ d  | d  ‖
:t, | d :d  | s, :l, | s, :l, | t, ‖ s,.f, | m, :l, | s, :-.f,  | m, :— | — ‖ f, | m, ‖
:s  | s :d  | d  :d  | d  :m  | s  ‖ r     | d  :d  | d  :t,    | d  :— | — ‖ l, | s, ‖
:s, | d :l, | m, :f, | d, :l, | s, ‖ s,    | l, :f, | s, :s,    | d, :— | — ‖ f, | d, ‖
                                                                         A-men.
```

PSALM LXIX.

13 But, in an acceptable time,
my pray'r, Lord, is to thee:
In truth of thy salvation, Lord,
and mercy great, hear me.

14 Deliver me out of the mire,
from sinking do me keep;
Free me from those that do me hate,
and from the waters deep.
15 Let not the flood on me prevail,
whose water overflows;
Nor deep me swallow, nor the pit
her mouth upon me close.

16 Hear me, O Lord, because thy love
and kindness is most good;
Turn unto me, according to
thy mercies' multitude.
17 Nor from thy servant hide thy face:
I'm troubled, soon attend.
18 Draw near my soul, and it redeem;
me from my foes defend.

19 To thee is my reproach well known,
my shame, and my disgrace:
Those that mine adversaries be
are all before thy face.
20 Reproach hath broke my heart; I'm full
of grief: I look'd for one
To pity me, but none I found;
comforters found I none.

21 They also bitter gall did give
unto me for my meat:
They gave me vinegar to drink,
when as my thirst was great.
22 Before them let their table prove
a snare; and do thou make
Their welfare and prosperity
a trap themselves to take.

23 Let thou their eyes so darken'd be,
that sight may them forsake;
And let their loins be made by thee
continually to shake.
24 Thy fury pour thou out on them,
and indignation;
And let thy wrathful anger, Lord,
fast hold take them upon.

25 All waste and desolate let be
their habitation;
And in their tabernacles all
inhabitants be none.
26 Because him they do persecute,
whom thou didst smite before;
They talk unto the grief of those
whom thou hast wounded sore.

HERMON. (C.M.)

Lah = F. Doh = A♭.

JEREMIAH CLARK, *c.* 1659–1707.

:m, | l, :t, | d :t, | l, :t,.l, | se, || t, | d :t, | d :r | m :— | — ||
:d, | m, :m, | m, :m, | f, :f, | m, || m, | m, :m, | l, :l, | se, :— | — ||
:l, | l, :se, | l, :t, | d :r | t, || se, | l, :t, | l, :l, | t, :— | — ||
:l_2 | d, :m, | l, :s, | f, :r, | m, || m, | l, :s, | f, :f, | m, :— | — ||

:m | s :f | m :r | d.m :r.d | t, || m | l, :t, | t, :-.l, | l, :— | — || l, | l, ||
:s, | s, :s, | s, :s,.f, | m, :l, | se, || se, | m, :f, | m, :r, | d, :— | — || r, | de, ||
:d | r :t, | d :t, | l, :f | t, || t, | l, :l, | l, :se, | l, :— | — || f, | m, ||
:d | t, :s, | d :s, | l, :r, | m, || m, | d, :r, | m, :m, | l_2 :— | — || r, | l_2 ||

A-men.

PSALMS LXIX, LXX.

27 Add thou iniquity unto
their former wickedness;
And do not let them come at all
into thy righteousness.
28 Out of the book of life let them
be raz'd and blotted quite;
Among the just and righteous
let not their names be writ.

29 But now become exceeding poor
and sorrowful am I:
By thy salvation, O my God,
let me be set on high.
30 The name of God I with a song
most cheerfully will praise;
And I, in giving thanks to him,
his name shall highly raise.

31 This to the Lord a sacrifice
more gracious shall prove
Than bullock, ox, or any beast
that hath both horn and hoof.
32 When this the humble men shall see,
it joy to them shall give:
O all ye that do seek the Lord,
your hearts shall ever live.

33 For God the poor hears, and will not
his prisoners contemn.
34 Let heav'n, and earth, and seas,
him praise,
and all that move in them.
35 For God will Judah's cities build,
and he will Sion save,
That they may dwell therein, and it
in sure possession have.

36 And they that are his servants' seed
inherit shall the same;
So shall they have their dwelling
there
that love his blessed name.

70

LORD, haste me to deliver;
with speed, Lord, succour me.
2 Let them that for my soul do seek
sham'd and confounded be:
Turn'd back be they, and sham'd,
that in my hurt delight.
3 Turn'd back be they, Ha, ha! that
say,
their shaming to requite.

4 In thee let all be glad,
and joy that seek for thee:
Let them who thy salvation love
say still, God praised be.

70

HOWARD. (C.M.) *Wilson's Collection,* 1825.

Doh = A. E.t. f.A.

```
:m  | m :s :f   | m :r :d    | r :l, :t,  | d :—  | r s  | l :t :d'  | s.f:m :r  | d s, :—
:s, | s,:—:s,   | s,:t, :d   | l,:—:s,    | s,:—  | s,d  | d :r :d   | d :—:t,   | d s, :—
:d  | d :m :r   | s :f :m    | r :—:f     | m :—  | t,m  | f :—:s    | l :s :f   | m t, :—
:d  | d :—:t,   | d :s, :l,  | f,:—:s,    | d,:—  | s,d  | f :r :m   | f :s :s,  | d s, :—

:d  | r :—:m    | f :—:m     | r :m :d        | d :t, | s,    | s :f :m    | r :l, :t,  | d :— || d  | d
:s, | s,:—:s,   | f,:—:s,    | l,:s,:m,.f,    | s,:—  | s,    | s,:t,:d    | l,:—:s,    | s,:— || l, | s,
:d  | t,:—:d    | d :—:d.t,  | l,:t,:d .r     | m :r  | t,    | d :r :m    | f :—:r     | m :— || f  | m
:m, | s,:—:d.ta,| l,:—:s,    | f,:s,:l,       | s,:—  | s,.f, | m,:r,:d,   | f,:—:s,    | d,:— || f, | d,
```

A-men.

PSALMS LXX, LXXI.

5 I poor and needy am;
come, Lord, and make no stay:
My help thou and deliv'rer art;
O Lord, make no delay.

70 (2)

ANOTHER OF THE SAME.

MAKE haste, O God, me to preserve;
with speed, Lord, succour me.
2 Let them that for my soul do seek
sham'd and confounded be:
Let them be turned back, and sham'd,
that in my hurt delight.
3 Turn'd back be they, Ha, ha! that say,
their shaming to requite.

4 O Lord, in thee let all be glad,
and joy that seek for thee:
Let them who thy salvation love
say still, God praised be.
5 But I both poor and needy am;
come, Lord, and make no stay:
My help thou and deliv'rer art;
O Lord, make no delay.

71

O LORD, my hope and confidence
is plac'd in thee alone;
Then let thy servant never be
put to confusion.
2 And let me, in thy righteousness,
from thee deliv'rance have;
Cause me escape, incline thine ear
unto me, and me save.

3 Be thou my dwelling-rock, to which
I ever may resort:
Thou gav'st commandment me to save,
for thou 'rt my rock and fort.
4 Free me, my God, from wicked hands,
hands cruel and unjust:
5 For thou, O Lord God, art my hope,
and from my youth my trust.

6 Thou from the womb didst hold me up;
thou art the same that me
Out of my mother's bowels took;
I ever will praise thee.
7 To many I a wonder am;
but thou 'rt my refuge strong.

HUDDERSFIELD. (C.M.) MARTIN MADAN, 1726-90.

Doh = E♭.

:d | s :—:l | s :—:d | f :m :r | d :— || t_1 | d :—:r | m.s:f :m | m :r ||
:d | d :—:d | d :—:d | d :—:t_1 | d :— || s_1 | s_1:—:t_1 | d.m:r :d | d :t_1 ||
:m | m :—:f | m :—:m | l :s :f | m :— || s | s :—:s | s :—:s | s :— ||
:d | d :—:d | d :—:l_1 | f_1:s_1 :s_1 | d :— || s.f | m :—:r | d :t_1 :d | s_1:— ||

:s | m.,r:d :d' | l :s :m | f .,m:r :d | m :r || s | d :r :m | f :m :r | d :— || d | d ||
:t_1 | d :—:d | d :—:d | t_1.,d:s_1 :l_1 | d :t_1 || t_1 | d :s_1 :s_1.d | d :—:t_1 | d :— || l_1 | s_1 ||
:s | s.,f:m :s | f :s :s | s :—:m.fe | s :— || s.f | m :r :d | l :s :f | m :— || f | m ||
:s_1 | d :—:m | f :m :d | r .,d:t_1 :l_1 | s_1:— || s_1 | l_1:t_1:d | f_1:s_1 :s_1 | d :— || f_1 | d ||

A-men.

PSALM LXXI.

8 Fill'd let my mouth be with thy praise
and honour all day long.

9 O do not cast me off, when as
old age doth overtake me;
And when my strength decayed is,
then do not thou forsake me.
10 For those that are mine enemies
against me speak with hate;
And they together counsel take
that for my soul lay wait.

11 They said, God leaves him; him pursue
and take: none will him save.
12 Be thou not far from me, my God:
thy speedy help I crave.
13 Confound, consume them, that unto
my soul are enemies:
Cloth'd be they with reproach and shame
that do my hurt devise.

14 But I with expectation
will hope continually;
And yet with praises more and more
I will thee magnify.
15 Thy justice and salvation
my mouth abroad shall shew,
Ev'n all the day; for I thereof
the numbers do not know.

16 And I will constantly go on
in strength of God the Lord;
And thine own righteousness, ev'n thine
alone, I will record.
17 For even from my youth, O God,
by thee I have been taught;
And hitherto I have declar'd
the wonders thou hast wrought.

18 And now, Lord, leave me not, when I
old and gray-headed grow:
Till to this age thy strength and pow'r
to all to come I shew.
19 And thy most perfect righteousness,
O Lord, is very high,
Who hast so great things done: O God,
who is like unto thee?

20 Thou, Lord, who great adversities,
and sore, to me didst shew,
Shalt quicken, and bring me again
from depths of earth below.

ICONIUM. (C.M.)
Doh = E♭.

JAMES NARES, 1715–83.

```
:s  |f  :m  |r  :d  |d  :t, |d  ‖m  |l  :s  |t  :d'  |r  :— |— ‖
:d  |d  :d  |t, :d  |l, :s, |s, ‖d  |d  :d  |f  :m.d |t, :— |— ‖
:m  |l  :s  |f  :m  |r  :r  |m  ‖s  |f  :s  |s  :s   |s  :— |— ‖
:d  |d  :d  |s, :l, |f, :s, |d  ‖d  |f  :m  |r  :d   |s, :— |— ‖

:s  |r  :m  |f  :m  |l  :r  |s  ‖m  |d  :f  |r  :s  |m  :— |— ‖f  |m ‖
:t, |t, :d  |r  :d  |d  :t, |d  ‖t, |d  :d  |d  :t, |d  :— |— ‖d  |d ‖
:s  |s  :s  |s  :s  |l  :s  |s  ‖se |l  :l  |s  :s  |s  :— |— ‖l  |s ‖
:s, |f  :m  |t, :d  |f, :f  |m  ‖m  |l, :f, |s, :s, |d  :— |— ‖f, |d ‖
                                                            A-men.
```

PSALMS LXXI, LXXII.

21 My greatness and my pow'r thou wilt
increase, and far extend:
On ev'ry side against all grief
thou wilt me comfort send.

22 Thee, ev'n thy truth, I'll also praise,
my God, with psaltery:
Thou Holy One of Israel,
with harp I'll sing to thee.
23 My lips shall much rejoice in thee,
when I thy praises sound;
My soul, which thou redeemed hast,
in joy shall much abound.

24 My tongue thy justice shall proclaim,
continuing all day long;
For they confounded are, and sham'd,
that seek to do me wrong.

72*

O LORD, thy judgments give the king,
his son thy righteousness.
2 With right he shall thy people judge,
thy poor with uprightness.
3 The lofty mountains shall bring forth
unto the people peace;
Likewise the little hills the same
shall do by righteousness.

4 The people's poor ones he shall judge,
the needy's children save;
And those shall he in pieces break
who them oppressed have.
5 They shall thee fear, while sun and moon
do last, through ages all.
6 Like rain on mown grass he shall drop,
or show'rs on earth that fall.

7 The just shall flourish in his days,
and prosper in his reign:
He shall, while doth the moon endure,
abundant peace maintain.
8 His large and great dominion shall
from sea to sea extend:
It from the river shall reach forth
unto earth's utmost end.

9 They in the wilderness that dwell
bow down before him must;

73

IRISH. (C.M.) *Hymns and Sacred Poems*, Dublin, 1749.

Doh=E.

:d | d :—:s_1 | d :r :m | f :m :r | m :— || s | m :f :s | d :r :t_1 | d :— ||
s_1 | s_1 :—:s_1 | l_1:t_1:d | d :—:t_1 | d :— || r | d :—:d | l_1:—:s_1 | s_1:— ||
:m | m :—:r | m :s :s | l :s :s | s :— || s | s :l :s | m :f :r | m :— ||
:d | d :—:t_1 | l_1:s_1:d | f_1:s_1:s_1 | d :— || t_1 | d :l_1:m_1 | l_1:f_1:s_1 | d :— ||

:s | d':s :l | s :f :m | l.,s:f :m | r :— || s | d'.,t:l :s | f :m :r | d :— || d | d ||
:d | d :m :d | d :t_1:d | d :r :s_1 | s_1:— || t_1 | d :—:d | r :d :t_1 | d :— || l_1 | s_1 ||
:m.f | s :—:f | s :—:s | f.,s:l.t:d' | t :— || s.f | m :f :s | l :s :f | m :— || f | m ||
:d.r | m :d :f | m :r :d | f.,m:r :d | s_1:— || s_1 | l_1 :f_1:m_1 | f_1:s_1:s_1 | d :— || f_1 | d ||

A-men.

And they that are his enemies
shall lick the very dust.
10 The kings of Tarshish, and the isles,
to him shall presents bring;
And unto him shall offer gifts
Sheba's and Seba's king.

11 Yea, all the mighty kings on earth
before him down shall fall;
And all the nations of the world
do service to him shall.
12 For he the needy shall preserve,
when he to him doth call;
The poor also, and him that hath
no help of man at all.

13 The poor man and the indigent
in mercy he shall spare;
He shall preserve alive the souls
of those that needy are.
14 Both from deceit and violence
their soul he shall set free;
And in his sight right precious
and dear their blood shall be.

15 Yea, he shall live, and giv'n to him
shall be of Sheba's gold:
For him still shall they pray, and he
shall daily be extoll'd.

16 Of corn an handful in the earth
on tops of mountains high,
With prosp'rous fruit shall shake, like trees
on Lebanon that be.
The city shall be flourishing,
her citizens abound
In number shall, like to the grass
that grows upon the ground.
17 His name for ever shall endure;
last like the sun it shall:
Men shall be bless'd in him, and bless'd
all nations shall him call.

18 Now blessed be the Lord our God,
the God of Israel,
For he alone doth wondrous works,
in glory that excel.
19 And blessed be his glorious name
to all eternity:
The whole earth let his glory fill.
Amen, so let it be.

73*

YET God is good to Israel,
to each pure-hearted one.
2 But as for me, my steps near slipp'd,
my feet were almost gone.

74

JACKSON. (C.M.)
Doh = D.

THOMAS JACKSON, 1715–81.

```
:s  |s  :d'.t |l  :s  |f  :s.f  |m  ||m  |s  :d'   |t  :l    |s  :— |— ||
:d  |d  :d    |d  :d  |d  :t,   |d  ||d  |r  :m    |r  :-.d  |t, :— |— ||
:m  |s  :m    |f  :s  |l  :s    |s  ||d' |t  :l.s  |s  :fe   |s  :— |— ||
:d  |m  :d    |f  :m  |r  :s,   |d  ||l, |t, :d    |r  :r    |s, :— |— ||
```

```
:s  |m  :m    |f  :s  |l  :r'.d' |t  ||d' |s  :l.f |m  :r    |d  :— |— ||d  |d  ||
:r  |d  :d    |d  :d  |d  :f.m   |r  ||m  |d  :d   |d  :t,   |d  :— |— ||l, |s, ||
:s  |s  :s    |f  :m  |f  :l     |t  ||s  |d' :l   |s  :s.f  |m  :— |— ||f  |m  ||
:t, |d  :ta,  |l, :d  |f  :r     |s  ||d  |m  :f   |s  :s,   |d  :— |— ||f, |d  ||
```

A-men.

PSALM LXXIII.

3 For I envious was, and grudg'd
the foolish folk to see,
When I perceiv'd the wicked sort
enjoy prosperity.

4 For still their strength continueth firm;
their death of bands is free.
5 They are not toil'd like other men,
nor plagu'd, as others be.
6 Therefore their pride, like to a chain,
them compasseth about;
And, as a garment, violence
doth cover them throughout.

7 Their eyes stand out with fat; they have
more than their hearts could wish.
8 They are corrupt; their talk of wrong
both lewd and lofty is.
9 They set their mouth against the heav'ns
in their blasphemous talk;
And their reproaching tongue throughout
the earth at large doth walk.

10 His people oftentimes for this
look back, and turn about;
Sith waters of so full a cup
to these are poured out.
11 And thus they say, How can it be
that God these things doth know?
Or, Can there in the Highest be
knowledge of things below?

12 Behold, these are the wicked ones,
yet prosper at their will
In worldly things; they do increase
in wealth and riches still.
13 I verily have done in vain
my heart to purify;
To no effect in innocence
washed my hands have I.

14 For daily, and all day throughout,
great plagues I suffer'd have;
Yea, ev'ry morning I of new
did chastisement receive.
15 If in this manner foolishly
to speak I would intend,
Thy children's generation,
behold, I should offend.

16 When I this thought to know, it was
too hard a thing for me;
17 Till to God's sanctuary I went,
then I their end did see.

75

KILMARNOCK. (C.M.)

Doh = E♭.

NEIL DOUGALL, 1776–1862.

:d |m :s |l :s.m |m :r |d ||l |s :d'.l |s :d.r |m :r |— ||
:s, |d :d |d :d |d :t, |d ||d |d :d |d :d |d :t, |— ||
:m |s :s |f :s |s :s.f |m ||f |s :m.f |m :fe |s :— |— ||
:d |d :m |f :m.d |s :s, |d ||f |m :d |d :l, |s, :— |— ||

:s |l :s |d' :m.r |d :r |m ||l |s :d.r |m :r |d :— |— ||d |d ||
:d |d :d.t, |d :se, |l, :t, |d ||d |d :d |d :t, |d :— |— ||l, |s, ||
:s |f :s.f |m :m |m :s |s ||f |s :l |s :s.f |m :— |— ||f |m ||
:m |f :m.r |d :t, |l, :s, |d ||f, |m, :f, |s, :s, |d :— |— ||f, |d ||

[There is a Faux-bourdon setting in the Revised Church Hymnary, No. 400.] A-men.

18 Assuredly thou didst them set
a slipp'ry place upon;
Them suddenly thou castedst down
into destruction.

19 How in a moment suddenly
to ruin brought are they!
With fearful terrors utterly
they are consum'd away.
20 Ev'n like unto a dream, when one
from sleeping doth arise;
So thou, O Lord, when thou awak'st,
their image shalt despise.

21 Thus grieved was my heart in me,
and me my reins opprest:
22 So rude was I, and ignorant,
and in thy sight a beast.
23 Nevertheless continually,
O Lord, I am with thee:
Thou dost me hold by my right hand,
and still upholdest me.

24 Thou, with thy counsel, while I live,
wilt me conduct and guide;
And to thy glory afterward
receive me to abide.
25 Whom have I in the heavens high
but thee, O Lord, alone?
And in the earth whom I desire
besides thee there is none.

26 My flesh and heart doth faint and fail,
but God doth fail me never:
For of my heart God is the strength
and portion for ever.
27 For, lo, they that are far from thee
for ever perish shall;
Them that a whoring from thee go
thou hast destroyed all.

28 But surely it is good for me
that I draw near to God:
In God I trust, that all thy works
I may declare abroad.

74

O GOD, why hast thou cast us off?
is it for evermore?
Against thy pasture-sheep why doth
thine anger smoke so sore?
2 O call to thy rememberance
thy congregation,
Which thou hast purchased of old;
still think the same upon:

76

KILSYTH. (C.M.)
Doh = B♭.

Adapted from *Geistliche Lieder*, Leipsic, 1545.

```
:d  |s,  :l,  |d  :m  |r  :r  |d  ‖m  |r  :d  |t,  :t,   |l,  :— |— ‖
:m, |s,  :f,  |s, :s, |l, :s, |m, ‖s, |f, :m, |m,  :-.r, |d,  :— |— ‖
:s, |d   :d   |d  :d  |d  :t, |d  ‖d  |l, :l, |l,  :se,  |l,  :— |— ‖
:d, |m,  :f,  |m, :d, |f, :s, |d, ‖d, |r, :l,, |m, :m,   |l,, :— |— ‖

:m  |f   :r   |m  :d  |r  :m  |l, ‖d   |s,  :m  |r  :r  |d  :— |— ‖d  |d  ‖
:l, |l,  :s,  |s, :s, |f, :m, |f, ‖f,  |f,  :m, |l, :s, |m, :— |— ‖f, |m, ‖
:d  |r   :t,  |d  :s, |t, :d  |d  ‖d   |r   :d  |d  :t, |d  :— |— ‖l, |s, ‖
:l, |r,  :s,  |d, :m, |r, :d, |f, ‖l,, |t,, :d, |f, :s, |d, :— |— ‖f, |d, ‖
```

A-men.

PSALM LXXIV.

The rod of thine inheritance,
which thou redeemed hast,
This Sion hill, wherein thou hadst
thy dwelling in times past.
3 To these long desolations
thy feet lift, do not tarry;
For all the ills thy foes have done
within thy sanctuary.

4 Amidst thy congregations
thine enemies do roar:
Their ensigns they set up for signs
of triumph thee before.
5 A man was famous, and was had
in estimation,
According as he lifted up
his axe thick trees upon.

6 But all at once with axes now
and hammers they go to,
And down the carved work thereof
they break, and quite undo.
7 They fired have thy sanctuary,
and have defil'd the same,
By casting down unto the ground
the place where dwelt thy name.

8 Thus said they in their hearts, Let us
destroy them out of hand:
They burnt up all the synagogues
of God within the land.
9 Our signs we do not now behold;
there is not us among
A prophet more, nor any one
that knows the time how long.

10 How long, Lord, shall the enemy
thus in reproach exclaim?
And shall the adversary thus
always blaspheme thy name?
11 Thy hand, ev'n thy right hand of might,
why dost thou thus draw back?
O from thy bosom pluck it out
for our deliv'rance' sake.

12 For certainly God is my King,
ev'n from the times of old,
Working in midst of all the earth
salvation manifold.
13 The sea, by thy great pow'r, to part
asunder thou didst make;
And thou the dragons' heads, O Lord,
within the waters brake.

14 The leviathan's head thou brak'st
in pieces, and didst give

KING'S NORTON. (C.M.) JEREMIAH CLARK, *c.* 1659–1707.

Lah = F. Doh = A♭.

```
|d :l,:-.t, |se,:m, :— |l,.,t,:d :r |m :— :— ||m :f .m:r .d |d :—:t, |d :— ||
|m,:f,:f,   |m, :m, :— |d, :f, :l,  |se,:— :— ||s,:l, :m,    |s,:—:s, |s,:— ||
|d :d :r    |t, :se,:— |l, :—:l,    |t, :— :— ||d :d :l,     |r :—:r  |m :— ||
|l,:f,:r,   |m, :m, :— |f, :—:f,    |m, :—.f,:m,.r, ||d,:f, :l, |s,:—:s, |d,:— ||

:m |s :r.m:f |f :d.r:m |r.,d:t,.d:t,.l, |se,:— |se |l.,s:f :f .m |d :—:t, .l, |l,:— ||l, l,  ||
:d |r :— :r  |d :— :l, |m, :— :re,      |m, :— |t, |d :—:l,      |m,:—:m,     |d,:— ||f, m,  ||
:s |s :— :s  |d :— :d  |m :— :l,        |t, :— |m  |m :f :l,     |l,:—:se,.l, |l,:— ||l, de  ||
:d |t,:— :t, |l,:— :l, |se, :l, :f,     |m, :  |m, |l,, :—:d,    |m,:—:m,     |l,,: ||r, l,, ||
```

A-men.

PSALMS LXXIV, LXXV.

Him to be meat unto the folk
in wilderness that live.
15 Thou clav'st the fountain and the flood,
which did with streams abound:
Thou dry'dst the mighty waters up
unto the very ground.

16 Thine only is the day, O Lord,
thine also is the night;
And thou alone prepared hast
the sun and shining light.
17 By thee the borders of the earth
were settled ev'ry where:
The summer and the winter both
by thee created were.

18 That th' enemy reproached hath,
O keep it in record;
And that the foolish people have
blasphem'd thy name, O Lord.
19 Unto the multitude do not
thy turtle's soul deliver:
The congregation of thy poor
do not forget for ever.

20 Unto thy cov'nant have respect;
for earth's dark places be
Full of the habitations
of horrid cruelty.

21 O let not those that be oppress'd
return again with shame:
Let those that poor and needy are
give praise unto thy name.

22 Do thou, O God, arise and plead
the cause that is thine own:
Remember how thou art reproach'd
still by the foolish one.
23 Do not forget the voice of those
that are thine enemies:
Of those the tumult ever grows
that do against thee rise.

75

TO thee, O God, do we give thanks,
we do give thanks to thee;
Because thy wondrous works declare
thy great name near to be.
2 I purpose, when I shall receive
the congregation,
That I shall judgment uprightly
render to ev'ry one.

78

LANCASTER. (C.M.)

Doh = A.

SAMUEL HOWARD, 1710–82.

```
:s, | d  :r  | m  :d  | f     :m     | r  || r  | m  :d  | t, :l,    | s, :— | — ||
:m, | s, :s, | s, :l, | l,    :s,    | s, || s, | s, :s, | s, :fe,   | s, :— | — ||
:d  | d  :t, | d  :d  | l,.t, :d     | t, || r  | d  :s, | r  :r.d   | t, :— | — ||
:d, | m, :s, | d  :l, | r,    :m,.f, | s, || t₂ | d, :m, | r, :r,    | s, :— | — ||

:s, | l, :t, | d  :t,     | d  :r  | m  || m  | s  :f  | m  :r      | d  :— | — || d  | d  ||
:s, | s, :f, | m, :s,     | d  :t, | d  || d  | s, :l, | s, :s,.f,  | m, :— | — || f, | m, ||
:d  | d  :r  | d  :r      | s  :f  | m  || d  | d  :d  | d  :t,     | d  :— | — || l, | s, ||
:m, | f, :r, | l, :s,.f,  | m, :r, | d, || l, | m, :f, | s, :s,     | d, :— | — || f, | d, ||
                                                                                  A-men.
```

PSALMS LXXV, LXXVI.

3 Dissolved is the land, with all
that in the same do dwell;
But I the pillars thereof do
bear up, and stablish well.
4 I to the foolish people said,
Do not deal foolishly;
And unto those that wicked are,
Lift not your horn on high.

5 Lift not your horn on high, nor speak
6 with stubborn neck. But know,
That not from east, nor west, nor south,
promotion doth flow.
7 But God is judge; he puts down one,
and sets another up.
8 For in the hand of God most high
of red wine is a cup:

'Tis full of mixture, he pours forth,
and makes the wicked all
Wring out the bitter dregs thereof;
yea, and they drink them shall.
9 But I for ever will declare,
I Jacob's God will praise.
10 All horns of lewd men I'll cut off;
but just men's horns will raise.

76

IN Judah's land God is well known,
his name 's in Isr'el great:
2 In Salem is his tabernacle,
in Sion is his seat.
3 There arrows of the bow he brake,
the shield, the sword, the war.
4 More glorious thou than hills of prey,
more excellent art far.

5 Those that were stout of heart are spoil'd,
they slept their sleep outright;
And none of those their hands did find,
that were the men of might.
6 When thy rebuke, O Jacob's God,
had forth against them past,
Their horses and their chariots both
were in a dead sleep cast.

7 Thou, Lord, ev'n thou art he that should
be fear'd; and who is he
That may stand up before thy sight,
if once thou angry be?

LANGHOLM. (C.M.)

Doh = E♭. *Dr. Arnold's Psalms*, 1791.

:s |f :m |l :d' |s :-.f |m ‖ s |d' :t |l :fe |s :— |— ‖
:d |d :d |d :d |r :t$_1$ |d ‖ d |d :r |m :r.d |t$_1$:— |— ‖
:m |l :s |f :s |l :s |s ‖ m |m.fe :s |d' :l |s :— |— ‖
:d |d :d |f :m |r :s$_1$ |d ‖ d |l$_1$:t$_1$ |d :r |s$_1$:— |— ‖

:s |f :m |l :s |t :d' |r ‖ l |s :f |m :r |d :— |— ‖ d |d ‖
:d |d :d |d :d |f :m.d |t$_1$ ‖ r |m :r |d :t$_1$ |d :— |— ‖ l$_1$ |s$_1$ ‖
:m |f :s |f :s |s :s |s ‖ l.t |d' :l |s :s.f |m :— |— ‖ f |m ‖
:d |l$_1$:d |f :m |r :d |s ‖ f |m :f |s :s$_1$ |d :— |— ‖ f$_1$ |d ‖

A-men.

PSALMS LXXVI, LXXVII.

8 From heav'n thou judgment caus'd be heard;
the earth was still with fear,
9 When God to judgment rose, to save
all meek on earth that were.

10 Surely the very wrath of man
unto thy praise redounds:
Thou to the remnant of his wrath
wilt set restraining bounds.
11 Vow to the Lord your God, and pay:
all ye that near him be,
Bring gifts and presents unto him;
for to be fear'd is he.

12 By him the sp'rits shall be cut off
of those that princes are:
Unto the kings that are on earth
he fearful doth appear.

77

UNTO the Lord I with my voice,
I unto God did cry;
Ev'n with my voice, and unto me
his ear he did apply.
2 I in my trouble sought the Lord,
my sore by night did run,
And ceased not; my grieved soul
did consolation shun.

3 I to remembrance God did call,
yet trouble did remain;
And overwhelm'd my spirit was,
whilst I did sore complain.
4 Mine eyes, debarr'd from rest and sleep,
thou makest still to wake;
My trouble is so great that I
unable am to speak.

5 The days of old to mind I call'd,
and oft did think upon
The times and ages that are past
full many years agone.
6 By night my song I call to mind,
and commune with my heart;
My sp'rit did carefully enquire
how I might ease my smart.

7 For ever will the Lord cast off,
and gracious be no more?
8 For ever is his mercy gone?
fails his word evermore?
9 Is't true that to be gracious
the Lord forgotten hath?
And that his tender mercies he
hath shut up in his wrath?

LINCOLN. (C.M.) *Ravenscroft's Psalter*, 1621.

Doh = G. f.C.

d :—	r :m	r :d	d :t,	d :—	ᵈs :—	r' :d'	d' :t	d' :—
s, :—	s, :s,	s, :m,	l, :s,	s, :—	ˢr :—	s :s	r :r	m :—
m :—	r :d	t, :d	f :r	m :—	ᵐt :—	t :d'	l :s	s :—
d :—	t, :d	s, :l,	f, :s,	d, :—	ᵈs, :—	s :m	f :s	d :—

G.t.

d' :—	t :l	se :l	t :t	l :—	ˢd :—	l, :d	d :t,	d :—	d	d
s :—	s :m	m :m	f :m.r	d :—	ᵗm, :—	l, :s,	l, :s,	s, :—	f,	m,
m' :—	r' :d'	t :l	l :se	l :—	ᵐl, :—	d :d	f.m :r	m :—	l,	s,
d :—	s, :l,	m :d	r :m	l, :—	ᵐl, :—	f, :m,	f, :s,	d, :—	f,	d,

A-men.

PSALM LXXVII.

10 Then did I say, That surely this
is mine infirmity:
I'll mind the years of the right hand
of him that is most High.
11 Yea, I remember will the works
performed by the Lord:
The wonders done of old by thee
I surely will record.

12 I also will of all thy works
my meditation make;
And of thy doings to discourse
great pleasure I will take.
13 O God, thy way most holy is
within thy sanctuary;
And what god is so great in pow'r
as is our God most high?

14 Thou art the God that wonders do'st
by thy right hand most strong:
Thy mighty pow'r thou hast declar'd
the nations among.
15 To thine own people with thine arm
thou didst redemption bring;
To Jacob's sons, and to the tribes
of Joseph that do spring.

16 The waters, Lord, perceived thee,
the waters saw thee well;
And they for fear aside did flee;
the depths on trembling fell.
17 The clouds in water forth were pour'd,
sound loudly did the sky;
And swiftly through the world abroad
thine arrows fierce did fly.

18 Thy thunder's voice alongst the heav'n
a mighty noise did make;
By lightnings lighten'd was the world,
th' earth tremble did and shake.
19 Thy way is in the sea, and in
the waters great thy path;
Yet are thy footsteps hid, O Lord;
none knowledge thereof hath.

20 Thy people thou didst safely lead,
like to a flock of sheep;
By Moses' hand and Aaron's thou
didst them conduct and keep.

81

LIVERPOOL. (C.M.)

ROBERT WAINWRIGHT, 1748–82.
Arranged by SAMUEL SEBASTIAN WESLEY, 1810–76.

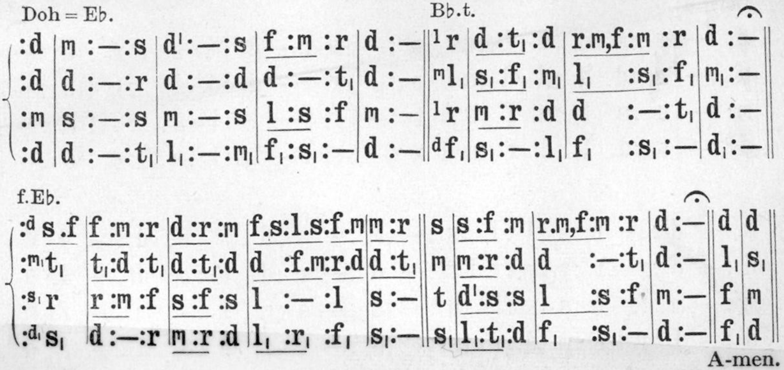

```
Doh = Eb.                                      Bb.t.
:d |m :— :s |d' :— :s |f :m :r |d :— ‖(l)r |d :t, :d |r.m,f :m :r |d :— ‖
:d |d :— :r |d :— :d |d :— :t, |d :— ‖(m)l, |s, :f, :m, |l, :s, :f, |m, :— ‖
:m |s :— :s |m :— :s |l :s :f |m :— ‖(l)r |m :r :d |d :— :t, |d :— ‖
:d |d :— :t, |l, :— :m, |f, :s, :— |d :— ‖(d)f, |s, :— :l, |f, :s, :— |d, :— ‖

f.Eb.
:(d)s .f |f :m :r |d :r :m |f.s:l.s:f.m |m :r ‖ s |s :f :m |r.m,f :m :r |d :— ‖ d |d ‖
:(m)t, |t, :d :t, |d :t, :d |d :f.m:r.d |d :t, ‖ m |m :r :d |d :— :t, |d :— ‖ l, |s, ‖
:(s,)r |r :m :f |s :f :s |l :— :l |s :— ‖ t |d' :s :s |l :s :f |m :— ‖ f |m ‖
:(d,)s, |d :— :r |m :r :d |l, :r, :f, |s, :— ‖ s, |l, :t, :d |f, :s, :— |d :— ‖ f, |d ‖
                                                                              A-men.
```

PSALM LXXVIII.

78*

ATTEND, my people, to my law;
 thereto give thou an ear;
The words that from my mouth proceed
 attentively do hear.
2 My mouth shall speak a parable,
 and sayings dark of old;
3 The same which we have heard and known,
 and us our fathers told.

4 We also will them not conceal
 from their posterity;
Them to the generation
 to come declare will we:
The praises of the Lord our God,
 and his almighty strength,
The wondrous works that he hath done,
 we will shew forth at length.

5 His testimony and his law
 in Isr'el he did place,
And charg'd our fathers it to show
 to their succeeding race;
6 That so the race which was to come
 might well them learn and know;
And sons unborn, who should arise,
 might to their sons them show:

7 That they might set their hope in God,
 and suffer not to fall
His mighty works out of their mind,
 but keep his precepts all:
8 And might not, like their fathers, be
 a stiff rebellious race;
A race not right in heart; with God
 whose sp'rit not stedfast was.

9 The sons of Ephraim, who nor bows
 nor other arms did lack,
When as the day of battle was,
 they faintly turned back.
10 They brake God's cov'nant, and refus'd
 in his commands to go;
11 His works and wonders they forgot,
 which he to them did shew.

LONDON NEW. (C.M.) *Scottish Psalter*, 1635.

Doh = D.

d :—	s :m	d' :s	l :d'	t :—	s :—	d' :m	s :r	d :—
d :—	r :d	d :d	d :m	r :—	r :—	d :d	d :t,	d :—
m :—	s :s	l :m	f :s.l	t :—	t :—	l :l	s :-.f	m :—
d :—	t, :d	l, :d	f :m.f	s :—	s, :—	l, :l,	m,.f, :s,	d :—

s :—	d' :l	t :s	l :l	s :—	m :—	s :d'	m :r	d :—	d	d
d :—	d :r	r :t,	m :r.d	t, :—	d :—	r :d	d :t,	d :—	l,	s,
m :—	m :fe	fe :s	s :fe	s :—	s :—	s :m.f	s :-.f	m :—	f	m
d :—	l, :r.d	t, :m	d :r	s, :—	d :—	t, :l,	s, :s,	d :—	f,	d

[*There is a Faux-bourdon setting in the Revised Church Hymnary, No.* 520.] A-men.

PSALM LXXVIII.

12 Things marvellous he brought to pass;
their fathers them beheld
Within the land of Egypt done,
yea, ev'n in Zoan's field.
13 By him divided was the sea,
he caus'd them through to pass;
And made the waters so to stand,
as like an heap it was.

14 With cloud by day, with light of fire
all night, he did them guide.
15 In desert rocks he clave, and drink,
as from great depths, supply'd.
16 He from the rock brought streams, like floods
made waters to run down.
17 Yet sinning more, in desert they
provok'd the Highest One.

18 For in their heart they tempted God,
and, speaking with mistrust,
They greedily did meat require
to satisfy their lust.
19 Against the Lord himself they spake,
and, murmuring, said thus,
A table in the wilderness
can God prepare for us?

20 Behold, he smote the rock, and thence
came streams and waters great;
But can he give his people bread?
and send them flesh to eat?
21 The Lord did hear, and waxed wroth;
so kindled was a flame
'Gainst Jacob, and 'gainst Israel
up indignation came.

22 For they believ'd not God, nor trust
in his salvation had;
23 Though clouds above he did command,
and heav'n's doors open made,
24 And manna rain'd on them, and gave
them corn of heav'n to eat.
25 Man angels' food did eat; to them
he to the full sent meat.

26 And in the heaven he did cause
an eastern wind to blow;
And by his power he let out
the southern wind to go.

LONDON NEW. (C.M.) DESCANT.

ALAN GRAY, 1855–

Doh = D.

Descant.

```
| m  :—  | s  :d'  | d' :m'.r' | d' :m' | r' :— || t :— | d' :d' | s :t  | d' :— ||
  Melody.
| d  :—  | s  :m   | d' :s     | l  :d' | t  :— || s :— | d' :m  | s :r  | d  :— ||

| d' :—  | m' :-.r' | r' :t    | d' :d' | t  :— || s :l | t  :d' | d' :t | d' :— ||
| s  :—  | d' :l    | t  :s    | l  :l  | s  :— || m :— | s  :d' | m  :r | d  :— ||
```

PSALM LXXVIII.

27 Then flesh as thick as dust he made
to rain down them among;
And feather'd fowls, like as the sand
which li'th the shore along.

28 At his command amidst their camp
these show'rs of flesh down fell,
All round about the tabernacles
and tents where they did dwell.
29 So they did eat abundantly,
and had of meat their fill;
For he did give to them what was
their own desire and will.

30 They from their lust had not estrang'd
their heart and their desire;
But while the meat was in their mouths,
which they did so require,
31 God's wrath upon them came, and slew
the fattest of them all;
So that the choice of Israel,
o'erthrown by death, did fall.

32 Yet, notwithstanding of all this,
they sinned still the more;
And though he had great wonders wrought,
believ'd him not therefore:
33 Wherefore their days in vanity
he did consume and waste;
And by his wrath their wretched years
away in trouble past.

34 But when he slew them, then they did
to seek him shew desire;
Yea, they return'd, and after God
right early did enquire.
35 And that the Lord had been their Rock
they did remember then;
Ev'n that the high almighty God
had their Redeemer been.

36 Yet with their mouth they flatter'd him,
and spake but feignedly;
And they unto the God of truth
with their false tongues did lie.
37 For though their words were good, their heart
with him was not sincere;
Unstedfast and perfidious
they in his cov'nant were.

83

MANCHESTER. (C.M.) ROBERT WAINWRIGHT, 1748–82.

Doh = E♭.

```
:d |m :— :r |d :— :d' |l :s :f   |m :— ||d' |s :f :m  |l :t :d' |m :r  ||
:d |d :— :t,|d :— :d  |d :— :d.t,|d :— ||m  |d :t, :d |d :r :m  |d :t, ||
:m |s :— :f |m :— :s  |f :m.f :s |s :— ||s  |s :— :s  |f :— :s  |s :—  ||
:d |d :— :s,|l,:— :m, |f,:s, :s, |d :— ||d  |m :r :d  |f :r :d  |s,:—  ||

:r |f :r :m  |l :— :s  |s :f :m  |m :r  ||t   |d':f :m  |f :m :r  |d :— ||d  |d  ||
:t,|d :r :d  |d :r :m  |t,:r :d  |d :t, ||r   |d :t, :d |d :— :t, |d :— ||l, |s, ||
:s |f :r :s  |l :t :d' |s :— :s  |s :—  ||s   |s :— :s  |l :s :f  |m :— ||f  |m  ||
:s,|l,:t, :d |f :— :m  |r :t, :d |s,:—  ||s.f |m :r :d  |f,:s, :s,|d :— ||f, |d  ||
```

A-men.

PSALM LXXVIII.

38 But, full of pity, he forgave
their sin, them did not slay;
Nor stirr'd up all his wrath, but oft
his anger turn'd away.
39 For that they were but fading flesh
to mind he did recall;
A wind that passeth soon away,
and not returns at all.

40 How often did they him provoke
within the wilderness!
And in the desert did him grieve
with their rebelliousness!
41 Yea, turning back, they tempted God,
and limits set upon
Him, who in midst of Isr'el is
the only Holy One.

42 They did not call to mind his pow'r,
nor yet the day when he
Deliver'd them out of the hand
of their fierce enemy;
43 Nor how great signs in Egypt land
he openly had wrought;
What miracles in Zoan's field
his hand to pass had brought.

44 How lakes and rivers ev'ry where
he turned into blood;
So that nor man nor beast could drink
of standing lake or flood.
45 He brought among them swarms of flies,
which did them sore annoy;
And divers kinds of filthy frogs
he sent them to destroy.

46 He to the caterpillar gave
the fruits of all their soil;
Their labours he deliver'd up
unto the locusts' spoil.
47 Their vines with hail, their sycamores
he with the frost did blast:
48 Their beasts to hail he gave; their flocks
hot thunderbolts did waste.

49 Fierce burning wrath he on them cast,
and indignation strong,
And troubles sore, by sending forth
ill angels them among.
50 He to his wrath made way; their soul
from death he did not save;
But over to the pestilence
the lives of them he gave.

51 In Egypt land the first-born all
he smote down ev'ry where;

84

[FIRST FORM]

MARTYRDOM. (C.M.)

Doh=G. HUGH WILSON, 1766–1824.

:s, |d :l, |s, :d.r |m :r |d ||m |s :m.r |d :m |r :— |— ||

:m, |s, :f, |m, :d |d :t, |d ||s, |s, :t, |d :s, |s, :— |— ||

:d |s, :l,.t, |d :m.f |s :s.f |m ||d |r :s |m :d |t, :— |— ||

:d, |m, :f, |d, :l, |s, :s, |d, ||d |t, :s, |l, :m, |s, :— |— ||

:s |m :r |d :m |f :m |r ||m |s,.l, :d.r |m :r |d :— |— ||d |d ||

:r |d :t, |l, :ta, |l,.t, :d |t, ||d |s,.f, :m,.l, |s, :s,.f, |m, :— |— ||f, |m, ||

:s |s :s |m :s |d.r :m.f |s ||s |d :d |d :t, |d :— |— ||l, |s, ||

:t, |d :s, |l, :s, |f, :d, |s, ||d, |m,.f, :l,.f, |s, :s, |d, :— |— ||f, |d, ||

A-men.

PSALM LXXVIII.

Among the tents of Ham, ev'n these
chief of their strength that were.
52 But his own people, like to sheep,
thence to go forth he made;
And he, amidst the wilderness,
them, as a flock, did lead.

53 And he them safely on did lead,
so that they did not fear;
Whereas their en'mies by the sea
quite overwhelmed were.
54 To borders of his sanctuary
the Lord his people led,
Ev'n to the mount which his right hand
for them had purchased.

55 The nations of Canaan,
by his almighty hand,
Before their face he did expel
out of their native land;
Which for inheritance to them
by line he did divide,
And made the tribes of Israel
within their tents abide.

56 Yet God most high they did provoke,
and tempted ever still;
And to observe his testimonies
did not incline their will:

57 But, like their fathers, turned back,
and dealt unfaithfully:
Aside they turned, like a bow
that shoots deceitfully.

58 For they to anger did provoke
him with their places high;
And with their graven images
mov'd him to jealousy.
59 When God heard this, he waxed wroth,
and much loath'd Isr'el then:
60 So Shiloh's tent he left, the tent
which he had plac'd with men.

61 And he his strength delivered
into captivity;
He left his glory in the hand
of his proud enemy.
62 His people also he gave o'er
unto the sword's fierce rage:
So sore his wrath inflamed was
against his heritage.

63 The fire consum'd their choice young men;
their maids no marriage had;
64 And when their priests fell by the sword,
their wives no mourning made.

85

[SECOND FORM]

MARTYRDOM. (C.M.) HUGH WILSON, 1766–1824.

Doh = G.

:s, | d :— :l, | s, :— :d .r | m :— :r | d :— || m | s :— :m | d :— :m | r :— ||
:m, | m, :— :f, | s, :— :m,.f, | s, :— :s,.f, | m, :— || s, | s, :— :s, | m, :—.f, :s, | s, :— ||
:d | d :s, :l,.t, | d :— :d | d :l, :t, | d :— || d | t, :— :t, | d :— :d | t, :— ||
:d, | d, :— :f, | m, :— :l, | s, :— :s, | d, :— || d, | m, :— :s, | l, :— :m, | s, :— ||

:s | m :— :r | d :— :m | f :— :m | r :— || m | s, :l, :d .r | m :— :r | d :— || d | d ||
:s, | s, :— :t, | d :— :ta, | l, :t, :d | t, :— || s, | s, :f, :m,.f, | s, :— :f, | m, :— || f, | m, ||
:r | d :— :f | m :— :d | d :r :m.f | s :— || d | d :— :d | d :l, :t, | d :— || l, | s, ||
:t, | d :— :s, | l, :— :s, | f, :— :d, | s, :— || d | m, :f, :l, | s, :— :s, | d, :— || f, | d, ||

A-men.

PSALMS LXXVIII, LXXIX.

65 But then the Lord arose, as one
that doth from sleep awake;
And like a giant that, by wine
refresh'd, a shout doth make:

66 Upon his en'mies' hinder parts
he made his stroke to fall;
And so upon them he did put
a shame perpetual.

67 Moreover, he the tabernacle
of Joseph did refuse;
The mighty tribe of Ephraim
he would in no wise chuse:

68 But he did chuse Jehudah's tribe
to be the rest above;
And of mount Sion he made choice,
which he so much did love.

69 And he his sanctuary built
like to a palace high,
Like to the earth which he did found
to perpetuity.

70 Of David, that his servant was,
he also choice did make,
And even from the folds of sheep
was pleased him to take:

71 From waiting on the ewes with young,
he brought him forth to feed
Israel, his inheritance,
his people, Jacob's seed.

72 So after the integrity
he of his heart them fed;
And by the good skill of his hands
them wisely governed.

79

O GOD, the heathen enter'd have
thine heritage; by them
Defiled is thy house: on heaps
they laid Jerusalem.

2 The bodies of thy servants they
have cast forth to be meat
To rav'nous fowls; thy dear saints' flesh
they gave to beasts to eat.

3 Their blood about Jerusalem
like water they have shed;
And there was none to bury them
when they were slain and dead.

4 Unto our neighbours a reproach
most base become are we;
A scorn and laughingstock to them
that round about us be.

85 *continued*]

DESCANT.

MARTYRDOM. (C.M.)

Doh = G. ALAN GRAY, 1855–

Descant.

```
:s, |m :—:f |s :d' :t.l |s :—:f |m :— ||s |s :—:s |m :-.f :s.l |r :— ||
Melody.
:s, |d :—:l, |s, :—:d.r |m :—:r |d :— ||m |s :—:m |d :— :m |r :— ||

:s |s :d' :t |l :—:ta |l :—:s |s :— ||s |d' :t .l :s.f |m :-.f :s.f |m :— ||
:s |m :—:r |d :—:m |f :—:m |r :— ||m |s, :l, :d.r |m :— :r |d :— ||
```

PSALMS LXXIX, LXXX.

5 How long, Lord, shall thine anger last?
wilt thou still keep the same?
And shall thy fervent jealousy
burn like unto a flame?
6 On heathen pour thy fury forth,
that have thee never known,
And on those kingdoms which thy name
have never call'd upon.

7 For these are they who Jacob have
devoured cruelly;
And they his habitation
have caused waste to lie.
8 Against us mind not former sins;
thy tender mercies show;
Let them prevent us speedily,
for we're brought very low.

9 For thy name's glory help us, Lord,
who hast our Saviour been:
Deliver us; for thy name's sake,
O purge away our sin.
10 Why say the heathen, Where's their God?
let him to them be known;
When those who shed thy servants' blood
are in our sight o'erthrown.

11 O let the pris'ner's sighs ascend
before thy sight on high;
Preserve those in thy mighty pow'r
that are design'd to die.
12 And to our neighbours' bosom cause
it sev'n-fold render'd be,
Ev'n the reproach wherewith they have,
O Lord, reproached thee.

13 So we thy folk, and pasture-sheep,
shall give thee thanks always;
And unto generations all
we will shew forth thy praise.

80*

HEAR, Isr'el's Shepherd! like a flock
thou that dost Joseph guide;
Shine forth, O thou that dost between
the cherubims abide.
2 In Ephraim's and Benjamin's,
and in Manasseh's sight,
O come for our salvation;
stir up thy strength and might.

3 Turn us again, O Lord our God,
and upon us vouchsafe

86

MARTYRS. (C.M.) *Scottish Psalter*, 1615.

Ray = D.

r :— | f :r | l :— | f :— | m :r | l :— ‖ l :— | d' :l | t.d' :r' | l :— ‖
l, :— | r :r | m :— | l, :t, | d :r | m :— ‖ f :— | s :f | r.m :f | m :— ‖
f :— | l :f | m :— | f :— | s :s | d' :— ‖ d' :— | d' :d' | s :l .t | de' :— ‖
r :— | r :r | d :— | r :— | d :t, | l, :— ‖ f :— | m :f | s :r | l :— ‖

l :— | d' :s | l :f | m :r | l :— ‖ d' :— | t :s.l | t :— | l :— | r :— | — :— ‖ d | r ‖
f :— | s :m | d :t, | d :r | m :— ‖ d :— | r :m | r :— | r :d | l, :— | — :— ‖ l, | l, ‖
d' :— | s :d' | f :f | s :s | d' :— ‖ m :— | s :s | s :— | m :— | f :— | — :— ‖ m | f ‖
f :— | m :d | f :r | d :t, | l, :— ‖ l, :— | t, :d | s, :— | l, :— | r :— | — :— ‖ l, | r ‖

A-men.

PSALM LXXX.

To make thy countenance to shine,
and so we shall be safe.
4 O Lord of hosts, almighty God,
how long shall kindled be
Thy wrath against the prayer made
by thine own folk to thee?

5 Thou tears of sorrow giv'st to them
instead of bread to eat;
Yea, tears instead of drink thou giv'st
to them in measure great.
6 Thou makest us a strife unto
our neighbours round about;
Our enemies among themselves
at us do laugh and flout.

7 Turn us again, O God of hosts,
and upon us vouchsafe
To make thy countenance to shine,
and so we shall be safe.
8 A vine from Egypt brought thou hast,
by thine outstretched hand;
And thou the heathen out didst cast
to plant it in their land.

9 Before it thou a room didst make,
where it might grow and stand;
Thou causedst it deep root to take,
and it did fill the land.

10 The mountains vail'd were with its shade,
as with a covering;
Like goodly cedars were the boughs
which out from it did spring.

11 Upon the one hand to the sea
her boughs she did out send;
On th' other side unto the flood
her branches did extend.
12 Why hast thou then thus broken down,
and ta'en her hedge away?
So that all passengers do pluck.
and make of her a prey.

13 The boar who from the forest comes
doth waste it at his pleasure;
The wild beast of the field also
devours it out of measure.
14 O God of hosts, we thee beseech,
return now unto thine;
Look down from heav'n in love, behold,
and visit this thy vine:

15 This vineyard, which thine own right hand
hath planted us among;

87

MELROSE. (C.M.)

Doh = G. *Scottish Psalter*, 1635.

```
| d  :—  | s  :m  | f  :s  | f  :r  | m  || f   | m  :d  | r  :m   | r  :—  ||
| s, :—  | s, :s, | l, :s, | l, :s, | s, || l,  | s, :s, | t, :d   | t, :—  ||
| m  :—  | r  :d  | d  :d  | d  :t, | d  || d   | m  :m  | f  :s   | s  :—  ||
| d  :—  | t, :d  | l, :m, | f, :s, | d  || f,  | d  :m  | r  :d   | s, :—  ||

| s  :—  | l  :s  | m  :s  | f  :m  | r  || f     | m  :d  | r  :r   | d  :—  || d  | d  ||
| d  :—  | d  :t, | d  :s, | l, :s, | s, || f,    | s, :l, | l, :t,  | d  :—  || l, | s, ||
| s  :—  | f  :r  | d  :d  | d  :d  | t, || l,.t, | d  :m  | r  :s.f | m  :—  || f  | m  ||
| m, :—  | f, :s, | l, :m, | f, :d, | s, || r,    | m, :l, | f, :s,  | d, :—  || f, | d, ||
                                                                         A-men.
```


And that same branch, which for thyself
thou hast made to be strong.
16 Burnt up it is with flaming fire,
it also is cut down:
They utterly are perished,
when as thy face doth frown.

17 O let thy hand be still upon
the Man of thy right hand,
The Son of man, whom for thyself
thou madest strong to stand.
18 So henceforth we will not go back,
nor turn from thee at all:
O do thou quicken us, and we
upon thy name will call.

19 Turn us again, Lord God of hosts,
and upon us vouchsafe
To make thy countenance to shine,
and so we shall be safe.

81

SING loud to God our strength; with joy
to Jacob's God do sing.
2 Take up a psalm, the pleasant harp,
timbrel and psalt'ry bring.
3 Blow trumpets at new-moon, what day
our feast appointed is:
4 For charge to Isr'el, and a law
of Jacob's God was this.

5 To Joseph this a testimony
he made, when Egypt land
He travell'd through, where speech I heard
I did not understand.
6 His shoulder I from burdens took,
his hands from pots did free.
7 Thou didst in trouble on me call,
and I deliver'd thee:

In secret place of thundering
I did thee answer make;
And at the streams of Meribah
of thee a proof did take.
8 O thou, my people, give an ear,
I'll testify to thee;
To thee, O Isr'el, if thou wilt
but hearken unto me.

9 In midst of thee there shall not be
any strange god at all;
Nor unto any god unknown
thou bowing down shalt fall.

88

MILTON. (C.M.) *Mason's Hallelujah*, 1854.

Doh = A.

| d :d .d | d :s, | l, :s, | s, ‖ r | m :r .d | t, :l, | s, :— ‖
| m, :m,.f, | s, :m, | f, :r, | m, ‖ s, | s, :l, | s, :fe, | s, :— ‖
| d :d .d | d :d | d :t, | d ‖ r | d :m | r :- .d | t, :— ‖
| d, :d,.r, | m, :d, | f, :s, | d ‖ t, | d :l, | r :r, | s, :— ‖

| m :m .m | d :d | f :m | r ‖ m .f | s :m .d | l, :t, | d :— ‖ d | d ‖
| m, :f,.s, | l, :l,.s, | f, :s,.l, | t, ‖ s, | s, :s, | s,.f, :m,.r, | m, :— ‖ f, | m, ‖
| d :d .d | d :d | r :d | t, ‖ t, | d :d | d :s, | s, :— ‖ l, | s, ‖
| d, :r,.m, | f, :f,.m, | r, :m,.f, | s, ‖ s,.f, | m, :d, | f, :s, | d, :— ‖ f, | d, ‖

A-men.

PSALMS LXXXI, LXXXII.

10 I am the Lord thy God, which did
from Egypt land thee guide;
I'll fill thy mouth abundantly,
do thou it open wide.

11 But yet my people to my voice
would not attentive be;
And ev'n my chosen Israel
he would have none of me.
12 So to the lust of their own hearts
I them delivered;
And then in counsels of their own
they vainly wandered.

13 O that my people had me heard,
Isr'el my ways had chose!
14 I had their en'mies soon subdu'd,
my hand turn'd on their foes.
15 The haters of the Lord to him
submission should have feign'd;
But as for them, their time should have
for evermore remain'd.

16 He should have also fed them with
the finest of the wheat;
Of honey from the rock thy fill
I should have made thee eat.

82

IN gods' assembly God doth stand;
he judgeth gods among.
2 How long, accepting persons vile,
will ye give judgment wrong?
3 Defend the poor and fatherless;
to poor oppress'd do right.
4 The poor and needy ones set free;
rid them from ill men's might.

5 They know not, nor will understand;
in darkness they walk on:
All the foundations of the earth
out of their course are gone.
6 I said that ye are gods, and are
sons of the Highest all:
7 But ye shall die like men, and as
one of the princes fall.

8 O God, do thou raise up thyself,
the earth to judgment call:
For thou, as thine inheritance,
shalt take the nations all.

MORAVIA. (C.M.)

Doh=F. Adapted from *Wolder's Gesangbuch*, 1598.

```
:d  |d  :s  |m  :d  |d  :m  |r  ||m |s  :f   |m  :r   |d :— |— ||
:s, |l, :s, |s, :s, |l, :d  |t, ||d |d  :d.r |d  :t,  |d :— |— ||
:m  |m  :r  |d  :d  |f  :s  |s  ||s |s  :l   |s  :s.f |m :— |— ||
:d  |l, :t, |d  :m, |f, :d  |s, ||d |m, :f,  |s, :s,  |d :— |— ||
```

```
:m  |s  :f  |m :d     |d  :m     |r  ||m |s  :f   |m  :r   |d :— |— ||d  |d  ||
:d  |t, :r  |d :d.ta, |l, :s,.l, |t, ||d |d  :d.r |d  :t,  |d :— |— ||l, |s, ||
:d  |r  :s  |s :s     |f  :m .fe |s  ||s |s  :l   |s  :s.f |m :— |— ||f  |m  ||
:l, |s, :t, |d :m,    |f, :d     |s, ||d |m, :f,  |s, :s,  |d :— |— ||f, |d  ||
                                                                      A-men.
```

PSALM LXXXIII.

83

KEEP not, O God, we thee entreat,
O keep not silence now:
Do thou not hold thy peace, O God,
and still no more be thou.
2 For, lo, thine enemies a noise
tumultuously have made;
And they that haters are of thee
have lifted up the head.

3 Against thy chosen people they
do crafty counsel take:
And they against thy hidden ones
do consultations make.
4 Come, let us cut them off, said they,
from being a nation,
That of the name of Isr'el may
no more be mention.

5 For with joint heart they plot, in league
against thee they combine.
6 The tents of Edom, Ishm'elites,
Moab's and Hagar's line;
7 Gebal, and Ammon, Amalek,
Philistines, those of Tyre;
8 And Assur join'd with them, to help
Lot's children they conspire.

9 Do to them as to Midian,
Jabin at Kison strand;
10 And Sis'ra, which at En-dor fell,
as dung to fat the land.
11 Like Oreb and like Zeeb make
their noble men to fall;
Like Zeba and Zalmunna like,
make thou their princes all;

12 Who said, For our possession
let us God's houses take.
13 My God, them like a wheel, as chaff
before the wind, them make.
14 As fire consumes the wood, as flame
doth mountains set on fire,
15 Chase and affright them with the storm
and tempest of thine ire.

16 Their faces fill with shame, O Lord,
that they may seek thy name.
17 Let them confounded be, and vex'd,
and perish in their shame:
18 That men may know that thou, to whom
alone doth appertain
The name JEHOVAH, dost most high
o'er all the earth remain.

MORVEN. (C.M.)

Doh = E♭. ROBERT ARCHIBALD SMITH, 1780–1829.

:d | r :m | s :d | l :s | m ‖ s | l :d^1 | l :s.m | m :s | — ‖
:d | s_1 :d | t_1 :l_1 | d :d.t_1 | d ‖ d | d :d | d :d | d :t_1 | — ‖
:m | s :s | s.f :m | f :r.s | s ‖ m | f.l :s.m | f :m | m :r | — ‖
:d | t_1 :d | s_1 :l_1 | f_1 :s_1 | d ‖ d | f :m.d | f_1 :s_1.l_1 | s_1 :— | — ‖

:m | r :d | l_1 :d.r | m :r.d | m.r ‖ s | d :l,s,m | r :r | d :— | — ‖ d | d ‖
:s_1 | t_1 :l_1 | l_1 :s_1 | s_1 :s_1.d | d.t_1 ‖ t_1 | d :d | d :t_1 | d :— | — ‖ l_1 | s_1 ‖
:d | s :m | f :s.f | m.d :r.fe | s ‖ r | d :d,m,s | l :s.f | m :— | — ‖ f | m ‖
:d | s_1 :l_1 | f_1.f :m.r | d :t_1.l_1 | s_1 ‖ s_1 | l_1 :m_1 | f_1 :s_1 | d :— | — ‖ f_1 | d ‖

A-men.

PSALM LXXXIV.

84*

HOW lovely is thy dwelling-place,
O Lord of hosts, to me!
The tabernacles of thy grace
how pleasant, Lord, they be!
2 My thirsty soul longs veh'mently,
yea faints, thy courts to see:
My very heart and flesh cry out,
O living God, for thee.

3 Behold, the sparrow findeth out
an house wherein to rest;
The swallow also for herself
hath purchased a nest;
Ev'n thine own altars, where she safe
her young ones forth may bring,
O thou almighty Lord of hosts,
who art my God and King.

4 Bless'd are they in thy house that dwell,
they ever give thee praise.
5 Bless'd is the man whose strength thou art,
in whose heart are thy ways:
6 Who passing thorough Baca's vale,
therein do dig up wells;
Also the rain that falleth down
the pools with water fills.

7 So they from strength unwearied go
still forward unto strength,
Until in Sion they appear
before the Lord at length.
8 Lord God of hosts, my prayer hear;
O Jacob's God, give ear.
9 See God our shield, look on the face
of thine anointed dear.

10 For in thy courts one day excels
a thousand; rather in
My God's house will I keep a door,
than dwell in tents of sin.
11 For God the Lord's a sun and shield:
he'll grace and glory give;
And will withhold no good from them
that uprightly do live.

12 O thou that art the Lord of hosts,
that man is truly blest,
Who by assured confidence
on thee alone doth rest.

91

NEWARK. (C.M.)

Lah = G. Doh = B♭. *Gawthorn's Harmonia Perfecta*, 1730.

:l, |d :t,.l, |se, :l, |l, :se, |l, ||d |r :m |f .m:r |d :— |— ||
:m, |l, :f, |m, :m, |m, :m, |m, ||m, |l, :s, |f, :s,.f, |m, :— |— ||
:d |m :r |t, :d |t, :t, |d ||d |d :d |l, :t, |d :— |— ||
:l$_2$ |l, :r, |m, :l$_2$ |m, :m, |l$_2$ ||l, |f, :m, |r, :s, |d, :— |— ||

:d |m :r |d :t,.d |r .d:t,.l, |se, ||d |t, :l, |l,:se, |l,:— |— ||l, |l, ||
:m, |s, :s,.f, |m,:s, |l, :f, |m, ||m, |m,.r,:d, |f,:m, |m,:— |— ||f, |m, ||
:d |d :t, |d :m |r :r .d |t, ||l, |se, :l, |t,:t, |d :— |— ||r |de ||
:d, |d :s, |l,:m, |f, :r, |m, ||l$_2$ |m, :f, |r,:m, |l$_2$:— |— ||r, |l$_2$ ||

A-men.

PSALMS LXXXV, LXXXVI.

85*

O LORD, thou hast been favourable
to thy beloved land:
Jacob's captivity thou hast
recall'd with mighty hand.
2 Thou pardoned thy people hast
all their iniquities;
Thou all their trespasses and sins
hast cover'd from thine eyes.

3 Thou took'st off all thine ire, and turn'dst
from thy wrath's furiousness.
4 Turn us, God of our health, and cause
thy wrath 'gainst us to cease.
5 Shall thy displeasure thus endure
against us without end?
Wilt thou to generations all
thine anger forth extend?

6 That in thee may thy people joy,
wilt thou not us revive?
7 Shew us thy mercy, Lord, to us
do thy salvation give.
8 I'll hear what God the Lord will speak:
to his folk he'll speak peace,
And to his saints; but let them not
return to foolishness.
9 To them that fear him surely near
is his salvation;
That glory in our land may have
her habitation.
10 Truth met with mercy, righteousness
and peace kiss'd mutually:
11 Truth springs from earth, and righteousness
looks down from heaven high.
12 Yea, what is good the Lord shall give;
our land shall yield increase:
13 Justice, to set us in his steps,
shall go before his face.

86*

O LORD, do thou bow down thine ear,
and hear me graciously;
Because I sore afflicted am,
and am in poverty.
2 Because I'm holy, let my soul
by thee preserved be:
O thou my God, thy servant save,
that puts his trust in thee.

NEWINGTON. (C.M.)

Doh = A♭.

WILLIAM JONES, 1726–1800.

```
:d  |s  :m  |d  :r.d |t,  :d     |r  || m.f |s  :d.r   |m  :r     |d  :— |— ||
:s, |s, :s, |l, :l,  |s,  :s,.fe,|s, || s,  |s, :m,.f, |s, :s,.f, |m, :— |— ||
:m  |r  :d  |m  :f.m |r   :d     |t, || d   |d  :d     |d  :t,    |d  :— |— ||
:d  |t, :d  |l, :f,  |s,  :l,    |s, || d   |m, :l,    |s, :s,    |d  :— |— ||

:m  |f  :r  |m  :f    |s  :r.d |t, || l, |s, :d.r   |m  :r     |d  :— |— || d  |d  ||
:s, |l, :s, |s, :s,   |s, :l,  |s, || r, |s, :m,.f, |s, :s,.f, |m, :— |— || f, |m, ||
:d  |d  :t, |d  :d.t, |d  :f.m |r  || t, |d  :d     |d  :t,    |d  :— |— || l, |s, ||
:d  |f, :s, |d, :r,   |m, :f,  |s, || f, |m, :l,    |s, :s,    |d, :— |— || f, |d, ||
```

A-men.

PSALM LXXXVI.

3 Sith unto thee I daily cry,
be merciful to me.
4 Rejoice thy servant's soul; for, Lord,
I lift my soul to thee.
5 For thou art gracious, O Lord,
and ready to forgive;
And rich in mercy, all that call
upon thee to relieve.

6 Hear, Lord, my pray'r; unto the voice
of my request attend:
7 In troublous times I'll call on thee;
for thou wilt answer send.
8 Lord, there is none among the gods
that may with thee compare;
And like the works which thou hast done,
not any work is there.

9 All nations whom thou mad'st shall come
and worship rev'rently
Before thy face; and they, O Lord,
thy name shall glorify.
10 Because thou art exceeding great,
and works by thee are done
Which are to be admir'd; and thou
art God thyself alone.

11 Teach me thy way, and in thy truth,
O Lord, then walk will I;
Unite my heart, that I thy name
may fear continually.
12 O Lord my God, with all my heart
to thee I will give praise;
And I the glory will ascribe
unto thy name always:

13 Because thy mercy toward me
in greatness doth excel;
And thou deliver'd hast my soul
out from the lowest hell.
14 O God, the proud against me rise,
and vi'lent men have met,
That for my soul have sought; and thee
before them have not set.

15 But thou art full of pity, Lord,
a God most gracious,
Long-suffering, and in thy truth
and mercy plenteous.
16 O turn to me thy countenance,
and mercy on me have;
Thy servant strengthen, and the son
of thine own handmaid save.

NEWINGTON. (C.M.) FAUX-BOURDON SETTING. HARVEY GRACE, 1874-

Doh = A♭.

```
:d  |s  :s    |l .s  :f .m  |r  :d       |t, ||s     |s  :m .f |s     :r  |m  :— |— ||
:d  |s, :d .t,|l,    :l,    |l, :s,.fe,  |s, ||d     |t, :d    |d .l, :t, |s, :— |— ||
:d  |s  :m    |d     :r .d  |t, :d       |r  ||m .f  |s  :d .r |m     :r  |d  :— |— ||
:d  |s, :d,   |f,.m, :r,    |f, :m,      |s, ||d,.r, |m, :l,   |s,    :s, |d, :— |— ||

:s   |d' :f      |t   :- .l |s    :f    |r  ||r .d |t,.r :s   |s     :- .f |m/d :— |— ||
:m.r |d  :r .d   |t,  :t,   |t,.d :l,   |s, ||r,   |s,   :s,  |s,.l, :t,   |s,  :— |— ||
:m   |f  :r      |m   :f    |s    :r .d |t, ||l,   |s,   :d .r|m     :r    |d   :— |— ||
:d.t,|l, :t,.l,  |se, :s,   |f,.m, :r,  |s, ||f,   |f,   :m,.f,|s,   :s,   |d,  :— |— ||
```

PSALMS LXXXVI, LXXXVII, LXXXVIII.

17 Shew me a sign for good, that they
which do me hate may see,
And be asham'd; because thou, Lord,
didst help and comfort me.

87

UPON the hills of holiness
he his foundation sets.
2 God, more than Jacob's dwellings all,
delights in Sion's gates.
3 Things glorious are said of thee,
thou city of the Lord.
4 Rahab and Babel I, to those
that know me, will record:

Behold ev'n Tyrus, and with it
the land of Palestine,
And likewise Ethiopia;
this man was born therein.
5 And it of Sion shall be said,
This man and that man there
Was born; and he that is most High
himself shall stablish her.

6 When God the people writes, he'll count
that this man born was there.
7 There be that sing and play; and all
my well-springs in thee are.

88

LORD God, my Saviour, day and night
before thee cry'd have I.
2 Before thee let my prayer come;
give ear unto my cry.
3 For troubles great do fill my soul;
my life draws nigh the grave.
4 I'm counted with those that go down
to pit, and no strength have.

5 Ev'n free among the dead, like them
that slain in grave do lie;
Cut off from thy hand, whom no more
thou hast in memory.
6 Thou hast me laid in lowest pit,
in deeps and darksome caves.
7 Thy wrath lies hard on me, thou hast
me press'd with all thy waves.

93

ORLINGTON. (C.M.) JOHN CAMPBELL, 1807–60.
Doh = C.

:s | m :s :d' | m' :r' :d' | l :— :t | d' :— ||
:s | d :m :s | s :— :s | f :— :f | m :— ||
:s | d' :— :s | d' :t :d' | d' :r' :s | s :— ||
:s | d' :s :m | d :r :m | f :r :s | d :— ||

:s | m :s :d' | l :f' :r' | d' :t || s | s .,l :s :f
:r | d :m :s | f :l :f | m :r || s | m .,f :m :r
:s | s :d' :d' | d' :— :l | s :— || | : :
:t, | d :— :m | f :— :f | s :— || | : :

PSALMS LXXXVIII, LXXXIX.

8 Thou hast put far from me my
friends,
thou mad'st them to abhor me;
And I am so shut up, that I
find no evasion for me.
9 By reason of affliction
mine eye mourns dolefully:
To thee, Lord, do I call, and stretch
my hands continually.

10 Wilt thou shew wonders to the
dead?
shall they rise, and thee bless?
11 Shall in the grave thy love be told?
in death thy faithfulness?
12 Shall thy great wonders in the dark,
or shall thy righteousness
Be known to any in the land
of deep forgetfulness?

13 But, Lord, to thee I cry'd; my
pray'r
at morn prevent shall thee.
14 Why, Lord, dost thou cast off my
soul,
and hid'st thy face from me?
15 Distress'd am I, and from my youth
I ready am to die;
Thy terrors I have borne, and am
distracted fearfully.

16 The dreadful fierceness of thy wrath
quite over me doth go:
Thy terrors great have cut me off,
they did pursue me so.
17 For round about me ev'ry day,
like water, they did roll;
And, gathering together, they
have compassed my soul.

18 My friends thou hast put far from
and him that did me love; [me,
And those that mine acquaintance
were
to darkness didst remove.

89*

GOD'S mercies I will ever sing;
and with my mouth I shall
Thy faithfulness make to be known
to generations all.
2 For mercy shall be built, said I,
for ever to endure;
Thy faithfulness, ev'n in the
heav'ns,
thou wilt establish sure.

3 I with my chosen One have made
a cov'nant graciously;
And to my servant, whom I lov'd,
to David sworn have I;

:||:

f :m :d'	d' :t :l	l :s	s	d' :— :r'	m' :— :d'
r :d :m	l :s :f	f :m	m	m.,f :s :s	s :— :m
: :	: :	:	s	m'.,r':d' :t	d' :— :d'
: :	: :	:	d	d.,r :m :s	d' :— :d'

f' :— :m'	r' :—	s	l :t :d'	r' :d' :t	d' :—	d'	d'
f.,s:l :s	s :—	s	f :—:s	f :m :r	m :—	f	m
d' :— :d'	t :—	d'	d' :r':d'	l :s :s	s :—	l	s
l.,s:f :d	s :—	m	f.,m:r :m	f :s :s,	d :—	f	d

A-men.

PSALM LXXXIX.

4 That I thy seed establish shall
for ever to remain,
And will to generations all
thy throne build and maintain.

5 The praises of thy wonders, Lord,
the heavens shall express;
And in the congregation
of saints thy faithfulness.

6 For who in heaven with the Lord
may once himself compare?
Who is like God among the sons
of those that mighty are?

7 Great fear in meeting of the saints
is due unto the Lord;
And he of all about him should
with rev'rence be ador'd.

8 O thou that art the Lord of hosts,
what Lord in mightiness
Is like to thee? who compass'd round
art with thy faithfulness.

9 Ev'n in the raging of the sea
thou over it dost reign;
And when the waves thereof do swell,
thou stillest them again.

10 Rahab in pieces thou didst break,
like one that slaughter'd is;
And with thy mighty arm thou hast
dispers'd thine enemies.

11 The heav'ns are thine, thou for thine own
the earth dost also take;
The world, and fulness of the same,
thy pow'r did found and make.

12 The north and south from thee alone
their first beginning had;
Both Tabor mount and Hermon hill
shall in thy name be glad.

13 Thou hast an arm that's full of pow'r,
thy hand is great in might;
And thy right hand exceedingly
exalted is in height.

14 Justice and judgment of thy throne
are made the dwelling-place;
Mercy, accompany'd with truth,
shall go before thy face.

15 O greatly bless'd the people are
the joyful sound that know;
In brightness of thy face, O Lord,
they ever on shall go.

16 They in thy name shall all the day
rejoice exceedingly;
And in thy righteousness shall they
exalted be on high.

94

PALESTRINA. (C.M.) Adapted from GIOVANNI PIERLUIGI DA PALESTRINA, 1525–94.

Doh = E.

s :s :s	l :—:s	s :f :m	s :—:—	m :m :m	m :r :d	r :—:—
d :d :d	d :—:d	t$_1$:r :d	r :—:—	d :d :t$_1$	d :l$_1$:l$_1$	t$_1$:—:—
m :m :m	f :—:m	s :l :l	t :—:—	s :l :s	s :f :m	s :—:—
d :d :d	f :—:d	m :r :l	s :—:—	d :l$_1$:m	d :r :l$_1$	s$_1$:—:—

m :s :s	l :—:m	s :f :f	m :—:—	m :r :d	r :—:r	m :—:—	f	m
d :d :d	d :—:d	t$_1$:r :r	t$_1$:—:—	d :t$_1$:l$_1$	l$_1$:—:t$_1$	d :—:—	d	d
s :m :m	f :—:s	s :l :l	se:—:—	s :s :m	f :—:s	s :—:—	l	s
d :d :d	f$_1$:—:d	m :r :r	m :—:—	d :s$_1$:l$_1$	r :—:s$_1$	d :—:—	f$_1$	d

A-men.

PSALM LXXXIX.

17 Because the glory of their strength
doth only stand in thee;
And in thy favour shall our horn
and pow'r exalted be.
18 For God is our defence; and he
to us doth safety bring:
The Holy One of Israel
is our almighty King.

19 In vision to thy Holy One
thou saidst, I help upon
A strong one laid; out of the folk
I rais'd a chosen one;
20 Ev'n David, I have found him out
a servant unto me;
And with my holy oil my King
anointed him to be.

21 With whom my hand shall stablish'd be;
mine arm shall make him strong.
22 On him the foe shall not exact,
nor son of mischief wrong.
23 I will beat down before his face
all his malicious foes;
I will them greatly plague who do
with hatred him oppose.

24 My mercy and my faithfulness
with him yet still shall be;
And in my name his horn and pow'r
men shall exalted see.
25 His hand and pow'r shall reach
afar;
I'll set it in the sea;
And his right hand established
shall in the rivers be.

26 Thou art my Father, he shall cry,
thou art my God alone;
And he shall say, Thou art the Rock
of my salvation.
27 I'll make him my first-born, more
than kings of any land. [high
28 My love I'll ever keep for him,
my cov'nant fast shall stand.

29 His seed I by my pow'r will make
for ever to endure; [throne
And, as the days of heav'n, his
shall stable be, and sure.
30 But if his children shall forsake
my laws, and go astray,
And in my judgments shall not
walk,
but wander from my way:

31 If they my laws break, and do not
keep my commandements;
32 I'll visit then their faults with rods,
their sins with chastisements.

PHILIPPI. (C.M.)
Doh = E♭.

SAMUEL WESLEY, 1766–1837.

```
:m | m :—:s  | s :—:d'  | d':t :l    | s :— || f  | m :r :d  | l :f :m   | r :—  ||
:d | d :—:r  | r :—:d   | d :—:d     | m :— || t, | d :t, :d | d :—:d    | t, :— ||
:s | s :—:s  | s :—:m   | m :—:f     | s :— || s  | s :f :m  | f :l :s   | s :—  ||
:d | d :—:t, | t, :—:l, | l, :s, :f, | d :— || s, | d :—:d   | f, :—:d   | s, :— ||

:s | m :s :f  | r :f :m  | d :m :r    | d :t,  || s  | f :m :l    | s :m :r    | d :— || d  | d  ||
:m | m :—:r   | r :—:d   | d :—:l,    | s, :—  || s, | l, :—:d    | d :—:t,    | d :— || l, | s, ||
:t | l :—:l   | s :—:s   | l :m :f    | m :r   || m  | r :d :f    | m :s :f    | m :— || f  | m  ||
:m | de :—:r  | t, :—:d  | l, :—:f,   | s, :—  || m, | l, :—:f,   | s, :—:s,   | d :— || f, | d  ||
                                                                                           A-men.
```

PSALM LXXXIX.

33 Yet I'll not take my love from him,
nor false my promise make.
34 My cov'nant I'll not break, nor change
what with my mouth I spake.
35 Once by my holiness I sware,
to David I'll not lie;
36 His seed and throne shall, as the
before me last for aye. [sun,
37 It, like the moon, shall ever be
establish'd stedfastly;
And like to that which in the heav'n
doth witness faithfully.
38 But thou, displeased, hast cast off,
thou didst abhor and loathe;
With him that thine anointed is
thou hast been very wroth.
39 Thou hast thy servant's covenant
made void, and quite cast by;
Thou hast profan'd his crown, while it
cast on the ground doth lie.
40 Thou all his hedges hast broke down,
his strong holds down hast torn.
41 He to all passers-by a spoil,
to neighbours is a scorn.
42 Thou hast set up his foes' right hand;
mad'st all his en'mies glad:
43 Turn'd his sword's edge, and him to
in battle hast not made. [stand
44 His glory thou hast made to cease,
his throne to ground down cast;
45 Shorten'd his days of youth, and him
with shame thou cover'd hast.
46 How long, Lord, wilt thou hide thy-
for ever, in thine ire? [self?
And shall thine indignation
burn like unto a fire?
47 Remember, Lord, how short a time
I shall on earth remain:
O wherefore is it so that thou
hast made all men in vain?
48 What man is he that liveth here,
and death shall never see?
Or from the power of the grave
what man his soul shall free?
49 Thy former loving-kindnesses,
O Lord, where be they now?
Those which in truth and faithfulness
to David sworn hast thou?
50 Mind, Lord, thy servant's sad re-
how I in bosom bear [proach;
The scornings of the people all,
who strong and mighty are.

96

PRAETORIUS. (C.M.)

Doh = F.

Görlitz Gesangbuch, 1599.

```
:d  |s  :s  |l  :s     |s  :-.f  |m  ‖d  |r     :m  |f  :f  |m  :— |— ‖
:s, |s, :d  |d  :d     |t, :-.t, |d  ‖m, |s,    :s, |l, :s, |s, :— |— ‖
:m  |r  :m  |f  :s     |r  :-.s  |s  ‖d  |t,    :d  |d  :t, |d  :— |— ‖
:d  |t, :d  |f, :m,.f, |s, :-.s, |d  ‖l, |s,.f, :m, |r, :s, |d, :— |— ‖

:m  |m  :s  |f  :r  |m  :d   |t, ‖s, |l, :d  |d  :t, |d    :— |— ‖d  |d    ‖
:s, |d  :s, |l, :s, |s, :fe, |s, ‖s, |f, :m, |s, :s, |s,   :— |— ‖l, |s,   ‖
:d  |d  :d  |d  :t, |d  :d   |r  ‖d  |d  :d  |r  :r  |m    :— |— ‖f  |m    ‖
:d  |l, :m, |f, :s, |d  :l,  |s, ‖m, |f, :l, |s, :s, |d/d, :— |— ‖f, |d/d, ‖
                                                                  A - men.
```

PSALMS LXXXIX, XC.

51 Wherewith thy raging enemies
reproach'd, O Lord, think on;
Wherewith they have reproach'd the steps
of thine anointed one.
52 All blessing to the Lord our God
let be ascribed then:
For evermore so let it be.
Amen, yea, and amen.

90*

LORD, thou hast been our dwelling-place
in generations all.
2 Before thou ever hadst brought forth
the mountains great or small;
Ere ever thou hadst form'd the earth,
and all the world abroad;
Ev'n thou from everlasting art
to everlasting God.

3 Thou dost unto destruction
man that is mortal turn;
And unto them thou say'st, Again,
ye sons of men, return.
4 Because a thousand years appear
no more before thy sight
Than yesterday, when it is past,
or than a watch by night.

5 As with an overflowing flood
thou carry'st them away:
They like a sleep are, like the grass
that grows at morn are they.
6 At morn it flourishes and grows,
cut down at ev'n doth fade.
7 For by thine anger we're consum'd,
thy wrath makes us afraid.

8 Our sins thou and iniquities
dost in thy presence place,
And sett'st our secret faults before
the brightness of thy face.
9 For in thine anger all our days
do pass on to an end;
And as a tale that hath been told,
so we our years do spend.

10 Threescore and ten years do sum up
our days and years, we see;
Or if, by reason of more strength,
in some fourscore they be:
Yet doth the strength of such old men
but grief and labour prove;
For it is soon cut off, and we
fly hence, and soon remove.

97

Adapted from THOMAS HAWEIS, 1734–1820, by SAMUEL WEBBE, the younger, 1770–1843.

RICHMOND. (C.M.)

Doh = G.

| s_1 :d :m | s :— :f | m :f :r | d :— ‖ m | r :s :d | t_1 :d :l_1 | s_1 :— ‖
| m_1 :s_1 :d | r :t_1 :l_1 | s_1 :l_1 :f_1 | m_1 :— ‖ fe_1 | s_1 :— :l_1 | s_1 :— :fe_1 | s_1 :— ‖
| d :m :s | s :— :d .r | m :d :t_1 | d :— ‖ d | r :— :m | r :— :d | t_1 :— ‖
| d :d :d | t_1 :s_1 :l_1.t_1 | d :f_1 :s_1 | d_1 :— ‖ l_1 | t_1 :— :d | r :— :r_1 | s_1 :— ‖

:r | m :r :d | f :m :r | s :f :m | l :— | s | l_1:f :m | m.r:d :t_1 | d :— :— ‖ d | d ‖
:s_1 | s_1:— :l_1 | f_1:— :s_1.l_1 | ta_1:— :ta_1 | l_1:— | d | l_1:t_1 :d | l_1 :s_1:s_1 | s_1:— :— ‖ l_1 | s_1 ‖
:t_1 | d :t_1 :l_1 | r :d :t_1 | d :r :m | d :— | s | f :— :s | f :m :r | m :— :— ‖ f | m ‖
:f_1 | m_1:— :l_1 | r_1:— :f_1 | m_1 :r_1 :d_1 | f_1:— | m_1 | m_1:r_1 :d_1 | f_1 :s_1:s_1 | d_1:— :— ‖ f_1 | d_1 ‖

A-men.

[*There is a Faux-bourdon setting in the Revised Church Hymnary, No.* 32.]

---

11 Who knows the power of thy wrath?
according to thy fear
12 So is thy wrath: Lord, teach thou us
our end in mind to bear;
And so to count our days, that we
our hearts may still apply
To learn thy wisdom and thy truth,
that we may live thereby.

13 Turn yet again to us, O Lord,
how long thus shall it be?
Let it repent thee now for those
that servants are to thee.
14 O with thy tender mercies, Lord,
us early satisfy;
So we rejoice shall all our days,
and still be glad in thee.

15 According as the days have been,
wherein we grief have had,
And years wherein we ill have seen,
so do thou make us glad.
16 O let thy work and pow'r appear
thy servants' face before;
And shew unto their children dear
thy glory evermore:

17 And let the beauty of the Lord
our God be us upon:
Our handy-works establish thou,
establish them each one.

91

HE that doth in the secret place
of the most High reside,
Under the shade of him that is
th' Almighty shall abide.
2 I of the Lord my God will say,
He is my refuge still,
He is my fortress, and my God,
and in him trust I will.

3 Assuredly he shall thee save,
and give deliverance
From subtile fowler's snare, and from
the noisome pestilence.
4 His feathers shall thee hide; thy trust
under his wings shall be:
His faithfulness shall be a shield
and buckler unto thee.

5 Thou shalt not need to be afraid
for terrors of the night;
Nor for the arrow that doth fly
by day, while it is light;

98

ROCHESTER. (C.M.) CHARLES HYLTON STEWART, 1884–

Doh = F. C.t.

:d |d :r :m |f :m :r |d :— :r |m :— |[fe]t |d' :— :s |f :m :r |d :— ||
:s, |m, :s, :d |l, :— :l, |s, :l, :s, |s, :— |[d]f |s :f :m |r :d :t, |d :— ||
:m |s :f :m |d :— :f |d :— :t, |d :— |[d']f' |m' :r' :d' |l :s :f |m :— ||
:d |d :— :d, |r, :m, :f, |m, :f, :r, |d, :— |[l,]r |m :— :m |f :s :s, |d :— ||

f.F.

:[m]t, |d :r :m |f :m :r |s :— :f |m :f |s |l :— :s |f :m :r |d :— ||d |d ||
:[d]s, |d :t, :d |f, :s, :t, |d :l, :t, |d :— |t, |l, :t, :d |d :— :t, |d :— ||l, |s, ||
:[s]r |s :f :s |d :— :r |d :m :r |d :— |m |f :— :s |l :— :r |m :— ||f |m ||
:[d]s, |m :r :d |l, :s, :f, |m, :f, :s, |l, :— |s, |f, :r, :m, |f, :— :s |d d, :— ||f, |d d, ||

[*Copyright*, 1924, *by J. Curwen & Sons, Ltd.*] A-men.

6 Nor for the pestilence, that walks
in darkness secretly;
Nor for destruction, that doth waste
at noon-day openly.

7 A thousand at thy side shall fall,
on thy right hand shall lie
Ten thousand dead; yet unto thee
it shall not once come nigh.
8 Only thou with thine eyes shalt
and a beholder be; [look,
And thou therein the just reward
of wicked men shalt see.

9 Because the Lord, who constantly
my refuge is alone,
Ev'n the most High, is made by
thy habitation; [thee
10 No plague shall near thy dwelling
come;
no ill shall thee befall:
11 For thee to keep in all thy ways
his angels charge he shall.

12 They in their hands shall bear thee
up,
still waiting thee upon;
Lest thou at any time should'st
dash
thy foot against a stone.

13 Upon the adder thou shalt tread,
and on the lion strong;
Thy feet on dragons trample shall,
and on the lions young.

14 Because on me he set his love,
I'll save and set him free;
Because my great name he hath
known,
I will him set on high.
15 He'll call on me, I'll answer him;
I will be with him still
In trouble, to deliver him,
and honour him I will.

16 With length of days unto his mind
I will him satisfy;
I also my salvation
will cause his eyes to see.

92*

TO render thanks unto the Lord
it is a comely thing,
And to thy name, O thou most High,
due praise aloud to sing.
2 Thy loving-kindness to shew forth
when shines the morning light;
And to declare thy faithfulness
with pleasure ev'ry night,

ST. ANDREW. (C.M.) *Tans'ur's New Harmony of Zion*, 1764.

Doh = A.

```
:d  |m  :—:m  |r  :—:m  |d  :—:t,  |d  :— ||m |s  :—:f  |m.,r:d  :m  |r  :— ||
:s, |s, :—:s, |s, :—:s, |m, :l,:s, |s, :— ||d |r  :t,:r  |d   :s, :d  |t, :— ||
:m  |d  :—:d  |t, :—:t, |d  :f :r  |m  :— ||s |s  :—:s   |s.,f:m  :s  |s  :— ||
:d, |d  :—:m, |s, :—:m, |l, :f,:s, |d, :— ||d |t, :s,:t, |d   :—  :d, |s, :— ||

:s,    |d  :—:r  |m  :—:s  |f  :—   :m     |r  :— ||r  |m  :—:d  |f  :m  :r    |d  :— ||d  |d  ||
:s,    |s, :—:s, |s, :—:s, |l, :d   :s,.l, |t, :— ||s, |s, :—:m, |l, :s, :-.f, |m, :— ||f, |m, ||
:t,    |d  :—:t, |d  :—:d  |d  :-.r:m .fe  |s  :— ||t, |d  :—:d  |d  :—  :t,   |d  :— ||l, |s, ||
:s,.f, |m, :—:s, |d  :—:m, |f, :l,  :d     |s, :— ||s, |d, :m,:l, |f, :s, :s,   |d, :— ||f, |d, ||
                                                                                         A-men.
```

PSALM XCII.

3 On a ten-stringed instrument,
upon the psaltery,
And on the harp with solemn sound,
and grave sweet melody.
4 For thou, Lord, by thy mighty works
hast made my heart right glad;
And I will triumph in the works
which by thine hands were made.

5 How great, Lord, are thy works! each thought
of thine a deep it is:
6 A brutish man it knoweth not;
fools understand not this.
7 When those that lewd and wicked are
spring quickly up like grass,
And workers of iniquity
do flourish all apace;

It is that they for ever may
destroyed be and slain:
8 But thou, O Lord, art the most High,
for ever to remain.
9 For, lo, thine enemies, O Lord,
thine en'mies perish shall;
The workers of iniquity
shall be dispersed all.

10 But thou shalt, like unto the horn
of th' unicorn, exalt
My horn on high: thou with fresh oil
anoint me also shalt.
11 Mine eyes shall also my desire
see on mine enemies;
Mine ears shall of the wicked hear
that do against me rise.

12 But like the palm-tree flourishing
shall be the righteous one;
He shall like to the cedar grow
that is in Lebanon.
13 Those that within the house of God
are planted by his grace,
They shall grow up, and flourish all
in our God's holy place.

14 And in old age, when others fade,
they fruit still forth shall bring;
They shall be fat, and full of sap,
and aye be flourishing;
15 To shew that upright is the Lord:
he is a rock to me;
And he from all unrighteousness
is altogether free.

100

ST. ANNE. (C.M.)

Doh = C.

William Croft, 1678–1727.

```
|s :— |m :l   |s :d' |d' :t |d' :— ||s :— |d' :s |l :fe |s :— ||
|d :— |d :d.r |m :m  |r :r  |m :—  ||m :— |m :m  |m :r  |r :— ||
|m :— |s :l.t |d' :d'|l :s  |s :—  ||d' :—|d' :t |l :l  |t :— ||
|d :— |d :f   |m :l  |f :s  |d :—  ||d :— |l, :m |d :r  |s :— ||

|t :— |d' :l |r' :t |d' :l  |t :—  ||s :— |l :d' |r' :t |d' :— ||d'   |d' ||
|r :— |m :d  |f :r  |m :-.r |t, :— ||d :— |f :m  |r :r  |m :—  ||f    |m  ||
|s :— |s :l  |l :s  |s :l   |se :— ||s :— |f :s  |l :s  |s :—  ||l    |s  ||
|s :— |d :f  |r :s  |d :f   |m :—  ||m :— |r :d  |f :s  |d :—  ||f/f, |d  ||
                                                                 A-men.
```

PSALMS XCIII, XCIV.

93*

THE Lord doth reign, and cloth'd is he
with majesty most bright;
His works do shew him cloth'd to be,
and girt about with might.
The world is also stablished,
that it cannot depart.
2 Thy throne is fix'd of old, and thou
from everlasting art.

3 The floods, O Lord, have lifted up,
they lifted up their voice;
The floods have lifted up their waves,
and made a mighty noise.
4 But yet the Lord, that is on high,
is more of might by far
Than noise of many waters is,
or great sea-billows are.

5 Thy testimonies ev'ry one
in faithfulness excel;
And holiness for ever, Lord,
thine house becometh well.

94

O LORD God, unto whom alone
all vengeance doth belong;
O mighty God, who vengeance own'st,
shine forth, avenging wrong.
2 Lift up thyself, thou of the earth
the sov'reign Judge that art;
And unto those that are so proud
a due reward impart.

3 How long, O mighty God, shall they
who lewd and wicked be,
How long shall they who wicked are
thus triumph haughtily?
4 How long shall things most hard by them
be uttered and told?
And all that work iniquity
to boast themselves be bold?

5 Thy folk they break in pieces, Lord,
thine heritage oppress:
6 The widow they and stranger slay,
and kill the fatherless.
7 Yet say they, God it shall not see
nor God of Jacob know.
8 Ye brutish people! understand;
fools! when wise will ye grow?

ST. ANNE. (C.M.)

FAUX-BOURDON SETTING.

Doh = C.

MARTIN SHAW, 1876–

:s	d' :d'	d' :m'	r' :r'	m' :—		r' :—	d' :t	m :r	r :—	
d :—	s :f	s :m	l :s	s :—		:r	m :-.r	d :l_1	t_1 :—	
s :—	m :l	s :d'	d' :t	d :—		s :—	d' :s	l :fe	s :—	
d :—	d :f	m :l	f :s	d :—		t_1 :—	l_1 :s_1	d :r	s_1 :—	

r' :—	d' :d'	t :t	l :-.l	se :—		t :—	d' :-.d'	f' :r'	m' :—	
:r	s :f	f :m	m :r	m :—		:r	l :s	f :s	s :—	
t :—	d' :l	r' :t	d' :l	t :—		s :—	l :d'	r' :t	d' :—	
s :—	m :f	r :s	f :f	m :—		s :—	f :m	r :s	d :—	

[*Copyright*, 1915, *by J. Curwen & Sons, Ltd.*]

PSALM XCIV.

9 The Lord did plant the ear of man,
and hear then shall not he?
He only form'd the eye, and then
shall he not clearly see?
10 He that the nations doth correct,
shall he not chastise you?
He knowledge unto man doth teach,
and shall himself not know?

11 Man's thoughts to be but vanity
the Lord doth well discern.
12 Bless'd is the man thou chast'nest, Lord,
and mak'st thy law to learn:
13 That thou may'st give him rest from days
of sad adversity,
Until the pit be digg'd for those
that work iniquity.

14 For sure the Lord will not cast off
those that his people be,
Neither his own inheritance
quit and forsake will he:
15 But judgment unto righteousness
shall yet return again;
And all shall follow after it
that are right-hearted men.

16 Who will rise up for me against
those that do wickedly?
Who will stand up for me 'gainst those
that work iniquity?
17 Unless the Lord had been my help
when I was sore opprest,
Almost my soul had in the house
of silence been at rest.

18 When I had uttered this word,
(my foot doth slip away,)
Thy mercy held me up, O Lord,
thy goodness did me stay.
19 Amidst the multitude of thoughts
which in my heart do fight,
My soul, lest it be overcharg'd,
thy comforts do delight.

20 Shall of iniquity the throne
have fellowship with thee,
Which mischief, cunningly contriv'd,
doth by a law decree?
21 Against the righteous souls they join,
they guiltless blood condemn.
22 But of my refuge God 's the rock,
and my defence from them.

23 On them their own iniquity
the Lord shall bring and lay,
And cut them off in their own sin;
our Lord God shall them slay.

ST. BERNARD. (C.M.)

Doh = E♭.

Tochter Sion, Cologne, 1741.
Probably adapted by JOHN RICHARDSON, 1816–79.

```
{:s  |d  :r  |m  :r.d |f  :m  |r  ||s  |m  :l  |fe :-.fe |s  :—  |—  ||
 :d  |d  :t, |d  :t,.d|t, :d  |t, ||r  |d  :d  |d  :-.d  |t, :—  |—  ||
 :m  |s  :s  |s  :s   |f  :s  |s  ||s  |s  :l  |l  :-.l  |s  :—  |—  ||
 :d  |m  :r  |d  :f.m |r  :d  |s, ||t, |d  :l, |r  :-.r  |s, :—  |—  ||

{:s  |d' :l  |s  :l   |f  :f  |m  ||d  |f  :m  |r  :r   |d  :—  |—  ||d  |d  ||
 :t, |d  :d  |d  :l,  |l, :r  |d  ||d  |t, :d  |d  :t,  |d  :—  |—  ||l, |s, ||
 :s  |s  :f  |m  :m   |f  :s  |s  ||s  |f  :s  |l  :s.f |m  :—  |—  ||f  |m  ||
 :s  |m  :f  |d  :de  |r  :t, |d  ||m  |r  :d  |f, :s,  |d  :—  |—  ||f, |d  ||
                                                                      A-men.
```

PSALMS XCV, XCVI.

95*

O COME, let us sing to the Lord:
  come, let us ev'ry one
A joyful noise make to the Rock
  of our salvation.
2 Let us before his presence come
  with praise and thankful voice;
Let us sing psalms to him with grace,
  and make a joyful noise.

3 For God, a great God, and great King,
  above all gods he is.
4 Depths of the earth are in his hand,
  the strength of hills is his.
5 To him the spacious sea belongs,
  for he the same did make;
The dry land also from his hands
  its form at first did take.

6 O come, and let us worship him,
  let us bow down withal,
And on our knees before the Lord
  our Maker let us fall.
7 For he 's our God, the people we
  of his own pasture are,
And of his hand the sheep; to-day,
  if ye his voice will hear,

8 Then harden not your hearts, as in the provocation,
As in the desert, on the day
  of the tentation:
9 When me your fathers tempt'd and prov'd,
  and did my working see;
10 Ev'n for the space of forty years
  this race hath grieved me.

I said, This people errs in heart,
  my ways they do not know:
11 To whom I sware in wrath, that to
  my rest they should not go.

96*

O SING a new song to the Lord:
  sing all the earth to God.
2 To God sing, bless his name, shew still
  his saving health abroad.
3 Among the heathen nations
  his glory do declare;
And unto all the people shew
  his works that wondrous are.

4 For great 's the Lord, and greatly he
  is to be magnify'd;

102

ST. COLUMBA (ERIN). (C.M.) Old Irish Hymn Melody

Doh = E♭.

:d.r |m :—:f |s :—:f .s |m :—:r |d :— || d .r |m :—:f |s :—:f.s.l |s :— ||
:s, |d :—:d |t, :—:d .r |r :d :t, |l, :— || l,.t, |d :—:d |d :—:l, |d :— ||
:m.f |s :—:f |r :—:d .s |s :—:s |m :— || f |s :—:l |s :—:d |m :— ||
:d |d :t, :l, |s, :—:l,.t, |d :—:s, |l, :— || f, |d :t, :l, |m, :—:f, |d :— ||

:s |d' :—:l |s :—:f |m :— :r |d :— || m |s :—:f |m :—:r |d :— || d |d ||
:t, |d :—:d |d :—:r |r :d :t, |d :— || d |d :—:d |d :—:t, |d :— || l, |s, ||
:s.f |m :—:f |s :—:l |s :— :f |m :— || m |d' :t :l |s :—:s.f |m :— || f |m ||
:s, |l, :s, :f, |f, :m, :r, |m, :—.f, :s, |l, :— || l, |m, :—:f, |s, :—:s, |d :— || f, |d ||

A-men.

PSALMS XCVI, XCVII.

Yea, worthy to be fear'd is he
above all gods beside.
5 For all the gods are idols dumb,
which blinded nations fear;
But our God is the Lord, by whom
the heav'ns created were.

6 Great honour is before his face,
and majesty divine;
Strength is within his holy place,
and there doth beauty shine.
7 Do ye ascribe unto the Lord,
of people ev'ry tribe,
Glory do ye unto the Lord,
and mighty pow'r ascribe.

8 Give ye the glory to the Lord
that to his name is due;
Come ye into his courts, and bring
an offering with you.
9 In beauty of his holiness,
O do the Lord adore;
Likewise let all the earth throughout
tremble his face before.

10 Among the heathen say, God reigns;
the world shall stedfastly
Be fix'd from moving; he shall judge
the people righteously.

11 Let heav'ns be glad before the Lord,
and let the earth rejoice;
Let seas, and all that is therein,
cry out, and make a noise.

12 Let fields rejoice, and ev'ry thing
that springeth of the earth:
Then woods and ev'ry tree shall sing
with gladness and with mirth
13 Before the Lord; because he comes,
to judge the earth comes he:
He'll judge the world with righteousness,
the people faithfully.

97*

GOD reigneth, let the earth be glad,
and isles rejoice each one.
2 Dark clouds him compass; and in right
with judgment dwells his throne.
3 Fire goes before him, and his foes
it burns up round about:
4 His lightnings lighten did the world;
earth saw, and shook throughout.

103

ST. DAVID. (C.M.)

Doh = E♭.

Ravenscroft's Psalter, 1621.

```
|d :— |s :d' |m :s |f    :m |r :— ‖ d :— |s :d |f :l |s :— ‖
|d :— |r :d  |d :d |l,.t,:d |t, :— ‖ l, :— |r :d |d :d |d :— ‖
|m :— |s :l  |d' :d' |f  :s |s :— ‖ m :— |s :m |f :f |m :— ‖
|d :— |t, :l, |l :m |r   :d |s, :— ‖ l, :— |t, :d |l, :f, |d :— ‖

|s :— |l :m |s :d |f    :m |r :— ‖ s :— |d :m |f :r |d :— ‖ d |d ‖
|d :— |d :d |d :d |l,.t,:d |t, :— ‖ r :— |d :d |d :t, |d :— ‖ l, |s, ‖
|m :— |f :s |s :m |f    :s |s :— ‖ s :— |m :l |l :s |m :— ‖ f |m ‖
|d :— |f, :d |m, :l, |r  :d |s, :— ‖ t, :— |d :l, |f, :s, |d :— ‖ f, |d ‖
                                                             A-men.
```

PSALMS XCVII, XCVIII.

5 Hills at the presence of the Lord,
like wax, did melt away;
Ev'n at the presence of the Lord
of all the earth, I say.
6 The heav'ns declare his righteous-
all men his glory see. [ness,
7 All who serve graven images,
confounded let them be.

Who do of idols boast themselves,
let shame upon them fall:
Ye that are called gods, see that
ye do him worship all.
8 Sion did hear, and joyful was,
glad Judah's daughters were;
They much rejoic'd, O Lord, because
thy judgments did appear.

9 For thou, O Lord, art high above
all things on earth that are;
Above all other gods thou art
exalted very far.
10 Hate ill, all ye that love the Lord:
his saints' souls keepeth he;
And from the hands of wicked men
he sets them safe and free.

11 For all those that be righteous
sown is a joyful light,
And gladness sown is for all those
that are in heart upright.
12 Ye righteous, in the Lord rejoice;
express your thankfulness,
When ye into your memory
do call his holiness.

98*

O SING a new song to the Lord,
for wonders he hath done:
His right hand and his holy arm
him victory hath won.
2 The Lord God his salvation
hath caused to be known;
His justice in the heathen's sight
he openly hath shown.

3 He mindful of his grace and truth
to Isr'el's house hath been;
And the salvation of our God
all ends of th' earth have seen.
4 Let all the earth unto the Lord
send forth a joyful noise;
Lift up your voice aloud to him,
sing praises, and rejoice.

5 With harp, with harp, and voice of psalms,
unto JEHOVAH sing:
6 With trumpets, cornets, gladly sound
before the Lord the King.

104

ST. ETHELDREDA. (C.M.)

Doh = F. THOMAS TURTON, 1780–1864.

```
:d  |d  :r  |m  :r     |d  :t,  |d  ||r   |m  :s  |f     :m  |r  :— |— ||
:s, |d  :t, |d  :l,    |s, :s,  |s, ||t,  |d  :d  |l,.t, :d  |t, :— |— ||
:m  |m  :s  |s  :f     |m  :r   |m  ||s   |s  :m  |f     :s  |s  :— |— ||
:d  |l, :s, |d  :f,    |s, :s,  |d  ||s,  |d  :m  |r     :d  |s, :— |— ||

:m  |f  :l  |s  :t,    |d  :f   |m  ||s   |l  :f  |m  :r    |d :— |— ||f  |m ||
:d  |d  :d  |d  :s,.f, |m, :s,  |s, ||ta, |l, :d  |d  :t,   |d :— |— ||d  |d ||
:s  |f  :f  |s  :m.r   |d  :r   |d  ||d   |d  :f  |s  :-.f  |m :— |— ||l  |s ||
:d  |l, :f, |m, :s,    |l, :t,  |d  ||m,  |f, :l, |s, :s,   |d :— |— ||f, |d ||
                                                                      A-men.
```

PSALMS XCVIII, XCIX, C.

7 Let seas and all their fulness roar;
the world, and dwellers there;
8 Let floods clap hands, and let the
together joy declare [hills
9 Before the Lord; because he comes,
to judge the earth comes he:
He'll judge the world with righteousness,
his folk with equity.

99

TH' eternal Lord doth reign as
king,
let all the people quake;
He sits between the cherubims,
let th' earth be mov'd and shake.
2 The Lord in Sion great and high
above all people is;
3 Thy great and dreadful name (for it
is holy) let them bless.
4 The king's strength also judgment
thou settlest equity: [loves;
Just judgment thou dost execute
in Jacob righteously.
5 The Lord our God exalt on high,
and rev'rently do ye
Before his footstool worship him:
the Holy One is he.
6 Moses and Aaron 'mong his priests,
Samuel, with them that call
Upon his name: these call'd on God,
and he them answer'd all.
7 Within the pillar of the cloud
he unto them did speak:
The testimonies he them taught,
and laws, they did not break.
8 Thou answer'dst them, O Lord our
thou wast a God that gave [God;
Pardon to them, though on their
deeds
thou wouldest vengeance have.
9 Do ye exalt the Lord our God,
and at his holy hill
Do ye him worship: for the Lord
our God is holy still.

100*

ALL people that on earth do dwell,
Sing to the Lord with cheerful
voice. [forth tell,
2 Him serve with mirth, his praise
Come ye before him and rejoice.
3 Know that the Lord is God indeed;
Without our aid he did us make:
We are his flock, he doth us feed,
And for his sheep he doth us take.

105

ST. FLAVIAN. (C.M.)

Doh = F.

English Psalter, 1562.

```
|d  :—  |d  :t, |d  :m  |r  :r  |d  :—  ||d  :—  |f  :m  |d  :r  |m  :—  ||
|s, :—  |s, :s, |s, :d  |d  :t, |d  :—  ||s, :—  |d  :d  |d  :l, |t, :—  ||
|m  :—  |r  :r  |m  :s  |l  :s  |m  :—  ||m  :—  |f  :s  |l  :l  |se :—  ||
|d  :—  |s, :s, |d  :m, |f, :s, |d, :—  ||d  :—  |l, :d  |f  :f  |m  :—  ||

|m  :—  |m  :f  |s  :m  |d  :r  |m  :—  ||m  :—  |r  :d  |d  :t, |d  :—  ||d  |d   ||
|d  :—  |d  :d  |r  :t, |l, :t, |d  :—  ||d  :—  |t, :d  |l, :s, |s, :—  ||l, |s,  ||
|s  :—  |s  :f  |r  :s  |m  :s  |s  :—  ||s  :—  |s  :m  |f  :r  |m  :—  ||f  |m   ||
|d  :—  |d  :l, |t, :s, |l, :s, |d  :—  ||d  :—  |s, :l, |f, :s, |d, :—  ||f, |d d,||
                                                                          A-men.
```

PSALMS C, CI.

4 O enter then his gates with praise,
Approach with joy his courts unto:
Praise, laud, and bless his name always,
For it is seemly so to do.
5 For why? the Lord our God is good,
His mercy is for ever sure;
His truth at all times firmly stood,
And shall from age to age endure.

100 (2)

ANOTHER OF THE SAME.

O ALL ye lands, unto the Lord
make ye a joyful noise.
2 Serve God with gladness, him before
come with a singing voice.
3 Know ye the Lord that he is God;
not we, but he us made:
We are his people, and the sheep
within his pasture fed.

4 Enter his gates and courts with praise,
to thank him go ye thither:
To him express your thankfulness,
and bless his name together.

5 Because the Lord our God is good,
his mercy faileth never;
And to all generations
his truth endureth ever.

101

I MERCY will and judgment sing,
Lord, I will sing to thee.
2 With wisdom in a perfect way
shall my behaviour be.
O when, in kindness unto me,
wilt thou be pleas'd to come?
I with a perfect heart will walk
within my house at home.

3 I will endure no wicked thing
before mine eyes to be:
I hate their work that turn aside,
it shall not cleave to me.
4 A stubborn and a froward heart
depart quite from me shall;
A person giv'n to wickedness
I will not know at all.

5 I'll cut him off that slandereth
his neighbour privily:
The haughty heart I will not bear,
nor him that looketh high.

[105 *continued*]

DESCANT.

ST. FLAVIAN. (C.M.) ALAN GRAY, 1855–

Doh = F.

Descant.

|m :— |s :r |m :m |l :s |m :— || s :— |l :s |d' :t.l |se :— ||

Melody.

|d :— |d :t, |d :m |r :r |d :— || d :— |f :m |d :r |m :— ||

|s :— |s :l |t :s |s :–.f |m :— || d' :— |t :l |l :s |s :— ||

|m :— |m :f |s :m |d :r |m :— || m :— |r :d |d :t, |d :— ||

PSALMS CI, CII.

6 Upon the faithful of the land
mine eyes shall be, that they
May dwell with me: he shall me serve
that walks in perfect way.

7 Who of deceit a worker is
in my house shall not dwell;
And in my presence shall he not
remain that lies doth tell.
8 Yea, all the wicked of the land
early destroy will I;
All from God's city to cut off
that work iniquity.

102

O LORD, unto my pray'r give ear,
my cry let come to thee;
2 And in the day of my distress
hide not thy face from me.
Give ear to me; what time I call,
to answer me make haste:
3 For, as an hearth, my bones are burnt,
my days, like smoke, do waste.

4 My heart within me smitten is,
and it is withered
Like very grass; so that I do
forget to eat my bread.
5 By reason of my groaning voice
my bones cleave to my skin.
6 Like pelican in wilderness
forsaken I have been:

I like an owl in desert am,
that nightly there doth moan;
7 I watch, and like a sparrow am
on the house-top alone.
8 My bitter en'mies all the day
reproaches cast on me;
And, being mad at me, with rage
against me sworn they be.

9 For why? I ashes eaten have
like bread, in sorrows deep;
My drink I also mingled have
with tears that I did weep.
10 Thy wrath and indignation
did cause this grief and pain;
For thou hast lift me up on high,
and cast me down again.

11 My days are like unto a shade,
which doth declining pass;
And I am dry'd and withered,
ev'n like unto the grass.

106

ST. FRANCES. (C.M.)
Doh = E♭.

GEORGE AUGUSTUS LÖHR, 1821–97.

```
:d  | f  :m   | r  :d  | s  :f  | m || m   | r  :s  | l  :l   | s  :— | — ||
:s, | d  :d   | t, :d  | r  :r  | d || d   | r  :t, | m  :r.d | t, :— | — ||
:m  | l  :s   | f  :m  | s  :s  | s || s   | s  :r  | m  :fe  | s  :— | — ||
:d  | d  :d   | s, :l, | t, :t, | d || d   | t, :s, | d  :r   | s, :— | — ||

:s  | d' :m   | f  :l  | s  :f  | m || m   | f  :r  | d  :t,  | d  :— | — || d  | d  ||
:r  | d  :ta, | l, :d  | t, :t, | d || ta, | l, :l, | s, :s,  | s, :— | — || l, | s, ||
:f  | m  :s   | f  :f  | r  :s  | s || s   | f  :f  | m  :r   | m  :— | — || f  | m  ||
:t, | d  :d   | f, :f, | s, :s, | d || d   | f, :f, | s, :s,  | d  :— | — || f, | d  ||
```

A-men.

PSALM CII.

12 But thou, Lord, everlasting art,
and thy remembrance shall
Continually endure, and be
to generations all.

13 Thou shalt arise, and mercy have
upon thy Sion yet;
The time to favour her is come,
the time that thou hast set.
14 For in her rubbish and her stones
thy servants pleasure take;
Yea, they the very dust thereof
do favour for her sake.

15 So shall the heathen people fear
the Lord's most holy name;
And all the kings on earth shall dread
thy glory and thy fame.
16 When Sion by the mighty Lord
built up again shall be,
In glory then and majesty
to men appear shall he.

17 The prayer of the destitute
he surely will regard;
Their prayer will he not despise,
by him it shall be heard.
18 For generations yet to come
this shall be on record:
So shall the people that shall be
created praise the Lord.

19 He from his sanctuary's height
hath downward cast his eye;
And from his glorious throne in heav'n
the Lord the earth did spy;
20 That of the mournful prisoner
the groanings he might hear,
To set them free that unto death
by men appointed are:

21 That they in Sion may declare
the Lord's most holy name,
And publish in Jerusalem
the praises of the same;
22 When as the people gather shall
in troops with one accord,
When kingdoms shall assembled be
to serve the highest Lord.

23 My wonted strength and force he hath
abated in the way,
And he my days hath shortened:
24 Thus therefore did I say,
My God, in mid-time of my days
take thou me not away:
From age to age eternally
thy years endure and stay.

107

ST. FULBERT. (C.M.)

Doh = E♭. HENRY JOHN GAUNTLETT, 1805–76.

:s | s :d | r :l | s :f | m || s | m :s | l :d^1 | t :— | — ||
:r | d :d | d :t_1 | d :r | d || r | d :d | l_1 :l_1 | r :— | — ||
:s | m :s | l :r^1 | s :s | s || s | s :s | s :fe | s :— | — ||
:t_1 | d :m | f :f | m :t_1 | d || t_1 | d :m | r :r | s_1 :— | — ||

:d^1 | s :l | s :d | f :f | m || m | r :m | f :r | d :— | — || f | m ||
:m | d :d | d :d | d :t_1 | d || d | d :d | d :t_1 | d :— | — || d | d ||
:s | s :f | s :s | l :s | s || l | l :s | l :f | m :— | — || l | s ||
:d | m :f | m :m | r :s_1 | d || l_1 | f_1 :m_1 | r_1 :s_1 | d :— | — || f_1 | d ||

A-men.

PSALM CII.

25 The firm foundation of the earth
of old time thou hast laid;
The heavens also are the work
which thine own hands have made.
26 Thou shalt for evermore endure,
but they shall perish all;
Yea, ev'ry one of them wax old,
like to a garment, shall:

Thou, as a vesture, shalt them change,
and they shall changed be:
27 But thou the same art, and thy years
are to eternity.
28 The children of thy servants shall
continually endure;
And in thy sight, O Lord, their seed
shall be establish'd sure.

102 (2)*

ANOTHER OF THE SAME.

LORD, hear my pray'r, and let my cry
Have speedy access unto thee;
2 In day of my calamity
O hide not thou thy face from me.
Hear when I call to thee; that day
An answer speedily return:
3 My days, like smoke, consume away,
And, as an hearth, my bones do burn.

4 My heart is wounded very sore,
And withered, like grass doth fade:
I am forgetful grown therefore
To take and eat my daily bread.
5 By reason of my smart within,
And voice of my most grievous groans,
My flesh consumed is, my skin,
All parch'd, doth cleave unto my bones.

6 The pelican of wilderness,
The owl in desert, I do match;
7 And, sparrow-like, companionless,
Upon the house's top, I watch.
8 I all day long am made a scorn,
Reproach'd by my malicious foes:
The madmen are against me sworn,
The men against me that arose.

9 For I have ashes eaten up,
To me as if they had been bread;
And with my drink I in my cup
Of bitter tears a mixture made.

108

ST. GEORGE. (C.M.)

Doh = F.

NICOLAUS HERMAN, 1485–1561.

```
:d  |s  :s   |s  :s    |l   :s.f |m  ||r  |m  :s    |s  :fe  |s  :— |— ||
:s, |d  :t,  |d  :d.t, |l,  :t,  |s, ||t, |d  :t,.d |r  :r.d |t, :— |— ||
:m  |s  :f   |m  :s    |f.m :r   |m  ||s  |s  :s    |l  :l   |s  :— |— ||
:d  |m  :r   |d  :m,   |f,  :s,  |d  ||s, |d  :m    |r  :r   |s, :— |— ||

:m  |s   :s  |s  :m  |s  :f.m |r  ||s  |f  :m |r  :r   |d :— |— ||d  |d  ||
:d  |r   :d  |t, :d  |d  :r.d |t, ||d  |d  :d |d  :t,  |d :— |— ||l, |s, ||
:s  |s.f :m  |r  :d  |s  :l   |r  ||d  |l  :s |s  :-.f |m :— |— ||f  |m  ||
:d  |t,  :d  |s, :l, |m, :f,  |s, ||m, |f, :d |s, :s,  |d :— |— ||f, |d  ||
                                                                    A-men.
```

PSALM CII.

10 Because thy wrath was not appeas'd,
And dreadful indignation: [rais'd,
Therefore it was that thou me
And thou again didst cast me down.

11 My days are like a shade alway,
Which doth declining swiftly pass;
And I am withered away,
Much like unto the fading grass.
12 But thou, O Lord, shalt still endure,
From change and all mutation free,
And to all generations sure
Shall thy remembrance ever be.

13 Thou shalt arise, and mercy yet
Thou to mount Sion shalt extend:
Her time for favour which was set,
Behold, is now come to an end.
14 Thy saints take pleasure in her stones,
Her very dust to them is dear.
15 All heathen lands and kingly thrones [fear.
On earth thy glorious name shall

16 God in his glory shall appear,
When Sion he builds and repairs.
17 He shall regard and lend his ear
Unto the needy's humble pray'rs:
Th' afflicted's pray'r he will not scorn.
18 All times this shall be on record:
And generations yet unborn
Shall praise and magnify the Lord.

19 He from his holy place look'd down,
The earth he view'd from heav'n on high; [groan,
20 To hear the pris'ner's mourning
And free them that are doom'd to
21 That Sion, and Jerus'lem too, [die;
His name and praise may well record,
22 When people and the kingdoms do
Assemble all to praise the Lord.

23 My strength he weaken'd in the
My days of life he shortened. [way,
24 My God, O take me not away
In mid-time of my days, I said:
Thy years throughout all ages last.
25 Of old thou hast established
The earth's foundation firm and fast:
Thy mighty hands the heav'ns have made.

26 They perish shall, as garments do,
But thou shalt evermore endure;

109

ST. GREGORY. (C.M.) — ROBERT WAINWRIGHT, 1748–82.

Doh = A.

:d	m :—:r.m	f :—:m	r :d :t,	d :—	m	r :s :t,	d :t, :l,	s, :—
:m,	s, :—:s,	f, :—:s,	l, :s, :s,	s, :—	s,	s, :—:s,	l, :s, :fe,	s, :—
:d	d :—:t,	d :—:d	f :m :r	m :—	d	r :—:m	m :r :d	t, :—
:d,	d :—:s,	l, :—:m,	f, :s, :s,	d, :—	d	t, :—:m,	d, :r, :r,	s, :—

:s,	d :—:ta,	l, :t, :d	r.m:f.m:r.d	d :t,	r	s :f :m	l,.r:d :t,	d :—	d	d
:s,	m,:f, :s,	f, :—:s,	l, :— :l,	s, :—	s,	s, :t, :d	l, :s, :s,	s, :—	l,	s,
:t,	d :—:d	d :r :m	r :— :r	m :r	t,	d :r :m	f :m :r	m :—	f	m
:s,	d, :r, :m,	f, :r, :d,	f, :r, :f,	s, :—	s,.f,	m, :r, :d,	f, :s, :s,	d, :—	f,	d,

A-men.

As vestures, thou shalt change them so;
And they shall all be changed sure:
27 But from all changes thou art free;
Thy endless years do last for aye.
28 Thy servants, and their seed who be,
Establish'd shall before thee stay.

103*

O THOU my soul, bless God the Lord;
and all that in me is
Be stirred up his holy name
to magnify and bless.

2 Bless, O my soul, the Lord thy God,
and not forgetful be
Of all his gracious benefits
he hath bestow'd on thee.

3 All thine iniquities who doth
most graciously forgive:
Who thy diseases all and pains
doth heal, and thee relieve.

4 Who doth redeem thy life, that thou
to death may'st not go down;
Who thee with loving-kindness doth
and tender mercies crown:

5 Who with abundance of good things
doth satisfy thy mouth;
So that, ev'n as the eagle's age,
renewed is thy youth.

6 God righteous judgment executes
for all oppressed ones.
7 His ways to Moses, he his acts
made known to Isr'el's sons.

8 The Lord our God is merciful,
and he is gracious,
Long-suffering, and slow to wrath,
in mercy plenteous.

9 He will not chide continually,
nor keep his anger still.
10 With us he dealt not as we sinn'd,
nor did requite our ill.

11 For as the heaven in its height
the earth surmounteth far;
So great to those that do him fear
his tender mercies are:

12 As far as east is distant from
the west, so far hath he
From us removed, in his love,
all our iniquity.

13 Such pity as a father hath
unto his children dear;
Like pity shews the Lord to such
as worship him in fear.

14 For he remembers we are dust,
and he our frame well knows.
15 Frail man, his days are like the grass,
as flow'r in field he grows:

ST. JAMES. (C.M.)

Doh = A. RAPHAEL COURTEVILLE, ? –1772.

```
:s,  |d  :r  |m  :d  |r  :f  |m  ||m  |l,  :t,  |d  :l,    |s, :— |— ||
:m,  |s, :s, |s, :s, |l, :s, |s, ||s, |fe, :s,  |s, :fe,   |s, :— |— ||
:d   |d  :t, |d  :d  |d  :t, |d  ||m  |r   :r   |m  :r.d   |t, :— |— ||
:d,  |m, :s, |d  :m, |f, :s, |d, ||d, |r,  :s,  |d, :r,    |s, :— |— ||
```

```
:r  |m  :d  |f  :m  |l, :r  |t, ||s,    |d  :m  |f  :r     |d  :— |— ||d  |d  ||
:s, |s, :s, |f, :s, |l, :l, |s, ||r,    |s, :m, |l, :s,.f, |m, :— |— ||f, |m, ||
:t, |d  :d  |t, :d  |d  :f  |r  ||t,    |d  :d  |d  :t,    |d  :— |— ||l, |s, ||
:s, |d, :m, |r, :d, |f, :r, |s, ||s,.f, |m, :d, |r, :s,    |d, :— |— ||f, |d, ||
```

A-men.

PSALMS CIII, CIV.

16 For over it the wind doth pass,
and it away is gone;
And of the place where once it was
it shall no more be known.
17 But unto them that do him fear
God's mercy never ends;
And to their children's children still
his righteousness extends:
18 To such as keep his covenant,
and mindful are alway
Of his most just commandements,
that they may them obey.
19 The Lord prepared hath his throne
in heavens firm to stand;
And ev'ry thing that being hath
his kingdom doth command.
20 O ye his angels, that excel
in strength, bless ye the Lord;
Ye who obey what he commands,
and hearken to his word.
21 O bless and magnify the Lord,
ye glorious hosts of his;
Ye ministers, that do fulfil
whate'er his pleasure is.
22 O bless the Lord, all ye his works,
wherewith the world is stor'd
In his dominions ev'ry where.
My soul, bless thou the Lord.

104*

BLESS God, my soul. O Lord my God,
thou art exceeding great;
With honour and with majesty
thou clothed art in state.
2 With light, as with a robe, thyself
thou coverest about;
And, like unto a curtain, thou
the heavens stretchest out.

3 Who of his chambers doth the beams
within the waters lay;
Who doth the clouds his chariot make,
on wings of wind make way.
4 Who flaming fire his ministers,
his angels sp'rits, doth make:
5 Who earth's foundations did lay,
that it should never shake.

6 Thou didst it cover with the deep,
as with a garment spread:
The waters stood above the hills,
when thou the word but said.
7 But at the voice of thy rebuke
they fled, and would not stay;
They at thy thunder's dreadful voice
did haste them fast away.

ST. KILDA. (C.M.)

Lah = E. Doh = G. WILLIAM ROBERT BROOMFIELD, 1826-88.

```
:l,  |l, :t,  |d  :m    |r  :d  |t,  || d  |l, :t,  |d  :r  |m :— |— ||
:m,  |m, :s,  |s, :s,.d |t, :l, |se, || l, |m, :se, |l, :t, |d :— |— ||
:d   |d  :r   |m  :s    |s  :m  |m   || m  |d  :r   |m  :s  |s :— |— ||
:l,  |l, :s,  |d, :d    |s, :l, |m,  || l, |d  :t,  |l, :s, |d :— |— ||
```

```
:m |r  :m |s :m |r  :d  |t,  || m  |l, :d  |t, :t,  |l, :— |— || l, |l, ||
:d |t, :d |r :d |t, :l, |se, || se, |l, :l, |l, :se, |l, :— |— || f, |m, ||
:s |s  :m |r :s |s  :m  |m   || m  |d  :m  |f  :m.r |d  :— |— || r  |de ||
:d |s, :d |t, :d |s, :l, |m,  || m,  |f, :d, |r, :m,  |l, :— |— || r, |l, ||
```

A-men.

PSALM CIV.

8 They by the mountains do ascend,
and by the valley-ground
Descend, unto that very place
which thou for them didst found.
9 Thou hast a bound unto them set,
that they may not pass over,
That they do not return again
the face of earth to cover.

10 He to the valleys sends the springs,
which run among the hills:
11 They to all beasts of field give drink,
wild asses drink their fills.
12 By them the fowls of heav'n shall have
their habitation,
Which do among the branches sing
with delectation.

13 He from his chambers watereth
the hills, when they are dry'd:
With fruit and increase of thy works
the earth is satisfy'd.
14 For cattle he makes grass to grow,
he makes the herb to spring
For th' use of man, that food to him
he from the earth may bring;

15 And wine, that to the heart of man
doth cheerfulness impart,
Oil that his face makes shine, and bread
that strengtheneth his heart.
16 The trees of God are full of sap;
the cedars that do stand
In Lebanon, which planted were
by his almighty hand.

17 Birds of the air upon their boughs
do chuse their nests to make;
As for the stork, the fir-tree she
doth for her dwelling take.
18 The lofty mountains for wild goats
a place of refuge be;
The conies also to the rocks
do for their safety flee.

19 He sets the moon in heav'n, thereby
the seasons to discern:
From him the sun his certain time
of going down doth learn.
20 Thou darkness mak'st, 'tis night, then beasts
of forests creep abroad.
21 The lions young roar for their prey,
and seek their meat from God.

22 The sun doth rise, and home they flock,
down in their dens they lie.

112

ST. LAWRENCE. (C.M.)

Doh = E♭.

ROBERT ARCHIBALD SMITH, 1780-1829.

:d	m :m.f	s :- .l	m :r	d ‖	s	l :d'	s.f :f.m	m :r	— ‖
:s,	d :d	d :m .d	d :t,	d ‖	d	d.r :m.d	t, :d	d :t,	— ‖
:m	s :l	s :d'.l	s :s.f	m ‖	d'.t	l :s	s :s	s :—	— ‖
:d	d :l,	m :- .f	s :s,	d ‖	m	f :m	r :d	s, :—	— ‖

:s	d :r	m.f :s	l.s :f .m	l ‖	d'	s :- .l	m :r	d :—	— ‖	d	d ‖
:t,	d.s, :l,.t,	d :r.s,	d.m :r .d	d ‖	d.r	m .f :m .r	d :t,	d :—	— ‖	l,	s, ‖
:s	s :s .f	m :r	m :s	f ‖	l.t	d'.t :d'.l	s :s.f	m :—	— ‖	f	m ‖
:s.f	m :r	d :t,	l, :t,.d	f, ‖	f	m .r :m .f	s :s,	d :—	— ‖	f,	d ‖

A-men.

PSALM CIV.

23 Man goes to work, his labour he
doth to the ev'ning ply.
24 How manifold, Lord, are thy works!
in wisdom wonderful
Thou ev'ry one of them hast made;
earth 's of thy riches full:

25 So is this great and spacious sea,
wherein things creeping are,
Which number'd cannot be; and beasts
both great and small are there.
26 There ships go; there thou mak'st to play
that leviathan great.
27 These all wait on thee, that thou may'st
in due time give them meat.

28 That which thou givest unto them
they gather for their food;
Thine hand thou open'st lib'rally,
they filled are with good.
29 Thou hid'st thy face; they troubled are,
their breath thou tak'st away;
Then do they die, and to their dust
return again do they.

30 Thy quick'ning spirit thou send'st forth,
then they created be;
And then the earth's decayed face
renewed is by thee.
31 The glory of the mighty Lord
continue shall for ever:
The Lord JEHOVAH shall rejoice
in all his works together.

32 Earth, as affrighted, trembleth all,
if he on it but look;
And if the mountains he but touch,
they presently do smoke.
33 I will sing to the Lord most high,
so long as I shall live;
And while I being have I shall
to my God praises give.

34 Of him my meditation shall
sweet thoughts to me afford;
And as for me, I will rejoice
in God, my only Lord.
35 From earth let sinners be consum'd,
let ill men no more be.
O thou my soul, bless thou the Lord.
Praise to the Lord give ye.

113

ST. LEONARD. (C.M.)

Doh = C. HENRY SMART, 1813–79.

```
:s  |s  :m  |l  :s  |l  :t  |d'  ||r'  |m' :d' |t  :l  |s :— |— ||
:m  |m  :d  |d  :d  |f  :f  |m   ||s   |s  :l  |s  :fe |s :— |— ||
:d' |d' :s  |f  :s  |f  :f  |s   ||t   |d' :m' |r' :d' |t :— |— ||
:d  |d  :d  |f  :m  |r  :r  |d   ||s   |d  :d  |r  :r  |s :— |— ||
```

```
:r' |t  :s   |d' :r' |m' :d' |l  ||r'  |s  :d' |d' :t |d' :— |— ||d' |d' ||
:s  |s  :r   |s  :s  |s  :s  |d  ||f   |m  :m  |r  :r |m  :— |— ||f  |m  ||
:t  |r' :t   |d' :t  |d' :s  |l  ||l.t |d' :d' |l  :s |s  :— |— ||l  |s  ||
:s  |s  :s.f |m  :r  |d  :m  |f  ||r   |m  :l  |f  :s |d  :— |— ||f  |d  ||
                                                                  A-men.
```

PSALM CV.

105*

GIVE thanks to God, call on his name;
to men his deeds make known.
2 Sing ye to him, sing psalms; proclaim
his wondrous works each one.
3 See that ye in his holy name
to glory do accord;
And let the heart of ev'ry one
rejoice that seeks the Lord.

4 The Lord Almighty, and his strength,
with stedfast hearts seek ye:
His blessed and his gracious face
seek ye continually.
5 Think on the works that he hath done,
which admiration breed;
His wonders, and the judgments all
which from his mouth proceed;

6 O ye that are of Abr'ham's race,
his servant well approv'n;
And ye that Jacob's children are,
whom he chose for his own.
7 Because he, and he only, is
the mighty Lord our God;
And his most righteous judgments are
in all the earth abroad.

8 His cov'nant he remember'd hath,
that it may ever stand:
To thousand generations
the word he did command.
9 Which covenant he firmly made
with faithful Abraham,
And unto Isaac, by his oath,
he did renew the same:

10 And unto Jacob, for a law,
he made it firm and sure,
A covenant to Israel,
which ever should endure.
11 He said, I'll give Canaan's land
for heritage to you;
12 While they were strangers there, and few,
in number very few:

13 While yet they went from land to land
without a sure abode;
And while through sundry kingdoms they
did wander far abroad;
14 Yet, notwithstanding, suffer'd he
no man to do them wrong:
Yea, for their sakes, he did reprove
kings, who were great and strong.

ST. MAGNUS (NOTTINGHAM). (C.M.)

Doh = G.

JEREMIAH CLARK, *c.* 1659–1707.

:s_1 | d :r | t_1 :s_1 | d :r | m ‖ r | m :d | m :fe | s :— | — ‖
:s_1 | l_1 :l_1 | s_1 :s_1 | s_1 :l_1.t_1 | d ‖ t_1 | d :s_1 | s_1 :d | t_1 :— | — ‖
:m | m :f | r :t_1 | d :f | m ‖ s | s :s.f | m.r :d | r :— | — ‖
:d | l_1 :f_1 | s_1 :s_1.f_1 | m_1 :r_1 | d_1 ‖ s_1 | d :m.r | d.t_1 :l_1 | s_1 :— | — ‖

:r | m :r | d :t_1 | l_1 :r | t_1 ‖ s_1 | s :s.f | m :r | d :— | — ‖ d | d ‖
:t_1 | d :t_1 | l_1 :s_1 | f_1 :l_1 | s_1 ‖ s_1 | d :d | d :t_1 | d :— | — ‖ l_1 | s_1 ‖
:s | s :s | m :m.r | d :f | r ‖ t_1 | d :l | s :-.f | m :— | — ‖ d | m ‖
:s_1 | d :s_1 | l_1 :m_1 | f_1 :r_1 | s_1 ‖ s_1.f_1 | m_1 :f_1 | s_1 :s_1 | d :— | — ‖ f_1 | d ‖

[*There is a Faux-bourdon setting in the Revised Church Hymnary, No.* 131.] A-men.

PSALM CV.

15 Thus did he say, Touch ye not those
that mine anointed be,
Nor do the prophets any harm
that do pertain to me.
16 He call'd for famine on the land,
he brake the staff of bread:
17 But yet he sent a man before,
by whom they should be fed;

Ev'n Joseph, whom unnat'rally
sell for a slave did they;
18 Whose feet with fetters they did [hurt,
and he in irons lay;
19 Until the time that his word came
to give him liberty;
The word and purpose of the Lord
did him in prison try.

20 Then sent the king, and did command
that he enlarg'd should be:
He that the people's ruler was
did send to set him free.
21 A lord to rule his family
he rais'd him, as most fit;
To him of all that he possess'd
he did the charge commit:

22 That he might at his pleasure bind
the princes of the land;
And he might teach his senators
wisdom to understand.
23 The people then of Israel
down into Egypt came;
And Jacob also sojourned
within the land of Ham.

24 And he did greatly by his pow'r
increase his people there;
And stronger than their enemies
they by his blessing were.
25 Their heart he turned to envy
his folk maliciously,
With those that his own servants [were
to deal in subtilty.

26 His servant Moses he did send,
Aaron his chosen one.
27 By these his signs and wonders great
in Ham's land were made known.
28 Darkness he sent, and made it dark;
his word they did obey.
29 He turn'd their waters into blood,
and he their fish did slay.

30 The land in plenty brought forth frogs
in chambers of their kings.
31 His word all sorts of flies and lice
in all their borders brings.

ST. MAGNUS (NOTTINGHAM). (C.M.) DESCANT. ALAN GRAY, 1855-

Doh = G.

Descant.

:m	l :l	s :t_1	d :f	m ‖ s_1	s :m.f	s :l	t :—	— ‖
Me	*lody.*							
:s_1	d :r	t_1 :s_1	d :r	m ‖ r	m :d	m :fe	s :—	— ‖

:t	d' :t	l :s	f :s.l	s ‖ s	s.d' :t.l	s :-.f	m :—	— ‖
:r	m :r	d :t_1	l_1 :r	t_1 ‖ s_1	s :s.f	m :r	d :—	— ‖

PSALMS CV, CVI.

32 He hail for rain, and flaming fire
into their land he sent:
33 And he their vines and fig-trees smote;
trees of their coasts he rent.

34 He spake, and caterpillars came,
locusts did much abound;
35 Which in their land all herbs consum'd,
and all fruits of their ground.
36 He smote all first-born in their land,
chief of their strength each one.
37 With gold and silver brought them forth,
weak in their tribes were none.

38 Egypt was glad when forth they went,
their fear on them did light.
39 He spread a cloud for covering,
and fire to shine by night.
40 They ask'd, and he brought quails: with bread
of heav'n he filled them.
41 He open'd rocks, floods gush'd, and
in deserts like a stream. [ran

42 For on his holy promise he,
and servant Abr'ham, thought.
43 With joy his people, his elect
with gladness, forth he brought.
44 And unto them the pleasant lands
he of the heathen gave;
That of the people's labour they
inheritance might have.

45 That they his statutes might observe
according to his word;
And that they might his laws obey.
Give praise unto the Lord.

106*

GIVE praise and thanks unto the Lord,
for bountiful is he;
His tender mercy doth endure
unto eternity.
2 God's mighty works who can express?
or shew forth all his praise?
3 Blessed are they that judgment
and justly do always. [keep,

4 Remember me, Lord, with that love
which thou to thine dost bear;
With thy salvation, O my God,
to visit me draw near:

115

ST. MARY. (C.M.)

Lah = D. Doh = F. *Prys's Psalms*, 1621.

| l, :— | d :t, | l, :l | s :f | m :— ‖ m :— | s :d | m :r | d :— ‖

| l, :— | l, :s, | f, :d | d :l, | l, :— ‖ s, :— | s, :l, | d :t, | d :— ‖

| d :— | m :m | d :f | m :r | de :— ‖ d :— | r :m | s :-.f | m :— ‖

| l, :— | l, :m, | f, :f, | d :r | l, :— ‖ d :— | t, :l, | m,.f, :s, | d :— ‖

| m :— | s :l | t :m | r :d | s :— ‖ r :— | m :l, | d :t, | l, :— ‖ l, | l, ‖

| d :— | r :d | t, :d | s, :d | t, :— ‖ s, :— | s, :l, | l, :se, | l, :— ‖ f, | m, ‖

| s :— | s :-.fe | s :s | r :m.fe | s :— ‖ t, :— | d :d.r | m :m.r | d :— ‖ r | de ‖

| d :— | t, :l, | s, :d | t, :l, | s, :— ‖ s, :— | d :f, | m, :m, | l, :— ‖ r, | l, ‖

A-men.

PSALM CVI.

5 That I thy chosen's good may see,
and in their joy rejoice;
And may with thine inheritance
triumph with cheerful voice.

6 We with our fathers sinned have,
and of iniquity
Too long we have the workers been;
we have done wickedly.
7 The wonders great, which thou, O Lord,
didst work in Egypt land,
Our fathers, though they saw, yet them
they did not understand:

And they thy mercies' multitude
kept not in memory;
But at the sea, ev'n the Red sea,
provok'd him grievously.
8 Nevertheless he saved them,
ev'n for his own name's sake;
That so he might to be well known
his mighty power make.

9 When he the Red sea did rebuke,
then dried up it was:
Through depths, as through the wilderness,
he safely made them pass.

10 From hands of those that hated them
he did his people save;
And from the en'my's cruel hand
to them redemption gave.

11 The waters overwhelm'd their foes;
not one was left alive.
12 Then they believ'd his word, and praise
to him in songs did give.
13 But soon did they his mighty works
forget unthankfully,
And on his counsel and his will
did not wait patiently;

14 But much did lust in wilderness,
and God in desert tempt.
15 He gave them what they sought, but to
their soul he leanness sent.
16 And against Moses in the camp
their envy did appear;
At Aaron they, the saint of God,
envious also were.

17 Therefore the earth did open wide,
and Dathan did devour,
And all Abiram's company
did cover in that hour.

DESCANT.

ST. MARY. (C.M.) — ALAN GRAY, 1855–

Lah = D. Doh = F.

Descant.

| m :— | l :s | f :f | m :r | de :— || d :— | r :m.f | s :—.f | m :— ||

Melody.

| l_1 :— | d :t_1 | l_1 :l | s :f | m :— || m :— | s :d | m :r | d :— ||

| s :— | s :—.fe | s :m.f | s :l | t :— || t :— | d^1 :f | m.ba :se | l :— ||

| m :— | s :l | t :m | r :d | s :— || r :— | m :l_1 | d :t_1 | l_1 :— ||

PSALM CVI.

18 Likewise among their company
a fire was kindled then;
And so the hot consuming flame
burnt up these wicked men.

19 Upon the hill of Horeb they
an idol-calf did frame,
A molten image they did make,
and worshipped the same.
20 And thus their glory, and their God,
most vainly changed they
Into the likeness of an ox
that eateth grass or hay.

21 They did forget the mighty God,
that had their saviour been,
By whom such great things brought to pass
they had in Egypt seen.
22 In Ham's land he did wondrous works,
things terrible did he,
When he his mighty hand and arm
stretch'd out at the Red sea.

23 Then said he, He would them destroy,
had not, his wrath to stay,
His chosen Moses stood in breach,
that them he should not slay.

24 Yea, they despis'd the pleasant land,
believed not his word:
25 But in their tents they murmured,
not heark'ning to the Lord.

26 Therefore in desert them to slay
he lifted up his hand:
27 'Mong nations to o'erthrow their seed,
and scatter in each land.
28 They unto Baal-peor did
themselves associate;
The sacrifices of the dead
they did profanely eat.

29 Thus, by their lewd inventions,
they did provoke his ire;
And then upon them suddenly
the plague brake in as fire.
30 Then Phin'has rose, and justice did,
and so the plague did cease;
31 That to all ages counted was
to him for righteousness.

32 And at the waters, where they strove,
they did him angry make,
In such sort, that it fared ill
with Moses for their sake:

116

ST. MATTHIAS (SONG 67). (C.M.)

Doh = D.

ORLANDO GIBBONS, 1583–1625.

```
|d  :—  |s  :m  |f    :s  |l  :l  |s  ‖s    |d' :l  |t  :t   |l  :—  |—  ‖
|d  :—  |r  :d  |d    :m  |m  :r  |m  ‖d    |d  :m  |m  :-.r |d  :—  |—  ‖
|m  :—  |s  :s  |d'   :t  |l  :t  |d' ‖m    |m  :l  |l  :se  |l  :—  |—  ‖
|d  :—  |t, :d  |l,   :s, |f, :f, |d  ‖d    |l, :d  |m  :m   |l, :—  |—  ‖

:d'   |t  :l   |s  :s  |f     :m |r  ‖s     |s   :d |m  :r   |d :— ‖d  |d  ‖
:d.r  |m  :f   |m  :d  |l,.t, :d |t, ‖t,.d  |r   :d |d  :t,  |d :— ‖l, |s, ‖
:m.f  |s  :l.t |d' :m  |f     :s |s  ‖s     |s.f :m |s  :-.f |m :— ‖f  |m  ‖
:l,   |s, :f,  |d  :m  |r     :d |s, ‖s,.l, |t,  :d |s, :s,  |d :— ‖f, |d  ‖
                                                                   A-men.
```

PSALM CVI.

33 Because they there his spirit meek
provoked bitterly,
So that he utter'd with his lips
words unadvisedly.

34 Nor, as the Lord commanded them,
did they the nations slay:
35 But with the heathen mingled were,
and learn'd of them their way.
36 And they their idols serv'd, which did
a snare unto them turn.
37 Their sons and daughters they to dev'ls
in sacrifice did burn.

38 In their own children's guiltless blood
their hands they did imbrue,
Whom to Canaan's idols they
for sacrifices slew:
So was the land defil'd with blood.
39 They stain'd with their own way,
And with their own inventions
a whoring they did stray.

40 Against his people kindled was
the wrath of God therefore,
Insomuch that he did his own
inheritance abhor.

41 He gave them to the heathe'ns hand;
their foes did them command.
42 Their en'mies them oppress'd, they were
made subject to their hand.

43 He many times deliver'd them;
but with their counsel so
They him provok'd, that for their sin
they were brought very low.
44 Yet their affliction he beheld,
when he did hear their cry:
45 And he for them his covenant
did call to memory;

After his mercies' multitude
46 he did repent: And made
Them to be pity'd of all those
who did them captive lead.
47 O Lord our God, us save, and gather
the heathen from among,
That we thy holy name may praise
in a triumphant song.

48 Bless'd be JEHOVAH, Isr'el's God,
to all eternity:
Let all the people say, Amen.
Praise to the Lord give ye.

117

ST. MIRREN. (C.M.)

Doh = C. ROBERT ARCHIBALD SMITH, 1780–1829.

```
:d' |d' :t  |d' :l   |s  :f  |m  ‖ s.  |l  :t  |d'.t :l  |s  :— |— ‖
:m  |m  :f  |s  :f   |m  :r  |d  ‖ r.s |fe :s  |s    :fe |s  :— |— ‖
:s  |s  :s  |s  :d'  |d' :t  |d' ‖ s.t |r' :r' |m'.r':d' |t  :— |— ‖
:d  |d  :r  |m  :f   |s  :s, |d  ‖ t,  |l, :s, |d    :r  |s, :— |— ‖

:t   |d' :m' |l.t   :d'  |r' :d' |t  ‖ d' |l :r' |s  :t  |d' :— |— ‖ d' |d' ‖
:s   |s  :s  |f     :s.m |f  :m  |r  ‖ m  |d :f  |m  :r  |m  :— |— ‖ f  |m  ‖
:r'  |d' :d' |d'.r' :s   |s  :s  |s  ‖ s  |l :l  |d' :s  |s  :— |— ‖ l  |s  ‖
:s.f |m  :d  |f.r   :m.d |t, :d  |s, ‖ d  |f :f  |s  :s, |d  :— |— ‖ f  |d  ‖
                                                                   A-men.
```

PSALM CVII.

107*

PRAISE God, for he is good: for still
his mercies lasting be.
2 Let God's redeem'd say so, whom he
from th' en'my's hand did free;
3 And gather'd them out of the lands,
from north, south, east, and west.
4 They stray'd in desert's pathless way,
no city found to rest.

5 For thirst and hunger in them faints
6 their soul. When straits them press,
They cry unto the Lord, and he
them frees from their distress.
7 Them also in a way to walk
that right is he did guide,
That they might to a city go,
wherein they might abide.

8 O that men to the Lord would give
praise for his goodness then,
And for his works of wonder done
unto the sons of men!
9 For he the soul that longing is
doth fully satisfy;
With goodness he the hungry soul
doth fill abundantly.

10 Such as shut up in darkness deep,
and in death's shade abide,
Whom strongly hath affliction bound,
and irons fast have ty'd:
11 Because against the words of God
they wrought rebelliously,
And they the counsel did contemn
of him that is most High:

12 Their heart he did bring down with grief,
they fell, no help could have.
13 In trouble then they cry'd to God,
he them from straits did save.
14 He out of darkness did them bring,
and from death's shade them take;
These bands, wherewith they had been bound,
asunder quite he brake.

15 O that men to the Lord would give
praise for his goodness then,
And for his works of wonder done
unto the sons of men!
16 Because the mighty gates of brass
in pieces he did tear,
By him in sunder also cut
the bars of iron were.

ST. NEOT. (C.M.) *Green's Collection*, 1715.

Lah = G. Doh = B♭.

```
:l₁ |d :—:t₁ |m :—:r |d :—:r |t₁ :— ||t₁ |d :r :m |r :d :t₁ |l₁ :— ||
:m₁ |m₁:—:m₁ |m₁:l₁ :se₁ |l₁:—:l₁ |se₁:— ||m₁ |m₁:f₁:l₁ |l₁:—:se₁ |l₁ :— ||
:d |l₁:—:se₁ |l₁:—:t₁ |d :m :f |m :— ||m |d :l₁:l₁ |f :m :m.r |d :— ||
:l₁ |l₁:—:m₁ |d₁:—:t₂ |l₂:—:r₁ |m₁ :— ||se₁ |l₁:f₁:d₁ |r₁:m₁ :m₁ |l₂ :— ||

:m |m :—:r |m :—:r |d :—:r |t₁ :— ||t₁ |m :—:l₁ |r :d :t₁ |l₁:— ||l₁ |l₁ ||
:s₁ |s₁:—:s₁ |s₁:—:s₁ |m₁:—:f₁ |m₁ :— ||m₁ |m₁:—:d₁ |f₁:m₁ :m₁.r₁ |d₁:— ||r₁ |de₁ ||
:d |d :—:t₁ |d :—:t₁ |l₁:—:l₁ |se₁:— ||se₁ |l₁:—:l₁ |l₁:—:se₁ |l₁:— ||f₁ |m₁ ||
:d₁ |d₁:m₁ :s₁ |d :m₁ :s₁ |l₁:l₂ :r₁ |m₁ :— ||m₁.r₁ |d₁:—:f₁ |r₁:m₁ :m₁ |l₂:— ||r₁ |l₂ ||
```

A-men.

PSALM CVII.

17 Fools, for their sin, and their offence,
do sore affliction bear;
18 All kind of meat their soul abhors;
they to death's gates draw near.
19 In grief they cry to God; he saves
them from their miseries.
20 He sends his word, them heals, and them
from their destructions frees.

21 O that men to the Lord would give
praise for his goodness then,
And for his works of wonder done
unto the sons of men!
22 And let them sacrifice to him
off'rings of thankfulness;
And let them shew abroad his works
in songs of joyfulness.

23 Who go to sea in ships, and in
great waters trading be,
24 Within the deep these men God's works
and his great wonders see.
25 For he commands, and forth in haste
the stormy tempest flies,
Which makes the sea with rolling waves
aloft to swell and rise.

26 They mount to heav'n, then to the depths
they do go down again;
Their soul doth faint and melt away
with trouble and with pain.
27 They reel and stagger like one drunk,
at their wit's end they be:
28 Then they to God in trouble cry,
who them from straits doth free.

29 The storm is chang'd into a calm
at his command and will;
So that the waves, which rag'd before,
now quiet are and still.
30 Then are they glad, because at rest
and quiet now they be:
So to the haven he them brings,
which they desir'd to see.

31 O that men to the Lord would give
praise for his goodness then,
And for his works of wonder done
unto the sons of men!
32 Among the people gathered
let them exalt his name;
Among assembled elders spread
his most renowned fame.

33 He to dry land turns water-springs,
and floods to wilderness;

119

ST. NICHOLAS. (C.M.) *Holdroyd's Spiritual Man's Companion*, 1753.

Lah = E. Doh = G.

```
:l, | d :—:m  | l :—:m  | f :m :r    | d :—  || t,  | l, :—:t,   | d :—:r    | m :—  ||
:l, | l, :—:t,| l, :—:l,| l, :—:se,  | l, :— || se, | l, :s, :f, | m, :—:l,  | se, :—||
:d  | m :—:t, | d :—:d  | d :t, :m   | m :—  || r   | d :—:r     | m :—:r    | t, :— ||
:l, | l, :—:s,| f, :—:l,| r, :m, :m, | l, :— || m,  | f, :m, :r, | l, :s, :f,| m, :— ||

:m  | s :—:m  | r :—:m   | d :—:r     | t, :— || m   | l :se :l   | d :—:t,   | l, :— || l, | l, ||
:s, | s, :—:d | t, :—:t, | l, :—:l,   | se, :—|| se, | l, :t, :d  | l, :—:se, | l, :— || f, | m, ||
:d  | r :—:s  | s :—:s   | m :f :f    | m :—  || m   | m :r :d.r  | m :—:m.r  | d :—  || r  | de ||
:d  | t, :—:d | s, :—:m, | l, :f, :r, | m, :— || m.r | d :t, :l,  | m, :—:m,  | l, :— || r, | l, ||
                                                                                     A-men.
```

PSALMS CVII, CVIII.

34 For sins of those that dwell therein,
fat land to barrenness.
35 The burnt and parched wilderness
to water-pools he brings;
The ground that was dry'd up before
he turns to water-springs:

36 And there, for dwelling, he a place
doth to the hungry give,
That they a city may prepare
commodiously to live.
37 There sow they fields, and vine-
yards plant,
to yield fruits of increase.
38 His blessing makes them multiply,
lets not their beasts decrease.

39 Again they are diminished,
and very low brought down,
Through sorrow and affliction,
and great oppression.
40 He upon princes pours contempt,
and causeth them to stray,
And wander in a wilderness,
wherein there is no way.

41 Yet setteth he the poor on high
from all his miseries,
And he, much like unto a flock,
doth make him families.
42 They that are righteous shall rejoice,
when they the same shall see;
And, as ashamed, stop her mouth
shall all iniquity.

43 Whoso is wise, and will these things
observe, and them record,
Ev'n they shall understand the love
and kindness of the Lord.

108

MY heart is fix'd, Lord; I will sing,
and with my glory praise.
2 Awake up psaltery and harp;
myself I'll early raise. [Lord;
3 I'll praise thee 'mong the people,
'mong nations sing will I:
4 For above heav'n thy mercy's great,
thy truth doth reach the sky.

5 Be thou above the heavens, Lord,
exalted gloriously;
Thy glory all the earth above
be lifted up on high.
6 That those who thy beloved are
delivered may be,
O do thou save with thy right hand,
and answer give to me.

120

ST. PAUL. (C.M.)

Doh = G. *Chalmers's Collection*, Aberdeen, 1749.

```
|d :—  |r :m   |s, :d   |r :t,  |d :—  ‖m :— |r :s   |f     :m |r :—  ‖
|s, :— |s, :s, |s, :m,  |l, :s, |s, :— ‖d :— |t, :d  |l,.t, :d |t, :— ‖
|m :—  |t, :d  |r :m    |f :r   |m :—  ‖s :— |s.f :m |f     :s |s :—  ‖
|d :—  |s, :d  |t, :l,  |f, :s, |d, :— ‖d :— |s, :m  |r     :d |s, :— ‖

|d :— |r :d   |f :m    |r :d        |t, :— ‖s, :— |l, :f   |m     :r   |d :—  ‖d  |d  ‖
|d :— |s, :s, |f, :s,  |l, :m,.fe,  |s, :— ‖s, :— |f, :l,  |d     :t,  |d :—  ‖l, |s, ‖
|m :— |r :d   |d :s    |f :d        |r :—  ‖d :—  |d :r    |s     :-.f |m :—  ‖f  |m  ‖
|d :— |t, :d  |l, :d   |f, :l,      |s, :— ‖m, :— |f, :r,  |m,.f, :s,  |d, :— ‖f, |d, ‖
```

A-men.

PSALMS CVIII, CIX.

7 God in his holiness hath said,
Herein I will take pleasure;
Shechem I will divide, and forth
will Succoth's valley measure.
8 Gilead I claim as mine by right;
Manasseh mine shall be;
Ephraim is of my head the strength;
Judah gives laws for me;

9 Moab 's my washing-pot; my shoe
I'll over Edom throw;
Over the land of Palestine
I will in triumph go.
10 O who is he will bring me to
the city fortify'd?
O who is he that to the land
of Edom will me guide?

11 O God, thou who hadst cast us off,
this thing wilt thou not do?
And wilt not thou, ev'n thou, O God,
forth with our armies go?
12 Do thou from trouble give us help,
for helpless is man's aid.
13 Through God we shall do valiantly;
our foes he shall down tread.

109

O THOU the God of all my praise,
do thou not hold thy peace;

2 For mouths of wicked men to speak
against me do not cease:
The mouths of vile deceitful men
against me open'd be;
And with a false and lying tongue
they have accused me.

3 They did beset me round about
with words of hateful spight;
And though to them no cause I gave,
against me they did fight.
4 They for my love became my foes,
but I me set to pray.
5 Evil for good, hatred for love,
to me they did repay.

6 Set thou the wicked over him;
and upon his right hand
Give thou his greatest enemy,
ev'n Satan, leave to stand.
7 And when by thee he shall be judg'd,
let him condemned be;
And let his pray'r be turn'd to sin,
when he shall call on thee.

8 Few be his days, and in his room
his charge another take.
9 His children let be fatherless,
his wife a widow make.

121

ST. PETER. (C.M.)

Doh = E♭. ALEXANDER ROBERT REINAGLE, 1799–1877.

:s | d' :t | l :s | s :f | m ‖ m | r :d | f :m | r :— | — ‖
:d | m :m | d :d | r :t_1 | d ‖ d | l_1 :s_1 | t_1 :d | t_1 :— | — ‖
:m | s :s | f :s | s :s | s ‖ s | f :s | s :s | s :— | — ‖
:d | d :m | f :m | t_1 :s_1 | d ‖ d | f :m | r :d | s_1 :— | — ‖

:m | f :m | l :s | s :f | m ‖ d | m :r | d :t_1 | d :— | — ‖ d | d ‖
:d | d :d.ta_1 | l_1.t_1:d | d :t_1 | d ‖ l_1 | d :l_1 | s_1 :s_1 | s_1 :— | — ‖ l_1 | s_1 ‖
:s | f :s | d .r :m | l :s | d ‖ m | s :f | m :r | m :— | — ‖ f | m ‖
:d.ta_1 | l_1 :s_1 | f_1 :m_1 | r_1 :s_1 | l_1 ‖ l_1 | m_1 :f_1 | s_1 :s_1 | d :— | — ‖ f_1 | d ‖

A-men.

PSALM CIX.

10 His children let be vagabonds,
and beg continually;
And from their places desolate
seek bread for their supply.

11 Let covetous extortioners
catch all he hath away:
Of all for which he labour'd hath
let strangers make a prey.
12 Let there be none to pity him,
let there be none at all
That on his children fatherless
will let his mercy fall.

13 Let his posterity from earth
cut off for ever be,
And in the foll'wing age their name
be blotted out by thee.
14 Let God his father's wickedness
still to remembrance call;
And never let his mother's sin
be blotted out at all.

15 But let them all before the Lord
appear continually,
That he may wholly from the earth
cut off their memory.
16 Because he mercy minded not,
but persecuted still
The poor and needy, that he might
the broken-hearted kill.

17 As he in cursing pleasure took,
so let it to him fall;
As he delighted not to bless,
so bless him not at all.
18 As cursing he like clothes put on,
into his bowels so,
Like water, and into his bones,
like oil, down let it go.

19 Like to the garment let it be
which doth himself array,
And for a girdle, wherewith he
is girt about alway.
20 From God let this be their reward
that en'mies are to me,
And their reward that speak against
my soul maliciously.

21 But do thou, for thine own name's
sake,
O God the Lord, for me:
Sith good and sweet thy mercy is,
from trouble set me free.
22 For I am poor and indigent,
afflicted sore am I,
My heart within me also is
wounded exceedingly.

ST. STEPHEN (ABRIDGE). (C.M.) | Isaac Smith, *c.* 1740–*c.* 1800.

Doh = E♭.

```
:d  |s :—:d' |d' :t :l  |s :f :m  |m :r  ||m |l  :—:s  |s :—:fe |s  :— ||
:s, |d :—:m  |r  :—:r   |s,:t,:d  |d :t, ||d |m  :—:r  |m :r :d |t, :— ||
:m  |s :—:s  |s  :—:l.t |d':s :s  |s :—  ||s |d' :—:t  |l :t :l |s  :— ||
:d  |m :—:d  |s  :—:f   |m :r :d  |s,:—  ||d |l, :—:t, |d :r :r |s, :— ||

:s  |m :f :l  |s :—:s  |l    :t :d' |d':t  ||s   |d':m :s  |f :m :r  |d :— ||d  |d  ||
:r  |d :—:d   |d :t,:d |d    :f :m  |m :r  ||t,  |d :—:d   |d :—:t,  |d :— ||l, |s, ||
:s  |s :f :f  |m :f :s |f    :s :s  |s :—  ||s   |s :—:ta  |l :s :f  |m :— ||f  |m  ||
:t, |d :l,:f, |d :r :m |f.,m :r :d  |s,:—  ||s.f |m :d :m  |f :s :s, |d :— ||f, |d  ||
```

A-men.

PSALMS CIX, CX.

23 I pass like a declining shade,
am like the locust tost:
24 My knees through fasting weaken'd are,
my flesh hath fatness lost.
25 I also am a vile reproach
unto them made to be;
And they that did upon me look
did shake their heads at me.

26 O do thou help and succour me,
who art my God and Lord:
And, for thy tender mercy's sake,
safety to me afford:
27 That thereby they may know that this
is thy almighty hand;
And that thou, Lord, hast done the same,
they may well understand.

28 Although they curse with spite, yet, Lord,
bless thou with loving voice:
Let them asham'd be when they rise;
thy servant let rejoice.
29 Let thou mine adversaries all
with shame be clothed over;
And let their own confusion
them, as a mantle, cover.

30 But as for me, I with my mouth
will greatly praise the Lord;
And I among the multitude
his praises will record.
31 For he shall stand at his right hand
who is in poverty,
To save him from all those that would
condemn his soul to die.

110

THE LORD did say unto my Lord,
Sit thou at my right hand,
Until I make thy foes a stool,
whereon thy feet may stand.
2 The Lord shall out of Sion send
the rod of thy great pow'r:
In midst of all thine enemies
be thou the governor.

3 A willing people in thy day
of pow'r shall come to thee,
In holy beauties from morn's womb;
thy youth like dew shall be.
4 The Lord himself hath made an oath,
and will repent him never,
Of th' order of Melchisedec
thou art a priest for ever.

5 The glorious and mighty Lord,
that sits at thy right hand,

FAUX-BOURDON SETTING.

ST. STEPHEN (ABRIDGE). (C.M.) GEOFFREY TURTON SHAW, 1879-

Doh = E♭.

```
:d' | d':t :l  | s :—:l.t | d':r':m' | s :—  || l  | l :r' :t  | s :d' :l   | t :—  ||
:m  | d :s :f.m | r :m :r  | d :t, :d | d :t, || de | de:r :r   | r.d:m :r   | t,:—  ||
:d  | s :—:d'  | d':t :l   | s :f :m  | m :r  || m  | l :—:s    | s :—:fe    | s :—  ||
:d  | m :—:f   | s :—:f    | m :r :d  | s,:—  || s, | f,:—:f    | m :d :r    | s,:—  ||

:ta | l :—:r'  | s :—:d'   | d':t :l  | s :—  || s  | s :d':m   | f :l :s    | m :—  ||
:r  | de:r :f  | r :m :s   | f :—:m   | f :m  || r  | d :—:d    | d :-.l,:t, | d :—  ||
:s  | m :f :l  | s :—:s    | l :t :d' | d':t  || s  | d':m :s   | f :m :r    | d :—  ||
:s, | l,:r :d  | t,:d :m   | r :—:d   | r :s  || f  | m :d :ta, | l,:f, :s,  | d :—  ||
```

PSALMS CX, CXI, CXII.

Shall, in his day of wrath, strike through
kings that do him withstand.
6 He shall among the heathen judge,
he shall with bodies dead
The places fill: o'er many lands
he wound shall ev'ry head.

7 The brook that runneth in the way
with drink shall him supply;
And, for this cause, in triumph he
shall lift his head on high.

111*

PRAISE ye the Lord: with my whole heart
I will God's praise declare,
Where the assemblies of the just
and congregations are.
2 The whole works of the Lord our God
are great above all measure,
Sought out they are of ev'ry one
that doth therein take pleasure.

3 His work most honourable is,
most glorious and pure,
And his untainted righteousness
for ever doth endure.
4 His works most wonderful he hath
made to be thought upon:
The Lord is gracious, and he is
full of compassion.
5 He giveth meat unto all those
that truly do him fear;
And evermore his covenant
he in his mind will bear.
6 He did the power of his works
unto his people show,
When he the heathen's heritage
upon them did bestow.
7 His handy-works are truth and right;
all his commands are sure:
8 And, done in truth and uprightness,
they evermore endure.
9 He sent redemption to his folk;
his covenant for aye
He did command: holy his name
and rev'rend is alway.
10 Wisdom's beginning is God's fear:
good understanding they
Have all that his commands fulfil
his praise endures for aye.

112

PRAISE ye the Lord. The man is bless'd
that fears the Lord aright,
He who in his commandements
doth greatly take delight.

123

ST. THOMAS. (C.M.) *Ashworth's Collection*, 1760 (?).

Doh = A.

```
:d  | m :—:r   | d :—:s,  | l,  :t, :d      | s, :— || s,    | d :r :m     | f :m :r       | d :—  ||
:m, | s, :—:f, | m, :—:s, | s,  :f, :m,     | r, :— || r,    | s, :—:s,    | l, :s, :s,.f, | m, :— ||
:d  | d :—:t,  | d :—:d   | d   :s, :d      | t, :— || t,    | d :t, :d    | d :—:t,       | d :—  ||
:d  | d :—:s,  | l, :—:m, | f,.,m, :r, :d,  | s, :— || s,.f, | m, :r, :d,  | f, :s, :s,    | d, :— ||
```

```
:d  | r :—:m   | s :—:m   | f :— :m       | r :—  || s  | m.,r :d :m  | f :m :r       | d :—  || d  | d  ||
:m, | s, :—:s, | s, :—:s, | l, :— :s,     | s, :— || s, | s, :—:d     | l, :s, :s,.f, | m, :— || l, | s  ||
:d  | t, :—:d  | r :—:d   | d :— :d       | t, :— || r  | d.,r :m :d  | d :—:t,       | d :—  || d  | m  ||
:d, | s, :—:d  | t, :—:d  | f, :l,.t, :d  | s, :— || t, | d :—:l,     | f, :s, :s,    | d, :— || f, | d, ||
```

A-men.

PSALMS CXII, CXIII.

2 His seed and offspring powerful
shall be the earth upon:
Of upright men blessed shall be
the generation.

3 Riches and wealth shall ever be
within his house in store;
And his unspotted righteousness
endures for evermore.

4 Unto the upright light doth rise,
though he in darkness be:
Compassionate, and merciful,
and righteous, is he.

5 A good man doth his favour shew,
and doth to others lend:
He with discretion his affairs
will guide unto the end.

6 Surely there is not any thing
that ever shall him move:
The righteous man's memorial
shall everlasting prove.

7 When he shall evil tidings hear,
he shall not be afraid:
His heart is fix'd, his confidence
upon the Lord is stay'd.

8 His heart is firmly stablished,
afraid he shall not be,
Until upon his enemies
he his desire shall see.

9 He hath dispers'd, giv'n to the poor,
his righteousness shall be
To ages all; with honour shall
his horn be raised high.

10 The wicked shall it see, and fret,
his teeth gnash, melt away:
What wicked men do most desire
shall utterly decay.

113

PRAISE God: ye servants of the Lord,
O praise, the Lord's name praise.

2 Yea, blessed be the name of God
from this time forth always.

3 From rising sun to where it sets,
God's name is to be prais'd.

4 Above all nations God is high,
'bove heav'ns his glory rais'd.

5 Unto the Lord our God that dwells
on high, who can compare?

6 Himself that humbleth things to see
in heav'n and earth that are.

7 He from the dust doth raise the poor,
that very low doth lie;
And from the dunghill lifts the man
oppress'd with poverty;

124

SALISBURY. (C.M.)

Doh = G. *Ravenscroft's Psalter*, 1621.

d :—	r :f	m :s	s :fe	s :—		m :—	l :s	f :f	m :—	
s, :—	l, :s,	d :t,	m :r.d	t, :—		d :—	l,.t, :d	d :t,	d :—	
m :—	f :r	s :s	l :l	s :—		s :—	f :s	l :f	s :—	
d :—	d :t,	d :m	d :r	s, :—		d :—	f :m	r :r	d :—	

s :—	m :f	r :m	d :r	t, :—		f :—	m :m	r :r	d :—		d	d	
s, :—	s, :l,	s, :t,	d :l,	s, :—		l, :-.t,	d :d	d :t,	d :—		l,	s,	
r :—	m :d	r :s	m :f	r :—		r :—	s :m	l :s.f	m :—		f	m	
t, :—	d :l,	t, :s,	l, :f,	s, :—		r, :—	m, :l,	f, :s,	d, :—		f,	d,	

A-men.

8 That he may highly him advance,
and with the princes set;
With those that of his people are
the chief, ev'n princes great.
The barren woman house to keep
he maketh, and to be
Of sons a mother full of joy.
Praise to the Lord give ye.

114

WHEN Isr'el out of Egypt went,
and did his dwelling change,
When Jacob's house went out from those
that were of language strange,
2 He Judah did his sanctuary,
his kingdom Isr'el make:
3 The sea it saw, and quickly fled,
Jordan was driven back.

4 Like rams the mountains, and like lambs
the hills skipp'd to and fro.
5 O sea, why fledd'st thou? Jordan,
why wast thou driven so? [back
6 Ye mountains great, wherefore was
that ye did skip like rams? [it
And wherefore was it, little hills,
that ye did leap like lambs?

7 O at the presence of the Lord,
earth, tremble thou for fear,
While as the presence of the God
of Jacob doth appear:
8 Who from the hard and stony rock
did standing water bring;
And by his pow'r did turn the flint
into a water-spring.

115*

NOT unto us, Lord, not to us,
but do thou glory take
Unto thy name, ev'n for thy truth,
and for thy mercy's sake.
2 O wherefore should the heathen say,
Where is their God now gone?
3 But our God in the heavens is,
what pleas'd him he hath done.

4 Their idols silver are and gold,
work of men's hands they be.
5 Mouths have they, but they do not speak;
and eyes, but do not see;
6 Ears have they, but they do not
noses, but savour not; [hear;
7 Hands, feet, but handle not, nor
walk; [throat.
nor speak they through their

125

SALZBURG. (C.M.) JOHANN MICHAEL HAYDN, 1737-1806.

Doh=E♭.

:d |m :—:s |s :f :m |m :—:r |d :— ||d |d :t, :d |s :f :m |m :r ||
:s, |d :—:d |r :—:d |d :—:t, |d :— ||l, |s, :—:s, |s, :r :d |d :t, ||
:m |s :—:s |s :—:s |s :—:f |m :— ||f |s :f :m |r :s :s |s :— ||
:d |d :—:m |t, :—:d |s, :—:se, |l, :— ||f |m :r :d |t, :—:d |s, :— ||

:d |d :—:l |s :m :d |d :—:l |s :— ||d' |d' :l :f |m :f :r |d :— ||d |d ||
:s, |d :—:d |d :—:s, |d :—:d |d :— ||d |d :—:d |d :t, :t, |d :— ||l, |s, ||
:m |f :—:f |m :s :m |f :—:f |m :— ||s |l :f :l |s :r :f |m :— ||f |m ||
:d.ta, |l, :—:f, |d :—:d.ta, |l, :—:f, |d :— ||m, |f, :—:f, |s, :—:s, |d :— ||f, |d ||

A-men.

PSALMS CXV, CXVI.

8 Like them their makers are, and all
on them their trust that build.
9 O Isr'el, trust thou in the Lord,
he is their help and shield.
10 O Aaron's house, trust in the Lord,
their help and shield is he.
11 Ye that fear God, trust in the Lord,
their help and shield he'll be.

12 The Lord of us hath mindful been,
and he will bless us still:
He will the house of Isr'el bless,
bless Aaron's house he will.
13 Both small and great, that fear the Lord,
he will them surely bless.
14 The Lord will you, you and your seed,
aye more and more increase.

15 O blessed are ye of the Lord,
who made the earth and heav'n.
16 The heav'n, ev'n heav'ns, are God's, but he
earth to men's sons hath giv'n.
17 The dead, nor who to silence go,
God's praise do not record.
18 But henceforth we for ever will
bless God. Praise ye the Lord.

116*

I LOVE the Lord, because my voice
and prayers he did hear.
2 I, while I live, will call on him,
who bow'd to me his ear.
3 Of death the cords and sorrows did
about me compass round;
The pains of hell took hold on me,
I grief and trouble found.

4 Upon the name of God the Lord
then did I call, and say,
Deliver thou my soul, O Lord,
I do thee humbly pray.
5 God merciful and righteous is,
yea, gracious is our Lord.
6 God saves the meek: I was brought low,
he did me help afford.

7 O thou my soul, do thou return
unto thy quiet rest;
For largely, lo, the Lord to thee
his bounty hath exprest.
8 For my distressed soul from death
deliver'd was by thee:
Thou didst my mourning eyes from tears,
my feet from falling, free.

SHEFFIELD. (C.M.)

Doh = A. WILLIAM MATHER, 1756–1808.

```
:s, |d  :m  |r  :f  |m    :r   |d  || t,.d |r.t, :l,.d |t, :l,  |s, :— |— ||
:m, |s, :s, |l, :f, |s,   :-.f,|m, || s,   |s,   :s,   |s, :fe, |s, :— |— ||
:d  |d  :d  |l, :-.t,|d   :t,  |d  || m    |r    :m    |r  :-.d |t, :— |— ||
:d, |m, :d, |f, :r, |m,.f, :s, |l, || m,   |t2   :d,   |r, :r,  |s, :— |— ||

:m.f |s     :r.m  |f     :d.r  |m     :r.d |r     || m.f   |s.m   :r.f |m  :r    |d  :— |— || d  |d  ||
:s,  |s,.l, :t,   |f,.s, :l,   |s,    :fe, |s,    || s,.f, |m,.s, :l,  |s, :s,.f,|m, :— |— || f, |m, ||
:d.r |m     :t,.d |r     :l,.t,|d     :d   |t,    || d.t,  |d     :d   |d  :t,   |d  :— |— || l, |s, ||
:d   |m,.f, :s,   |r,.m, :f,   |d,.m, :l,  |s,.f, || m,.r, |d,    :f,  |s, :s,   |d, :— |— || f, |d, ||
                                                                                              A-men.
```

PSALMS CXVI, CXVII, CXVIII.

9 I in the land of those that live
will walk the Lord before.
10 I did believe, therefore I spake:
I was afflicted sore.
11 I said, when I was in my haste,
that all men liars be.
12 What shall I render to the Lord
for all his gifts to me?

13 I'll of salvation take the cup,
on God's name will I call:
14 I'll pay my vows now to the Lord
before his people all.
15 Dear in God's sight is his saints' death.
16 Thy servant, Lord, am I;
Thy servant sure, thine handmaid's son:
my bands thou didst untie.

17 Thank-off'rings I to thee will give,
and on God's name will call.
18 I'll pay my vows now to the Lord
before his people all;
19 Within the courts of God's own house,
within the midst of thee,
O city of Jerusalem.
Praise to the Lord give ye.

117*

O GIVE ye praise unto the Lord,
all nations that be;
Likewise, ye people all, accord
his name to magnify.
2 For great to us-ward ever are
his loving-kindnesses:
His truth endures for evermore.
The Lord O do ye bless.

118*

O PRAISE the Lord, for he is good;
his mercy lasteth ever.
2 Let those of Israel now say,
His mercy faileth never.
3 Now let the house of Aaron say,
His mercy lasteth ever.
4 Let those that fear the Lord now say,
His mercy faileth never.

5 I in distress call'd on the Lord;
the Lord did answer me:
He in a large place did me set,
from trouble made me free.
6 The mighty Lord is on my side,
I will not be afraid;
For any thing that man can do
I shall not be dismay'd.

127

SIDON. (C.M.) WILLIAM CROTCH, 1775–1847.

Lah=D. Doh=F.

:m |l :s :f |m :— :l, |r :d :t, |d :— ||d |s :—.f :m |r :m :f |m :— ||
:l, |d :— :l,.t, |d :— :l, |l, :s, :s, |s, :— ||d |d :r :d |d :— :d |t, :— ||
:d |m :— :f .s |l :— :d |f :m :r |m :— ||l |s :— :s |l :— :l |se :— ||
:l, |l, :d :r |l, :— :l,.s, |f, :s, :s, |d :— ||l, |m :t, :d |f :m :r |m :— ||

:d |l, :— :r |d :t, :m |d :— :f |m :r ||l |se :— :l |r :d :t, |l, :— ||r |de ||
:l, |l, :— :l, |l, :se, :t, |l, :— :r |d :t, ||t, |t, :— :m.d |t, :l, :se, |l, :— ||l, |l, ||
:m |m :d :r |m :— :m |m :f :l |s :— ||r |m :— :m |f :m :m.r |d :— ||f |m ||
:l, |d :l, :f, |m, :— :se, |l, :f, :r, |s, :— ||f, |m, :m :d |r :m :m, |l, :— ||r, |l, ||

A-men.

PSALM CXVIII.

7 The Lord doth take my part with them
that help to succour me:
Therefore on those that do me hate
I my desire shall see.
8 Better it is to trust in God
than trust in man's defence;
9 Better to trust in God than make
princes our confidence.

10 The nations, joining all in one,
did compass me about:
But in the Lord's most holy name
I shall them all root out.
11 They compass'd me about; I say,
they compass'd me about:
But in the Lord's most holy name
I shall them all root out.

12 Like bees they compass'd me about;
like unto thorns that flame
They quenched are: for them shall I
destroy in God's own name.
13 Thou sore hast thrust, that I might fall,
but my Lord helped me.
14 God my salvation is become,
my strength and song is he.

15 In dwellings of the righteous
is heard the melody
Of joy and health: the Lord's right hand
doth ever valiantly.
16 The right hand of the mighty Lord
exalted is on high;
The right hand of the mighty Lord
doth ever valiantly.

17 I shall not die, but live, and shall
the works of God discover.
18 The Lord hath me chastised sore,
but not to death giv'n over.
19 O set ye open unto me
the gates of righteousness;
Then will I enter into them,
and I the Lord will bless.

20 This is the gate of God, by it
the just shall enter in.
21 Thee will I praise, for thou me heard'st,
and hast my safety been.
22 That stone is made head corner-stone,
which builders did despise:
23 This is the doing of the Lord,
and wondrous in our eyes.

24 This is the day God made, in it
we'll joy triumphantly.
25 Save now, I pray thee, Lord; I pray
send now prosperity.

128

SOLOMON. (C.M.)

Doh = E♭.

Arranged from *Solomon.*
George Frederick Handel, 1685–1759.

```
:d |m  :-.f |s   :-.s |l    :l    |s  ||s |l :s |t  :d' |r  :— |— ||
:d |d  :t,  |d   :d   |d.t, :d.r  |m  ||d |d :d |f  :m  |t, :— |— ||
:m |s  :s   |s.f :m   |l.s  :l.t  |d' ||m |f :s |s  :s  |s  :— |— ||
:d |d  :r   |m.r :d   |f    :f    |d  ||d |f :m |r  :d  |s, :— |— ||
```

```
:s |l :-.l |s :-.l |f :-.m |m ||r  |s  :d  |r  :d.t, |d  :— |— ||d  |d  ||
:d |d :r   |r :d   |d :t,  |d ||t, |d  :d  |l, :s,   |s, :— |— ||l, |s, ||
:s |f :l   |t :s   |l :s   |s ||s  |s  :m  |f  :r    |m  :— |— ||f  |m  ||
:m |f :f   |f :m   |r :s,  |d ||f, |m, :l, |f, :s,   |d  :— |— ||f, |d  ||
                                                                  A-men.
```

PSALMS CXVIII, CXIX.

26 Blessed is he in God's great name
that cometh us to save:
We, from the house which to the Lord
pertains, you blessed have.

27 God is the Lord, who unto us
hath made light to arise:
Bind ye unto the altar's horns
with cords the sacrifice.

28 Thou art my God, I'll thee exalt;
my God, I will thee praise.

29 Give thanks to God, for he is good:
his mercy lasts always.

119*

BLESSED are they that undefil'd,
and straight are in the way;
Who in the Lord's most holy law
do walk, and do not stray.

2 Blessed are they who to observe
his statutes are inclin'd;
And who do seek the living God
with their whole heart and mind.

3 Such in his ways do walk, and they
do no iniquity.

4 Thou hast commanded us to keep
thy precepts carefully.

5 O that thy statutes to observe
thou would'st my ways direct!

6 Then shall I not be sham'd, when I
thy precepts all respect.

7 Then with integrity of heart
thee will I praise and bless,
When I the judgments all have learn'd
of thy pure righteousness.

8 That I will keep thy statutes all
firmly resolv'd have I:
O do not then, most gracious God,
forsake me utterly.

*BETH. The Second Part.

9 By what means shall a young man learn
his way to purify?
If he according to thy word
thereto attentive be.

10 Unfeignedly thee have I sought
with all my soul and heart:
O let me not from the right path
of thy commands depart.

11 Thy word I in my heart have hid,
that I offend not thee.

129

SOUTHWARK. (C.M.)

Doh = A.

Adapted from Christopher Tye, *c.* 1508–72.

:s_1 |d :r |m :f |s :-.f |m ||f |m :-.r |d :d |t_1 :— |— ||
:s_1 |s_1 :s_1 |s_1 :l_1 |t_1 :-.t_1 |d ||l_1 |s_1 :-.f_1 |m_1 :l_1 |s_1 :— |— ||
:m |m :r |d :d |r :-.r |d ||d |d :-.t_1 |d :f |r :— |— ||
:d |d :t_1 |d :l_1 |s_1 :-.s_1 |d ||f_1 |d :-.s_1 |l_1 :f_1 |s_1 :— |— ||

:r |r :de |r :d |d :t_1 |d ||m |r :s |f :r |d :— |— ||d |d ||
:ta_1 |l_1 :s_1 |f_1 :l_1 |s_1 :f_1 |m_1 ||d |t_1 :d |l_1 :t_1 |d :— |— ||l_1 |s_1 ||
:s |m :m |f :f |r :r |d ||s |s :-.d |r :f |m :— |— ||f |m ||
:s_1 |l_1 :l_1 |r_1 :f_1 |s_1 :s_1 |d_1 ||d_1 |s_1 :m_1 |f_1 :s_1 |d :— |— ||f_1 |d_1 ||

A-men.

PSALM CXIX.

12 O Lord, thou ever blessed art,
thy statutes teach thou me.
13 The judgments of thy mouth each one
my lips declared have:
14 More joy thy testimonies' way
than riches all me gave.

15 I will thy holy precepts make
my meditation;
And carefully I'll have respect
unto thy ways each one.
16 Upon thy statutes my delight
shall constantly be set:
And, by thy grace, I never will
thy holy word forget.

GIMEL. The Third Part.

17 With me thy servant, in thy grace,
deal bountifully, Lord;
That by thy favour I may live,
and duly keep thy word.
18 Open mine eyes, that of thy law
the wonders I may see.
19 I am a stranger on this earth,
hide not thy laws from me.

20 My soul within me breaks, and doth
much fainting still endure,
Through longing that it hath all times
unto thy judgments pure.
21 Thou hast rebuk'd the cursed proud,
who from thy precepts swerve.
22 Reproach and shame remove from me,
for I thy laws observe.

23 Against me princes spake with spite,
while they in council sat:
But I thy servant did upon
thy statutes meditate.
24 My comfort, and my heart's delight,
thy testimonies be;
And they, in all my doubts and fears,
are counsellors to me.

DALETH. The Fourth Part.

25 My soul to dust cleaves: quicken me,
according to thy word.
26 My ways I shew'd, and me thou heard'st:
teach me thy statutes, Lord.
27 Thy way of thy commandements
make me aright to know;
So all thy works that wondrous are
I shall to others show.

130

SOUTHWELL. (C.M.)

Doh = E. HERBERT STEPHEN IRONS, 1834-1905.

```
:d   | m :m | s  :d    | d  :l     | s || s    | d' :m   | r  :r  | r  :— | — ||
:s,  | d :d | t, :d.t, | l, :l,.t, | d || m.r  | d  :d.t, | l, :l, | t, :— | — ||
:m   | s :l | r  :s    | f  :d.r   | m || s    | l  :l.s  | s  :fe | s  :— | — ||
:d   | d :l,| s, :m,   | f, :f,    | d || d.t, | l, :d    | r  :r  | s, :— | — ||
```

```
:s   | s :l.s | f    :f   | f   :s.f | m || d     | d  :f  | m  :r   | d :— | — || d  | d  ||
:r   | m :m   | m.de :r   | r.d :t,  | d || d.ta, | l, :r  | d  :t,  | d :— | — || l, | s, ||
:t   | t :l   | l    :l   | s   :s   | s || s     | l  :l  | s  :s.f | m :— | — || f  | m  ||
:s.f | m :de  | r    :r.d | t,  :s,  | d || m,    | f, :r, | s, :s,  | d :— | — || f, | d  ||
                                                                              A-men.
```

PSALM CXIX.

28 My soul doth melt, and drop away,
for heaviness and grief:
To me, according to thy word,
give strength, and send relief.
29 From me the wicked way of lies
let far removed be;
And graciously thy holy law
do thou grant unto me.

30 I chosen have the perfect way
of truth and verity:
Thy judgments that most righteous are
before me laid have I.
31 I to thy testimonies cleave;
shame do not on me cast.
32 I'll run thy precepts' way, when thou
my heart enlarged hast.

*HE. THE FIFTH PART.

33 Teach me, O Lord, the perfect way
of thy precepts divine,
And to observe it to the end
I shall my heart incline.
34 Give understanding unto me,
so keep thy law shall I;
Yea, ev'n with my whole heart I shall
observe it carefully.

35 In thy law's path make me to go;
for I delight therein.
36 My heart unto thy testimonies,
and not to greed, incline.
37 Turn thou away my sight and eyes
from viewing vanity;
And in thy good and holy way
be pleas'd to quicken me.

38 Confirm to me thy gracious word,
which I did gladly hear,
Ev'n to thy servant, Lord, who is
devoted to thy fear.
39 Turn thou away my fear'd reproach;
for good thy judgments be.
40 Lo, for thy precepts I have long'd;
in thy truth quicken me.

VAU. THE SIXTH PART.

41 Let thy sweet mercies also come
and visit me, O Lord;
Ev'n thy benign salvation,
according to thy word.
42 So shall I have wherewith I may
give him an answer just,
Who spitefully reproacheth me;
for in thy word I trust.

131

SPOHR. (C.M.) Adapted from LUDWIG SPOHR, 1784–1859.

Doh = G.

| :s_1 | m :— :m | s :— :d | m :— :r | d :— ‖ d | l :s :m | f :— :s | m :— ‖
| :s_1 | d :— :d | s_1 :— :l_1 | d :— :t_1 | d :— ‖ d | d :— :d | r :–.d :t_1 | d :— ‖
| :s | s :— :d | d :— :m | s :— :f | m :— ‖ m | f :s :l | l :— :s | s :— ‖
| :s_1 | d :— :l_1 | m_1 :— :l_1 | s_1 :— :s_1 | d :— ‖ d | f_1 :m_1 :l_1 | r_1 :— :s_1 | d :— ‖

| :m | r :— :de | r :— :m | f :— :l | s :— ‖ f | m :— :f | r :— :r | d :— ‖ d | d ‖
| :d | t_1 :— :le_1 | t_1 :— :de | r :— :ma | r :— ‖ r | d :— :d | d :— :t_1 | d :— ‖ l_1 | s_1 ‖
| :s | s :f :m | r :— :s | l :— :fe | s :— ‖ s | s :— :l | r :s :f | m :— ‖ f | m ‖
| :d | s_1 :— :s_1 | s_1 :f_1 :m_1 | r_1 :r :d | t_1 :— ‖ t_1 | d :— :f_1 | s_1 :— :s_1 | d_1 :— ‖ f_1 | d_1 ‖

A-men.

PSALM CXIX.

43 The word of truth out of my mouth
take thou not utterly;
For on thy judgments righteous
my hope doth still rely.
44 So shall I keep for evermore
thy law continually.
45 And, sith that I thy precepts seek,
I'll walk at liberty.

46 I'll speak thy word to kings, and I
with shame shall not be mov'd;
47 And will delight myself always
in thy laws, which I lov'd.
48 To thy commandments, which I lov'd,
my hands lift up I will;
And I will also meditate
upon thy statutes still.

ZAIN. THE SEVENTH PART.

49 Remember, Lord, thy gracious word
thou to thy servant spake,
Which, for a ground of my sure hope,
thou causedst me to take.
50 This word of thine my comfort is
in mine affliction:
For in my straits I am reviv'd
by this thy word alone.

51 The men whose hearts with pride are stuff'd
did greatly me deride;
Yet from thy straight commandements
I have not turn'd aside.
52 Thy judgments righteous, O Lord,
which thou of old forth gave,
I did remember, and myself
by them comforted have.
53 Horror took hold on me, because
ill men thy law forsake.
54 I in my house of pilgrimage
thy laws my songs do make.
55 Thy name by night, Lord, I did mind,
and I have kept thy law.
56 And this I had, because thy word
I kept, and stood in awe.

CHETH. THE EIGHTH PART.

57 Thou my sure portion art alone,
which I did chuse, O Lord:
I have resolv'd, and said, that I
would keep thy holy word.
58 With my whole heart I did entreat
thy face and favour free:
According to thy gracious word
be merciful to me.

STOCKTON. (C.M.)

Doh = E. THOMAS WRIGHT, 1763–1829.

```
:d  |m  :f    |s  :d'  |f  :m   |r  ‖ r  |m  :fe  |s  :fe   |s  :— |— ‖
:d  |d  :d.t, |d  :d   |r  :d   |t, ‖ t, |d  :d   |r  :d.l, |t, :— |— ‖
:m  |s  :f    |m  :l   |s  :s   |s  ‖ s  |s  :l   |s  :l    |s  :— |— ‖
:d  |d  :r    |m  :l,  |t, :d   |s, ‖ s, |d  :l,  |t, :r    |s, :— |— ‖

:d' |m  :l    |s  :d   |r  :f   |m  ‖ s  |l.t:d'  |m  :r    |d  :— |— ‖ d  |d  ‖
:d  |d  :d    |d  :d   |d  :t,  |d  ‖ d  |d  :d   |d  :t,   |d  :— |— ‖ l, |s, ‖
:s  |s  :f    |s  :s   |l  :s   |s  ‖ s  |f  :s.l |s  :-.f  |m  :— |— ‖ f  |m  ‖
:m  |d  :f    |m  :m,  |f, :s,  |d  ‖ m  |f  :m.f |s  :s,   |d  :— |— ‖ f, |d  ‖
                                                                      A-men.
```

PSALM CXIX.

59 I thought upon my former ways,
and did my life well try;
And to thy testimonies pure
my feet then turned I.
60 I did not stay, nor linger long,
as those that slothful are;
But hastily thy laws to keep
myself I did prepare.

61 Bands of ill men me robb'd; yet I
thy precepts did not slight.
62 I'll rise at midnight thee to praise,
ev'n for thy judgments right.
63 I am companion to all those
who fear, and thee obey.
64 O Lord, thy mercy fills the earth:
teach me thy laws, I pray.

TETH. THE NINTH PART.

65 Well hast thou with thy servant dealt,
as thou didst promise give.
66 Good judgment me, and knowledge teach,
for I thy word believe.
67 Ere I afflicted was I stray'd;
but now I keep thy word.
68 Both good thou art, and good thou do'st:
teach me thy statutes, Lord.

69 The men that are puff'd up with pride
against me forg'd a lie;
Yet thy commandements observe
with my whole heart will I.
70 Their hearts, through worldly ease and wealth,
as fat as grease they be:
But in thy holy law I take
delight continually.

71 It hath been very good for me
that I afflicted was,
That I might well instructed be,
and learn thy holy laws.
72 The word that cometh from thy mouth
is better unto me
Than many thousands and great sums
of gold and silver be.

JOD. THE TENTH PART.

73 Thou mad'st and fashion'dst me: thy laws
to know give wisdom, Lord.
74 So who thee fear shall joy to see
me trusting in thy word.
75 That very right thy judgments are
I know, and do confess;
And that thou hast afflicted me
in truth and faithfulness.

STRACATHRO. (C.M.) CHARLES HUTCHESON, 1792–1860.

Doh = D.

:d | m :— :r | d :— :r | m :d' :t | l :— || d' | s :m :d | m :— :r | d :— ||
:d | d :— :t_1 | l_1 :— :s_1 | s_1 :m :r | d :— || m | r :d :d | d :— :t_1 | d :— ||
:m | s :— :s.f | m :— :s | m :-.ba :se | l :— || l | r :s :l | s :— :f | m :— ||
:d | d :— :s_1 | l_1 :— :t_1 | d :-.r :m | f :— || l_1 | t_1 :d :l_1 | m_1 :-.f_1 :s_1 | d :— ||

:m | m :— :r | d :m :s | l :r' :d' | t :— || t | d' :s :l | m :— :r | d :— || f | m ||
:d | d :— :t_1 | d :s_1 :s | d :f :m | r :— || r | d :— :d | d :— :t_1 | d :— || d | d ||
:s | s :— :s | s :d' :t | l :— :s.l | t :— || s | s :d'.t :l | s :— :s.f | m :— || l | s ||
:d | d :s :f | m :d :m | f :r :m.f | s :— || s.f | m :— :f | s :— :s_1 | d :— || f_1 | d ||

A-men.

PSALM CXIX.

76 O let thy kindness merciful,
I pray thee, comfort me,
As to thy servant faithfully
was promised by thee.
77 And let thy tender mercies come
to me, that I may live;
Because thy holy laws to me
sweet delectation give.

78 Lord, let the proud ashamed be;
for they, without a cause,
With me perversely dealt: but I
will muse upon thy laws.
79 Let such as fear thee, and have known
thy statutes, turn to me.
80 My heart let in thy laws be sound,
that sham'd I never be.

CAPH. THE ELEVENTH PART.

81 My soul for thy salvation faints;
yet I thy word believe.
82 Mine eyes fail for thy word: I say,
When wilt thou comfort give?
83 For like a bottle I'm become,
that in the smoke is set:
I'm black, and parch'd with grief; yet I
thy statutes not forget.

84 How many are thy servant's days?
when wilt thou execute
Just judgment on these wicked men
that do me persecute?
85 The proud have digged pits for me,
which is against thy laws.
86 Thy words all faithful are: help me,
pursu'd without a cause.

87 They so consum'd me, that on earth
my life they scarce did leave:
Thy precepts yet forsook I not,
but close to them did cleave.
88 After thy loving-kindness, Lord,
me quicken, and preserve:
The testimony of thy mouth
so shall I still observe.

*LAMED. THE TWELFTH PART.

89 Thy word for ever is, O Lord,
in heaven settled fast;
90 Unto all generations
thy faithfulness doth last:
The earth thou hast established,
and it abides by thee.
91 This day they stand as thou ordain'dst;
for all thy servants be.

134

STROUDWATER. (C.M.) *Wilkins's Psalmody, c.* 1730.

Doh = A.

```
:d  |s, :—:d  |s  :—:m  |f :m :r    |d :—  ||d  |r  :—:m  |f  :—:m  |r  :— ||
:s, |s, :—:l, |t, :—:d  |d :—:t,    |d :—  ||s, |s, :—:s, |l, :—:s, |s, :— ||
:m  |r  :—:d  |r  :—:d  |l :s :s.f  |m :—  ||d  |t, :—:d  |d  :—:d  |t, :— ||
:d  |t, :—:l, |s, :—:l, |f,:s, :s,  |d,:—  ||m, |s, :—:d  |f, :—:d, |s, :— ||
```

```
:m  |r :—:d     |s,:—:t,  |d :— :r      |s :—  ||s.f |m :r :d       |f :m :r       |d :— ||d |d  ||
:s, |s,:f, :m,  |s,:—:s,  |s,:— :fe,    |s,:—  ||s,  |s,:—.f, :m,    |l,:s, :s,.f,  |m,:— ||l,|s, ||
:d  |t,:—:d     |d :—:r   |m :—.r :d    |t,:—  ||r   |d :t, :d       |d :—:t,       |d :— ||d |m  ||
:d  |s,:—:l,    |m,:—:s,  |d :—.t, :l,  |s,:—  ||t,  |d :s, :l,      |f,:s, :s,     |d,:— ||f,|d, ||
```

A-men.

PSALM CXIX.

92 Unless in thy most perfect law
my soul delights had found,
I should have perished, when as
my troubles did abound.
93 Thy precepts I will ne'er forget;
they quick'ning to me brought.
94 Lord, I am thine; O save thou me:
thy precepts I have sought.

95 For me the wicked have laid wait,
me seeking to destroy:
But I thy testimonies true
consider will with joy.
96 An end of all perfection
here have I seen, O God:
But as for thy commandement,
it is exceeding broad.

MEM. The Thirteenth Part.

97 O how love I thy law! it is
my study all the day:
98 It makes me wiser than my foes;
for it doth with me stay.
99 Than all my teachers now I have
more understanding far;
Because my meditation
thy testimonies are.

100 In understanding I excel
those that are ancients;
For I endeavoured to keep
all thy commandements.
101 My feet from each ill way I stay'd,
that I may keep thy word.
102 I from thy judgments have not swerv'd;
for thou hast taught me, Lord.

103 How sweet unto my taste, O Lord,
are all thy words of truth!
Yea, I do find them sweeter far
than honey to my mouth.
104 I through thy precepts, that are pure,
do understanding get;
I therefore ev'ry way that's false
with all my heart do hate.

NUN. The Fourteenth Part.

105 Thy word is to my feet a lamp,
and to my path a light.
106 I sworn have, and I will perform,
to keep thy judgments right.
107 I am with sore affliction
ev'n overwhelm'd, O Lord:
In mercy raise and quicken me,
according to thy word.

TALLIS. (C.M.)

Doh = E♭. THOMAS TALLIS, *c.* 1505–85.

:d |m :f |s :s |l :l |s ‖s |d' :t |l :l |s :— |— ‖
:d |d :d |r :m |f :f |m ‖d |m :r |r :r |t_1 :— |— ‖
:m |s :l |t :s |d' :d' |d' ‖m |s :s |s :fe |s :— |— ‖
:d |d :l_1 |s_1 :d |f_1 :f_1 |d ‖d |d :s_1 |r :r |s_1 :— |— ‖

:d |m :f |s :s |l :l |s ‖d |f :m |r :r |d :— |— ‖d |d ‖
:d |d :d |t_1 :d |d :d |d ‖d |d :d |d :t_1 |d :— |— ‖l_1 |s_1 ‖
:m |s :f |r :m |f :f |m ‖m |l :s |s :s |m :— |— ‖f |m ‖
:d |d :l_1 |s_1 :d |f :f_1 |d ‖d |l_1 :d |s_1 :s_1 |d :— |— ‖f_1 |d ‖

A-men.

PSALM CXIX.

108 The free-will-off'rings of my mouth
accept, I thee beseech:
And unto me thy servant, Lord,
thy judgments clearly teach.
109 Though still my soul be in my hand,
thy laws I'll not forget.
110 I err'd not from them, though for me
the wicked snares did set.

111 I of thy testimonies have
above all things made choice,
To be my heritage for aye;
for they my heart rejoice.
112 I carefully inclined have
my heart still to attend;
That I thy statutes may perform
alway unto the end.

SAMECH. THE FIFTEENTH PART.

113 I hate the thoughts of vanity,
but love thy law do I.
114 My shield and hiding-place thou art:
I on thy word rely.
115 All ye that evil-doers are
from me depart away;
For the commandments of my God
I purpose to obey.

116 According to thy faithful word
uphold and stablish me,
That I may live, and of my hope
ashamed never be.
117 Hold thou me up, so shall I be
in peace and safety still;
And to thy statutes have respect
continually I will.

118 Thou tread'st down all that love to stray;
false their deceit doth prove.
119 Lewd men, like dross, away thou putt'st;
therefore thy law I love.
120 For fear of thee my very flesh
doth tremble, all dismay'd;
And of thy righteous judgments, Lord,
my soul is much afraid.

TIVERTON. (C.M.) — Grigg, in *John Rippon's Selection of Psalm and Hymn Tunes*, c. 1795.

Doh = B♭.

```
:s,  |d   :r    |m  :d.t,  |l,  :t,  |d   ||m     |r   :s,.d   |t,  :l,   |s,  :—  |—  ||
:m,  |s,  :s,   |s, :s,    |f,  :f,  |s,  ||s,    |s,  :s,.l,  |s,  :fe,  |s,  :—  |—  ||
:d   |d   :t,   |d  :d     |d   :r   |s,  ||d     |r   :m      |r   :r.d  |t,  :—  |—  ||
:d,  |m,  :s,   |d  :m,    |f,  :r,  |m,  ||d,    |t,, :d,     |r,  :r,   |s,  :—  |—  ||

:r   |d.t, :l,.s, |d  :r.m    |f   :m   |r   ||d     |s, :l,.f   |m  :r     |d  :— |—  ||d  |d  ||
:s,  |s,   :r,    |s, :s,     |s,  :s,  |s,  ||m,.f, |s, :f,.l,  |s, :s,.f, |m, :— |—  ||f, |m, ||
:t,  |r    :l,.t, |d  :t,.d   |r   :d   |t,  ||d     |d  :d      |d  :t,    |d  :— |—  ||l, |s, ||
:s,  |s,   :f,    |m, :r,.d,  |t,, :d,  |s,  ||l,    |m, :f,.r,  |s, :s,    |d, :— |—  ||f, |d, ||
                                                                                        A-men.
```

PSALM CXIX.

AIN. The Sixteenth Part.

121 To all men I have judgment done,
performing justice right;
Then let me not be left unto
my fierce oppressors' might.
122 For good unto thy servant, Lord,
thy servant's surety be:
From the oppression of the proud
do thou deliver me.

123 Mine eyes do fail with looking long
for thy salvation,
The word of thy pure righteousness
while I do wait upon.
124 In mercy with thy servant deal,
thy laws me teach and show.
125 I am thy servant, wisdom give,
that I thy laws may know.

126 'Tis time thou work, Lord; for they have
made void thy law divine.
127 Therefore thy precepts more I love
than gold, yea, gold most fine.
128 Concerning all things thy commands
all right I judge therefore;
And ev'ry false and wicked way
I perfectly abhor.

PE. The Seventeenth Part.

129 Thy statutes, Lord, are wonderful,
my soul them keeps with care.
130 The entrance of thy words gives light,
makes wise who simple are.
131 My mouth I have wide opened,
and panted earnestly,
While after thy commandements
I long'd exceedingly.

132 Look on me, Lord, and merciful
do thou unto me prove,
As thou art wont to do to those
thy name who truly love.
133 O let my footsteps in thy word
aright still order'd be:
Let no iniquity obtain
dominion over me.

134 From man's oppression save thou me;
so keep thy laws I will.
135 Thy face make on thy servant shine;
teach me thy statutes still.
136 Rivers of waters from mine eyes
did run down, when I saw
How wicked men run on in sin,
and do not keep thy law.

137

UNIVERSITY. (C.M.)

Doh = C. JOHN RANDALL, 1715–99.

```
:s  |f.m:r .d|d' :r'.m'|s :f  |m :- ||.s |m.d:l.s|f  :m |r  :— |— ||
:d  |d :t,.d |d.s:f .m |r :t, |d :- ||.r |d :d   |d.t,:d|t, :— |— ||
:m  |l.s:f .m|s :t .d' |r' :s |s :- ||.s |s :f.s |l.f :s |s  :— |— ||
:d  |d :d    |m :r .d  |t, :s,|d :- ||.t,|d.m:f.m|r  :d |s, :— |— ||

:s  |d':d'.t|l :s    |d :r.m  |f :- ||.s |l.d':s .l|m :r   |d :—|—||f |m ||
:r  |s :m   |d.r:m   |d :d    |d :- ||.d |d :d     |d :t,  |d :—|—||d |d ||
:t  |d':s   |l.t:d'  |d':-.t  |l :- ||.s |f.l :d'.l|s :-.f |m :—|—||l |s ||
:s.f|m :d   |f :m    |l :s    |f :- ||.m |f :m .f  |s :s,  |d :—|—||f,|d ||
```

A-men.

PSALM CXIX.

TSADDI. The Eighteenth Part.

137 O Lord, thou art most righteous;
thy judgments are upright.
138 Thy testimonies thou command'st
most faithful are and right.
139 My zeal hath ev'n consumed me,
because mine enemies
Thy holy words forgotten have,
and do thy laws despise.

140 Thy word 's most pure, therefore on it
thy servant's love is set.
141 Small, and despis'd I am, yet I
thy precepts not forget.
142 Thy righteousness is righteousness
which ever doth endure:
Thy holy law, Lord, also is
the very truth most pure.

143 Trouble and anguish have me found,
and taken hold on me:
Yet in my trouble my delight
thy just commandments be.
144 Eternal righteousness is in
thy testimonies all:
Lord, to me understanding give,
and ever live I shall.

KOPH. The Nineteenth Part.

145 With my whole heart I cry'd, Lord, hear;
I will thy word obey.
146 I cry'd to thee; save me, and I
will keep thy laws alway.
147 I of the morning did prevent
the dawning, and did cry:
For all mine expectation
did on thy word rely.

148 Mine eyes did timeously prevent
the watches of the night.
That in thy word with careful mind
then meditate I might.
149 After thy loving-kindness hear
my voice, that calls on thee:
According to thy judgment, Lord,
revive and quicken me.

150 Who follow mischief they draw nigh;
they from thy law are far:
151 But thou art near, Lord; most firm truth
all thy commandments are.
152 As for thy testimonies all,
of old this have I try'd,
That thou hast surely founded [them
for ever to abide.

UXBRIDGE. (C.M.)

Doh = A. *Dibdin's Standard Psalm Tune Book*, 1857.

:s_1	d :t_1	d :r	d :t_1	d ‖	r	m :d	t_1 :l_1	s_1 :—	— ‖
:m_1	s_1 :s_1	s_1 :l_1	s_1 :s_1	s_1 ‖	s_1	s_1 :l_1	s_1 :fe_1	s_1 :—	— ‖
:d	d :r	m :f	m :r	m ‖	t_1	d :m	r :r.d	t_1 :—	— ‖
:d_1	m_1 :s_1	d :f_1	s_1 :s_1	d_1 ‖	s_1	d_1 :d_1	r_1 :r_1	s_1 :—	— ‖

:r	r :r	f :r	m :r.d	t_1 ‖	d	l_1.t_1 :d	d :t_1	d :—	— ‖	d	d ‖
:s_1	s_1 :s_1	f_1 :s_1	s_1 :l_1	s_1 ‖	s_1	f_1 :s_1.l_1	s_1 :s_1	s_1 :—	— ‖	l_1	s_1 ‖
:t_1	r :t_1	d :r	d :f	r ‖	d	d.r :d.f	m :r	m :—	— ‖	f	m ‖
:s_1	t_1 :s_1	l_1 :t_1	d :f_1	s_1 ‖	m_1	f_1.r_1 :m_1.f_1	s_1 :s_1	d_1 :—	— ‖	f_1	d_1 ‖

A-men.

PSALM CXIX.

RESH. The Twentieth Part.

153 Consider mine affliction,
in safety do me set:
Deliver me, O Lord, for I
thy law do not forget.
154 After thy word revive thou me:
save me, and plead my cause.
155 Salvation is from sinners far;
for they seek not thy laws.

156 O Lord, both great and manifold
thy tender mercies be:
According to thy judgments just,
revive and quicken me.
157 My persecutors many are,
and foes that do combine;
Yet from thy testimonies pure
my heart doth not decline.

158 I saw transgressors, and was griev'd;
for they keep not thy word.
159 See how I love thy law! as thou
art kind, me quicken, Lord.
160 From the beginning all thy word
hath been most true and sure:
Thy righteous judgments ev'ry one
for evermore endure.

SCHIN. The Twenty-first Part.

161 Princes have persecuted me,
although no cause they saw:
But still of thy most holy word
my heart doth stand in awe.
162 I at thy word rejoice, as one
of spoil that finds great store.
163 Thy law I love; but lying all
I hate and do abhor.

164 Sev'n times a-day it is my care
to give due praise to thee;
Because of all thy judgments, Lord,
which righteous ever be.
165 Great peace have they who love thy law;
offence they shall have none.
166 I hop'd for thy salvation, Lord,
and thy commands have done.

167 My soul thy testimonies pure
observed carefully;
On them my heart is set, and them
I love exceedingly.
168 Thy testimonies and thy laws
I kept with special care;
For all my works and ways each one
before thee open are.

WALSALL. (C.M.)
Lah=F. Doh=A♭.

Anchors' Collection of Psalm Tunes, c. 1720.

```
:l, |d  :t,.l, |m, :m  |r.d:t, |l, ||d |l, :se, |l,.t,:d.r|m   :— |— ||
:m, |m, :m,    |m, :l, |f, :r, |d, ||l,|m, :r,  |m,   :l, |se, :— |— ||
:d  |l, :l,    |se,:d  |l, :se,|l, ||m |d  :r   |d    :l, |t,  :— |— ||
:l,,|l, :d,    |m, :l,,|r, :m, |l, ||l,|d  :t,  |l,   :f, |m,  :— |— ||

:m  |m :m  |r :d.t,|l,:r.d|t, ||m |l,.se,:l,.t,|d.r :t,.,l,|l, :—|—||l,|l,     ||
:s, |s,:s, |s,:s,  |f,:l, |s, ||s,|f,    :l,   |l,   :se,  |l, :—|—||f,|m,     ||
:d  |d :d  |t,:d   |d :f  |r  ||d |d     :f    |m.f  :r    |d  :—|—||r |de     ||
:d, |m,:d, |s,:m,  |f,:r, |s, ||d,|f,    :r,   |m,.r,:m,   |l,,:—|—||r,|l, l,, ||
```

A-men.

PSALMS CXIX, CXX, CXXI.

*TAU. The Twenty-second Part.

169 O let my earnest pray'r and cry
come near before thee, Lord:
Give understanding unto me,
according to thy word.
170 Let my request before thee come:
after thy word me free.
171 My lips shall utter praise, when thou
hast taught thy laws to me.
172 My tongue of thy most blessed word
shall speak, and it confess;
Because all thy commandements
are perfect righteousness.
173 Let thy strong hand make help to me:
thy precepts are my choice.
174 I long'd for thy salvation, Lord,
and in thy law rejoice.
175 O let my soul live, and it shall
give praises unto thee;
And let thy judgments gracious
be helpful unto me.
176 I, like a lost sheep, went astray;
thy servant seek, and find:
For thy commands I suffer'd not
to slip out of my mind.

120

IN my distress to God I cry'd,
and he gave ear to me.
2 From lying lips, and guileful tongue,
O Lord, my soul set free.
3 What shall be giv'n thee? or what shall
be done to thee, false tongue?
4 Ev'n burning coals of juniper,
sharp arrows of the strong.
5 Woe 's me that I in Mesech am
a sojourner so long;
That I in tabernacles dwell
to Kedar that belong.
6 My soul with him that hateth peace
hath long a dweller been.
7 I am for peace; but when I speak,
for battle they are keen.

121*

I TO the hills will lift mine eyes,
from whence doth come mine aid.
2 My safety cometh from the Lord,
who heav'n and earth hath made.
3 Thy foot he'll not let slide, nor will
he slumber that thee keeps.
4 Behold, he that keeps Israel,
he slumbers not, nor sleeps.

140

WARWICK. (C.M.)

Doh = D. SAMUEL STANLEY, 1767–1822.

```
:d |m.s:d'.l |s  :f.l |s.m:r  |d  ||m.fe|s  :l.d' |t.l :s.fe|s  :— |— ||
:d |d  :d    |d  :d.f |m.d:t, |d  ||d   |r  :m    |r   :r   |t, :— |— ||
:m |s.m:s.l  |d' :d'  |d'.s:s.f|m ||l   |s  :m    |s.d':t.l |s  :— |— ||
:d |d  :m.f  |m  :l.f |s  :s, |d  ||l,  |t, :d.l, |r   :r   |s, :— |— ||

:s |l.f:d'.l |s  :m |f.r:s.f |m ||s |l.t:d'.r' |d' :t  |d' :— |— ||d' |d' ||
:d |d  :f    |s  :d |r  :r   |d ||d |d.f:m.r   |m  :r  |m  :— |— ||f  |m  ||
:m |f.l:l.d' |d' :d'|l.f:s   |s ||s |f  :s.l   |s  :s  |s  :— |— ||l  |s  ||
:d |f  :l.f  |m  :l |r  :t,  |d ||m |f.r:m.f   |s  :s, |d  :— |— ||f  |d  ||
```

A-men.

PSALMS CXXI, CXXII, CXXIII.

5 The Lord thee keeps, the Lord thy shade
on thy right hand doth stay:
6 The moon by night thee shall not smite,
nor yet the sun by day.
7 The Lord shall keep thy soul; he shall
preserve thee from all ill.
8 Henceforth thy going out and in
God keep for ever will.

122*

I JOY'D when to the house of God,
Go up, they said to me.
2 Jerusalem, within thy gates
our feet shall standing be.
3 Jerus'lem, as a city, is
compactly built together:
4 Unto that place the tribes go up,
the tribes of God go thither:

To Isr'el's testimony, there
to God's name thanks to pay.
5 For thrones of judgment, ev'n the thrones
of David's house, there stay.
6 Pray that Jerusalem may have
peace and felicity:
Let them that love thee and thy peace
have still prosperity.
7 Therefore I wish that peace may still
within thy walls remain,
And ever may thy palaces
prosperity retain.
8 Now, for my friends' and brethren's sakes,
Peace be in thee, I'll say.
9 And for the house of God our Lord,
I'll seek thy good alway.

123

O THOU that dwellest in the heav'ns,
I lift mine eyes to thee.
2 Behold, as servants' eyes do look
their masters' hand to see,
As handmaid's eyes her mistress' hand;
so do our eyes attend
Upon the Lord our God, until
to us he mercy send.

3 O Lord, be gracious to us,
unto us gracious be;
Because replenish'd with contempt
exceedingly are we.

141

WESTMINSTER. (C.M.)

Doh = C. JAMES TURLE, 1802-82.

:m |s :s |d :d' |t :l |s ||s |m' :t |d' :r' |s :— |— ||
:d |m :r |d :m |m :d.r |m ||f |m :s.f |m :f.m |r :— |— ||
:s |s :r |m :d' |m' :l.t |d' ||t |d' :m'.r' |d' :l |t :— |— ||
:d |d :t, |l, :l |s :f |m ||r |d :s |l :f |s :— |— ||

:s |t :l |se :l |d' :t |l ||l |s :d |r :f |m :— |— ||f |m ||
:r |r :r |r :d |m :m.r |d ||f |m :d |d :t, |d :— |— ||d |d ||
:t |s :l |t :l |l :se |l ||r' |s :s |l :s |s :— |— ||l |s ||
:s |s :f |m :f |m :m |l, ||t, |d :m |f :s |d :— |— ||f f, |d ||

A-men.

4 Our soul is fill'd with scorn of those
that at their ease abide,
And with the insolent contempt
of those that swell in pride.

124

HAD not the Lord been on our side,
may Israel now say;
2 Had not the Lord been on our side,
when men rose us to slay;
3 They had us swallow'd quick, when as
their wrath 'gainst us did flame:
4 Waters had cover'd us, our soul
had sunk beneath the stream.

5 Then had the waters, swelling high,
over our soul made way.
6 Bless'd be the Lord, who to their teeth
us gave not for a prey.
7 Our soul 's escaped, as a bird
out of the fowler's snare;
The snare asunder broken is,
and we escaped are.

8 Our sure and all-sufficient help
is in JEHOVAH'S name;
His name who did the heav'n create,
and who the earth did frame.

124 (2)*

ANOTHER OF THE SAME.

NOW Israel
may say, and that truly,
If that the Lord
had not our cause maintain'd;
2 If that the Lord
had not our right sustain'd,
When cruel men
against us furiously
Rose up in wrath,
to make of us their prey;

3 Then certainly
they had devour'd us all,
And swallow'd quick,
for ought that we could deem;
Such was their rage,
as we might well esteem.
4 And as fierce floods
before them all things drown,
So had they brought
our soul to death quite down.

5 The raging streams,
with their proud swelling waves,
Had then our soul
o'erwhelmed in the deep.

WETHERBY. (C.M.) SAMUEL SEBASTIAN WESLEY, 1810–76.

Doh = D.

:m | s :—:m.r | d :—:s | l :—:l | s :— || s | d' :—:t | t.l :s :fe | s :— ||
:d | m :—:t_1 | d :—:d | d :—:d | d :— || r | d :—:r | m :r :r | t_1 :— ||
:s | s :—:s.f | m :—:d | d :f :d.r | m :— || s | m :fe :s | d' :t :l | s :— ||
:d | d :—:s_1 | l_1 :—:m_1 | f_1 :l_1 :f_1 | d :— || t_1 | l_1 :—:t_1 | d :r :r | s_1 :— ||

:s | t :—:r' | d' :—:s | s :f :m | f :— || l | s :—:d | r :m :r | d :— || d | d ||
:r | r :—:t_1 | d :—:m | m :r :de | r :— || f | m :—:d | d :—:t_1 | d :— || l_1 | s_1 ||
:t | t :—:s | s :—:t | l :—:l | l :— || r | m :—:s | l :s :s.f | m :— || f | m ||
:s_1 | s :—:f | m :—:m | l_1 :—:l_1 | r :— || t_1 | d :—:m | f :s :s_1 | d :— || f_1 | d ||

A-men.

6 But bless'd be God,
who doth us safely keep,
And hath not giv'n
us for a living prey
Unto their teeth,
and bloody cruelty.

7 Ev'n as a bird
out of the fowler's snare
Escapes away,
so is our soul set free:
Broke are their nets,
and thus escaped we.
8 Therefore our help
is in the Lord's great name,
Who heav'n and earth
by his great pow'r did frame.

125*

THEY in the Lord that firmly trust
shall be like Sion hill,
Which at no time can be remov'd,
but standeth ever still.
2 As round about Jerusalem
the mountains stand alway,
The Lord his folk doth compass so,
from henceforth and for aye.

3 For ill men's rod upon the lot
of just men shall not lie;
Lest righteous men stretch forth their hands
unto iniquity.
4 Do thou to all those that be good
thy goodness, Lord, impart;
And do thou good to those that are
upright within their heart.

5 But as for such as turn aside
after their crooked way,
God shall lead forth with wicked men:
on Isr'el peace shall stay.

126*

WHEN Sion's bondage God turn'd back,
as men that dream'd were we.
2 Then fill'd with laughter was our mouth,
our tongue with melody:
They 'mong the heathen said, The Lord
great things for them hath wrought.
3 The Lord hath done great things for us,
whence joy to us is brought.

WIGTOWN. (C.M.)

Doh = F. *Scottish Psalter*, 1635.

```
|m  :—  |m  :m  |f  :-.m  |r .d  :r    |d  :—  ||m :— |m :r  |m    :f  |s  :— ||
|s, :—  |s, :l, |l, :-.d  |l,    :t,   |d  :—  ||d :— |s,:s, |s,   :d  |t, :— ||
|s  :—  |m  :d  |r  :-.s  |f .m  :s.f  |m  :—  ||s :— |d :r  |d    :d  |r  :— ||
|d  :—  |d  :l, |r, :-.m, |f,.l, :s,   |d  :—  ||d :— |d :t, |d.t, :l, |s, :— ||

|r  :—  |r  :m  |l  :s  |f     :m     |r  :— ||r  :— |m  :f  |r  :r     |d  :— |— :— ||d  |d  ||
|ta,:—  |ta,:d  |l, :t, |d .s, :s,.l, |t, :— ||s, :— |s, :l, |s, :-.f, |m, :— |— :— ||l, |s, ||
|s  :—  |s  :s  |f  :m  |m .r  :m .f  |s  :— ||s  :— |m  :d  |d  :t,    |d  :— |— :— ||d  |m  ||
|s, :—  |s, :d  |f, :s, |l,.t, :d     |s, :— ||t, :— |d  :f, |s, :s,    |d, :— |— :— ||f, |d, ||
```

A-men.

PSALMS CXXVI, CXXVII, CXXVIII, CXXIX.

4 As streams of water in the south,
our bondage, Lord, recall.
5 Who sow in tears, a reaping time
of joy enjoy they shall.
6 That man who, bearing precious seed,
in going forth doth mourn,
He doubtless, bringing back his sheaves,
rejoicing shall return.

127

EXCEPT the Lord do build the house,
the builders lose their pain:
Except the Lord the city keep,
the watchmen watch in vain.
2 'Tis vain for you to rise betimes,
or late from rest to keep,
To feed on sorrows' bread; so gives
he his beloved sleep.

3 Lo, children are God's heritage,
the womb's fruit his reward.
4 The sons of youth as arrows are,
for strong men's hands prepar'd.
5 O happy is the man that hath
his quiver fill'd with those;
They unashamed in the gate
shall speak unto their foes.

128

BLESS'D is each one that fears the Lord,
and walketh in his ways;
2 For of thy labour thou shalt eat,
and happy be always.
3 Thy wife shall as a fruitful vine
by thy house' sides be found:
Thy children like to olive-plants
about thy table round.

4 Behold, the man that fears the Lord,
thus blessed shall he be.
5 The Lord shall out of Sion give
his blessing unto thee:
Thou shalt Jerus'lem's good behold
whilst thou on earth dost dwell.
6 Thou shalt thy children's children see,
and peace on Israel.

129

OFT did they vex me from my youth,
may Isr'el now declare;
2 Oft did they vex me from my youth,
yet not victorious were.

FAUX-BOURDON SETTING.

WIGTOWN. (C.M.)

Doh = F. THOMAS CUTHBERTSON LEITHEAD PRITCHARD, 1885-

m :—	m :s	l :s	m :r	m :f		s :—	l :-.t	d'.r':d'	t :—	
s, :—	d :t,	l, :t,	l, :f,	l, :—		d :-.t,	l, :r	d :f	r :—	
m :—	m :m	f :-.m	r.d :r	d :—		m :—	m :r	m :f	s :—	
d :t,	l, :s,	f, :s,	l, :r,	l, :f,		m, :d,	f, :f,	l, :r,	s, :—	

ta :—	l :s	f :m	r :de	r :—		s :—	m :l	s :-.f	m :—	—:—	
r :—	l,.t, :de	r :ta,	l, :l,	f, :—		s, :—	s, :d	d :t,	d :—	—:—	
r :—	r :m	l :s	f :m	r :—		r :—	m :f	r :r	d :—	—:—	
ta, :—	f, :m,	r, :s,	l, :l,	r :—		t, :—	d :f,	s, :s,	d :—	—:—	

[*Copyright*, 1929, *by Oxford University Press.*]

PSALMS CXXIX, CXXX, CXXXI.

3 The plowers plow'd upon my back;
they long their furrows drew.
4 The righteous Lord did cut the cords
of the ungodly crew.

5 Let Sion's haters all be turn'd
back with confusion.
6 As grass on houses' tops be they,
which fades ere it be grown:
7 Whereof enough to fill his hand
the mower cannot find;
Nor can the man his bosom fill,
whose work is sheaves to bind.

8 Neither say they who do go by,
God's blessing on you rest:
We in the name of God the Lord
do wish you to be blest.

130*

LORD, from the depths to thee
I cry'd.
2 My voice, Lord, do thou hear:
Unto my supplications' voice
give an attentive ear.
3 Lord, who shall stand, if thou, O
Lord,
should'st mark iniquity?
4 But yet with thee forgiveness is,
that fear'd thou mayest be.

5 I wait for God, my soul doth wait,
my hope is in his word.
6 More than they that for morning
watch,
my soul waits for the Lord;
I say, more than they that do watch
the morning light to see.
7 Let Israel hope in the Lord,
for with him mercies be;

And plenteous redemption
is ever found with him.
8 And from all his iniquities
he Isr'el shall redeem.

131

MY heart not haughty is, O Lord,
mine eyes not lofty be;
Nor do I deal in matters great,
or things too high for me.
2 I surely have myself behav'd
with quiet sp'rit and mild,
As child of mother wean'd: my soul
is like a weaned child.

3 Upon the Lord let all the hope
of Israel rely,
Ev'n from the time that present is
unto eternity.

144

WILTSHIRE. (C.M.) GEORGE THOMAS SMART, 1776–1867.

Doh = B♭.

:s, | m, :s, :d | d :t, :d | f :m :r | r :m || s, | s, :— :s, | s, :m :d | d :t, ||
:m, | m, :— :s, | s, :f, :m, | l, :s, :s, | f, :m, || m, | r, :m, :f, | m, :— :s,.l, | s, :— ||
:d | d :— :m | m :r :d | d :— :t, | t, :d || s, | s, :— :s, | d :s, :d | m :r ||
:d, | d, :m, :d, | s, :— :l, | f, :s, :s, | d, :— || d, | t,, :d, :r, | d, :— :m,.f, | s, :— ||

:r | d :— :t, | d :— :r | m :f :m | m :r || m.d | l, :— :r.d | t, :-.l, :t, | d :— || d | d ||
:f, | m, :s, :f, | m, :s, :— | s, :— :s, | d :t, || s, | s, :f, :l, | s, :-.l, :s,.f, | m, :— || f, | m, ||
:t, | d :— :r | d :— :t, | d :r :m.f | s :— || d | d :r.m :f | r :-.d :r | d :— || l, | s, ||
:s, | d :m, :s, | d, :m, :s, | d :t, :d | s, :— || m, | f, :— :r, | s, :— :s, | d, :— || f, | d, ||

A-men.

PSALM CXXXII.

132*

DAVID, and his afflictions all,
Lord, do thou think upon;
2 How unto God he sware, and vow'd
to Jacob's mighty One.
3 I will not come within my house,
nor rest in bed at all;
4 Nor shall mine eyes take any sleep,
nor eyelids slumber shall;

5 Till for the Lord a place I find,
where he may make abode;
A place of habitation
for Jacob's mighty God.
6 Lo, at the place of Ephratah
of it we understood;
And we did find it in the fields,
and city of the wood.

7 We'll go into his tabernacles,
and at his footstool bow.
8 Arise, O Lord, into thy rest,
th' ark of thy strength, and thou.
9 O let thy priests be clothed, Lord,
with truth and righteousness;
And let all those that are thy saints
shout loud for joyfulness.

10 For thine own servant David's sake,
do not deny thy grace;
Nor of thine own anointed one
turn thou away the face.
11 The Lord in truth to David sware,
he will not turn from it,
I of thy body's fruit will make
upon thy throne to sit.

12 My cov'nant if thy sons will keep,
and laws to them made known,
Their children then shall also sit
for ever on thy throne.
13 For God of Sion hath made choice;
there he desires to dwell.
14 This is my rest, here still I'll stay;
for I do like it well.

15 Her food I'll greatly bless; her poor
with bread will satisfy.
16 Her priests I'll clothe with health; her saints
shall shout forth joyfully.
17 And there will I make David's horn
to bud forth pleasantly:
For him that mine anointed is
a lamp ordain'd have I.

18 As with a garment I will clothe
with shame his en'mies all:
But yet the crown that he doth wear
upon him flourish shall.

WILTSHIRE. (C.M.) DESCANT.

Doh = B♭. ALAN GRAY, 1855–

Descant.

:m |m :—:d |m :r :d |l :s :f |f :m ||m |r :m :f |m :—:s.f |m :r ||

Me lody.

:s$_1$ |m$_1$:s$_1$:d |d :t$_1$:d |f :m :r |r :m ||s$_1$ |s$_1$:—:s$_1$ |s$_1$:m :d |d :t$_1$ ||

:f |m :s :f |m :—:r |d :r :m |m :r ||s |s :f :l |s :-.f :m.r |d :— ||

:r |d :—:t$_1$ |d :—:r |m :f :m |m :r ||m.d |l$_1$:—:r.d |t$_1$:-.l$_1$:t$_1$ |d :— ||

PSALMS CXXXIII, CXXXIV, CXXXV.

133*

BEHOLD, how good a thing it is,
and how becoming well,
Together such as brethren are
in unity to dwell!
2 Like precious ointment on the head,
that down the beard did flow,
Ev'n Aaron's beard, and to the skirts
did of his garments go.

3 As Hermon's dew, the dew that doth
on Sion' hills descend:
For there the blessing God commands,
life that shall never end.

134

BEHOLD, bless ye the Lord, all ye
that his attendants are,
Ev'n you that in God's temple be,
and praise him nightly there.
2 Your hands within God's holy place
lift up, and praise his name.
3 From Sion' hill the Lord thee bless,
that heav'n and earth did frame.

135

PRAISE ye the Lord, the Lord's name praise;
his servants, praise ye God.
2 Who stand in God's house, in the courts
of our God make abode.
3 Praise ye the Lord, for he is good;
unto him praises sing:
Sing praises to his name, because
it is a pleasant thing.

4 For Jacob to himself the Lord
did chuse of his good pleasure,
And he hath chosen Israel
for his peculiar treasure.
5 Because I know assuredly
the Lord is very great,
And that our Lord above all gods
in glory hath his seat.

6 What things soever pleas'd the Lord,
that in the heav'n did he,
And in the earth, the seas, and all
the places deep that be.
7 He from the ends of earth doth make
the vapours to ascend;
With rain he lightnings makes, and wind
doth from his treasures send.

145

WINCHESTER. (C.M.)

Doh = F. *Este's Psalter*, 1592.

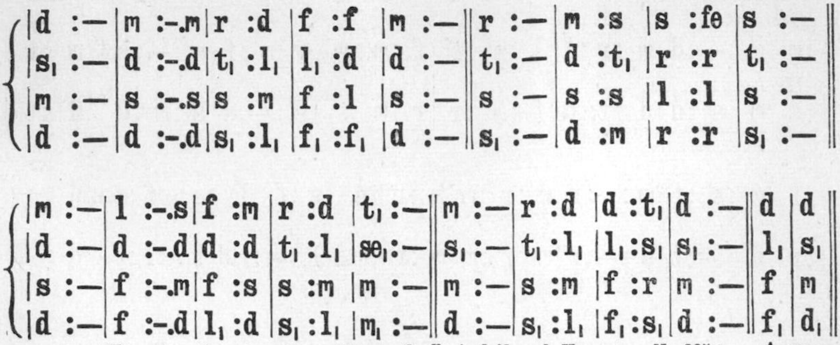

d :—	m :-.m	r :d	f :f	m :—		r :—	m :s	s :fe	s :—	
s_1 :—	d :-.d	t_1 :l_1	l_1 :d	d :—		t_1 :—	d :t_1	r :r	t_1 :—	
m :—	s :-.s	s :m	f :l	s :—		s :—	s :s	l :l	s :—	
d :—	d :-.d	s_1 :l_1	f_1 :f_1	d :—		s_1 :—	d :m	r :r	s_1 :—	

m :—	l :-.s	f :m	r :d	t_1 :—		m :—	r :d	d :t_1	d :—		d	d	
d :—	d :-.d	d :d	t_1 :l_1	se_1 :—		s_1 :—	t_1 :l_1	l_1 :s_1	s_1 :—		l_1	s_1	
s :—	f :-.m	f :s	s :m	m :—		m :—	s :m	f :r	m :—		f	m	
d :—	f :-.d	l_1 :d	s_1 :l_1	m_1 :—		d :—	s_1 :l_1	f_1 :s_1	d :—		f_1	d_1	

[*There is a Faux-bourdon setting in the Revised Church Hymnary, No.* 385.] **A-men.**

8 Egypt's first-born, from man to beast
9 who smote. Strange tokens he
On Phar'oh and his servants sent,
Egypt, in midst of thee.
10 He smote great nations, slew great kings:
11 Sihon of Heshbon king,
And Og of Bashan, and to nought
did Canaan's kingdoms bring:

12 And for a wealthy heritage
their pleasant land he gave,
An heritage which Israel,
his chosen folk, should have.
13 Thy name, O Lord, shall still endure,
and thy memorial
With honour shall continu'd be
to generations all.

14 For why? the righteous God will judge
his people righteously;
Concerning those that do him serve,
himself repent will he.
15 The idols of the nations
of silver are and gold,
And by the hands of men is made
their fashion and mould.

16 Mouths have they, but they do not speak;
eyes, but they do not see;
17 Ears have they, but hear not; and in
their mouths no breathing be.
18 Their makers are like them; so are
all that on them rely.
19 O Isr'el's house, bless God; bless God,
O Aaron's family.

20 O bless the Lord, of Levi's house
ye who his servants are;
And bless the holy name of God,
all ye the Lord that fear.
21 And blessed be the Lord our God
from Sion's holy hill,
Who dwelleth at Jerusalem.
The Lord O praise ye still.

136

GIVE thanks to God, for good is [he:
for mercy hath he ever.
2 Thanks to the God of gods give ye:
for his grace faileth never.
3 Thanks give the Lord of lords unto:
for mercy hath he ever.
4 Who only wonders great can do:
for his grace faileth never.

146

YORK. (C.M.) *Scottish Psalter*, 1615.

Doh = F. Arranged by John Milton, *c.* 1563–1647.

d :—	m :s	f :l	m :s	r :—		r :—	m :s	s :fe	s :—	
s, :—	d :ta,	ta, :l,	l, :s,	s, :—		t, :—	d :t,.d	r :r	t, :—	
m :—	s :s	r :d	d :t,	t, :—		s :—	s :s	l :l	s :—	
d :—	d :s,	ta, :f,	l, :m,	s, :—		s, :—	d :m	r :r	s, :—	

d :—	m :s	f :l	m :s	r :—		m :—	f :m	r :r	d :—		d	d	
d :—	d :ta,	ta, :l,	l, :s,	s, :—		s, :—	l, :d	d :t,	d :—		l,	s,	
m :—	s :s	r :f	d :m	t, :—		d :—	d :m.f	s :s	m :—		f	m	
d :—	d :s,	ta, :f,	l, :m,	s, :—		d :—	f, :d	s, :s,	d, :—		f,	d (d,)	

A-men.

PSALM CXXXVI.

5 Who by his wisdom made heav'ns high:
for mercy hath he ever.
6 Who stretch'd the earth above the sea:
for his grace faileth never.
7 To him that made the great lights shine:
for mercy hath he ever.
8 The sun to rule till day decline:
for his grace faileth never.

9 The moon and stars to rule by night:
for mercy hath he ever.
10 Who Egypt's first-born kill'd outright:
for his grace faileth never.
11 And Isr'el brought from Egypt land:
for mercy hath he ever.
12 With stretch'd-out arm, and with strong hand:
for his grace faileth never.

13 By whom the Red sea parted was:
for mercy hath he ever.
14 And through its midst made Isr'el pass:
for his grace faileth never.
15 But Phar'oh and his host did drown:
for mercy hath he ever.
16 Who through the desert led his own:
for his grace faileth never.

17 To him great kings who overthrew:
for he hath mercy ever.
18 Yea, famous kings in battle slew:
for his grace faileth never.
19 Ev'n Sihon king of Amorites:
for he hath mercy ever.
20 And Og the king of Bashanites:
for his grace faileth never.

21 Their land in heritage to have:
(for mercy hath he ever.)
22 His servant Isr'el right he gave:
for his grace faileth never.
23 In our low state who on us thought:
for he hath mercy ever.
24 And from our foes our freedom wrought:
for his grace faileth never.

25 Who doth all flesh with food relieve:
for he hath mercy ever.
26 Thanks to the God of heaven give:
for his grace faileth never.

147

EVANGEL. (D.C.M.)

Doh = B♭.

Gottfried Wilhelm Fink, 1783–1846.

:s, |d :d |t, :l, |s, :-.l, |s, ‖ s, |l, :r |d :t, |d :— |— ‖

:s, |m, :s, |s, :f, |m, :-.f, |m, ‖ s, |f, :l, |s, :s, |s, :— |— ‖

:s, |d :d |d :d |d :-.d |d ‖ d |d :f |m :r |m :— |— ‖

:s, |d, :m, |f, :l, |d :-.f, |d ‖ m, |f, :r, |s, :s, |d, :— |— ‖

:s, |d :d |t, :l, |s, :-.l, |s, ‖ m |r :d |t, :l, |s, :— |— ‖

:s, |m, :s, |s, :f, |m, :-.f, |m, ‖ m,.fe, |s, :l, |s, :fe, |s, :— |— ‖

:s, |d :d |d :d |d :-.d |d ‖ s,.l, |t, :m |r :d |t, :— |— ‖

:s, |d, :m, |f, :l, |d :-.f, |d ‖ d, |t_2 :d, |r, :r, |s, :— |— ‖

PSALM CXXXVI.

136 (2)*

ANOTHER OF THE SAME.

PRAISE God, for he is kind:
His mercy lasts for aye.
2 Give thanks with heart and mind
To God of gods alway:
For certainly
His mercies dure
Most firm and sure
Eternally.

3 The Lord of lords praise ye,
Whose mercies still endure.
4 Great wonders only he
Doth work by his great pow'r:
For certainly, &c.

5 Which God omnipotent,
By might and wisdom high,
The heav'n and firmament
Did frame, as we may see:
For certainly, &c.

6 To him who did outstretch
This earth so great and wide,
Above the waters' reach
Making it to abide:
For certainly, &c.

7 Great lights he made to be;
For his grace lasteth aye:
8 Such as the sun we see,
To rule the lightsome day:
For certainly, &c.

9 Also the moon so clear,
Which shineth in our sight;
The stars that do appear,
To guide the darksome night:
For certainly, &c.

10 To him that Egypt smote,
Who did his message scorn;
And in his anger hot
Did kill all their first-born:
For certainly, &c.

11 Thence Isr'el out he brought;
For his grace lasteth ever.
12 With a strong hand he wrought,
And stretch'd-out arm deliver:
For certainly, &c.

13 The sea he cut in two;
For his grace lasteth still.
14 And through its midst to go
Made his own Israel:
For certainly, &c.

:s, |t, :s, |d :s, |r :s, |m ||d |f :m |r :d |d :— |t, ||
:s, |s, :s, |s, :s, |f, :f, |m, ||m, |f, :s, |l, :l, |s, :— |— ||
:t, |r :t, |d :d |t, :t, |d ||d |d :d |l, :r |r :— |— ||
:s, |f, :f, |m, :m, |r, :r, |d, ||ta, |l, :s, |f, :fe, |s, :— |— ||

:s, |d :d |t, :l, |s, :-.l, |s, ||s, |l, :r |d :t, |d :— |— ||d |d ||
:s, |s, :s, |s, :f, |f, :-.f, |m, ||s, |f, :l, |s, :s, |s, :— |— ||l, |s, ||
:t, |d :d |d :d |r :t, |d ||d |d :f |m :r |m :— |— ||f |m ||
:f, |m, :m, |f, :l, |t, :s, |d ||m, |f, :r, |s, :s, |d, :— |— ||f, |d, ||

A-men.

PSALMS CXXXVI, CXXXVII.

15 But overwhelm'd and lost
Was proud king Pharaoh,
With all his mighty host,
And chariots there also:
For certainly, &c.

16 To him who pow'rfully
His chosen people led,
Ev'n through the desert dry,
And in that place them fed:
For certainly, &c.

17 To him great kings who smote;
For his grace hath no bound.
18 Who slew, and spared not
Kings famous and renown'd:
For certainly, &c.

19 Sihon the Am'rites' king;
For his grace lasteth ever:
20 Og also, who did reign
The land of Bashan over:
For certainly, &c.

21 Their land by lot he gave;
For his grace faileth never,
22 That Isr'el might it have
In heritage for ever:
For certainly, &c.

23 Who hath remembered
Us in our low estate;
24 And us delivered
From foes which did us hate:
For certainly, &c.

25 Who to all flesh gives food;
For his grace faileth never.
26 Give thanks to God most good,
The God of heav'n, for ever:
For certainly, &c.

137*

BY Babel's streams we sat and wept,
when Sion we thought on.
2 In midst thereof we hang'd our harps
the willow-trees upon.
3 For there a song required they,
who did us captive bring:
Our spoilers call'd for mirth, and said,
A song of Sion sing.
4 O how the Lord's song shall we sing
within a foreign land?
5 If thee, Jerus'lem, I forget,
skill part from my right hand.
6 My tongue to my mouth's roof let cleave,
if I do thee forget,
Jerusalem, and thee above
my chief joy do not set.

148

HEREFORD. (D.C.M.)

Doh = G.

WILLIAM HAYES, 1706–77.

:d |m :s |f :m |l :s.f |m ‖ s |l :s |f :m |r :— |— ‖

:s, |s, :s, |l,.t, :d |d :t, |d ‖ d |d :d |t, :d |t, :— |— ‖

:m |m :r |d :d |f.m :r |d ‖ m |f :s |s :s |s :— |— ‖

:d |d :t, |l, :s, |f, :s, |d, ‖ d |f :m |r :d |s, :— |— ‖

D.t.

:r |s :r |m :-.m |[l]r' :d' |t ‖ -.t |d' :f |m :r |d :— |— ‖

:t, |r :t, |d :-.s, |[d]f :fe |s ‖ -.r |d :d |d :t, |d :— |— ‖

:s |s :s |s :-.d |[m]l :r' |r' ‖ -.s |s :l |s :-.f |m :— |— ‖

:s, |t, :s, |d :-.d |[l]r :r |s ‖ -.f |m :f |s :s, |d :— |— ‖

---

7 Remember Edom's children, Lord,
who in Jerus'lem's day,
Ev'n unto its foundation,
Raze, raze it quite, did say.
8 O daughter thou of Babylon,
near to destruction;
Bless'd shall he be that thee rewards,
as thou to us hast done.

9 Yea, happy surely shall he be
thy tender little ones
Who shall lay hold upon, and them
shall dash against the stones.

138*

THEE will I praise with all my heart,
I will sing praise to thee
2 Before the gods: And worship will
toward thy sanctuary.
I'll praise thy name, ev'n for thy truth,
and kindness of thy love;
For thou thy word hast magnify'd
all thy great name above.

3 Thou didst me answer in the day
when I to thee did cry;
And thou my fainting soul with strength
didst strengthen inwardly.
4 All kings upon the earth that are
shall give thee praise, O Lord;
When as they from thy mouth shall hear
thy true and faithful word.

5 Yea, in the righteous ways of God
with gladness they shall sing:
For great 's the glory of the Lord,
who doth for ever reign.
6 Though God be high, yet he respects
all those that lowly be;
Whereas the proud and lofty ones
afar off knoweth he.

7 Though I in midst of trouble walk,
I life from thee shall have:
'Gainst my foes' wrath thou'lt stretch thine hand;
thy right hand shall me save.
8 Surely that which concerneth me
the Lord will perfect make:
Lord, still thy mercy lasts; do not
thine own hands' works forsake.

d.f.C. G.t.

:s l |r' :t |se :-.se |l :t |[d]f ||r |s :s |s :f |m :— |— ||
:d r |r :f |m :-.m |m :r |[d]f_1 ||s_1 |s_1 :t_1 |d :s_1 |s_1 :— |— ||
:[ma]f |l :t |t :-.t |l :se |[l]r ||t_1 |d :r |m :r |m :— |— ||
:d r |f :r |m :-.r |d :t_1 |[l]r_1 ||f_1 |m_1 :s_1 |d :t_1 |d :— |— ||

:s |l :s |l :-.s |f :m |r ||f |m :r.d |d :t_1 |d :— |— ||d |d ||
:d |d :d |d :-.d |t_1 :d |t_1 ||r |d :l_1 |s_1 :s_1 |s_1 :— |— ||l_1 |s_1 ||
:m |f :m |f :-.s |s :s |s ||s |s :f.m |r :s.f |m :— |— ||f |m ||
:d |f :d |f :-.m |r :d |s_1 ||t_1 |d :f_1 |s_1 :s_1 |d_1 :— |— ||f_1 |d_1 ||

A-men.

PSALM CXXXIX.

139*

O LORD, thou hast me search'd
and known.
2 Thou know'st my sitting down,
And rising up; yea, all my thoughts
afar to thee are known.
3 My footsteps, and my lying down,
thou compassest always;
Thou also most entirely art
acquaint with all my ways.

4 For in my tongue, before I speak,
not any word can be,
But altogether, lo, O Lord,
it is well known to thee.
5 Behind, before, thou hast beset,
and laid on me thine hand.
6 Such knowledge is too strange for
too high to understand. [me,

7 From thy Sp'rit whither shall I go?
or from thy presence fly?
8 Ascend I heav'n, lo, thou art there;
there, if in hell I lie.
9 Take I the morning wings, and dwell
in utmost parts of sea;
10 Ev'n there, Lord, shall thy hand me
lead,
thy right hand hold shall me.

11 If I do say that darkness shall
me cover from thy sight,
Then surely shall the very night
about me be as light.
12 Yea, darkness hideth not from thee,
but night doth shine as day:
To thee the darkness and the light
are both alike alway.

13 For thou possessed hast my reins,
and thou hast cover'd me,
When I within my mother's womb
inclosed was by thee.
14 Thee will I praise; for fearfully
and strangely made I am; [well
Thy works are marv'llous, and right
my soul doth know the same.

15 My substance was not hid from thee,
when as in secret I [parts
Was made; and in earth's lowest
was wrought most curiously.
16 Thine eyes my substance did behold,
yet being unperfect;
And in the volume of thy book
my members all were writ;

Which after in continuance
were fashion'd ev'ry one,
When as they yet all shapeless were,
and of them there was none.

149

OLD 18TH. (D.C.M.)

English Psalter, 1561.

Lah = G. Doh = B♭. Arranged by JAMES SMITH ANDERSON, 1853–

l_1 :— :l_1 :se_1 :l_1 :d :t_1 :t_1 :m_1 ‖ m_1 :l_1 :d :t_1 :t_1 :l_1 :— ‖
m_1 :— :m_1 :m_1 :d_1 :m_1 :m_1 :re_1 :m_1 ‖ d_1 :m_1 :m_1 :m_1 :m_1 :d_1 :— ‖
d :— :d :t_1 :l_1 :l_1 :fe_1 :t_1 :s_1 ‖ l_1 :l_1 :l_1 :l_1 :se_1 :l_1 :— ‖
l_1 :— :l_1 :m_1 :f_1 :l_2 :t_2 :t_2 :d_1 ‖ l_2 :d_1 :l_2 :m_1 :m_1 :l_2 :— ‖

m :— :r :d :t_1 :d :t_1 :l_1 :se_1 ‖ d :t_1 :l_1 :l_1 :se_1 :l_1 :— ‖
s_1 :— :s_1 :m_1 :se_1 :l_1 :m_1 :d_1 :m_1 ‖ m_1 :m_1 :d_1 :m_1 :m_1 :d_1 :— ‖
s_1 :— :t_1 :d :m :m :s_1 :l_1 :t_1 ‖ l_1 :se_1 :l_1 :t_1 :t_1 :l_1 :— ‖
d_1 :— :s_1 :l_1 :m_1 :l_1 :s_1 :f_1 :m_1 ‖ d_1 :m_1 :f_1 :m_1 :m_1 :l_2 :— ‖

17 How precious also are thy thoughts,
O gracious God, to me!
And in their sum how passing great
and numberless they be!

18 If I should count them, than the
they more in number be: [sand
What time soever I awake,
I ever am with thee. [slay:
19 Thou, Lord, wilt sure the wicked
hence from me bloody men.
20 Thy foes against thee loudly speak,
and take thy name in vain.

21 Do not I hate all those, O Lord,
that hatred bear to thee?
With those that up against thee rise
can I but grieved be?
22 With perfect hatred them I hate,
my foes I them do hold.
23 Search me, O God, and know my
heart,
try me, my thoughts unfold:

24 And see if any wicked way
there be at all in me;
And in thine everlasting way
to me a leader be.

140

LORD, from the ill and froward man
give me deliverance,
And do thou safe preserve me from
the man of violence:
2 Who in their heart mischievous
things
are meditating ever;
And they for war assembled are
continually together.

3 Much like unto a serpent's tongue
their tongues they sharp do make;
And underneath their lips there lies
the poison of a snake.
4 Lord, keep me from the wicked's
hands,
from vi'lent men me save;
Who utterly to overthrow
my goings purpos'd have.

5 The proud for me a snare have hid,
and cords; yea, they a net
Have by the way-side for me spread;
they gins for me have set.
6 I said unto the Lord, Thou art
my God: unto the cry
Of all my supplications,
Lord, do thine ear apply.

```
l, :— :d  :t, :l, :m  :m  :re :m  :—  ‖ m  :— :r  :d  :t, :l, :se, :—  ‖
m, :— :l, :se,:l, :l, :ba,:ba,:se, :—  ‖ s, :— :s, :m, :se,:m, :m,  :—  ‖
d  :— :m  :m  :d  :d  :t, :t, :t,  :—  ‖ d  :— :t, :d  :m  :d  :t,  :—  ‖
l, :— :l, :m, :l, :l, :t, :t, :m,  :—  ‖ d, :— :s, :l, :m, :l,,:m,  :—  ‖

d  :— :s, :l, :t, :d  :r  :d  :t,  :—  ‖ d  :— :t, :— :l, :l, :— :se, :l, :—  ‖ l, ‖ l,   ‖
s, :— :s, :m, :se,:l, :l, :l, :se, :—  ‖ l, :— :m, :— :m, :m, :— :m,  :de,:—  ‖ r, ‖ de,  ‖
m  :— :m  :d  :m  :m  :f  :m  :m   :—  ‖ m  :— :t, :— :d  :t, :— :t,  :l, :—  ‖ f, ‖ m,   ‖
d, :— :d, :l,,:m, :l, :r, :l, :m,  :—  ‖ l, :— :se,:— :l, :m, :— :m,  :l,,:—  ‖ r, ‖ l,,  ‖
                                                                                  A-men.
```


7 O God the Lord, who art the strength
of my salvation:
A cov'ring in the day of war
my head thou hast put on.
8 Unto the wicked man, O Lord,
his wishes do not grant;
Nor further thou his ill device,
lest they themselves should vaunt.

9 As for the head and chief of those
about that compass me,
Ev'n by the mischief of the lips
let thou them cover'd be.
10 Let burning coals upon them fall,
them throw in fiery flame,
And in deep pits, that they no more
may rise out of the same.

11 Let not an evil speaker be
on earth established:
Mischief shall hunt the vi'lent man,
till he be ruined.
12 I know God will th' afflicted's cause
maintain, and poor men's right.
13 Surely the just shall praise thy name;
th' upright dwell in thy sight.

141

O LORD, I unto thee do cry,
do thou make haste to me,
And give an ear unto my voice,
when I cry unto thee.
2 As incense let my prayer be
directed in thine eyes;
And the uplifting of my hands
as th' ev'ning sacrifice.

3 Set, Lord, a watch before my mouth,
keep of my lips the door.
4 My heart incline thou not unto
the ills I should abhor,
To practise wicked works with men
that work iniquity;
And with their delicates my taste
let me not satisfy.

5 Let him that righteous is me smite,
it shall a kindness be;
Let him reprove, I shall it count
a precious oil to me:
Such smiting shall not break my head;
for yet the time shall fall,
When I in their calamities
to God pray for them shall.

150

OLD 22ND. (D.C.M.) *Anglo-Genevan Psalter*, 1556.

Doh = E♭.

d :—	d :r	m :—	s :—	f :f	m :—	— ‖ d	f :m	r :r	d :— 𝄐 ‖
s_1 :—	l_1 :t_1	d :—	d :—	d :t_1	d :—	— ‖ d	l_1 :d	d :t_1	d :— ‖
m :—	m :s	s :—	s :—	l :f	s :—	— ‖ l	l :s	s :s	m :— ‖
d :—	l_1 :s_1	d :—	m :—	r :r	d :—	— ‖ l_1	f_1 :d	s_1 :s_1	d :— ‖

s :—	l :t	d' :—	t :—	l :l	s :— ‖	m :—	f :m	r :—	r :—	d :— 𝄐 ‖
d :—	m :r	d :—	r :—	m :r	t_1 :— ‖	d :—	l_1 :d	d :—	t_1 :—	d :— ‖
m :—	m :s	l :—	s :—	m :fe	s :— ‖	d :—	r :s	l :—	s :f	m :— ‖
d :—	d :t_1	l_1 :—	t_1 :—	d :r	s_1 :— ‖	l_1 :—	r_1 :m_1	f_1 :—	s_1 :—	d :— ‖

PSALMS CXLI, CXLII, CXLIII.

6 When as their judges down shall be
in stony places cast, [they
Then shall they hear my words; for
shall sweet be to their taste.
7 About the grave's devouring mouth
our bones are scatter'd round,
As wood which men do cut and
cleave
lies scatter'd on the ground.

8 But unto thee, O God the Lord,
mine eyes uplifted be:
My soul do not leave destitute;
my trust is set on thee.
9 Lord, keep me safely from the snares
which they for me prepare;
And from the subtile gins of them
that wicked workers are.

10 Let workers of iniquity
into their own nets fall,
Whilst I do, by thine help, escape
the danger of them all.

142

I WITH my voice cry'd to the Lord,
with it made my request:
2 Pour'd out to him my plaint, to him
my trouble I exprest.

3 When in me was o'erwhelm'd my
sp'rit,
then well thou knew'st my way;
Where I did walk a snare for me
they privily did lay.

4 I look'd on my right hand, and
view'd,
but none to know me were;
All refuge failed me, no man
did for my soul take care.
5 I cry'd to thee; I said, Thou art
my refuge, Lord, alone;
And in the land of those that live
thou art my portion.

6 Because I am brought very low,
attend unto my cry:
Me from my persecutors save,
who stronger are than I.
7 From prison bring my soul, that I
thy name may glorify: [thou
The just shall compass me, when
with me deal'st bounteously.

143

LORD, hear my pray'r, attend my
and in thy faithfulness [suits;
Give thou an answer unto me,
and in thy righteousness.

f. A♭.

|d' :— |t :l |s :l |t :— |l :— |s :— ‖ ^{l}m :— |t_{1} :d |r :m |r :— ‖
|m :— |m :d |d :d |t_{1}:r |r :d |t_{1} :— ‖ $^{l}m_{1}$:— |m_{1} :m_{1} |f_{1} :s_{1} |s_{1} :— ‖
|l :— |s :f |m :fe |s :— |fe :— |s :— ‖ ^{f}d :— |t_{1} :l_{1} |l_{1} :d |t_{1} :— ‖
|l :— |m :f |d :l_{1} |s_{1}:t_{1} |r :— |s_{1} :— ‖ $^{r}l_{1}$:— |se_{1} :l_{1} |f_{1} :d_{1} |s_{1} :— ‖

E♭. t.

|^{t}m :— |m :r |m :d |m :fe |s :— ‖ m :— |r :m |f :— |r :— |d :— ‖ d |d ‖
|^{s}d :— |d :t_{1} |d :s_{1} |s_{1} :d |t_{1} :— ‖ s_{1} :— |r :d |d :— |t_{1} :— |d :— ‖ l_{1} |s_{1} ‖
|^{r}s :— |s :s |s :m |m :d |r :— ‖ m :— |s :s |l :— |s :f |m :— ‖ f |m ‖
|^{s}d :— |m_{1} :s_{1} |d :m.r |d :l_{1} |s_{1} :— ‖ d :— |t_{1} :d |f_{1} :— |s_{1} :— |d :— ‖ f_{1} |d ‖

A-men.

PSALM CXLIII.

2 Thy servant also bring thou not
in judgment to be try'd:
Because no living man can be
in thy sight justify'd.

3 For th' en'my hath pursu'd my soul,
my life to ground down tread:
In darkness he hath made me dwell,
as who have long been dead.
4 My sp'rit is therefore overwhelm'd
in me perplexedly;
Within me is my very heart
amazed wondrously.

5 I call to mind the days of old,
to meditate I use
On all thy works; upon the deeds
I of thy hands do muse.
6 My hands to thee I stretch; my soul
thirsts, as dry land, for thee.
7 Haste, Lord, to hear, my spirit fails:
hide not thy face from me;

Lest like to them I do become
that go down to the dust.
8 At morn let me thy kindness hear;
for in thee do I trust.
Teach me the way that I should
walk:
I lift my soul to thee.

9 Lord, free me from my foes; I flee
to thee to cover me.

10 Because thou art my God, to do
thy will do me instruct:
Thy Sp'rit is good, me to the land
of uprightness conduct.
11 Revive and quicken me, O Lord,
ev'n for thine own name's sake;
And do thou, for thy righteousness,
my soul from trouble take.

12 And of thy mercy slay my foes;
let all destroyed be
That do afflict my soul: for I
a servant am to thee.

143 (2)*

ANOTHER OF THE SAME.

OH, hear my prayer, Lord,
And unto my desire
To bow thine ear accord,
I humbly thee require;
And, in thy faithfulness,
Unto me answer make,
And, in thy righteousness,
Upon me pity take.

151

OLD 29TH. (D.C.M.)

Doh = D.

Anglo-Genevan Psalter, 1556.

|d' :— |d' :t |d' :s |l :l |s :— ‖ l :— |r' :d' |t :l |s :— ‖
|m :— |s :s.f |m :m |m :f |m :— ‖ d :— |f :d |r :r.d |t, :— ‖
|s :— |d' :r' |d' :t |d' :d' |d' :— ‖ l :— |l :l |s :fe |s :— ‖
|d :— |m :s |d :m |l :f |d :— ‖ f :— |r :l, |t,.d :r |s, :— ‖

|s :— |m :r |d :m |f :s |l :— ‖ t :— |d' :r' |d' :t |d' :— ‖
|r :— |d :l,.t, |d :d |d :d |d :— ‖ f :— |m :r |s :r |m :— ‖
|s :— |s :f |s :s |d.r :m |f :— ‖ r' :— |d' :l |s :s |s :— ‖
|t, :— |d :r |m :d |l, :d |f :— ‖ r :— |l :f |m :s |d :— ‖

PSALM CXLIII.

2 In judgment enter not
With me thy servant poor;
For why, this well I wot,
No sinner can endure
The sight of thee, O God:
If thou his deeds shalt try,
He dare make none abode
Himself to justify.

3 Behold, the cruel foe
Me persecutes with spite,
My soul to overthrow:
Yea, he my life down quite
Unto the ground hath smote,
And made me dwell full low
In darkness, as forgot,
Or men dead long ago.

4 Therefore my sp'rit much vex'd,
O'erwhelm'd is me within;
My heart right sore perplex'd
And desolate hath been.
5 Yet I do call to mind
What ancient days record,
Thy works of ev'ry kind
I think upon, O Lord.

6 Lo, I do stretch my hands
To thee, my help alone;
For thou well understands
All my complaint and moan:
My thirsting soul desires,
And longeth after thee,
As thirsty ground requires
With rain refresh'd to be.

7 Lord, let my pray'r prevail,
To answer it make speed;
For, lo, my sp'rit doth fail:
Hide not thy face in need;
Lest I be like to those
That do in darkness sit,
Or him that downward goes
Into the dreadful pit.

8 Because I trust in thee,
O Lord, cause me to hear
Thy loving-kindness free,
When morning doth appear:
Cause me to know the way
Wherein my path should be;
For why, my soul on high
I do lift up to thee.

9 From my fierce enemy
In safety do me guide,
Because I flee to thee,
Lord, that thou may'st me hide.
10 My God alone art thou,
Teach me thy righteousness:

|s :— |d' :t |l :s |m :f |s :— ‖ l :— |t :d' |l :l |s :— ‖
|d :— |d :r |m :m |d :d |d :— ‖ d :— |f :m |r :r |t, :— ‖
|m :— |s :s |d' :d'.t |l :l |s :— ‖ f :— |f :s |s :fe |s :— ‖
|d :— |m :s |d :m |l.s :f |m :— ‖ f :— |r :d |r :r |s :— ‖

|d' :— |t :l |m :f |s :f |m :— ‖ d :— |r :m |r :r |d :— ‖ d |d ‖
|d :— |s :m |m :d |m :r.d |t, :— ‖ d :— |l, :d |d :t, |d :— ‖ l, |s, ‖
|s :— |r' :d' |t :l |d'.t :l |se :— ‖ l :— |l :s |s :s.f |m :— ‖ f |m ‖
|m :— |s :l |s :f |d :r |m :— ‖ l, :— |f, :m,.f, |s, :s, |d :— ‖ f, |d ‖

A-men.

Thy Sp'rit's good, lead me to
The land of uprightness.

11 O Lord, for thy name's sake,
Be pleas'd to quicken me;
And, for thy truth, forth take
My soul from misery.
12 And of thy grace destroy
My foes, and put to shame
All who my soul annoy;
For I thy servant am.

144

O BLESSED ever be the Lord,
who is my strength and might,
Who doth instruct my hands to war,
my fingers teach to fight.
2 My goodness, fortress, my high tow'r,
deliverer, and shield,
In whom I trust: who under me
my people makes to yield.

3 Lord, what is man, that thou of him
dost so much knowledge take?
Or son of man, that thou of him
so great account dost make?
4 Man is like vanity; his days,
as shadows, pass away.

5 Lord, bow thy heav'ns, come down, touch thou
the hills, and smoke shall they.

6 Cast forth thy lightning, scatter them;
thine arrows shoot, them rout.
7 Thine hand send from above, me save;
from great depths draw me out;
And from the hand of children strange,
8 Whose mouth speaks vanity;
And their right hand is a right hand
that works deceitfully.

9 A new song I to thee will sing,
Lord, on a psaltery;
I on a ten-string'd instrument
will praises sing to thee.
10 Ev'n he it is that unto kings
salvation doth send;
Who his own servant David doth
from hurtful sword defend.

11 O free me from strange children's hand,
whose mouth speaks vanity;
And their right hand a right hand is
that works deceitfully.

152

OLD 44TH. (D.C.M.)

Doh = A♭.

Anglo-Genevan Psalter, 1556.

```
:d  |d  :t, |d  :l, |s, :s, |d  || s  |f     :m  |r  :r     |d  :— |— ||
:s, |l, :s, |m, :f, |r, :r, |s, || m, |f,    :s, |l, :s,    |m, :— |— ||
:m  |f  :r  |d  :d  |t, :t, |d  || d  |l,.t, :d  |d  :t,    |d  :— |— ||
:d, |f, :s, |l, :f, |s, :f, |m, || d, |r,    :m, |f, :s,    |d, :— |— ||

:d  |d  :t, |d  :l, |s, :s, |d  || m  |f     :m  |r  :r     |d  :— |— ||
:s, |l, :s, |m, :f, |r, :r, |s, || s, |l,    :s, |s, :s,.f, |m, :— |— ||
:m  |f  :r  |d  :d  |t, :t, |d  || d  |d     :d  |d  :t,    |d  :— |— ||
:d, |f, :s, |l, :f, |s, :f, |m, || d, |f,    :d, |s, :s,    |d, :— |— ||
```


12 That, as the plants, our sons may be
in youth grown up that are;
Our daughters like to corner-stones,
carv'd like a palace fair.

13 That to afford all kind of store
our garners may be fill'd;
That our sheep thousands, in our streets
ten thousands they may yield.

14 That strong our oxen be for work,
that no in-breaking be,
Nor going out; and that our streets
may from complaints be free.

15 Those people blessed are who be
in such a case as this;
Yea, blessed all those people are,
whose God JEHOVAH is.

145

I'LL thee extol, my God, O King;
I'll bless thy name always.

2 Thee will I bless each day, and will
thy name for ever praise.

3 Great is the Lord, much to be prais'd;
his greatness search exceeds.

4 Race unto race shall praise thy works,
and show thy mighty deeds.

5 I of thy glorious majesty
the honour will record;
I'll speak of all thy mighty works,
which wondrous are, O Lord.

6 Men of thine acts the might shall show,
thine acts that dreadful are;
And I, thy glory to advance,
thy greatness will declare.

7 The mem'ry of thy goodness great
they largely shall express;
With songs of praise they shall extol
thy perfect righteousness.

8 The Lord is very gracious,
in him compassions flow;
In mercy he is very great,
and is to anger slow.

9 The Lord JEHOVAH unto all
his goodness doth declare;
And over all his other works
his tender mercies are.

10 Thee all thy works shall praise, O Lord,
and thee thy saints shall bless;

11 They shall thy kingdom's glory show,
thy pow'r by speech express:

```
:d  |d  :r  |m  :f  |s  :f  |m  ‖r  |d  :l, |t, :d  |r  :—  |—  ‖
:m, |m, :s, |s, :l, |t, :t, |d  ‖l, |s, :f, |f, :m, |s, :—  |—  ‖
:d  |d  :t, |d  :d  |r  :r  |d  ‖f  |m  :d  |r  :d  |t, :—  |—  ‖
:d  |l, :s, |d  :l, |s, :s, |l, ‖r, |m, :f, |r, :l, |s, :—  |—  ‖
```

```
:d  |s, :l, |t, :d  |r  :m  |r  ‖d  |t, :d  |r  :r     |d  :—  |—  ‖d  |d  ‖
:s, |s, :f, |r, :m, |f, :s, |s, ‖m, |s, :s, |l, :s, f, |m, :—  |—  ‖f, |m, ‖
:m  |d  :d  |s, :s, |l, :d  |t, ‖d  |r  :d  |d  :t,    |d  :—  |—  ‖l, |s, ‖
:d, |m, :f, |s, :m, |r, :d, |s, ‖l, |s, :m, |f, :s,    |d, :—  |—  ‖f, |d, ‖
                                                                    A-men.
```

PSALM CXLV.

12 To make the sons of men to know
his acts done mightily,
And of his kingdom th' excellent
and glorious majesty.
13 Thy kingdom shall for ever stand,
thy reign through ages all.
14 God raiseth all that are bow'd down,
upholdeth all that fall.

15 The eyes of all things wait on thee,
the giver of all good;
And thou, in time convenient,
bestow'st on them their food:
16 Thine hand thou open'st lib'rally,
and of thy bounty gives
Enough to satisfy the need
of ev'ry thing that lives.

17 The Lord is just in all his ways,
holy in his works all.
18 God 's near to all that call on him,
in truth that on him call.
19 He will accomplish the desire
of those that do him fear:
He also will deliver them,
and he their cry will hear.

20 The Lord preserves all who him love,
that nought can them annoy:
But he all those that wicked are
will utterly destroy.

21 My mouth the praises of the Lord
to publish cease shall never:
Let all flesh bless his holy name
for ever and for ever.

145 (2)*

ANOTHER OF THE SAME.

O LORD, thou art my God and King;
Thee will I magnify and praise:
I will thee bless, and gladly sing
Unto thy holy name always.
2 Each day I rise I will thee bless,
And praise thy name time without end.
3 Much to be prais'd, and great God is;
His greatness none can comprehend.

4 Race shall thy works praise unto race,
The mighty acts show done by thee.
5 I will speak of the glorious grace,
And honour of thy majesty;
Thy wondrous works I will record.
6 By men the might shall be extoll'd
Of all thy dreadful acts, O Lord:
And I thy greatness will unfold.

153

OLD 68TH. (D.C.M.)

Doh = G. *Anglo-Genevan Psalter*, 1558.

```
| d  :—  | d  :t,  | l,  :s,  | d   :r   | m  :— || m  :— | r  :d  | f  :m  | r  :— ||
| s, :—  | l, :s,  | f,  :m,  | m,  :s,  | s, :— || s, :— | s, :m, | l, :s, | s, :— ||
| m  :—  | m  :m   | d   :d   | d   :t,  | d  :— || d  :— | t, :d  | d  :d  | t, :— ||
| d  :—  | l, :m,  | f,  :d,  | l,  :s,  | d  :— || d, :— | s, :l, | f, :d, | s, :— ||

| d  :—  | m  :f   | s   :d   | f    :m  | r  :— || d  :—  | t, :d  | r  :r  | d  :— ||
| m, :—  | s, :l,  | s,  :m,  | f,   :s, | s, :— || m, :f, | s, :s, | s, :s, | m, :— ||
| d  :—  | t, :d   | d   :d   | l,.t,:d  | t, :— || l, :—  | r  :d  | d  :t, | d  :— ||
| l, :—  | s, :f,  | m,  :l,  | r,   :d, | s, :— || l, :—  | s, :m, | s, :s, | d  :— ||
```

PSALM CXLV.

7 They utter shall abundantly
The mem'ry of thy goodness great;
And shall sing praises cheerfully,
Whilst they thy righteousness relate.
8 The Lord our God is gracious,
Compassionate is he also;
In mercy he is plenteous,
But unto wrath and anger slow.

9 Good unto all men is the Lord:
O'er all his works his mercy is.
10 Thy works all praise to thee afford:
Thy saints, O Lord, thy name shall bless.
11 The glory of thy kingdom show
Shall they, and of thy power tell:
12 That so men's sons his deeds may know,
His kingdom's grace that doth excel.

13 Thy kingdom hath none end at all,
It doth through ages all remain.
14 The Lord upholdeth all that fall,
The cast-down raiseth up again.
15 The eyes of all things, Lord, attend,
And on thee wait that here do live,
And thou, in season due, dost send
Sufficient food them to relieve.

16 Yea, thou thine hand dost open wide,
And ev'ry thing dost satisfy
That lives, and doth on earth abide,
Of thy great liberality.
17 The Lord is just in his ways all,
And holy in his works each one.
18 He 's near to all that on him call,
Who call in truth on him alone.

19 God will the just desire fulfil
Of such as do him fear and dread:
Their cry regard, and hear he will,
And save them in the time of need.
20 The Lord preserves all, more and less,
That bear to him a loving heart:
But workers all of wickedness
Destroy will he, and clean subvert.

21 Therefore my mouth and lips I'll frame
To speak the praises of the Lord:
To magnify his holy name
For ever let all flesh accord.

```
|s  :— |m  :f  |s  :s  |l  :l  |s  :— ||r  :— |m  :s    |s  :fe |s  :— ||
|s, :— |s, :d  |t, :d  |d  :d  |d  :— ||r  :— |d  :t,.d  |r  :l, |t, :— ||
|r  :— |d  :d  |r  :m  |f  :f  |m  :— ||s  :— |s  :s    |l  :r  |r  :— ||
|t, :— |d  :l, |s, :d  |f, :l, |d  :— ||t, :— |d  :m    |r  :r  |s, :— ||
```

```
|f  :— |m  :d  |r  :t,    |d  :l, |s, :— ||t, :— |d  :m     |r  :r     |d  :— ||d  |d  ||
|l, :t,|d  :l, |l, :s,.f, |m, :f, |m, :— ||s, :— |m, :s,    |s, :s,.f, |m, :— ||f, |m, ||
|r  :— |s  :m  |f  :m.r   |d  :d  |d  :— ||r  :— |d  :d     |d  :t,    |d  :— ||l, |s, ||
|r, :— |m, :l, |f, :s,    |l, :f, |d  :— ||s, :— |l, :m,.f, |s, :s,    |d, :— ||f, |d, ||
                                                                              A-men.
```

PSALMS CXLVI, CXLVII.

146*

PRAISE God. The Lord praise,
O my soul.
2 I'll praise God while I live;
While I have being to my God
in songs I'll praises give.
3 Trust not in princes, nor man's son,
in whom there is no stay:
4 His breath departs, to 's earth he turns;
that day his thoughts decay.

5 O happy is that man and blest,
whom Jacob's God doth aid;
Whose hope upon the Lord doth rest,
and on his God is stay'd: [high,
6 Who made the earth and heavens
who made the swelling deep,
And all that is within the same;
who truth doth ever keep:

7 Who righteous judgment executes
for those oppress'd that be,
Who to the hungry giveth food;
God sets the pris'ners free.
8 The Lord doth give the blind their sight,
the bowed down doth raise:
The Lord doth dearly love all those
that walk in upright ways.

9 The stranger's shield, the widow's
the orphan's help, is he: [stay,
But yet by him the wicked's way
turn'd upside down shall be.
10 The Lord shall reign for evermore:
thy God, O Sion, he
Reigns to all generations.
Praise to the Lord give ye.

147*

PRAISE ye the Lord; for it is good
praise to our God to sing:
For it is pleasant, and to praise
it is a comely thing.
2 God doth build up Jerusalem;
and he it is alone
That the dispers'd of Israel
doth gather into one.

3 Those that are broken in their heart,
and grieved in their minds,
He healeth, and their painful wounds
he tenderly up-binds.
4 He counts the number of the stars;
he names them ev'ry one.
5 Great is our Lord, and of great pow'r;
his wisdom search can none.

154

OLD 81ST. (D.C.M.)

Doh = D. *English Psalter*, 1562.

```
d :m :f :s :—:s :l :—:l :s :— || s :l :t :d' :—:l :t :—
d :d :d :t, :—:d :d :—:d :d :— || d :d :m :m :—:r :r :—
m :s :l :r :—:m :f :—:f :m :— || m :l :s :s :—:fe :s :—
d :d :l, :s, :—:d :l, :f, :—:d :— || d :l, :m :d :—:r :s, :—

s :d' :—:t :l :—:s :f :m :s :— || m :l :—:s :s :—:fe :s :—
d :m :—:m :d :—:d :l, :d :t, :— || d :d :—:t, :d :—:l, :t, :—
m :l :—:s :f :—:m :r :s :s :— || s :f :—:r :m :—:r :r :—
d :l, :—:m :f :—:d :r :d :s, :— || d :f, :—:s, :d :—:r :s, :—
```


6 The Lord lifts up the meek; and casts
the wicked to the ground.
7 Sing to the Lord, and give him thanks;
on harp his praises sound;
8 Who covereth the heav'n with clouds,
who for the earth below
Prepareth rain, who maketh grass
upon the mountains grow.

9 He gives the beast his food, he feeds
the ravens young that cry.
10 His pleasure not in horses' strength,
nor in man's legs, doth lie.
11 But in all those that do him fear
the Lord doth pleasure take;
In those that to his mercy do
by hope themselves betake.

12 The Lord praise, O Jerusalem;
Sion, thy God confess:
13 For thy gates' bars he maketh strong;
thy sons in thee doth bless.
14 He in thy borders maketh peace;
with fine wheat filleth thee.
15 He sends forth his command on earth,
his word runs speedily.

16 Hoar-frost, like ashes, scatt'reth he;
like wool he snow doth give:
17 Like morsels casteth forth his ice;
who in its cold can live?
18 He sendeth forth his mighty word,
and melteth them again;
His wind he makes to blow, and then
the waters flow amain.

19 The doctrine of his holy word
to Jacob he doth show;
His statutes and his judgments he
gives Israel to know.
20 To any nation never he
such favour did afford;
For they his judgments have not known.
O do ye praise the Lord.

148

PRAISE God. From heavens praise the Lord,
in heights praise to him be.
2 All ye his angels, praise ye him;
his hosts all, praise him ye.
3 O praise ye him, both sun and moon;
praise him, all stars of light.
4 Ye heav'ns of heav'ns him praise, and floods
above the heavens' height.

|s :d^1 :t :l :—:s :f :—:m :r :—‖m :f :—:m :m :r :—:m :—‖
|d :m :m :d :—:d :l$_1$:d :—:t$_1$:—‖d :d :—:d :d :t$_1$:—:d :—‖
|m :l :s :f :—:m :f :l :s :s :—‖s :l :—:s :s :s :—:s :—‖
|d :l$_1$:m$_1$:f$_1$:—:d :r :l$_1$:d :s$_1$:—‖d :f$_1$:—:d :d :s$_1$:—:d :—‖

|m :l :s :f :—:m :r :—:d :t$_1$:—‖m :r :—:d :d :—:t$_1$:d :—‖d |d‖
|d :d :ta$_1$:ta$_1$:—:s$_1$:t$_1$:—:d :s$_1$:—‖s$_1$:t$_1$:—:d :l$_1$:—:s$_1$:s$_1$:—‖l$_1$ |s$_1$‖
|s :f :r :r :—:m :s :—:m :s :—‖d :r :s :—:f :—:r :m :—‖f |m‖
|d :f$_1$:s$_1$:ta$_1$:—:d :s$_1$:—:l$_1$:s$_1$:—‖d :s$_1$:—:m$_1$:f$_1$:—:s$_1$:d :—‖f$_1$ |d‖

A-men.

PSALM CXLVIII.

5 Let all the creatures praise the name
of our almighty Lord:
For he commanded, and they were
created by his word.
6 He also, for all times to come,
hath them establish'd sure;
He hath appointed them a law,
which ever shall endure.

7 Praise ye JEHOVAH from the earth,
dragons, and ev'ry deep:
8 Fire, hail, snow, vapour, stormy wind,
his word that fully keep.
9 All hills and mountains, fruitful trees,
and all ye cedars high:
10 Beasts, and all cattle, creeping things,
and all ye birds that fly.

11 Kings of the earth, all nations,
princes, earth's judges all:
12 Both young men, yea, and maidens too,
old men, and children small.
13 Let them God's name praise; for his name
alone is excellent:
His glory reacheth far above
the earth and firmament.

14 His people's horn, the praise of all
his saints, exalteth he;
Ev'n Isr'el's seed, a people near
to him. The Lord praise ye.

148 (2)*

ANOTHER OF THE SAME.

THE Lord of heav'n confess,
On high his glory raise.
2 Him let all angels bless,
Him all his armies praise.
3 Him glorify
Sun, moon, and stars;
4 Ye higher spheres,
And cloudy sky.

5 From God your beings are,
Him therefore famous make;
You all created were,
When he the word but spake.
6 And from that place,
Where fix'd you be
By his decree,
You cannot pass.

7 Praise God from earth below,
Ye dragons, and ye deeps:
8 Fire, hail, clouds, wind, and snow,
Whom in command he keeps.

OLD 137TH. (D.C.M.)

Doh = G.

Anglo-Genevan Psalter, 1556.

```
d   :t,.l, |s,  :d   |m     :r   |d   :—  ‖ d   :r .m |f   :r   |m   :—  ‖
m,  :f,.f, |s,  :l,  |s,    :s,  |m,  :—  ‖ l,  :t,.d |d   :t,  |d   :—  ‖
s,  :t,.t, |d   :m   |d     :t,  |d   :—  ‖ m   :s .s |l   :s   |s   :—  ‖
d,  :r,.r, |m,  :l,  |m,.f, :s,  |d,  :—  ‖ l,  :s,.d |f,  :s,  |d   :—  ‖

m   :r .d  |t,  :d   |l,.l,  :s, |—  ‖ s,  |d   :-.r  |m     :r   |d   :—  ‖
d   :s,.s, |s,  :s,  |s,.fe, :s, |—  ‖ s,  |l,  :-.t, |d     :t,  |d   :—  ‖
s   :r .m  |r   :d   |m .r   :t, |—  ‖ d   |m   :-.s  |s     :s.f |m   :—  ‖
d   :t,.d  |s,  :m,  |d,.r,  :s, |—  ‖ m,  |l,  :-.s, |m,.f, :s,  |d,  :—  ‖
```

PSALMS CXLVIII, CXLIX.

9 Praise ye his name,
Hills great and small,
Trees low and tall;
10 Beasts wild and tame;

All things that creep or fly.
11 Ye kings, ye vulgar throng,
All princes mean or high;
12 Both men and virgins young,
Ev'n young and old,
13 Exalt his name;
For much his fame
Should be extoll'd.

O let God's name be prais'd
Above both earth and sky;
14 For he his saints hath rais'd,
And set their horn on high;
Ev'n those that be
Of Isr'el's race,
Near to his grace.
The Lord praise ye.

149

PRAISE ye the Lord: unto him sing
a new song, and his praise
In the assembly of his saints
in sweet psalms do ye raise.

2 Let Isr'el in his Maker joy,
and to him praises sing:
Let all that Sion's children are
be joyful in their King.

3 O let them unto his great name
give praises in the dance;
Let them with timbrel and with harp
in songs his praise advance.
4 For God doth pleasure take in those
that his own people be;
And he with his salvation
the meek will beautify.

5 And in his glory excellent
let all his saints rejoice:
Let them to him upon their beds
aloud lift up their voice.
6 Let in their mouth aloft be rais'd
the high praise of the Lord,
And let them have in their right hand
a sharp two-edged sword;

7 To execute the vengeance due
upon the heathen all,
And make deserved punishment
upon the people fall.

|s_1 :— |d :-.r |m :d |f :-.f |m :— ‖d :l_1.t_1 |d :r |d :— ‖
|m_1 :— |l_1 :-.l_1 |t_1 :d |r :-.r |de :— ‖l_1 :l_1.se_1 |l_1.d :-.t_1 |d :— ‖
|d :— |m :-.l |se :m |l :-.l |l :— ‖m :m.r |d.m :s |m :— ‖
|d :— |l_1 :-.f_1 |m_1 :l_1 |r_1 :-.f_1 |l_1 :— ‖l_1 :d.t_1 |l_1 :s_1 |d :— ‖

|d :— |m.f :s.s |l :-.l |s :— ‖m :r.m |f :r |d :— ‖d |d ‖
|s_1 :— |d.d :t_1.d |d :-.d |d :— ‖d :t_1.d |r.d :-.t_1 |d :— ‖l_1 |s_1 ‖
|m :— |s.d :r.s |f :-.f |m :— ‖s :s.s |l :s |m :— ‖f |m ‖
|d :— |d.l_1 :s_1.m_1 |f_1 :-.f_1 |d :— ‖d :s_1.d |f_1 :s_1 |d_1 :— ‖f_1 |d_1 ‖

A-men.

PSALMS CXLIX, CL.

8 And ev'n with chains, as pris'ners, bind
their kings that them command;
Yea, and with iron fetters strong,
the nobles of their land.

9 On them the judgment to perform
found written in his word:
This honour is to all his saints.
O do ye praise the Lord.

150*

PRAISE ye the Lord. God's praise within
his sanctuary raise;
And to him in the firmament
of his pow'r give ye praise.

2 Because of all his mighty acts,
with praise him magnify:
O praise him, as he doth excel
in glorious majesty.

3 Praise him with trumpet's sound; his praise
with psaltery advance:
4 With timbrel, harp, string'd instruments,
and organs, in the dance.
5 Praise him on cymbals loud; him praise
on cymbals sounding high.
6 Let each thing breathing praise the Lord.
Praise to the Lord give ye.

END OF THE PSALMS.

157

PSALM 107. (D.C.M.)

French Psalter, 1543.

Lah = D. Doh = F. Composed or arranged by LOUIS BOURGEOIS, 1510– ? .

```
:l,    |l,   :m     :l .l  |s .s  :m   ||m  |f .m  :d   :r    |d   :—     ||
:m,    |l,   :l,.t, :l,.t, |d .d  :t,  ||l, |f,.s, :m,  :s,.f,|m,  :—     ||
:d .r  |m .r :d .m  :m .r  |m .m  :s   ||d  |r .d  :d   :t,   |d   :—     ||
:l,.t, |d .t,:l,.s, :f,.f, |d,.d, :m,  ||l, |r,.m, :l,  :s,   |d,  :—     ||

:l,    |l,   :m     :l .l  |s .s  :m   ||d  |r .m  :d   :t,   |l,  :— :— ||
:m,    |l,   :l,    :t,.t, |t,.t, :l,  ||s, |s,.s, :fe, :se,  |l,  :— :— ||
:d     |r    :— .d  :f .f  |m .m  :d   ||m  |s .m  :fe  :t,   |d   :— :— ||
:l,.s, |f,   :m,    :r,.r, |m,.m, :l,  ||d  |t,.d  :r,  :m,   |l,  :— :— ||
```

TRANSLATIONS AND PARAPHRASES, IN VERSE,

OF

SEVERAL PASSAGES OF SACRED SCRIPTURE.

1

GENESIS i.

LET heav'n arise, let earth appear,
said the Almighty Lord:
The heav'n arose, the earth appear'd,
at his creating word.

2 Thick darkness brooded o'er the deep:
God said, 'Let there be light':
The light shone forth with smiling ray,
and scatter'd ancient night.

3 He bade the clouds ascend on high;
the clouds ascend, and bear
A wat'ry treasure to the sky,
and float upon the air.

4 The liquid element below
was gather'd by his hand;
The rolling seas together flow,
and leave the solid land.

5 With herbs, and plants, and fruitful trees,
the new-form'd globe he crown'd,
Ere there was rain to bless the soil,
or sun to warm the ground.

6 Then high in heav'n's resplendent arch
he plac'd two orbs of light,
He set the sun to rule the day,
the moon to rule the night.

l :m.fe:s.l	s :fe	m :—	l :t.l	m :fe	m :—
l_1 :l_1.d :t_1.d	t_1 :$t_1.l_1$	se_1 :—	l_1 :m.d	s_1 :$t_1.l_1$	se_1 :—
d.r :m.l :s.m	m :re	m :—	m :s.m	m :re	m :—
$l_1.t_1$:d.r :m.l_1	$m_1.s_1$:t_1	m_1 :—	d :$s_1.l_1$	d :t_1	m_1 :—

m :s.fe :m.m	r.r :d	d	r.m :r :t_1	l_1 :—	l_1	l_1
l_1.d :t_1.r :r.d	d.t_1 :l_1	$l_1.s_1$	$f_1.m_1$:$fe_1.l_1$:-.se_1	l_1 :—	f_1	m_1
d.l :s.t :s.s	s.f :m	f.d	$l_1.l_1$:r.fe :m.r	d :—	r	de
l_1 :m.t_1 :d.d	$s_1.s_1$:$l_1.s_1$	$f_1.m_1$	$r_1.d_1$:r_1 :m_1	l_1 :—	r_1	l_1

A-men.

PARAPHRASES I, II, III.

7 Next, from the deep, th' Almighty King
did vital beings frame;
Fowls of the air of ev'ry wing,
and fish of ev'ry name.
8 To all the various brutal tribes
he gave their wondrous birth;
At once the lion and the worm
sprung from the teeming earth.

9 Then, chief o'er all his works below,
at last was Adam made;
His Maker's image bless'd his soul,
and glory crown'd his head.
10 Fair in th' Almighty Maker's eye
the whole creation stood.
He view'd the fabric he had rais'd;
his word pronounc'd it good.

2*

Genesis xxviii. 20–22.

O GOD of Bethel! by whose hand
thy people still are fed;
Who through this weary pilgrimage
hast all our fathers led:
2 Our vows, our pray'rs, we now present
before thy throne of grace:
God of our fathers! be the God
of their succeeding race.

3 Through each perplexing path of life
our wand'ring footsteps guide;
Give us each day our daily bread,
and raiment fit provide.
4 O spread thy cov'ring wings around,
till all our wand'rings cease,
And at our Father's lov'd abode
our souls arrive in peace.

5 Such blessings from thy gracious hand
our humble pray'rs implore;
And thou shalt be our chosen God,
and portion evermore.

3

Job i. 21.

NAKED as from the earth we came,
and enter'd life at first;
Naked we to the earth return,
and mix with kindred dust.
2 Whate'er we fondly call our own
belongs to heav'n's great Lord;
The blessings lent us for a day
are soon to be restor'd.

158

ST. ASAPH. (D.C.M.)

Doh = G.

Giovanni Marie Giornovichi, 1745–1804.

:s, | d :d | r :r | m :s.f | m || s | f :f | m :m | r :— | — ||
:s, | l, :d | d :t, | d :d.t, | d || d | d :r | d :d | t, :— | — ||
:m | m :s | l :s | s :m.f | s || s | l :l | s :l | r :— | — ||
:d | l, :m, | f, :s, | d :m.r | d || m, | f, :r, | m, :f, | s, :— | — ||

:s, | d :d | r :r | m :m.f | s || s | f :f | m :r | d :— | — ||
:s, | s, :m, | l, :s, | s, :d | d || t, | d :r | d :t, | d :— | — ||
:t, | d :d | d :t, | d :d.r | m || r | f :l | s :f | m :— | — ||
:s,.f, | m, :l, | f, :s, | d :l, | m, || s, | l, :r, | m,.f, :s, | d, :— | — ||

PARAPHRASES III, IV, V.

3 'Tis God that lifts our comforts high,
or sinks them in the grave:
He gives; and, when he takes away,
he takes but what he gave.

4 Then, ever blessed be his name!
his goodness swell'd our store;
His justice but resumes its own;
'tis ours still to adore.

4

JOB iii. 17–20.

HOW still and peaceful is the grave!
where, life's vain tumults past,
Th' appointed house, by Heav'n's decree,
receives us all at last.

2 The wicked there from troubling cease,
their passions rage no more;
And there the weary pilgrim rests
from all the toils he bore.

3 There rest the pris'ners, now releas'd
from slav'ry's sad abode;
No more they hear th' oppressor's voice,
or dread the tyrant's rod.

4 There servants, masters, small and great,
partake the same repose;
And there, in peace, the ashes mix
of those who once were foes.

5 All, levell'd by the hand of Death,
lie sleeping in the tomb;
Till God in judgment calls them forth,
to meet their final doom.

5

JOB v. 6–12.

THOUGH trouble springs not from the dust,
nor sorrow from the ground;
Yet ills on ills, by Heav'n's decree,
in man's estate are found.

2 As sparks in close succession rise,
so man, the child of woe,
Is doom'd to endless cares and toils
through all his life below.

3 But with my God I leave my cause;
from him I seek relief;
To him, in confidence of pray'r,
unbosom all my grief.

𝄋

```
:m   |f  :f  |r  :r  |s  :m.f  |s  ||s  |l  :s  |f  :m    |r  :— |— ||
:d   |d  :d  |t, :t, |d  :d.t, |d  ||d  |d  :de |r  :d    |t, :— |— ||
:s   |f  :l  |s  :s  |s  :s.f  |m  ||s  |f  :m  |f  :s.l  |r  :— |— ||
:d   |l, :f, |s, :s, |m  :d.r  |m  ||m, |f, :l, |r, :m,.f,|s, :— |— ||
```

D.S. for v. 7 of Par. 66.

```
:s,     |d  :d  |r  :r  |m  :s.f  |m  ||s  |f  :f  |m     :r    |d  :— |— ||d  |d  ||
:s,     |s, :d  |d  :t, |d  :d.t, |d  ||d  |d  :r  |d     :t,   |d  :— |— ||l, |s, ||
:t,     |d  :m  |l  :s  |s  :m.f  |s  ||s  |l  :l  |s     :-.f  |m  :— |— ||f  |m  ||
:s,.f,  |m, :l, |f, :s, |d  :m.r  |d  ||m, |f, :r, |m,.f, :s,   |d, :— |— ||f, |d, ||
```

A-men.

PARAPHRASES V, VI, VII.

4 Unnumber'd are his wondrous works,
unsearchable his ways;
'Tis his the mourning soul to cheer,
the bowed down to raise.

6

Job viii. 11–22.

THE rush may rise where waters flow,
and flags beside the stream;
But soon their verdure fades and dies
before the scorching beam:

2 So is the sinner's hope cut off;
or, if it transient rise,
'Tis like the spider's airy web,
from ev'ry breath that flies.

3 Fix'd on his house he leans; his house
and all its props decay:
He holds it fast; but, while he holds,
the tott'ring frame gives way.

4 Fair, in his garden, to the sun,
his boughs with verdure smile;
And, deeply fix'd, his spreading roots
unshaken stand a while.

5 But forth the sentence flies from Heav'n,
that sweeps him from his place;
Which then denies him for its lord,
nor owns it knew his face.

6 Lo! this the joy of wicked men,
who Heav'n's high laws despise:
They quickly fall; and in their room
as quickly others rise.

7 But, for the just, with gracious care,
God will his pow'r employ;
He'll teach their lips to sing his praise,
and fill their hearts with joy.

7

Job ix. 2–10.

HOW should the sons of Adam's race
be pure before their God?
If he contends in righteousness,
we sink beneath his rod.

2 If he should mark my words and thoughts
with strict enquiring eyes,
Could I for one of thousand faults
the least excuse devise?

159

ST. MATTHEW. (D.C.M.) WILLIAM CROFT, 1678–1727.

Doh = B♭.

:s_1 | m_1 :—:s_1 | d :—:m | r :d :t_1 | d :— || m | r :—:s_1 | l_1:s_1 :fe_1 | s_1 :— ||
:r_1 | m_1 :—:m_1 | m_1 :—:s_1 | f_1:m_1:r_1 | m_1 :— || s_1 | s_1 :—:s_1 | m_1:r_1 :r_1 | r_1 :— ||
:s_1 | d :—:t_1 | d :—:d | l_1:s_1:s_1 | s_1 :— || d | r :—:t_1 | d :t_1 :l_1 | t_1 :— ||
:t_2 | d_1 :—:m_1 | l_1 :—:m_1 | f_1:s_1:s_2 | d_1 :— || d_1 | t_2 :—:m_1 | d_1:r_1 :r_1 | s_1 :— ||

:r | t_1 :—:s_1 | d :—:m | m :r :d | d :t_1 || s_1 | d :—:m | r :d :t_1 | d :— ||
:s_1 | s_1 :—:s_1 | s_1 :—:s_1 | l_1 :—:m_1.f_1 | s_1 :— || r_1 | s_1 :—:s_1 | f_1:m_1:r_1 | m_1 :— ||
:t_1 | r :—:r | d :—:d | d :r :l_1 | r :— || t_1 | d :—:d | l_1:s_1:s_1 | s_1 :— ||
:s_1 | s_1 :—:f_1 | m_1 :—:d_1 | f_1 :—:l_1 | s_1 :— || f_1 | m_1 :—:d_1 | f_1:s_1:s_1 | d_1 :— ||

3 Strong is his arm, his heart is wise;
who dares with him contend?
Or who, that tries th' unequal strife,
shall prosper in the end?
4 He makes the mountains feel his wrath,
and their old seats forsake;
The trembling earth deserts her place,
and all her pillars shake.

5 He bids the sun forbear to rise;
th' obedient sun forbears:
His hand with sackcloth spreads the skies,
and seals up all the stars.
6 He walks upon the raging sea;
flies on the stormy wind:
None can explore his wondrous way,
or his dark footsteps find.

8

JOB xiv. 1–15.

FEW are thy days, and full of woe,
O man, of woman born!
Thy doom is written, 'Dust thou art,
and shalt to dust return.'
2 Behold the emblem of thy state
in flow'rs that bloom and die,
Or in the shadow's fleeting form,
that mocks the gazer's eye.

3 Guilty and frail, how shalt thou stand
before thy sov'reign Lord?
Can troubled and polluted springs
a hallow'd stream afford?
4 Determin'd are the days that fly
successive o'er thy head;
The number'd hour is on the wing
that lays thee with the dead.

5 Great God! afflict not in thy wrath
the short allotted span,
That bounds the few and weary days
of pilgrimage to man.
6 All nature dies, and lives again:
the flow'r that paints the field,
The trees that crown the mountain's brow,
and boughs and blossoms yield,

7 Resign the honours of their form
at Winter's stormy blast,
And leave the naked leafless plain
a desolated waste.

						F.t.		f.Bb.
:m_1	m_1:—:l_1	l_1:se_1:l_1	t_1:l_1:se_1	l_1:— | t_1	^{d}f:—:m.r	d :—:t_1	$^{l}m_1$:—
:r_1	d_1:—:m_1	m :—:d_1	f_1:m_1:m_1	m_1:— | se_1	^{l}r:—:l_1	l_1:—:se_1	$^{l}m_1$:—
:se_1	l_1:—:l_1	d :t_1 :l_1	r :d :t_1	d :— | m	^{m}l:se:l.f	m :—:r	$^{d}s_1$:—
:t_2	l_2:—:d_1	m_1:—:f_1	r_1:m_1:m_1	l_1:— | m_1	^{l}r:t_1:d.r	m :—:m_1	$^{l}m_1$:—

:s_1	s_1:—:d	l_1:—:l_1	r :—:d	d :t_1 | s_1	d :—:m	r :d :t_1	d:—	d	d
:f_1	m_1:f_1 :s_1	f_1:—:s_1	fe_1:s_1 :l_1	s_1:— | s_1	s_1:f_1 :m_1	l_1:s_1:s_1	s_1:—	f_1	m_1
:t_1	d :—:d	d :—:de	r :—:r	r :— | t_1	d :—:s	f :m :r	m:—	l_1	s_1
:r_1	d_1:r_1 :m_1	f_1:—:m_1	r_1 :m_1 :fe_1	s_1:— | f_1	m_1:r_1 :d_1	f_1:s_1:s_2	d_1:—	f_1	d_1

A-men.

PARAPHRASES VIII, IX.

8 Yet soon reviving plants and flow'rs
anew shall deck the plain;
The woods shall hear the voice of Spring,
and flourish green again.

9 But man forsakes this earthly scene,
ah! never to return:
Shall any foll'wing spring revive
the ashes of the urn?

10 The mighty flood that rolls along
its torrents to the main,
Can ne'er recall its waters lost
from that abyss again.

11 So days, and years, and ages past,
descending down to night,
Can henceforth never more return
back to the gates of light;

12 And man, when laid in lonesome grave,
shall sleep in Death's dark gloom,
Until th' eternal morning wake
the slumbers of the tomb.

13 O may the grave become to me
the bed of peaceful rest,
Whence I shall gladly rise at length,
and mingle with the blest!

14 Cheer'd by this hope, with patient mind,
I'll wait Heav'n's high decree,
Till the appointed period come,
when death shall set me free.

9

Job xxvi. 6, to the end.

WHO can resist th' Almighty arm
that made the starry sky?
Or who elude the certain glance
of God's all-seeing eye?

2 From him no cov'ring vails our crimes;
hell opens to his sight;
And all Destruction's secret snares
lie full disclos'd in light.

3 Firm on the boundless void of space
he pois'd the steady pole,
And in the circle of his clouds
bade secret waters roll.

4 While nature's universal frame
its Maker's pow'r reveals,
His throne, remote from mortal eyes,
an awful cloud conceals.

160

AYNHOE. (S.M.)

Doh = B♭.

JAMES NARES, 1715–83.

:d |d :t, :l, |s, :l, :t, |d :— || t,.d |r :-.d :t, |d :t, :l, |s, :— ||
:m, |m, :— :f, |s, :— :f, |m, :— || s, |s, :r, :s, |l, :s, :fe, |s, :— ||
:s, |s, :— :l,.t, |d :— :r |s, :— || s, |s, :t,.d :r |m :r :r.d |t, :— ||
:d, |d, :— :f, |m, :f,.m, :r, |d, :— || m, |t,, :s,, :s, |d, :r, :— |s, :— ||

:s, |d :— :r |m :-.r :d |f :— :m |r :— || m |l, :t, :d |d :-.r :t, |d :— || d |d ||
:s, |s, :— :f, |m, :-.f, :s, |l, :s, :s, |s, :— || s, |f, :— :s,.l, |s, :— :s, |s, :— || f, |m, ||
:t, |d :s,.l, :t, |d :s.f :m |d :r :d |t, :— || d |d :r :d.f |m :-.f :r |m :— || l, |s, ||
:s,.f, |m, :— :r, |d, :— :d |l, :t, :d |s, :— || d, |f, :r, :m,.f, |s, :— :s, |d, :— || f, |d, ||

A-men.

PARAPHRASES IX, X.

5 From where the rising day ascends,
to where it sets in night,
He compasses the floods with bounds,
and checks their threat'ning might.

6 The pillars that support the sky
tremble at his rebuke;
Through all its caverns quakes the earth,
as though its centre shook.

7 He brings the waters from their beds,
although no tempest blows,
And smites the kingdom of the proud
without the hand of foes.

8 With bright inhabitants above
he fills the heav'nly land,
And all the crooked serpent's breed
dismay'd before him stand.

9 Few of his works can we survey;
these few our skill transcend:
But the full thunder of his pow'r
what heart can comprehend?

10

PROV. i. 20–31.

IN streets, and op'nings of the gates,
where pours the busy crowd,
Thus heav'nly Wisdom lifts her voice,
and cries to men aloud:

2 How long, ye scorners of the truth,
scornful will ye remain?
How long shall fools their folly love,
and hear my words in vain?

3 O turn, at last, at my reproof!
and, in that happy hour,
His bless'd effusions on your heart
my Spirit down shall pour.

4 But since so long, with earnest voice,
to you in vain I call,
Since all my counsels and reproofs
thus ineffectual fall;

5 The time will come, when humbled low,
in Sorrow's evil day,
Your voice by anguish shall be taught,
but taught too late, to pray.

6 When, like the whirlwind, o'er the deep
comes Desolation's blast;
Pray'rs then extorted shall be vain,
the hour of mercy past.

7 The choice you made has fix'd your doom;
for this is Heav'n's decree,
That with the fruits of what he sow'd
the sinner fill'd shall be.

161

BREDON. (S.M.)

Doh = E♭.

HENRY JOHN GAUNTLETT, 1805–76.

:m | f :m | m :r | d :— | — ‖ s | f :m | l :f | r :— | — ‖
:d | r :d | t_1 :t_1 | d :— | — ‖ d | d :d | d :r | t_1 :— | — ‖
:s | s :s | s :f | m :— | — ‖ m | f :s | l :l | s :— | — ‖
:d | t_1 :d | s_1 :s_1 | l_1 :— | — ‖ m_1 | l_1 :s_1 | f_1 :f_1 | s_1 :— | — ‖

:s | s :t | d^1 :t | t :l | s ‖ m | f :m | m :r | d :— | — ‖ d | d ‖
:t_1 | r :s_1 | d :d | d :d | r ‖ d | d :d | d :t_1 | d :— | — ‖ l_1 | s_1 ‖
:s | t :r^1 | s :s | s :f | r ‖ s | f :l | s :-.f | m :— | — ‖ f | m ‖
:s_1 | s :f | m :m_1 | f_1 :l_1 | t_1 ‖ d | l_1 :f_1 | s_1 :s_1 | d :— | — ‖ f_1 | d ‖

A-men.

PARAPHRASES XI, XII, XIII.

11*

PROV. iii. 13–17.

O HAPPY is the man who hears
 Instruction's warning voice;
And who celestial Wisdom makes
 his early, only choice.
2 For she has treasures greater far
 than east or west unfold;
And her rewards more precious are
 than all their stores of gold.

3 In her right hand she holds to view
 a length of happy days;
Riches, with splendid honours join'd,
 are what her left displays.
4 She guides the young with innocence,
 in pleasure's paths to tread,
A crown of glory she bestows
 upon the hoary head.

5 According as her labours rise,
 so her rewards increase;
Her ways are ways of pleasantness,
 and all her paths are peace.

12

PROV. vi. 6–12.

YE indolent and slothful! rise,
 View the ant's labours, and be
 wise;
She has no guide to point her way,
No ruler chiding her delay:
2 Yet see with what incessant cares
She for the winter's storm prepares;
In summer she provides her meat,
And harvest finds her store complete.

3 But when will slothful man arise?
How long shall sleep seal up his eyes?
Sloth more indulgence still demands;
Sloth shuts the eyes, and folds the
 hands.
4 But mark the end; want shall assail,
When all your strength and vigour
 fail;
Want, like an armed man, shall rush
The hoary head of age to crush.

13

PROV. viii. 22, to the end.

KEEP silence, all ye sons of men,
 and hear with rev'rence due;
Eternal Wisdom from above
 thus lifts her voice to you:
2 I was th' Almighty's chief delight
 from everlasting days,
Ere yet his arm was stretched forth
 the heav'ns and earth to raise.

CARLISLE. (S.M.)

Doh = E♭.

CHARLES LOCKHART, 1745-1815.

:d |s :d |m .r :d .t, |d :— |— ||d |f :s .l |s :d .f |m :r |— ||
:s, |s, :l, |l, :s, |s, :— |— ||s, |d :d |d :l,.r |d :t, |— ||
:m |r :m |f :m .r |m :— |— ||m |f :m .f |s :l |s :— |— ||
:d |t, :l, |f, :s, |d :— |— ||d .t, |l, :s,.f, |m, :f, |s, :— |— ||

:r |m :r .d |f :m.r |s :f .m |l ||t |d' :d.f |m :r |d :— |— ||d |d ||
:t, |d :t,.d |r :d.t, |d :d |d ||r |d :d.r |d :t, |d :— |— ||l, |s, ||
:s |s :s |l :s |s :d'.ta |l ||f |s :l |s :-.f |m :— |— ||f |m ||
:s, |d :f .m |r :s.f |m :l .s |f ||r |m :f.r |s :s, |d :— |— ||f, |d ||

A-men.

3 Before the sea began to flow,
and leave the solid land,
Before the hills and mountains rose,
I dwelt at his right hand.

4 When first he rear'd the arch of heav'n,
and spread the clouds on air,
When first the fountains of the deep
he open'd, I was there.

5 There I was with him, when he stretch'd
his compass o'er the deep,
And charg'd the ocean's swelling waves
within their bounds to keep.

6 With joy I saw th' abode prepar'd
which men were soon to fill:
Them from the first of days I lov'd,
unchang'd, I love them still.

7 Now therefore hearken to my words,
ye children, and be wise:
Happy the man that keeps my ways;
the man that shuns them dies.

8 Where dubious paths perplex the mind,
direction I afford;
Life shall be his that follows me,
and favour from the Lord.

9 But he who scorns my sacred laws
shall deeply wound his heart,
He courts destruction who contemns
the counsel I impart.

14

ECCLES. vii. 2–6.

WHILE others crowd the house of mirth,
and haunt the gaudy show,
Let such as would with Wisdom dwell,
frequent the house of woe.

2 Better to weep with those who weep,
and share th' afflicted's smart,
Than mix with fools in giddy joys
that cheat and wound the heart.

3 When virtuous sorrow clouds the face,
and tears bedim the eye,
The soul is led to solemn thought,
and wafted to the sky.

4 The wise in heart revisit oft
grief's dark sequester'd cell;
The thoughtless still with levity
and mirth delight to dwell.

163

EGHAM. (S.M.) — William Turner, 1651–1740.

Doh = E♭. — Arranged by Samuel Sebastian Wesley, 1810–76

:m | r :d | f :m | l :— | — || t | d' :s | m :f | r :— | — ||
:d | t_1 :d | r :d | d :— | — || r | d :r | d :r | t_1 :— | — ||
:s | f :m | s :s | l :— | — || s | s :s | s :l | s :— | — ||
:d | s_1 :l_1 | t_1 :d | f :— | — || f | m :t_1 | d :f_1 | s_1 :— | — ||

:r | m :s | f :l | s :t | d' || m | f :m | r :r | d :— | — || d | d ||
:t_1 | d :d | d :d | d :r | d || de | r.t_1 :d | d :t_1 | d :— | — || l_1 | s_1 ||
:s | s :m | f :f | s :f | m || l | f :s.l | r.m :f | m :— | — || f | m ||
:s_1 | d :ta_1 | l_1 :f_1 | m_1 :se_1 | l_1 || l_1 | r_1 :m_1.f_1 | s_1 :s_1 | d :— | — || f_1 | d ||

A-men.

PARAPHRASES XIV, XV, XVI.

5 The noisy laughter of the fool,
is like the crackling sound
Of blazing thorns, which quickly fall
in ashes to the ground.

15

ECCLES. ix. 4, 5, 6, 10.

As long as life its term extends,
Hope's blest dominion never ends;
For while the lamp holds on to burn,
The greatest sinner may return.
2 Life is the season God hath giv'n
To fly from hell, and rise to heav'n;
That day of grace fleets fast away,
And none its rapid course can stay.

3 The living know that they must die;
But all the dead forgotten lie:
Their mem'ry and their name is gone,
Alike unknowing and unknown.
4 Their hatred and their love is lost,
Their envy bury'd in the dust;
They have no share in all that 's done
Beneath the circuit of the sun.

5 Then what thy thoughts design to do,
Still let thy hands with might pursue;
Since no device nor work is found,
Nor wisdom underneath the ground.
6 In the cold grave, to which we haste,
There are no acts of pardon past:
But fix'd the doom of all remains,
And everlasting silence reigns.

16

ECCLES. xii. 1.

In life's gay morn, when sprightly youth
with vital ardour glows,
And shines in all the fairest charms
which beauty can disclose;
2 Deep on thy soul, before its pow'rs
are yet by vice enslav'd,
Be thy Creator's glorious name
and character engrav'd.

3 For soon the shades of grief shall cloud
the sunshine of thy days;
And cares, and toils, in endless round
encompass all thy ways.
4 Soon shall thy heart the woes of age
in mournful groans deplore,
And sadly muse on former joys
that now return no more.

164

FRANCONIA. (S.M.)

Doh = E♭.

König's Choralbuch, 1738.

```
:d  |r  :m  |f  :s  |m  :—  |—  ||s  |l  :d' |f  :m  |r  :—  |—  ||
:s, |t, :d  |d  :t, |d  :—  |—  ||d  |d  :d  |t, :d  |t, :—  |—  ||
:m  |s  :s  |f  :r  |m  :—  |—  ||m  |f  :s  |f  :s  |s  :—  |—  ||
:d  |s, :d  |l, :s, |d  :—  |—  ||d  |f  :m  |r  :d  |s, :—  |—  ||

:s  |d' :t  |l  :s   |l   :l   |s  ||s  |d  :m  |r  :r   |d  :—  |—  ||d  |d  ||
:r  |d  :r  |m  :m   |m   :r.d |t, ||t, |d  :d  |d  :t,  |d  :—  |—  ||l, |s, ||
:t  |s  :s  |d' :t   |l.s :fe  |s  ||s  |m  :s  |l  :s.f |m  :—  |—  ||f  |m  ||
:s  |m  :s  |d  :m.r |d   :r   |s, ||s, |l, :m, |f, :s,  |d  :—  |—  ||f, |d  ||
                                                                         A-men.
```

PARAPHRASES XVII, XVIII.

17

ISAIAH i. 10–19.

RULERS of Sodom! hear the voice
of heav'n's eternal Lord;
Men of Gomorrah! bend your ear
submissive to his word.

2 'Tis thus he speaks: To what intent
are your oblations vain?
Why load my altars with your gifts,
polluted and profane?

3 Burnt-off'rings long may blaze to heav'n,
and incense cloud the skies;
The worship and the worshipper
are hateful in my eyes.

4 Your rites, your fasts, your pray'rs, I scorn,
and pomp of solemn days:
I know your hearts are full of guile,
and crooked are your ways.

5 But cleanse your hands, ye guilty race,
and cease from deeds of sin;
Learn in your actions to be just,
and pure in heart within.

6 Mock not my name with honours vain,
but keep my holy laws;
Do justice to the friendless poor,
and plead the widow's cause.

7 Then though your guilty souls are stain'd
with sins of crimson dye,
Yet, through my grace, with snow itself
in whiteness they shall vie.

18*

ISAIAH ii. 2–6.

BEHOLD! the mountain of the Lord
in latter days shall rise
On mountain tops above the hills,
and draw the wond'ring eyes.

2 To this the joyful nations round,
all tribes and tongues shall flow;
Up to the hill of God, they'll say,
and to his house we'll go.

3 The beam that shines from Sion hill
shall lighten ev'ry land;
The King who reigns in Salem's tow'rs
shall all the world command.

DESCANT.

FRANCONIA. (S.M.) — ALAN GRAY, 1855-

Doh = E♭.

Descant.

:s |t :d' |d' :t |d' :— |— ||s |l :d' |t :d' |r' :— |— ||

Melody.

:d |r :m |f :s |m :— |— ||s |l :d' |f :m |r :— |— ||

:s |m' :r' |d' :d' |l :r'.d' |t ||t |d' :s |l :s.f |m :— |— ||

:s |d' :t |l :s |l :l |s ||s |d :m |r :r |d :— |— ||

PARAPHRASES XVIII, XIX, XX.

4 Among the nations he shall judge;
his judgments truth shall guide;
His sceptre shall protect the just,
and quell the sinner's pride.

5 No strife shall rage, nor hostile feuds
disturb those peaceful years;
To ploughshares men shall beat their swords,
to pruning-hooks their spears.
6 No longer hosts encount'ring hosts
shall crowds of slain deplore:
They hang the trumpet in the hall
and study war no more.

7 Come then, O house of Jacob! come
to worship at his shrine;
And, walking in the light of God,
with holy beauties shine.

19*

ISAIAH ix. 2–8.

THE race that long in darkness pin'd
have seen a glorious light;
The people dwell in day, who dwelt
in death's surrounding night.
2 To hail thy rise, thou better Sun!
the gath'ring nations come,
Joyous, as when the reapers bear
the harvest treasures home.

3 For thou our burden hast remov'd,
and quell'd th' oppressor's sway,
Quick as the slaughter'd squadrons fell
in Midian's evil day.
4 To us a Child of hope is born;
to us a Son is giv'n;
Him shall the tribes of earth obey,
him all the hosts of heav'n.

5 His name shall be the Prince of Peace,
for evermore ador'd,
The Wonderful, the Counsellor,
the great and mighty Lord.
6 His pow'r increasing still shall spread,
his reign no end shall know;
Justice shall guard his throne above,
and peace abound below.

20*

ISAIAH xxvi. 1–7.

HOW glorious Sion's courts appear,
the city of our God!
His throne he hath establish'd here,
here fix'd his lov'd abode.

165

HAMPTON. (S.M.)

Doh = D.

Williams's Psalmody, 1770.

:s	m .l :s :t	d' :—	‖ d'	t .d' :t :l	s :—	‖
:d	d .d :d :f	m :—	‖ m	r .m :r :r .d	t, :—	‖
:m	s .f :s :s	s :—	‖ s	s .s :s :fe	s :—	‖
:d	d .f :m :r	d :—	‖ d	s .d :r :r	s, :—	‖

:m	f .s :l :s	f .m :r	‖ s	d'.f :m :r	d :—	‖ f	m ‖
:d	d .d :d :t,	d .d :t,	‖ r	s,.d :d :t,	d :—	‖ d	d ‖
:s	f .m :f :r	l .s :s	‖ t	d'.l :s :s .f	m :—	‖ l	s ‖
:d	l,.d :f, :s,	l,.d :s,	‖ s .f	m .f :s :s,	d :—	‖ f,	d ‖

A-men.

PARAPHRASES XX, XXI.

2 Its walls, defended by his grace,
no pow'r shall e'er o'erthrow,
Salvation is its bulwark sure
against th' assailing foe.

3 Lift up the everlasting gates,
the doors wide open fling;
Enter, ye nations, who obey
the statutes of our King.

4 Here shall ye taste unmingled joys,
and dwell in perfect peace,
Ye, who have known JEHOVAH's name,
and trusted in his grace.

5 Trust in the Lord, for ever trust,
and banish all your fears;
Strength in the Lord JEHOVAH dwells
eternal as his years.

6 What though the wicked dwell on high,
his arm shall bring them low;
Low as the caverns of the grave
their lofty heads shall bow.

7 Along the dust shall then be spread
their tow'rs, that brave the skies:
On them the needy's feet shall tread,
and on their ruins rise.

21*

Isaiah xxxiii. 13–18.

ATTEND, ye tribes that dwell remote,
ye tribes at hand, give ear;
Th' upright in heart alone have hope
the false in heart have fear.

2 The man who walks with God in truth,
and ev'ry guile disdains;
Who hates to lift oppression's rod,
and scorns its shameful gains;

3 Whose soul abhors the impious bribe
that tempts from truth to stray,
And from th' enticing snares of vice
who turns his eyes away:

4 His dwelling, 'midst the strength of rocks,
shall ever stand secure;
His Father will provide his bread,
his water shall be sure.

5 For him the kingdom of the just
afar doth glorious shine;
And he the King of kings shall see
in majesty divine.

166

NARENZA. (S.M.) *Kirchen Gesäng*, Cologne, 1619.

Doh = B♭. Arranged by WILLIAM HENRY HAVERGAL, 1793–1870.

```
:d  |t,  :s,  |l,  :t,  |d   :—  |—  ||m   |r   :t,  |d   :l,  |s,  :—  |—  ||
:s, |s,  :s,  |d,  :f,  |m,  :—  |—  ||s,  |fe, :s,  |m,  :r,  |t,, :—  |—  ||
:m  |r   :d   |d   :r   |s,  :—  |—  ||d   |l,  :s,  |s,  :fe, |s,  :—  |—  ||
:d, |s,  :m,  |f,  :r,  |d,  :—  |—  ||d,  |r,  :m,  |d,  :r,  |s,  :—  |—  ||

:s, |s,  :s,  |l,  :t,  |d   :l,  |t,  ||m   |r   :d   |r   :r     |d   :—  |—  ||d   |d   ||
:m, |f,  :m,  |f,  :f,  |m,  :l,  |se, ||s,  |s,  :m,  |l,  :s,.f, |m,  :—  |—  ||f,  |m,  ||
:s, |r   :d   |d   :r   |d   :r   |t,  ||d   |t,  :d   |d   :t,    |d   :—  |—  ||l,  |s,  ||
:d, |t,, :d,  |f,  :r,  |l,  :f,  |m,  ||d,  |s,  :l,  |f,  :s,    |d,  :—  |—  ||f,  |d,  ||
                                                                                  A-men.
```

PARAPHRASES XXII, XXIII.

22*

ISAIAH xl. 27, to the end.

WHY pour'st thou forth thine anxious plaint,
despairing of relief,
As if the Lord o'erlook'd thy cause,
and did not heed thy grief?

2 Hast thou not known, hast thou not heard,
that firm remains on high
The everlasting throne of Him
who form'd the earth and sky?

3 Art thou afraid his pow'r shall fail
when comes thy evil day?
And can an all-creating arm
grow weary or decay?

4 Supreme in wisdom as in pow'r
the Rock of ages stands;
Though him thou canst not see, nor trace
the working of his hands.

5 He gives the conquest to the weak,
supports the fainting heart;
And courage in the evil hour
his heav'nly aids impart.

6 Mere human pow'r shall fast decay,
and youthful vigour cease;
But they who wait upon the Lord
in strength shall still increase.

7 They with unweary'd feet shall tread
the path of life divine;
With growing ardour onward move,
with growing brightness shine.

8 On eagles' wings they mount, they soar,
their wings are faith and love,
Till, past the cloudy regions here,
they rise to heav'n above.

23*

ISAIAH xlii. 1–13.

BEHOLD my Servant! see him rise
exalted in my might!
Him have I chosen, and in him
I place supreme delight.

2 On him, in rich effusion pour'd,
my Spirit shall descend;
My truths and judgments he shall show
to earth's remotest end.

3 Gentle and still shall be his voice,
no threats from him proceed;
The smoking flax he shall not quench,
nor break the bruised reed.

167

OLD 134TH (ST. MICHAEL). (S.M.)
Doh = A♭.

French Psalter, 1551 Composed or arranged by Louis Bourgeois, 1510– ?

|s_1 :— |d :m |r :r |m :— ‖s :— |f :m |r :r |d :— ‖

|m_1 :— |m_1 :s_1 |l_1 :s_1 |s_1 :— ‖s_1 :— |d :d |d :t_1 |d :— ‖

|d :— |d :d |d :t_1 |d :— ‖r :— |f :s |s :-.f |m :— ‖

|d :— |l_1 :m_1 |f_1 :s_1 |d :— ‖t_1 :— |l_1 :d |s_1 :s_1 |d_1 :— ‖

|d :— |t_1 :l_1 |s_1 :d |d :r |m :— ‖m :— |r :d |d :t_1 |d :— ‖d |d ‖

|l_1 :— |s_1 :f_1 |m_1 :s_1 |l_1 :l_1 |se_1 :— ‖s_1 :— |f_1 :s_1 |l_1 :s_1 |s_1 :— ‖l_1 |s_1 ‖

|m :— |m :d |d :d |m :r |t_1 :— ‖d :— |l_1.t_1 :d |f :r |m :— ‖f |m ‖

|l_1 :— |m_1 :f_1 |d_1 :m_1 |l_1 :f_1 |m_1 :— ‖d_1 :— |r_1 :m_1 |f_1 :s_1 |d_1 :— ‖f_1 |d_1 ‖

A-men.

PARAPHRASE XXIII.

4 The feeble spark to flames he'll raise;
the weak will not despise;
Judgment he shall bring forth to truth,
and make the fallen rise.

5 The progress of his zeal and pow'r
shall never know decline,
Till foreign lands and distant isles
receive the law divine.

6 He who erected heav'n's bright arch,
and bade the planets roll,
Who peopled all the climes of earth,
and form'd the human soul,

7 Thus saith the Lord, Thee have I rais'd,
my Prophet thee install;
In right I've rais'd thee, and in strength
I'll succour whom I call.

8 I will establish with the lands
a covenant in thee,
To give the Gentile nations light,
and set the pris'ners free:

9 Asunder burst the gates of brass;
the iron fetters fall;
And gladsome light and liberty
are straight restor'd to all.

10 I am the Lord, and by the name
of great JEHOVAH known;
No idol shall usurp my praise,
nor mount into my throne.

11 Lo! former scenes, predicted once,
conspicuous rise to view;
And future scenes, predicted now,
shall be accomplish'd too.

12 Sing to the Lord in joyful strains!
let earth his praise resound,
Ye who upon the ocean dwell,
and fill the isles around!

13 O city of the Lord! begin
the universal song;
And let the scatter'd villages
the cheerful notes prolong.

14 Let Kedar's wilderness afar
lift up its lonely voice;
And let the tenants of the rock
with accents rude rejoice;

15 Till 'midst the streams of distant lands
the islands sound his praise;
And all combin'd, with one accord,
JEHOVAH's glories raise.

POTSDAM. (S.M.)

Doh = E. Adapted from JOHANN SEBASTIAN BACH, 1685-1750.

```
:d  |r  :f  |m   :r   |d :— |— ||s  |l :d' |t :l   |s  :— |— ||
:s, |s, :d  |d   :t,  |d :— |— ||r  |m :m  |r :r.d |t, :— |— ||
:m  |r  :d  |d.m :s.f |m :— |— ||s  |s :s  |s :fe  |s  :— |— ||
:d  |t, :l, |s,  :s,  |d :— |— ||t, |d :l, |r :r   |s, :— |— ||
```

```
:m |f  :l  |s  :f  |m :fe |s  ||d  |r  :f  |m  :r   |d :— |— ||d  |d  ||
:d |d  :d  |t, :r  |d :d  |t, ||d  |l, :r  |d  :t,  |d :— |— ||l, |s, ||
:s |f  :f  |r  :s  |s :d  |r  ||d  |f  :l  |s  :s.f |m :— |— ||f  |m  ||
:d |l, :f, |s, :t, |d :l, |s, ||l, |f, :r, |s, :s,  |d :— |— ||f, |d  ||
                                                               A-men.
```

PARAPHRASES XXIV, XXV.

24*

ISAIAH xlix. 13–17.

YE heav'ns, send forth your song of praise!
earth, raise your voice below!
Let hills and mountains join the hymn,
and joy through nature flow.

2 Behold how gracious is our God!
hear the consoling strains,
In which he cheers our drooping hearts,
and mitigates our pains.

3 Cease ye, when days of darkness come,
in sad dismay to mourn,
As if the Lord could leave his saints
forsaken or forlorn.

4 Can the fond mother e'er forget
the infant whom she bore?
And can its plaintive cries be heard,
nor move compassion more?

5 She may forget: nature may fail
a parent's heart to move;
But Sion on my heart shall dwell
in everlasting love.

6 Full in my sight, upon my hands
I have engrav'd her name:
My hands shall build her ruin'd walls,
and raise her broken frame.

25*

ISAIAH liii.

HOW few receive with cordial faith
the tidings which we bring?
How few have seen the arm reveal'd
of heav'n's eternal King?

2 The Saviour comes! no outward pomp
bespeaks his presence nigh;
No earthly beauty shines in him
to draw the carnal eye.

3 Fair as a beauteous tender flow'r
amidst the desert grows,
So slighted by a rebel race
the heav'nly Saviour rose.

4 Rejected and despis'd of men,
behold a man of woe!
Grief was his close companion still
through all his life below.

5 Yet all the griefs he felt were ours,
ours were the woes he bore:
Pangs, not his own, his spotless soul
with bitter anguish tore.

6 We held him as condemn'd by Heav'n,
an outcast from his God,
While for our sins he groan'd, he bled,
beneath his Father's rod.

PRAGUE. (S.M.) LOUIS RENATUS WEST, 1753–1826.

Doh = D. A.t.

```
:d  |m  :s  |d'  :l  |s  :— |— ||f  |m  :d    |(m)l, :t, |d  :— |— ||
:d  |d  :r  |d   :d  |d  :— |— ||r  |d  :d    |(d)f, :f, |m, :— |— ||
:m  |s  :s  |m   :f  |m  :— |— ||s  |s  :s.f  |(m)l, :r  |s, :— |— ||
:d  |d  :t, |l,  :f, |d  :— |— ||t, |d  :m.r  |(d)f, :r, |d, :— |— ||
```

f.D.

```
:d  |s  :f  |m  :d  |d  :t,     |(d)s  ||s  |d' :m  |f  :r   |d :— |— ||d  |d  ||
:m, |s, :t, |s, :l, |l, :s,.f,  |(m)t, ||t, |d  :d  |r  :t,  |d :— |— ||l, |s, ||
:d  |r  :r  |d  :m  |r  :r      |(d)s  ||r' |s  :l  |l  :s.f |m :— |— ||f  |m  ||
:l, |t, :s, |d  :l, |f, :s,     |(d,)s,||f  |m  :l, |f, :s,  |d :— |— ||f, |d  ||
```

A-men.

PARAPHRASES XXV, XXVI.

7 His sacred blood hath wash'd our souls
from sin's polluted stain;
His stripes have heal'd us, and his death
reviv'd our souls again.

8 We all, like sheep, had gone astray
in ruin's fatal road:
On him were our transgressions laid;
he bore the mighty load.

9 Wrong'd and oppress'd, how meekly he
in patient silence stood!
Mute, as the peaceful harmless lamb,
when brought to shed its blood.

10 Who can his generation tell?
from prison see him led!
With impious show of law condemn'd,
and number'd with the dead.

11 'Midst sinners low in dust he lay;
the rich a grave supply'd:
Unspotted was his blameless life;
unstain'd by sin he dy'd.

12 Yet God shall raise his head on high,
though thus he brought him low;
His sacred off'ring, when complete,
shall terminate his woe.

13 For, saith the Lord, my pleasure then
shall prosper in his hand;
His shall a num'rous offspring be,
and still his honours stand.

14 His soul, rejoicing, shall behold
the purchase of his pain;
And all the guilty whom he sav'd
shall bless Messiah's reign.

15 He with the great shall share the spoil,
and baffle all his foes;
Though rank'd with sinners, here he fell,
a conqueror he rose.

16 He dy'd to bear the guilt of men,
that sin might be forgiv'n:
He lives to bless them and defend,
and plead their cause in heav'n.

26*

ISAIAH lv.

HO! ye that thirst, approach the spring
where living waters flow:
Free to that sacred fountain all
without a price may go.

2 How long to streams of false delight
will ye in crowds repair?

170

ST. BRIDE. (S.M.)

Lah = G. Doh = B♭. SAMUEL HOWARD, 1710–82.

|l_1 :— |m_1 :l_1 |d :t_1 |l_1 :— ‖ d :— |s_1 :d |m :r |d :— ‖
|m_1 :— |m_1 :d_1.r_1 |m_1 :m_1.r_1 |d_1 :— ‖ m_1 :— |m_1 :–.f_1 |s_1 :s_1.f_1 |m_1 :— ‖
|d :— |l_1 :l_1 |l_1 :se_1 |l_1 :— ‖ m :— |d :d |d :t_1 |d :— ‖
|l_2 :— |d_1 :f_1 |m_1 :m_1 |l_2 :— ‖ l_1 :— |d.t_1 :l_1 |s_1 :s_1 |d_1 :— ‖

|m :— |r :d |t_1 :l_1 |s_1 :f_1 |m_1 :— ‖ m :— |l_1 :r |d :t_1 |l_1 :— ‖ l_1 |l_1 ‖
|s_1 :— |s_1 :m_1 |s_1 :f_1 |m_1 :r_1.d_1 |t_2 :— ‖ m_1 :— |d_1 :f_1 |l_1 :se_1 |l_1 :— ‖ f_1 |m_1 ‖
|d :— |t_1 :d |m :d |d.t_1 :l_1 |se_1 :— ‖ se_1 :— |l_1 :l_1.t_1 |d.r :m.r |d :— ‖ r |de ‖
|d :— |s_1 :l_1 |m_1 :f_1 |d_1 :r_1 |m_1 :— ‖ m_1 :— |f_1 :r_1 |m_1 :r_1 |l_2 :— ‖ r_1 |l_2 ‖

A-men.

PARAPHRASE XXVI.

How long your strength and substance waste
on trifles, light as air?

3 My stores afford those rich supplies
that health and pleasure give:
Incline your ear, and come to me;
the soul that hears shall live.

4 With you a cov'nant I will make,
that ever shall endure;
The hope which gladden'd David's heart
my mercy hath made sure.

5 Behold he comes! your leader comes,
with might and honour crown'd;
A witness who shall spread my name
to earth's remotest bound.

6 See! nations hasten to his call
from ev'ry distant shore;
Isles, yet unknown, shall bow to him,
and Isr'el's God adore.

7 Seek ye the Lord while yet his ear
is open to your call;
While offer'd mercy still is near,
before his footstool fall.

8 Let sinners quit their evil ways,
their evil thoughts forego:
And God, when they to him return,
returning grace will show.

9 He pardons with o'erflowing love:
for, hear the voice divine!
My nature is not like to yours,
nor like your ways are mine:

10 But far as heav'n's resplendent orbs
beyond earth's spot extend,
As far my thoughts, as far my ways,
your ways and thoughts transcend.

11 And as the rains from heav'n distil,
nor thither mount again,
But swell the earth with fruitful juice,
and all its tribes sustain:

12 So not a word that flows from me
shall ineffectual fall;
But universal nature prove
obedient to my call.

13 With joy and peace shall then be led
the glad converted lands;
The lofty mountains then shall sing,
the forests clap their hands.

14 Where briers grew 'midst barren wilds,
shall firs and myrtles spring;
And nature, through its utmost bounds,
eternal praises sing.

171

ST. OLAVE. (S.M.)

Doh = C. HENRY JOHN GAUNTLETT, 1805–76.

:m | f :l | s :f | m :— | — || m' | r' :d' | d' :t | d' :— | — ||
:d | d :d | d :t, | d :— | — || s | s :m | s :s | m :— | — ||
:s | l :f | s :s | s :— | — || d' | t :d' | r' :r' | d' :— | — ||
:d | f :f | m :r | d :— | — || d' | s :l | s :s | d :— | — ||

:s | l :fe | s :t | r' :-.r' | d' || l | s :m | r :m.f | m :— | — || f | m ||
:m | m :r | r :s | s :-.s | s || d | d :d | d :t, | d :— | — || d | d ||
:t | d' :l | t :r' | t :-.t | d' || d' | s :s | s :s | s :— | — || l | s ||
:m | d :r | s :s | f :-.f | m || f | m :d | s, :s, | d :— | — || f, | d ||

A-men.

PARAPHRASES XXVII, XXVIII.

27*

ISAIAH lvii. 15, 16.

THUS speaks the high and lofty One;
ye tribes of earth, give ear;
The words of your Almighty King
with sacred rev'rence hear:
2 Amidst the majesty of heav'n
my throne is fix'd on high;
And through eternity I hear
the praises of the sky:

3 Yet, looking down, I visit oft
the humble hallow'd cell;
And with the penitent who mourn
'tis my delight to dwell;
4 The downcast spirit to revive,
the sad in soul to cheer;
And from the bed of dust the man
of heart contrite to rear.

5 With me dwells no relentless wrath
against the human race;
The souls which I have form'd shall find
a refuge in my grace.

28*

ISAIAH lviii. 5–9.

ATTEND, and mark the solemn fast
which to the Lord is dear;
Disdain the false unhallow'd mask
which vain dissemblers wear.
2 Do I delight in sorrow's dress?
saith he who reigns above;
The hanging head and rueful look,
will they attract my love?

3 Let such as feel oppression's load
thy tender pity share:
And let the helpless, homeless poor,
be thy peculiar care.
4 Go, bid the hungry orphan be
with thy abundance blest;
Invite the wand'rer to thy gate,
and spread the couch of rest.

5 Let him who pines with piercing cold
by thee be warm'd and clad;
Be thine the blissful task to make
the downcast mourner glad.
6 Then, bright as morning, shall come forth,
in peace and joy, thy days;
And glory from the Lord above
shall shine on all thy ways.

172

ST. THOMAS. (S.M.)

Doh = G. *Williams's Psalmody*, 1770.

```
:s, |d  :d  |m  :r.d |r  :— |— ||m.f |s  :f.m  |f    :m     |r  :— |— ||
:s, |s, :l, |s, :s,  |s, :— |— ||s,  |s, :d    |l,.t,:d     |t, :— |— ||
:t, |d  :d  |d  :d   |t, :— |— ||t,  |d  :d    |f    :s     |s  :— |— ||
:s, |m, :f, |d, :m,  |s, :— |— ||s,  |m, :l,   |r,   :m,.f, |s, :— |— ||

:s  |m :d |r   :s,   |d  :m.,f |s  ||s    |l  :s.f   |m  :r   |d  :— |— ||d  |d  ||
:r  |d :d |t,  :s,   |s, :d    |t, ||d.t, |l, :d     |d  :t,  |d  :— |— ||l, |s, ||
:s  |s :s |s   :s.f  |m  :d    |r  ||d    |d  :s.l   |s  :-.f |m  :— |— ||f  |m  ||
:t, |d :m |s.f :m.r  |d  :l,   |s, ||m,   |f, :m,.f, |s, :s,  |d, :— |— ||f, |d, ||
                                                                            A-men.
```

PARAPHRASES XXIX, XXX.

29

LAMENT. iii. 37–40.

AMIDST the mighty, where is he
who saith, and it is done?
Each varying scene of changeful life
is from the Lord alone.

2 He gives in gladsome bow'rs to dwell,
or clothes in sorrow's shroud;
His hand hath form'd the light, his hand
hath form'd the dark'ning cloud.

3 Why should a living man complain
beneath the chast'ning rod?
Our sins afflict us; and the cross
must bring us back to God.

4 O sons of men! with anxious care
your hearts and ways explore;
Return from paths of vice to God:
return, and sin no more!

30*

HOSEA vi. 1–4.

COME, let us to the Lord our God
with contrite hearts return;
Our God is gracious, nor will leave
the desolate to mourn.

2 His voice commands the tempest forth,
and stills the stormy wave;
And though his arm be strong to smite,
'tis also strong to save.

3 Long hath the night of sorrow reign'd,
the dawn shall bring us light:
God shall appear, and we shall rise
with gladness in his sight.

4 Our hearts, if God we seek to know,
shall know him, and rejoice;
His coming like the morn shall be,
like morning songs his voice.

5 As dew upon the tender herb,
diffusing fragrance round;
As show'rs that usher in the spring,
and cheer the thirsty ground:

6 So shall his presence bless our souls,
and shed a joyful light;
That hallow'd morn shall chase away
the sorrows of the night.

173

SELMA. (S.M.)

Doh = E. ROBERT ARCHIBALD SMITH, 1780–1829.

:d |m :r |d :r.m |s :— |— ‖ s |l :s |m :s.,l |l :— |— ‖

:s, |d :t, |d :s, |t, :— |— ‖ d |d :d |d :d |d :— |— ‖

:m |s :s.f |m :r.d |r :— |— ‖ m |f :s |s :m.,f |f :— |— ‖

:d |d :s, |l, :t,.d |s, :— |— ‖ d |f :m |d :d |f, :— |— ‖

:l |s :l.d' |d' :s |l :m |r ‖ d |r.m:s |r :r |d :— |— ‖ d |d ‖

:d |d :d |d :d |d :d |t, ‖ d |s, :d |d :t, |d :— |— ‖ l, |s, ‖

:f |m :l |s :m |f :s |s ‖ m |r.d:s |l :s.f |m :— |— ‖ f |m ‖

:f, |d :f |m :d |f, :d |s, ‖ l, |t,.d:m, |f, :s, |d :— |— ‖ f, |d ‖

A-men.

PARAPHRASES XXXI, XXXII.

31

MICAH vi. 6–9.

THUS speaks the heathen: How shall man
the Pow'r Supreme adore?
With what accepted off'rings come
his mercy to implore?

2 Shall clouds of incense to the skies
with grateful odour speed?
Or victims from a thousand hills
upon the altar bleed?

3 Does justice nobler blood demand
to save the sinner's life?
Shall, trembling, in his offspring's side
the father plunge the knife?

4 No: God rejects the bloody rites
which blindfold zeal began;
His oracles of truth proclaim
the message brought to man.

5 He what is good hath clearly shown,
O favour'd race! to thee;
And what doth God require of those
who bend to him the knee?

6 Thy deeds, let sacred justice rule;
thy heart, let mercy fill;
And, walking humbly with thy God,
to him resign thy will.

32*

HABAK. iii. 17, 18.

WHAT though no flow'rs the fig-tree clothe,
though vines their fruit deny,
The labour of the olive fail,
and fields no meat supply?

2 Though from the fold, with sad surprise,
my flock cut off I see;
Though famine pine in empty stalls,
where herds were wont to be?

3 Yet in the Lord will I be glad,
and glory in his love;
In him I'll joy, who will the God
of my salvation prove.

4 He to my tardy feet shall lend
the swiftness of the roe;
Till, rais'd on high, I safely dwell
beyond the reach of woe.

5 God is the treasure of my soul,
the source of lasting joy;
A joy which want shall not impair,
nor death itself destroy.

SERENITY. (S.M.) CORNELIUS BRYAN, c. 1775–1840

Doh=G. D.t. f.G.

```
:m  |m  :r  :m  |f  :— :t, |d  :— ||(d)f  |m  :s  :d' |d' :— :t |(d')s :— ||
:d  |l, :— :s,  |f, :l, :s, |s, :— ||(s,)d |d  :— :m  |r  :m :f |(m)t, :— ||
:s  |s  :f  :de |r  :— :r  |m  :— ||(d)f  |s  :d' :s  |s  :— :s |(s)r  :— ||
:d  |f, :— :l,  |r, :— :s, |d, :— ||(m,)l,|s, :m  :d  |s  :— :s |(d)s, :— ||

:s  |s  :f  :m  |m  :r  :d  |d  :t, :l, |s, :—   ||d.t, |l, :-.t, :d .r    |m  :— :r  |d  :— ||d  |d  ||
:t, |d  :— :t,  |l, :— :l,  |f, :— :f,  |r, :—   ||s,   |s, :f,   :s,.l,   |s, :d :t,  |d  :— ||l, |s, ||
:m  |d  :r  :m  |s  :f  :m  |m  :r  :d  |d  :t,  ||d    |d  :-.r  :d       |d  :m :f   |m  :— ||f  |m  ||
:m, |l, :— :s,  |f, :— :l,  |r, :— :r,  |s, :-.f,||m,   |f, :-.r, :m,.f,   |s, :— :s,  |d, :— ||f, |d, ||
                                                                                               A-men.
```

PARAPHRASES XXXIII, XXXIV.

33*

MATT. vi. 9–14.

FATHER of all! we bow to thee,
who dwell'st in heav'n ador'd;
But present still through all thy works,
the universal Lord.

2 For ever hallow'd be thy name
by all beneath the skies;
And may thy kingdom still advance,
till grace to glory rise.

3 A grateful homage may we yield,
with hearts resign'd to thee;
And as in heav'n thy will is done,
on earth so let it be.

4 From day to day we humbly own
the hand that feeds us still:
Give us our bread, and teach to rest
contented in thy will.

5 Our sins before thee we confess;
O may they be forgiv'n!
As we to others mercy show,
we mercy beg from Heav'n.

6 Still let thy grace our life direct;
from evil guard our way;
And in temptation's fatal path
permit us not to stray.

7 For thine the pow'r, the kingdom thine;
all glory 's due to thee:
Thine from eternity they were,
and thine shall ever be.

34*

MATT. xi. 25, to the end.

THUS spoke the Saviour of the world,
and rais'd his eyes to heav'n:
To thee, O Father! Lord of all,
eternal praise be giv'n.

2 Thou to the pure and lowly heart
hast heav'nly truth reveal'd;
Which from the self-conceited mind
thy wisdom hath conceal'd.

3 Ev'n so! thou, Father, hast ordain'd
thy high decree to stand;
Nor men nor angels may presume
the reason to demand.

4 Thou only know'st the Son: from thee
my kingdom I receive;
And none the Father know but they
who in the Son believe.

175

SOUTHWELL. (S.M.)

Lah = E. Doh = G. *Damon's Psalmes*, 1579.

```
|l, :— |d  :d  |t, :t,  |l, :— ‖l, :— |d  :d  |r  :r  |m  :— ‖
|m, :— |m, :l, |l, :se, |l, :— ‖m, :— |l, :d  |d  :t, |d  :— ‖
|d  :— |d  :d  |f  :m   |d  :— ‖d  :— |m  :m  |l  :s  |s  :— ‖
|l, :— |l, :f, |r, :m,  |l, :— ‖l, :— |l, :s, |f, :s, |d  :— ‖

|m :— |s  :s  |f  :f  |m  :m  |r  :— ‖m  :— |r  :d  |t, :t,  |l, :— ‖l, |l, ‖
|d :— |d  :t, |l, :s, |s, :d  |t, :— ‖d  :— |t, :l, |l, :se, |l, :— ‖f, |m, ‖
|m :— |r  :r  |d  :r  |m  :s  |s  :— ‖s  :— |s  :m  |f  :m   |d  :— ‖r  |de ‖
|d :— |s, :s, |l, :t, |d  :m, |s, :— ‖d, :— |s, :l, |r, :m,  |l, :— ‖r, |l, ‖
                                                                    A-men.
```


5 Come then to me, all ye who groan,
with guilt and fears opprest;
Resign to me the willing heart,
and I will give you rest.
6 Take up my yoke, and learn of me
the meek and lowly mind;
And thus your weary troubled souls
repose and peace shall find.

7 For light and gentle is my yoke;
the burden I impose
Shall ease the heart, which groan'd before
beneath a load of woes.

35*

MATT. xxvi. 26–29.

'TWAS on that night, when doom'd to know
The eager rage of ev'ry foe,
That night in which he was betray'd,
The Saviour of the world took bread:
2 And, after thanks and glory giv'n
To him that rules in earth and heav'n,
That symbol of his flesh he broke,
And thus to all his foll'wers spoke:

3 My broken body thus I give
For you, for all; take, eat, and live;
And oft the sacred rite renew,
That brings my wondrous love to view.
4 Then in his hands the cup he rais'd,
And God anew he thank'd and prais'd;
While kindness in his bosom glow'd,
And from his lips salvation flow'd:

5 My blood I thus pour forth, he cries,
To cleanse the soul in sin that lies;
In this the covenant is seal'd,
And Heav'n's eternal grace reveal'd.
6 With love to man this cup is fraught,
Let all partake the sacred draught;
Through latest ages let it pour,
In mem'ry of my dying hour.

36*

LUKE i. 46–56.

MY soul and spirit, fill'd with joy,
my God and Saviour praise,
Whose goodness did from poor estate
his humble handmaid raise.
2 Me bless'd of God, the God of might,
all ages shall proclaim;
From age to age his mercy lasts,
and holy is his name.

176

SWABIA. (S.M.)

Doh = D. *Spiess's Gesangbuch*, Heidelberg, 1745.

```
:s  |m  :f  |r  :r  |d  :—  |—  ||r  |m .fe:s |s  :fe |s  :—  |—  ||
:m  |d  :d  |d  :t, |d  :—  |—  ||t, |d   :r.m|r  :r  |r  :—  |—  ||
:d' |s  :l  |s  :s  |m  :—  |—  ||s  |s   :t  |l  :l  |t  :—  |—  ||
:d  |d  :f, |s, :s, |l, :—  |—  ||s, |d  :t,.d|r  :r  |s, :—  |—  ||

:s  |l  :s  |l  :t  |d' :d' |d' ||s  |f   :m  |r  :r  |d  :—  |—  ||d  |d  ||
:m  |f  :m  |f  :f  |m  :f  |m  ||m  |r   :d  |d  :t, |d  :—  |—  ||l, |s, ||
:d' |d' :d' |d' :r' |d' :l  |s  ||d' |l .t:d' |s  :s  |m  :—  |—  ||f  |m  ||
:d  |f  :d  |f  :r  |l  :f  |d  ||d  |r  :m.f |s  :s, |d  :—  |—  ||f, |d  ||
                                                                  A-men.
```

PARAPHRASES XXXVI, XXXVII, XXXVIII.

3 Strength with his arm th' Almighty shew'd;
the proud his looks abas'd;
He cast the mighty to the ground,
the meek to honour rais'd.

4 The hungry with good things were fill'd,
the rich with hunger pin'd:
He sent his servant Isr'el help,
and call'd his love to mind;

5 Which to our fathers' ancient race
his promise did ensure,
To Abrah'm and his chosen seed,
for ever to endure.

37*

LUKE ii. 8–15.

WHILE humble shepherds watch'd their flocks
in Bethleh'm's plains by night,
An angel sent from heav'n appear'd,
and fill'd the plains with light.

2 Fear not, he said, (for sudden dread
had seiz'd their troubled mind;)
Glad tidings of great joy I bring
to you, and all mankind.

3 To you, in David's town, this day
is born, of David's line,
The Saviour, who is Christ the Lord;
and this shall be the sign:

4 The heav'nly Babe you there shall find
to human view display'd,
All meanly wrapt in swaddling-bands,
and in a manger laid.

5 Thus spake the seraph; and forthwith
appear'd a shining throng
Of angels, praising God; and thus
address'd their joyful song:

6 All glory be to God on high,
and to the earth be peace;
Good-will is shown by Heav'n to men,
and never more shall cease.

38*

LUKE ii. 25–33.

JUST and devout old Simeon liv'd;
to him it was reveal'd,
That Christ, the Lord, his eyes should see
ere death his eyelids seal'd.

2 For this consoling gift of Heav'n
to Isr'el's fallen state,
From year to year, with patient hope,
the aged saint did wait.

177

OLD 25TH. (D.S.M.)

Doh = G. *Anglo-Genevan Psalter*, 1558.

d :—	m :r	m :f	s :—		m :—	m :d	f :r	d :—	
s, :—	d :r	d :d	t, :—		s, :—	l, :d	d :t,	d :—	
m :—	s :s	m :d	r :—		d :—	d :m	l :s.f	m :—	
d :—	d :t,	l, :l,	s, :—		d :—	l, :-.s,	f, :s,	d, :—	

f.C.

m :—	r :d	s :f	m :r	m :—		lm :—	l :s	d' :t	l :—	
s, :—	s, :l,	t, :r	d :t,	d :—		lm :—	m.fe :s	l :se	l :—	
d :—	r :m.f	s :l	s :s	s :—		fd' :—	l :r'	m' :-.r'	d' :—	
d :—	t, :l,	s, :r,	m, :s,	d, :—		fd :—	d :t,	l, :m	l, :—	

3 Nor did he wait in vain; for, lo!
revolving years brought round,
In season due, the happy day,
which all his wishes crown'd.

4 When Jesus, to the temple brought
by Mary's pious care,
As Heav'n's appointed rites requir'd,
to God was offer'd there,

5 Simeon into those sacred courts
a heav'nly impulse drew;
He saw the Virgin hold her Son,
and straight his Lord he knew.

6 With holy joy upon his face
the good old father smil'd;
Then fondly in his wither'd arms
he clasp'd the promis'd child:

7 And while he held the heav'n-born Babe,
ordain'd to bless mankind,
Thus spoke, with earnest look, and heart
exulting, yet resign'd:

8 Now, Lord! according to thy word,
let me in peace depart;
Mine eyes have thy salvation seen,
and gladness fills my heart.

9 At length my arms embrace my Lord,
now let their vigour cease;
At last my eyes my Saviour see,
now let them close in peace.

10 This great salvation, long prepar'd,
and now disclos'd to view,
Hath prov'd thy love was constant still,
and promises were true.

11 That Sun I now behold, whose light
shall heathen darkness chase,
And rays of brightest glory pour
around thy chosen race.

39*

LUKE iv. 18, 19.

HARK, the glad sound, the Saviour comes!
the Saviour promis'd long;
Let ev'ry heart exult with joy,
and ev'ry voice be song!

2 On him the Spirit, largely shed,
exerts its sacred fire;
Wisdom and might, and zeal and love,
his holy breast inspire.

3 He comes! the pris'ners to relieve,
in Satan's bondage held;

G.t.

^{t}m :—	m :f	s :f	m :—		d :—	l_1 :t_1	d :r	m :—	
^{s}d :—	d :d	d :l_1	s_1 :—		s_1 :—	f_1 :f_1.s_1	l_1 :l_1	se_1 :—	
^{t}m :—	m :l	s :d	d :—		d :—	d :r	m :r	t_1 :—	
$^m l_1$:—	l_1 :f_1	m_1 :f_1	d :—		m_1 :—	f_1 :r_1	l_1 :f_1	m_1 :—	

d :—	m :m	l :s	f :m	r :—		d :—	s :m	f :r	d :—		d	d	
m_1 :—	d :t_1	l_1 :t_1	l_1.s_1 :d	t_1 :—		l_1 :—	t_1 :d	d :t_1	d :—		l_1	s_1	
l_1 :—	m :m	f :m.r	d.r :m.f	s :—		m :—	m :d	l :s.f	m :—		f	m	
l_1 :—	l_1 :s_1	f_1 :s_1	l_1.t_1 :d	s_1 :—		l_1 :—	m_1 :l_1	f_1 :s_1	d_1 :—		f_1	d_1	

A-men.

The gates of brass before him burst,
the iron fetters yield.

4 He comes! from dark'ning scales of vice
to clear the inward sight;
And on the eye-balls of the blind
to pour celestial light.

5 He comes! the broken hearts to bind,
the bleeding souls to cure;
And with the treasures of his grace
t' enrich the humble poor.

6 The sacred year has now revolv'd,
accepted of the Lord,
When Heav'n's high promise is fulfill'd,
and Isr'el is restor'd.

7 Our glad hosannahs, Prince of Peace!
thy welcome shall proclaim;
And heav'n's exalted arches ring
with thy most honour'd name.

40

LUKE XV. 13–25.

THE wretched prodigal behold
in mis'ry lying low,
Whom vice had sunk from high estate,
and plung'd in want and woe.

2 While I, despis'd and scorn'd, he cries,
starve in a foreign land,
The meanest in my father's house
is fed with bounteous hand:

3 I'll go, and with a mourning voice,
fall down before his face:
Father! I've sinn'd 'gainst Heav'n and thee,
nor can deserve thy grace.

4 He said, and hasten'd to his home,
to seek his father's love:
The father sees him from afar,
and all his bowels move.

5 He ran, and fell upon his neck,
embrac'd and kiss'd his son:
The grieving prodigal bewail'd
the follies he had done.

6 No more, my father, can I hope
to find paternal grace;
My utmost wish is to obtain
a servant's humble place.

7 Bring forth the fairest robe for him,
the joyful father said;
To him each mark of grace be shown,
and ev'ry honour paid.

8 A day of feasting I ordain;
let mirth and song abound:

LAWES (PSALM 32). (66. 66.)

Doh = G. HENRY LAWES, 1596–1662.

| d :— | r :d | f :f | m :— ‖ m :— | s :r | f :m | r :— ‖
| s_1 :— | l_1 :d | d :t_1 | d :— ‖ s_1 :— | s_1 :s_1 | l_1 :s_1.l_1 | t_1 :— ‖
| m :— | f :s | l :f | s :— ‖ m :— | r :r | d :m.f | s :— ‖
| d :— | f :m | r :r | d :— ‖ d :— | t_1 :ta_1 | l_1 :d | s_1 :— ‖

| r :— | r :m | d :r | t_1 :— ‖ s :— | f :s | m :r | d :— ‖ d | d ‖
| s_1 :— | s_1 :s_1 | l_1 :l_1 | s_1 :— ‖ s_1 :— | l_1 :s_1 | s_1.l_1 :t_1 | d :— ‖ l_1 | s_1 ‖
| t_1 :-.d | r :d | m :f | r :— ‖ d :— | d :d | d :r | m :— ‖ f | m ‖
| s_1 :-.l_1 | t_1 :d | l_1 :f_1 | s_1 :— ‖ m_1 :— | f_1 :m_1.f_1 | s_1 :s_1 | d d_1 :— ‖ f_1 | d_1 ‖

A-men.

PARAPHRASES XL, XLI, XLII.

My son was dead, and lives again!
was lost, and now is found!

9 Thus joy abounds in paradise
among the hosts of heav'n,
Soon as the sinner quits his sins,
repents, and is forgiv'n.

41*

JOHN iii. 14–19.

AS when the Hebrew prophet rais'd
the brazen serpent high,
The wounded look'd, and straight were cur'd,
the people ceas'd to die:
2 So from the Saviour on the cross
a healing virtue flows;
Who looks to him with lively faith
is sav'd from endless woes.

3 For God gave up his Son to death,
so gen'rous was his love,
That all the faithful might enjoy
eternal life above.
4 Not to condemn the sons of men
the Son of God appear'd;
No weapons in his hand are seen,
nor voice of terror heard:

5 He came to raise our fallen state,
and our lost hopes restore:
Faith leads us to the mercy-seat,
and bids us fear no more.
6 But vengeance just for ever lies
on all the rebel race,
Who God's eternal Son despise,
and scorn his offer'd grace.

42*

JOHN xiv. 1–7.

LET not your hearts with anxious thoughts
be troubled or dismay'd;
But trust in Providence divine,
and trust my gracious aid.
2 I to my Father's house return;
there num'rous mansions stand,
And glory manifold abounds
through all the happy land.

3 I go your entrance to secure,
and your abode prepare;
Regions unknown are safe to you,
when I, your friend, am there.
4 Thence shall I come, when ages close,
to take you home with me;
There we shall meet to part no more,
and still together be.

179

LEUCHARS. (66. 66.)

Doh = F. THOMAS LEGERWOOD HATELY, 1815–67.

```
|m  :—  |m  :s  |f  :m  |r  :—  ||m  :—  |d  :d  |r  :r  |m  :—  ||
|d  :—  |d  :t, |r  :d  |t, :—  ||t, :—  |l, :l, |t, :t, |d  :—  ||
|s  :—  |s  :s  |s  :s  |s  :—  ||s  :—  |m  :m  |s  :s  |s  :—  ||
|d  :—  |d  :s, |t, :d  |s, :—  ||m, :—  |l, :l, |s, :s, |d  :—  ||

|m  :—  |f  :m  |r  :d  |t,  :— ||d  :—  |r  :m  |r  :r  |d  :— ||d  |d  ||
|d  :—  |l, :d  |t, :l, |se, :— ||l, :—  |t, :d  |d  :t, |d  :— ||l, |s, ||
|s  :—  |f  :s  |s  :m  |m   :— ||m  :—  |s  :s  |l  :s  |m  :— ||f  |m  ||
|d  :—  |r  :d  |s, :l, |m,  :— ||l, :—  |s, :m, |f, :s, |d  :— ||f, |d  ||
                                                                   A-men.
```

PARAPHRASES XLII, XLIII, XLIV.

5 I am the way, the truth, the life:
no son of human race,
But such as I conduct and guide,
shall see my Father's face.

43*

JOHN xiv. 25–28.

YOU now must hear my voice no more;
my Father calls me home;
But soon from heav'n the Holy Ghost,
your Comforter, shall come.
2 That heav'nly Teacher, sent from God,
shall your whole soul inspire;
Your minds shall fill with sacred truth,
your hearts with sacred fire.

3 Peace is the gift I leave with you;
my peace to you bequeath;
Peace that shall comfort you through life,
and cheer your souls in death.
4 I give not as the world bestows,
with promise false and vain;
Nor cares, nor fears, shall wound the heart
in which my words remain.

44*

JOHN xix. 30.

BEHOLD the Saviour on the cross,
a spectacle of woe!
See from his agonizing wounds
the blood incessant flow;
2 Till death's pale ensigns o'er his cheek
and trembling lips were spread;
Till light forsook his closing eyes,
and life his drooping head!

3 'Tis finish'd—was his latest voice;
these sacred accents o'er,
He bow'd his head, gave up the ghost,
and suffer'd pain no more.
4 'Tis finish'd—The Messiah dies
for sins, but not his own;
The great redemption is complete,
and Satan's pow'r o'erthrown.

5 'Tis finish'd—All his groans are past;
his blood, his pain, and toils,
Have fully vanquished our foes,
and crown'd him with their spoils.
6 'Tis finish'd—Legal worship ends,
and gospel ages run;
All old things now are past away,
and a new world begun.

180

CROFT'S 136TH. (66. 66. 88.)

Doh = C.

WILLIAM CROFT, 1678–1727.

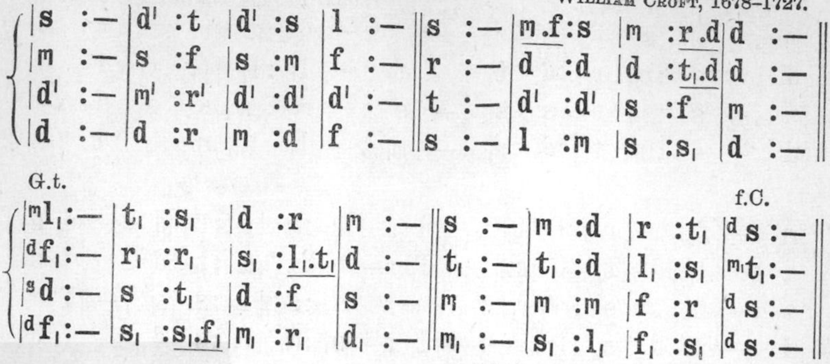

```
|s  :—  |d' :t   |d' :s  |l  :—  ||s  :—  |m.f :s  |m  :r.d  |d  :—  ||
|m  :—  |s  :f   |s  :m  |f  :—  ||r  :—  |d   :d  |d  :t,.d |d  :—  ||
|d' :—  |m' :r'  |d' :d' |d' :—  ||t  :—  |d'  :d' |s  :f    |m  :—  ||
|d  :—  |d  :r   |m  :d  |f  :—  ||s  :—  |l   :m  |s  :s,   |d  :—  ||
```

G.t.   f.C.

```
|(m)l, :— |t, :s,    |d  :r     |m  :— ||s  :— |m  :d  |r  :t, |(d)s  :— ||
|(d)f, :— |r, :r,    |s, :l,.t, |d  :— ||t, :— |t, :d  |l, :s, |(m)t, :— ||
|(s)d  :— |s  :t,    |d  :f     |s  :— ||m  :— |m  :m  |f  :r  |(d)s  :— ||
|(d)f, :— |s, :s,.f, |m, :r,    |d, :— ||m, :— |s, :l, |f, :s, |(d)s  :— ||
```

PARAPHRASES XLV, XLVI, XLVII.

45

ROMANS ii. 4–8.

UNGRATEFUL sinners! whence this scorn
of God's long-suff'ring grace?
And whence this madness that insults
th' Almighty to his face?
2 Is it because his patience waits,
and pitying bowels move,
You multiply transgressions more,
and scorn his offer'd love?

3 Dost thou not know, self-blinded man!
his goodness is design'd
To wake repentance in thy soul,
and melt thy harden'd mind?
4 And wilt thou rather chuse to meet
th' Almighty as thy foe,
And treasure up his wrath in store
against the day of woe?

5 Soon shall that fatal day approach
that must thy sentence seal,
And righteous judgments, now unknown,
in awful pomp reveal;
6 While they, who full of holy deeds
to glory seek to rise,
Continuing patient to the end,
shall gain th' immortal prize.

46

ROMANS iii. 19–22.

VAIN are the hopes the sons of men
upon their works have built;
Their hearts by nature are unclean,
their actions full of guilt.
2 Silent let Jew and Gentile stand,
without one vaunting word;
And, humbled low, confess their guilt
before heav'n's righteous Lord.

3 No hope can on the law be built
of justifying grace;
The law, that shows the sinner's guilt,
condemns him to his face.
4 Jesus! how glorious is thy grace!
when in thy name we trust,
Our faith receives a righteousness
that makes the sinner just.

47*

ROMANS vi. 1–7.

AND shall we then go on to sin,
that grace may more abound?
Great God, forbid that such a thought
should in our breast be found!

[**180** *continued*]

t :—	d' :s	l :—	d' :—	t :l	se :—	
r :—	d :m	f :—	s :—	f :d.r	m :—	
s :—	s :d'	d' :—	d' :—	r' :l	t :—	
s :—	m :d	f :—	m :—	r :f	m :—	

se :—	l :t	d' :—	s :—	m :r.d	d :—		f	m	
m :—	m :r	d :—	d :—	d :t,	d :—		d	d	
t :—	l :se	l :—	s :—	s :f	m :—		l	s	
r :—	d :t,	l, :—	m :—	s :s,	d :—		f,	d	

A-men.

PARAPHRASES XLVII, XLVIII.

2 When to the sacred font we came,
did not the rite proclaim,
That, wash'd from sin, and all its stains,
new creatures we became?

3 With Christ the Lord we dy'd to sin;
with him to life we rise,
To life, which now begun on earth,
is perfect in the skies.

4 Too long enthrall'd to Satan's sway,
we now are slaves no more;
For Christ hath vanquish'd death and sin,
our freedom to restore.

48*

ROMANS viii. 31, to the end.

LET Christian faith and hope dispel
the fears of guilt and woe;
The Lord Almighty is our friend,
and who can prove a foe?

2 He who his Son, most dear and lov'd,
gave up for us to die,
Shall he not all things freely give
that goodness can supply?

3 Behold the best, the greatest gift,
of everlasting love!
Behold the pledge of peace below,
and perfect bliss above!

4 Where is the judge who can condemn,
since God hath justify'd?
Who shall charge those with guilt or crime
for whom the Saviour dy'd?

5 The Saviour dy'd, but rose again
triumphant from the grave;
And pleads our cause at God's right hand,
omnipotent to save.

6 Who then can e'er divide us more
from Jesus and his love,
Or break the sacred chain that binds
the earth to heav'n above?

7 Let troubles rise, and terrors frown,
and days of darkness fall;
Through him all dangers we'll defy,
and more than conquer all.

8 Nor death nor life, nor earth nor hell,
nor time's destroying sway,
Can e'er efface us from his heart,
or make his love decay.

9 Each future period that will bless,
as it has bless'd the past;
He lov'd us from the first of time,
he loves us to the last.

181

DARWALL. (66. 66. 88.)

Doh = D.

JOHN DARWALL, 1731–89.

:d	m :d	s :m	d' :—	— :t	l :s	f :m
:d	d :d	r :m	m :—	— :m	f :d	t, :d
:m	s :m	s :s	l :—	— :t	d' :s	s :s
:d	d :d	t, :d	l :—	— :s	f :m	r :d

r :—	— ‖ r	m :d	l :s	fe :r	r' :d'
t, :—	— ‖ t,	d :d	m :r	r :r	r :m
s :—	— ‖ s	s :s	d' :t	l :fe	s :s
s, :—	— ‖ s,	d :m	l, :t,.d	r :r.d	t, :d

PARAPHRASE XLIX.

49*

1 COR. xiii.

THOUGH perfect eloquence adorn'd
my sweet persuading tongue,
Though I could speak in higher strains
than ever angel sung;

2 Though prophecy my soul inspir'd,
and made all myst'ries plain:
Yet, were I void of Christian love
these gifts were all in vain.

3 Nay, though my faith with boundless pow'r
ev'n mountains could remove,
I still am nothing, if I'm void
of charity and love.

4 Although with lib'ral hand I gave
my goods the poor to feed,
Nay, gave my body to the flames,
still fruitless were the deed.

5 Love suffers long; love envies not;
but love is ever kind;
She never boasteth of herself,
nor proudly lifts the mind.

6 Love harbours no suspicious thought,
is patient to the bad;
Griev'd when she hears of sins and crimes,
and in the truth is glad.

7 Love no unseemly carriage shows,
nor selfishly confin'd;
She glows with social tenderness,
and feels for all mankind.

8 Love beareth much, much she believes,
and still she hopes the best;
Love meekly suffers many a wrong,
though sore with hardship press'd.

9 Love still shall hold an endless reign
in earth and heav'n above,
When tongues shall cease, and prophets fail,
and ev'ry gift but love.

10 Here all our gifts imperfect are;
but better days draw nigh,
When perfect light shall pour its rays,
and all those shadows fly.

11 Like children here we speak and think,
amus'd with childish toys;
But when our pow'rs their manhood reach,
we'll scorn our present joys.

t :— |l :— |s :— |— ||s |l :— |t :— |d' :— |— :d
r :— |r :d |t, :— |— |d |d :— |f :— |m :— |— :d
s :— |fe :— |s :— |— |m |f :— |f :— |l :— |— :s
r :— |r :— |s, :— |— |d |f :— |r :— |l, :— |— :m

r :m |f :s |l :t |d' :r' |d' :— |t :— |d' :— |— ||d' |d'
t, :d |d :d |d :f |m :r |m :— |r :f |m :— |— |f |m
s :s |f :m |f :f |s :l |s :— |s :— |s :— |— |l |s
r :d |l, :d |f :r |m :f |s :— |s, :— |d :— |— |f |d

A-men.

[*There is a Faux-bourdon setting on the following page.*]

PARAPHRASES XLIX, L.

12 Now dark and dim, as through a glass,
are God and truth beheld;
Then shall we see as face to face,
and God shall be unvail'd.

13 Faith, Hope, and Love, now dwell on earth,
and earth by them is blest;
But Faith and Hope must yield to [Love,
of all the graces best.
14 Hope shall to full fruition rise,
and Faith be sight above:
These are the means, but this the end;
for saints for ever love.

50

1 Cor. xv. 52, to the end.

WHEN the last trumpet's awful voice
this rending earth shall shake,
When op'ning graves shall yield their charge,
and dust to life awake;
2 Those bodies that corrupted fell
shall incorrupted rise,
And mortal forms shall spring to life
immortal in the skies.

3 Behold what heav'nly prophets sung
is now at last fulfill'd, [reign,
That Death should yield his ancient
and, vanquish'd, quit the field.
4 Let Faith exalt her joyful voice,
and thus begin to sing;
O Grave! where is thy triumph now?
and where, O Death! thy sting?

5 Thy sting was sin, and conscious guilt,
'twas this that arm'd thy dart;
The law gave sin its strength and force
to pierce the sinner's heart:
6 But God, whose name be ever bless'd!
disarms that foe we dread,
And makes us conqu'rors when we die,
through Christ our living head.

7 Then stedfast let us still remain,
though dangers rise around,
And in the work prescrib'd by God
yet more and more abound;
8 Assur'd that though we labour now,
we labour not in vain,
But, through the grace of heav'n's great Lord,
th' eternal crown shall gain.

[**181** *continued*]

FAUX-BOURDON SETTING.

DARWALL. (66. 66. 88.) THOMAS CUTHBERTSON LEITHEAD PRITCHARD, 1885–

Doh = D.

```
:d  |m :d |s  :m  |d' :—    |— :m  |f  :s  |l.t :d' |r' :t |s  ||
:d  |m :d |s  :m  |d' :s    |m :d  |d  :de |r   :m  |t, :— |r  ||
:d  |m :d |s  :m  |d' :—    |— :t  |l  :s  |f   :m  |r  :— |—  ||
:d  |m :d |s  :m  |d' :m    |s :d  |f  :l, |r   :d  |s, :— |t, ||

:f  |m :s |d' :m' |r' :d'   |t  :l  |s  :— |fe :— |s  :— |— ||
:t, |d :m |m  :d  |r  :m.fe |s  :m  |r  :m |r  :d |t, :r |d ||
:r  |m :d |l  :s  |fe :r    |r' :d' |t  :— |l  :— |s  :— |— ||
:s, |d :d |l, :l, |r  :r    |s, :l, |t, :d |r  :— |s  :f |m ||
```

PARAPHRASES LI, LII.

51

2 COR. v. 1–11.

SOON shall this earthly frame, dissolv'd,
in death and ruins lie;
But better mansions wait the just,
prepar'd above the sky.

2 An house eternal, built by God,
shall lodge the holy mind,
When once those prison-walls have fall'n
by which 'tis now confin'd.

3 Hence, burden'd with a weight of clay,
we groan beneath the load,
Waiting the hour which sets us free,
and brings us home to God.

4 We know, that when the soul, uncloth'd,
shall from this body fly,
'Twill animate a purer frame
with life that cannot die.

5 Such are the hopes that cheer the just;
these hopes their God hath giv'n;
His Spirit is the earnest now,
and seals their souls for heav'n.

6 We walk by faith of joys to come,
faith grounded on his word;
But while this body is our home,
we mourn an absent Lord.

7 What faith rejoices to believe,
we long and pant to see;
We would be absent from the flesh
and present, Lord! with thee.

8 But still, or here, or going hence,
to this our labours tend,
That, in his service spent, our life
may in his favour end.

9 For, lo! before the Son, as judge,
th' assembled world shall stand,
To take the punishment or prize
from his unerring hand.

10 Impartial retributions then
our diff'rent lives await;
Our present actions, good or bad,
shall fix our future fate.

52*

PHIL. ii. 6–12.

YE who the name of Jesus bear,
his sacred steps pursue;
And let that mind which was in him
be also found in you.

:d'	d' :t	l :se	l :d'	s :m	f :s	d .r :m
:m	m :—	m :—	m :—	d :d	d :t_1	l_1 :d
:s	l :—	t :—	d' :—	— :d	r :m	f :s
:d	l_1 :—	m :—	l :—	m :d	l_1 :s_1	f_1 :d

f :s	l :t	d' :r'	m' :f'	m' :—	—	d'	d'
d :r	m :f	s :l	s :—	s :—	—	f	m
l :t	d' :r'	d' :—	t :—	d' :—	—	l	s
f :f	m :r	m :f	s :—	d :—	—	f	d

[*Copyright*, 1929, *by Oxford University Press.*]

A - men.

PARAPHRASES LII, LIII.

2 Though in the form of God he was,
his only Son declar'd,
Nor to be equally ador'd
as robb'ry did regard;

3 His greatness he for us abas'd,
for us his glory vail'd;
In human likeness dwelt on earth,
his majesty conceal'd:

4 Nor only as a man appears,
but stoops a servant low;
Submits to death, nay, bears the cross,
in all its shame and woe.

5 Hence God this gen'rous love to men
with honours just hath crown'd,
And rais'd the name of Jesus far
above all names renown'd:

6 That at this name, with sacred awe,
each humble knee should bow,
Of hosts immortal in the skies,
and nations spread below:

7 That all the prostrate pow'rs of hell
might tremble at his word,
And ev'ry tribe, and ev'ry tongue,
confess that he is Lord.

53*

1 Thess. iv. 13, to the end.

TAKE comfort, Christians, when your friends
in Jesus fall asleep;
Their better being never ends;
why then dejected weep?

2 Why inconsolable, as those
to whom no hope is giv'n?
Death is the messenger of peace,
and calls the soul to heav'n.

3 As Jesus dy'd, and rose again
victorious from the dead;
So his disciples rise, and reign
with their triumphant Head.

4 The time draws nigh, when from the clouds
Christ shall with shouts descend,
And the last trumpet's awful voice
the heav'ns and earth shall rend.

5 Then they who live shall changed be,
and they who sleep shall wake;
The graves shall yield their ancient charge,
and earth's foundations shake.

182

LAWES (PSALM 47). (66. 66. 88.)

Doh = F. HENRY LAWES, 1596-1662.

m :—	r :s	d :r	m :—	m :—	r :s	s :fe	s :—
d :—	t_1 :t_1	l_1 :t_1	d :—	d :—	t_1 :t_1	r :r.d	t_1 :—
s :—	s :s	f :f	s :—	s :—	s :s	l :l	s :—
d :—	s_1 :m_1	f_1 :r_1	d_1 :—	d :—	s_1 :m_1	r_1 :r_1	s_1 :—

s :—	s :s	l :f	s :—	s :—	f :r	m :d	r :—
r :—	r :d	d :r	d :—	d :—	l_1 :s_1	s_1 :l_1	t_1 :—
t :—	t :s	f :l	s :—	m :—	r :r	d :m	s :—
s_1 :—	s :m	f :r	m :—	d :—	r :t_1	d :l_1	s_1 :—

PARAPHRASES LIII, LIV, LV.

6 The saints of God, from death set free,
with joy shall mount on high;
The heav'nly hosts with praises loud
shall meet them in the sky.

7 Together to their Father's house
with joyful hearts they go;
And dwell for ever with the Lord,
beyond the reach of woe.

8 A few short years of evil past,
we reach the happy shore,
Where death-divided friends at last
shall meet, to part no more.

54*

2 TIM. i. 12.

I'M not asham'd to own my Lord,
or to defend his cause,
Maintain the glory of his cross,
and honour all his laws.

2 Jesus, my Lord! I know his name,
his name is all my boast;
Nor will he put my soul to shame,
nor let my hope be lost.

3 I know that safe with him remains,
protected by his pow'r,
What I've committed to his trust,
till the decisive hour.

4 Then will he own his servant's name
before his Father's face,
And in the New Jerusalem
appoint my soul a place.

55

2 TIM. iv. 6, 7, 8, 18.

MY race is run; my warfare's o'er;
the solemn hour is nigh,
When, offer'd up to God, my soul
shall wing its flight on high.

2 With heav'nly weapons I have fought
the battles of the Lord;
Finish'd my course, and kept the faith,
depending on his word.

3 Henceforth there is laid up for me
a crown which cannot fade;
The righteous Judge at that great day
shall place it on my head.

4 Nor hath the Sov'reign Lord decreed
this prize for me alone;
But for all such as love like me
th' appearance of his Son.

5 From ev'ry snare and evil work
his grace shall me defend,
And to his heav'nly kingdom safe
shall bring me in the end.

r :—	m :f	s :m	f :r	t, :—
t, :—	d :d	r :d	d :l,	s, :—
s :—	s :f	r :s	l :l	r :—
s, :—	d :l,	t, :d	l, :f,	s, :—

d :—	d :r	t, :d	m :r	d :—	d	d
s, :—	l, :l,	s, :s	d :t,	d :—	l,	s,
d :—	d :f	r :m	s :s .f	m :—	f	m
m, :—	f, :r,	s, :d	s, :s,	d, :—	f,	d
					A-men.	

PARAPHRASES LVI, LVII.

56*

TIT. iii. 3–9.

HOW wretched was our former state,
when, slaves to Satan's sway,
With hearts disorder'd and impure,
o'erwhelm'd in sin we lay!
2 But, O my soul! for ever praise,
for ever love his name,
Who turn'd thee from the fatal paths
of folly, sin, and shame.

3 Vain and presumptuous is the trust
which in our works we place,
Salvation from a higher source
flows to the human race.
4 'Tis from the mercy of our God
that all our hopes begin;
His mercy sav'd our souls from death,
and wash'd our souls from sin.

5 His Spirit, through the Saviour shed,
its sacred fire imparts,
Refines our dross, and love divine
rekindles in our hearts.
6 Thence rais'd from death, we live anew;
and, justify'd by grace,
We hope in glory to appear,
and see our Father's face.

7 Let all who hold this faith and hope
in holy deeds abound;
Thus faith approves itself sincere,
by active virtue crown'd.

57

HEB. iv. 14, to the end.

JESUS, the Son of God, who once
for us his life resign'd,
Now lives in heav'n, our great High Priest,
and never-dying friend.
2 Through life, through death, let us to him
with constancy adhere;
Faith shall supply new strength, and hope
shall banish ev'ry fear.

3 To human weakness not severe
is our High Priest above;
His heart o'erflows with tenderness,
his bowels melt with love.
4 With sympathetic feelings touch'd,
he knows our feeble frame;

183

ST. JOHN. (66. 66. 88.)

Doh = D. *Parish Choir*, 1851.

:d |m :m |s :s |d' :— |— ||d' |t :l |s :fe |s :— |— ||

:d |d :m |r :r |d :— |— ||d |r :m |r :r |r :— |— ||

:m |s :s |s :s |m :— |— ||m |s :d' |t :l |t :— |— ||

:d |d :d |t, :t, |l, :— |— ||l, |t, :d |r :r |s, :— |— ||

:s |l :t |d' :l |s :— |— ||s |f :m |r :r |d :— |— ||

:m |f :f |s :f |m :— |— ||d |d :d |d :t, |d :— |— ||

:d' |d' :r' |d' :d' |d' :— |— ||s |l :s |s :f |m :— |— ||

:d |f :r |m :f |d :— |— ||m |l, :d |s, :s, |d :— |— ||

He knows what sore temptations are,
for he has felt the same.

5 But though he felt temptation's pow'r,
unconquer'd he remain'd;
Nor, 'midst the frailty of our frame,
by sin was ever stain'd,
6 As, in the days of feeble flesh,
he pour'd forth cries and tears;
So, though exalted, still he feels
what ev'ry Christian bears.

7 Then let us, with a filial heart,
come boldly to the throne
Of grace supreme, to tell our griefs,
and all our wants make known:
8 That mercy we may there obtain
for sins and errors past,
And grace to help in time of need,
while days of trial last.

58*

ANOTHER VERSION OF THE SAME PASSAGE.

WHERE high the heav'nly temple stands,
The house of God not made with hands,
A great High Priest our nature wears,
The guardian of mankind appears.
2 He who for men their surety stood,
And pour'd on earth his precious blood,
Pursues in heav'n his mighty plan,
The Saviour and the friend of man.

3 Though now ascended up on high,
He bends on earth a brother's eye;
Partaker of the human name,
He knows the frailty of our frame.
4 Our fellow-suff'rer yet retains
A fellow-feeling of our pains;
And still remembers in the skies
His tears, his agonies, and cries.

5 In ev'ry pang that rends the heart,
The Man of sorrows had a part;
He sympathizes with our grief,
And to the suff'rer sends relief.
6 With boldness, therefore, at the throne,
Let us make all our sorrows known;
And ask the aids of heav'nly pow'r
To help us in the evil hour.

:d	d	:r	m	:d	m	:f	s		
:d	d	:t_1	d	:d	d	:d	r		
:m	m	:s	s	:s	s	:l	t		
:d	l_1	:s_1	d	:m	d	:l_1	s_1		

:s	l	:t	d'	:d'	r'	:—	t	:—	d'	:—	—	d'	d'		
:m	f	:f	s	:m	f	:—	r	:—	m	:—	—	f	m		
:d'	d'	:r'	d'	:d'	l	:—	s	:—	s	:—	—	l	s		
:d	f	:r	m	:l	f	:—	s	:—	d	:—	—	f	d		

A-men.

[*There is a Descant on the following page.*]

PARAPHRASE LIX.

59*

HEB. xii. 1–13.

BEHOLD what witnesses unseen
encompass us around;
Men, once like us, with suff'ring try'd,
but now with glory crown'd.

2 Let us, with zeal like theirs inspir'd,
begin the Christian race,
And, freed from each encumb'ring weight,
their holy footsteps trace.

3 Behold a witness nobler still,
who trod affliction's path,
Jesus, at once the finisher
and author of our faith.

4 He for the joy before him set,
so gen'rous was his love,
Endur'd the cross, despis'd the shame,
and now he reigns above.

5 If he the scorn of wicked men
with patience did sustain,
Becomes it those for whom he dy'd
to murmur or complain?

6 Have ye like him to blood, to death,
the cause of truth maintain'd?
And is your heav'nly Father's voice
forgotten or disdain'd?

7 My son, saith he, with patient mind
endure the chast'ning rod;
Believe, when by afflictions try'd,
that thou art lov'd by God.

8 His children thus most dear to him,
their heav'nly Father trains,
Through all the hard experience led
of sorrows and of pains.

9 We know he owns us for his sons,
when we correction share;
Nor wander as a bastard race,
without our Father's care.

10 A father's voice with rev'rence we
on earth have often heard;
The Father of our spirits now
demands the same regard.

11 Parents may err; but he is wise,
nor lifts the rod in vain;
His chast'nings serve to cure the soul
by salutary pain.

12 Affliction, when it spreads around,
may seem a field of woe;
Yet there, at last, the happy fruits
of righteousness shall grow.

[183 *continued*]

DESCANT.

ST. JOHN. (66. 66. 88.) THOMAS CUTHBERTSON LEITHEAD PRITCHARD, 1885–

Doh = D.

Descant.
:d |m :m |s :s |d' :— |— ||m' |r' :d' |t :l |s :— |— ||
Melody.
:d |m :m |s :s |d' :— |— ||d' |t :l |s :fe |s :— |— ||

:s |s :f |m :d' |r' :d' |t ||d' |l :d' |s :f |m :f |s ||
:s |l :t |d' :l |s :— |— ||s |f :m |r :r |d :— |— ||

PARAPHRASES LIX, LX, LXI, LXII.

13 Then let our hearts no more despond,
our hands be weak no more;
Still let us trust our Father's love,
his wisdom still adore.

60*

HEB. xiii. 20, 21.

FATHER of peace, and God of love!
we own thy pow'r to save,
That pow'r by which our Shepherd rose
victorious o'er the grave.
2 Him from the dead thou brought'st again,
when, by his sacred blood,
Confirm'd and seal'd for evermore,
th' eternal cov'nant stood.

3 O may thy Spirit seal our souls,
and mould them to thy will,
That our weak hearts no more may stray,
but keep thy precepts still;
4 That to perfection's sacred height
we nearer still may rise,
And all we think, and all we do,
be pleasing in thine eyes.

61*

1 PET. i. 3–5.

BLESS'D be the everlasting God,
the Father of our Lord;
Be his abounding mercy prais'd,
his majesty ador'd.
2 When from the dead he rais'd his Son,
and call'd him to the sky,
He gave our souls a lively hope
that they should never die.

3 To an inheritance divine
he taught our hearts to rise;
'Tis uncorrupted, undefil'd,
unfading in the skies.
4 Saints by the pow'r of God are kept
till the salvation come:
We walk by faith as strangers here;
but Christ shall call us home.

62

2 PET. iii. 3–14.

LO! in the last of days behold
a faithless race arise;
Their lawless lust their only rule;
and thus the scoffer cries;

```
{:l   |s   :f   |m   :d'  |t   :l   |s   ||
{:d   |d   :r   |m   :d   |m   :f   |s   ||

{:m'  |m'  :r'  |d'  :l   |f'  :—   |m'  :r'  |m'  :—   |—   ||d' |d' ||
{:s   |l   :t   |d'  :d'  |r'  :—   |t   :—   |d'  :—   |—   ||d' |d' ||
```

[*Copyright*, 1929, *by Oxford University Press.*] A - men.

PARAPHRASE LXII.

2 Where is the promise, deem'd so true,
that spoke the Saviour near?
E'er since our fathers slept in dust,
no change has reach'd our ear.

3 Years roll'd on years successive glide,
since first the world began,
And on the tide of time still floats,
secure, the bark of man.
4 Thus speaks the scoffer; but his words
conceal the truth he knows,
That from the waters' dark abyss
the earth at first arose.

5 But when the sons of men began
with one consent to stray,
At Heav'n's command a deluge swept
the godless race away.
6 A diff'rent fate is now prepar'd
for Nature's trembling frame;
Soon shall her orbs be all enwrapt
in one devouring flame.

7 Reserv'd are sinners for the hour
when to the gulf below,
Arm'd with the hand of sov'reign pow'r,
the Judge consigns his foe.

8 Though now, ye just! the time appears
protracted, dark, unknown,
An hour, a day, a thousand years,
to heav'n's great Lord are one.

9 Still all may share his sov'reign
in ev'ry change secure; [grace,
The meek, the suppliant contrite
shall find his mercy sure. [race,
10 The contrite race he counts his friends,
forbids the suppliant's fall;
Condemns reluctant, but extends
the hope of grace to all.

11 Yet as the night-wrapp'd thief who lurks
to seize th' expected prize,
Thus steals the hour when Christ shall come,
and thunder rend the skies.
12 Then at the loud, the solemn peal,
the heav'ns shall burst away;
The elements shall melt in flame,
at Nature's final day.

13 Since all this frame of things must end,
as Heav'n has so decreed,

184

GENEVA. (87. 87. D.)

Doh=A♭.

Adapted from Psalm 42.
French Psalter, 1551.

```
:d  |d  :r  |m  :r  |d     :t,   |l,  ||s,  |d  :r  |m  :f  |m    :r    |d
:m, |m, :s, |s, :s, |m,    :s,   |f,  ||m,  |m, :s, |s, :l, |s,   :-.f, |m,
:d  |d  :t, |d  :t, |d     :m    |d   ||d   |d  :t, |d  :d  |d    :t,   |d
:d  |l, :s, |d, :s, |l,    :m,   |f,  ||d,  |l, :s, |d  :f, |s,   :—    |d,

:d  |d  :r  |m  :r  |d     :t,   |l,  ||s,  |d  :r  |m  :f  |m    :r    |d
:m, |s, :s, |s, :s, |m,.fe,:s,   |fe, ||s,  |s, :s, |s, :f, |s,   :-.f, |m,
:d  |d  :t, |d  :s, |d     :r.m  |l,  ||t,  |d  :t, |d  :l, |d    :t,   |d
:l, |m, :s, |d, :t,,|l,,   :t,,.d,|r, ||s,  |m, :s, |d, :r, |m,.f,:s,   |d,
```

PARAPHRASES LXII, LXIII, LXIV.

How wise our inmost thoughts to guard,
and watch o'er ev'ry deed;
14 Expecting calm th' appointed hour,
when, Nature's conflict o'er,
A new and better world shall rise,
where sin is known no more.

63*

1 John iii. 1–4.

BEHOLD th' amazing gift of love
the Father hath bestow'd
On us, the sinful sons of men,
to call us sons of God!
2 Conceal'd as yet this honour lies,
by this dark world unknown,
A world that knew not when he came,
ev'n God's eternal Son.

3 High is the rank we now possess;
but higher we shall rise;
Though what we shall hereafter be
is hid from mortal eyes:
4 Our souls, we know, when he appears,
shall bear his image bright;
For all his glory, full disclos'd,
shall open to our sight.

5 A hope so great, and so divine,
may trials well endure;
And purge the soul from sense and sin,
as Christ himself is pure.

64*

Rev. i. 5–9.

TO him that lov'd the souls of men,
and wash'd us in his blood,
To royal honours rais'd our head,
and made us priests to God;
2 To him let ev'ry tongue be praise,
and ev'ry heart be love!
All grateful honours paid on earth,
and nobler songs above!

3 Behold, on flying clouds he comes!
his saints shall bless the day;
While they that pierc'd him sadly mourn
in anguish and dismay.
4 I am the First, and I the Last;
time centres all in me;
Th' Almighty God, who was, and is,
and evermore shall be.

```
:d  |m  :m  |s  :f  |m  :r  |m   ||m  |s  :s  |l  :s  |f     :m     |r  ||
:m, |s, :d  |t, :l, |l, :l, |se, ||l, |t, :d  |d  :t, |l,    :s,.l, |t, ||
:d  |d  :d  |r  :r  |d  :l, |t,  ||d  |r  :m  |f  :r  |d.r   :m.f   |s  ||
:d, |d  :l, |s, :r, |l, :f, |m,  ||l, |s, :d  |f, :s, |l,.t, :d     |s, ||

:r  |m  :s  |f  :m  |d  :r  |m  ||d  |m  :m  |f  :m  |r  :t, |d  ||d  |d  ||
:t, |d  :d  |l, :s, |l, :t, |d  ||s, |s, :l, |l, :d  |l, :s, |s, ||f, |m, ||
:s  |s  :m  |f  :d  |m  :s  |s  ||m  |d  :d  |r  :s  |f  :r  |m  ||l, |s, ||
:s, |d  :d, |f, :d  |l, :s, |d, ||d  |d  :l, |r, :m, |f, :s, |d, ||f, |d, ||
                                                                   A-men.
```

PARAPHRASE LXV.

65*

REV. v. 6, to the end.

BEHOLD the glories of the Lamb,
amidst his Father's throne;
Prepare new honours for his name,
and songs before unknown.

2 Lo! elders worship at his feet;
the church adores around,
With vials full of odours rich,
and harps of sweetest sound.

3 These odours are the pray'rs of saints,
these sounds the hymns they raise;
God bends his ear to their requests,
he loves to hear their praise.

4 Who shall the Father's record search,
and hidden things reveal?
Behold the Son that record takes,
and opens ev'ry seal.

5 Hark how th' adoring hosts above
with songs surround the throne!
Ten thousand thousand are their tongues;
but all their hearts are one.

6 Worthy the Lamb that dy'd, they cry,
to be exalted thus;
Worthy the Lamb, let us reply;
for he was slain for us.

7 To him be pow'r divine ascrib'd,
and endless blessings paid;
Salvation, glory, joy, remain
for ever on his head!

8 Thou hast redeem'd us with thy blood,
and set the pris'ners free;
Thou mad'st us kings and priests to God,
and we shall reign with thee.

9 From ev'ry kindred, ev'ry tongue,
thou brought'st thy chosen race;
And distant lands and isles have shar'd
the riches of thy grace.

10 Let all that dwell above the sky,
or on the earth below,
With fields, and floods, and ocean's shores,
to thee their homage show.

11 To Him who sits upon the throne,
the God whom we adore,
And to the Lamb that once was slain,
be glory evermore.

185

OLD 124TH. (10 10 10 10 10.)

Doh = G. *French Psalter*, 1551.

```
| d    :r .m  | f     :m       | r .d   :d .t,   | d   :—  || m     :f .s   |
| d    :t, .d | d     :d       | l, .s, :l, .s,  | s,  :—  || d     :d .d   |
| m    :s .s  | l     :s       | f .m   :r .r    | m   :—  || s     :f .m   |
| d    :s, .d | f,    :d,      | r, .m, :f, .s,  | d,  :—  || d .t, :l, .s, |

| l    :s     | f .m    :r .d    | t,  :—  || s,  :d .d    | t,  :d   |
| d    :d     | l,,t,.d :l, .l,  | s,  :—  || s,  :s, .s,  | s,  :s,  |
| f    :m     | f .s    :r .r    | r   :—  || t,  :d .m    | r   :d   |
| f,   :d,    | r, .m,  :f, .fe, | s,  :—  || s,  :m, .d,  | s,  :m,  |
```

PARAPHRASES LXVI, LXVII.

66*

REV. vii. 13, to the end.

HOW bright these glorious spirits shine!
whence all their white array?
How came they to the blissful seats
of everlasting day?
2 Lo! these are they from suff'rings great,
who came to realms of light,
And in the blood of Christ have wash'd
those robes which shine so bright.

3 Now, with triumphal palms, they stand
before the throne on high,
And serve the God they love, amidst
the glories of the sky.
4 His presence fills each heart with joy,
tunes ev'ry mouth to sing:
By day, by night, the sacred courts
with glad hosannahs ring.

5 Hunger and thirst are felt no more,
nor suns with scorching ray;
God is their sun, whose cheering beams
diffuse eternal day.
6 The Lamb which dwells amidst the throne
shall o'er them still preside;
Feed them with nourishment divine,
and all their footsteps guide.

7 'Mong pastures green he'll lead his flock,
where living streams appear;
And God the Lord from ev'ry eye
shall wipe off ev'ry tear.

67*

REV. xxi. 1–9.

LO! what a glorious sight appears
to our admiring eyes!
The former seas have pass'd away,
the former earth and skies.
2 From heav'n the New Jerus'lem comes,
all worthy of its Lord;
See all things now at last renew'd,
and paradise restor'd!

r .f :m .r	m :—		s :s .f	m :r	m .s :s .fe	s :—	
l_1 .l_1 :s_1 .s_1	s_1 :—		d :d .t_1	d :t_1	d .d :l_1,t_1.d	t_1 :—	
d .d :d .t_1	d :—		m :s .s	s :s	s .s :l .r	r :—	
f_1 .r_1 :s_1 .s_1	d_1 :—		d :m .r	d :s_1	d .m :r .r_1	s_1 :—	

m :r .d	t_1 .d :r .f	m :r	d :—		d	d	
d :t_1 .l_1	se_1 .l_1 :l_1.l_1,t_1	d :t_1	s_1 :—		f_1	m_1	
d :s .m	m .m :r .r	s :- .f	m :—		l_1	s_1	
d :s_1 .l_1	m_1 .l_1 :f_1.r_1	m_1 .f_1 :s_1	d_1 :—		f_1	d_1	

A-men.

[*There is a Descant on the following page.*]

PARAPHRASE LXVII.

3 Attending angels shout for joy,
and the bright armies sing;
Mortals! behold the sacred seat
of your descending King!

4 The God of glory down to men
removes his bless'd abode;
He dwells with men; his people they,
and he his people's God.

5 His gracious hand shall wipe the tears
from ev'ry weeping eye:
And pains and groans, and griefs and fears,
and death itself, shall die.

6 Behold, I change all human things!
saith he, whose words are true;
Lo! what was old is pass'd away,
and all things are made new!

7 I am the First, and I the Last,
through endless years the same;
I AM, is my memorial still,
and my eternal name.

8 Ho, ye that thirst! to you my grace
shall hidden streams disclose,
And open full the sacred spring,
whence life for ever flows.

9 Bless'd is the man that overcomes;
I'll own him for a son;
A rich inheritance rewards
the conquests he hath won.

10 But bloody hands and hearts unclean,
and all the lying race,
The faithless, and the scoffing crew,
who spurn at offer'd grace;

11 They, seiz'd by justice, shall be doom'd
in dark abyss to lie,
And in the fiery burning lake
the second death shall die.

12 O may we stand before the Lamb,
when earth and seas are fled,
And hear the Judge pronounce our name,
with blessings on our head!

DESCANT.

OLD 124TH. (10 10 10 10 10.) THOMAS CUTHBERTSON LEITHEAD PRITCHARD, 1885–

Doh = G.

Descant.

|m :s .s |l :- .s |f .m :r .f |m :— ||s :d' .d' |

Melody.

|d :r .m |f :m |r .d :d .t_1 |d :— ||m :f .s |

|d' :- .t |l .s :f .m |r :— ||m :d .d |r :m .s |

|l :s |f .m :r .d |t_1 :— ||s_1 :d .d |t_1 :d |

HYMNS

1

WHEN all thy mercies, O my God!
my rising soul surveys,
Transported with the view, I'm lost
in wonder, love, and praise.

2 O how shall words, with equal warmth,
the gratitude declare
That glows within my ravish'd heart!
but thou canst read it there.

3 Thy Providence my life sustain'd,
and all my wants redrest,
When in the silent womb I lay,
and hung upon the breast.

4 To all my weak complaints and cries
thy mercy lent an ear,
Ere yet my feeble thoughts had learn'd
to form themselves in pray'r.

5 Unnumber'd comforts to my soul
thy tender care bestow'd,
Before my infant heart conceiv'd
from whom these comforts flow'd.

6 When in the slipp'ry paths of youth
with heedless steps I ran;
Thine arm, unseen, convey'd me safe,
and led me up to man:

7 Through hidden dangers, toils, and deaths,
it gently clear'd my way;
And through the pleasing snares of vice,
more to be fear'd than they.

8 When worn with sickness, oft hast thou
with health renew'd my face;
And, when in sins and sorrows sunk,
reviv'd my soul with grace.

| f .l :s .f | m :— || r :m .f | s :s | s .d' :l .l | t :— ||
| r .f :m .r | m :— || s :s .f | m :r | m .s :s .fe | s :— ||

| d' .s :f .m | r .d :f .l | s :- .f | m :— || d | d ||
| m :r .d | t, .d :r .f | m :r | d :— || d | d ||

A-men.

[*Copyright*, 1929, *by Oxford University Press.*]

HYMNS I, II.

9 Thy bounteous hand with worldly bliss
hath made my cup run o'er;
And, in a kind and faithful friend,
hath doubled all my store.
10 Ten thousand thousand precious gifts
my daily thanks employ;
Nor is the least a cheerful heart,
that tastes these gifts with joy.

11 Through ev'ry period of my life
thy goodness I'll proclaim;
And after death, in distant worlds,
resume the glorious theme.
12 When nature fails, and day and night
divide thy works no more,
My ever grateful heart, O Lord,
thy mercy shall adore.

13 Through all eternity to thee
a joyful song I'll raise;
For, oh! eternity's too short
to utter all thy praise.

2

THE spacious firmament on high,
With all the blue ethereal sky,
And spangled heav'ns, a shining frame,
Their great Original proclaim.
2 Th' unweary'd sun, from day to day,
Does his Creator's pow'r display;
And publishes to ev'ry land
The work of an Almighty hand.

3 Soon as the ev'ning shades prevail,
The moon takes up the wondrous tale,
And, nightly to the list'ning earth,
Repeats the story of her birth;
4 While all the stars that round her burn,
And all the planets in their turn,
Confirm the tidings as they roll,
And spread the truth from pole to pole.

5 What though in solemn silence all
Move round the dark terrestrial ball?
What though no real voice, nor sound,
Amidst their radiant orbs be found?
6 In Reason's ear they all rejoice,
And utter forth a glorious voice;
For ever singing, as they shine,
'The hand that made us is divine.'

186

CASTLEFORD. (C.M.)

Sacred Harmony, Leeds, *c.* 1720.
Arranged by SAMUEL SEBASTIAN WESLEY, 1810–76.

Doh = E.

:d |m :r |d :l |s :f |m ||m |s :d' |t :l |s :— |— ||
:d |d :t, |d :d |d :-.t, |d ||d |r :m |r :-.d |t, :— |— ||
:m |s :-.f |m :f |r :s |s ||s |s :s |s :fe |s :— |— ||
:d |d :s, |l, :f, |s, :s, |d ||d |t, :l, |r :r |s, :— |— ||

:s |m :d |l :s |l.t :d' |t ||s |d' :d.f |m :r |d :— |— ||d |d ||
:r |d :d |d :d |f :m |r ||t, |d :d |d :t, |d :— |— ||l, |s, ||
:s |s :s |l :m |f :s |s ||s.f |m :l |s :-.f |m :— |— ||f |m ||
:t, |d :m |f :m |r :d |s, ||s, |l, :f, |s, :s, |d :— |— ||f, |d ||

A-men.

HYMNS III, IV.

3

WHEN rising from the bed of death,
o'erwhelm'd with guilt and fear,
I see my Maker face to face,
O how shall I appear!

2 If yet while pardon may be found,
and mercy may be sought,
My heart with inward horror shrinks,
and trembles at the thought;

3 When thou, O Lord! shalt stand disclos'd
in majesty severe,
And sit in judgment on my soul,
O how shall I appear!

4 But thou hast told the troubled mind,
who doth her sins lament,
That timely grief for errors past
shall future woe prevent.

5 Then see the sorrows of my heart,
ere yet it be too late;
And hear my Saviour's dying groans,
to give those sorrows weight.

6 For never shall my soul despair
of mercy at thy throne,
Who knows thine only Son has dy'd
thy justice to atone.

4

BLEST morning! whose first dawning rays
beheld the Son of God
Arise triumphant from the grave,
and leave his dark abode.

2 Wrapt in the silence of the tomb
the great Redeemer lay,
Till the revolving skies had brought
the third, th' appointed day.

3 Hell and the grave combin'd their force
to hold our Lord in vain;
Sudden the Conqueror arose,
and burst their feeble chain.

4 To thy great name, Almighty Lord!
we sacred honours pay,
And loud hosannahs shall proclaim
the triumphs of the day.

5 Salvation and immortal praise
to our victorious King!
Let heav'n and earth, and rocks and seas,
with glad hosannahs ring.

6 To Father, Son, and Holy Ghost,
the God whom we adore,
Be glory, as it was, and is,
and shall be evermore.

EPWORTH. (C.M.)

Doh = E♭. CHARLES WESLEY, 1757–1834.

:d	m :s	d' :-.m	r.l :s.f	m	s	d' :t	l.s :fe	s :—	—					
:d	d :r	d :d	d :t_1	d	d	d :r	m :r	r :—	—					
:m	s :s	m :m	f :r	m	m	m.fe :s	d' :l	t :—	—					
:d	d :t_1	l_1 :s_1	f_1 :s_1	d	d.t_1	l_1 :t_1	d :r	s_1 :—	—					

:s	f :m	l :-.f	m :r	s	s	d' :d.r	m :r	d :—	—	d	d
:m	r :de	r :-.r	d :t_1	d	d	d :d	d :t_1	d :—	—	l_1	s_1
:t	l :l	l :-.l	s :s	s	m	m :l	s :-.f	m :—	—	f	m
:m	l :s	f :m.r	s :f	m	d	l_1 :f_1	s_1 :s_1	d :—	—	f_1	d

A-men.

HYMN V.

5

THE hour of my departure's come;
I hear the voice that calls me home;
At last, O Lord! let trouble cease,
And let thy servant die in peace.

2 The race appointed I have run;
The combat 's o'er, the prize is won;
And now my witness is on high,
And now my record 's in the sky.

3 Not in mine innocence I trust;
I bow before thee in the dust;
And through my Saviour's blood alone
I look for mercy at thy throne.

4 I leave the world without a tear,
Save for the friends I held so dear;
To heal their sorrows, Lord, descend,
And to the friendless prove a friend.

5 I come, I come, at thy command,
I give my spirit to thy hand;
Stretch forth thine everlasting arms,
And shield me in the last alarms.

6 The hour of my departure 's come;
I hear the voice that calls me home:
Now, O my God! let trouble cease;
Now let thy servant die in peace.

188

NORWICH. (C.M.)

Lah = E. Doh = G. *Ravenscroft's Psalter*, 1621.

```
|l, :—  |d  :r  |m  :m  |f  :f   |m  :— || m  :— |f  :d  |r  :r     |d  :— ||
|m, :—  |l, :l, |se,:l, |l, :s,  |s, :— || s, :— |l, :m, |s, :s,.f, |m, :— ||
|d  :—  |m  :r  |t, :d  |d  :t,  |d  :— || d  :— |d  :d  |d  :t,    |d  :— ||
|l, :—  |l, :f, |m, :l, |r, :s,  |d, :— || d, :— |f, :l, |s, :s,    |d, :— ||

|d  :—  |m  :f  |s  :m  |r  :d      |t, :— || m  :— |r     :l,   |d  :t,  |l, :— || l, |l, ||
|m, :—  |t, :l, |s, :s, |l, :m,.f,  |s, :— || m, :— |l,    :l,   |l, :se, |l, :— || f, |m, ||
|l, :—  |t, :d  |d  :m  |f  :d      |r  :— || d  :— |l,.t, :d.r  |m  :-.r |d  :— || r  |de ||
|l, :—  |s, :f, |m, :d  |f, :l,     |s, :— || d, :— |f,    :f,   |m, :m,  |l, :— || r, |l, ||
                                                                               A-men.
```

PASSAGES OF SCRIPTURE PARAPHRASED.

HYMNS.

189

INVOCATION. (D.C.M.) ROBERT ARCHIBALD SMITH, 1780–1829.

Psalm xliii. 3–5.

Doh = E♭.

```
:d .m |s  :s .f |m  :f  |m  :r   |d    || r  |m  :l .s  |s .f :m.s,f |m  :r  ||
:d    |m  :r    |d  :d  |d  :t,  |d    || t, |d  :f .m  |m .r :d.m,r |d  :t, ||
3. O   send thy  light forth and thy truth; let them be guides to me,
5. Why art thou  then cast down, my soul?   what should dis- cour - age thee?
:m .s |d' :t    |d' :l  |s  :s .f |m   || s  |s  :d'    |s  :s       |s  :—  ||
:d    |d  :s,   |l, :f, |s, :s,  |d    || s, |d  :d     |t, :d       |s, :—  ||
```

B♭.t.

```
:r  |s  :f  |m  :s  |d'f .m   :r .d    |d .t, |r .m,f |m .s :f .r |d  :t,    |r  :d
:t, |t, :r  |d  :r  |m l, .s, :f, .l,  |s,    |s,     |s,  :l,    |s, :s,    |s, :—
And bring me to thine ho - ly hill, ev'n where thy dwell-ing be.
And why with vex-ing thoughts art thou dis- qui - et - ed in me?
:s  |r  :s  |s  :t  |d'f .d   :r .f    |m .r  |t,.d,r |d .m :r .f |m  :r.m,f |f  :m
:s, |s, :t, |d  :t, |l r, .m, :f,      |s,    |s,     |d   :f,    |s, :s,    |d, :—
```

f.E♭.

```
:d s .f |m  :s  |d' :s .d' |t.l :s.f |m  || m .f |s .l :t.d' |l  :r' |d' :t
:m t,   |d  :r  |m  :m     |f   :m.r |d  || d .r |m .f :r.m  |f  :f  |m  :r
4. Then will I to God's al - tar go, to God my chief-est joy:
Still trust in God; for him to praise good cause I yet shall have:
:d s    |s  :t  |d' :d'    |d'  :t   |d' ||      |     :     |   :    |    :
:d s,   |d  :t, |l, :d     |f,  :s,  |d  ||      |     :     |   :    |    :
```

```
:t      |d' :s  |s .f :m     |f .m  :l  |s  :     |    :m .s
:r.m,f  |m  :m  |r    :d     |d     :d  |d  :     |    :d .r
Yea, God, my God, thy name to praise, my harp, my
He of my count' - nance is the health, my God, my
:s      |s  :s  |s    :s     |f .m  :f  |m  :s .f |m   :d' .t
:s      |d  :d  |t,   :d .ta,|l, .s, :f,|d  :m .r |d   :
```

rallentando.

```
|d' :s  |l  :l  |s  :s .f |m  :f  |m  :r  |d  || d  |d  ||
|m  :m  |f  :f  |m  :r    |d  :d  |d  :t, |d  || l, |s, ||
harp, my harp I will em - ploy, I will em - ploy.
God, my God, that doth me save, that doth me save. A - men.
|l  :d' |d' :d' |d' :t    |d' :l  |s  :s .f |m || f  |m  ||
|   :d  |f, :f, |s, :s,   |l, :f, |s, :s,   |d || f, |d  ||
```

190

ST. GEORGE'S, EDINBURGH. (D.C.M.) ANDREW MITCHELL THOMSON, 1788–1831.

Psalm xxiv. 7–10.

Doh = F.

: |d :— |d :r |m :f |s :— |s :— |s :— |— :s |f :m |r :d
: |d :— |d :t, |d :r |m :— |f :— |m :— |— :m |r :d |t, :d
7. Ye gates, lift up your heads on high; ye doors that last for
9. Ye gates, lift up your heads; ye doors, doors that do last for
: |m :— |s :s |s :f |m :d' |t :— |d' :— |— :s |s :s |s :s
: |d :— |m :f |m :r |d :— |s, :— |d :— |— :d |t, :d |f :m.d

|m :— |r |r |m :f |s :d'.t |l :-.s |s :d.r |m :s |f :r |d :— |—
|d :— |t, |t, |d :t, |d :d |d :-.d |d :d.t, |d :d |r :t, |d :— |—
aye, . . Be lift - ed up, that so the King of glo - ry en - ter may.
aye, . . Be lift - ed up, that so the King of glo - ry en - ter may.
|s :— |— |s |s :s |s :s |l :-.d' |d' :s |s :s |l :s.f |m :— |—
|s :— |— |s, |d :r |m :m.s |f :-.m |m :m.r |d :m, |f, :s, |d :— |—

1st time.

: | : | : | : | : | : | :s |d' :s |m :d |s :— |—
: | : | : | : | : | : | :s |d' :s |m :d |s :— |—
8. But who of glo-ry is the King? The migh-ty Lord is this;
:m |s :— |— :s |s :s |s :fe |s :— |— :s |d' :s |m :d |s :— |—
:d |t, :— |— :m |d :t, |l, :r |s, :— |— :s, |d :s, |m, :d, |s, :— |—

2nd time.

: | : | : | : | : | : .s |s :s |d' :s |m :d |s :— |—
: | : | : | : | : | : .s |s :s |d' :s |m :d |s :— |—
10. But who is he that is the King, the King of glo - ry? who is this?
:m |s :— |— :s |s :-.s |s :fe |s :-.s |s :s |d' :s |m :d |s :— |—
:d |t, :— |— :m |d :-.t, |l, :r |s, :-.s, |s, :s, |d :s, |m, :d, |s, :— |—

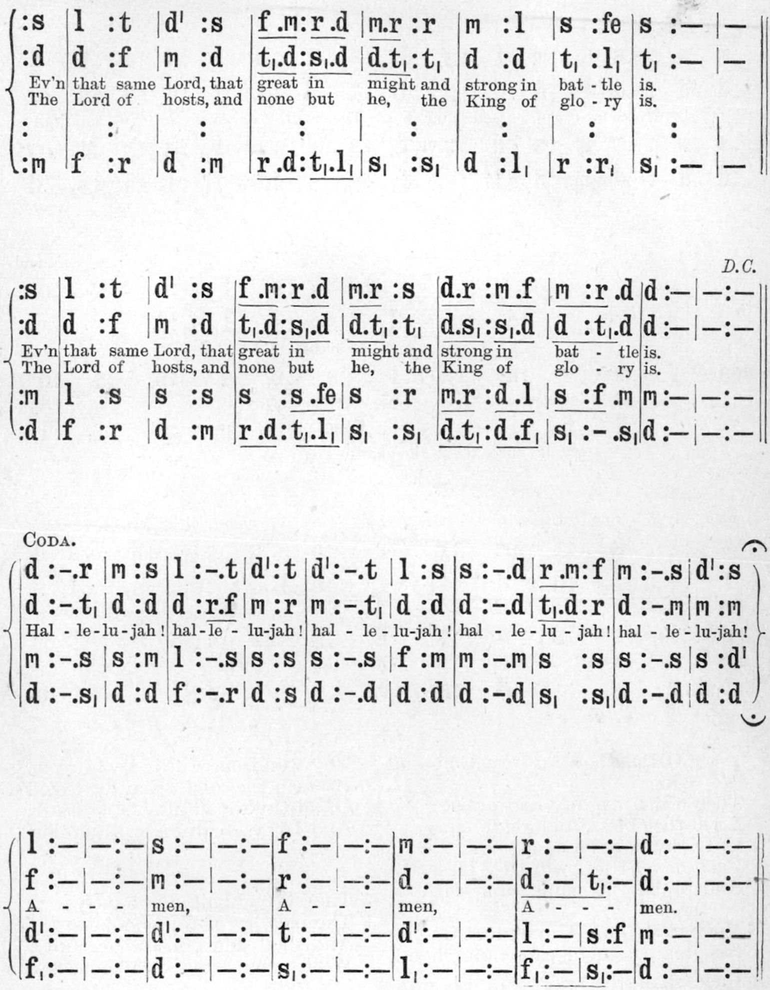

:s |l :t |d' :s |f .m:r .d |m.r :r |m :l |s :fe |s :— |—

:d |d :f |m :d |t,.d:s,.d |d.t,:t, |d :d |t, :l, |t, :— |—

Ev'n that same Lord, that great in might and strong in bat - tle is.

The Lord of hosts, and none but he, the King of glo - ry is.

: | : | : | : | : | : | : | : |

:m |f :r |d :m |r .d:t,.l, |s, :s, |d :l, |r :r, |s, :— |—

D.C.

:s |l :t |d' :s |f .m:r .d |m.r :s |d.r :m .f |m :r .d |d :— |— :—

:d |d :f |m :d |t,.d:s,.d |d.t,:t, |d.s,:s,.d |d :t,.d |d :— |— :—

Ev'n that same Lord, that great in might and strong in bat - tle is.

The Lord of hosts, and none but he, the King of glo - ry is.

:m |l :s |s :s |s :s .fe |s :r |m.r :d .l |s :f .m |m :— |— :—

:d |f :r |d :m |r .d:t,.l, |s, :s, |d.t,:d .f, |s, :- .s, |d :— |— :—

Coda.

d :-.r |m :s |l :-.t |d' :t |d' :-.t |l :s |s :-.d |r .m:f |m :-.s |d' :s

d :-.t, |d :d |d :r.f |m :r |m :-.t, |d :d |d :-.d |t,.d:r |d :-.m |m :m

Hal - le-lu-jah! hal-le - lu-jah! hal - le-lu-jah! hal - le-lu - jah! hal - le-lu-jah!

m :-.s |s :m |l :-.s |s :s |s :-.s |f :m |m :-.m |s :s |s :-.s |s :d'

d :-.s, |d :d |f :-.r |d :s |d :-.d |d :d |d :-.d |s, :s, |d :-.d |d :d

l :— |— :— |s :— |— :— |f :— |— :— |m :— |— :— |r :— |— :— |d :— |— :—

f :— |— :— |m :— |— :— |r :— |— :— |d :— |— :— |d :— |t, :— |d :— |— :—

A - - - men, A - - - men, A - - - men.

d' :— |— :— |d' :— |— :— |t :— |— :— |d' :— |— :— |l :— |s :f |m :— |— :—

f, :— |— :— |d :— |— :— |s, :— |— :— |l, :— |— :— |f, :— |s, :— |d :— |— :—

191

ABERFELDY. (L.M.) *Scottish Psalter*, Aberdeen, 1633.

Psalm cxlv. 1–8 (second version).

Doh = F.

```
:m |s :-.s |s :m |f :s |l :s |f :m |r :d |d :t, |d ||
:d |d :-.d |r :d |d :ta, |l, :d |d :d.t, |l, :d |s, :s, |s, ||
1. O Lord, thou art my God and King; Thee will I mag - ni - fy and praise:
:s |m :-.m |s :s |d :r.m |f :s |l :s |f :m.f |r :r |m ||
:d |d :-.d |t, :d |l, :s, |f, :m, |l, :d |f, :l, |s, :s, |d ||

I will thee bless, and
: | : | : | : | :s |f :m |r :d'
: | : | :d |t, :l, |s, :s, |l,.t, :d |r :m
I will thee bless, and glad - ly sing Un -
:s |f :m |r :d |r.m :f |s :s |s :s |s :d
I will thee bless, and glad - ly sing Un - to thy ho - ly
: | :d |t, :l, |s,.s, :f,.f, |m, :m |r :d |t, :l,
I will thee bless, and glad-ly sing

glad - ly sing Un - to thy ho - ly name al - ways.
t :l |s :f |m :r |r :d |d :t, |d ||d |d ||
r :-.d |t, :d.r |d :t, |l, :s,.l, |s, :s, |s, ||l, |s, ||
to . . . . . thy ho - ly . . . . name al - ways. A- men.
r.m :fe |s :s |s :s |f :m |r :r |m ||f |m ||
name al - ways, Un- to thy ho - ly name al - ways.
t,.d :r |s, :l,.t, |d :s, |r, :m,.f, |s, :s, |d, ||f, |d, ||
```

O LORD, thou art my God and King;
Thee will I magnify and praise:
I will thee bless, and gladly sing
Unto thy holy name always.

2 Each day I rise I will thee bless,
And praise thy name time without end.

3 Much to be prais'd, and great God is;
His greatness none can comprehend.

4 Race shall thy works praise unto race,
The mighty acts show done by thee.

5 I will speak of the glorious grace,
And honour of thy majesty;
Thy wondrous works I will record.

6 By men the might shall be extoll'd
Of all thy dreadful acts, O Lord:
And I thy greatness will unfold.

7 They utter shall abundantly
The mem'ry of thy goodness great;
And shall sing praises cheerfully,
Whilst they thy righteousness relate.

8 The Lord our God is gracious,
Compassionate is he also;
In mercy he is plenteous,
But unto wrath and anger slow.

192

BON ACCORD. (C.M.) Psalm xcv. *Scottish Psalter*, Aberdeen, 1625

Doh = G.

:s |s :d |t, :-.d |r :m |r :s |m :d |r :r |d :— |— ||
:d |d :s, |s, :-.s, |s, :-.l, |t, :s, |s, :d |d :t, |d :— |— ||
1. O | come, let us sing | to the Lord : come, | let us ev' - ry | one
:m |m :s |f :-.m |r :d |r :r |d :m |s :f |m :— |— ||
:d |d :m |r :-.d |t, :d |s, :t, |d :l, |s, :s, |d :— |— ||

A joy - ful noise make
: | : | : | : | :s |f :m |r :d
: | : | :d |t, :l, |s, :d |l,.t, :d |l,.r, :m,.fe,
A joy - ful noise make to the Rock of our sal-
:s |f :m |r :d |r.m :f |s :m |f :s |l :d
A joy - ful noise make to the Rock of our . . . . . sal -
: | :d |t, :l, |s, :f, |m, :d, |r, :m, |f, :l,
A joy - ful noise make to the Rock of our sal

to the Rock
t, :-.d |r :m |r :d |d :t, |d :— |— || d |d ||
s, :-.fe, |s, :s, |l, :m,.f, |s,.l, :s,.f, |m, :— |— || f, |m, ||
va - tion, of our sal - va - tion. A- men.
r :-.r |r :d |l, :d |r :r |d :— |— || l, |s, ||
va - tion.
s, :-.l, |t, :d |f, :l, |s, :s, |d, :— |— || f, |d, ||
va - tion, of our sal - va - tion.

O COME, let us sing to the Lord:
come, let us ev'ry one
A joyful noise make to the Rock
of our salvation.

2 Let us before his presence come
with praise and thankful voice;
Let us sing psalms to him with grace,
and make a joyful noise.

3 For God, a great God, and great King,
above all gods he is.
4 Depths of the earth are in his hand,
the strength of hills is his.

5 To him the spacious sea belongs,
for he the same did make;
The dry land also from his hands
its form at first did take.

6 O come, and let us worship him,
let us bow down withal,
And on our knees before the Lord
our Maker let us fall.

7 For he 's our God, the people we
of his own pasture are,
And of his hand the sheep; to-day,
if ye his voice will hear,

8 Then harden not your hearts, as in
the provocation,
As in the desert, on the day
of the tentation:

9 When me your fathers tempt'd and prov'd,
and did my working see;
10 Ev'n for the space of forty years
this race hath grieved me.

I said, This people errs in heart,
my ways they do not know:
11 To whom I sware in wrath, that to
my rest they should not go.

ALPHABETICAL INDEX OF TUNES

* *Denotes that the tune has at the numbers so marked a Descant or Faux-bourdon, or that there is a varied accompaniment for unison singing in the Appendix of the Staff notation editions.*

(*Where the name of a tune appears in alphabetical order in brackets, the tune is indexed elsewhere under another name.*)

METRICAL INDEX OF TUNES

** Denotes that the tune has a Descant, Faux-bourdon, or varied accompaniment in the Staff notation editions.*

DOUBLE COMMON METRE (D.C.M.)

LONG METRE (L.M.)

DOUBLE LONG METRE (D.L.M.)

6666

66 66 88

87 87 D.

10 10 10 10 10

FAUX-BOURDONS

DESCANTS

VARIED ACCOMPANIMENTS
(in Appendix to Staff notation editions)

INDEX OF COMPOSERS, ARRANGERS, AND SOURCES OF TUNES

** Denotes a Descant, Faux-bourdon, or arrangement by the person named. App. signifies the Appendix to the Staff notation editions.*

Anchors' Collection of Psalm Tunes, c. 1720.
Walsall, 139.
ANDERSON, JAMES SMITH, 1853–.
*Old 18th, 149.
Anglo-Genevan Psalter, 1556. Old 22nd, 150.
Old 29th, 151.
Old 44th, 152.
Old 137th, 155.
1558. Old 25th, 177.
Old 68th, 153.
ARNOLD, SAMUEL, 1740–1802.
Arnold, 25.
Arnold's (Dr.) Psalms, 1791.
Langholm, 79.
As Hymnodus Sacer, Leipsic, 1625.
Breslau, 3.
Ashworth's Collection, c. 1760.
St. Thomas, 123.

BACH, JOHANN SEBASTIAN, 1685–1750.
Potsdam, 168.
Barton's Psalms, 1706.
Coleshill, 42.
BEETHOVEN, LUDWIG VAN, 1770–1827.
Consolation, 43.
BOURGEOIS, LOUIS, 1510–?
*Old 134th, 167.
*Psalm 107, 157.
BROOMFIELD, WILLIAM ROBERT, 1826–88.
St. Kilda, 111.
BRYAN, CORNELIUS, c. 1775–1840.
Serenity, 174.

CAMPBELL, JOHN, 1807–60.
Orlington, 93.
Chalmers's Collection, Aberdeen, 1749.
St. Paul, 120.
Chetham's Psalmody, 1718.
Burford, 36.
CLARK, JEREMIAH, c. 1659–1707.
Bishopthorpe, 32.
Brockham (Confidence), 4.
Hermon, 69.
King's Norton, 77.
St. Magnus (Nottingham), 114.
Uffingham, 18.
CLARK, THOMAS, 1775–1859.
Crediton, 46.
COCKBURN, ROBERT WILLIAM, 1879–.
*Old 100th, *App.* 13.
COOPER, GEORGE, 1820–76.
St. Sepulchre, 15.
COURTEVILLE, RAPHAEL, ?–1772.
St. James, 110.
CROFT, WILLIAM, 1678–1727.
Croft's 136th, 180.
Eatington, 54.
St. Anne, 100.
St. Matthew, 159.
CROTCH, WILLIAM, 1775–1847.
Sidon, 127.
CRÜGER, JOHANN, 1598–1662.
Gräfenberg, 65.

Damon's Psalmes.
1579. Southwell, 175.
1591. Dundee (Windsor), 51.
DARWALL, JOHN, 1731–89.
Darwall, 181.
Dibdin's Standard Psalm Tune Book, 1857.
Uxbridge, 138.
DOUGALL, NEIL, 1776–1862.
Kilmarnock, 75.

English Psalter.
1561. Old 18th, 149.
1562. Old 81st, 154.
St. Flavian, 105.
Este's Psalter, 1592.
Cheshire, 39.
Winchester, 145.

FARRANT, RICHARD, c. 1530–80.
Farrant, 59.
FINK, GOTTFRIED WILHELM, 1783–1846.
Evangel, 147.

INDEX OF FIRST LINES WITH SUGGESTED TUNES

The Selections most suitable for use in Public Worship are indicated in italics.

PSALMS

INDEX OF FIRST LINES

PARAPHRASES

INDEX OF FIRST LINES

INDEX OF FIRST LINES

HYMNS

SUBJECT INDEX TO THE SELECTION OF PSALMS AND PARAPHRASES

SUBJECT INDEX

SUBJECT INDEX

SUBJECT INDEX

SUBJECT INDEX

SELECTION OF PSALMS AND PARAPHRASES MOST SUITABLE FOR USE IN PUBLIC WORSHIP WITH SUGGESTED TUNES

PSALMS

No. of Psalm.	First Line.	Tune.
1	That man hath perfect blessedness	Tallis, 135; Jackson, 74.
4	Give ear unto me when I call (1, 6–8)	Durham, 53; Abbey, 24.
5	Give ear unto my words, O Lord (1, *5a*–7)	Moravia, 89.
8	How excellent in all the earth	Winchester, 145.
9	God shall endure for aye; he doth (7–11)	Stroudwater, 134.
15	Within thy tabernacle, Lord	Gräfenberg, 65.
16	God is of mine inheritance (5–11)	Salisbury, 124; Dunfermline, 52.
19	The heavens God's glory do declare (1–6)	Aspurg, 26.
	God's law is perfect, and converts (7–14)	St. Andrew, 99.
20	Jehovah hear thee in the day (1–5)	St. Matthias, 116; St. Neot, 118.
22	Praise ye the Lord, who do him fear (23–28)	Old 22nd, 150; Praetorius, 96.
23	The Lord 's my shepherd, I'll not want	Wiltshire, 144; Martyrdom, 84, 85.
24	The earth belongs unto the Lord (1–5)	Tallis, 135.
	Ye gates, lift up your heads on high (7–10)	St. Magnus, 114; St. George's, Edinburgh, 190.
25	(i) Shew me thy ways, O Lord (4–10)	Old 25th, 177; Franconia, 164.
	God good and upright is (8–12)	Old 134th, 167; Aynhoe, 160.
	O do thou keep my soul (20–22)	St. Bride, 170.
26	Mine hands in innocence, O Lord (6–8)	St. Thomas, 123.
27	The Lord 's my light and saving health (1–4)	Durham, 53; Drumclog, 49.
	One thing I of the Lord desired (4–6)	Bishopthorpe, 32.
	O Lord, give ear unto my voice (7–8, 13–14)	Cheshire, 39.
28	For ever blessed be the Lord (6–9)	Gloucester, 64.
30	Lord, I will thee extol, for thou (1–5)	Norwich, 188; St. David, 103.
31	In thee, O Lord, I put my trust (1–3, 5)	St. David, 103.
	How great 's the goodness thou for them (19–20, 23–24)	Caithness, 37; Bloxham, 33.
32	O blessed is the man to whom (1–2, 5–7)	Wigtown, 143.
33	Ye righteous, in the Lord rejoice (1–5)	Colchester, 41.
	That nation blessed is, whose God (12–14, 18–22)	St. Matthias, 116.

No. of Psalm.	First Line.	Tune.
34	God will I bless all times: his praise (1–9)	St. Thomas, 123; St. David, 103.
	O children, hither do ye come (11–15, 17–19)	St. Flavian, 105; Salisbury, 124.
36	Thy mercy, Lord, is in the heavens (5–10)	London New, 82.
37	Set thou thy trust upon the Lord (3–7, 23–24)	Bristol, 34.
40	I waited for the Lord my God (1–5)	Ballerma, 27.
42	Like as the hart for water-brooks (1–5)	Glenluce, 63; Elgin, 57.
43	O send thy light forth and thy truth (3–5)	Martyrs, 86; Invocation, 189.
45	(ii) My heart inditing is (1–4, 6)	Narenza, 166; Old 134th, 167.
46	God is our refuge and our strength (1–5)	Stroudwater, 134.
	The Lord of hosts upon our side (7–11)	St. Nicholas, 119.
48	Great is the Lord, and greatly he (1–2, 10–14)	St. Magnus, 114.
50	(i) The mighty God, the Lord (1–6)	Hampton, 165.
51	After thy loving-kindness, Lord (1–3, 7–13)	St. Mary, 115; St. Kilda, 111.
	My closed lips, O Lord, by thee (15–18)	Lincoln, 80.
57	Be merciful to me, O God (1–3)	Martyrdom, 84, 85.
	Be thou exalted very high (5, 7–11)	Colchester, 41.
61	O God, give ear unto my cry (1–5, 8)	Salzburg, 125; Old 18th, 149.
62	My soul, wait thou with patience (5–8)	Howard, 70.
63	Lord, thee, my God, I'll early seek (1–8)	Jackson, 74.
65	Praise waits for thee in Sion, Lord (1–4)	St. Stephen, 122.
	O God of our salvation (5–8)	Tallis, 135.
	The earth thou visit'st, watering it (9–13)	Glasgow, 62.
66	All lands to God, in joyful sounds (1–4, 8–9, 20)	Crediton, 46.
67	(i) Lord, bless and pity us	Selma, 173.
68	O God, what time thou didst go forth (7–11)	St. Anne, 100.
	Thou hast, O Lord, most glorious (18–20)	Sheffield, 126.
	O all ye kingdoms of the earth (32–35)	Old 68th, 153; Southwark, 129.
72	O Lord, thy judgments give the king (1–8)	Liverpool, 81; Petersham, 156.
	His large and great dominion shall (8–16)	Warwick, 140.
	His name for ever shall endure (17–19)	Effingham, 56; St. Lawrence, 112.
73	Yet God is good to Israel (1–2, 23–26)	Melrose, 87; Westminster, 141.
78	The praises of the Lord our God (4*b*–7)	Caithness, 37.
80	O God of hosts, we thee beseech (14–15, 17–19)	Morven, 90; Caroline, 38.
84	How lovely is thy dwelling-place (1–5)	Harington, 66; Arnold, 25.
	Lord God of hosts, my prayer hear (8–12)	Wetherby, 142; Melrose, 87.
85	I'll hear what God the Lord will speak (8–13)	Wigtown, 143.
86	Hear, Lord, my prayer: unto the voice (6–12)	Burford, 36.

No. of Psalm.	First Line.	Tune.
89	God's mercies I will ever sing (1–2, 5–7)	University, 137.
	O thou that art the Lord of hosts (8–9, 13–14)	Culross, 48.
	O greatly bless'd the people are (15–18)	Newington, 92.
90	Lord, thou hast been our dwelling-place (1–2, 14–17)	Dundee, 51; St. Anne, 100.
	O with thy tender mercies, Lord (14–17)	Kilmarnock, 75.
92	To render thanks unto the Lord (1–4)	Howard, 70; St. Stephen, 122.
93	The Lord doth reign, and cloth'd is he	Stroudwater, 134.
95	O come, let us sing to the Lord (1–6)	Bon Accord, 192; Irish, 73.
96	O sing a new song to the Lord (1–6)	Southwark, 129.
	Give ye the glory to the Lord (8–13)	Praetorius, 96.
97	God reigneth, let the earth be glad (1–2, 9–12)	Stockton, 132.
98	O sing a new song to the Lord	St. Magnus, 114.
100	(i) All people that on earth do dwell	Old 100th, 13.
102	(ii) Thou shalt arise, and mercy yet (13–22)	Duke Street, 9.
	Thy years throughout all ages last (24*b*–28)	Saxony, 16.
103	O thou my soul, bless God the Lord (1–5)	Coleshill, 42.
	The Lord our God is merciful (8–13)	Chichester, 40.
	Such pity as a father hath (13–18)	Kilmarnock, 75.
	The Lord prepared hath his throne (19–22)	Gloucester, 64.
104	Bless God, my soul. O Lord my God (1–5, 33–34)	Bishopthorpe, 32.
105	Give thanks to God, call on his name (1–5, 7)	St. Gregory, 109.
106	Give praise and thanks unto the Lord (1–5)	Dunfermline, 52.
	Bless'd be Jehovah, Isr'el's God (48)	St. Lawrence, 112.
107	Praise God, for he is good: for still (1–9)	Psalm 107, 157; York, 146.
	O that men to the Lord would give (21–25, 29–31)	St. Nicholas, 119.
111	Praise ye the Lord, with my whole heart (1–5, 9–10)	Manchester, 83.
115	Not unto us, Lord, not to us (1, 12–16)	St. Mirren, 117.
116	I love the Lord, because my voice (1–7)	Manchester, 83; Kilmarnock, 75.
	I'll of salvation take the cup (13–19)	Wigtown, 143; Kilmarnock, 75.
117	O give ye praise unto the Lord	Tiverton, 136.
118	O set ye open unto me (19–25, 28–29)	Irish, 73; Southwark, 129.
119	Blessed are they that undefiled (1–8)	Jackson, 74.
	By what means shall a young man learn (9–16)	St. Flavian, 105.
	Teach me, O Lord, the perfect way (33–40)	York, 146.
	Thy word for ever is, O Lord (89–94)	London New, 82.
	O let my earnest pray'r and cry (169–176)	Farrant, 59.
121	I to the hills will lift mine eyes	French, 61.
122	I joy'd when to the house of God	Harington, 66.
	Pray that Jerusalem may have (6–9)	St. Paul, 120.
124	(ii) Now Israel may say	Old 124th, 185.
125	They in the Lord that firmly trust	St. David, 103.
126	When Sion's bondage God turned back	Abbey, 24.
130	Lord, from the depths to thee I cried	Martyrdom, 84, 85.

No. of Psalm.	First Line.	Tune.
132	We'll go into his tabernacles (7–9, 13–16)	Colchester, 41.
133	Behold, how good a thing it is	Newington, 92.
136	(ii) Praise God, for he is kind (1–5, 23–26)	Darwall, 181; Croft's 136th, 180.
137	By Babel's streams we sat and wept (1–6)	Old 137th, 155.
138	Thee will I praise with all my heart	Bedford, 29.
139	O Lord, thou hast me searched and known (1–6, 17–18)	Hermon, 69; St. Andrew, 99.
143	(ii) Oh, hear my prayer, Lord (1, 6–8)	Leuchars, 179; Lawes (Ps. 32), 178.
145	(ii) O Lord, thou art my God and King (1–7)	Aberfeldy, 191; Duke Street, 9.
	Good unto all men is the Lord (9–16)	Crasselius, 7; Melcombe, 12.
	The Lord is just in his ways all (17–21)	Doversdale, 8.
146	Praise God. The Lord praise, O my soul (1–2, 5–10)	St. Stephen, 122.
147	Praise ye the Lord, for it is good (1–7)	Huddersfield, 71; Dunfermline, 52.
148	(ii) The Lord of heav'n confess	St. John, 182; Lawes (Ps. 47), 182.
150	Praise ye the Lord. God's praise within	Crediton, 46.

PARAPHRASES

No. of Paraphrase.	First Line.	Tune.
2	O God of Bethel! by whose hand	Salzburg, 125; St. Paul, 120.
11	O happy is the man who hears	St. Bernard, 101; Newington, 92.
18	Behold! the mountain of the Lord	Glasgow, 62.
19	The race that long in darkness pined	Tiverton, 136.
20	How glorious Sion's courts appear (1–5)	Irish, 73; Aspurg, 26.
21	Attend, ye tribes that dwell remote	Liverpool, 81.
22	Why pour'st thou forth thy anxious plaint	Sidon, 127; St. Stephen, 122.
23	Behold my servant! see him rise (1–5)	Huddersfield, 71.
	Sing to the Lord in joyful strains (12–15)	Crediton, 46.
24	Ye heavens, send forth your song of praise	St. Lawrence, 112; Wetherby, 142.
25	The Saviour comes! no outward pomp (2–7)	St. Mary, 115.
26	Ho! ye that thirst, approach the spring (1–6)	Wetherby, 142.
	Seek ye the Lord while yet his ear (7–14)	Felix, 60; Iconium, 72.

No. of Paraphrase.	First Line.	Tune.
27	Thus speaks the high and lofty one	Caithness, 37.
28	Let such as feel oppression's load (3–6)	Bristol, 34.
30	Come, let us to the Lord our God	Kilmarnock, 75.
32	What though no flowers the fig-tree clothe	Bishopthorpe, 32.
33	Father of all! we bow to thee	Palestrina, 94.
34	Thus spoke the Saviour of the world	St. Etheldreda, 104.
35	'Twas on that night when doomed to know	Rockingham, 14.
36	My soul and spirit, filled with joy	Praetorius, 96.
37	While humble shepherds watch'd their flocks	Evangel, 147.
38	When Jesus, to the temple brought (4–11)	St. Andrew, 99; Kilsyth, 76.
39	Hark, the glad sound, the Saviour comes	Crediton, 46.
41	As when the Hebrew prophet raised (1–5)	St. Thomas, 123.
42	Let not your hearts with anxious thoughts	Kilmarnock, 75.
43	You now must hear my voice no more	St. Thomas, 123.
44	'Tis finished—was his latest voice (3–6)	Dundee, 51.
47	And shall we then go on to sin	Tallis, 135.
48	Let Christian faith and hope dispel (1–6)	Gloucester, 64.
	The Saviour dy'd, but rose again (5–9)	St. Andrew, 99.
49	Love suffers long, love envies not (5–9)	Howard, 70.
52	Ye who the name of Jesus bear	St. Peter, 121; St. Flavian, 105.
53	Take comfort, Christians, when your friends (1–3, 7, 8)	Ballerma, 27.
54	I'm not ashamed to own my Lord	Lancaster, 78; Jackson, 74.
56	'Tis from the mercy of our God (4–7)	Bedford, 29.
58	Where high the heavenly temple stands	Soldau, 17.
59	Behold what witnesses unseen (1–4, 13)	Wetherby, 142; St. Nicholas, 119.
60	Father of peace, and God of love	Caithness, 37; St. Paul, 120.
61	Bless'd be the everlasting God	Bishopthorpe, 32.
63	Behold th' amazing gift of love	Newington, 92.
64	To him that loved the souls of men	St. Gregory, 109.
65	Hark how th' adoring hosts above (5–11)	Hebdomadal, 67; St. Magnus, 114.
66	How bright these glorious spirits shine	St. Asaph, 158; Gloucester, 64.
67	Lo! what a glorious sight appears (1–7, 12)	St. Matthias, 116.
	O may we stand before the Lamb (12)	St. Anne, 100.

7½.54

SET IN GREAT BRITAIN AT THE UNIVERSITY PRESS, OXFORD, AND REPRINTED FROM PLATES BY THE RIVERSIDE PRESS, EDINBURGH

THE
CHURCH HYMNARY
REVISED EDITION

Authorized for Use in Public Worship

by

THE CHURCH OF SCOTLAND
THE UNITED FREE CHURCH OF SCOTLAND
THE PRESBYTERIAN CHURCH IN IRELAND
THE PRESBYTERIAN CHURCH OF ENGLAND
THE PRESBYTERIAN CHURCH OF WALES
THE PRESBYTERIAN CHURCH OF AUSTRALIA
THE PRESBYTERIAN CHURCH OF NEW ZEALAND
THE PRESBYTERIAN CHURCH
OF SOUTH AFRICA

With Music

GEOFFREY CUMBERLEGE
OXFORD UNIVERSITY PRESS
LONDON GLASGOW NEW YORK

14 *R. Crown* 8*vo Sol-fa*

HANDBOOK TO THE CHURCH HYMNARY

Edited by the REV. PROFESSOR JAMES MOFFATT, D.D., D.LITT., with Notes on Words and Music

Biographical and Historical Notes on Authors and Composers

Calendar and Indexes of Scripture Texts and Subjects, &c.

With *SUPPLEMENT*, edited by the REV. MILLAR PATRICK, D.D.

The *SUPPLEMENT* also separately

PRINTED IN GREAT BRITAIN

PREFACE

THE original edition of the Church Hymnary appeared in 1898, and its wide circulation has been the best proof of its popularity. In 1922 the General Assemblies of the Churches interested, the Church of Scotland, the United Free Church of Scotland, and the Presbyterian Church in Ireland, recognizing that the time had come for the preparation of a revised edition, instructed their Praise Committees to proceed with the revision of the Hymnary both as to words and music.

The work was entrusted to a Joint Revision Committee formed of representatives from these Committees; but the Presbyterian Church of England and the Presbyterian Church of Wales having expressed a desire to co-operate, the General Assemblies of 1923 of the Scottish and Irish Churches instructed the Committees to admit representatives of these Churches to take part in the work, and the Joint Revision Committee was augmented accordingly. The Presbyterian Churches of South Africa, Australia, and New Zealand also appointed Committees to co-operate with the revisers, and two of the members of the Revision Committee acted in the interests of these Churches. In 1925 the General Assemblies approved the draft of the words of the Revised Hymnary and, subject to adjustments, authorized its publication on the completion of the choice and arrangement of the music.

In the revision of the music the Committee has been fortunate in having the co-operation of representatives of the Societies of Organists in Edinburgh, Glasgow, Aberdeen, and Ulster, and musicians from England and Wales. Thanks are due to these gentlemen, whose practical experience has been of the utmost value, and particularly to Dr. David Evans, Professor of Music in the University of Wales, who has not only acted as chief musical editor, but has transcribed the tunes for the sol-fa and melody editions. The Committee desires likewise to put on record its special indebtedness to the secretary, Mr. W. M. Page, who has spared neither time nor labour in its service. Great care has been taken to trace the authors or proprietors of words and music. If there has been any infringement of copyright or omission of acknowledgement it is unintentional, and the Committee trusts that it will be pardoned.

The Church Hymnary in this revised form is issued with the prayer that its use may be to the glory of God and the good of His people.

April 1927.

THE MUSIC

DURING recent years the Presbyterian Churches have come to attach a greater importance to music as an aid in Church worship, and to set a much higher value upon it.

A widespread reaction has set in against much of the music that was in vogue and popular at the beginning of this century. It has been generally realized that religious feeling demands for its expression the best and noblest music, and that the number of weakly sentimental tunes retained in use should be reduced to a minimum.

From various countries and different ages there has come into the Church's possession a fine body of tunes, fitted to give expression, in a dignified and artistic manner, to all phases of religious emotion. A large number of these noble spiritual songs has been included in this book, in the belief that they will be appreciated wherever they come to be known. The singing of them should bring to all who participate a great spiritual enrichment.

Congregational singing. The tunes included, with the exception of a small number intended for choir use only, have been selected and arranged with a view to congregational singing. It is hoped that the time will soon come when every member of a congregation will be able to take an effective vocal part in the Church's offering of praise. This, however, involves much preliminary training and preparation by means of congregational rehearsals and the institution of Psalmody Festivals. These are already in use in some sections of the Churches for which this book is provided, and they ought to be made available for many more.

Where this is not possible, it is strongly recommended that the whole congregation should sing the *melody* only. A *Melody Edition* has been provided with this in view, so that each member may become familiar with, and be encouraged to join in, the tune. To facilitate such unison singing, many of the tunes have been lowered in pitch.

In the old Psalter tunes the original long initial note has been restored, as being more in keeping with the broad and dignified character of these melodies. In some of them the original rhythm has also been restored.

Pace. There is a general tendency to sing hymn-tunes much too fast, thereby robbing them of their dignity and reverence. Especially is this true of old Chorales and Psalter tunes, which should always move slowly and with a stately stride, without any sense of hurry. Slow movement need not be unrhythmic or lifeless. It is inartistic to adhere rigidly to a metronomic rate and to rush breathlessly through four lines of a tune without a break. Most Chorales and Psalter tunes should be sung in single lines with a slight pause at the end of each. More modern tunes move more quickly, and require only a short break at the end of every second or third line, as the case may be. Any choirmaster giving serious thought to the matter may safely trust his musical instinct.

The speed at which a tune should be sung depends on a number of factors, such as the number and powers of the singers, and the nature of the building, which must be estimated by the choirmaster. But in the belief that some indication of the *tempo* of each tune might be helpful, a suggestion has been inserted in each case. These indications must be regarded merely as our opinion of the rate at which the tunes should be taken. No exact metronomic equivalent can be stated, as the same tune may be sung with good effect at different speeds on various occasions. But the following may be given as approximate equivalents : *Slow*=M.M. 50–66 ; *Moderately slow* = 60–72 ; *Moderate time* = 72–96 ; *Moderately quick*= 80–112.

Choirmasters will realize that it is not desirable in *every* hymn to slacken the pace at the end of each verse, or even at the end of the last verse. Where the sentiment of the words is joyous, the singing ought to be carried on to the very last word without any *rallentando*, and oftentimes end with a triumphant 'Amen'.

Special care should be given to the rendering of the 'Amen'. The listless and half-hearted manner in which it is often sung makes it worse than useless. It is the summing up of all that precedes it. It is the people's affirmation, and should often become a veritable paean of praise.

Faux-bourdon. Settings of some well-known tunes are given in Faux-bourdon. This ensures variety and artistic interest. Here the choir and the congregation have their definite part to take. The latter must sing the *melody only.* In a hymn of five or six verses, two may be Faux-bourdon verses. Care should be taken in selecting the verses for this treatment.

Plainsong. In Plainsong melodies the notes have no fixed time-values, but take their rhythm from the words to which they are sung. The rhythm is essentially that of *speech.* The melodies should flow lightly and easily and have the variety of inflexion obtained in reading intelligently and rather slowly.

Accompaniments. The accompaniments in every case must be light.

DAVID EVANS.

DIRECTIONS FOR CHANTING

Gregorian Chants. In Gregorian chants the phrases should be sung smoothly and lightly, due emphasis being given to the accented syllables. The notes take their value from the words to which they are sung. The rhythm must be quite free and rigidity avoided. To assist the congregation, the words have been placed under the notes to which they are to be sung.

Various simple accompaniments have been suggested, and the capable organist will doubtless think of many others equally appropriate. Merbecke's *Pater Noster* had better be sung unaccompanied, but a simple organ arrangement has been provided in case it is desired.

Anglican Chants. The notes in the Anglican chants also have no definite time-values, and may be lengthened or shortened at will. It follows that they vary to some degree with every verse.

The chant must not be viewed as a *short hymn-tune* to which a verse has to be fitted, but rather as a series of notes on which a verse or verses should be recited. Chanting should be good reading intensified.

(*a*) The bars and double-bars in the text correspond with those in the chant.

(*b*) In the melodic portion of the chant, two words or syllables in a bar, or three *equal* words or syllables in a bar, have no additional sign, and are sung as halves or triplets (in the latter the first pulse-note in the bar is repeated):

Doh = G.
{| m :r }
Ho - ly

Doh = G.
{| m :m :r } (3)
Ma - jes - ty

(*c*) Whenever the bar is divided into anything smaller, a dot (·) marks the division of the words between the pulse-notes to which they are sung:

Doh = B♭.
{:r .r | m .m :r .d | d :t, | d :— ||
and ex - | alted · them of | low de - | gree ||

Doh = B♭.
{:r .r ,r | m .m :r .d | d :t, | d .d :—. ||
all gener- | ations · shall | call me | blessed ||

When this division occurs between syllables, a hyphen is used instead of a dot:

Doh = B♭.
{| m .,m :r .d | d :t, | d :— ||
| world with-out | end. A - | men. ||

The two-pulse note at the end of a section is sometimes replaced by two pulse-notes. Whenever there are more than two syllables to be sung to such pulse-notes, the dot or hyphen is inserted to mark the division:

For He hath regarded the | lowliness | of His | hand-maiden : ||

(*d*) An asterisk (*) denotes a stop, and that breath should be taken.

ACKNOWLEDGEMENTS

PERMISSION to use copyright hymns and music has been granted as stated below. *A blank in the second column indicates that the author or composer is also the owner of the copyright, or that permission was granted in the lifetime of authors now dead. An asterisk denotes that permission has been obtained on payment of a fee.*

HYMNS

AUTHOR	OWNER OF COPYRIGHT	NO. OF HYMN
ADAMS, Miss Jessie	*The Trustees of the Fellowship Hymn Book	528.
Ainger, A. C.	*The Society for Promoting Christian Knowledge	380.
Alexander, Mrs.	Miss E. Alexander	101.
,,	Association for Promoting Christian Knowledge, Dublin	506.
Alford, Dean	Rev. H. E. T. Cruso	579.
Armitage, Mrs.		355.
BAKER, Rev. Sir H. W.	*Proprietors of 'Hymns Ancient and Modern'	102, 316.
Baring-Gould, Rev. Sabine	*Messrs. A. W. Ridley & Co.	214, 288, 535.
B. E.	Mrs. H. C. A. Dixon	699.
Beeching, Dean	Mrs. Beeching	673.
Benson, Rev. L. F., D.D.		74.
Bevan, Mrs.	*Messrs. James Nisbet & Co., Ltd.	394.
Bickersteth, Bishop	Messrs. Longmans, Green & Co., Ltd.	321, 370, 444.
Blatchford, Rev. A. N.	*Messrs. Reid Bros., Ltd.	28.
Bliss, Philipp	The John Church Company	664.
Blunt, Rev. A. G. W.	Mr. R. Blunt	347.
Bonar, Rev. Horatius, D.D.	Rev. H. N. Bonar	488.
Borthwick, Miss	Messrs. Thomas Nelson & Sons, Ltd.	602.
Bright, Canon William	The Rev. The Warden, Keble College, Oxford	320.
Brooke, Rev. Stopford A.	Miss Honor Brooke	80, 85, 231.
Brownlie, Rev. John, D.D.	*Messrs. Morgan & Scott, Ltd.	458.
Bruce, Rev. William, D.D.	Hymnal Trustees of the United Presbyterian Church	204.
Burke, Miss Christian	The Mothers' Union	652.
Butler, Miss Mary	*The National Sunday School Union	674.
CANTON, W.		555.
Chadwick, Rev. J. W.	Mrs. Chadwick	614.
Charteris, Rev. A. H., D.D.	Brig.-General J. Charteris, M.P.	521.
Chatfield, Rev. A. W.	Mr. Kyrle Chatfield	403.
Chesterton, G. K.	English Hymnal Committee	638.
Codner, Mrs.	Mr. William Wood	687.
Coghill, Mrs.	Mrs. Dalzell	357.
Collins, Rev. H.	Rev. P. L. Carew	430.
Conder, Rev. E. R., D.D.	Miss E. M. Conder	75.
Coster, Rev. G. T.	Mr. A. Vennell Coster	492.
Cousin, Mrs.	Mr. D. R. Cousin	581.
DEARMER, Rev. P., D.D.	English Hymnal Committee	263, 349.
Deck, Mrs.	The Religious Tract Society	480.
Dobree, Mrs.	*Messrs. Seeley, Service & Co., Ltd.	328.
Dodgshun, Ernest		644.
Draper, Rev. W. H.	*	13.
Dugmore, Canon E. E.		503.
EDDIS, E. W.	The Representatives of the late Mr. E. W. Eddis	315.
Edwards, Rev. Lewis, D.D.	Mrs. Lilian Charles-Edwards	596.
Ellerton, Rev. John	Oxford University Press	100, 237, 242, 271, 289, 326, 330, 336, 360, 584, 634, 641.

ACKNOWLEDGEMENTS

AUTHOR	OWNER OF COPYRIGHT	NO. OF HYMN
FALCONER, Rev. Hugh, D.D.	....	59.
Farningham, Miss Marianne	*Messrs. James Clarke & Co., Ltd.	497.
Farrar, Dean	Rev. E. M. Farrar..............	43.
Fletcher, Frank	....	146.
Freer, Miss	Mr. William de Caux	452.
GILL, T. H.	Mr. E. W. B. Gill	211, 498, 608.
Gladden, Rev. Washington, D.D.	Miss Alice Gladden	339.
Gray, Rev. H. B., D.D. .	....	676.
Greenaway, Miss	*Proprietors of 'Hymns Ancient and Modern'...............	97.
Greenwell, Miss	Messrs. H. R. Allenson, Ltd. ...	698.
Gurney, Mrs.	....	327
HANKEY, Miss Kate	Miss Rashdall	682.
Hasloch, Miss	Canon J. Hasloch Potter	343.
Hatch, Rev. Edwin, D.D.	Miss Hatch	194.
Havergal, Miss	*Messrs. James Nisbet & Co., Ltd.	133, 157, 338, 375, 443, 512, 519, 695.
Hawkins, Mrs. H. Periam	....	603.
Hensley, Canon L.	Miss L. Hensley...............	152.
Holland, Canon H. Scott	English Hymnal Committee	636.
Hopps, Rev. J. P.	*The National Sunday School Union	565.
Horne, Rev. C. Silvester .	Hon. Mrs. Silvester Horne......	212.
Hosmer, Rev. F. L., D.D.	....	153, 331.
Housman, Laurence	....	645.
How, Bishop	Mr. F. D. How	70, 76, 117, 342, 436, 610, 613, 621, 622, 635, 675.
Howells, Dr. W.	....	384.
Hull, Miss Eleanor	.... and Messrs. Chatto & Windus .	477.
Hunter, Rev. John, D.D.	Canon L. S. Hunter	460.
JENKINS, W. Vaughan ..	Mrs. H. Vaughan Jenkins	325.
Jones, Miss Edith	....	630.
KINGSLEY, Canon Charles	Messrs. Macmillan & Co., Ltd. ...	351.
Kipling, Rudyard	*.............................. and Messrs. Methuen & Co., Ltd. (from 'The Five Nations')	637.
,, ...	*.............................. and Messrs. Macmillan & Co., Ltd. (from 'Puck of Pook's Hill')	647.
Kirkland, Rev. P. M. ...	....	127.
LATHBURY, Miss........	Chautauqua Press	202.
Lewis, Rev. H. Elvet ...	....	337, 628.
Lewis, Mrs.	....	226.
Lewis, R. M.	Mr. D. Lleufer Thomas	445.
Lowry, Rev. S. C.	....	359.
Luke, Mrs.	The National Sunday School Union	82.
MACALISTER, Professor R. A. S.	....	203, 505.
Macbean, Lachlan	....	53, 570 (from 'Songs and Hymns of the Gael').
MacDonald, Dr. George..	Dr. Greville MacDonald	264.
Macgregor, Rev. D.	Mrs. Macgregor	179, 454.
Maclagan, Archbishop ..	Mr. Eric Maclagan	98, 219.
Macnicol, Rev. Nicol ...	....	406.
Mathams, Rev. Walter J.	....	667.
Matheson, Miss	National Sunday School Union .	361.
Matheson, Rev. George, D.D.	Messrs. Novello & Co., Ltd.	424.
,,	Trustees of the late Miss Jane G. Matheson's Estate..........	464.
Mathews, B. J.	....	373.
Maude, Mrs.	Miss Mary J. Maude	504.

ACKNOWLEDGEMENTS

Author	Owner of Copyright	No. of Hymn
Merrill, Rev. W. P., D.D.	.... and 'The Continent', Chicago	344.
Merrington, Rev. E. N., Ph.D.	....	642.
Midlane, Albert	*Messrs. Reid Bros., Ltd.	593.
,, ...	*Mrs. Mills	679.
Parker, W. H.	The National Sunday School Union	189.
Pennefather, Rev. William	Mr. W. S. Pennefather	248.
Piggot, Rev. W. Charter	....	218.
Plumptre, Dean	Oxford University Press	215.
Plunket, Archbishop	Bishop of Meath	125.
Pollock, Rev. T. B.	*The Incumbent, St. Alban's, Birmingham	94, 95, 208, 399, 469.
Pott, Rev. Francis	Miss Mary F. Pott	79, 122, 252.
Rawnsley, Canon H. D.	Mrs. Rawnsley	353.
Rhodes, Mrs.	Sheffield Sunday School Union..	20.
Richards, Rev. C. H.	Messrs. Charles E. Merrill Company	486.
Roberts, Rev. R. R.	....	572.
Robinson, Rev. G. Wade	Miss E. Wade Robinson........	434.
Rooker, Alfred	Miss M. Rooker	244.
Rossetti, Miss Christina G.	*Messrs. Macmillan & Co., Ltd. ..	50.
,, ..	*The Society for Promoting Christian Knowledge	52, 358, 412, 545, 586.
Rowley, Rev. F. H., D.D.	....	683.
Shairp, Principal J. C. .	Messrs. Macmillan & Co., Ltd. ..	559.
Shuttleworth, Canon H. C.	Oxford University Press	493.
Sidebotham, Miss	Rev. F. W. G. Sidebotham	404.
Smith, Canon I. G.	Mr. G. Murray-Smith	114.
Smith, Rev. W. Chalmers, D.D.	Mr. William Galbraith	12, 461.
Stevenson, Miss	Mrs. L. J. Neale Bubb	629.
Stone, Rev. S. J.	Rev. W. G. Boyd	348.
Symonds, J. A.	*Mr. John Murray	639.
Tennyson, Alfred, Lord	Messrs. Macmillan & Co., Ltd. ..	588.
Threlfall, Miss	The family of the late Mr. Joseph Keech Aston	93, 573.
Thring, Rev. Godfrey ...	Mr. Leonard G. P. Thring	66, 352.
,, ..	* ,, ...	136, 200, 487.
Walmsley, Robert	Miss Clara S. Walmsley	273.
Waring, Miss	The Society for Promoting Christian Knowledge	442.
,, ...	* ,, ,, ,, ...	446, 548.
Watt, Rev. Lauchlan MacLean, D.D.	....	112, 402.
Whittier, J. G.	Messrs. Houghton Mifflin Co. ..	245, 254, 589.
Willcox, Mrs.	Mrs. A. H. Gunn	374.
Wordsworth, Bishop	Rev. Christopher Wordsworth ..	213.
Wotherspoon, Rev. A. W. and Rev. W. Mair, D.D.	.... and Mrs. Mair	108.
Wright, William........	The Publishers of the Y.M.C.A. Hymnal	537.

Also thanks to Dr. Robert Bridges for hymns Nos. 217, 250, 278, 284, 440, 448 from the Yattendon Hymnal.

MUSIC

Composer	Owner of Copyright	No. of Hymn
Adcock, J.	*Miss C. M. Brunt	669.
Anderson, J. S.	*Oxford University Press	81, 97, 104, 141, 460, 543[1], 586[2], 645.
Armes, Dr. P.	*Mr. A. H. H. Armes	647[1].
Arthur, Edward	*..............................	17, 192, 218, 303, 427, 544, 614, 671.
Baker, H.	Miss M. Morley Horder	501[1].
Baring-Gould, Rev. S. ..	*Messrs. A. W. Ridley & Co.	288[2].
Barnby, Sir J.	*Messrs. Novello & Co., Ltd.	128, 327, 430, 566, 588, 606, 705.

ACKNOWLEDGEMENTS

Composer	Owner of Copyright	No. of Hymn
Barnby, Sir J.	Wesleyan Methodist Sunday School Department	653.
Barnes, Dr. A. F.	*Oxford University Press	373, 638.
Bell, J. M.	The Trustees for the late Mr. J. M. Bell	346.
Bell, W. H.		383.
Blunt, F. W.	*Messrs. Novello & Co., Ltd.	288^{1}.
Booth, J.		20.
„	*	674.
Boyd, Rev. W.	*	517^{1}.
Brown, Arthur Henry	*Oxford University Press	269, 287, 395^{1}, 497.
Buck, Dr. P. C.		23.
Bunnett, Dr. E.	Messrs. Longmans, Green & Co., Ltd.	399.
Button, H. E.	*Messrs. Novello & Co., Ltd.	670.
CALDBECK, G. T.	Messrs. Longmans, Green & Co., Ltd.	444^{1}.
Calkin, J. B.	Lady Carbery	328.
„	Miss A. Calkin	361.
„	Messrs. John F. Shaw & Co., Ltd.	482.
Crosbie, Rev. H. A.	Mrs. E. A. Crosbie	375.
DALE, Rev. R. F.	Miss Milicent Pickersgill-Cunliffe	348.
Davies, Sir H. Walford	*	10, 155^{1}, 317, 446.
„	*Miss M. Morley Horder	48^{1}.
Dix, L. L.		456^{2}.
Doane, W. H.	Mrs. George W. Doane	679^{2}, 707.
Drewett, E.	*Mrs. Drewett	487^{2}.
ELLIOTT, J. W.	*Messrs. Novello & Co., Ltd.	25, 231, 508^{2}.
Ellis, W.		159.
Elvey, Sir G. J.	*Mr. E. S. Elvey	204.
„	*Messrs. Seeley, Service & Co., Ltd.	602, 696 (altered by permission).
Evans, D. Emlyn	Mrs. J. W. Jones	294^{2}.
„	*The Caniedydd Committee of the Union of Welsh Independents	560.
Evans, Professor David	*	127, 146, 247, 298, 321, 391^{2}, 393, 424^{1}, 461, 529^{1}, 568^{1}, 673.
FARMER, John	*Messrs. Joseph Williams, Ltd.	43 (from 'Christ and His Soldiers').
Farrer, J. Downing	*Oxford University Press	238.
Ferguson, Rev. W. H.		139^{2}, 178^{1}, 508^{1}.
Finlay, K. G.	*	358, 491^{1}, 663.
Foster, Myles B.	*Miss M. Morley Horder	85.
GALLOWAY, Rev. A.	Miss Elizabeth E. Galloway	219^{1}
Gilbert, Dr. W. B.	*Messrs. Novello & Co., Ltd.	235, 389.
Gladstone, W. H.	*Messrs. Novello & Co., Ltd.	24.
„	Hon. Mrs. W. H. Gladstone	111, 325.
Goldsmith, E. W.		124^{1}.
Goss, Sir John	Lady Carbery	21.
„	*Messrs. Novello & Co., Ltd.	51, 200, 267^{2}.
„	Messrs. James Nisbet & Co., Ltd., and the Presbyterian Church of England	519.
Grace, Harvey	*The Faith Press, Ltd.	9 Faux-bourdon (from the 'Tenor Tune Book').
Griffith, W.	*Oxford University Press	667.
HADOW, Sir W. H.		496.
Harwood, Dr. Basil	*	15^{1}, 143, 215, 330^{2}, 380, 441^{1}.
Hately, W.	*Miss Hately	556^{2}.
Havergal, Miss	Messrs. James Nisbet & Co., Ltd., and the Presbyterian Church of England	133.
Holst, Gustav	*	50, 180^{1}.
Hopkins, Dr. E. J.	*Messrs. A. Weekes & Co., Ltd., on behalf of the Executors of the late Dr. E. J. Hopkins	37, 363, 573.

ACKNOWLEDGEMENTS

Composer	Owner of Copyright	No. of Hymn
Hurst, W.	*Proprietors of 'Hymns Ancient and Modern'	316.
	*	76[1].
IRELAND, John	Mr. E. T. Jeboult	426.
JEBOULT, H. A.	Miss Nellie D. Jenkins	464[2].
Jenkins, D.	* ,,	684.
,,	Mrs. D. P. Morris	161.
Jones, G. H. (Gutyn Arfon)	Hope Publishing Company, Chicago	657.
KIRKPATRICK, W. J.	Miss M. Morley Horder	617.
LAHEE, H.	Hymnal Trustees of the United Presbyterian Church	362.
Lamb, Rev. J.	*Messrs. Novello & Co., Ltd.	2[1], 323, 378, 605.
Langran, J.	Miss Theodora C. M. Legge	174[1].
Legge, A.		331.
Ley, Dr. H. G.	The Caniedydd Committee of the Union of Welsh Independents	73, 183, 390[2].
Lloyd, J. A.	Miss B. Ambrose Lloyd	470[2].
Lloyd, J. A. (Junior)	*Oxford University Press	68[1], 408, 575, 650, 727[2].
Lloyd, J. M.		
MACALISTER, Professor R. A. S.	*Oxford University Press	15[2], 92[2], 144, 438[2], 505, 610
Macfarren, Walter Cecil	*Mrs. Mary Rose	265.
McGranahan, J.	*Mrs. H. C. A. Dixon	699.
Maclagan, Archbishop	Mr. Eric Maclagan	340.
Maker, F. C.	*The Psalms and Hymns Trust	441[2], 691.
Mann, Dr. A. H.		71, 171, 268.
Mansfield, P. J.	*Messrs. Bayley & Ferguson	400 (Faux-bourdon).
Martin, Sir George C.	*Messrs. Novello & Co., Ltd.	503.
Martin, G. W.	*Messrs. Novello & Co., Ltd.	464[1].
Matthews, Rev. T. R.	*Messrs. Novello & Co., Ltd.	67, 188[2], 343, 470[1].
Mendelssohn-Bartholdy, F.	*Messrs. Novello & Co., Ltd.	46.
Moffatt, Rev. James, D.D.	*Oxford University Press	586[1].
Monk, Dr. W. H.	*Miss Florence Monk for the Representatives of Dr. W. H. Monk	66, 157, 178[2], 248. 266, 320, 629.
Morgan, A. P.	*	523[2].
Morley, H. K.	Mrs. H. Periam Hawkins	36.
Mountain, Rev. J., D.D.	Messrs. Marshall Bros., Ltd	443.
NAYLOR, Dr. E. W.		534[2].
Nisbet, J. M.	*Oxford University Press	315.
Nyberg, Pastor Huugo		402.
OAKELEY, Sir H. S.	*Mr. E. M. Oakeley	267[1].
,,	,,	292[1].
Ouseley, Rev. Sir F. A. G.	*Messrs. Cassell & Co., Ltd.	18[2].
PARRATT, Sir Walter	Miss K. Parratt	240.
Parry, Sir C. H. H.	*Messrs. Novello & Co., Ltd.	168[1].
,,	*Proprietors of 'Hymns Ancient and Modern'	485.
,,	*The Executors of the late Sir Hubert Parry and Messrs. J. Curwen & Sons, Ltd.	640 (from Curwen Edn., No. 40009).
Parry, Dr. J.	*Messrs. Hughes & Son	414[2].
,,	*The Caniedydd Committee of the Union of Welsh Independents	703.
Peace, Dr. A. L.	*Messrs. Novello & Co., Ltd.	424[2].
,,	*The Trustees of the late Dr. A. L. Peace	521.
Poole, C. W.	*Miss M. Morley Horder	398, 528[1].
Price, J. (Beulah)	*Oxford University Press	411[2].
Price, Tom	Mr. T. J. Price	465.
Pritchard, T. C. L.	*Oxford University Press	34, 570, 576[2], 589.
Prout, Dr. E.	*Congregational Union of England and Wales	211[2], 630.
QUAILE, R. N.		213.
,,	Wesleyan Methodist Sunday School Department	659.

ACKNOWLEDGEMENTS

Composer	Owner of Copyright	No. of Hymn
Rees, J. T.	*Mr. D. J. Snell	190².
Richards, J. (Isalaw) ...	*Messrs. Hughes & Son	2².
Ridsdale, Rev. C. J.	....	412 (from 'New Office Hymn Book').
Roberts, A. O.	....	347, 487¹.
Roberts, Rev. J. (Ieuan Gwyllt)	Calvinistic Methodist Book Agency	108², 243¹, 475¹, 572, 687.
Roberts, J. H.	*The J. H. Roberts Music Publishing Co., Liverpool	466.
,, ...	The J. H. Roberts Music Publishing Co., Liverpool	718.
Roberts, L. J.	*	158².
Roberts, Robert	*	404.
Ross, Dr. W. B.	....	61.
Ryley, Rev. G. C. E. ...	....	436¹.
Scholefield, Rev. C. C.	*English Hymnal Committee	289³.
,,	Presbyterian Church of England	584.
Scott-Gatty, Sir A.	*Mr. C. T. Gatty	648.
Shaw, Geoffrey T.	*The Faith Press, Ltd.	106, 131 (Faux-bourdons) from the 'TenorTuneBook'.
,, ...	*Messrs. J. Curwen & Sons, Ltd..	221¹ (from Curwen Edition, No. 6300).
Shaw, Martin	*Messrs. J. Curwen & Sons, Ltd. .	155² (from Curwen Edn., No. 71487).
,, ...	*Messrs. J. Curwen & Sons, Ltd. .	214², 372, 601 (Faux-bourdon), 662¹ (from Curwen Edition, No. 6300).
,, ...	*The Faith Press, Ltd.	32, 209, 520² (Faux-bourdons) from the 'TenorTuneBook'.
Sibelius, Jean	*Messrs. Breitkopf & Härtel, Leipzig	556¹.
Silas, E.	*Messrs. Novello & Co., Ltd.	84.
Smart, H.	Lady Carbery	198.
,, ...	Hymnal Trustees of the United Presbyterian Church	232.
,, ...	*Proprietors of 'Hymns Ancient and Modern'	411¹.
,, ...	Messrs. James Nisbet & Co., Ltd.	531², 611.
,, ...	*Messrs. Novello & Co., Ltd.	579, 718.
Smith, Canon H. P.	Miss M. Morley Horder	420¹.
Smith, S.	*Messrs. Novello & Co., Ltd.	59, 613.
Stainer, Sir J.	*Messrs. Novello & Co., Ltd.	18¹, 194¹, 219², 273, 437, 488, 578, 654, 662², 728⁴, 728⁵.
,, ...	*Mr. J. F. R. Stainer	72, 281, 593.
Stanford, Sir C. V.	*Messrs. Stainer & Bell, Ltd.	506¹.
Stewart, C. Hylton	*Messrs. J. Curwen & Sons, Ltd..	422¹ (from Curwen Edn., No. 80632).
,, ...	*The Composer and the Society for Promoting Christian Knowledge	718¹.
Stewart, Sir R. P.	Association for Promoting Christian Knowledge, Dublin	210, 335, 609¹, 695.
Stocks, Dr. G. G.	The Governors, Repton School .	48², 271¹.
Strong, Right Rev. T. B., D.D.	*Oxford University Press	175.
Sullivan, Sir Arthur S. ..	*Messrs. Novello & Co., Ltd.	47, 75, 115, 126, 251, 308, 314², 370, 453, 469, 475³, 535, 616, 622.
Swift, J. F.	Wesleyan Methodist Sunday School Department	189 (reharmonized by Dr. Evans).
Taylor, J. P.	*Oxford University Press	125.
Terry, Sir R. R.	....	506².
Thomas, J.	Mrs. G. T. Lewis	387².

ACKNOWLEDGEMENTS

COMPOSER	OWNER OF COPYRIGHT	NO. OF HYMN
Thorne, Dr. E. H.	*Proprietors of 'Hymns Ancient and Modern'	500.
Tyler, J. S.	Miss Mary A. Tyler	480.
VINCENT, Dr. C. J.	Messrs. Longmans, Green & Co., Ltd.	444^{1}.
WALTON, H. F. R.	*...........................	68^{2}.
Westbrook, B. V.	Congregational Union of England and Wales	716.
Williams, B.	Miss Jennie Williams	28.
Williams, Dr. R. Vaughan	*...........................	33, 70, 243^{2}, 550^{1}, 576^{1}, 612, 623^{2}.
"	*English Hymnal Committee	191, 220, 624.
Williams, T. J.	Messrs. W. Gwenlyn Evans & Son	701^{1}.
Wilson, Canon David F. R.	....	452^{1}.
Wood, Dr. Charles	Mrs. Charlotte G. Wood	637^{1}.
Wooldridge, H. E.	Dr. Robert Bridges	528^{2}.
YOAKLEY, J.	....	202^{1}.

Thanks are also due to the following, who have kindly allowed the inclusion of versions and harmonizations of traditional and other melodies, which are their copyright:

Mr. G. E. P. Arkwright	'Newbury' (655).
Association for Promoting Christian Knowledge (Dublin)	'Moville' (179).
Mr. Arthur Darley	'Dun Aluinn' (525^{1}).
The Educational Company of Ireland, Ltd.	'Lorica Patricii' (505). 'Durrow' (454) and 'Slane' (477) from Dr. Joyce's *Old Irish Music*.
English Hymnal Committee	'O Lux Beata Trinitas' (4^{1}). 'Pange Lingua' (108^{1}).
*The Faith Press, Ltd.	Faux-bourdon to 'Winchester' (385^{2}) from the 'Tenor Tune Book'.
Mr. C. T. Gatty	'Omni die' (395^{2}).
Irish Literary Society	'Gartan' (52). 'Moville' (179). 'St. Patrick' (506) from the Petrie *Collection of Ancient Irish Music*.
Miss Maud Karpeles	'Mendip' (592^{1}).
Messrs. A. R. Mowbray & Co., Ltd. ...	'Cherry-tree Carol' (463).
*Oxford University Press.............	'Devonshire' (270, 621). 'Kingsfold' (74). 'King's Langley' (608). 'St. Hugh' (557). 'Shipston' (495^{2}). 'St. Columba' (196).
Miss Stanford	'Childhood' (80).
*University of Wales (Students' Hymnal)	'Quinta' (120^{2}).

The copyrights in the following tunes are the property of the Trustees for the Church Hymnary:

Nos. 62^{2}, 110, 245, 425, 680, 682, 685^{2}.

The following tunes have been harmonized or adapted by the musical editor:

Nos. 3, 4^{2}, 11^{1}, 16, 30, 38^{2}, 41, 44, 45, 49, 52, 53, 62^{1}, 65^{1}, 77, 82, 88, 91, 103, 106, 112, 114, 116, 119^{2}, 124^{2}, 140, 158^{1}, 172, 176, 177, 185, 207, 212, 214^{1}, 223^{1}, 223^{2}, 224, 226, 230, 234, 237, 243^{1}, 246^{1}, 250, 253, 259, 262, 263, 274^{2}, 276^{2}, 280, 283, 289^{1}, 295, 296, 299, 300, 302^{2}, 305^{1}, 305^{2}, 310, 311, 312, 313^{1}, 318, 324, 337, 341, 349, 352, 356, 357, 364^{1}, 368, 371^{1}, 371^{2}, 376, 377, 384, 385^{1}, 388, 397, 403, 409, 415^{1}, 434, 435^{2}, 442, 445, 451^{2}, 454, 455, 457^{2}, 458, 459^{2}, 477, 479, 481^{2}, 492, 493^{2}, 494, 499, 502^{2}, 507^{2}, 517^{2}, 518, 520^{1}, 525^{1}, 530^{2}, 539, 540, 546^{2}, 549^{2}, 552, 563, 564^{2}, 571, 581, 583^{1}, 583^{2}, 587, 596, 597^{2}, 598, 600, 604, 607, 615, 618, 627, 632, 633, 634^{2}, 639, 641, 643, 644, 651, 652, 658, 661, 677, 678, 679^{1}, 683, 685^{1}, 688, 689, 692, 697, 714^{1}, 715^{1}, 716^{1}, 716^{2}, 720, 723^{1}, 723^{2}, 724, 725.

The Committee desires to express its thanks to Mr. E. Noel Burghes for his services in obtaining the permissions acknowledged in the foregoing list.

CONTENTS

CONTENTS

GOD: HIS BEING, WORKS, AND WORD

THE HOLY TRINITY

1 NICÆA. (11 12. 12 10.)

Doh = E♭. *Moderately slow.* JOHN BACCHUS DYKES, 1823–76.

```
|d  :d  |m  :m  |s  :—  |s  :—  |l  :—  |l  :l  |s  :—  |m  :—  ||
|s, :s, |d  :d  |t, :r  |d  :t, |l, :t, |d  :r  |m  :—  |d  :—  ||
|m  :m  |d  :d  |r  :f  |m  :s  |f  :s  |l  :t  |d' :s  |s  :—  ||
|d  :d  |l, :l, |s, :—  |d  :—  |f, :—  |f  :f  |d  :—  |d  :—  ||

B♭. t.                                          f. E♭.
|ˢd  :-.d  |d  :d  |f  :—  |m  :d  |s, :d  |r  :-.d  |ᵈs  :— |— :— ||
|ʳs, :s,   |l, :s, |f, :s, |s, :l, |s, :m, |f, :-.m, |ᵐt, :— |— :— ||
|ˢd  :d    |d  :d  |l, :t, |d  :d  |m  :d  |t, :-.d  |ᵈs  :— |f :— ||
|ᵗm, :m,   |f, :m, |r, :—  |m, :f, |s, :s, |s, :-.d, |ᵈs, :— |— :— ||

|d  :d  |m  :m  |s  :—  |s  :—  |l  :-.l  |l  :l  |s  :—  |s  :—  ||
|s, :s, |d  :d  |t, :r  |d  :t, |l, :t,   |d  :r  |m  :—  |d  :—  ||
|m  :m  |d  :d  |r  :f  |m  :s  |f  :s    |l  :t  |d' :s  |m  :—  ||
|d  :d  |l, :l, |s, :—  |d  :—  |f, :-.f, |f  :f  |d  :—  |d  :—  ||

|d' :—  |s  :s  |l  :—  |m  :—   |f  :r  |r  :-.d |d :— |— :— || d  | d  ||
|d  :—  |d  :d  |d  :—  |d  :ta, |l, :l, |t, :-.d |d :— |— :— || l, | s, ||
|m  :f  |s  :ta |l  :—  |s  :—   |f  :f  |f  :-.m |m :— |— :— || f  | m  ||
|l, :—  |m, :m, |f, :—  |d  :—   |f, :f, |s, :-.d |d :— |— :— || f, | d  ||
                                                               A - men.
```

HOLY, holy, holy, Lord God Almighty!
Early in the morning our song shall rise to Thee;
Holy, holy, holy, merciful and mighty,
God in Three Persons, blessèd Trinity!

2 Holy, holy, holy! all the saints adore Thee,
Casting down their golden crowns around the glassy sea,
Cherubim and seraphim falling down before Thee,
Which wert, and art, and evermore shalt be.

3 Holy, holy, holy! though the darkness hide Thee,
Though the eye of sinful man Thy glory may not see,
Only Thou art holy; there is none beside Thee,
Perfect in power, in love, and purity.

4 Holy, holy, holy, Lord God Almighty!
All Thy works shall praise Thy Name in earth and sky and sea;
Holy, holy, holy, merciful and mighty,
God in Three Persons, blessèd Trinity!

REGINALD HEBER, 1783–1826.

2 DEERHURST. (8 7. 8 7. D.)

Doh = F. *In moderate time.* JAMES LANGRAN, 1835–1909.

```
m :s  |m :d  |t, :d  |r :m  |f :m    |r :s  |t :l  |s :—
d :r  |d :s, |s, :s, |s, :s,|d :d.t, |l, :r |r :d  |t, :—
s :s  |s :s  |f :m   |r :d  |l :s    |fe :s |s :fe |s :—
d :t, |d :m  |r :d   |t, :d |d :d    |d :t, |r :r  |s, :—
```

```
m :s  |m :d  |t, :d  |r :m   |f :m   |l :s   |m :r   |d :—
d :r  |d :s, |s, :s, |s, :s, |d :d   |d :d   |d :t,  |d :—
s :s  |s :s  |f :m   |r :d   |d :m   |f :s   |s :f   |m :—
d :t, |d :m  |r :d   |t, :d  |l, :s, |f, :m, |s, :s, |d :—
```

```
m :s  |d' :l |s :d |f :m  |r :m  |s :f |d :r  |m :—
d :t, |d :d  |d :d |t, :d |r :de |r :r |d :l, |t, :—
s :s  |s :f  |s :s |s :s  |l :l  |l :l |l :l  |se :—
d :r  |m :f  |m :m |r :d  |f :m  |r :r |f :f  |m :—
```

```
m :s   |d' :l |s :d |f :m  |r :m  |s :f      |l, :t, |d :—  || d  |d  ||
d :r   |d :d  |d :d |t, :d |r :de |r :l,     |l, :s, |s, :— || l, |s, ||
l :s.f |m :f  |s :s |s :s  |l :l  |l :r      |r :f   |m :—  || f  |m  ||
l, :t, |d :f  |m :m |r :d  |f :m  |r :r,.m,  |f, :s, |d, :— || f, |d  ||
                                                              A - men.
```

[*By permission of Novello & Co., Ltd.*]

SANCTUS. (8 7. 8 7. D.)

Doh = C. *In moderate time.* JOHN RICHARDS (ISALAW), 1843–1908.

```
d' :-.d' |t :l |s :l |s :m |s :-.s   |s :s    |l :d'   |t :—
d' :-.d' |t :l |s :l |s :m |r :-.m   |f :m    |r :l    |s :—
d' :-.d' |t :l |s :l |s :m |s :-.d'  |t :de'  |r' :r'  |r' :—
d' :-.d' |t :l |s :l |s :m |t, :-.d  |r :m    |f :fe   |s :—
```

```
d' :-.d' |t :l |s :l |s :m |m' :-.r' |d' :r' |s :t |d' :— ||
d' :-.d' |t :l |s :l |s :m |s  :-.f  |s  :f  |m :f |m  :— ||
d' :-.d' |t :l |s :l |s :m |d' :-.t  |d' :l  |d':r'|d' :— ||
d' :-.d' |t :l |s :l |s :m |d  :-.r  |m  :f  |s :s |d  :— ||

l :m |d':t |l :se|l :m |l :m |m':r'|d':t |l :— ||t :t |d':d'
m :m |m :m |m :m |m :m |l :m |m :f |m :r |d :— ||m :m |m :fe
d':t |l :se|l :m |d':t |l :m |l :l |l :se|l :— ||l :se|l :d'
l :se|l :m |d':t |l :se|l :m |d :r |m :m |l, :—||m :m |l :l

r':r'|m':m'|d':— |d':— |d':— |l :— |d':— |r':— |d':— |— :— ||d'|d'||
s :s |s :s |l :— |m :— |f :— |f :— |m :— |s :f |m :— |— :— ||f |m ||
d':t |d':d'|m':— |d':— |l :— |d':— |d':— |t :— |d':— |— :— ||l |s ||
s :s |d':d'|l :— |l :— |f :— |f :— |s :— |s :— |d :— |— :— ||f |d ||
                                                          A-men.
```

[By permission of Hughes & Son, Wrexham.]

ROUND the Lord in glory seated,
Cherubim and seraphim
Filled His temple, and repeated
Each to each the alternate hymn:
'Lord, Thy glory fills the heaven;
Earth is with its fulness stored;
Unto Thee be glory given,
Holy, holy, holy Lord.'

2 Heaven is still with glory ringing,
Earth takes up the angels' cry,
'Holy, holy, holy,' singing,
'Lord of hosts, the Lord most high.
Lord, Thy glory fills the heaven;
Earth is with its fulness stored;
Unto Thee be glory given,
Holy, holy, holy Lord.'

3 With His seraph train before Him,
With His holy Church below,
Thus conspire we to adore Him,
Bid we thus our anthem flow:
'Lord, Thy glory fills the heaven;
Earth is with its fulness stored;
Unto Thee be glory given,
Holy, holy, holy Lord.'

RICHARD MANT, 1776–1848.

3 BROCKHAM (CONFIDENCE). (L.M.)

JEREMIAH CLARK, 1670–1707.

Doh = G. *Moderately fast.*

:s, |d :r |m :t, |d :r |t, :r |f :-.f |m :d |m :fe |s ||
:s, |s, :s, |s, :-.f, |m, :l, |s, :t, |l, :-.l, |s, :s, |s, :d |t, ||
:s, |d :t, |d :r |d :f |r :s |d :-.r |m :s |m.r :d |r ||
:s, |m, :s, |d :s, |l, :f, |s, :s, |l, :-.t, |d :m |d.t, :l, |s, ||

:s |m :d |l, :m |f :r |t, :s, |d :-.r |m :s |m :r.d |d ||d |d ||
:r |d :s, |l, :s, |f, :l, |s, :s, |s, :-.t, |d :s, |d :t,.d |s, ||l, |s, ||
:s |s :d |d :de |r :r |r :s, |s :-.f |m :d |s :f |m ||f |m ||
:t, |d :m, |f, :m, |r, :f, |s, :s,.f, |m, :-.r, |d, :m, |s, :s, |d, ||f, |d, ||

A-men.

Te Deum laudamus.

WE praise, we worship Thee, O God;
Thy sovereign power we sound abroad;
All nations bow before Thy throne,
And Thee the great Jehovah own.

2 Loud hallelujahs to Thy Name
Angels and seraphim proclaim;
By all the powers and thrones in heaven
Eternal praise to Thee is given.

3 O holy, holy, holy Lord,
Thou God of hosts, by all adored,
Earth and the heavens are full of Thee,
Thy light, Thy power, Thy majesty.

4 Apostles join the glorious throng,
And swell the loud triumphant song;
Prophets and martyrs hear the sound,
And spread the hallelujah round.

5 Glory to Thee, O God most high!
Father, we praise Thy majesty:
The Son, the Spirit we adore—
One Godhead, blest for evermore.

Tr. in PHILIP GELL'S *Psalms and Hymns*, 1815.

4 O LUX BEATA TRINITAS.

Doh = D. *Unison. In free rhythm.*

Plainsong Melody. Mode viii.

s :l :s :f :m :f :r :m :f :s :l :l :s :s ||

1. O Trin - i - ty, O bless - ed Light,
2. Let us with songs of praise di - vine
3. To God the Fa - ther, glo - ry great,

s :l :s :f :m :f :r :m :f :s :l :l :s :s ||

O Un - i - ty, most prin - ci - pal,
At morn and even - ing Thee im - plore;
And glo - ry to His on - ly Son,

| s: l | :d' :t | :d' :l | :s :f | :s :l | :s :f | :m :m ||

The fie - ry sun now leaves our sight:
And let our glo - ry, bowed to Thine,
And to the Ho - ly Pa - ra - clete,

| f :s | :s :f | :m :f | :r :m | :f :s | :l :l | :s :s :— || s :l :s :s :— ||

Cause in our hearts Thy beams to fall.
Thee glo - ri - fy for ev - er - more.
Both now and still while a - ges run. A - men.

AETERNA CHRISTI MUNERA. (L.M.)

Doh = G. *With movement.* Rouen Church Melody.

```
:s  | f :m :r  | m :d :r  | m :r :-.d   | d :— :m   | s :— :s
:s, | d :— :r  | d :— :t, | t, :— :-.l, | l, :— :s, | s, :— :s,
:d  | d :m :s  | s :m :s  | s :— :-.m   | m :— :d   | r :— :t,
:m, | l, :— :t,| d :— :s, | m, :s, :-.l,| l, :— :d  | t, :— :s,

m :— :d   | f :m :r    | r :— || r  | m :— :d  | l, :— :r  | d :t, :l,
s, :— :d  | d :— :d    | t, :— || t, | d :— :s, | l, :— :l, | s, :— :f,
d :— :m   | l :— :l    | s :— || s  | s :— :m  | d :— :f   | m :r :d
d :— :l,  | r, :m, :f, | s, :— || s, | d :— :m, | f, :— :r, | m, :— :f,

s, :— :s  | r :m :d   | f :m :r   | m :r :-.d    | d :—  || d  | d  ||
r, :— :s, | s, :— :d  | t, :d :t, | t, :— :-.d   | d :—  || l, | s, ||
t, :— :d  | t, :d :s  | f :s :s   | s :— :-.m    | m :—  || f  | m  ||
s, :— :m, | s, :d :m  | r :d :s,  | m, :s, :-.d, | d, :— || f, | d, ||
                                                            A - men.
```

O Lux beata Trinitas.

O TRINITY, O blessèd Light,
O Unity, most principal,
The fiery sun now leaves our sight:
Cause in our hearts Thy beams to fall.

2 Let us with songs of praise divine
At morn and evening Thee implore;
And let our glory, bowed to Thine,
Thee glorify for evermore.

3 To God the Father, glory great,
And glory to His only Son,
And to the Holy Paraclete,
Both now and still while ages run.

St. Ambrose, 340–97; *tr.* by
Wm. Drummond of Hawthornden, 1585–1649.

5 DAS LEIDEN DES HERRN. (L.M.)

Lah = E. Doh = G. *Very slow.* German Traditional Melody.

l, :l, :l,	m :-.f :m	m :r :d	t, :— :—		r :r :r	r :-.d :t,
l, :l, :l,	l, :— :l,	d :t, :l,	l, :s, :—		f, :l, :t,	m, :— :m,
l, :l,.t, :d.r	m :-.r :m	fe :— :fe	r :— :m		f :f :r	l :— :m
l, :l, :l,.t,	d :-.t, :d	r :— :r,	s, :— :—		r, :f, :s,	l, :— :s,

d :r :m	l, :—		m	r :t, :d.t,	l, :— :s,	d :— :r	m :— :—	
l, :— :s,	s, :f,		d	t, :s, :s,	f, :m, :r,	l, :— :l,	l, :— :se,	
l, :t, :d	r :—		s	s :r :d	d :— :t,	m :— :r	t, :— :—	
f, :— :m,	r, :—		d,	s, :f, :m,	f, :— :s,	l, :s, :f,	m, :— :—	

m :m :m	r :— :m	d :t, :—	l, :— :—		l,	l,	
l, :t, :de	r.d :t,.l, :se,	l, :— :se,	m, :— :—		f,	m,	
de :m :l	l.s :f.m :r	m :m :-.r	d :— :—		r	de	
l, :se, :l,.s,	f,.m, :r,.d, :t,,	d,.r, :m, :—	l, :— :—		r,	l,	

A-men.

RIVAULX. (L.M.)

Doh = D. *In moderate time.* JOHN BACCHUS DYKES, 1823–76.

s :s :s	s :— :s	l :— :l	s :— :—	d' :d' :l	r :— :m
d :m :m	f :— :m.r	d :— :r	m :— :—	d :d :d	d :— :d
m :s :d'	r' :— :d'.t	l :— :t	d' :— :—	s :s :l	l :— :s
d :d :d	t, :— :d	f :— :f	d :— :—	m :m :f	f :— :m

f :— :f	m :—		d	m :— :m	m :— :m	s :— :s
d :t, :—	d :—		l,	t, :d :r	d :— :d	r :m :f
l :s :f	s :—		l	l :— :se	l :— :d'	d' :— :t
r :— :r	d :—		f	m :— :m,{m}	l, :— :l	s :— :s,{s}

s :— :—	d' :t :l	s :— :f	m :— :r	d :— :—		d	d	
m :— :—	m :m :f	s :s, :l,	d :t, :—	d :— :—		l,	s,	
d' :— :t	l :t :d'	d' :— :f	s :— :f	m :— :—		f	m	
d :— :—	l :s :f	m :— :r	d :s, :—	d :— :—		f,	d	

A-men.

FATHER of heaven, whose love profound
A ransom for our souls hath found,
Before Thy throne we sinners bend;
To us Thy pardoning love extend.

2 Almighty Son, Incarnate Word,
Our Prophet, Priest, Redeemer, Lord,
Before Thy throne we sinners bend;
To us Thy saving grace extend.

3 Eternal Spirit, by whose breath
The soul is raised from sin and death,
Before Thy throne we sinners bend;
To us Thy quickening power extend.

4 Jehovah—Father, Spirit, Son—
Mysterious Godhead, Three in One,
Before Thy throne we sinners bend;
Grace, pardon, life to us extend.

EDWARD COOPER, 1770–1833.

6 LEICESTER. (8 8. 8 8. 8 8.)

Lah = A. Doh = C. *Moderately slow.* JOHN BISHOP, 1665–1737.

```
:m  |m    :l    |se :l    |r'.d':t.l  |se :-.se |l  :s.f |m    :l
:d  |m    :m.f  |m  :m    |r.m  :f    |m  :-.m  |m  :r   |d.r  :m.f
:l  |d'.r':d'   |t  :d'.t |l    :r'.d'|t  :-.t  |d' :r'  |s    :m'.r'
:l, |l,.t,:d.r  |m  :l.s  |f    :r    |m  :-.m  |l, :t,  |d.t, :d.r

|l  :se |l  ||m  |m    :l    |se :l    |r'.d':t.l  |se :-.se
|m  :m  |m  ||d  |m    :m.f  |m  :m    |r.m  :f    |m  :-.m
|d' :t  |d' ||l  |d'.r':d'   |t  :d'.t |l    :r'.d'|t  :-.t
|m  :m  |l, ||l, |l,.t,:d.r  |m  :l.s  |f    :r    |m  :-.m

|l  :t   |d' :r'.d' |d' :t  |d' ||d' |m' :r'  |d' :t
|m  :s   |s  :f.m   |m  :r  |m  ||m  |s  :s   |s  :se
|d' :r'  |d' :l     |s  :s  |s  ||s  |d' :t   |d' :m'
|l  :s.f |m  :f     |s  :s, |d  ||d  |d  :s.f |m  :m.r

|l  :t.l   |se :-.se |l  :s.f |m    :l     |l  :se  |l  ||l |l
|l  :f     |m  :-.m  |m  :r   |d.r  :m.f   |m  :m.r |d  ||r |de
|m' :r'.d' |t  :-.t  |d' :r'  |s    :m'.r' |d' :t   |l  ||f |m
|d  :r     |m  :-.m  |l, :t,  |d.t, :d.r   |m  :m   |l, ||r |l,
                                                         A - men.
```

O KING of kings, before whose throne
The angels bow, no gift can we
Present that is indeed our own,
Since heaven and earth belong to Thee:
Yet this our souls through grace impart,
The offering of a thankful heart.

2 O Jesus, set at God's right hand,
With Thine eternal Father plead
For all Thy loyal-hearted band,
Who still on earth Thy succour need:
For them in weakness strength provide,
And through the world their footsteps guide.

3 O Holy Spirit, Fount of breath,
Whose comforts never fail nor fade,
Vouchsafe the life that knows no death,
Vouchsafe the light that knows no shade;
And grant that we, through all our days,
May share Thy gifts and sing Thy praise.

JOHN QUARLES, 1624–65; and THOMAS DARLING, 1816–93.

7 REGENT SQUARE. (8 7. 8 7. 8 7.)

Doh = B♭. *Moderately fast.* HENRY SMART, 1813–79.

```
s, :m, |d  :s,  |m  :-.r  |d  :s,  |l, :l,  |s, :d   |s, :f,  |m, :—  ||
m, :d, |s, :m,  |s, :-.s, |s, :s,  |d, :d,  |d, :d,  |r, :t2  |d, :—  ||
d  :s, |s, :d   |d  :-.t, |d  :d   |l, :d   |s, :l,  |s, :s,  |s, :—  ||
d, :d, |m, :d,  |s, :-.f, |m, :m,  |f, :f,  |m, :l2  |t2 :s2  |d, :—  ||

s, :m, |d  :s,    |m  :-.r  |d  :t,  |d  :t,  |l, :t,.d |t, :l,  |s, :—  ||
m, :d, |s, :s,.f, |m, :-.f, |m, :m,  |m, :m,  |m, :m,   |s, :fe, |s, :—  ||
d  :d  |s, :s,    |d  :-.t, |l, :se, |l, :se, |m  :r.d  |r  :d   |t, :—  ||
d  :s, |m, :m,.r, |d, :-.r, |m, :m,  |l, :m,  |d, :l2   |r, :r,  |s2 :—  ||

                   //:
r  :-.r  |t, :s, |m  :-.r  |d  :l, |f  :m  |r     :d    |d  :t,   |d  :— ||d  |d  ||
s, :-.s, |s, :s, |s, :-.m, |f, :f, |l, :s, |f,    :m,.f,|s, :-.f, |m, :— ||f, |m, ||
t, :-.t, |r  :t, |d  :-.ta,|l, :d  |r  :s, |l,.t, :d    |r  :r    |d  :— ||l, |s, ||
s, :-.s, |s, :s, |d, :-.d, |f, :f, |r, :m, |f,.s, :l,   |s, :s2   |d, :— ||f, |d, ||
                                                                            A-men.
```

GLORY be to God the Father,
Glory be to God the Son,
Glory be to God the Spirit,—
Great Jehovah, Three in One!
Glory, glory
While eternal ages run!

2 Glory be to Him who loved us,
Washed us from each spot and stain!
Glory be to Him who bought us,
Made us kings with Him to reign!
Glory, glory
To the Lamb that once was slain!

3 Glory to the King of angels,
Glory to the Church's King,
Glory to the King of nations!
Heaven and earth, your praises bring;
Glory, glory
To the King of Glory bring!

4 'Glory, blessing, praise eternal!'
Thus the choir of angels sings;
'Honour, riches, power, dominion!'
Thus its praise creation brings;
Glory, glory,
Glory to the King of kings!

HORATIUS BONAR, 1808–89.

Also the following:

8

ST. FLAVIAN. (C.M.)

Doh = F. *In moderate time.* *English Psalter*, 1562.

d :—	d :t,	d :m	r :r	d :—		d :—	f :m	d :r	m :—	
s, :—	s, :s,	s, :d	d :t,	d :—		s, :—	d :d	d :l,	t, :—	
m :—	r :r	m :s	l :s	m :—		m :—	f :s	l :l	se :—	
d :—	s, :s,	d :m,	f, :s,	d, :—		d :—	l, :d	f :f	m :—	

m :—	m :f	s :m	d :r	m :—		m :—	r :d	d :t,	d :—		d	d	
d :—	d :d	r :t,	l, :t,	d :—		d :—	t, :d	l, :s,	s, :—		l,	s,	
s :—	s :f	r :s	m :s	s :—		s :—	s :m	f :r	m :—		f	m	
d :—	d :l,	t, :s,	l, :s,	d :—		d :—	s, :l,	f, :s,	d, :—		f,	d,	

A-men.

THERE is a book, who runs may read,
Which heavenly truth imparts,
And all the lore its scholars need,
Pure eyes and Christian hearts.

2 The works of God, above, below,
Within us and around,
Are pages in that book, to show
How God Himself is found.

3 The glorious sky, embracing all,
Is like the Maker's love,
Wherewith encompassed, great and small
In peace and order move.

4 The dew of heaven is like Thy grace :
It steals in silence down ;
But, where it lights, the favoured place
By richest fruits is known.

5 One Name, above all glorious names,
With its ten thousand tongues
The everlasting sea proclaims,
Echoing angelic songs.

6 Two worlds are ours ; 'tis only sin
Forbids us to descry
The mystic heaven and earth within,
Plain as the sea and sky.

7 Thou who hast given me eyes to see
And love this sight so fair,
Give me a heart to find out Thee,
And read Thee everywhere.

JOHN KEBLE, 1792–1866.

9 HANOVER. (10 10. 11 11.)

Doh = A. *In moderate time.* WILLIAM CROFT, 1678–1727.

:s, | d :d :r | m :— :s | d :r :t, | d :— ||
:m, | s, :s, :s, | s, :— :s, | l, :l, :s, | s, :— ||
:d | m :d :t, | d :— :r | m :f :r | m :— ||
:d, | d, :m, :s, | d :— :t, | l, :f, :s, | d, :— ||

:r | m :r :d | t, :— :d | r :d.t, :l, | s, :— ||
:s, | s, :s, :s,.fe, | s, :— :s, | s, :l,.s, :fe, | s, :— ||
:t, | d :r :m.r | r :— :m | r :l, :r | t, :— ||
:s, | d :t, :l, | s, :— :m, | t_2 :d, :r, | s, :— ||

:t, | d :r :m | d :l, :f | m :r :d | s :— ||
:se, | l, :l, :se, | l, :m, :s, | s, :s, :d | t, :— ||
:m | m :l, :t, | d :d :r | d :r :m.fe | s :— ||
:m, | l, :f, :m, | l, :l, :t, | d :t, :l, | s, :— ||

:s, | l, :t, :d | r :s, :m | l, :r :t, | d :— || d | d ||
:s, | s, :f, :s, | s, :m, :s, | f, :l, :s, | s, :— || l, | s, ||
:d | d :r :m | r :t, :d | d :f :r | m :— || f | m ||
:m, | f, :r, :d, | t_2 :m, :d, | f, :r, :s, | d, :— || f, | d, ||

A - men.

From Psalm civ.

O WORSHIP the King all-glorious above,
O gratefully sing His power and His love,
Our Shield and Defender, the Ancient of Days,
Pavilioned in splendour, and girded with praise.

2 O tell of His might, O sing of His grace,
Whose robe is the light, whose canopy space.
His chariots of wrath the deep thunder-clouds form,
And dark is His path on the wings of the storm.

Unison. 3 The earth with its store of wonders untold,
Almighty, Thy power hath founded of old,
Hath stablished it fast by a changeless decree,
And round it hath cast, like a mantle, the sea.

FAUX-BOURDON SETTING *

Doh = A. HARVEY GRACE, 1874–

:s_1 | d :d :l | s :— :f.m | f :f :m.r | m :— ||
:s_1 | d :d :d.t_1 | d :s_1 :d | d :l_1 :s_1 | s_1 :— ||
:s_1 | d :d :r | m :— :s | d :r :t_1 | d :— ||
:s_1 | d :d :f_1 | m_1 :d/d_1 :ta_1 | l_1 :f_1 :s_1 | d_1 :— ||

:f | m :t_1 :d | r.m :f :m | r :– .m :d | d :t_1 ||
:s_1 | s_1 :l_1 :s_1 | f_1.s_1 :l_1 :s_1 | s_1 :s_1 :fe_1 | s_1 :— ||
:r | m :r :d | t_1 :— :d | r :d.t_1 :l_1 | s_1 :— ||
:t_2 | d_1 :f_1 :m_1 | r_1 :— :m_1 | t_2 :d_1 :r_1 | s_1 :— ||

:r | m :r :d.t_1 | d.r :m :l | s :s :f.m | r :— ||
:t_1 | l_1 :t_1.l_1 :se_1 | l_1.t_1 :d :m.r | m :s_1 :l_1 | t_1 :— ||
:t_1 | d :r :m | d :l_1 :f | m :r :d | s :— ||
:s_1 | fe_1 :f_1 :m_1 | l_1 :l_1 :t_1 | d :t_1 :d | s_1 :— ||

:d | d.r :m.r :m.f | s :ta :– .ta | l :f :m.r | d :— ||
:s_1 | f_1 :s_1 :s_1.l_1 | ta_1.d :r :d | d :l_1 :s_1.f_1 | m_1 :— ||
:s_1 | l_1 :t_1 .d | r :s_1 :m | l_1 :r :t_1 | d :— ||
:m_1 | l_1 :s_1 :d | s_1 :s_1 :d_1 | f_1 :f_1 :s_1 | d_1 :— ||

Unison. 4 Thy bountiful care what tongue can recite ?
It breathes in the air ; it shines in the light ;
It streams from the hills ; it descends to the plain,
And sweetly distils in the dew and the rain.

Harmony. 5 Frail children of dust, and feeble as frail,
In Thee do we trust, nor find Thee to fail ;
Thy mercies how tender, how firm to the end,
Our Maker, Defender, Redeemer, and Friend !

6 O measureless Might ! ineffable Love !
While angels delight to hymn Thee above,
The humbler creation, though feeble their lays,
With true adoration shall lisp to Thy praise.

ROBERT GRANT, 1779–1838

* See Preface.

10

FIRMAMENT. (D.L.M.)

1st and 3rd verses Unison.
2nd verse Harmony.

Doh = A. *In moderate time.* HENRY WALFORD DAVIES, 1869–

:s, | s, :– .s, | s, .l, :t, .d | m :r | d :– .d (:d)
:s, | m, :f, | s, :m, .s, | d :t, | l, :– .m,
1. The | spa - cious | fir - ma - | ment on | high, With
2. Soon | as the | ev - 'ning | shades pre - | vail, The
3. What | though in | sol - emn | si - lence | all Move
:s, | m :t, | d :m | s :f | m :– .d
:s, | d, :r, | m, :d, | s, :s, | l, :– .l,

d :t, .l, | s, :d | s, :– .f, | m, :s,
f, :f, | r, :d, | m, :– .r, | d, :m,
all the | blue e - | the - real | sky, And
moon takes | up the | won - drous | tale, And
round the | dark ter - | res - trial | ball? What
l, :t, .d | t, :s, | l, :t, | s, :s,
r, :r, | f, :m, | r, :s, | d, :d,

s, :– .s, | s, .l, :t, .d | m :r | d :– .d
m, :f, | s, :m, .s, | d :t, | l, :s,
span - gled | heavens, a | shi - ning | frame, Their
night - ly | to the | listen - ing | earth Re -
though no | real . . . | voice nor | sound A -
m :t, | d :m | s :f | m :d
d, :r, | m, :d, | s, :s, | l, :l,

d :t, .l, | r :t, | l, :– .s, | s, :s, .s,
fe, :m, .fe, | s, :s, | s, :fe, | s, :s,
great O - | rig - i - | nal pro - | claim. The un-
peats the | sto - ry | of her | birth; While
midst their | ra - diant | orbs be | found? In
l, :r | r :r | m :d | t, :s,
r, :d | t, :s, | d, :r, | s, :s,

m :– .r | d :s_1 | m :– .r | d :d
s_1 :– .s_1 | s_1 :s_1 | s_1 :– .s_1 | s_1 :s_1
wea - ried sun, from day to day, Does
all the stars that round her burn, And
rea - son's ear they all re - joice, And
t_1 :– .t_1 | d :s_1 | l_1 :– .t_1 | d :d
f_1 :– .f_1 | m_1 :s_1 | s_1 :– .f_1 | m_1 :m_1

f.D. *B minor.* A.t.

$^{f}d^1$:– .t | l :m | d^1 :– .t | ^{l}r :r
^{l_1}m :– .m | m :m | m :– .m | $^{m}l_1$:d
his Cre - a - tor's power dis - play, And
all the plan - ets, in their turn, Con -
ut - ter forth a glo - rious voice, For
^{de}se :– .se | l :d^1 | se :ba .se | ^{l}r :l
^{l_1}m :– .r | d :l_1 | m :r | $^{d}f_1$:f_1

s :t_1 | d :r .m | s_1 :f_1 | m_1 :– .s_1
t_1 :– .l_1 | s_1 .l_1 :t_1 .d | m_1 :r_1 | d_1 :– .s_1
pub - lish - es to ev - ery land The
firm the ti - dings, as they roll, And
ev - er sing - ing, as they shine, 'The
s :– .s | s :f .m | d :r | m :– .s_1
f :– .f | m :r .d | l_1 :t_1 | d :– .s_1

d :–.d | d :s_1 | m :r .d | l_1 :— | s_1 :— ‖ l_1 :— | s_1 :f_1 | d :— | — :—
d :–.d | d :s_1 | d :s_1 | f_1 :— | m_1 :— ‖ d_1 :— | — :— | f_1 :— | m_1 :—
work of an al - migh - ty hand.
spread the truth from pole to pole.
hand that made us is di - vine.' A - men.
d :–.d | d :s_1 | s :f .m | d :— | — :— ‖ d :— | t_1 :l_1 | l_1 :— | s_1 :—
d :–.d | d :s_1 | d_1 :r_1.m_1 | f_1 :— | d_1 :— ‖ f_1 :— | — :— | d_1 :— | — :—

From Psalm xix. JOSEPH ADDISON, 1672–1719.

11

HARTS. (77. 77.)

Doh = A♭. *In moderate time.*

Benjamin Milgrove, 1731–1810.

s, :s,	d :d	r :r	m :—	d :d	f :m.r	d :m	r :—	
m, :r,	m, :s,	l, :s,	s, :—	s, :m,	l, :s,	s, :d	t, :—	
d :r	d :d	d :t,	d :—	d :d	d :t,	d :s	s :—	
d :t,	l, :m,	f, :s,	d :—	m, :l,	r, :s,.f,	m, :d,	s, :—	

s :s	m :m	f :f	r :—	m :f	s :f	m :r	d :—		d	d	
s, :s,	l, :l,	d :d	t, :—	s, :l,	d :d	d :t,	d :—		l,	s,	
r :m	d :d.m	l :l	s :—	s :d	s :l	s :—.f	m :—		f	m	
t, :m,	l, :l,.s,	f, :r,	s, :—	d :l,	m, :f,	s, :s,	d, :—		f,	d,	

A-men.

MELLING. (77. 77.)

Doh = G. *In moderate time.*

A New Set of Sacred Music, by John Fawcett, c. 1822.

d :s,	d.r :m.f	m :r	d :—	r :m.d	l, :r.d	t, :l,	s, :—	
s, :s,	l,.t, :d.d	d :t,	d :—	t, :s,	fe, :s,.l,	s, :fe,	s, :—	
m :r	m.s :—.l	s :s	m :—	s :m	r :r.m	r :r	t, :—	
d :t,	l,.s, :d.f,	s, :s,	d, :—	s, :d	r.d :t,.d	r :r,	s, :—	

d :d.r	m.d :l,.t,	d.r :m.d	r :—	m.s :f.l	s :—.f	m :r	d :—		d	d	
s, :l,	s, :l,.s,	s, :—.fe,	s, :—	s, :t,	d :—.r	d :t,	s, :—		l,	s,	
d :f	m :d.r	m.r :d	d :t,	s.m :f	m.,f :s.l	s :s	m :—		f	m	
m, :f,	d, :f,	m, :l,	s, :—	d :r	m.,r :m.f	s :s,	d :—		f,	d,	

A-men.

From Psalm cxxxvi.

LET us with a gladsome mind
Praise the Lord, for He is kind :
For His mercies aye endure,
Ever faithful, ever sure.

2 Let us blaze His Name abroad,
For of gods He is the God :
For His mercies aye endure,
Ever faithful, ever sure.

3 He, with all-commanding might,
Filled the new-made world with light :
For His mercies aye endure,
Ever faithful, ever sure.

4 All things living He doth feed ;
His full hand supplies their need :
For His mercies aye endure,
Ever faithful, ever sure.

5 He His chosen race did bless
In the wasteful wilderness :
For His mercies aye endure,
Ever faithful, ever sure.

6 He hath with a piteous eye
Looked upon our misery :
For His mercies aye endure,
Ever faithful, ever sure.

7 Let us then with gladsome mind
Praise the Lord, for He is kind :
For His mercies aye endure,
Ever faithful, ever sure.

John Milton, 1608–74.

12 JOANNA. (11 11. 11 11).

Welsh Hymn Melody.

Doh = A. *In moderate time.* *D.C.*

:d	l, :f, :r	t, :s, :d.r	m :m :r	d :—
:s,	f, :f, :l,	s, :s, :m,.f,	s, :s, :s,.f,	m, :—
:m	d :l, :f	r :t, :d	d :d :t,	d :—
:d,	f, :f, :r,	s, :s, :l,	s, :s, :s,	d, :—

:d	m :m :s	m :d :d	m :m :s	r :—
:s,	d :d :r	s, :s, :s,	s, :l, :s,	s, :—
:m	s :s :r	m :m :s.f	m :d :d	t, :—
:d,	d :d :t,	d :d :m.r	d :l, :m,.f,	s, :—

:m	d :l, :r	t, :s, :d.r	m :m :r	d :—	d	d
:s,	l, :f, :l,	s, :s, :m,.f,	s, :d :t,	d :—	l,	s,
:d	d :d :f	r :t, :d	d :s :s.f	m :—	f	m
:d,	f, :f, :r,	s, :s, :l,	s, :s, :s,	d, :—	f,	d,
					A -	men.

IMMORTAL, invisible, God only wise,
In light inaccessible hid from our eyes,
Most blessèd, most glorious, the Ancient of Days,
Almighty, victorious, Thy great Name we praise.

2 Unresting, unhasting, and silent as light,
Nor wanting, nor wasting, Thou rulest in might;
Thy justice like mountains high soaring above
Thy clouds which are fountains of goodness and love.

3 To all, life Thou givest—to both great and small;
In all life Thou livest, the true life of all;
We blossom and flourish as leaves on the tree,
And wither and perish—but nought changeth Thee.

4 Great Father of Glory, pure Father of Light,
Thine angels adore Thee, all veiling their sight;
All laud we would render: O help us to see
'Tis only the splendour of light hideth Thee.

WALTER CHALMERS SMITH, 1824–1908.

13

LASST UNS ERFREUEN. (88. 44. 88. and Refrain.)

Doh = E♭. *With vigour.* *Geistliche Kirchengesäng*, Cologne, 1623.

:d | d .r :m .d :m .f | s :— :d | d .r :m .d :m .f | s :— ||
:d | d .r :m .d :m .f | s :— :d | d .r :m .d :m .f | s :— ||
:d | d .r :m .d :m .f | s :— :d | d .r :m .d :m .f | s :— ||
:d | d .r :m .d :m .f | s :— :d | d .r :m .d :m .f | s :— ||

:d'.t | l :s :d'.t | l :s || d' | d' .s :s .f :m .f
:s .s | s .f :m :d .r | m .r :t, || d' | d' .s :s .f :m .f
:d'.d' | d' :d' :m .s | s .fe :s || d' | d' .s :s .f :m .f
:m .m | f :d :l,.t, | d .r :s, || d' | d' .s :s .f :m .f

REFRAIN.

| s :— :d' | d' .s :s .f :m .f | s :— || f .m | r :d :f .m
| s :— :d' | d' .s :s .f :m .f | s :— || d | d .t, :d :d
| s :— :d' | d' .s :s .f :m .f | s :— || l | l .s :s :l .s
| s :— :d' | d' .s :s .f :m .f | s :— || l, .s, | f, :m, :r,.m,

r :d :d'.t	l :s :d'.t	l :s :f.m	r :— :—	d :—		d	d	
d .t, :l, :m .r	m .r :t, :d'.t	l :s :f.m	r :— :—	d :—		l,	s,	
l .f :m :m .s	s .fe :s :d'.t	l :s :f.m	r :— :—	d :—		f	m	
f,.s, :l, :l,.t,	d .r :s, :d'.t	l :s :f.m	r :— :—	d :—		f,	d	

A - men.

Laudato sia Dio mio Signore.

ALL creatures of our God and King,
Lift up your voice and with us sing
Alleluia, Alleluia!
Thou burning sun with golden beam,
Thou silver moon with softer gleam,
O praise Him, O praise Him,
Alleluia, Alleluia, Alleluia!

2 Thou rushing wind that art so strong,
Ye clouds that sail in heaven along,
O praise Him, Alleluia!
Thou rising morn, in praise rejoice,
Ye lights of evening, find a voice.

3 Thou flowing water, pure and clear,
Make music for thy Lord to hear,
Alleluia, Alleluia!
Thou fire so masterful and bright,
That givest man both warmth and light.

4 Dear mother earth, who day by day
Unfoldest blessings on our way,
O praise Him, Alleluia!
The flowers and fruits that in thee grow,
Let them His glory also show.

5 And all ye men of tender heart,
Forgiving others, take your part,
O sing ye, Alleluia!
Ye who long pain and sorrow bear,
Praise God and on Him cast your care.

6 And thou, most kind and gentle death,
Waiting to hush our latest breath,
O praise Him, Alleluia!
Thou leadest home the child of God,
And Christ our Lord the way hath trod.

7 Let all things their Creator bless,
And worship Him in humbleness,
O praise Him, Alleluia!
Praise, praise the Father, praise the Son,
And praise the Spirit, Three in One.

St. Francis of Assisi, 1182–1226;
tr. by William Henry Draper, 1855–

14

TROYTE NO. 2. (Irr.) ARTHUR HENRY DYKE TROYTE, 1811–57.

Doh = G. *In moderate time.*

Me	m :r	d :—	Fah	f :m	r :—
Doh	d :t,	d :—	Lah,	s, :d	t, :—
Soh	s :f	m :—	Doh	r :s	s :—
Doh	d :s,	l, :—	Lah,	t, :d	s, :—

Cantemus cuncti melodum.

THE strain upraise of joy and praise, Alle-	-lu - - - ia!	To the glory of their King Let the ransomed	peo - ple sing
2 And the choirs that . . .	dwell on high	Swell the chorus	in the sky,
3 Ye through the fields of	Paradise that roam,	Ye blessèd ones, repeat through	that bright home,
Unison. 4 Ye planets, glittering on your	heaven - ly way,	Ye shining constellations,	join and say
Harmony. 5 Ye clouds that onward sweep, Ye winds on	pin - ions light,	Ye thunders, echoing loud and deep, Ye lightnings	wild - ly bright,
6 Ye floods and ocean billows, Ye storms and	winter snow,	Ye days of cloudless beauty, Hoar frost and	sum - mer glow,
7 First let the birds, with painted	plum - age gay,	Exalt their great Creator's	praise, and say
8 Then let the beasts of earth, with	vary - ing strain,	Join in creation's hymn, and	cry a - gain
Unison. 9 Here let the mountains thunder forth so-	-nor - - ous	Alle - - - - -	-lu - - ia!
10 Thou jubilant abyss of .	o - cean, cry	Alle - - - - -	-lu - - ia!
Harmony. 11 To God, who all cre - -	-a - tion made,	The frequent hymn be	du - ly paid,
12 This is the strain, the eternal strain, the Lord of	all things loves:	Alle - - - - -	-lu - - ia!
13 Wherefore we sing, both heart and voice a-	-wak - - ing,	Alle - - - - -	-lu - - ia!
Unison. 14 Now from all men . . .	be out-poured	Alleluia	to the Lord.
Harmony. 15 Praise be done to the . .	Three in One,	Alle - - - - -	-lu - ia!

Soh	s :f | m :— ‖	Ray	r :— | d :— ‖	d	d ‖
Te_{l}	d :r | d :— ‖	Lah_{l}	t_{l} :— | d :— ‖	l_{l}	s_{l} ‖
Soh	m :s | s :— ‖	Fah	f :— | m :— ‖	f	m ‖
Me	l_{l} :t_{l} | d :— ‖	Fah_{l}	s_{l} :— | d_{l} :— ‖	f_{l}	d_{l} ‖
				A-men.	

Alle - - - -	-lu - - ia!	Alle - - -	- lu - ia!
(2) Alle - - - -	-lu - - ia!	Alle - - -	- lu - ia!
(3) Alle - - - -	-lu - - ia!	Alle - - -	- lu - ia!
(4) Alle - - - -	-lu - - ia!	Alle - - -	- lu - ia!
(5) In sweet con - - -	-sent u - nite	your Alle - -	- lu - ia!
(6) Ye groves that wave in spring, And glorious	fo - rests, sing	Alle - - -	- lu - ia!
(7) Alle - - - -	-lu - - ia!	Alle - - -	- lu - ia!
(8) Alle - - - -	-lu - - ia!	Alle - - -	- lu - ia!
(9) There let the valleys sing in gentler	cho - - rus,	Alle - - -	- lu - ia!
(10) Ye tracts of earth and conti-	-nents, re - ply	Alle - - -	- lu - ia!
(11) Alle - - - -	-lu - - ia!	Alle - - -	- lu - ia!
(12) This is the song, the heavenly song, that Christ Him-	-self ap - proves:	Alle - - -	- lu - ia!
Trebles only. (13) And children's voices echo, answer	mak - - ing,	Alle - - -	- lu - ia!
(14) With Alleluia	e - ver - more	The Son and Spirit	we adore.
(15) Alle - - - -	-lu - - ia!	Alle - - -	- lu - ia!

Attributed to BALBULUS NOTKER, 840–912; *tr.* by JOHN MASON NEALE, 1818-66.

15 LUCKINGTON. (10 4. 6 6. 6 6. 10 4.)

Doh = E♭. *Moderately quick.* BASIL HARWOOD, 1859–

:d |m :— |s :— |d' :— |— :d |r :l |s :f |m :— ‖
:s, |d :— |r :— |m :— |— :d |d :d |d :t, |d :— ‖
:m |s :— |t :— |d' :— |— :s |l :f |r' :s |s :— ‖
:d |d :— |t, :— |l, :— |— :m |f :r |s :s |d :— ‖

|s :— |l :— |r :— |t :— |— ‖d' |l :f |r :t |d' :— ‖
|r :— |m :— |r :— |r :— |— ‖d' |l :f |r :t |d' :— ‖
|s :— |s :— |fe :— |s :— |— ‖d' |l :f |r :t |d' :— ‖
|t, :— |d :— |r :— |s, :— |— ‖d' |l :f |r :t |d' :— ‖

B♭.t.

|d' :— |l :f |r :t |d' :— ‖(s)d :— |l, :f, |r, :s, |m, :— ‖
|d :— |d :d |d :r |d :— ‖(s)d :— |l, :f, |r, :s, |m, :— ‖
|s :— |f :l |s :f |m :— ‖(s)d :— |l, :f, |r, :s, |m, :— ‖
|m :— |f :r |s :s, |d :— ‖(s)d :— |l, :f, |r, :s, |m, :— ‖

f.E♭.

|d :— |l, :f, |r, :s, |m, :— ‖ :(f)d |m :— |s :— |d' :— |— :d
|s, :— |f, :d, |r, :r, |d, :— ‖ :(d)s, |l, :— |t, :— |d :— |— :d
|d :— |d :d |d :t, |s, :— ‖ :(l)m |d :— |r :— |s :— |— :s
|m, :— |f, :l, |s, :s, |d, :— ‖ :(f)d |l, :— |s, :— |m, :— |— :m

|r :l |s :f |m :— ‖d' :— |r' :— |s :— |d' :— |— ‖d' |d' ‖
|d :d |t, :r |d :— ‖s :— |l :— |s :f |m :— |— ‖f |m ‖
|l :f |r :s |s :— ‖d' :— |d' :— |t :— |d' :— |— ‖l |s ‖
|f :r |s, :t, |d :— ‖m :— |f :— |s :— |d :— |— ‖f |d ‖

A - men.

LET all the world in every corner sing,
'My God and King!'
The heavens are not too high,
His praise may thither fly;
The earth is not too low,
His praises there may grow.
Let all the world in every corner sing,
'My God and King!'

ST. DARERCA. (10 4. 6 6. 6 6. 10 4.)

ROBERT ALEXANDER STEWART MACALISTER, 1870– .

Doh = C. *In moderate time.* *rall.* > > >

:d' | t :s | l :m | s :d | r :m | s :– | – :– | – :d | r :m
:d' | t :s | l :m | s :d | r :m | s :– | – :– | – :d | l, :d
:d' | t :s | l :m | s :d | r :m | s :– | – :– | – :s | l :l
:d' | t :s | l :m | s :d | r :m | s :– | – :– | – :m | f :d

A tempo.

| s :– | – :– | – :– || :s | l :–.s | f :l | r' :– | d' :–
| r :– | – :– | – :– || :m | f :–.m | f :f | f :– | m :fe
| t :– | – :– | – :– || :d' | d' :–.d' | d' :d' | d' :t | d' :–
| s, :– | – :– | – :– || :d | f :–.s | l :f | r :– | l :–

| t.d' :r' | t :l | s :– | m :– | f :–.m | r :f | t :– | l :–
| s :s | s :fe | r :– | d :– | r :–.d | r :r | r :– | r :re
| r' :s.l | t.d' :r' | t :– | d' :– | l :l | l :l | l :se | l :–
| s :t,.d | r :r | s :– | l :– | r :–.m | f :d | t, :– | f :–

E.t.m.l.r. r.s.d.f.C.

| ^se^m.f :s | m :r | ^d^m :– | – :d' | t :s | l :m | s :d | r :m
| ^m^d :d | d :t, | ^d^m :– | – :m | m :m | m :m | d :d | d :d
| ^t^s :d.r | m.f :s | ^m^se :– | – :l | s :t | d' :d' | d' :s | s :s
| ^m^d :m,.f, | s, :s, | ^d^m :– | – :l | m :m | l, :l | m :m | d :d

> > > >

s :–	– :f	s :–	l :–	d' :–	– :–	– :–		d'	d'	
r :–	– :r	r :–	r :–	m :–	– :–	– :–		f	m	
ta :–	– :d'	ta :–	l :–	s :–	– :–	– :–		l	s	
s, :–	– :r	m :–	f :–	d :–	– :–	– :–		f	d	

A-men.

[*Copyright*, 1927, *by Oxford University Press.*]

2 Let all the world in every corner sing,
'My God and King!'
The Church with psalms must shout,
No door can keep them out;
But, above all, the heart
Must bear the longest part.
Let all the world in every corner sing,
'My God and King!'

GEORGE HERBERT, 1593–1632.

16

LLANFAIR. (77. 77. and Hallelujahs.)

Doh = G. *Moderately quick time.* ROBERT WILLIAMS, c. 1781–1821.

D.C.

d :d	m :m	s :f.m	r :—	s :—.f	m :f.m	r :—	d :—	
s, :s,	d :d	d :r.d	t, :—	s, :l,.t,	d :d	d :t,	d :—	
m :m	d :d	s :l	r :—	m :—.f	s :f.s	l :s	m :—	
d :d	l, :l,	m, :f,	s, :—	m :—.r	d :l,.s,	f, :s,	d :—	

m :m	s :s	l.s :f.m	r :—	m :—.r	m :fe	s :—	s :—	
s, :l,	s, :d	l, :t,.d	t, :—	d :—.r	d :d	t, :—.d	t, :—	
m :d	r :m	f :s	s :—	s :—	— :d	r :—.m	r :—	
d :l,	t, :d	f.m :r.d	s, :—	d :—.t,	d :l,	s, :—	s, :—	

d :d	m :m	s :f.m	r :—	s :—.f	m :f.m	r :—	d :—	
d :s,	s, :d	d :r.d	t, :—	s, :l,.t,	d :d	d :t,	d :—	
m :s.f	m :d	s :l	r :—	m :—.f	s :f.s	l :s	m :—	
d :m.r	d :l,	m, :f,	s, :—	m :—.r	d :l,.s,	f, :s,	d, :—	

From Psalm cl.

PRAISE the Lord, His glories show, *Hallelujah!*
Saints within His courts below, *Hallelujah!*
Angels round His throne above, *Hallelujah!*
All that see and share His love. *Hallelujah!*

2 Earth to heaven, and heaven to earth, *Hallelujah!*
Tell His wonders, sing His worth; *Hallelujah!*
Age to age and shore to shore, *Hallelujah!*
Praise Him, praise Him evermore! *Hallelujah!*

3 Praise the Lord, His mercies trace; *Hallelujah!*
Praise His providence and grace, *Hallelujah!*
All that He for man hath done, *Hallelujah!*
All He sends us through His Son. *Hallelujah!*

4 Strings and voices, hands and hearts, *Hallelujah!*
In the concert bear your parts; *Hallelujah!*
All that breathe, your Lord adore, *Hallelujah!*
Praise Him, praise Him evermore! *Hallelujah!*

HENRY FRANCIS LYTE, 1793–1847.

f :—	l :—	s :—	— :—	
d :—	l, :t,	d :—	— :—	
f :—	d :r	m :—	— :—	
l, :—	f, :—	d :—	— :—	
A - - men.

17 LUCERNA LAUDONIAE. (77. 77. 77.)

Doh = A♭. *In moderate time.* EDWARD ARTHUR, 1874–

```
:s,.s, |m   :-.d  :r.m   |l,  :—   :s,.d  |f   :-.m  :d.m   |r   :—  ||
:s,.s, |s,  :-.s, :f,.m, |m,  :r,  :s,.s, |f,  :-.s, :l,.s, |s,  :—  ||
:s,.s, |s,  :-.d  :t,.d  |d   :t,  :d.s,  |l,  :t,.d :m.d   |t,  :—  ||
:s,.s, |d,  :-.m, :r,.d, |f,  :—   :m,.m, |r,  :-.d, :l,.m, |s,  :—  ||

:m.d   |l,  :s,   :d.r   |m   :—   :s,.l, |t,.d  :r   :r    |s,  :—  ||
:s,.s, |f,  :r,   :s,.s, |s,  :—   :s,.m, |s,.s, :s,  :fe,  |s,  :—  ||
:d.d   |d   :t,   :d.t,  |d   :—   :r.d   |r.s,  :t,  :l,   |t,  :—  ||
:d,.m, |f,  :s,   :m,.s, |d   :—   :t,.l, |s,.m, :r,  :r,   |s,  :—  ||

|d  :l,.d  |m   :-.d  |f   :m     |r   :m.f  |s   :m  |r   :r   |d   :—  ||d   |d  ||
|m, :m,    |m,  :-.m, |l,  :s,.l, |t,  :d.d  |s,  :d  |d   :t,  |d   :—  ||l,  |s, ||
|d  :m.d   |t,  :-.d  |d   :d     |s   :s.d  |r   :s  |l   :s   |m   :—  ||f   |m  ||
|l, :d.l,  |se, :-.l, |r,  :m,.f, |s,  :d.l, |t,  :d  |f,  :s,  |d,  :—  ||f,  |d, ||
                                                                         A-men.
```

[*Copyright*, 1927, *by Edward Arthur.*]

FOR the beauty of the earth,
For the beauty of the skies,
For the love which from our birth
Over and around us lies,
Christ, our God, to Thee we raise
This our sacrifice of praise.

2 For the beauty of each hour
Of the day and of the night,
Hill and vale, and tree and flower,
Sun and moon and stars of light,
Christ, our God, to Thee we raise
This our sacrifice of praise.

3 For the joy of ear and eye,
For the heart and mind's delight,
For the mystic harmony
Linking sense to sound and sight,
Christ, our God, to Thee we raise
This our sacrifice of praise.

4 For the joy of human love,
Brother, sister, parent, child,
Friends on earth and friends above,
For all gentle thoughts and mild,
Christ, our God, to Thee we raise
This our sacrifice of praise.

5 For each perfect gift of Thine
To our race so freely given,
Graces human and divine,
Flowers of earth and buds of heaven,
Christ, our God, to Thee we raise
This our sacrifice of praise.

FOLLIOTT SANDFORD PIERPOINT, 1835–1917.

18 GOD IN NATURE. (76. 76. D.)

Doh = G. *In moderate time.* JOHN STAINER, 1840–1901.

```
           v. 1.
                        r :-.s | s  :                     D.t.
:s,  |d  :f  |f  :m  |r  :—   |s  :s,  |d  :f  |f  :{m}l  |s  :— |— ||
:s,  |s, :d  |d  :d  |t, :—   |d  :s,  |s, :d  |d  :{d}f  |r  :— |— ||
:s,  |m  :l  |l  :s  |f  :—   |m  :m   |m  :l  |l  :{s}d' |t  :— |— ||
:s,  |d  :d  |d  :d  |d  :—   |d  :d   |d  :d  |d  :{d}f  |f  :r |s ||
v. 1.  All things bright and beau - ti - ful,

                                                          f. G.
:s   |s  :d' |t  :l  |l  :-.l  |s  :f  |m  :s  |m  :r    |{d}s, :— |— ||
:r   |s  :s  |f  :m  |f  :-.f  |m  :r  |d  :d  |d  :t,   |{d}s, :— |— ||
:t   |d' :d' |f  :l  |r  :-.r  |s  :s  |s  :s  |s  :-.f  |{m}t, :— |— ||
:f   |m  :m  |r  :d  |t, :-.t, |t, :t, |d  :m, |s, :s,   |{d}s, :— |— ||
v. 1.  All things wise and won - der - ful.

:r   |m  :r  |t, :s, |d  :—  |d  :m  |l   :s   |m   :d   |f  :— |— ||
:s,  |s, :s, |s, :s, |s, :—  |s, :s, |d   :d   |d   :d   |d  :— |— ||
:t,  |t, :t, |r  :t, |d  :—  |d  :d  |m   :m   |s   :m   |f  :— |— ||
:s,  |f, :f, |f, :f, |m, :—  |m, :d  |ta, :ta, |ta, :ta, |l, :— |— ||

:f   |m  :r  |s  :f  |m  :r   |d  :l,  |s, :d  |d  :t,  |d  :— |— ||d  |d  ||
:d   |d  :t, |d  :t, |d  :se, |l, :r,  |m, :s, |f, :f,  |m, :— |— ||f, |m, ||
:f   |s  :s  |s  :s  |s  :m   |m  :d   |d  :m  |r  :r   |d  :— |— ||l, |s, ||
:l,  |s, :f  |m  :r  |d  :t,  |l, :fe, |s, :s, |s, :s,  |d, :— |— ||f, |d, ||
                                                                    A - men.
```

[*Copyright*, 1897, *by Novello, Ewer & Co., Ltd.*]

ALL things bright and beautiful,
All creatures great and small,
All things wise and wonderful—
The Lord God made them all.

2 Each little flower that opens,
Each little bird that sings—
He made their glowing colours,
He made their tiny wings.

3 The purple-headed mountain,
The river running by,
The sunset, and the morning
That brightens up the sky,

ALL THINGS BRIGHT. (76. 76.)

Doh = D. *In moderate time.* FREDERICK ARTHUR GORE OUSELEY, 1825–89.

v. 1.

```
d  :d   |m  :f  |s  :-.l |s  :s   |d' :m  |s  :f.m |r  :—     |—:
s, :s,  |d  :d  |r  :r   |m  :f   |m  :d  |d  :r.d |d  :t,.l, |t,:
m  :m   |m  :l  |t  :t   |d' :t   |d' :d' |s  :l   |r  :—     |—:
d  :-.t,|l, :l, |s, :f   |m  :r   |d  :l, |m, :f,  |s, :—     |—:
```

```
f   :f  |m  :r   |d  :-.r  |m  :f.s |l.t   :d'  |m  :r   |d  :— |—
r   :r  |t, :t,  |l, :-.t, |d  :d.m |f.r   :d   |d  :t,  |d  :— |—
f.s :l  |se :m   |m  :-.m  |l  :d'  |d'.r' :s   |s  :-.f |m  :— |—
r   :t, |m  :se, |l, :-.l, |l, :l.s |f     :m.f |s  :s,  |d  :— |—
```

vv. 2–6.

```
:d |d  :d   |m  :f  |s  :-.l |s  :s  |d' :m  |s  :f.m |r  :—     |—
:d |s, :s,  |d  :d  |r  :—   |m  :f  |m  :d  |d  :r.d |d  :t,.l, |t,
:d |m  :m   |m  :l  |t  :—   |d' :t  |d' :d' |s  :l   |r  :—     |—
:d |d  :-.t,|l, :l, |s, :f   |m  :r  |d  :l, |m, :f,  |s, :—     |—
```

```
:r.m  |f   :f  |m  :r   |d  :-.r  |m  :f.s |l.t   :d'  |m :r   |d :— |— ||f  |m ||
:r.de |r   :r  |t, :t,  |l, :-.t, |d  :d.m |f.r   :d   |d :t,  |d :— |— ||d  |d ||
:l.s  |f.s :l  |se :m   |m  :—    |l  :d'  |d'.r' :s   |s :-.f |m :— |— ||l  |s ||
:f.m  |r   :t, |m  :se, |l, :—    |l, :l.s |f     :m.f |s :s,  |d :— |— ||f, |d ||
```

A-men.

4 The cold wind in the winter,
The pleasant summer sun,
The ripe fruits in the garden—
He made them every one.

5 The tall trees in the greenwood,
The meadows where we play,
The rushes, by the water,
We gather every day—
6 He gave us eyes to see them,
And lips that we might tell
How great is God Almighty,
Who has made all things well.

CECIL FRANCES ALEXANDER, 1823–95.

19 ES IST KEIN TAG. (88. 84.)

Doh = D. *Moderately slow.* JOHANN DAVID MEJER, 1692.

:s |d' :t .l |s :l .s |f .m :r |d || m .f
:d .t, |d :f |m .r :d |d .l, :t, |d || d
:m .f |s :t |d' .t :l .t |d' :s |m || s
:d .r |m :r |m :f .s |l .f :s |d || d .r

s :s |l :t |d' :d'.r' |t || d'.t |l :s |f :r
s .f :m .r |d :f .s |m :r |r || d |d .r :m |l, :r
d'.r' :d'.t |l :r' |s :l |s || s |l .t :d' |l :s
m :m |f .m :r |m :fe |s || m |f :m |r :t,

m :-.f |s || d .r |m :— |r :— |d :— |— || d |d
d :d |d || d |d :— |— :t, |d :— |— || l, |s,
s :l |s || m .f |s :l |r :— |m :— |— || f |m
d.t, :l, |m, || l, |s, :f, |s, :— |d :— |— || f, |d

A-men.

O LORD of heaven and earth and sea,
To Thee all praise and glory be;
How shall we show our love to Thee,
Who givest all?

2 The golden sunshine, vernal air,
Sweet flowers and fruits Thy love declare;
Where harvests ripen, Thou art there,
Who givest all.

3 For peaceful homes and healthful days,
For all the blessings earth displays,
We owe Thee thankfulness and praise,
Who givest all.

ALMSGIVING. (88. 84.)

Doh = G. *In moderate time.* JOHN BACCHUS DYKES, 1823–76.

```
m  :m  :r     | d  :—   :s,   | d  :—  :r  | m  :— :— || s, :d  :m
s, :s, :s,.f, | m, :-.f,:s,   | s, :f, :—  | m, :— :— || s, :s, :d
d  :d  :t,    | d  :-.r :m.r  | d  :—  :t, | d  :— :— || m  :m  :m
d, :m, :s,    | d  :—   :d.t, | l, :—  :s, | d, :— :— || d  :d  :l,

s  :—     :f  | m  :r  :d  | r  :— :— || t, :d  :r  | d  :— :d
d  :t,.l, :t, | s, :—  :d  | t, :— :— || s, :s, :f, | m, :— :f,
m  :r.d   :r  | d  :r  :m  | s  :— :— || f  :m  :t, | d  :s  :f
s, :—     :s, | d  :t, :l, | s, :— :— || s, :s, :s, | d  :m  :r

m     :f  :s    | l  :— :— | s, :m  :-.r  | d :— :— || d  | d  ||
s,    :d  :ta,  | l, :— :— | s, :d  :-.t, | d :— :— || l, | s, ||
m     :d  :r.m  | f  :d :r | m.d :s :-.f  | m :— :— || f  | m  ||
d.ta, :l, :s,   | f, :— :— | s, :s, :s,   | d :— :— || f, | d, ||
                                                        A-men.
```

4 Thou didst not spare Thine only Son,
But gav'st Him for a world undone,
And freely with that blessèd One
Thou givest all.

5 Thou giv'st the Spirit's blessèd dower,
Spirit of life and love and power,
And dost His sevenfold graces shower
Upon us all.

6 For souls redeemed, for sins forgiven,
For means of grace and hopes of heaven,
Father, all praise to Thee be given,
Who givest all.

CHRISTOPHER WORDSWORTH, 1807–85.

20

BEECHWOOD. (5 6. 6 4.)

Doh = A♭. *In moderate time.* JOSIAH BOOTH, 1852-

```
|m  :r  |d  :r  |t, :—  |—  :s, |d  :d  |r  :r  |m  :—  |—  ||
|d  :t, |l, :l, |s, :—  |—  :s, |s, :m, |l, :s, |s, :—  |—  ||
|s  :f  |m  :f  |r  :—  |—  :t, |d  :d  |d  :t, |d  :—  |—  ||
|d  :s, |l, :f, |s, :—  |—  :f, |m, :l, |f, :s, |d, :—  |—  ||

:m  |s  :m  |d  :t, |l, :—  |—  :—  |f  :—  |m  :r  |d  :—  |—  :—  ||d  |d  ||
:s, |s, :t, |l, :s, |f, :—  |—  :—  |l, :—  |s, :f, |m, :—  |—  :—  ||f, |m, ||
:d  |r  :s  |m  :d  |d  :—  |—  :—  |r  :—  |t, :t, |d  :—  |—  :—  ||l, |s, ||
:d  |t, :s, |l, :m, |f, :—  |—  :—  |r, :—  |s, :s, |d, :—  |—  :—  ||f, |d, ||
                                                                    A - men.
```

GOD, who made the earth,
The air, the sky, the sea,
Who gave the light its birth,
Careth for me.

2 God, who made the grass,
The flower, the fruit, the tree,
The day and night to pass,
Careth for me.

3 God, who made the sun,
The moon, the stars, is He
Who, when life's clouds come on,
Careth for me.

4 God, who made all things,
On earth, in air, in sea,
Who changing seasons brings,
Careth for me.

5 God, who sent His Son
To die on Calvary,
He, if I lean on Him,
Will care for me.

6 When in heaven's bright land
I all His loved ones see,
I'll sing with that blest band,
'God cared for me.'

SARAH BETTS RHODES, 1870.

21

PRAISE, MY SOUL.* (87. 87. 87.)

Doh = D. *In moderate time.* JOHN GOSS, 1800–80.

vv. 1 and 5 in *Unison*, vv. 2 and 4 in *Harmony*, v. 3 Trebles only.

s :s	s :s	d' :t	l :—	s :—	f :m	l :s	m :f
d :d	t, :t,	d :s	s :f	m :—	d :d	d :d	d :r
m :m	f :f	s :s	l :t	d' :—	f :s	f :s	l :l
d :d	r :r	m :m	f :—	d :—	l, :d	f :m	l :r

r :—	m :m	m :m	l :s	s :fe	s :l	t :d'	m :fe	s :—
t, :—	t, :r	d :t,	l, :l,	d :d	t, :r	r :d	d :d	t, :—
s :f	m :t,	d :r	m :l	l :l	s :d'	t :s	l :l	s :—
s, :—	se, :se,	l, :t,	d :de	r :re	m :fe	s :m	d :r	s, :—

d' :t	l :s	d' :t	l :s	l :s	f :r	d :t,	d :—	f	m
d :-.d	d :t,	d :r.m	f :f	m :r	d :l,	s, :s,	s, :—	d	d
s :-.s	f :f	m :r.d	r :s	d' :t	l :f	m :r.f	m :—	l	s
m :-.m,	f, :s,	l, :-.l,	t, :t,	d :r.m	f :f,	s, :s,	d :—	f,	d d,

* May be sung in Harmony throughout. A - men.

From Psalm ciii.

PRAISE, my soul, the King of heaven;
To His feet thy tribute bring;
Ransom'd, heal'd, restor'd, forgiven,
Who like me His praise should sing?
Praise Him! Praise Him!
Praise Him! Praise Him!
Praise the everlasting King.

2 Praise Him for His grace and favour
To our fathers in distress;
Praise Him, still the same for ever,
Slow to chide and swift to bless:
Praise Him! Praise Him!
Praise Him! Praise Him!
Glorious in His faithfulness.

3 Father-like He tends and spares us:
Well our feeble frame He knows;
In His hands He gently bears us,
Rescues us from all our foes:
Praise Him! Praise Him!
Praise Him! Praise Him!
Widely as His mercy flows.

4 Frail as summer's flower we flourish;
Blows the wind and it is gone;
But, while mortals rise and perish,
God endures unchanging on:
Praise Him! Praise Him!
Praise Him! Praise Him!
Praise the high eternal One.

5 Angels, help us to adore Him;
Ye behold Him face to face;
Sun and moon, bow down before Him;
Dwellers all in time and space.
Praise Him! Praise Him!
Praise Him! Praise Him!
Praise with us the God of grace. Amen.

HENRY FRANCIS LYTE, 1793–1847.

[May be sung to REGENT SQUARE, No. 7.]

22 LOBE DEN HERREN. (14 14. 4 7 8.)

Doh = G. *Moderately slow.* *Stralsund Gesangbuch*, 1665.

D.C.

d :d :s	m :-.r :d	t, :l, :s,	l, :t, :d	r :— :—	d :— :—	
s, :l, :s,	d :-.t, :l,	s, :f, :m,	f, :f, :m,	l, :s, :f,	m, :— :—	
m :m :r	s :-.s :m	m :d :d	d :r :d	d :t, :—	d :— :—	
d :l, :t,	d :-.s, :l,	m, :f, :d,	f, :r, :l,	f, :s, :—	d, :— :—	

s :s :s	l :— :—		m :f :s	s :f :m	r :— :—	
d :r :d	d :— :—		d :d :r	d :l,.t, :d	t, :— :—	
m :r :m	f :— :—		s :f :r	m :f :s	s :— :—	
d :t, :d	f, :— :—		d :l, :t,	d :r :m.d	s, :— :—	

s, :l, :t,	d :r :m	r :— :—	d :— :—		d	d	
s, :f, :f,	m, :l, :se,	l, :— :s,	m, :— :—		f,	m,	
d :d :r	d :l, :t,	l, :r.d :t,	d :— :—		l,	s,	
m, :f, :r,	l, :f, :m,	f, :— :s,	d, :— :—		f,	d,	

A - men.

From Psalms ciii, cl.

Lobe den Herren, den mächtigen König der Ehren.

Unison. PRAISE to the Lord, the Almighty, the King of creation;
O my soul, praise Him, for He is thy health and salvation;
All ye who hear,
Now to His temple draw near,
Joining in glad adoration.

Harmony. 2 Praise to the Lord, who o'er all things so wondrously reigneth,
Shieldeth thee gently from harm, or when fainting sustaineth;
Hast thou not seen
How thy heart's wishes have been
Granted in what He ordaineth?

3 Praise to the Lord, who doth prosper thy work and defend thee;
Surely His goodness and mercy shall daily attend thee;
Ponder anew
What the Almighty can do,
If with His love He befriend thee.

Unison. 4 Praise to the Lord! O let all that is in me adore Him!
All that hath life and breath, come now with praises before Him!
Let the Amen
Sound from His people again:
Gladly for aye we adore Him.

JOACHIM NEANDER, 1650–80; *tr.* by CATHERINE WINKWORTH, 1829–78, and others.

23

GONFALON ROYAL. (L.M.)

Doh = A♭. *Unison.* *With firm rhythm.* PERCY CARTER BUCK, 1871–

{ :s, | l, :d | f :m.r | m :d | l, :— | — :l, | r :t, }

{ | s, :d | f.m :r.d | r :— | — || r | s :m | d :— .d }

{ | f :r | t, :l,.t, | d.r :m.r | f :m | r :l, | s, :— | — ‖

SING to the Lord a joyful song,
  Lift up your hearts, your voices raise;
To us His gracious gifts belong,
  To Him our songs of love and praise.

2 For life and love, for rest and food,
  For daily help and nightly care,
Sing to the Lord, for He is good,
  And praise His Name, for it is fair.

3 For strength to those who on Him wait
  His truth to prove, His will to do,
Praise ye our God, for He is great,
  Trust in His Name, for it is true.

4 For joys untold, that from above
  Cheer those who love His sweet employ,
Sing to our God, for He is love,
  Exalt His Name, for it is joy.

5 For He is Lord of heaven and earth,
  Whom angels serve and saints adore,
The Father, Son, and Holy Ghost,
  To whom be praise for evermore.

:s, | l, :d | r :— | d :— | — ‖
:m, | m, :l,.s, | f, :r, | m, :— | — ‖
:m | d :— | — :t, | d :— | — ‖
:d | l, :f,.m, | r, :s, | d, :— | — ‖

A - - - - - men.

JOHN SAMUEL BEWLEY MONSELL, 1811–75.

24 OMBERSLEY. (L.M.)

Doh = C. *In moderate time.* WILLIAM HENRY GLADSTONE, 1840-91.

```
| m  :r  :d  | f  :— :f  | f  :— :f   | m :— :— | m :f  :s | l :— :l
| d  :t, :d  | d  :— :r  | r  :d  :t, | d :— :— | d :d  :d | d :— :d
| s  :f  :m  | l  :— :l  | s  :— :s   | s :— :— | s :f  :m | f :— :f
| d  :d  :d  | d  :— :d  | t, :l, :s, | d :— :— | d :l, :d | f :— :f

| r' :— :d' | t :— :— || s :l :t  | d' :— :r' | m' :r' :d'
| f  :— :r  | r :— :— || d :d :m  | m  :— :f  | m  :f  :s
| l  :— :l  | s :— :— || m :l :se | l  :— :t  | d' :t  :d'
| r  :— :f  | s :— :— || d :f :m  | l  :— :s  | d  :r  :m

| l  :— :— | s  :m  :r  | d  :— :d  | m  :— :r  | d :— :— || f  | m ||
| d  :— :— | d  :t, :t, | d  :— :d  | d  :— :t, | d :— :— || d  | d ||
| d' :— :— | d' :s  :f  | m  :— :l  | s  :— :f  | m :— :— || l  | s ||
| f  :— :— | m  :s  :s, | l, :— :f, | s, :— :s, | d :— :— || f, | d ||
```

A-men.

[*By permission of Novello & Co., Ltd.*]

LORD of all being, throned afar,
Thy glory flames from sun and star;
Centre and soul of every sphere,
Yet to each loving heart how near!

2 Sun of our life, Thy quickening ray
Sheds on our path the glow of day;
Star of our hope, Thy softened light
Cheers the long watches of the night.

3 Our midnight is Thy smile withdrawn,
Our noontide is Thy gracious dawn,
Our rainbow arch Thy mercy's sign;
All, save the clouds of sin, are Thine.

4 Lord of all life, below, above,
Whose light is truth, whose warmth is love,
Before Thy ever-blazing throne
We ask no lustre of our own.

5 Grant us Thy truth to make us free,
And kindling hearts that burn for Thee,
Till all Thy living altars claim
One holy light, one heavenly flame.

OLIVER WENDELL HOLMES, 1809-94.

25

CHURCH TRIUMPHANT. (L.M.)

Doh = B♭. *In moderate time.* JAMES WILLIAM ELLIOTT, 1833–1915.

:s, |d :s, |m :r |d :l, |s, :m, .f,
:m, |m, :m, |s, :f, |m, :f, |m, :d, .r,
:d |s, :d |m :t, |d :d |d :s,
:d, |d, :d, |d :s, |l, :f, |d, :d,

|s, :l,.t, |d :m |r :–.d |t, ||s, |l, :l, |t, :m,
|m, :s, |m, :m, |l, :fe, |s, ||r, |r, :r, |r, :r,
|m :r |d :t, |l, :r |r ||t, |l, :l, |l, :se,
|d :t, |l, :s, |fe, :r, |s, ||s, |f, :f, |m, :m,

d :d	r :s,	m :m	f :l,	t, :–.r	d		d	d	
d, :f,	f, :f,	m, :s,	f, :f,	s, :f,	m,		f,	m,	
m :d	d :t,	d :d	d :r	r :–.t,	d		l,	s,	
l, :l,	s, :s,	d, :ta,	l, :r,	s, :s$_2$	d,		f,	d,	

A-men.

[*By permission of Novello & Co., Ltd.*]

Unison.

THE Lord is King! lift up thy voice,
O earth, and, all ye heavens, rejoice;
From world to world the joy shall ring,
'The Lord Omnipotent is King!'

Harmony.

2 The Lord is King! who then shall dare
Resist His will, distrust His care,
Or murmur at His wise decrees,
Or doubt His royal promises?

3 The Lord is King! child of the dust,
The Judge of all the earth is just;
Holy and true are all His ways:
Let every creature speak His praise.

4 He reigns! ye saints, exalt your strains;
Your God is King, your Father reigns;
And He is at the Father's side,
The Man of Love, the Crucified.

5 Come, make your wants, your burdens known;
He will present them at the throne;
And angel bands are waiting there
His messages of love to bear.

Unison.

6 One Lord, one empire, all secures;
He reigns, and life and death are yours:
Through earth and heaven one song shall ring,
'The Lord Omnipotent is King!'

JOSIAH CONDER, 1789–1855.

26 BELGRAVE. (C.M.)

Doh = E♭. *In moderate time.* WILLIAM HORSLEY, 1774–1858.

:s |m :— :s |d' :— :m |f :s :l |r :— :s.,f
:d |d :— :r |d :— :d |d :— :d |t, :— :r
:m |s :— :r |m :— :s |f :m :r |s :— :s
:d |d :— :t, |l, :— :ta, |l, :s, :f, |s, :— :t,

|m :fe :s.,l |t :— :l |s :— ||d' |m :— :l |r :— :s
|d :— :r.,m |r :— :r.d |t, :— ||d |d :— :d |t, :— :d
|s :l :s |s :— :fe |s :— ||s |d' :t :l |s :— :s
|d :l, :t,.,d |r :— :r |s, :— ||m |l :s :f |s :f :m

d :r :m	m :r :s	s :f :m	m.,r:d :t,	d :—		d	d	
l, :t, :d	d :t, :t,	d :r :d	l, :s, :s,	s, :—		l,	s,	
l.,s:f :m	s :— :r	s :— :s	f :m :r	m :—		f	m	
f.,m:r :d	s, :— :s,	l, :t, :d	f, :s, :s,	d :—		f,	d	

A-men.

WHEN all Thy mercies, O my God!
My rising soul surveys,
Transported with the view, I'm lost
In wonder, love, and praise.

2 O how shall words, with equal warmth,
The gratitude declare
That glows within my ravished heart!
But Thou canst read it there.

3 Unnumbered comforts to my soul
Thy tender care bestowed,
Before my infant heart conceived
From whom these comforts flowed.

4 When in the slippery paths of youth
With heedless steps I ran,
Thine arm, unseen, conveyed me safe,
And led me up to man.

5 When worn with sickness, oft hast Thou
With health renewed my face;
And, when in sins and sorrows sunk,
Revived my soul with grace.

6 Ten thousand thousand precious gifts
My daily thanks employ;
Nor is the least a cheerful heart,
That tastes those gifts with joy.

7 Through every period of my life
Thy goodness I'll pursue;
And after death, in distant worlds,
The glorious theme renew.

JOSEPH ADDISON, 1672–1719.

27

WESTMINSTER. (C.M.)

Doh = C. *Moderately slow.* JAMES TURLE, 1802–82.

:m	s :s	d :d'	t :l	s :s
:d	m :r	d :m	m :d .r	m :f
:s	s :r	m :d'	m' :l .t	d' :t
:d	d :t,	l, :l	s :f	m :r

m' :t	d' :r'	s :—	—	s	t :l	se :l
m :s .f	m :f .m	r :—	—	r	r :r	r :d
d' :m'.r'	d' :l	t :—	—	t	s :l	t :l
d :s	l :f	s :—	—	s	s :f	m :f

d' :t	l :l	s :d	r :f	m :—	—	f	m
m :m .r	d :f	m :d	d :t,	d :—	—	d	d
l :se	l :r'	s :s	l :s	s :—	—	l	s
m :m	l, :t,	d :m	f :s	d :—	—	f,	d

A - men.

MY God, how wonderful Thou art,
Thy majesty how bright!
How beautiful Thy mercy-seat,
In depths of burning light!

2 How dread are Thine eternal years,
O everlasting Lord,
By prostrate spirits day and night
Incessantly adored!

3 O how I fear Thee, living God,
With deepest, tenderest fears,
And worship Thee with trembling hope
And penitential tears!

4 Yet I may love Thee too, O Lord,
Almighty as Thou art,
For Thou hast stooped to ask of me
The love of my poor heart.

5 No earthly father loves like Thee;
No mother, e'er so mild,
Bears and forbears as Thou hast done
With me, Thy sinful child.

6 How beautiful, how beautiful
The sight of Thee must be,
Thine endless wisdom, boundless power,
And awful purity!

FREDERICK WILLIAM FABER, 1814–63.

28

DEGANWY. (87. 87. Iambic.)

Doh = Ab. *In moderate time.* BENJAMIN WILLIAMS, 1839–1918.

:s, |m :r |d :t, |l, :d |s, :d
:m, |s, :f, |m, :s, |f, :f, |s, :s,
:d |d :t, |d :m .r |d :f |m :m
:d, |d, :s, |l, :m, |f, :l, |d :d,

|t, :d |r :m |m :— |r ||r |m :f |m :r
|s, :s, |s,.f, :m,.s, |s, :— |s, ||s, |s, :-.s, |s, :t,
|r :d |t, :d |d :— |t, ||t, |d :r |d.m :s .f
|s, :m, |r, :d, |s, :— |s, ||s, |d :t, |d :s,

d :d	r :r	m :s	s :f	m :r	d		d	d	
l, :fe,	s, :t,	d :d	d :d	d :t,	d		l,	s,	
m :d	t, :s	s :s	l :l	s :-.f	m		f	m	
l, :l,	s, :s,	d :m,	f, :f,	s, :—	d,		f,	d,	

A-men.

A GLADSOME hymn of praise we sing,
And thankfully we gather
To bless the love of God above,
Our everlasting Father.

2 In Him rejoice with heart and voice,
Whose glory fadeth never,
Whose providence is our defence,
Who lives and loves for ever.

3 Full in His sight His children stand,
By His strong arm defended,
And He whose wisdom guides the world
Our footsteps hath attended.

4 For nothing falls unknown to Him,
Or care or joy or sorrow,
And He, whose mercy ruled the past,
Will be our stay to-morrow.

5 Then praise the Lord with one accord,
To His great Name give glory,
And of His never-changing love
Repeat the wondrous story.

AMBROSE NICHOLS BLATCHFORD, 1842–1924.

29

NUN DANKET. (67. 67. 66. 66.)

Doh = F. *Very slow.* JOHANN CRÜGER, 1598–1662.

```
:s  |s  :s    |l       :l      |s :— |— :s    |f    :m      |r    :m     |r    :—   |d
:d  |d  :d    |d       :l,.t,  |d :— |— :d.ta,|l,   :d      |t,   :d     |d    :t,  |d
:m  |m  :s    |f       :d.r    |m :— |— :m    |f    :s      |s.f  :m     |f    :—   |m
:d  |d  :m    |f       :f,     |d :— |— :d,   |r,   :m,.f,  |s,   :d,    |s,   :—   |d,

:s  |s  :s    |l       :l      |s :— |— :s    |f    :m      |r    :m     |r    :—   |d
:d  |d  :d    |d       :d.t,   |d :— |— :d    |d    :d.t,   |l,   :t,    |l,   :t,  |d
:m  |m  :m    |f       :f      |m :— |— :m    |f    :s      |l    :-.se  |l    :s.f |m
:d  |d  :d.ta,|l,.s,   :f,     |d :— |— :d.t, |l,   :s,     |f,   :m,    |f,   :s,  |d,

C.t.
:(r)s   |s  :s     |l     :d'     |s :— |— :s    |l.t  :d'     |r'   :t     |d' :— |—
:(t,)m  |f  :m.s   |s     :f      |m :— |— :d    |d.r  :m      |f    :m     |m  :— |—
:(s)d'  |r' :d'.t  |l     :l      |s :— |— :d'   |d'   :d'     |d'.t :l.se  |l  :— |—
:(s,)d  |t, :d     |f,.s, :l,.t,  |d :— |— :m    |f    :m      |r    :m     |l, :— |—

f.F.
:(d')s    |l  :s      |f  :m   |f  :— |— :m     |r      :d     |d  :t,    |d  :— |— ||d  |d
:(m)t,    |l, :l,     |l, :de  |r  :— |— :s,    |l,     :m,.f, |s, :s,.f, |m, :— |— ||f, |m,
:(l)m     |m  :r.m    |f  :s   |f  :— |— :d.t,  |l,.t,  :d.r   |m  :r     |d  :— |— ||l, |s,
:(l,)m.r  |de :t,.de  |r  :l,  |r, :— |— :m,    |f,     :l,    |s, :s,    |d, :— |— ||f, |d,
                                                                                      A-men.
```

Nun danket alle Gott.

Unison.

NOW thank we all our God,
With heart and hands and voices,
Who wondrous things hath done,
In whom His world rejoices,—
Who, from our mothers' arms,
Hath blessed us on our way
With countless gifts of love,
And still is ours to-day.

Harmony.

2 O may this bounteous God
Through all our life be near us,
With ever-joyful hearts
And blessèd peace to cheer us,
And keep us in His grace,
And guide us when perplexed,
And free us from all ills
In this world and the next.

Unison. 3 All praise and thanks to God
The Father now be given,
The Son, and Him who reigns
With Them in highest heaven,—
The one, eternal God,
Whom earth and heaven adore;
For thus it was, is now,
And shall be evermore.

MARTIN RINKART, 1586–1649; *tr.* by
CATHERINE WINKWORTH, 1829–78.

30

OLD 104TH. (10 10. 11 11.)

Lah = D. Doh = F. *Slow.* *Ravenscroft's Psalter*, 1621.

```
:l, | d  :t,  :l,  | m  :—  :d  | r  :f  :m     | r  :— || r  | m :s  :fe
:l, | l, :m,  :l,  | se,:—  :l, | l, :-.t, :d   | t, :— || t, | d :t, :r
:d  | m  :m   :l,  | t, :—  :d  | f  :f  :s     | s  :— || s  | s :m  :l
:l, | l, :s,  :f,  | m, :—  :l, | f, :r, :m,.f, | s, :— || s, | d :m  :r.d

s  :— :d  | m  :r  :r  | d  :— || d  | d  :d     :r  | m  :d  :d  | r  :f   :m
r  :— :d  | d  :d  :t, | d  :— || s, | l, :l,    :t, | d  :s, :l, | l, :r   :de
s  :— :m  | s  :l  :s  | m  :— || m  | m  :f     :f  | s  :m  :m  | f  :l   :l
t, :— :l, | m, :f, :s, | d, :— || d  | l, :f,.m, :r, | d, :d  :l, | f, :-.s, :l,

r :— || l | s :d :f  | m :r    :d  | r  :—  | m  :—  | t,  :— | l, :— || l, | l,  ||
r :— || d | d :d :t, | d :t,   :l, | l, :—  | l,  :— | se, :— | l, :— || f, | m,  ||
f :— || f | s :l :f  | s :-.f  :m  | l  :f  | m  :—  | m   :r | d  :— || r  | de  ||
r :— || f | m :f :r  | d :s,   :l, | f, :r, | d, :r, | m,  :— | l, :— || r, | l,  ||
                                                                        A - men.
```

THOUGH troubles assail and dangers affright,
Though friends should all fail and foes all unite,
Yet one thing secures us, whatever betide,
The Scripture assures us the Lord will provide.

2 The birds without barn or storehouse are fed;
From them let us learn to trust for our bread;
His saints what is fitting shall ne'er be denied,
So long as 'tis written, 'The Lord will provide.'

3 His call we obey, like Abram of old,
Not knowing our way, but faith makes us bold;
For, though we are strangers, we have a good guide,
And trust, in all dangers, the Lord will provide.

4 No strength of our own or goodness we claim;
Yet, since we have known the Saviour's great Name,
In this our strong tower for safety we hide,—
The Lord is our power, the Lord will provide.

JOHN NEWTON, 1725–1807.

[May be sung to HANOVER, No. 9.]

31

COLESHILL. (C.M.)

Lah = A. Doh = C. *Slow.* *Barton's Psalms*, 1706.

l :—	l :s	d' :s	l :l	m		d'	m' :r'	d' :s	d' :—	—	
m :—	f :r	s :m	d :d	d		m	s :f	m :r	m :—	—	
d' :—	d' :t	d' :d'	l :f	s		s	d' :l	s :t	d' :—	—	
l :—	f :s	m :d	f :f	d		d	d :r	m :s	d :—	—	

:d' |m' :r' |d' :s |l :l |m ||d' |s :l |r'.d' :t |l :— ||l |l ||
:s |s :s |m :d |d :d |d ||m |m.r :d |f .m :r |d :— ||r |de ||
:m' |d' :t |d' :d' |l :f |s ||d' |t :l |l :se |l :— ||f |m ||
:d |d' :s |l :m |f :f |d ||d |m :f |r :m |l, :— ||r |l, ||

A - men.

ST. DAVID. (C.M.)

Doh = E♭. *Moderately slow.* *Ravenscroft's Psalter*, 1621.

d :—	s :d'	m :s	f :m	r :—		d :—	s :d	f :l	s :—	
d :—	r :d	d :d	l,.t, :d	t, :—		l, :—	r :d	d :d	d :—	
m :—	s :l	d' :d'	f :s	s :—		m :—	s :m	f :f	m :—	
d :—	t, :l,	l :m	r :d	s, :—		l, :—	t, :d	l, :f,	d :—	

s :—	l :m	s :d	f :m	r :—		s :—	d :m	f :r	d :—		d	d	
d :—	d :d	d :d	l,.t, :d	t, :—		r :—	d :d	d :t,	d :—		l,	s,	
m :—	f :s	s :m	f :s	s :—		s :—	m :l	l :s	m :—		f	m	
d :—	f, :d	m, :l,	r :d	s, :—		t, :—	d :l,	f, :s,	d :—		f,	d	

A-men.

GOD moves in a mysterious way,
His wonders to perform ;
He plants His footsteps in the sea,
And rides upon the storm.

2 Deep in unfathomable mines
Of never-failing skill
He treasures up His bright designs,
And works His sovereign will.

Unison.

3 Ye fearful saints, fresh courage take ;
The clouds ye so much dread
Are big with mercy, and shall break
In blessings on your head.

Harmony.

4 Judge not the Lord by feeble sense,
But trust Him for His grace ;
Behind a frowning providence
He hides a smiling face.

5 His purposes will ripen fast,
Unfolding every hour ;
The bud may have a bitter taste,
But sweet will be the flower.

6 Blind unbelief is sure to err,
And scan His work in vain ;
God is His own interpreter,
And He will make it plain.

WILLIAM COWPER, 1731–1800.

32 RICHMOND. (C.M.)

Doh = G. *Moderately slow.*

Adapted from THOMAS HAWEIS, 1734–1820, by SAMUEL WEBBE, the younger, 1770–1843.

s, :d :m	s :— :f	m :f :r	d :— :m	r :s :d
m, :s, :d	r :t, :l,	s, :l, :f,	m, :— :fe,	s, :— :l,
d :m :s	s :— :d.r	m :d :t,	d :— :d	r :— :m
d :d :d	t, :s, :l,.t,	d :f, :s,	d, :— :l,	t, :— :d

t, :d :l,	s, :— ‖ r	m :r :d	f :m :r	s :f :m
s, :— :fe,	s, :— ‖ s,	s, :— :l,	f, :— :s,.l,	ta, :— :ta,
r :— :d	t, :— ‖ t,	d :t, :l,	r :d :t,	d :r :m
r :— :r,	s, :— ‖ f,	m, :— :l,	r, :— :f,	m, :r, :d,

l :— :s	l, :f :m	m.r:d :t,	d :— :— ‖ d	d ‖
l, :— :d	l, :t, :d	l, :s, :s,	s, :— :— ‖ l,	s, ‖
d :— :s	f :— :s	f :m :r	m :— :— ‖ d	m ‖
f, :— :m,	m, :r, :d,	f, :s, :s,	d, :— :— ‖ f,	d, ‖

A-men.

FAUX-BOURDON VERSION.

Doh = G.

MARTIN SHAW, 1876– .

s :m :d	s, :l, :t,	d :— :r	m :— :s
s :m :d	s, :— :s,	s, :l, :t,	d :— :s,
s, :d :m	s :— :f	m :f :r	d :— :m
s, :d :m	s :— :r	m :f :r	d :— :d,

C.t.

r :— :m	s, :— :l,	t, :— ‖ r	s :— :m	[l]m' :— :d'
s, :— :s,	r, :m, :fe,	s, :— ‖ t,	s, :— :d	[l]m :— :l
r :s :d	t, :d :l,	s, :— ‖ r	m :r :d	[f]d' :t :l
t_2 :— :d,	r, :— :r,	s, :— ‖ s,	m, :— :l,	[f]d :— :f

f.G.

f' :m' :r'	[s']d' :— :d	l :— :s	s.f:m :r	m :— :— ‖
l :— :t	[d']f :— :d	f :t, :d	l, :d :s,	s, :— :— ‖
r' :d' :t	[m']l :— :s	l, :f :m	m.r:d :t,	d :— :— ‖
r :— :s	[d] f, :— :m,	r, :— :m,	f, :s, :s,	d, :— :— ‖

GERONTIUS. (C.M.)

Doh = A. *In moderate time.* JOHN BACCHUS DYKES, 1823–76.

m :m :r	d :— :s,	d :— :m	s :— :—	m :r :s,
s, :s, :f,	m, :— :s,	s, :— :d	t, :— :—	s, :s, :s,
s, :l, :t,	d :s :f	m :— :d	r :— :—	d :t, :d.s,
d, :d, :d,	d, :d :r	d :— :l,	s, :— :—	d, :f, :m,

s, :— :s,	s, :— :—		l, :r :m	f :— :m	m :r :d
f, :— :m,	m, :r, :—		m, :l, :s,	f, :— :s,	l, :— :l,
l, :t, :d	d :t, :—		de :r :l,	l, :t, :d	d :f :m
r, :— :d,	s, :— :—		s, :f, :de,	r, :— :m,	f, :— :fe,

t, :— :d	r :— :f	m :— :r	d :— :—		d	d	
s, :f, :m,	l, :— :l,	s, :— :f,	m, :— :—		f,	m,	
r :— :d	d :— :d	d :—.l, :t,	d :— :—		l,	s,	
s, :— :l,	f, :— :r,	s, :—.f, :s	d, :— :—		f,	d,	

A-men.

Unison.

PRAISE to the Holiest in the height,
And in the depth be praise,—
In all His words most wonderful,
Most sure in all His ways.

Harmony.

2 O loving wisdom of our God!
When all was sin and shame,
A second Adam to the fight
And to the rescue came.

3 O wisest love! that flesh and blood,
Which did in Adam fail,
Should strive afresh against the foe,
Should strive and should prevail;

4 And that a higher gift than grace
Should flesh and blood refine,
God's presence, and His very self
And essence all-divine.

5 O generous love! that He who smote
In Man, for man, the foe,
The double agony in Man,
For man, should undergo,

6 And in the garden secretly,
And on the Cross on high,
Should teach His brethren, and inspire
To suffer and to die.

Unison. 7 Praise to the Holiest in the height,
And in the depth be praise,—
In all His words most wonderful,
Most sure in all His ways.

JOHN HENRY NEWMAN, 1801–90.

33

SUSSEX. (87. 87.)

Adapted from an English Traditional Melody.

Doh = G. *In moderate time.*

m :m	m :-.r	d.r :m.r	d :l$_1$	f :f	m :-.r
d :d	d :-.t$_1$	l$_1$:s$_1$	l$_1$:l$_1$	l$_1$:d	d :-.t$_1$
s :s	s :-.s	m :m	m :d	f :f	s :-.s
d :d	d :-.s$_1$	l$_1$:m$_1$	l$_1$:l$_1$	f$_1$:l$_1$	d :-.s$_1$

d :m	r :—		d :d	l$_1$:s$_1$	d :-.d	r.m :f
d :d	t$_1$:—		s$_1$:s$_1$	f$_1$.m$_1$:r$_1$	s$_1$:-.l$_1$	t$_1$:d
m :d	r :—		m :d	d :t$_1$	d :-.m	s :l
l$_1$:m$_1$	s$_1$:—		d$_1$:m$_1$	f$_1$:s$_1$	m$_1$:-.l$_1$	s$_1$:f$_1$

s :-.s	f :m.d	r :r	d :—		d	d	
d :-.s$_1$	t$_1$:d	d :t$_1$	d :—		l$_1$	s$_1$	
s :-.d	f :s	l :s.f	m :—		f	m	
m$_1$:-.m$_1$	r$_1$:m$_1$	f$_1$:s$_1$	d$_1$:—		f$_1$	d$_1$	

A-men.

GOD is love: His mercy brightens
All the path in which we rove;
Bliss He wakes, and woe He lightens:
God is wisdom, God is love.

2 Chance and change are busy ever;
Man decays, and ages move;
But His mercy waneth never:
God is wisdom, God is love.

3 Even the hour that darkest seemeth
Will His changeless goodness prove;
From the mist His brightness streameth:
God is wisdom, God is love.

4 He with earthly cares entwineth
Hope and comfort from above;
Everywhere His glory shineth:
God is wisdom, God is love!

JOHN BOWRING, 1792–1872.

34

BELHAVEN. (11 10. 11 10.)

THOMAS CUTHBERTSON LEITHEAD PRITCHARD, 1885–

Doh = A. *In moderate time.*

```
d  :—  |r  :-.r |m  :—  |m  :—  |f  :f  |m  :r  |d  :—  |s, :s,
d  :—  |r  :-.r |m  :—  |m  :—  |f  :f  |m  :r  |d  :—  |s, :m,
d  :—  |r  :-.r |m  :—  |m  :—  |f  :f  |m  :r  |d  :—  |s, :d
d  :—  |r  :-.r |m  :—  |m  :—  |f  :f  |m  :r  |d  :—  |s, :d,

l, :—  |—  :t,  |d  :—  |s, :d  |m  :m  |r  :d  |r  :—  |—  :—
f, :—  |—  :s,  |s, :—  |m, :s, |s, :d  |t, :l, |t, :—  |—  :—
d  :f  |m  :r   |d  :—  |d  :—  |d  :s  |fe :fe |s  :—  |—  :—
f, :—  |—  :f,  |m, :s, |d  :t, |l, :l, |r  :r  |s, :—  |—  :—
```

Doh = D.

```
(f)d'  :—  |t  :l  |d' :d' |t  :l  |s  :—  |—  :r  |m  :—  |s  :—
(l)m   :—  |m  :m  |f  :f  |f  :m  |r  :—  |—  :t, |d  :—  |d  :—
(f)d'  :—  |d' :d' |l  :l  |r' :d' |d' :—  |t  :s  |s  :—  |m  :—
(r)l   :—  |l  :l  |f  :f  |f  :f  |s  :—  |—  :s  |d  :—  |d  :—
```

Doh = A.

```
(s)d   :—  |m  :f  |s  :—  |m  :d  |m  :m  |m  :r  |d  :—  |—  :—  ||d  |d
(r)s,  :—  |d  :d  |r  :t, |s, :f, |s, :d  |l, :t, |d  :—  |—  :—  ||l, |s,
(s)d   :—  |d  :f  |r  :—  |s  :d  |d  :m  |s  :f  |m  :—  |—  :—  ||f  |m
(t)m,  :—  |l, :l, |t, :r  |d  :l, |s, :s, |s, :s, |d, :—  |—  :—  ||f, |d,
                                                                     A - men.
```

[*Copyright*, 1927, *by Oxford University Press.*]

PRAISE ye Jehovah, praise the Lord most holy,
Who cheers the contrite, girds with strength the weak;
Praise Him who will with glory crown the lowly,
And with salvation beautify the meek.

2 Praise ye the Lord for all His loving-kindness,
And all the tender mercy He hath shown;
Praise Him who pardons all our sin and blindness,
And calls us sons, and takes us for His own.

3 Praise ye Jehovah, Source of all our blessing;
Before His gifts earth's richest boons wax dim;
Resting in Him, His peace and joy possessing,
All things are ours, for we have all in Him.

4 Praise ye the Father, God the Lord, who gave us,
With full and perfect love, His only Son;
Praise ye the Son, who died Himself to save us;
Praise ye the Spirit: praise the Three in One.

[May be sung to PSALM 12 (DONNE SECOURS), No. 360.]

MARGARET COCKBURN-CAMPBELL, 1808–41.

35 LAUS DEO. (8 7. 8 7.)

Doh = A♭. *In moderate time.* RICHARD REDHEAD, 1820–1901.

| d :t, | d :m | r :d | d :t, | l, :r | s, :d | l, :l, | s, :— ||

| s, :s, | m, :s, | l, :m,.f, | s, :s, | m, :r, | r, :s, | s, :fe, | s, :— ||

| m :r | d :d | d :d | r :r | d :l, | t, :d | r :r.d | t, :— ||

| d :s, | l, :m, | f, :l, | s, :s, | s, :f, | f, :m, | r, :r, | s, :— ||

| s, :d | d :t, | r :m | f :m | m :s | s :f | m :r | d :— || d | d ||

| s, :s, | s, :s, | s, :s, | l,.f, :s, | s, :s, | l, :d | d :t, | d :— || l, | s, ||

| d :m | m :r | t, :d | d .t, :d | d :d | d :l | s :-.f | m :— || f | m ||

| m, :d, | s, :s, | f, :m, | r, :d, | d, :m, | f, :f, | s, :s, | d, :— || f, | d, ||

A-men.

From Psalm cxlviii.

PRAISE the Lord ! ye heavens, adore Him ;
Praise Him, angels, in the height ;
Sun and moon, rejoice before Him,
Praise Him, all ye stars and light.

2 Praise the Lord ! for He hath spoken ;
Worlds His mighty voice obeyed ;
Laws which never shall be broken
For their guidance hath He made.

3 Praise the Lord ! for He is glorious ;
Never shall His promise fail ;
God hath made His saints victorious ;
Sin and death shall not prevail.

4 Praise the God of our salvation !
Hosts on high, His power proclaim ;
Heaven, and earth, and all creation,
Laud and magnify His Name.

Foundling Hospital Hymns, 1809.

36

NEWCASTLE. (8 6. 8 8 6.)

Doh = G. *In moderate time.* HENRY KILLICK MORLEY, *c.* 1855–

```
:d  |d  :-.t, |t,  :r  |r  :-.d  |d  :m  |s    :f  |d  :r   |m  :— |— ||
:s, |s, :-.s, |s,  :s, |s, :-.s, |s, :s, |d.ta,:l, |l, :la, |s, :— |— ||
:m  |f  :-.f  |f   :f  |f  :-.m  |m  :d  |d    :d  |d  :t,  |d  :— |— ||
:d  |r  :-.r  |r   :t, |d  :-.d  |d  :d  |m,   :f, |f, :f,  |d, :— |— ||

:m  |m   :-.t,  |d  :d  |r   :-.l,  |t, :t, |d :r  |m :m
:s, |se, :-.se, |l, :l, |l,  :-.fe, |s, :s, |d :t, |d :d
:d  |t,  :-.m   |m  :m  |r   :-.r   |r  :s  |s :s  |s :s
:d, |m,  :-.m,  |l, :s, |fe, :-.r,  |s, :f  |m :r  |d :ta,

f  :s  |l   :r  |s  :— |d  :f  |m  :— |— :r  |d  :— |— || d  |d  ||
d  :d  |d   :t, |d  :— |d  :f, |s, :— |— :f, |m, :— |— || f, |m, ||
f  :m  |r   :s  |s  :— |m  :r  |d  :— |— :t, |d  :— |— || l, |s, ||
l, :s, |fe, :f, |m, :— |l, :r, |s, :— |— :s, |d, :— |— || f, |d, ||
                                                           A-men.

         |l :r |s :— |d :f |m :— |— :r |d :— |— ||
Last v.   Light, Through the e - ter  -    nal Love.
```

ETERNAL Light! eternal Light!
How pure the soul must be,
When, placed within Thy searching sight,
It shrinks not, but, with calm delight,
Can live, and look on Thee!

2 The spirits that surround Thy throne
May bear the burning bliss;
But that is surely theirs alone,
Since they have never, never known
A fallen world like this.

3 O how shall I, whose native sphere
Is dark, whose mind is dim,
Before the Ineffable appear,
And on my naked spirit bear
The uncreated beam?

4 There is a way for man to rise
To that sublime abode:
An offering and a sacrifice,
A Holy Spirit's energies,
An Advocate with God.

5 These, these prepare us for the sight
Of holiness above:
The sons of ignorance and night
May dwell in the eternal Light,
Through the eternal Love!

THOMAS BINNEY, 1798–1874.

37

CHILDREN'S VOICES. (6 6 6 6. 4 4 4 4.)

TREBLE VOICES. EDWARD JOHN HOPKINS, 1818–1901.

Doh = G. *In moderate time.*

:m |f :— :m |r :— :m |d :— :— |— :— :t_1
1. A - bove the clear blue sky, In

|l_1 :— :t_1 |d :— :r |s_1 :— :— |— :— ||
hea - ven's bright a - bode,

:m |f :— :m |r :— :m |d :— :m |r :— :t_1
The an - gel host on high Sing prais - es

|d :— :t_1 |l_1 :— :t_1 |s_1 :— :— |— :— : ||
to their God.

|r :— :— |s :— :r |m :— :— |d :— :d
Hal - - - - le - lu - - jah! They

|f :— :s |m :r ||d |s :— :l |f :— :—
love to sing To God their King,

|m :r :d |r :— :— |d :— :— |— :— ||d |d ||
'Hal - le - lu - - jah!' A-men.

2 But God from children's tongues
On earth receiveth praise;
We then our cheerful songs
In sweet accord will raise.
Hallelujah!
We too will sing
To God our King,
'Hallelujah!'

3 O blessèd Lord, Thy truth
In love to us impart,
And teach us in our youth
To know Thee as Thou art.
Hallelujah!
Then shall we sing
To God our King,
'Hallelujah!'

4 O may Thy holy word
Spread all the world around;
All then with one accord
Uplift the joyful sound.
Hallelujah!
All then shall sing
To God their King,
'Hallelujah!'

JOHN CHANDLER, 1806–76.

38

MONKLAND. (77. 7 7.)

Original unknown; arranged by JOHN BERNARD WILKES, 1785–1869.

Doh = C. *In moderate time.*

```
d  :m  |s  :m  |f.s :l.t  |d' :— |m'  :m'  |r' :d' |t  :l    |s  :—
d  :d  |r  :d  |d   :f    |m  :— |s   :s   |s  :s  |s  :fe   |s  :—
m  :l  |t  :s  |l   :f    |s  :— |d'  :d'  |t  :d' |r' :-.d' |t  :—
d  :l, |s, :d  |f   :r    |d  :— |d.r :m.f |s  :m  |r  :r    |s, :—

r' :r'.d' |t :s   |d' :m' |r' :— |m' :r'.d' |t  :d' |d' :t  |d' :— || d' |d'
s  :r     |r :s   |s  :s  |s  :— |s  :s     |s  :s  |s  :r  |m  :— || f  |m
t  :l     |s :t   |d' :d' |t  :— |d' :t.d'  |r' :d' |r' :s  |s  :— || l  |s
s  :fe    |s :s.f |m  :d  |s  :— |d  :r.m   |f  :m  |s  :s, |d  :— || f  |d
```

A-men.

CULBACH. (77. 77.)

Doh = E♭. *In moderate time.* *Heilige Seelenlust*, 1657.

```
d  :m  |s  :s  |f  :s  |m :— |d' :d'  |t  :t  |l :l   |s  :—
s, :d  |r  :t, |d  :s, |d :— |d  :r   |r  :r  |m :r.d |t, :—
m  :s  |s  :s  |d  :r  |m :— |m  :l   |s  :s  |s :fe  |s  :—
d  :d  |t, :s, |l, :t, |d :— |l, :fe, |s, :t, |d :r   |s, :—

s :t |d' :s |l  :s  |m  :— |s  :s |f  :m |r :r   |d :— || d  |d
d :f |m  :d |d  :t, |d  :— |s, :d |t, :d |d :t,  |d :— || l, |s,
m :f |s  :m |f  :r  |d  :— |r  :m |f  :s |l :s.f |m :— || f  |m
m :r |d  :d |f, :s, |l, :— |t, :d |r  :m |f :s   |d :— || f, |d
```

A-men.

SONGS of praise the angels sang,
Heaven with hallelujahs rang,
When creation was begun,
When God spake, and it was done.

2 Songs of praise awoke the morn
When the Prince of Peace was born;
Songs of praise arose when He
Captive led captivity.

3 Heaven and earth must pass away:
Songs of praise shall crown that day;
God will make new heavens, new earth:
Songs of praise shall hail their birth.

4 And can man alone be dumb,
Till that glorious Kingdom come?
No! the Church delights to raise
Psalms, and hymns, and songs of praise.

5 Saints below, with heart and voice,
Still in songs of praise rejoice,
Learning here, by faith and love,
Songs of praise to sing above.

6 Borne upon their latest breath,
Songs of praise shall conquer death;
Then, amidst eternal joy,
Songs of praise their powers employ.

JAMES MONTGOMERY, 1771–1854.

39

CROFT'S 136TH. (6 6. 6 6. 4 4. 4 4.) — WILLIAM CROFT, 1678–1727.

Doh = C. *In moderate time.*

G.t.

|s :— |d' :t |d' :s |l :— |s :— |m.f :s |m :r.d |d :— ||ᵐl, :— |t, :s, |d :r
|m :— |s :f |s :m |f :— |r :— |d :d |d :t,.d |d :— ||ᵈf, :— |r, :r, |s, :l,.t,
|d' :— |m' :r' |d' :d' |d' :— |t :— |d' :d' |s :f |m :— ||ˢd :— |s :t, |d :f
|d :— |d :r |m :d |f :— |s :— |l :m |s :s, |d :— ||ᵈf, :— |s, :s,.f, |m, :r,

f.C.

|m :— |s :— |m :d |r :t, |ᵈs :— ||t :— |d' :s |l :— |d' :—
|d :— |t, :— |t, :d |l, :s, |ᵐt, :— ||r :— |d :m |f :— |s :—
|s :— |m :— |m :m |f :r |ᵈs :— ||s :— |s :d' |d' :— |d' :—
|d, :— |m, :— |s, :l, |f, :s, |ᵈs :— ||s :— |m :d |f :— |m :—

t :l	se :—		se :—	l :t	d' :—	s :—	m :r.d	d :—		f	m	
f :d.r	m :—		m :—	m :r	d :—	d :—	d :t,	d :—		d	d	
r' :l	t :—		t :—	l :se	l :—	s :—	s :f	m :—		l	s	
r :f	m :—		r :—	d :t,	l, :—	m :—	s :s,	d :—		f,	d	

A-men.

YE holy angels bright,
Who wait at God's right hand,
Or through the realms of light
Fly at your Lord's command,
Assist our song,
Or else the theme
Too high doth seem
For mortal tongue.

2 Ye blessèd souls at rest,
Who ran this earthly race,
And now, from sin released,
Behold the Saviour's face,
His praises sound,
As in His light
With sweet delight
Ye do abound.

3 Ye saints, who toil below,
Adore your heavenly King,
And, onward as ye go,
Some joyful anthem sing;
Take what He gives,
And praise Him still
Through good and ill,
Who ever lives.

4 My soul, bear thou thy part,
Triumph in God above,
And with a well-tuned heart
Sing thou the songs of love.
Let all thy days
Till life shall end,
Whate'er He send,
Be filled with praise.

RICHARD BAXTER, 1615–91, and others.

[May be sung to DARWALL, No. 135.]

Also the following:

2 Round the Lord in glory seated
3 We praise, we worship Thee, O God
228 From all that dwell below the skies
229 All people that on earth do dwell
230 Before Jehovah's awful throne
231 All lands and peoples, all the earth

THE LORD JESUS CHRIST

HIS INCARNATION

40 CREDITON. (C.M.)

Doh = C. *In moderate time.* THOMAS CLARK, 1775–1859.

:(s)|d' .,d' :t |d' :s |l :s.f |m :s |l.t :d' |f :m |r :— |— ||
:(m)|m .,m :f |s :m |f :m.r |d :d |d :d |t, :d |t, :— |— ||
v. 1. Hark, the glad sound
:(s)|s .,s :s |s :d' |d' :t |d' :d'.t |l :s |s :s |s :— |— ||
:(d)|d .,d :r |m :d |f :s |d :m |f :m |r :d |s, :— |— ||

Harmony.

:s |s :l.t |d' :m' |r' :d' |t :s |l.t :d' |m'.r' :d'.t |d' :— |— || d' |d' ||
:r |s :f |m :s |s.r :m.fe |s :s |f :s |f :m.r |m :— |— || f |m ||
:t |d' :f |s :d' |r' :l |r' :d' |d'.r' :d' |l :s |s :— |— || l |s ||
:s.f |m :r |d :d' |t :l |s :m |f :m |f :s |d :— |— || f |d ||

A-men.

From St. Luke iv. 18, 19.

HARK, the glad sound! the Saviour comes,
The Saviour promised long;
Let every heart exult with joy,
And every voice be song!

2 On Him the Spirit, largely shed,
Exerts its sacred fire;
Wisdom and might, and zeal and love,
His holy breast inspire.

3 He comes, the prisoners to relieve,
In Satan's bondage held;
The gates of brass before Him burst,
The iron fetters yield.

4 He comes, from darkening scales of vice
To clear the inward sight;
And on the eye-balls of the blind
To pour celestial light.

5 He comes, the broken hearts to bind,
The bleeding souls to cure;
And with the treasures of His grace
To enrich the humble poor.

6 The sacred year has now revolved,
Accepted of the Lord,
When heaven's high promise is fulfilled,
And Israel is restored.

Unison. 7 Our glad hosannas, Prince of Peace,
Thy welcome shall proclaim;
And heaven's exalted arches ring
With Thy most honoured Name.

PHILIP DODDRIDGE, 1702–51, as in *Scottish Paraphrases*, 1781

41 BONN. (8336. 8336.)

Doh = G. *Slow.* JOHANN GEORG EBELING, 1637–76.

d :— |r :— |m :— |— :r |m :s |l :— |s :— |— :—
s, :— |l, :t, |d :— |— :t, |d :t, |r :—.d |t, :— |— :—
m :— |f :— |s :— |— :s |s :s |s :fe |s :— |— :—
m :— |r :— |d :— |— :s, |d :m |r :— |s, :— |— :—

s :l |f :— |f :s |m :— |m :s |f :m |r :— |d :—
d :d |l, :— |l, :s, |s, :— |s, :s, |d :d |d :t, |d :—
m :m |f :— |d :r |m :— |d :r.m |f :s |s :— |m :—
d :l, |r :— |l, :t, |d :— |d :t, |l, :d |s, :— |d :—

s :— |f :— |m :— |— :r |d :t, |l, :— |s, :— |— :—
d :— |l, :t, |d :— |— :s, |m, :s, |s, :fe, |s, :— |— :—
m :— |f :— |s :— |— :t, |d :r |m :r |t, :— |— :—
d, :— |r, :— |m, :— |— :s, |l, :t, |d :r |s, :— |— :—

s :l |f :— |f :s |m :— |m :r |f :m |r :— |d :— || d |d ||
t, :d |l, :— |l, :t, |s, :— |s, :s, |d :d |d :t, |d :— || l, |s, ||
s :m |r :— |f :r |d :— |d :s |f :s |l :s |m :— || f |m ||
m :d |r :— |r :s, |d :— |d :t, |l, :s, |f, :s, |d, :— || f, |d, ||

A-men.

Fröhlich soll mein Herze springen.

ALL my heart this night rejoices,
As I hear, far and near,
Sweetest angel voices;
'Christ is born!' their choirs are singing,
Till the air, everywhere,
Now with joy is ringing.

2 Hark! a voice from yonder manger,
Soft and sweet, doth entreat:
'Flee from woe and danger;
Brethren, come: from all doth grieve you
You are freed; all you need
I will surely give you.'

3 Come, then, let us hasten yonder;
Here let all, great and small,
Kneel in awe and wonder.
Love Him who with love is yearning;
Hail the Star that, from far,
Bright with hope is burning.

4 Thee, O Lord, with heed I'll cherish,
Live to Thee, and with Thee
Dying, shall not perish,
But shall dwell with Thee for ever
Far on high, in the joy
That can alter never.

PAUL GERHARDT, 1607–76;
tr. by CATHERINE WINKWORTH, 1829–78.

42 EVANGEL. (D.C.M.)

Doh = B♭. *Moderately.* GOTTFRIED WILHELM FINK, 1783–1846.

```
:s, | d  :d  | t, :l, | s, :-.l, | s, :s,     | l, :r  | d  :t,  | d  :— | — ||
:s, | m, :s, | s, :f, | m, :-.f, | m, :s,     | f, :l, | s, :s,  | s, :— | — ||
:s, | d  :d  | d  :d  | d  :-.d  | d  :d      | d  :f  | m  :r   | m  :— | — ||
:s, | d, :m, | f, :l, | d  :-.f, | d  :m,     | f, :r, | s, :s,  | d, :— | — ||

:s, | d  :d  | t, :l, | s, :-.l, | s, :m      | r  :d  | t, :l,  | s, :— | — ||
:s, | m, :s, | s, :f, | m, :-.f, | m, :m,.fe, | s, :l, | s, :fe, | s, :— | — ||
:s, | d  :d  | d  :d  | d  :-.d  | d  :s,.l,  | t, :m  | r  :d   | t, :— | — ||
:s, | d, :m, | f, :l, | d  :-.f, | d  :d,     | t,, :d, | r, :r, | s, :— | — ||

:s, | t, :s, | d  :s, | r  :s,   | m  :d      | f  :m  | r  :d   | d  :— | t, ||
:s, | s, :s, | s, :s, | f, :f,   | m, :m,     | f, :s, | l, :l,  | s, :— | —  ||
:t, | r  :t, | d  :d  | t, :t,   | d  :d      | d  :d  | l, :r   | r  :— | —  ||
:s, | f, :f, | m, :m, | r, :r,   | d, :ta,    | l, :s, | f, :fe, | s, :— | —  ||

:s, | d  :d  | t, :l, | s, :-.l, | s, :s,     | l, :r  | d  :t,  | d  :— | — || d  | d  ||
:s, | s, :s, | s, :f, | f, :-.f, | m, :s,     | f, :l, | s, :s,  | s, :— | — || l, | s, ||
:t, | d  :d  | d  :d  | r  :t,   | d  :d      | d  :f  | m  :r   | m  :— | — || f  | m  ||
:f, | m, :m, | f, :l, | t, :s,   | d  :m,     | f, :r, | s, :s,  | d, :— | — || f, | d, ||
```

A-men.

From St. Luke ii. 8–15.

WHILE humble shepherds watched their flocks
In Bethlehem's plains by night,
An angel sent from heaven appeared,
And filled the plains with light.
'Fear not,' he said, for sudden dread
Had seized their troubled mind;
'Glad tidings of great joy I bring
To you and all mankind.

2 'To you, in David's town, this day,
Is born, of David's line,
The Saviour, who is Christ the Lord;
And this shall be the sign:
'The heavenly Babe you there shall find
To human view displayed,
All meanly wrapped in swaddling-bands,
And in a manger laid.'

3 Thus spake the seraph; and forthwith
Appeared a shining throng
Of angels, praising God, and thus
Addressed their joyful song:
'All glory be to God on high,
And to the earth be peace;
Good will is shown by heaven to men,
And never more shall cease.'

NAHUM TATE, 1652–1715, as in *Scottish Paraphrases*, 1781.

[May be sung to WINCHESTER, No. 181.]

43 IN THE FIELD. (Irr.)

Doh = G. SOLO. *In moderate time.* JOHN FARMER, 1836–1901.

{| 11 *measures Instrumental* |d' :— |— :m .f |s :m .r |d .d :r .r}
1. In the field with their flocks a -
2. 'To you in the ci - ty of
3. And the shep - herds came to the

{|s, :-.l, |s, :d .r |m :m .m |f :r |s :— |— :m .f}
bid - ing, They lay on the dew - y ground, And
Da - vid A Sa - viour is born to - - day.' And
man - ger, And gazed on the Ho - ly Child; And

{|s :m .r |d :r .r |s, :-.l, |s, :d .r |m :f |r :r}
glimm - 'ring un - der the star - light The sheep lay white a -
sud - den a host of the heaven - ly ones Flashed forth to join the
calm - ly o'er that rude cra - dle The vir - gin mo - ther

D.t.
{|d :— |— :s .s |l :d' .d' |t :l |s :-.f |m :d}
round, When the light of the Lord streamed o'er them, And
lay. O ne - ver hath sweet-er mes - sage Thrilled
smiled; And the sky, in the star - lit si - lence, Seemed

{|m :m .m |f :r .r |s :— |— :s .s |l :d' .d' |t .t :l .l}
lo! from the hea - ven a - bove, An an - gel leaned from the
home to the souls of men; And the heavens them-selves had
full of the an - gel lay,— 'To you in the ci - ty of

rit.
{|s : -.f |m :d |m :m .m |f :r}
glo - - - ry, And sang his song of
ne - ver heard A glad - der choir till
Da - - - vid A Sa - viour is born to -

f.G. CHORUS. Trebles and Altos.

a tempo.
{|r :— |— :s, .s, |d :d .d |r :r |m :-.f |s :s}
love; He sang, that first sweet Christ - mas, The
then; For they sang that Christ - mas ca - rol That
- day.' O they sang—and I ween that ne - ver The

All.
{|f .f :f .f |m :m |r :— |— : |d :d .d |r :r .r}
song that shall ne - ver cease,— 'Glo - ry to God in the
ne-ver on earth shall cease,— 'Glo - ry to God in the
ca-rol on earth shall cease,— 'Glo - ry to God in the

{|m :-.f |s :f |m :f |r :r |d :— :— ||d |d||}
high - est, On earth good - will and peace!'
high - est, On earth good - will and peace!'
high - est, On earth good - will and peace!' A - men.

[*By permission of Joseph Williams, Ltd.*] FREDERIC WILLIAM FARRAR, 1831–1903.

44 CHARTRES. (87. 87. D.)

Lah = G. Doh = B♭. *In moderate time.* Old French Noël.

:l,.l, | m :- .m :t,.d | r :r :l,.t, | d :- .r :t,.d | l, :— ||

:m,.m, | l, :m, :m,.m, | f, :f, :l,.l, | l,.m, :f, :m, | d, :— ||

:d .d | m :d :r .d | d :t, :l,.f | m .d :l, :se, | l, :— ||

:l,.l, | d :l, :se,.l, | r, :r, :f,.r, | d,.l_2 :r, :m, | l, :— ||

:l,.l, | m :- .m :t,.d | r :r :l,.t, | d :- .r :t,.d | l, :— ||

:m,.l, | l, :se,.l, :l,.s, | f, :f,.l, :s,.f, | m,.d, :f, :m, | d, :— ||

:m .d | r :t,.d :r .m | f :t, :d .r | m .l, :l, :se, | l, :— ||

:d .l, | t, :m, :f,.m, | r, :r, :m,.r, | d,.f, :r, :m, | l_2 :— ||

:l,.l, | t, :-.se, :l, .t, | d :d :l,.l, | r :- .d :t,.l, | se, :— ||

:m,.m, | m, :m, :m,.m, | m, :l, :m,.l, | se, :l, :f,.f, | m, :— ||

:d .d | t, :r :d .t, | l, :m :d .m | f :m :r .d | t, :— ||

:l,.l, | se, :m, :ba,.se, | l, :l_2 :d,.d, | t_2 :d, :r,.r, | m, :— ||

:l,.l, | t, :-.se, :l,.t, | d :d :l,.l, | t, :-.l, :l,.se, | l, :— || l, | l, ||

:m,.m, | m, :m, :m,.s, | s, :m, :l,.s, | f, :f, :m,.m, | m, :— || f, | m, ||

:m .d | t, :r :d .r | m :d :d .d | r :d :t,.t, | d :— || r | de ||

:d .l, | se, :m, :l,.s, | d :d, :f,.m, | r, :r, :m,.m, | l_2 :— || r, | l_2 ||

A - men.

LITTLE children, wake and listen!
Songs are breaking o'er the earth;
While the stars in heaven glisten,
Hear the news of Jesus' birth.
Long ago, to lonely meadows,
Angels brought the message down;
Still, each year, through midnight shadows,
It is heard in every town.

2 What is this that they are telling,
Singing in the quiet street?
While their voices high are swelling,
What sweet words do they repeat?
Words to bring us greater gladness,
Though our hearts from care are free;
Words to chase away our sadness,
Cheerless though our hearts may be.

3 Christ has left His throne of glory,
And a lowly cradle found;
Well might angels tell the story,
Well may we their words resound.
Little children, wake and listen!
Songs are ringing through the earth;
While the stars in heaven glisten,
Hail with joy your Saviour's birth.

S.P.C.K. Appendix, 1869.

45 THE FIRST NOWELL. (Irr.)

Doh = D. *Moderately quick.*

Old English Carol.

:m .r | d :- .r :m .f | s :— :l .t | d' :t :l
:d .t, | d :— :d | r :— :s | s :s :fe
:s .f | m :- .f :s .l | s :— :m' .r' | d' :r' :d'
:d | d :— :d | d :t, :d .t, | l, :t, .d :r

s :— :l .t | d' :t :l | s :l :t | d' :s :f
s :— :s .s | s :f :m | f :m :r | d .r :m :r
t :— :d' .r' | s :s :l | r' :d' :t .l | s .l :s :s
s, :s :s .f | m :r :d | t, :d :r | m .f :s :s,

m :— || m .r | d :- .r :m .f | s :— :l .t | d' :t :l
d :— || t, | d :— :d | r :— :r | d :d :d .r
s :— || s | s :- .f :m .d' | d' :t :l | s :s :l .t
d :— || s .f | m :- .r :d .l, | s, :s :f | m :m :f

s :— :l .t | d' :t :l | s :l :t | d' :s :f | m :— ||
m :— :r .r | s :f :m | f :m :r | d .r :m :r | d :— ||
d' :— :l .s | s :s :l | r' :d' :t .l | s .l :s :s | s :— ||
d :— :f .f | m :r :d | t, :d :r | m .f :s :s, | d :— ||

REFRAIN.

:m .r | d :- .r :m .f | s :— :d' .t | l :— :l | s :— :—
:t, | d :— :d | r :— :d .r | m :s :fe | s :— :—
:s .f | m :— :d' | d' :t :s | s :m' :r' .d' | t :— :—
:s, | l, :— :l, | s, :— :m .r | d :— :r | s :— :f

d' :t :l | s :l :t | d' :s :f | m :— || f | m ||
s :s :f | m :— :s | s .f :m :r | d :— || d | d ||
d' :d' :d' | d' :— :r' | s .l :d' :t | d' :— || l | s ||
m :m :f .l | d' .t :l :s .f | m .f :s :s, | d :— || f, | d ||

A-men.

THE first Nowell the angel did say
Was to certain poor shepherds in fields as they lay :
In fields where they lay a-keeping their sheep
On a cold winter's night that was so deep.
Nowell, Nowell, Nowell, Nowell,
Born is the King of Israel.

2 They lookèd up and saw a star,
Shining in the east, beyond them far;
And to the earth it gave great light,
And so it continued both day and night.

3 And by the light of that same star,
Three wise men came from country far ;
To seek for a King was their intent,
And to follow the star wherever it went.

4 This star drew nigh to the north-west,
O'er Bethlehem it took its rest,
And there it did both stop and stay
Right over the place where Jesus lay.

5 Then entered in those wise men three,
Full reverently upon their knee,
And offered there in His presence
Their gold and myrrh and frankincense.

6 Then let us all with one accord
Sing praises to our Heavenly Lord,
That hath made heaven and earth of nought,
And with His blood mankind hath bought.

Traditional Carol.

46

BETHLEHEM. (77. 77. D. and refrain).

Doh = F. *In moderate time.* FELIX MENDELSSOHN-BARTHOLDY, 1809–47.

s_1 :d	d :-.t_1	d :m	m :r	s :s	s :-.f	m :r	m :—	
s_1 :s_1	s_1 :-.s_1	s_1 :d	d :t_1	d :t_1	l_1 :r	d :t_1	d :—	
m :m	m :-.r	d :s	s :—	s :s	l :l	s :s	s :—	
d :d	d :s_1	m_1 :d_1	s_1 :—	m_1 :m_1	f_1 :f_1	s_1 :s_1	d :—	

C.t. f.F.

s_1 :d	d :-.t_1	d :^{m}l	l :s	d^1 :s	s :-.m	m :r	$^{d}s_1$:—	
s_1 :s_1	s_1 :-.s_1	s_1 :^{d}f	r :—	s :t_1	d :-.d	d :t_1	$^{d}s_1$:—	
s :m	m :-.r	d :$^{s}d^1$	d^1 :t	d^1 :f^1	m^1 :d^1	s :s.f	$^{m}t_1$:—	
m :d	s_1 :f_1	m_1 :$^{d}f_1$	:—	m :r	d :m	s :s_1	$^{d}s_1$:—	

s :s	s :d	f :m	m :r	s :s	s :d	f :m	m :r	
s_1 :s_1	s_1 :d	r :d	d :t_1	s_1 :s_1	s_1 :d	r :d	d :t_1	
s :s	s :s	s :s	s :—	s :s	s :s	s :s	s :—	
s :s	s :m	t_1 :d	s_1 :—	s :s	s :m	t_1 :d	s_1 :—	

l :-.l	l :s	f :m	f :—	r :m.f	s :-.d	d :r	m :—	
f :-.f	f :m	r :de	r :—	t_1 :t_1	d :-.s_1	s_1 :t_1	d :—	
l :-.l	l :ta	l :s	f :s.l	s :s	s :-.m	m :s	s :—	
f_1 :-.f_1	f_1 :s_1	l_1 :l_1	r :m.f	s :f	m :d	s_1 :s_1	d :—	

REFRAIN.

l :-.l	l :s	f :m	f :—	r :m.f	s :-.d	d :r	d :—		d	d	
f :-.f	f :m	r :de	r :—	r :m.f	s :-.d	d :r	d :—		l_1	s_1	
l :-.l	l :s	f :m	f :—	r :m.f	s :-.d	d :r	d :—		f	m	
f :-.f	f :m	r :de	r :—	r :m.f	s :-.d	d :r	d :—		f_1	d_1	

A-men.

[*By permission of Novello & Co., Ltd.*]

HARK! the herald angels sing,
'Glory to the new-born King.
Peace on earth, and mercy mild,
God and sinners reconciled!'
Joyful, all ye nations, rise,
Join the triumph of the skies,
With the angelic host proclaim,
'Christ is born in Bethlehem.'
Hark! the herald angels sing,
'Glory to the new-born King.'

2 Christ, by highest heaven adored,
Christ, the everlasting Lord,
Late in time behold Him come,
Offspring of a virgin's womb.
Veiled in flesh the Godhead see;
Hail, the Incarnate Deity,
Pleased as Man with man to dwell,
Jesus, our Immanuel!

3 Hail, the heaven-born Prince of Peace!
Hail, the Sun of Righteousness!
Light and life to all He brings,
Risen with healing in His wings.
Mild He lays His glory by,
Born that man no more may die,
Born to raise the sons of earth,
Born to give them second birth.

CHARLES WESLEY, 1707-88.

47 NOEL. (D.C.M.)

Doh = F. *In moderate time.* Arranged by ARTHUR SEYMOUR SULLIVAN, 1842–1900.

```
:d.r |m  :r  |d  :r.m  |f  :m  |r  :s  |s  :m  |f.s :l  |s  :— |— ‖
:d   |d  :t, |d  :l,.d |t, :d  |t, :t, |d  :d  |d   :d  |d  :— |— ‖
:m.f |s  :s  |m  :l.s  |f  :s  |s  :s  |s  :s  |f   :f  |m  :— |— ‖
:d   |d  :s, |d  :f.m  |r  :d  |s, :f  |m  :d  |l,  :f, |d  :— |— ‖
```

```
:m.f |s  :s  |m  :d  |f  :m |r  :d.r |m.f :s     |m  :r  |d  :— |— ‖
:d   |t, :t, |d  :d  |d  :d |t, :d   |d   :s,    |d  :t, |d  :— |— ‖
:s   |s  :r  |d  :m  |l  :s |s  :m   |d   :d     |s  :f  |m  :— |— ‖
:d   |s, :s, |l, :l, |f, :d |s, :d   |l,  :m,.f, |s, :s, |d, :— |— ‖
```

```
:d  |t,  :l, |t, :r   |d  :-.t,  |l, :m  |r  :d  |t, :l,  |s, :— |— ‖
:l, |se, :l, |l, :se, |l, :-.se, |l, :d  |t, :l, |s, :fe, |s, :— |— ‖
:d  |r   :m  |f  :m   |m  :-.r   |d  :fe |s  :m  |r  :d   |t, :— |— ‖
:l, |t,  :d  |r  :m   |l, :-.l,  |l, :l, |t, :d  |r  :r,  |s, :— |— ‖
```

```
:s, |s  :f     |m  :r.m    |f    :m     |r  :d.r |m.f :s     |m  :r  |d  :— |— ‖ d  |d  ‖
:s, |m  :r     |de :t,.de  |r.t, :d     |t, :d   |d.r :m     |d  :t, |d  :— |— ‖ l, |s, ‖
:s, |s  :s     |s  :f.m    |r    :s,    |s  :m   |s   :-.s   |s  :f  |m  :— |— ‖ f  |m  ‖
:s, |m, :f,.s, |l, :l,     |r,   :m,.f, |s, :l,  |m,  :r,.d, |s, :s, |d, :— |— ‖ f, |d, ‖
                                                                                  A-men.
```

[*By permission of Novello & Co., Ltd.*]

IT came upon the midnight clear,
   That glorious song of old,
From angels bending near the earth
   To touch their harps of gold :—
'Peace on the earth, good will to men,
   From heaven's all-gracious King!'
The world in solemn stillness lay
   To hear the angels sing.

2 Still through the cloven skies they come
With peaceful wings unfurled ;
And still their heavenly music floats
O'er all the weary world ;
Above its sad and lowly plains
They bend on hovering wing,
And ever o'er its Babel sounds
The blessèd angels sing.

3 But with the woes of sin and strife
The world has suffered long ;
Beneath the angel strain have rolled
Two thousand years of wrong ;
And man, at war with man, hears not
The love song which they bring ;
O hush the noise, ye men of strife,
And hear the angels sing.

4 And ye, beneath life's crushing load
Whose forms are bending low,
Who toil along the climbing way
With painful steps and slow,
Look now ! for glad and golden hours
Come swiftly on the wing ;
O rest beside the weary road,
And hear the angels sing.

5 For, lo ! the days are hastening on,
By prophet bards foretold,
When with the ever-circling years
Comes round the Age of Gold,
When peace shall over all the earth
Its ancient splendours fling,
* And the whole world give back the song
Which now the angels sing.

*v. 5, line 7.

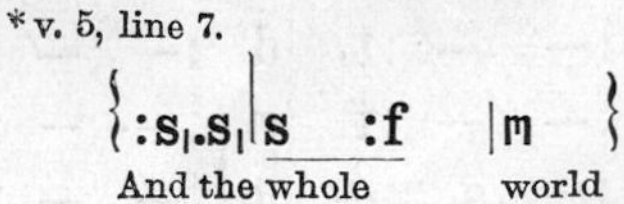

Edmund Hamilton Sears, 1810–76.

FIRST TUNE.

48 CHRISTMAS CAROL. (86. 86. 76. 86.)

vv. 1, 2, 3 Sopranos only. v. 4 in *Harmony.*

Doh = G. *In moderate time.* HENRY WALFORD DAVIES, 1869-

Two measures Instrumental.

d' :— |— :m |r :-.m |d :m |r :-.m |d :m
:d |t, :-.t, |d :d |t, :-.t, |d :d
:s |f :-.s |m :s |f :-.s |m :s
:d |s, :-.s, |d :d |s, :-.s, |d :d

D.t.

l :s |m :r .d |m :— |— ||m |r :-.m |d :m |m.r :r .m |d :[s]d .r
d :d |s, :s,.fe, |s, :— |— ||s, |s, :l,.t, |d :s, |s, :l,.t, |d :[m]l,.t,
f :s |d :r .l, |t, :— |— ||s |f :-.s |m :s |s.f :f .s |m :[m]l
f :m |d :t,.l, |m, :— |— ||s,.l, |t, :s, |d :s,.l, |t, :s, |d :[d]f

m :d' |t :-.l |l :— |— ||m.ba |se :m |l :m |t :m |d' :d'.r'
d :m |m :-.m |m :— |— ||d |t, :d.t, |l, :d |r :— |d :d
l :m.ba |se :r' |d' :— |— ||m |m :m |m :m.ba |se :ba.se |l :m
m :d.l, |m, :m |l, :— |— ||m |r :m.r |d :m |t, :m |l, :l,

f.G.

m' :d' |s :-.f |m :— |— ||[d]s |f :-.s |m :s |s .f :f .s |m :d
d :m.d |l, :t, |d :— |— ||[m]t,.d |r :t, |s, :t,.d |d .r :r .t, |s, :d
m :s.d' |m' :r' |s :— |— ||[l]m |r :-.m |d :m |m .r :r .m |d :s
s, :d.m |s :s, |d :— |— ||[d]s,.l, |t, :s, |d :s,.l, |l,.t, :t,.s, |d :m

l :s |m :d |m :— |— :r |d :— |— : || d :— |d :—
d :— |— :d |t, :— |— :t, |d :— |— : || l, :— |s, :—
f :s |l :m |s :— |— :f |m :— |— : || d :— |m :—
f :m |d :l, |m, :— |s, :— |s,/d, :— |— : || f, :— |d, :—

A - men.

[*Copyright*, 1905, *by W. Garrett Horder.*]

SECOND TUNE.

VILLAGE. (86. 86. 76. 86.)

Doh = E♭. *In moderate time.* GEORGE GILBERT STOCKS, 1877–

{ :s | f :s | m :r | d :l, | s, :l, | d :l, | d :r | d :— | — :s }

{ | f :s | m :r | d :l, | d :r | m :d | m :r | m :— | — :s }

{ | f :l | d' :l | s :f | — :m | r :f | l :m | r :— | — :s | f :s | m :r }

{ | d :l, | s, :l, | d :l, | d :r | d :— | — ‖ d | d ‖
A - men.

O LITTLE town of Bethlehem,
How still we see thee lie !
Above thy deep and dreamless sleep
The silent stars go by :
Yet in thy dark streets shineth
The everlasting Light ;
The hopes and fears of all the years
Are met in thee to-night.

2 For Christ is born of Mary ;
And, gathered all above,
While mortals sleep, the angels keep
Their watch of wondering love.
O morning stars, together
Proclaim the holy birth,
And praises sing to God the King,
And peace to men on earth.

3 How silently, how silently,
The wondrous gift is given !
So God imparts to human hearts
The blessings of His heaven.
No ear may hear His coming ;
But in this world of sin,
Where meek souls will receive Him, still
The dear Christ enters in.

4 O Holy Child of Bethlehem,
Descend to us, we pray ;
Cast out our sin, and enter in ;
Be born in us to-day.
We hear the Christmas angels
The great glad tidings tell ;
O come to us, abide with us,
Our Lord Immanuel.

PHILLIPS BROOKS, 1835–93.

49

STILLE NACHT. (Irr.)

Doh = C. *Moderately slow.* FRANZ GRUBER, 1787–1863.

```
s :-.l:s   |m :— :—   |s :-.l :s    |m :— :—   |r' :— :r'     |t :— :—
m :-.f:m   |d :— :—   |m :-.f :m    |d :— :m   |f :— :f       |f :-.s :f
d' :— :d'  |s :-.l:s  |d' :-.d':d'  |s :-.l:s  |t :— :t       |r' :-.m':r'
d :— :d    |d :— :—   |d :-.d :d    |d :— :—   |s :— :s       |s :— :—

d' :—:d'   |s :— :—      ||l :-.l :l    |d' :-.t:l  |s :-.l:s   |m :— :—
m :—:m     |s :-.f :m    ||f :-.f :f    |l :-.s:f   |s :-.f:s   |d :— :m
d' :—:s    |m' :-.r':d'  ||d' :-.d':d'  |l :-.t:d'  |d' :— :d'  |d' :— :—
d :—:d     |d :— :—      ||f :-.f :f    |f :-.f:f   |m :-.f:m   |s :-.l:s

l :-.l :l     |d' :-.t:l  |s :-.l :s  |m :— :—   |r' :-.r':r'   |f' :-.r':t
f :-.f :f     |f :— :f    |s :— :d    |d :— :—   |f :-.f :f     |r :-.r :f
d' :-.d':d'   |l :-.t:d'  |d' :— :s   |s :-.l:s  |t :-.t :t     |t :-.t :r'
f :-.f :f     |l :-.s:f   |m :-.f :m  |d :— :—   |s, :-.s,:s,   |s :-.s :s

                         ://:
d' :— :—    |m' :—:—   |d' :-.s:m  |s :-.f :r     |d :—:—  |—:—:—  ||f  |m  ||
m :-.f:m    |s :—:—    |m :-.m:d   |t, :-.t,:t,   |d :—:—  |—:—:—  ||d  |d  ||
d' :-.l:s   |d' :—:—   |s :-.s:s   |f :-.f:f      |m :—:—  |—:—:—  ||l  |s  ||
d :— :—     |d :—:m    |s :-.s:s   |s, :-.s,:s,   |d :—:—  |—:—:—  ||f, |d  ||
                                                                     A-men.
```

Stille Nacht, heilige Nacht.

STILL the night, holy the night!
Sleeps the world; hid from sight,
Mary and Joseph in stable bare
Watch o'er the Child beloved and fair,
Sleeping in heavenly rest.

2 Still the night, holy the night!
Shepherds first saw the light,
Heard resounding clear and long,
Far and near, the angel-song,
'Christ the Redeemer is here!'

3 Still the night, holy the night!
Son of God, O how bright
Love is smiling from Thy face!
Strikes for us now the hour of grace,
Saviour, since Thou art born!

JOSEPH MOHR, 1792–1848.

50

CRANHAM. (Irr.)

Doh = F. *In moderate time.*

GUSTAV HOLST, 1874-

1. In the bleak mid-winter,
Frosty wind made moan,
Earth stood hard as iron,
Water like a stone;
Snow had fallen, snow on snow,
Snow on snow,
In the bleak mid-winter,
Long ago.

2. Our God, heaven cannot hold Him,
Nor . . earth sustain;
Heaven and earth shall flee away
When He comes to reign:
In the bleak mid-winter A
stable place sufficed
The Lord God Almighty,
Jesus Christ.

3. Angels and archangels
May have gathered there,
Cherubim and seraphim
Thronged the air—
But His mother only,
In her maiden bliss,
Worshipped the Beloved
With a kiss.

4. What can I give Him,
Poor . . as I am?
If I were a shepherd,
I would bring a lamb;
If I were a wise man,
I would do my part;
Yet what I can I give Him—
Give my heart.
Amen.

51 HUMILITY. (77. 77. and refrain.)

Unison.

Doh = G. *In moderate time.* JOHN GOSS, 1800–80.

d :-.r | d :t, | l, :-.s, | s, :— | d :r | f :m | m :-.r | r :— ||

d :-.r | d :t, | l, :-.s, | s, :— | d :r | m :f | r :-.d | d :— ||

REFRAIN. *Harmony.*

s :-.s | f :m | r :d | t, :— | s :-.s | f :m | r :d | t, :— ||
d :-.d | d :d | s, :s, | s, :— | s, :-.d | d :d | l, :s, | s, :— ||
m :-.m | l :s | f :m | r :— | d :-.d | l :s | f :m | r :— ||
d :-.d | d :d | t, :d | s, :— | m, :-.m, | f, :d, | r, :m,.f, | s, :— ||

d :-.r | d :t, | l, :-.s, | s, :— | s :-.m | d :f | m :r | d :— || d | d ||
m, :-.m, | fe, :s, | s, :fe, | s, :— | s, :-.s, | l, :d | t, :t, | d :— || l, | s, ||
d :-.d | l, :s, | m :r.d | t, :— | d :-.d | d :l | s :f | m :— || f | m ||
l, :-.l, | r, :m, | d, :r, | s, :f, | m, :-.m, | f, :r, | s, :s, | d, :— || f, | d, ||

A-men.

[*By permission of Novello & Co., Ltd.*]

SEE ! in yonder manger low,
Born for us on earth below,
See ! the tender Lamb appears,
Promised from eternal years.
Hail, thou ever-blessèd morn !
Hail, redemption's happy dawn!
Sing through all Jerusalem,
'Christ is born in Bethlehem !'

2 Lo ! within a manger lies
He who built the starry skies,
He who, throned in height sublime,
Sits amid the cherubim.

3 Say, ye holy shepherds, say,
What your joyful news to-day ;
Wherefore have ye left your sheep
On the lonely mountain steep ?

4 'As we watched at dead of night,
Lo ! we saw a wondrous light :
Angels, singing peace on earth,
Told us of the Saviour's birth.'

5 Sacred Infant, all Divine,
What a tender love was Thine,
Thus to come from highest bliss
Down to such a world as this !

6 Teach, O teach us, Holy Child,
By Thy face so meek and mild,
Teach us to resemble Thee
In Thy sweet humility.

EDWARD CASWALL, 1814–78.

52 GARTAN. (67. 67.)

Doh = F. *In moderate time.* Traditional Irish Air.

d :-.r | m :l | s :— | s :— | s :-.s | s.m :r.m | s :-.s | s.m :r.m ||
d :-.t, | d :d | d :t, | d :— | s, :l,.t, | d :d | r :d | d :t, ||
s :-.f | m :f | r :— | m :— | s :f | m.s :f.m | r :m | s :— ||
m :-.r | d :f, | s, :— | d :— | m :r | d :d | t, :d | s, :— ||

d :-.r	m :l	s :—	s :—	s :-.s	s.m:r.m	d :d	d :—	
d :-.d	d :d.r	m :d	t_1 :d	r :d	t_1 :t_1	l_1 :l_1	s_1 :—	
m :f	s :l.t	d' :s	f :m	r :m	m.s:s.f	m :f	m :—	
l_1 :-.l_1	s_1 :f_1	m_1 :m	r :d	t_1 :d	m_1 :s_1	l_1 :f_1	d d_1 :—	

LOVE came down at Christmas,
  Love all lovely, Love Divine;
Love was born at Christmas,
  Star and angels gave the sign.

2 Worship we the Godhead,
  Love Incarnate, Love Divine;
Worship we our Jesus:
  But wherewith for sacred sign?

3 Love shall be our token,
  Love be yours and love be mine,
Love to God and all men,
  Love for plea and gift and sign.

CHRISTINA GEORGINA ROSSETTI, 1830–94.

	l_1 :—	d	
	f_1 :—	s_1	
	d :r	m	
	f_1 :—	d_1	
A - men.

53

BUNESSAN. (5 5. 5 3. D.)

Doh = C. *Unison.* *In moderate time.* Gaelic Melody.

| d :m :s | d' :— :— | r' :— :— | t :l :s | l :— :— | s :— :— ||
1. Child in the man - ger, In - fant of Ma - ry;

| d :r :m | s :— :— | l :— :— | s :m :d | r :— :— | — :— :— ||
Out-cast and stran - ger, Lord of all!

| s :m :s | d' :— :— | l :— :— | s :m :d | d :— :— | r :— :— ||
Child who in - her - its All our trans-gres - sions,

| m :r :m | s :— :— | l :— :— | r :m :r | d :— :— | — :— :— || f | m ||
All our de - mer - its On Him fall. A - men.

Leanabh an aigh.

2 Once the most holy
  Child of salvation
Gently and lowly
  Lived below;
Now, as our glorious
  Mighty Redeemer,
See Him victorious
  O'er each foe.

3 Prophets foretold Him,
  Infant of wonder;
Angels behold Him
  On His throne;
Worthy our Saviour
  Of all their praises
Happy for ever
  Are His own.

MARY MACDONALD, 1817–*c.* 1890; *tr.* by LACHLAN MACBEAN, 1853– .

54 STOCKPORT. (10 10. 10 10. 10 10.)

Doh = C. *In moderate time, dignified.* JOHN WAINWRIGHT, 1723–68.

d :— |d :r |m :— |— :f |s :m |f :s |l :— |— :—
d :— |d :t, |d :— |— :t, |d :d |d :d |d :— |— :—
m :— |m :s |s :— |— :s |s :s |s :s |f :— |— :—
d :— |d :s, |d :— |— :r |m :d |r :m |f :— |— :—

s :— |l :t |d' :r' |m' :r' |d' :— |t :— |d' :— |— :—
d :— |d :f |s :f |m :f |m :— |r :— |m :— |— :—
s :— |d' :r' |d' :t |d' :l |s :— |s :— |s :— |— :—
m :— |f :r |m :r |d :f |s :— |s, :— |d :— |— :—

d' :— |m' :s |l :— |— :s |l :t |d' :r' |t :— |— :—
m :— |m :s |f :— |— :d |f :f |s :f |r :— |— :—
s :— |d' :d' |d' :— |— :d' |d' :r' |d' :l |s :— |— :—
d :— |d :m |f :— |— :m |f :r |m :f |s :— |— :—

t :— |d' :t |l :se |l :t |d' :— |t :— |l :— |— :—
m :— |m :se |l :m |d :f |m :— |m :r |d :— |— :—
se :— |l :r' |m' :t |l :l |l :— |se :— |l :— |— :—
m :— |l, :t, |d :m |f :r |m :— |m :— |l, :— |— :—

l :— |s :f |m :— |d :— |f :m |r :d |s :— |— :s
d :— |r :t, |d :— |d :— |t, :d |s, :d |t, :— |— :d
m :— |s :s |s :— |s :— |s :s |s :fe |s :— |— :s
l, :— |t, :s, |d :— |m :— |r :d |t, :l, |s, :— |— :m

l :— |t :— |d' :r' |m' :r' |d' :— |t :— |d' :— |— :— || d' |d'
d :— |f :— |s :s |s :l |s :— |s :— |s :— |— :— || l |s
f :— |f :— |d' :t |d' :f' |m' :— |r' :— |m' :— |— :— || f' |m'
f :— |r :— |m :s |d' :f |s :— |s, :— |d :— |— :— || f |d

A-men.

CHRISTIANS, awake, salute the happy morn,
Whereon the Saviour of the world was born;
Rise to adore the mystery of love,
Which hosts of angels chanted from above;
With them the joyful tidings first begun
Of God Incarnate and the Virgin's Son:

2 Then to the watchful shepherds it was told,
Who heard the angelic herald's voice, 'Behold,
I bring good tidings of a Saviour's birth
To you and all the nations upon earth;
This day hath God fulfilled His promised word,
This day is born a Saviour, Christ the Lord.'

3 He spake; and straightway the celestial choir,
In hymns of joy unknown before, conspire.
The praises of redeeming love they sang,
And heaven's whole orb with hallelujahs rang:
God's highest glory was their anthem still,
Peace upon earth, and mutual goodwill.

4 To Bethlehem straight the enlightened shepherds ran,
To see the wonder God had wrought for man,
And found, with Joseph and the blessèd Maid,
Her Son, the Saviour, in a manger laid;
Amazed, the wondrous story they proclaim,
The first apostles of His infant fame.

5 Like Mary, let us ponder in our mind
God's wondrous love in saving lost mankind;
Trace we the Babe, who has retrieved our loss,
From His poor manger to His bitter Cross;
Treading His steps, assisted by His grace,
Till man's first heavenly state again takes place.

6 Then may we hope, the angelic thrones among,
To sing, redeemed, a glad triumphal song.
He that was born upon this joyful day
Around us all His glory shall display;
Saved by His love, incessant we shall sing
Of angels and of angel men the King.

JOHN BYROM, 1691–1763.

55

ADESTE FIDELES. (Irr.)

Doh = A. *In moderate time.* 18th cent.

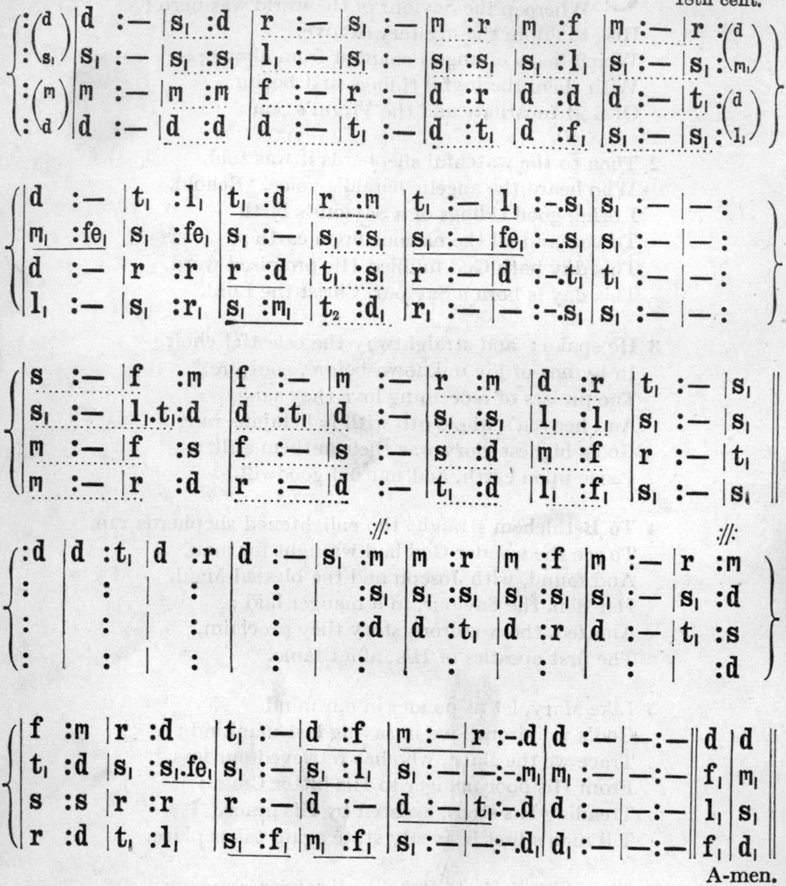

A-men.

Adeste fideles.

FIRST FORM.

O COME, all ye faithful,
Joyful and triumphant,
O come ye, O come ye to Bethlehem;
Come and behold Him
Born the King of angels;
O come, let us adore Him, Christ the Lord.

2 God of God,
Light of Light,
Lo! He abhors not the Virgin's womb;
Very God,
Begotten, not created;
O come, let us adore Him, Christ the Lord.

3 Sing, choirs of angels,
Sing in exultation,
Sing, all ye citizens of heaven above,
'Glory to God
In the highest.'
O come, let us adore Him, Christ the Lord.

4 Yea, Lord, we greet Thee,
Born this happy morning;
Jesus, to Thee be glory given:
Word of the Father,
Now in flesh appearing;
O come, let us adore Him, Christ the Lord.

18th century; *tr.* by Frederick Oakeley, 1802-80.

SECOND FORM.

O COME, all ye faithful,
Joyfully triumphant,
To Bethlehem hasten now with glad accord;
Lo! in a manger
Lies the King of angels;
O come, let us adore Him, Christ the Lord.

2 Though true God of true God,
Light of Light eternal,
The womb of a virgin He hath not abhorred;
Son of the Father,
Not made, but begotten;
O come, let us adore Him, Christ the Lord.

3 Raise, raise, choirs of angels,
Songs of loudest triumph,
Through heaven's high arches be your praises poured,
'Now to our God be
Glory in the highest.'
O come, let us adore Him, Christ the Lord.

4 Amen! Lord, we bless Thee,
Born for our salvation!
O Jesus, for ever be Thy Name adored:
Word of the Father,
Now in flesh appearing;
O come, let us adore Him, Christ the Lord.

18th century; *tr.* by William Mercer, 1811-73.

56 VOM HIMMEL HOCH. (L.M.)

Attributed to MARTIN LUTHER, 1483–1546.
Doh = C. *Slow and dignified.* Arranged by JOHANN SEBASTIAN BACH, 1685–1750.

```
:d' |t    :l    |t    :s    |l    :t  |d'  ||d'   |d'   :s   |s  :m.f
:s  |s.fe :m    |r    :m.r  |d    :r  |m   ||m.f  |s.f  :m   |r  :d
:m' |r'   :d'   |t    :d'.t |l.s  :f  |s   ||s    |d'   :d'  |t  :ta.l
:d  |s    :-.fe |s.f  :m    |f.m  :r  |d   ||d.r  |m    :m.f |s  :s.f

                   G.t.                                              f.C.
|s    :f    |m  ||m l,      |r    :r     |d.r    :m    |f.m    :r       |d s  ||
|d    :r    |d  ||d f,.s,   |l,   :s,    |s,.t,  :d    |d      :d.t,    |d s  ||
|s    :s    |s  ||s d       |d    :t,    |d.f    :m.r  |d.m    :l.s     |m t  ||
|m.r  :d.t, |d  ||d f,      |fe,  :s,.f, |m,.r,  :d,   |l,.s,  :f,.s,   |d s  ||

:d'   |t    :l    |s     :l.s  |f.m   :r    |d   ||f  |m  ||
:m.r  |r.m  :m.r  |r.d   :d    |d.l,  :t,   |d   ||d  |d  ||
:l    |s    :s.f  |f.m   :l.t  |d'    :s.f  |m   ||l  |s  ||
:s.fe |s.m  :d.r  |t,.d  :f.s  |l.f   :s.s, |d   ||f, |d  ||
                                                    A-men.
```

Vom Himmel hoch da komm ich her.

'FROM heaven above to earth I come,
To bear good news to every home;
Glad tidings of great joy I bring,
Whereof I now will say and sing,—

2 '"To you this night is born a Child
Of Mary, chosen mother mild";
This little Child, of lowly birth,
Shall be the joy of all your earth.

3 ''Tis Christ our God, who far on high
Hath heard your sad and bitter cry;
Himself will your salvation be;
Himself from sin will make you free.'

4 Welcome to earth, Thou noble Guest,
Through whom even wicked men are blest!
Thou com'st to share our misery;
What can we render, Lord, to Thee?

5 Were earth a thousand times as fair,
Beset with gold and jewels rare,
She yet were far too poor to be
A narrow cradle, Lord, for Thee.

6 Ah! dearest Jesus, Holy Child,
Make Thee a bed, soft, undefiled,
Within my heart, that it may be
A quiet chamber kept for Thee.

7 My heart for very joy doth leap;
My lips no more can silence keep;
I too must raise with joyful tongue
That sweetest ancient cradle song,—

Unison.

8 'Glory to God in highest heaven,
Who unto man His Son hath given!'
While angels sing with pious mirth
A glad New Year to all the earth.

MARTIN LUTHER, 1483–1546; *tr.* by CATHERINE WINKWORTH, 1829–78.

57

TIVERTON. (C.M.) — Grigg, in *John Rippon's Selection of Psalm and Hymn Tunes*, c. 1795.

Doh = B♭. *In moderate time.*

```
:s, |d  :r  |m  :d.t, |l, :t, |d  :m  |r   :s,.d  |t, :l,  |s, :— |— ||
:m, |s, :s, |s, :s,   |f, :f, |s, :s, |s,  :s,.l, |s, :fe, |s, :— |— ||
:d  |d  :t, |d  :d    |d  :r  |s, :d  |r   :m     |r  :r.d |t, :— |— ||
:d, |m, :s, |d  :m,   |f, :r, |m, :d, |t,, :d,    |r, :r,  |s, :— |— ||

:r  |d.t, :l,.s, |d  :r.m    |f   :m  |r  :d     |s, :l,.f  |m  :r     |d  :— |— ||d  |d  ||
:s, |s,   :r,    |s, :s,     |s,  :s, |s, :m,.f, |s, :f,.l, |s, :s,.f, |m, :— |— ||f, |m, ||
:t, |r    :l,.t, |d  :t,.d   |r   :d  |t, :d     |d  :d     |d  :t,    |d  :— |— ||l, |s, ||
:s, |s,   :f,    |m, :r,.d,  |t,, :d, |s, :l,    |m, :f,.r, |s, :s,    |d, :— |— ||f, |d, ||
                                                                                   A-men.
```

From Isaiah ix. 2, 8.

THE race that long in darkness pined
Have seen a glorious light;
The people dwell in day, who dwelt
In death's surrounding night.

2 To hail Thy rise, Thou better Sun!
The gathering nations come,
Joyous, as when the reapers bear
The harvest treasures home.

3 For Thou our burden hast removed,
And quelled the oppressor's sway,
Quick as the slaughtered squadrons fell
In Midian's evil day.

4 To us a Child of hope is born;
To us a Son is given;
Him shall the tribes of earth obey,
Him all the hosts of heaven.

5 His name shall be the Prince of Peace,
For evermore adored,
The Wonderful, the Counsellor,
The great and mighty Lord.

6 His power increasing still shall spread,
His reign no end shall know;
Justice shall guard His throne above,
And peace abound below.

John Morison, 1750–98, as in *Scottish Paraphrases*, 1781.

58

IN DULCI JUBILO. (Irr.)

Doh = F. *Moderately quick.* Early German Melody.

```
:d  |d  :— :d  |m  :—  :f  |s  :— :l |s  :—  ||s
:s, |l, :— :s, |d  :t, :l, |s, :— :d |t, :—  ||d
:m  |f  :— :m  |s  :—  :f  |m  :— :f |r  :—  ||m
:d  |d  :— :d  |d  :—  :d  |d  :— :— |—  :—  ||d

d  :— :d  |m :—  :f  |s :— :l  |s  :— : |s  :— :l  |s  :— :f
l, :— :s, |d :t, :l, |d :— :—  |t, :— : |d  :— :d  |t, :— :t,
f  :— :m  |s :—  :f  |m :— :f  |r  :— : |s  :— :f  |r  :— :s
d  :— :d  |d :—  :d  |d :— :f, |s, :— : |m, :— :f, |s, :— :s,

m :— :t, |d :— :— ||d :— :— |d  :— :— ||r  :— :r  |m  :— :r
d :— :t, |d :— :— ||d :— :— |d  :— :— ||l, :— :r  |d  :— :t,
s :— :f  |m :— :— ||d :— :— |m  :— :— ||f  :— :l  |s  :— :f
d :— :s, |d :— :— ||d :— :— |l, :— :— ||r, :— :f, |s, :— :s,

d :— :r |m :— : ||s :— :l |s :— :f  |m :— :r  |d  :— ||
d :— :d |d :— : ||d :— :d |d :— :t, |d :— :t, |l, :— ||
m :— :f |s :— : ||s :— :f |s :— :s  |s :— :f  |m  :— ||
d :— :d |d :— : ||m :— :f |m :— :r  |d :— :s, |l, :— ||

:d  |r  :— :r  |m  :— :r  |d :— :r |m :— : ||l, :— :l, |t, :— :t,
:d  |d  :— :d  |d  :— :t, |d :— :d |d :— : ||l, :— :f, |s, :— :s,
:s  |l  :— :l  |s  :— :f  |m :— :f |s :— : ||f  :— :d  |r  :— :r
:m, |f, :— :f, |s, :— :s, |d :— :d |d :— : ||f, :— :f, |f, :— :f,

                              ://:
d  :— :— |s :— :—  ||m :— :m  |r  :— :r  |d :— :— |— :— ||f  |m ||
s, :— :— |d :— :t, ||d :— :d  |d  :— :t, |d :— :— |— :— ||d  |d ||
d  :— :— |m :— :f  ||s :— :l  |l  :— :s  |m :— :— |— :— ||l  |s ||
m, :— :— |m :— :r  ||d :— :l, |f, :— :s, |d :— :— |— :— ||f, |d ||
                                                          A-men.
```

GOOD Christian men, rejoice
With heart and soul and voice!
Give ye heed to what we say:
News! News!
Jesus Christ is born to-day.
Ox and ass before Him bow,
And He is in the manger now:
Christ is born to-day.

2 Good Christian men, rejoice
With heart and soul and voice!
Now ye hear of endless bliss:
Joy! Joy!
Jesus Christ was born for this.
He hath oped the heavenly door,
And man is blessed for evermore.
Christ was born for this.

3 Good Christian men, rejoice
With heart and soul and voice!
Now ye need not fear the grave:
Peace! Peace!
Jesus Christ was born to save;
Calls you one, and calls you all,
To gain His everlasting hall.
Christ was born to save.

JOHN MASON NEALE, 1818–66.

59 NEWTON FERNS. (8 7. 8 7.)

Doh = E♭. *In moderate time.* SAMUEL SMITH, 1821–1917.

s :m	l :f	r :s	m :d	d' :t	l :s	f :r	t_1 :—
d :d	d :d	d :t_1	d :s_1	d :d	d :de	r :l_1	s_1 :—
m :s	f :l	s :s	s :m	m :s	f :s	l :f	r :—
d :d	f_1 :f_1	s_1 :s_1	d :d	d :m	f :m	r :f_1	s_1 :—

m :d	l_1 :l_1	f :r	t_1 :t_1	s :s	f :l_1	d :t_1	d :—	f	m
s_1 :s_1	s_1 :f_1	l_1 :l_1	l_1 :s_1	s_1 :ta_1	l_1 :l_1	s_1 :s_1	s_1 :—	d	d
d :d	d :d	r :r	r :r	d :d	d :f	m :r	m :—	l	s
d :m_1	f_1 :f_1.m_1	r_1 :f_1	s_1 :s_1.f_1	m_1 :m_1	f_1 :f_1	s_1 :s_1	d :—	f_1	d

A-men.

[*By permission of Novello & Co., Ltd.*]

GOD and Father, we adore Thee
For the Son, Thine image bright,
In whom all Thy holy nature
Dawned on our once hopeless night.

2 Far from Thee our footsteps wandered,
On dark paths of sin and shame;
But our midnight turned to morning,
When the Lord of Glory came.

3 Word Incarnate, God revealing,
Longed-for while dim ages ran,
Love Divine, we bow before Thee,
Son of God and Son of Man.

4 Let our life be new created,
Ever-living Lord, in Thee,
Till we wake with Thy pure likeness,
When Thy face in heaven we see;

5 Where the saints of all the ages,
Where our fathers glorified,
Clouds and darkness far beneath them,
In unending day abide.

6 God and Father, now we bless Thee
For the Son, Thine image bright,
In whom all Thy holy nature
Dawns on our adoring sight.

Verse 1 attributed to JOHN NELSON DARBY, 1800–82;
verses 2–5 and adaptation of verse 6, HUGH FALCONER, 1859–

60 CORDE NATUS. (87. 87. 877.)

Doh = E. *Unison.* *Moderately fast.* *Piae Cantiones*, 1582.

| d :—:r | m :—:f | m :—:r | m :—:r | d :—:— || m :—:f | s :—:l |

| s :m :f | s :—:— || l :—:t | d' :—:s | s :—:f | m :—:r | d :—:— ||

| l_1 :—:t_1 | d :—:r | d :l_1 :t_1 | d :—:— || d :—:r | m :—:f | m :—:r |

| s :—:l | s :m :f | s :—:— || d :—:t_1 | l_1 :—:t_1 | d :—:l_1 | s_1 :—:— ||

| d :— :r | m :— :s | m :— :d | r :— :— | d :— :— || r d | t_1 d | s m | s_1 d ||

A-men.

Corde natus ex Parentis.

OF the Father's love begotten
  Ere the worlds began to be,
He is Alpha and Omega,
  He the source, the ending He,
Of the things that are, that have been,
  And that future years shall see,
    Evermore and evermore.

2 O that birth for ever blessèd,
  When the Virgin, full of grace,
By the Holy Ghost conceiving,
  Bare the Saviour of our race,
And the Babe, the world's Redeemer,
  First revealed His sacred face,
    Evermore and evermore!

3 This is He whom seers in old time
  Chanted of with one accord,
Whom the voices of the prophets
  Promised in their faithful word;
Now He shines, the Long-expected;
  Let creation praise its Lord,
    Evermore and evermore.

4 O ye heights of heaven, adore Him;
  Angel hosts, His praises sing;
All dominions, bow before Him,
  And extol our God and King;
Let no tongue on earth be silent,
  Every voice in concert ring,
    Evermore and evermore.

5 Christ, to Thee, with God the Father,
  And, O Holy Ghost, to Thee,
Hymn, and chant, and high thanksgiving,
  And unwearied praises be,
Honour, glory, and dominion,
  And eternal victory,
        Evermore and evermore.

AURELIUS CLEMENS PRUDENTIUS, 348–413; *tr.* by JOHN MASON NEALE, 1818–66.

61 CARILLON. (6 6 10. 6 6 10. 8 12.)

Doh = C. *Unison.* *With dignity.* WILLIAM BAIRD ROSS, 1871–

| d' :— | t :s | l :m | s :— | — :d' | t :s | l :m | G.t. sd :— | — :t, |

1. Ring out, ye crys-tal spheres! Once bless our hu - man ears, If
2. For, if such ho - ly song En - wrap our fan-cy long, Time
3. Yea, Truth and Jus - tice then Will down re - turn to men, Orbed

| l, :t, | d :r | m :r.m | f :—.m | s :— | s :s | f :r | m :d |

ye have power to touch our sen - ses so: And let your sil - ver
will run back, and fetch the Age of Gold, And speck-led Van - i -
in a rain-bow; and, like glo - ries wear - ing, Mer-cy will sit be-

| r :— | — :r | d :l, | t, :se, | l, :— | — :l, | se, :l, | t, :d |

chime Move in me - lo - dious time: And let the bass of
-ty Will sick-en soon and die, And lep - rous Sin will
-tween, Throned in ce - les-tial sheen, With ra - diant feet the

| r :m | f.m :r | d :— | d f.C. :ds | m :r | d :m | l :s | f :m.r |

heaven's deep or - gan blow: And with your nine-fold har - mo - ny Make
melt from earth-ly mould; And Hell it - self will pass a - way, And
tis-sued clouds down steer - ing: And Heaven, as at some fes - ti - val, Will

| s :f | m :s | d' :t | l :t.d' | r' :— | — :r' | d' :— || d' f l f | d' m s d ||

up full con - sort to the an - gel - ic sym - pho - ny.
leave her dolo - rous man-sions to the peer - ing day.
o - pen wide the gates of her high pa - lace-hall.

A-men.

JOHN MILTON, 1608–74.

[*Copyright*, 1925, *by W. B. Ross.*]

62

PSALM 136 (LOUEZ DIEU). (77. 77.)

Doh = G. *In moderate time.* *French Psalter*, 1562.

s, :s,	d .r :m .f	s :—	m :s	f .m :d :r	d :—	
m, :m,	m,.s, :s,.d	d :t,	s, :d	l,.s, :m, :s,	m, :—	
d :t,	l,.t, :d .d	r :—	d :m	r .t, :l, .d :-.t,	d :—	
d, :m,	l,.s, :d .l,	s, :—	d :d,	r,.m, :l, :s,	d, :—	

m :r	d .d :f .f	m :—	d :r	t,.d :l,.l,	s, :—		s,	s,	
d :t,	t,.l, :r .d	t, :—	l, :l,	s,.s, :s,.f,	r, :—		m,	r,	
s :s	m .m :l .l	se :—	m :f	r .d :d .r	t, :—		d	t,	
d :s,	l,.l, :r,.r,	m, :—	l, :f,	s,.m, :f,.r,	s, :—		d,	s,	

A-men.

NOMEN DOMINI. (77. 77.)

Doh = G. *In moderate time.* *Horn's Gesangbuch*, 1544.

d :r	d :s,	l, :t,	d :—	m :s	s :m	r :fe	s :—	
s, :s,	s, :d,	l, :s,	s, :—	d :m	r :d	t, :r.d	t, :—	
m :r	m :d	f.m :r	m :—	s :d	r :s	s :l	s :—	
d :t,	d :m,	f, :s,	d :—	d :d	t, :d	r :r	s, :—	

s :l	s :r	m :s	r :—	m :s	f :r	d :t,	d :—		d	d	
d :l,.t,	d :r	d :s,.l,	t, :—	d :d	d :l,	s, :s,	s, :—		l,	s,	
s :f	s :s.f	m :d	s :—	s :m	f :f	m :r	m :—		f	m	
m :f	m :t,	d :m,	s, :—	d :ta,	l, :f,	s, :s,	d :—		f,	d,	

A-men.

'JESUS!' Name of wondrous love;
Name all other names above,
Unto which must every knee
Bow in deep humility.

2 'Jesus!' Name of priceless worth
To the fallen sons of earth,
For the promise that it gave,—
'Jesus shall His people save.'

3 'Jesus!' Name of mercy mild,
Given to the Holy Child
When the cup of human woe
First He tasted here below.

4 'Jesus!' only Name that's given
Under all the mighty heaven
Whereby man, to sin enslaved,
Bursts his fetters, and is saved.

5 'Jesus!' Name of wondrous love;
Human Name of God above;
Pleading only this, we flee,
Helpless, O our God, to Thee.

WILLIAM WALSHAM HOW, 1823–97.

63 DIX. (77. 77. 77.)

CONRAD KOCHER, 1786–1872.

Doh = G. *In moderate time.* *D.C.*

d :t,.d	r :d	f :f	m :—	l, :t,	d :l,	s, :s,	s, :—	
s, :s,	s, :s,	f, :s,	s, :—	l, :s,	s, :f,	m, :r,	m, :—	
m :f.m	r :m	d :r	d :—	d :r	d :d	d :t,	d :—	
d :r.d	t, :d	l, :t,	d :—	f, :f,	m, :f,	s, :s,	d, :—	

m :r	d :m	s :-.f	m :—	l, :t,	d :f	m :r	d :—		d	d	
s, :s,	s, :s,	s, :s,	s, :—	l, :s,	s, :f,	s, :-.f,	m, :—		f,	m,	
d :s.f	m :d	r :t,	d :—	d :r	d :d	d :t,	d :—		l,	s,	
d :t,	d :d	t, :s,	d :—	f, :f,	m, :l,	s, :s,	d, :—		f,	d,	

A-men.

As with gladness men of old
Did the guiding star behold,
As with joy they hailed its light,
Leading onward, beaming bright,—
So, most gracious Lord, may we
Evermore be led to Thee.

2 As with joyful steps they sped,
Saviour, to Thy lowly bed,
There to bend the knee before
Thee, whom heaven and earth adore,—
So may we with willing feet
Ever seek Thy mercy-seat.

3 As they offered gifts most rare
At Thy cradle rude and bare,—
So may we with holy joy,
Pure, and free from sin's alloy,
All our costliest treasures bring,
Christ, to Thee, our heavenly King.

4 Holy Jesus, every day
Keep us in the narrow way ;
And, when earthly things are past,
Bring our ransomed souls at last
Where they need no star to guide,
Where no clouds Thy glory hide.

5 In the heavenly country bright
Need they no created light ;
Thou its light, its joy, its crown,
Thou its sun which goes not down ;
There for ever may we sing
Hallelujahs to our King.

WILLIAM CHATTERTON DIX, 1837–98.

64 SPRINGFIELD. (11 10. 11 10. Dactylic.)

Doh = E. *In moderate time.* HENRY JOHN GAUNTLETT, 1805–76.

```
s  :f  :m  |m  :r  :d  |r  :m  :f  |f  :—  :m  |r  :f  :m
d  :t, :d  |d  :t, :d  |d  :d  :t, |r  :—  :d  |t, :r  :d
s  :s  :s  |s  :s  :s  |l  :s  :s  |s  :—  :s  |s  :s  :s
m  :r  :d  |s  :f  :m  |f  :s  :s, |d  :—  :d  |s, :t, :d
```

```
l  :l  :s  |d  :f  :m  |r  :—  :—  ||s  :f  :m  |m  :r  :d  |d' :t  :l
d  :t, :d  |l, :r  :d  |t, :—  :—  ||d  :r  :d  |d  :t, :d  |d  :d  :d
f  :f  :s  |l  :s  :s  |s  :—  :—  ||s  :s  :s  |s  :f  :m  |l  :s  :f
f  :r  :m  |l, :t, :d  |s, :—  :—  ||m  :t, :d  |d  :s, :l, |f, :f, :f,
```

```
l  :—  :s  |f  :m  :r  |s  :s  :d  |d  :r  :t, |d  :—  :—  ||d  |d  ||
d  :—  :d  |d  :d  :t, |d  :d  :l, |s, :s, :s, |s, :—  :—  ||l, |s, ||
f  :—  :m  |f  :s  :s  |s  :s  :f  |m  :f  :r  |m  :—  :—  ||f  |m  ||
d  :—  :d  |l, :s, :f, |m, :m, :f, |s, :s, :s, |d  :—  :—  ||f, |d  ||
                                                              A-men.
```

EPIPHANY. (11 10. 11 10. Dactylic.)

Doh = D. *Cheerfully.* JOSEPH FRANCIS THRUPP, 1827–67.

```
m  :— |r  :d  |s  :— |l  :t  |d' :— |t  :l  |s  :f |m  :— |r  :— |d  :d |f  :—
d  :— |d  :d  |r  :— |r  :r  |d  :— |d  :d  |r  :— |d  :— |t, :— |d  :d |t, :—
s  :— |f  :m  |s  :— |s  :s  |m  :— |m  :m  |s  :— |s  :— |s  :— |s  :s |s  :—
d  :— |d  :d  |t, :— |t, :t, |l, :— |l, :l, |t, :— |d  :— |f  :— |m  :m |r  :—
```

```
m :m |l :— |f :-.m  |r  :— |— :— ||s :— |d' :d' |t  :s  |f :f |m  :— |l  :l  |s :—
d :d |d :— |r :-.l, |t, :— |— :— ||d :— |m  :m  |r  :t, |r :r |d  :— |r  :r  |r :—
s :s |f :— |f :f    |s  :— |— :— ||s :— |s  :s  |r' :—  |t :t |d' :— |d' :d' |t :—
d :d |f :— |r :r    |s, :— |— :— ||m :— |d  :d  |s, :—  |s :s |l  :— |fe :fe |s :—
```

```
t :— |d' :— |d' :d' |d' :— |t  :l  |s  :— |r  :m  |d :— |— :— ||d  |d  ||
r :— |d  :— |d  :d  |r  :— |r  :r  |m  :— |t, :t, |d :— |— :— ||l, |s, ||
s :— |s  :m |f  :s  |l  :— |t  :d' |d' :s |f  :f  |m :— |— :— ||f  |m  ||
s :f |m  :d |r  :m  |f  :— |f, :f, |s, :— |s, :s, |d :— |— :— ||f, |d  ||
                                                                  A-men.
```

LIEBSTER IMMANUEL. (11 10. 11 10. Dactylic.) *Himmels-Lust*, Jena, 1679.
Lah = B. Doh = D. *Slow.* Arranged by JOHANN SEBASTIAN BACH, 1685–1750.

```
d' :d' :d'     | t  :-.l:s   | l :f    :m  | r :—  :d   || s :s :m | l   :-.t:d'
m  :m  :re.m   | fe :re  :m  | d :d.t, :d  | d :t, :s,  || d :d :d | d   :f  :m
l  :l  :l.s    | fe :t   :t  | l :l    :s  | s :-.f:m   || s :s :s | f.s:l   :l
l, :l.s:fe.m   | re :t,  :m  | f :r    :m  | s :s, :d   || m :m :d | f   :r  :l,

d  :r     :-.m    | m  :— :— || m  :m  :f | s  :m :-.m | l :se :l
l, :l,.d  :t,.l,  | t, :— :— || d  :d  :d | r  :d :-.d | m :r  :m
l  :l     :se.l   | se :— :— || l  :l  :l | s  :s :-.s | l :t  :d'
f, :f,    :f      | m  :— :— || l, :l, :r | t, :d :-.d | d :t, :l,

t  :m  :— || d' :t  :l | se :-.m:l | t.d'   :se :-.l | l  :— :— || l | l
m  :m  :— || m  :f  :r | m  :-.m:m | f      :m  :m   | m  :— :— || r | de
se :se :— || l  :se :l | t  :-.t:l | r'.d'  :t  :t   | d' :— :— || f | m
m  :m  :— || l  :r  :f | m  :r  :d | r      :m  :m,  | l, :— :— || r | l,
                                                                  A-men.
```

BRIGHTEST and best of the sons of the morning,
  Dawn on our darkness, and lend us thine aid;
Star of the east, the horizon adorning,
  Guide where our infant Redeemer is laid.

2 Cold on His cradle the dew-drops are shining;
  Low lies His head with the beasts of the stall;
Angels adore Him in slumber reclining,
  Maker and Monarch and Saviour of all.

3 Say, shall we yield Him, in costly devotion,
  Odours of Edom, and offerings divine,
Gems of the mountains and pearls of the ocean,
  Myrrh from the forest or gold from the mine?

4 Vainly we offer each ample oblation,
  Vainly with gifts would His favour secure;
Richer by far is the heart's adoration;
  Dearer to God are the prayers of the poor.

5 Brightest and best of the sons of the morning,
  Dawn on our darkness, and lend us thine aid;
Star of the east, the horizon adorning,
  Guide where our infant Redeemer is laid.

REGINALD HEBER, 1783–1826.

65 LEWES. (87. 87. 87.)

Doh = F. *In moderate time.* JOHN RANDALL, 1715–99.

```
m :-.f |r :s  |d :r  |t, :d  |f :m  |l :s  |f :m.f |m :r  ||
d :-.d |r :t, |d :l, |s, :s, |d :d  |d :d  |d.r :d |d :t, ||
s :-.l |s :f  |m :f  |r :m   |l :s  |f :s  |l :s   |s :—  ||
d :-.d |t, :s, |l, :f, |s, :d |l, :d |f :m |l,.t, :d |s, :— ||

m :-.f |r :s  |d :r  |t, :d  |f :m  |r.fe :s.l  |s :fe  |s :—  ||
d :-.d |r :t, |d :l, |s, :s, |d :d  |s,.d :r.d  |t, :l, |t, :— ||
s :-.l |s :f  |m :f  |r :m   |f :s  |r :r.m     |r :r   |r :—  ||
d :-.d |t, :s, |l, :f, |s, :d |l, :d |t,.l, :t,.d |r :r, |s, :— ||

m :-.f  |r.d :r    |f :-.s   |m.r :m  |s :-.m   |s :f.m |m :r   |d :—  || d  |d  ||
d :-.d  |t,.l, :t, |l, :-.r  |d.t, :d |d :-.d   |r :d   |d :t,  |d :—  || l, |s, ||
d :-.l  |s :s      |l :-.s   |s :s    |s :-.m   |s :s   |s :f   |m :—  || f  |m  ||
d :-.f, |s, :s,    |r :-.t,  |d :d    |m :-.l,  |t, :d  |s, :s, |d, :— || f, |d, ||
```

A-men.

LLANDINAM. (87. 87. 87.)

Doh = A♭. *In moderate time.* THOMAS WILLIAMS, 1807–94.

```
m :s :t,    |d :m :s,   |l, :d :t,   |r :d :    |m :— :r   |f :— :m
s, :— :f,   |m, :— :d,  |f, :s, :s,  |s, :s, :  |s, :— :s, |f, :s, :s,
d :— :r     |d :— :d    |d :— :r     |f :m :    |d :— :r   |d :r :m
d, :m, :s,  |l, :— :m,  |f, :m, :s,  |d, :d, :  |d :— :t,  |l, :t, :d

r :t, :d.r      |d :t, : |m :s :t,        |d :-.r :m    |r.m :f :m        |m :r :
l, :s, :s,.l,   |s, :— : |s, :— :s,       |s, :— :s,    |l, :-.s, :s,     |s, :s, :
f :r :d.f       |m :r :  |d :— :r         |d :-.t, :d   |l, :-.t, :d      |d :t, :
f, :— :m,.f,    |s, :— : |d, :m, :s,.f,   |m, :-.r, :d, |f,.m, :r, :d,    |s, :s, :
```

Eb.t. f.Ab.

[m]l:s :t |d':t.l:s.f |m :— :r |[d]s,:— : ||d :m :d |t, :l, :
[s]d:— :f |m :-.f:m.r |d :— :t, |[d]s,:— : ||s, :d :s, |s, :f, :
[d]f:s :s |s :-.f:s.l |s :— :f |[m]t,:— : ||m :s :d |d :d :
[d]f:m :r |d :-.r:m.f |s :— :s, |[d]s,:— : ||d, :— :m, |f, :f, :

://:

r :f :r |d :t, : |d :m :s |s :f :m.r |d :—:t, |d :—: ||d |d
l, :r :l, |s, :s, : |s, :d :ta, |l, :—:l, |s, :—:f, |m, :—: ||f, |m,
f :l :r |m :r : |m :s :d |d :—:s.f |m :—:r |d :—: ||l, |s,
r, :—:f, |s, :s, : |d :—:m, |f, :—:f, |s, :—:s, |d, :—: ||f, |d,

A-men.

ANGELS from the realms of glory,
Wing your flight o'er all the earth ;
Ye who sang creation's story,
Now proclaim Messiah's birth ;
Come and worship,
Worship Christ, the new-born King.

2 Shepherds, in the fields abiding,
Watching o'er your flock by night,
God with man is now residing,
Yonder shines the infant Light ;
Come and worship,
Worship Christ, the new-born King.

3 Sages, leave your contemplations ;
Brighter visions beam afar ;
Seek the great Desire of nations ;
Ye have seen His natal star ;
Come and worship,
Worship Christ, the new-born King.

4 Saints, before the altar bending,
Waiting long in hope and fear,
Suddenly the Lord, descending,
In His temple shall appear ;
Come and worship,
Worship Christ, the new-born King.

JAMES MONTGOMERY, 1771–1854.

[May be sung to WILDERSMOUTH, No. 573.]

66 COLYTON. (65. 65. D.)

Doh = C. *Brightly.* WILLIAM HENRY MONK, 1823–89.

|m.s :l.t |d' :d' |t.l :s.f |m :— ||m.m :f.m |m :l
|d.m :f.f |m :m |s.f :m.r |d :— ||d.m :r.r |d :d.r
|d'.d' :d'.s |s :d' |d'.d' :s.s |s :— ||l.l :l.se |l :l.t
|d.d :f.r |d :d |m.f :t,.t, |d :— ||l,.d :r.m |l :f

|s.f :m.r |m :— ||s.s :d'.t |t :l ||l.l :r'.d' |t :—
|m.r :d.t, |d :— ||s.f :m.s |s :f ||f.s :fe.l |s :—
|d'.l :s.s |s :— ||d'.t :d'.d' |d' :d' ||d'.de' :r'.r' |r' :—
|m.f :s.s, |d :— ||m.r :d.m |f :f ||f.m :r.fe |s :—

t.t :d'.r'	m' :d'	s.s :l.s	d' :—		d'	d'	
s.r :m.f	s :m	m.m :f.f	m :—		f	m	
r'.s :s.s	s :d'	d'.d' :t.t	d' :—		l	s	
s.f :m.r	d :d.m	s.s :s.s	d :—		f	d	

A-men.

FROM the eastern mountains,
Pressing on, they come,
Wise men in their wisdom,
To His humble home,
Stirred by deep devotion,
Hasting from afar,
Ever journeying onward,
Guided by a star.

2 There their Lord and Saviour
Meek and lowly lay,
Wondrous Light that led them
Onward on their way,
Ever now to lighten
Nations from afar,
As they journey homeward
By that guiding Star.

3 Thou who in a manger
Once hast lowly lain,
Who dost now in glory
O'er all kingdoms reign,
Gather in the heathen,
Who in lands afar
Ne'er have seen the brightness
Of Thy guiding star.

4 Gather in the outcasts,
All who've gone astray,
Throw Thy radiance o'er them,
Guide them on their way;
Those who never knew Thee,
Those who've wandered far,
Guide them by the brightness
Of Thy guiding star.

5 Onward through the darkness
Of the lonely night,
Shining still before them
With Thy kindly light,
Guide them, Jew and Gentile,
Homeward from afar,
Young and old together,
By Thy guiding star.

GODFREY THRING, 1823–1903.

Also the following:

67-93 *Hymns on our Lord's Life and Example* | **657** Away in a manger, no crib for a bed

67 MARGARET. (Irr.)

Doh = D. *In moderate time.* TIMOTHY RICHARD MATTHEWS, 1826–1910.

:d.r |m :m.m |f :m.r |d :r.r |m :m.fe |s :s.s |m :d.d |r :— |— ||
:d.d |d :d.d |l_1 :t_1.t_1 |d :l_1.l_1 |t_1 :d.d |t_1 :r.r |d :d.d |t_1 :— |— ||
:m.f |s :l.l |f :s.f |m :l.l |se :l.l |r :s.s |s :s.s |s :— |— ||
:d.d |d :l_1.l_1 |r :s_1.s_1 |l_1 :f_1.f_1 |m_1 :l_1.l_1 |s_1 :t_1.t_1 |d :m.m |s :— |— ||

A.t. f.D.

:$^{r}s_1$.s_1 |l_1 :l_1.l_1 |t_1 :t_1 .t_1 |d :d .d |r :r .r |m :d .d |r :-.m |^{d}s :— |— ||
:$^{t}m_1$.m_1 |f_1 :l_1.l_1 |l_1 :se_1.se_1 |m_1 :f_1 .f_1 |f_1 :f_1.f_1 |m_1 :s_1.s_1 |s_1 :f_1 |$^{m}t_1$:— |— ||
:^{s}d .d |d :d .d |r :r .r |d :d .d |d :t_1.t_1 |d :d .d |d :t_1 |^{d}s :— |— ||
:$^{s}d_1$.d_1 |f_1 :f_1.f_1 |m_1 :m_1 .m_1 |l_1 :la_1.la_1 |s_1 :s_1.s_1 |d_1 :m_1.m_1 |s_1 :s_1 |$^{d}s_1$:— |— ||

:s |s :m.f |s :d^1 |d^1 :— |t :l.l |s :d.r |m :r |d :— |— || f |m ||
:t_1 |d :d.d |d :m |f :— |f :r.r |m :d.d |d :t_1 |d :— |— || d |d ||
:f |m :s.s |s :s |r^1 :— |r^1 :t.t |d^1 :fe.fe |s :-.f |m :— |— || l |s ||
:s_1 |d :d.r |m :d |r :— |r :f.f |m :l_1.l_1 |s_1 :s_1 |d :— |— || f_1 |d ||

A-men.

[*By permission of Novello & Co., Ltd.*]

THOU didst leave Thy throne
And Thy kingly crown
When Thou camest to earth for me,
But in Bethlehem's home
Was there found no room
For Thy holy nativity:
O come to my heart, Lord Jesus;
There is room in my heart for Thee.

2 Heaven's arches rang
When the angels sang,
Proclaiming Thy royal degree;
But of lowly birth
Cam'st Thou, Lord, on earth,
And in great humility:
O come to my heart, Lord Jesus;
There is room in my heart for Thee.

3 The foxes found rest,
And the bird its nest,
In the shade of the forest tree;
But Thy couch was the sod,
O Thou Son of God,
In the deserts of Galilee:
O come to my heart, Lord Jesus;
There is room in my heart for Thee.

4 Thou camest, O Lord,
With the living word
That should set Thy people free;
But, with mocking scorn,
And with crown of thorn,
They bore Thee to Calvary:
O come to my heart, Lord Jesus;
Thy Cross is my only plea.

5 When heaven's arches ring,
And her choirs shall sing,
At Thy coming to victory,
Let Thy voice call me home,
Saying, 'Yet there is room,
There is room at My side for thee!'
And my heart shall rejoice, Lord Jesus,
When Thou comest and callest for me.

EMILY ELIZABETH STEELE ELLIOTT, 1836–97.

68 NADOLIG. (Irr.)

FIRST TUNE.

Lah = D. Doh = F. *In moderate time.* JOHN MORGAN LLOYD, 1880–

{| : | :l, ||d :m.,m | l :s.f | m :-.r | d :r.,r | m :l, | — :s, }

1. There came a lit - tle Child to earth Long a-
2. Far a - way in a good - ly land, Fair and
3. sing how the Lord of that world so fair A child was
4. put on His king-ly ap-par - el now, In that good - ly

{| l, :— | — :l,.,l, | d :m.,m | l :s.f | m :-.r | d :m | s :-.s | s :fe }

go; And the an - gels of God pro-claimed His birth, High and
bright, Chil-dren with crowns of glo - ry stand, Robed in
born, And, that they might a crown of glo - ry wear, Wore a crown of
land; And He leads, to where fountains of wa - ter flow, That cho - sen

{| m :— | — :m.,m | f :l,.,l, | se, :t,.,t, | m :-.r | d :m.,m }

low. Out on the night, so calm and still, Their
white, In white more pure than the spot - less snow; And their
thorn, And in mor - tal weak - ness, in want and pain, Came
band; And for ev - er - more, in their robes most fair And

{| s :— | f :— | m :— | — :m.,m | l :s.f | m :m.,m }

song was heard; For they knew that the Child on
tongues u - nite In the psalm which the an - gels
forth to die, That the chil - dren of earth might for
un - de - filed, Those ran - somed chil - dren His

D.S.

{| l :s.f | m :d.r | m :l, | — :s, | l, :— | — :— | : | :l,.,l, ||

Beth-lehem's hill Was Christ the Lord.
sang long a - go On that still night.
ev - er reign With Him on high. 3. They
praise de - clare Who was once a 4. He has

v. 4.

{| l, :— | — :— || d :r | m.r :d | t, :— | — :— | l, :— | — :— ||

child. A - - men, A - - men.

[*Copyright*, 1927, *by Oxford University Press.*]

EMILY ELIZABETH STEELE ELLIOTT, 1836–97.

68 CHILDREN'S SONG. (Irr.)

SECOND TUNE.

Doh = D. *In moderate time.* HERBERT FRANCIS RAINE WALTON, 1869–

:d.d | m :m :m | m :r :d | f :— :f | m :— :m.m
:d.d | d :d :d | d :d :d | d :— :d | d :— :d.d

1. There came a lit - tle Child to earth
2. Far a - way in a good - ly land,
3. They sing how the Lord of that world so fair A
4. He has put on His king - ly ap - par - el now, In that

:m.m | s :s :s | s :f :m | l :— :l | s :— :s.s
:d.d | d :d :d | d :d :d | d :— :d | d :— :d.d

d :— :— | r :— :— | d :— :— | — :— :m.m | s :s :s | s :f :m
d :— :— | t_1 :— :— | d :— :— | — :— :d.d | d :d :d | d :t_1 :d
Long a - go; And the angels of God pro-
Fair and bright, Children with crowns of
child was born, And, that they might a crown of
good - ly land; And He leads to where foun-tains of
m :— :— | f :— :— | m :— :— | — :— :s.s | s :s :s | s :s :s
s_1 :— :— | s_1 :— :— | d :— :— | — :— :d.d | m :m :m | m :r :d

l :— :l | s :— :s.s | s :— :— | l :— :— | s :— :— | — :— :s.s
d :— :d | d :— :d.d | t_1 :— :— | d :— :— | t_1 :— :— | — :— :r.r
claimed His birth, High and low.
glo - ry stand, Robed in white, In
glo - ry wear, Wore a crown of thorn, And in
wa - ter flow, That cho - sen band; And for
f :— :f | s :— :s.s | s :— :— | fe :— :— | s :— :— | — :— :t.t
f :— :f | m :— :m.m | r :— :— | r :— :— | s_1 :— :— | — :— :s.s

s :l :t | d' :d' :d' | t :— :l | s :— :f.f | m :— :— | f :— :—
r :r :r | d :d :d | r :— :r | r :— :t_1.t_1 | d :— :— | d :— :—
Out on the night, so calm and still, Their song was
white more pure than the spot - less snow; And their tongues u - -
mor - tal weakness, in want and pain, Came forth to
ev - er - more, in their robes most fair And un - de -
t :t :s | s :s :s | s :— :fe | s :— :s.s | s :— :— | l :— :—
f :f :f | m :m :m | r :— :d | t_1 :— :r.r | d :— :— | f_1 :— :—

r :— :— | — :d :r | m :r :m | s :s :s | d' :t :l | s :f :m .m
t_1 :— :— | — :d :t_1 | d :d :d | d :d :d | d :— :d | r :— :d .d
heard; For they knew that the Child on Beth-lehem's hill Was
nite In the psalm which the an-gels sang long a - go On
die, That the chil-dren of earth might for ev - er reign With
filed, Those ran - somed children His praise de - clare Who was
s :— :— | — :s :s | s :s :s | s :s :s | l :— :m | r :— :s .s
s_1 :— :— | f :m :r | d :d :d | m :m :m | l_1 :— :l_1 | t_1 :— :d .d

f :— :— | r :— :— | d :— :— | — :— :— | d | d
d :— :— | t_1 :— :— | d :— :— | — :— :— | l_1 | s_1
Christ the Lord.
that still night.
Him on high.
once a child. A- men.
l :— :— | s :— :f | m :— :— | — :— :— | f | m
f_1 :— :— | s_1 :— :— | d :— :— | — :— :— | f_1 | d

[May be sung to TROYTE'S CHANT, No. 14.] EMILY ELIZABETH STEELE ELLIOTT, 1836–97.

69 IRBY. (87. 87. 77.)

Doh = G. *In moderate time.* HENRY JOHN GAUNTLETT, 1805–76.

| s, :t, | d :- .d | d .t, :d .r | r :d | d :m
| s, :f, | s, :- .s, | s, :s, .t, | t, :d | s, :d
| m :r | d :- .m | m .r :m .f | f :m | m :d
| d, :r, | m, :- .d, | s, :s, | s, :d | d :l,

| s :-.m | m .r :d .t, | d :— || s, :t, | d :- .d | d .t, :d .r
| d :-.d | l, :s, | s, :— || s, :f, | s, :- .s, | fe, :fe,
| d :-.s | s .f :m .r | m :— || m :r | d :- .m | d :d
| m, :-.d, | f, :s, | d, :— || d, :r, | m, :- .d, | l, :r,

| r :d | d :m | s :-.m | m .r :d .t, | d :— || l :l
| s,.f, :m, | s, :d | d :-.d | l, :s, | s, :— || l, :d
| t, :d | m :d | d :-.s | s .f :m .r | m :— || f :f
| s, :d | d :l, | m, :-.d, | f, :s, | d, :— || f, .s, :l, .t,

s :-.d	f :f	m :—	l :l	s : .m	m .r :d .t,	d :—		d	d	
d .t, :d.d	d :t,	d :—	l,.t, :d .r	s,.t, :d .s,	l, :s,	s, :—		l,	s,	
m .f :s.m	r :s	s :—	f :f	f .r :m .s	s .f :m .r	m :—		f	m	
d .r :m.d	s, :s,	d :—	f,.s, :l,.t,	d :-.d	f, :s,	d, :—		f,	d,	

A-men.

ONCE in royal David's city
Stood a lowly cattle-shed,
Where a mother laid her Baby
In a manger for His bed.
Mary was that mother mild,
Jesus Christ her little Child.

2 He came down to earth from heaven
Who is God and Lord of all,
And His shelter was a stable,
And His cradle was a stall.
With the poor and mean and lowly
Lived on earth our Saviour holy.

3 And through all His wondrous childhood
He would honour and obey,
Love, and watch the lowly maiden
In whose gentle arms He lay.
Christian children all must be
Mild, obedient, good as He.

4 For He is our childhood's pattern:
Day by day like us He grew;
He was little, weak, and helpless;
Tears and smiles like us He knew:
And He feeleth for our sadness,
And He shareth in our gladness.

5 And our eyes at last shall see Him,
Through His own redeeming love;
For that Child so dear and gentle
Is our Lord in heaven above;
And He leads His children on
To the place where He is gone.

6 Not in that poor lowly stable,
With the oxen standing by,
We shall see Him, but in heaven,
Set at God's right hand on high,
When, like stars, His children crowned
All in white shall wait around.

CECIL FRANCES ALEXANDER, 1823–95.

70 GOSTERWOOD. (7 6. 7 6. D.)

Doh = G. *In moderate time.* English Traditional Melody.

:d |d :-.l, |t, :d |r :m |d :s |f :m |r.d:r |d :— |—
:m, |s, :-.f, |f, :s, |l, :s, |d :t, |l, :s, |f, :f, |m, :— |—
:d |d :-.d |f :m |r :t, |d :d |d :d |d :t, |d :— |—
:d, |m, :-.f, |r, :m, |f, :s, |l, :m, |f, :s, |l, :s, |d, :— |—

:d |d :-.l, |t, :d |r :m |d :s |f :m |r.d:r |d :— |—
:m, |s, :-.f, |f, :s, |l, :s, |d :t, |l, :s, |f, :f, |m, :— |—
:d |d :-.d |f :m |r :t, |d :d |d :d |d :t, |d :— |—
:d, |m, :-.f, |r, :m, |f, :s, |l, :m, |f, :s, |l, :s, |d, :— |—

:m.f |s :-.f |m :r |m :d |l, :m |f :m |r :r.t, |s, :— |—
:d |d :-.t, |d :t, |s, :— |f, :s, |l, :s, |l, :f, |s, :— |—
:s |s :-.r |m :s |d :— |d :de |r :s |r :r |t, :d |t,
:d.r |m :-.r |d :s, |m, :— |f, :m, |r, :m, |f, :r, |s, :l, |s,

:l,.t, |d :-.l, |t, :d |r :— |m :s |f :m |r.d:r |d :— |— || d |d
:s, |s, :-.s, |s, :s, |d :t, |d :ta, |l, :s, |f, :f, |m, :— |— || f, |m,
:r |d :-.d |r :d |f :— |m :d |d :d |d :t, |d :— |— || l, |s,
:f, |m, :-.m, |f, :m, |r, :— |d, :m, |f, :s, |l, :s, |d, :— |— || f, |d,

A-men.

COME, praise your Lord and Saviour
In strains of holy mirth;
Give thanks to Him, O children,
Who lived a child on earth.
He loved the little children,
And called them to His side;
His loving arms embraced them,
And for their sake He died.

Boys only.

2 O Jesus, we would praise Thee
With songs of holy joy,
For Thou on earth didst sojourn,
A pure and spotless boy.
Make us like Thee, obedient,
Like Thee from sin-stains free,
Like Thee in God's own temple,
In lowly home like Thee.

Girls only.

3 O Jesus, we too praise Thee,
The lowly maiden's Son;
In Thee all gentlest graces
Are gathered into one.
O give that best adornment
That Christian maid can wear,
The meek and quiet spirit
Which shone in Thee so fair.

All.

4 O Lord, with voices blended
We sing our songs of praise;
Be Thou the light and pattern
Of all our childhood's days;
And lead us ever onward,
That, while we stay below,
We may, like Thee, O Jesus,
In grace and wisdom grow.

WILLIAM WALSHAM HOW, 1823–97.

71

ANGELS' STORY. (76. 76. D.)

Doh = G. *In moderate time.* ARTHUR HENRY MANN, 1850-

:m |m :-.m |r :d |d :— |t, :s, |f :-.f |m :r |m :— |— ‖
:s, |s, :-.s, |f, :m,.s, |s, :— |s, :s, |s, :t, |d :s, |s, :— |— ‖
:d |s, :l, |t, :d |m :— |r :t, |t, :r |d :f |m :— |— ‖
:d |d, :d, |d, :d,.m, |s, :— |s, :s, |s, :-.s, |l, :t, |d :— |— ‖

:m |s :-.s |f :m |m :— |f :m |r :-.d |t, :d |r :— |— ‖
:d |de :-.de |r :l, |l, :— |l, :l, |l, :-.fe, |fe, :fe, |f, :— |— ‖
:m |m :-.m |l :m |s :— |f :s |fe :-.m |r :d |d :— |t, ‖
:d |l, :-.l, |t, :de |de :— |r :r |r :-.r, |r, :r, |s, :— |— ‖

:re |m :-.m |r :d |d :— |t, :s, |f :-.f |m :r |m :— |— ‖
:f, |m, :s, |f, :m,.s, |s, :— |s, :s, |s, :t, |d :s, |s, :— |— ‖
:t, |d :s,.l, |t, :d |m :— |r :t, |t, :r |d :f |m :— |— ‖
:s, |d, :d, |d, :d,.m, |s, :— |s, :s, |s, :-.s, |l, :t, |d :— |— ‖

:m |l :-.s |f :m |s :— |f :l, |d :-.t, |l, :t, |d :— |— ‖ d |d ‖
:d |de :-.de |r :l, |l, :— |l, :f, |s, :-.f, |f, :f, |m, :— |— ‖ f, |m, ‖
:m |m :-.m |l :s |m :— |f :r |m :-.r |d :r |d :— |— ‖ l, |s, ‖
:d |l, :-.l, |t, :de |de :— |r :r, |s, :-.s, |s, :s, |d, :— |— ‖ f, |d, ‖

A-men.

I LOVE to hear the story
  Which angel voices tell,
How once the King of Glory
  Came down on earth to dwell.
I am both weak and sinful,
  But this I surely know,
The Lord came down to save me,
  Because He loved me so.

2 I'm glad my blessèd Saviour
  Was once a child like me,
To show how pure and holy
  His little ones might be;
And, if I try to follow
  His footsteps here below,
He never will forsake me,
  Because He loves me so.

3 To sing His love and mercy
  My sweetest songs I'll raise,
And, though I cannot see Him,
  I know He hears my praise;
For He has kindly promised
  That even I may go
To sing among His angels,
  Because He loves me so.

EMILY HUNTINGTON MILLER, 1833–1913.

72 CREDO. (88. 88. 88.)

Lah = C. Doh = E♭. *In moderate time.* JOHN STAINER, 1840–1901.

```
:sm | m  :m  | m  :l  | se :l  | m   :r   | d  :m  | s  :f  | m  :r  | d  ||
:sm | t, :m  | m  :m  | r  :d  | t,  :se, | l, :d  | m  :r  | d  :t, | d  ||
:sm | se :se | l  :l  | t  :m  | m   :m   | m  :l  | l  :l  | s  :f  | m  ||
:sm | m  :r  | d  :d  | t, :l, | se, :m,  | l, :l, | f, :f, | s, :s, | d  ||

:d | f  :-.f  | m  :d  | l  :l | s :d | r  :f | f  :m | d  :r  | m  : ||
:d | d  :-.d  | d  :d  | d  :d | d :d | l, :r | r  :d | l, :t, | t, : ||
:m | f  :-.f  | s  :m  | f  :f | s :s | l  :l | s  :s | l  :l  | se : ||
:d | l, :-.l, | s, :s, | f, :f | m :m | f  :r | t, :d | f  :f  | m  : ||
```

C.t.m.l. *A little slower.*

```
| ms :s.,s | d' :-.d' | t  :l   | s  :s  | d' :-.d' | d' :r' | m' :r'   | d' || d' | d' ||
| ms :s.,s | d' :-.m  | s  :f   | m  :m  | m  :-.m  | f  :fe | s  :s    | s  || f  | m  ||
| ms :s.,s | d' :-.d' | d' :l.t | d' :d' | d' :-.d' | d' :d' | d' :t.f' | m' || l  | s  ||
| ms :s.,s | d' :-.l  | m  :f   | d  :d' | ta :-.ta | l  :la | s  :s    | d  || f  | d  ||
                                                                                A-men.
```

WE saw Thee not when Thou
didst come
To this poor world of sin and
death,
Nor e'er beheld Thy cottage home
In that despisèd Nazareth;
But we believe Thy footsteps trod
Its streets and plains, Thou Son of
God.

2 We did not see Thee lifted high
Amid that wild and savage crew,
Nor heard Thy meek, imploring cry,
'Forgive, they know not what
they do';
Yet we believe the deed was done
Which shook the earth, and veiled
the sun.

3 We stood not by the empty tomb
Where late Thy sacred body lay,
Nor sat within that upper room,
Nor met Thee in the open way;
But we believe that angels said,
'Why seek the living with the dead?'

4 We did not mark the chosen few,
When Thou didst through the
clouds ascend,
First lift to heaven their wondering
view,
Then to the earth all prostrate
bend;
Yet we believe that mortal eyes
Beheld that journey to the skies.

5 And now that Thou dost reign on
high,
And thence Thy waiting people
bless,
No ray of glory from the sky
Doth shine upon our wilderness;
But we believe Thy faithful word,
And trust in our redeeming Lord.

JOHN HAMPDEN GURNEY, 1802–62;
based on ANNE RICHTER, *d.* 1857.

73 HENRYD. (8 7. 8 7. D.)

Lah = E. Doh = G. *Moderately slow.* JOHN AMBROSE LLOYD, 1815–74.

| m :m | m :-.r | d :m | r :t, | l, :d | t, :m
| d :t, | l, :-.se, | l, :l, | l, :se, | m, :l, | se, :l,
| m :m.r | d :-.t, | l, :l, | f :m | d :m | m :m
| l, :se, | l, :-.m, | f, :d, | r, :m, | l, :l, | m, :d,

| r :d | t, :— || m :m | m :-.r | d :m | r :t,
| l, :l, | se, :— || se, :t, | l, :-.t, | l, :l, | l, :se,
| f :m | m :— || t, :m.r | d :-.m | m :m | f :m
| r, :l, | m, :— || m, :se, | l, :-.se, | l, :d | t, :m

| l, :d | t, :m | r.d :t, | l, :— || m :l | s :m
| l, :l, | se, :l, | l, :se, | l, :— || s, :l,.t, | d :d
| m :m | m :m | f :t,.r | d :— || s :f | s :s
| d :l, | m, :d, | r, :m, | l, :— || d :f | m :d

| r :s.f | m :r | d :f | m :d | t, :l, | m :— || m :m | m :-.r
| t, :d | d :t, | l, :l, | se, :m, | m, :l, | se, :— || l, :l, | t, :-.se,
| s :s.l | s :s | m :r.d | t, :l, | t, :d.l, | t, :— || d :m.l | se :-.m
| s, :m,.f, | s, :s, | l, :r, | m, :l, | s, :f, | m, :— || l, :d | m :-.m,

d :m	r :t,	l, :d	t, :m	r.d :t,	l, :—		l,	l,	
l, :l,	l, :se,	l, :l,	se, :l,	l, :se,	l, :—		f,	m,	
m :m	f :m	d :m	m :m	f.m :r.m	d :—		r	de	
l, :d,	r, :m,	f, :m,.r,	m,.r, :d,	r, :m,	l, :—		r,	l,	

A-men.

WHO is this, so weak and helpless,
Child of lowly Hebrew maid,
Rudely in a stable sheltered,
Coldly in a manger laid?
'Tis the Lord of all creation,
Who this wondrous path hath trod;
He is God from everlasting,
And to everlasting God.

2 Who is this, a Man of Sorrows,
Walking sadly life's hard way,
Homeless, weary, sighing, weeping
Over sin and Satan's sway?
'Tis our God, our glorious Saviour,
Who above the starry sky
Now for us a place prepareth,
Where no tear can dim the eye.

3 Who is this? behold Him shedding
Drops of blood upon the ground!
Who is this, despised, rejected,
Mocked, insulted, beaten, bound?
'Tis our God, who gifts and graces
Poureth on His Church below,
Now, in royal might victorious,
Triumphing o'er every foe.

4 Who is this that hangeth dying
While the rude world scoffs and scorns,
Numbered with the malefactors,
Pierced with nails, and crowned with thorns?
'Tis the God who ever liveth
'Mid the shining ones on high,
In the glorious golden city
Reigning everlastingly.

WILLIAM WALSHAM HOW, 1823–97.

74 KINGSFOLD. (D.C.M.)

Lah = E. Doh = G. *In moderate time.*

Arranged from an English Traditional Melody.

:d.t, | l, :l, | l, :s, | d :d | r :d.r | m :m | r.d :l, | s, :— | — ||
:l, | m, :m, | f, :r, | s, :m, | s, :s,.t, | d :d | l, :f, | r, :— | — ||
:m.r | d :d | d :t, | d :d | t, :d.f | m :s | f :d | d :— | t, ||
:l, | l, :l,.s, | f, :f, | m, :l, | s, :m,.r, | d, :d, | r, :f, | s, :— | — ||

:d.t, | l, :l, | l, :s, | d :d | r :d.r | m :m | r.d :l, | l, :— | — ||
:s, | s, :f, | f,.m, :r, | s, :fe, | s, :s,.f, | m, :s, | f, :f, | m, :— | — ||
:d | d :d | d :t, | d :d | t, :d.t, | d :d | l, :l,.t, | d :— | — ||
:m, | f, :f,.m, | r, :s, | m, :l, | s,.f, :m,.r, | d, :m, | f, :r, | l, :— | — ||

:m.f | s :m | m.r :d | r :r | m :— | m :m.r | d :l, | s, :— | — ||
:l, | t, :t, | d.s, :s, | l, :s, | s, :— | d :d.t, | s, :f,.m, | r, :— | — ||
:d | m :s | s.f :m | r.d :t, | d :— | s :s.f | m :d | d :— | t, ||
:l, | m, :m | l,.t, :d | f, :s, | d, :— | d, :d,.r, | m, :f, | s, :— | — ||

:d.t, | l, :l, | l,.s, :l,.t, | d :d | r :d.r | m :m | r.d :l, | l, :— | — || l, | l, ||
:s, | s, :s, | f, :f, | s, :s,.fe, | s, :s,.f, | m, :s, | l, :f, | m, :— | — || f, | m, ||
:d | d :d | r :f | m.r :d | t, :d.t, | d :t, | l, :l,.t, | d :— | — || r | de ||
:m, | f, :f,.m, | r, :r | d.t, :l, | s, :m,.r, | d, :m, | f, :r, | l, :— | — || r, | l, ||

A-men.

In vv. 2, 3, 4, lines 5 and 6 run thus:

:m.f | s :m | m.r :d | r :r | m :d.r | m :m.r | d :l, | s, :— | — ||
:l, | t, :t, | d.s, :s, | l, :s, | s, :s,.t, | d :d.t, | s, :f,.m, | r, :— | — ||
For | now the | flowers of | Naz-ar-eth | In | ev-ery | heart may | grow;
:d | m :s | s.f :m | r.d :t, | d :s.f | m :s.f | m :d | d :— | t, ||
:l, | m, :m | l,.t, :d | f, :s, | d :m,.r, | d, :d,.r, | m, :f, | s, :— | — ||

O SING a song of Bethlehem,
Of shepherds watching there,
And of the news that came to them
From angels in the air:
The light that shone on Bethlehem
Fills all the world to-day;
Of Jesus' birth and peace on earth
The angels sing alway.

2 O sing a song of Nazareth,
Of sunny days of joy;
O sing of fragrant flowers' breath,
And of the sinless Boy:
For now the flowers of Nazareth
In every heart may grow;
Now spreads the fame of His dear Name
On all the winds that blow.

3 O sing a song of Galilee,
Of lake and woods and hill,
Of Him who walked upon the sea,
And bade its waves be still :
For though, like waves on Galilee,
Dark seas of trouble roll,
When faith has heard the Master's word,
Falls peace upon the soul.

4 O sing a song of Calvary,
Its glory and dismay ;
Of Him who hung upon the Tree,
And took our sins away :
For He who died on Calvary
Is risen from the grave,
And Christ, our Lord, by heaven adored,
Is mighty now to save.

LOUIS FITZGERALD BENSON, 1855–

75 SAINTS OF GOD. (88. 88. 88.)

Doh = D. *In moderate time.* ARTHUR SEYMOUR SULLIVAN, 1842–1900.

```
:m |s  :-.s |s  :s  |d' :t  |l  :l  |s  :f  |m :s  |r  :-.r |d  ||
:d |m  :-.m |f  :f  |s  :s  |f  :f  |r  :r  |d :d  |d  :t,  |d  ||
:s |d' :-.d'|t  :t  |d' :d' |d' :d' |s  :s  |s :s  |f.m:f   |m  ||
:d |d  :-.d |r  :r  |m  :m  |f  :l, |t, :t, |d :m, |s, :s,  |d  ||

                                     A.t.                      f.D.
:m |s  :-.s |s  :s  |d' :t  |l  :l  |t m    :-.r   |d :r  |t, :t,  |l m ||
:d |m  :-.m |f  :f  |s  :se |l  :m  |fe t,  :-.t,  |l,:l, |l, :se, |l m ||
:s |d' :-.d'|t  :t  |d' :r' |d' :d' |t m    :-.m   |m :f  |t, :r   |d s ||
:d |d  :-.d |r  :r  |m  :m  |l  :l  |re se, :-.se, |l,:r, |m, :m,  |l m ||

:s |s :-.l|s  :d' |s :-.l|s  :d' |l  :f  |m  :l   |s  :t, |d  ||d  |d  ||
:m |r :-.r|s  :s  |f :-.f|m  :s  |f  :d  |d  :d   |t, :s, |s, ||l, |s, ||
:t |t :-.t|d' :d' |t :-.t|d' :d' |d' :f  |s  :r   |r  :f  |m  ||f  |m  ||
:m |f :-.f|m  :m  |s :-.s|d' :m  |f  :l, |s, :fe, |s, :s, |d  ||f, |d  ||
                                                               A-men.
```

[*By permission of Novello & Co., Ltd.*]

YE fair green hills of Galilee,
That girdle quiet Nazareth,
What glorious vision did ye see,
When He who conquered sin and death
Your flowery slopes and summits trod,
And grew in grace with man and God ?

2 'We saw no glory crown His head,
As childhood ripened into youth ;
No angels on His errands sped ;
He wrought no sign ; but meekness, truth,
And duty marked each step He trod,
And love to man, and love to God.'

3 Jesus ! my Saviour, Master, King,
Who didst for me the burden bear,
While saints in heaven Thy glory sing,
Let me on earth Thy likeness wear ;
Mine be the path Thy feet have trod,—
Duty, and love to man and God.

EUSTACE ROGERS CONDER, 1820–92.

76

LOVE UNKNOWN. (66. 66. 88.)

Doh = E♭. *Unison.* *In moderate time.* JOHN IRELAND, 1879–

:m	s .l :m :r	d :– .r	m .f :s .m	l :– .l
t .l :s .s	d' .t :l .s	s .m :– .fe	s :–.	f.A♭. ^{s}r	f .m :d :– .d
m .r :s_1 :– . E♭.t. ^{l}r	m .f :s .m	m :r	d :– .	d d / l_1 s_1 / f m / f_1 d

A-men.

WESLEY. (66. 66. 88.)

Doh = F. *Moderately fast.* Source unknown.

:d	m :r :d	s :f :m	r :–:–	–:–:m	f :s :l	m :– :r
:d	d :– :d	d :t_1 :d	t_1 :–:–	–:–:d	d :– :d	d :– :t_1
:m	s :f :m	s :– :s	s :–:–	–:–:s	f :m :f	m :f :s
:d	d :– :d	m :r :d	s_1 :–:–	–:–:d	l_1 :s_1 :f_1	s_1 :– :s_1

d :–:–	–:–	*D.C.* s	s :f :m	f :– :f	f :m :r	m :– :s
d :–:–	–:–	r	de :r :de	r :– :d	t_1 :d :t_1	d :– :r
m :–:–	–:–	r	m :f :l	l :– :r	r :m :s	s :– :s
d :–:–	–:–	ta_1	l_1 :– :l_1	r :– :r	s_1 :– :s_1	d :– :t_1

d :r :m	l :s :f	m :– :r	d :–	d d
d :– :ta_1	l_1 :d :d	d :– :t_1	d :–	l_1 s_1
m :– :m	f :s :l	s :– :f	m :–	f m
l_1 :– :s_1	f_1 :m_1 :f_1	s_1 :– :s_1	d :–	f_1 d

A-men.

BEHOLD a little Child,
Laid in a manger bed;
The wintry blasts blow wild
Around His infant head.
But who is this, so lowly laid?
'Tis He by whom the worlds were made.

2 Alas! in what poor state
The Son of God is seen
Why doth the Lord so great
Choose out a home so mean?
That we may learn from pride to flee,
And follow His humility.

3 Where Joseph plies his trade,
Lo, Jesus labours too;
The hands that all things made
An earthly craft pursue,
That weary men in Him may rest,
And faithful toil through Him be blest.

4 Among the doctors see
The Boy so full of grace;
Say, wherefore taketh He
The scholar's lowly place?
That Christian boys, with reverence meet,
May sit and learn at Jesus' feet.

5 Christ, once Thyself a boy!
Our boyhood guard and guide;
Be Thou its light and joy,
And still with us abide,
That Thy dear love, so great and free,
May draw us evermore to Thee.

William Walsham How, 1823–97.

77 LOWLINESS. (7 7. and refrain.)

Doh = B♭. *In moderate time.* Benjamin Russell Hanby, 1833–67.

```
:s,.s, |s,  :-.s, :s,.s, |l,  :—  :l,.l, |s,  :-.s, :d .d  |r   :—  ||
:m,.m, |r,  :-.m, :f,.m, |r,  :—  :f,.f, |s,  :-.m, :d,.m, |s,  :—  ||
:d .d  |r   :-.d  :t,.d  |d   :—  :d .t, |d   :-.d  :m .d  |t,  :—  ||
:d,.d, |t,, :-.d, :r,.m, |f,  :—  :r,.r, |m,  :-.d, :l,.l, |s,  :—  ||

:d .r  |m   :-.m  :f .m  |m   :r   :t,.d  |r   :-.r  :m .r  |r   :d  ||
:s,.s, |s,  :-.s, :s,.s, |s,  :s,  :t,.l, |s,  :-.t, :d .t, |t,  :d  ||
:m .r  |d   :-.d  :r .d  |d   :t,  :f .m  |r   :-.s  :s .f  |f   :m  ||
:l,.t, |d   :-.d  :t,.d  |s,  :s,  :s,.l, |t,  :-.s, :d .s, |d,  :d, ||

:d .d  |d   :-.d  :d .s, |l,  :—  :d .r  |m   :-.m  :r .r  |d   :—  ||d  |d  ||
:m,.f, |s,  :-.m, :f,.s, |f,  :—  :m,.f, |s,  :-.s, :f,.f, |m,  :—  ||f, |m, ||
:s,.s, |s,  :-.s, :d .d  |d   :—  :d .d  |d   :-.s, :l,.t, |d   :—  ||l, |s, ||
:d,.r, |m,  :-.d, :r,.m, |f,  :—  :l,.l, |s,  :-.s, :s,.s, |d,  :—  ||f, |d, ||
                                                                      A-men.
```

WHO is He, in yonder stall,
At whose feet the shepherds fall?
'Tis the Lord! O wondrous story!
'Tis the Lord, the King of Glory!
At His feet we humbly fall;
Crown Him, crown Him Lord of all.

2 Who is He, in yonder cot,
Bending to His toilsome lot?

3 Who is He, in deep distress,
Fasting in the wilderness?

4 Who is He that stands and weeps
At the grave where Lazarus sleeps?

5 Lo! at midnight, who is He
Prays in dark Gethsemane?

6 Who is He, in Calvary's throes,
Asks for blessings on His foes?

7 Who is He that from the grave
Comes to heal and help and save?

8 Who is He that on yon throne
Rules the world of light alone?

Benjamin Russell Hanby, 1833–67.

78 SOLEMNIS HAEC FESTIVITAS. (L.M.)

Doh = E♭. *Unison. In moderate time.* Angers Church Melody.

```
{ :d |m :— :f |s :— :s |l :s :f |s :— :s |l :— :t }
{ |d' :— :s |m :— :f |s :— :m |s :— :f |r :— :m |f :m :r }
{ |m :— :s |d :— :r |m :d :f |m :— :r |d :— :— || d  | d  ||
                                                   l, | s, ||
                                                   f  | m  ||
                                                   f, | d  ||
```

Iordanis oras praevia. A-men.

ON Jordan's bank the Baptist's cry
Announces that the Lord is nigh;
Come then and hearken, for he brings
Glad tidings from the King of kings.

2 Then cleansed be every breast from sin;
Make straight the way for God within;
Prepare we in our hearts a home,
Where such a mighty Guest may come.

3 For Thou art our salvation, Lord,
Our refuge, and our great reward;
Without Thy grace we waste away,
Like flowers that wither and decay.

4 Stretch forth Thine hand, to heal our sore,
And make us rise to fall no more;
Once more upon Thy people shine,
And fill the world with love divine.

5 To Him who left the throne of heaven
To save mankind, all praise be given;
Like praise be to the Father done,
And Holy Spirit, Three in One.

CHARLES COFFIN, 1676–1749; *tr.* by JOHN CHANDLER, 1806–76.

79

AUS DER TIEFE (HEINLEIN). (7 7. 7 7.)

Lah = D. Doh = F. *Slow.* C.t. Attributed to MARTIN HERBST, 1654–81.

```
| m   :m   | l,  :t,  | d   :r   | m   :—  | [m]l  :l   | d'  :d'  | t   :t   | l   :—  ||
| l,  :l,  | l,  :se, | l,  :l,  | t,  :—  | [d]f  :f   | m   :m   | f   :m   | de  :—  ||
| d   :d   | m   :r   | d   :l   | se  :—  | [l]r' :r'  | d'  :l   | l   :se  | l   :—  ||
| l,  :l,  | d   :t,  | l,  :f,  | m,  :—  | [l,]r :f   | l   :d   | r   :m   | l,  :—  ||
```

f.F.

```
| [l]m   :m   | f   :f   | r   :r   | m   :—  | m   :m   | r   :d   | t,  :t,  | l,  :—  || l,  | l,  ||
| [r]l,  :de  | r   :l,  | t,  :r   | d   :—  | s,  :d   | t,  :l,  | l,  :se, | l,  :—  || f,  | m,  ||
| [fe]de :m   | l   :l   | s   :s   | s   :—  | m   :s   | s   :m   | m   :t,  | d   :—  || r   | de  ||
| [r]l,  :l,  | f,  :r,  | s,  :t,  | d   :—  | d   :d   | s,  :l,  | m,  :m,  | l,  :—  || r,  | l,  ||
```

A-men.

FORTY days and forty nights
  Thou wast fasting in the wild,
Forty days and forty nights
  Tempted, and yet undefiled,—

2 Sunbeams scorching all the day,
  Chilly dewdrops nightly shed,
Prowling beasts about Thy way,
  Stones Thy pillow, earth Thy bed.

3 Shall we not Thy sorrow share,
  And from earthly joys abstain,
Fasting with unceasing prayer,
  Glad with Thee to suffer pain?

4 And if Satan, vexing sore,
  Flesh or spirit should assail,
Thou, his Vanquisher before,
  Grant we may not faint nor fail.

5 So shall we have peace divine;
  Holier gladness ours shall be;
Round us too shall angels shine,
  Such as ministered to Thee.

GEORGE HUNT SMYTTAN, 1822–70; and FRANCIS POTT, 1832–1909.

80 CHILDHOOD. (88. 86.)

Doh = F. *In moderate time.* 'University of Wales' (*Students' Hymnal*), 1923.

:d.m | s :-.l | s.f :m.r | d :d | d :s, | l, :t, | d :r | m :r.d | r ||
:d | d :-.d | d :d.t, | d :l, | s, :s, | l, :t, | d :r | d :t,.l, | t, ||
:m | m :-.f | m.l :s.f | m :f | m :m | f :r | m :s | d :m | s ||
:d | d :-.d | d :d | d :f, | d :m | f :r | m :s | d :m | s ||

:s | l :s.f | s :m | f.m :r.d | t, :s, | l, :d | d :m.r | d :— :— || d | d ||
:d | d :d | d :s, | d :l, | s, :s, | l, :d | d :t, | d :— :— || l, | s, ||
:s | f :s.l | s :s | f :f.m | r :m | f :m | m :s.f | m :— :— || f | m ||
:m | f :m.r | m :d | l, :r | s, :d | f, :l, | l, :s, | d :— :— || f, | d, ||

A-men.

IT fell upon a summer day,
When Jesus walked in Galilee,
The mothers from a village brought
Their children to His knee.

2 He took them in His arms, and laid
His hands on each remembered head;
'Suffer these little ones to come
To Me,' He gently said.

3 'Forbid them not; unless ye bear
The childlike heart your hearts within,
Unto My Kingdom ye may come,
But may not enter in.'

4 Master, I fain would enter there;
O let me follow Thee, and share
Thy meek and lowly heart, and be
Freed from all worldly care.

5 Of innocence, and love, and trust,
Of quiet work, and simple word,
Of joy, and thoughtlessness of self,
Build up my life, good Lord.

6 All happy thoughts, and gentle ways,
And loving-kindness daily given,
And freedom through obedience gained,
Make in my heart Thy heaven.

7 O happy thus to live and move!
And sweet this world, where I shall find
God's beauty everywhere, His love,
His good in all mankind.

8 Then, Father, grant this childlike heart,
That I may come to Christ, and feel
His hands on me in blessing laid,
Love-giving, strong to heal.

STOPFORD AUGUSTUS BROOKE, 1832–1916.

81

ES IST EIN ROS' ENTSPRUNGEN. (76. 76. D.)

Adapted by JAMES SMITH ANDERSON, 1853– , From an ancient German melody.

Doh = F. *In moderate time.*

```
:s  |s  :s  |l  :s  |s  :—  |m  :f  |m.r:d  |d  :t, |d  :—  |—  ‖
:d  |r  :d  |d  :d  |t, :—  |d  :d  |t, :l, |l, :s, |s, :—  |—  ‖
:m  |r  :m  |f  :m  |r  :—  |d  :l  |s.f:m  |f  :r  |m  :—  |—  ‖
:d  |t, :d  |f, :d  |s, :—  |l, :f, |s, :l, |f, :s, |d  :—  |—  ‖

:s  |s  :s  |l  :s  |s  :—     |m  :f  |m.r:d  |d  :t, |d  :—  |—  ‖
:m  |r  :d  |d  :d  |d.l,:t,   |d  :d  |t, :l, |l, :s, |s, :—  |—  ‖
:s  |s  :m  |f  :m  |r  :—     |d  :l  |s.f:m  |f  :r  |m  :—  |—  ‖
:d  |t, :d  |l, :d  |s, :—     |l, :f, |s, :l, |f, :s, |d  :—  |—  ‖
```

C.t. ... f.F.

```
:^m l  |s  :m  |f  :r  |m  :-.r |m  :l   |s  :m  |f  :r   |^d s, :—  |— :—  ‖
:^d f  |d  :d  |d  :t, |d  :-.r |m  :f   |d  :d  |d  :t,  |^d s, :—  |— :—  ‖
:^s d' |d' :s  |f  :s  |m  :-.f |s  :l.t |d' :s  |f  :s.f |^m t, :—  |— :—  ‖
:^d f  |m  :d  |r  :s, |d  :—   |d  :f   |m  :d  |r  :s,  |^d s, :—  |— :—  ‖

|s  :s.s |l  :s  |s  :—  |m  :f  |m.r:d  |d  :t, |d  :—  |—  ‖ d  |d  ‖
|r  :d.d |d  :d  |d  :t, |d  :d  |t, :l, |l, :s, |s, :—  |—  ‖ l, |s, ‖
|s  :m.m |f  :m  |r  :—  |d  :l  |s  :m  |f  :r  |m  :—  |—  ‖ f  |m  ‖
|t, :d.d |l, :d  |s, :—  |l, :r, |m, :l, |f, :s, |d, :—  |—  ‖ f, |d, ‖
                                                               A-men.
```

GOD, who hath made the daisies,
And every lovely thing,
He will accept our praises,
And hearken while we sing.
He says, though we are simple,
Though ignorant we be,
'Suffer the little children,
And let them come to Me.'

2 Though we are young and simple,
In praise we may be bold;
The children in the temple
He heard in days of old;
And if our hearts are humble,
He says to you and me,
'Suffer the little children,
And let them come to Me.'

3 He sees the bird that wingeth
Its way o'er earth and sky;
He hears the lark that singeth
Up in the heaven so high;
He sees the heart's low breathings,
And says, well pleased to see,
'Suffer the little children,
And let them come to Me.'

4 Therefore we will come near Him,
And joyfully we'll sing;
No cause to shrink or fear Him,
We'll make our voices ring;
For in our temple speaking,
He says to you and me,
'Suffer the little children,
And let them come to Me.'

EDWIN PAXTON HOOD, 1820–85.

82 SALAMIS. (Irr.)

Doh = E♭. *In moderate time.* Greek Air.

```
:d .r |m  :r .m |s .f :m .f |l   :s .s  |s  :m .f |s .m :d'.t  |l .s :f .m
:d    |d  :d .d |r    :d .d |d   :d .t, |d  :m .r |d    :d .r  |m    :r .d
:m .f |s  :f .s |s    :s .f |r   :m .f  |s  :s .f |m    :l .s  |m    :f .s,l
:d    |d  :d .d |t,   :d .l,|f,.f:m .r  |m  :d .d |d    :l,.t, |d    :r .m,f

m  :—  |r   ||d .r |m    :r .m  |s .f :m .f |l    :s .s   |s   :f .r
d  :—  |t,  ||d .t,|d    :t,.d  |s,   :s,.d |d    :d .t,  |d   :l,.l,
s  :—  |—   ||s .f |m .s :f .m  |r    :m .d |r .f :m .r   |s   :l .f
s  :—  |s,  ||m .r |d    :d .d  |t,   :d .l,|f,   :s,.f,  |m,  :f,.f,

d   :d .m  |m .r :d .t, |d  :—  |—  ||m .f |s    :t .l  |s .f :m .r
s,  :d .d  |l,   :s,.s, |s  :—  |—  ||d .t,|d .m :r .d  |t,   :d .r
m   :m .d  |f    :m .r  |m  :—  |—  ||s .f |m .s :s .fe |s    :s .s
s,  :l,.l, |f,   :s,.s, |d  :—  |—  ||d .r |m .d :r .r  |s,   :l,.t,

f  :m .m  |m  :m .f  |s .m :d'.t  |l .s :f .m   |m  :—  |r   ||d .r
d  :d .s, |d  :d .t, |d    :d .r  |m    :r .d   |d  :—  |t,  ||d .t,
l  :s .m  |s  :s .f  |m .s :l .s  |m    :f .s,l |s  :—  |—   ||s .f
d  :d .d  |d  :d .r  |m    :l,.t, |d    :r .m,f |s  :—  |s,  ||m .r

m   :r .m |s.f :m .f |l   :s .s  |s   :f .r  |d  :d .m  |m.r :d .t, |d  :—|—||d  |d  ||
d   :t,.d |s,  :s,.d |d   :d .t, |d   :l,.l, |s, :d .d  |l,  :s,.s, |s, :—|—||l, |s, ||
m.s :f .m |r   :m .d |r.f :m .r  |s   :l .f  |m  :m .d  |f   :m .r  |m  :—|—||f  |m  ||
d   :d .d |t,  :d .l,|f,  :s,.f, |m,  :f,.f, |s, :l,.l, |f,  :s,.s, |d  :—|—||f, |d  ||
                                                                          A-men.
```

I THINK, when I read that sweet story of old,
  When Jesus was here among men,
How He called little children as lambs to His fold,
  I should like to have been with them then;
I wish that His hands had been placed on my head,
  That His arm had been thrown around me,
And that I might have seen His kind look when He said,
  'Let the little ones come unto Me.'

2 Yet still to His footstool in prayer I may go,
  And ask for a share in His love;
And, if I now earnestly seek Him below,
  I shall see Him and hear Him above,

In that beautiful place He is gone to prepare
For all who are washed and forgiven ;
And many dear children are gathering there,
For of such is the Kingdom of heaven.

3 But thousands and thousands, who wander and fall,
Never heard of that heavenly home ;
I should like them to know there is room for them all,
And that Jesus has bid them to come.
I long for the joy of that glorious time,
The sweetest and brightest and best,
When the dear little children of every clime
Shall crowd to His arms and be blest.

JEMIMA LUKE, 1813–1906.

83

ST. AËLRED. (88. 83.)

Lah = C. Doh = E♭. *In moderate time.* JOHN BACCHUS DYKES, 1823–76.

```
| m  :m     :m    | m  :—  :m   | f  :—    :f    | m  :—  :—  | l  :d'  :t  |
| d  :d     :d    | t, :—  :d   | r  :—    :r    | d  :—  :—  | m  :m   :s  |
| l  :l     :l    | se :—  :l   | l  :—    :l    | l  :—  :—  | d' :d'  :s  |
| l, :l,.t, :d.r  | m  :—  :l,  | r  :r.m  :f.s  | l  :—  :—  | l  :l   :m  |

| l  :—   :s   | f  :—  :f   | m  :—  :—  || m  :m  :m  | s  :—  :s  |
| f  :—   :m   | l, :r  :d   | t, :—  :—  || d  :d  :d  | t, :—  :t, |
| l  :d'  :d'  | d' :t  :l   | se :—  :—  || l  :l  :d  | r  :—  :m  |
| f  :—   :d   | r  :—  :r   | m  :—  :—  || l, :l, :l, | s, :—  :s, |

| l  :— :s   | f  :—:— | d  :—:— | r  :—:— | m      :—:— | —:—:— || f  | m ||
| l, :— :ta, | l, :—:— | d  :—:— | d  :—:— | d      :—:— | —:—:— || d  | d ||
| f  :— :d   | d  :—:— | l  :—:— | l  :—:— | s      :—:— | —:—:— || l  | s ||
| f, :— :f,  | f, :—:— | f, :—:— | f, :—:— | {d d,} :—:— | —:—:— || f, | d ||
                                                                      A-men.
```

FIERCE raged the tempest o'er the deep,
Watch did Thine anxious servants keep,
But Thou wast wrapt in guileless sleep,
Calm and still.

2 'Save, Lord, we perish,' was their cry,
'O save us in our agony !'
Thy word above the storm rose high,
'Peace, be still.'

3 The wild winds hushed, the angry deep
Sank like a little child to sleep,
The sullen billows ceased to leap,
At Thy will.

4 So, when our life is clouded o'er,
And storm-winds drift us from the shore,
Say, lest we sink to rise no more,
'Peace, be still.'

GODFREY THRING, 1823–1903.

84

SILAS. (64. 64. D.)

Lah = A. Doh = C. *In moderate time.* ÉDOUARD SILAS, 1827–1909.

```
l  :r'.r' :t  | d' :-.t  :l   | se  :l  :-.t | m  :—  :—  || l  :l  :s  | s  :-.f :f
m  :r.r   :f  | m  :-.m  :m   | m   :m  :-.f | t, :—  :—  || m  :m  :m  | m  :-.r :r
d  :l.l   :l  | l  :-.r' :d'  | t   :l  :-.l | se :—  :—  || m  :l  :ta | ta :-.l :l
l  :f.f   :r  | l, :-.l, :l,  | m.r :d  :-.r | m  :—  :—  || d  :d  :de | r  :-.r :r
```

v. 1. was the wild bil - low.

```
                                G.t.                                          f.C.
f  :m  :-.d  | r  :—  :—  || ᵐl, :r :-.t, | m :-.d :l, | r :r :f | ˡm' :— :— ||
r  :d  :-.s, | t, :—  :—  || ᵐl, :r :-.t, | m :-.d :l, | r :r :f | ˡm  :— :— ||
s  :s  :-.m  | s  :—  :—  || ᵐl, :r :-.t, | m :-.d :l, | r :r :f | ˡm' :— :— ||
t, :d  :-.d  | s, :—  :—  || ᵐl, :r :-.t, | m :-.d :l, | r :r :f | ˡm  :— :— ||
```

```
l  :m  :-.m  | f  :-.m    :r  | m  :-.m  :m  | m  :— :— || l  :— :— | l  :— :— ||
m  :d  :-.d  | d  :t,.t,  :t, | t, :-.t, :t, | de :— :— || de :m :r | de :— :— ||
l  :l  :-.l  | l  :-.l    :l  | l  :-.l  :se | l  :— :— || m  :s :f | m  :— :— ||
d  :l, :-.l, | r  :-.m    :f  | m  :-.m  :m  | l, :— :— || l, :— :— | l, :— :— ||
                                                            A    -     men.
```

[By permission of Novello & Co., Ltd.]

Ζοφερᾶς τρικυμίας.

FIERCE was the wild billow,
  Dark was the night;
Oars laboured heavily,
  Foam glimmered white;
Trembled the mariners,
  Peril was nigh:
Then said the God of God,
  'Peace! It is I.'

2 Ridge of the mountain-wave,
  Lower thy crest!
Wail of Euroclydon,
  Be thou at rest!
Sorrow can never be,
  Darkness must fly,
Where saith the Light of Light,
  'Peace! It is I.'

3 Jesus, Deliverer,
  Come Thou to me;
Soothe Thou my voyaging
  Over life's sea:
Thou, when the storm of death
  Roars, sweeping by,
Whisper, O Truth of Truth,
  'Peace! It is I.'

8th century; *tr.* by JOHN MASON NEALE, 1818–66.

85 SALVATOR. (775. 775.)

Doh = G. *In moderate time.* MYLES BIRKET FOSTER, 1851–1922.

```
m  :-.r  |d  :t,  |l,  :d  |d  :—  |r  :-.r  |m  :d  |f  :m  |r  :—
d  :-.t, |l, :se, |l,  :l, |s, :—  |s, :-.t, |d  :d  |t, :d  |r  :d
s  :-.f  |m  :r   |d   :f  |f  :m  |r  :-.s  |s  :s  |s  :s  |s  :fe
d  :-.s, |l, :m,  |f,  :f, |d  :—  |t, :-.s, |d  :m  |r  :d  |t, :l,

r  :-.s, |d  :d   |t,  :—  |—  :   ||r  :-.t, |d  :m  |s  :f  |m  :—
t, :-.s, |s, :fe, |s,  :—  |—  :   ||s, :-.s, |s, :d  |d  :r  |m  :—
s  :-.r  |m  :r   |r   :—  |—  :   ||f  :-.f  |m  :m  |m  :s  |s  :—
s, :-.t, |l, :r,  |s,  :—  |—  :   ||s, :-.s, |s, :s, |l, :t, |d  :—

m  :-.de |r  :f  |l  :s  |f  :—  |m :r .d |s  :-.t, |d  :—  |—  : ||d  |d
de :-.l, |l, :r  |r  :m  |r  :—  |d :fe,  |s, :s,   |s, :—  |—  : ||l, |s,
s  :-.s  |f  :f  |f  :l  |l  :s  |s :d .r |m  :f    |m  :—  |—  : ||f  |m
l, :-.l, |l, :l, |t, :de |r  :t, |d :l,   |s, :s,   |d, :—  |—  : ||f, |d,
                                                                   A-men.
```

[*Copyright*, 1905, *by W. Garrett Horder.*]

WHEN the Lord of Love was here,
Happy hearts to Him were dear,
Though His heart was sad;
Worn and lonely for our sake,
Yet He turned aside to make
All the weary glad.

2 Meek and lowly were His ways;
From His loving grew His praise,
From His giving, prayer:
All the outcasts thronged to hear;
All the sorrowful drew near
To enjoy His care.

3 When He walked the fields, He drew
From the flowers, and birds, and dew,
Parables of God;
For within His heart of love
All the soul of man did move
God had His abode.

4 Lord, be ours Thy power to keep,
In the very heart of grief,
And in trial, love;
In our meekness to be wise,
And through sorrow to arise
To our God above.

5 Fill us with Thy deep desire
All the sinful to inspire
With the Father's life;
Free us from the cares that press
On the heart of worldliness,
From the fret and strife.

6 And, when in the fields and woods
We are filled with Nature's moods,
May the grace be given
With Thy faithful heart to say,
'All I see and feel to-day
Is my Father's heaven.'

STOPFORD AUGUSTUS BROOKE, 1832–1916.

86 ST. MATTHEW. (D.C.M.)

Doh = B♭. *In moderate time.* WILLIAM CROFT, 1678–1727.

:s, | m, :— :s, | d :— :m | r :d :t, | d :— :m | r :— :s, | l, :s, :fe,
:r, | m, :— :m, | m, :— :s, | f, :m, :r, | m, :— :s, | s, :— :s, | m, :r, :r,
:s, | d :— :t, | d :— :d | l, :s, :s, | s, :— :d | r :— :t, | d :t, :l,
:t,, | d, :— :m, | l, :— :m, | f, :s, :s,, | d, :— :d, | t,, :— :m, | d, :r, :r,

s, :— ‖ r | t, :— :s, | d :— :m | m :r :d | d :t, :s, | d :— :m
r, :— ‖ s, | s, :— :s, | s, :— :s, | l, :— :m,.f, | s, :— :r, | s, :— :s,
t, :— ‖ t, | r :— :r | d :— :d | d :r :l, | r :— :t, | d :— :d
s, :— ‖ s, | s, :— :f, | m, :— :d, | f, :— :l, | s, :— :f, | m, :— :d,

r :d :t, | d :— ‖ m, | m, :— :l, | l, :se, :l, | t, :l, :se, | l, :— :t,
f, :m, :r, | m, :— ‖ r, | d, :— :m, | m, :— :d, | f, :m, :m, | m, :— :se,
l, :s, :s, | s, :— ‖ se, | l, :— :l, | d :t, :l, | r :d :t, | d :— :m
f, :s, :s, | d, :— ‖ t,, | l,, :— :d, | m, :— :f, | r, :m, :m, | l, :— :m,

F.t. f.B♭.

(d)f :— :m.r | d :— :t, | (l)m, :— ‖ s, | s, :— :d | l, :— :l,
(l)r :— :l, | l, :— :se, | (l)m, :— ‖ f, | m, :f, :s, | f, :— :s,
(m)l :se :l.f | m :— :r | (d)s, :— ‖ t, | d :— :d | d :— :de
(l)r :t, :d.r | m :— :m, | (l)m, :— ‖ r, | d, :r, :m, | f, :— :m,

r :— :d | d :t, :s, | d :— :m | r :d :t, | d :— ‖ d | d
fe, :s, :l, | s, :— :s, | s, :f, :m, | l, :s, :s, | s, :— ‖ f, | m,
r :— :r | r :— :t, | d :— :s | f :m :r | m :— ‖ l, | s,
r, :m, :fe, | s, :— :f, | m, :r, :d, | f, :s, :s,, | d, :— ‖ f, | d,

A-men.

THINE arm, O Lord, in days of old,
Was strong to heal and save;
It triumphed o'er disease and death,
O'er darkness and the grave.
To Thee they went—the blind, the dumb,
The palsied, and the lame,
The leper with his tainted life,
The sick with fevered frame;

2 And, lo! Thy touch brought life and health,
Gave speech, and strength, and sight;
And youth renewed and frenzy calmed
Owned Thee, the Lord of light.
And now, O Lord, be near to bless,
Almighty as of yore,
In crowded street, by restless couch,
As by Gennesaret's shore.

3 Be Thou our great Deliverer still,
Thou Lord of life and death;
Restore and quicken, soothe and bless,
With Thine almighty breath;
To hands that work and eyes that see
Give wisdom's heavenly lore,
That whole and sick, and weak and strong,
May praise Thee evermore.

EDWARD HAYES PLUMPTRE, 1821–91.

87 ST. BERNARD. (C.M.)

Tochter Sion, Cologne, 1741.
Doh = E♭. *In moderate time.* Probably adapted by JOHN RICHARDSON, 1816–79.

```
:s |d  :r  |m :r.d |f  :m |r  :s  |m :l  |fe :-.fe|s  :— |— ||
:d |d  :t, |d :t,.d|t, :d |t, :r  |d :d  |d  :-.d |t, :— |— ||
:m |s  :s  |s :s   |f  :s |s  :s  |s :l  |l  :-.l |s  :— |— ||
:d |m  :r  |d :f.m |r  :d |s, :t, |d :l, |r  :-.r |s, :— |— ||

:s |d' :l  |s :l   |f  :f |m  :d  |f  :m |r  :r   |d  :— |— ||
:t,|d  :d  |d :l,  |l, :r |d  :d  |t, :d |d  :t,  |d  :— |— ||
:s |s  :f  |m :m   |f  :s |s  :s  |f  :s |l  :s.f |m  :— |— ||
:s |m  :f  |d :de  |r  :t,|d  :m  |r  :d |f, :s,  |d  :— |— ||
```

WHAT grace, O Lord, and beauty shone
Around Thy steps below!
What patient love was seen in all
Thy life and death of woe!

2 For ever on Thy burdened heart
A weight of sorrow hung,
Yet no ungentle, murmuring word
Escaped Thy silent tongue.

3 Thy foes might hate, despise, revile,
Thy friends unfaithful prove:
Unwearied in forgiveness still,
Thy heart could only love.

4 O give us hearts to love like Thee,
Like Thee, O Lord, to grieve
Far more for others' sins than all
The wrongs that we receive.

5 One with Thyself, may every eye
In us, Thy brethren, see
That gentleness and grace that spring
From union, Lord, with Thee.

EDWARD DENNY, 1796–1889.

```
|d  |d  ||
|l, |s, ||
|f  |m  ||
|f, |d  ||
A-men.
```

88

WER DA WONET. (D.L.M.)

St. Gall Gesangbuch, 1863.
Adapted from VEHE's *Gesangbüchlein*, 1537.

Doh = D. *In moderate time.*

```
:d  |d :—:m  |s :—:m  |f :s :l   |s :—:d'  |t :—:l  |s :m :s
:s, |s, :—:d |r :—:d  |d :—:d    |t, :—:d  |r :—:d  |r :m :d
:m  |m :—:l  |s :—:s  |f :m :f   |r :—:s   |f :s :l |r :s :l
:d  |d :t, :l, |t, :—:d |l, :s, :f, |s, :—:m |r :m :f |t, :d :l,

                 D.C.
|f :m :f   |m :—  ||s  |l :—:t |d' :—:s |f :m :r   |d :—:d
|d :—:t,   |d :—  ||d  |d :—:r |s :—:m  |r :d :t,  |d :—:d
|l :—:s    |s :—  ||s  |f :—:f |s :—:d' |l :—:f    |m :—:f
|r :—:s,   |d :—  ||m  |f :—:r |m :—:d  |r :—:s,   |l, :—:l,

|m :—:f    |s :—:l   |f :—:m    |r :—  ||r   |m :—:fe |s :—:l
|d :t, :d  |d :—:m   |l, :r :d  |t, :— ||t,  |d :—:r  |r :—:m
|s :—:l    |s :f :m  |f :—.s:l  |t :—  ||s   |s :—:l  |s :—:s
|s, :s :f  |m :r :d  |r :—.m:f  |s :—  ||s,  |d :—:d  |t, :—:d

|t :d' :l  |s :—:d'  |t :—:l  |s :—:f     |m :f :r    |d :—  ||d  |d  ||
|r :—:d    |t, :—:d  |r :—:d  |f :m :r    |d :—:t,    |d :—  ||l, |s, ||
|s :—:fe   |s :—:s   |f :s :l |r' :d' :l  |s :—:f     |m :—  ||f  |m  ||
|r :—:r    |s, :—:m  |r :m :f |t, :d :f,  |s, :—:s,   |d :—  ||f, |d  ||
                                                                 A-men.
```

O MASTER, it is good to be
High on the mountain here with Thee,
Where stand revealed to mortal gaze
The great old saints of other days,
Who once received, on Horeb's height,
The eternal laws of truth and right,
Or caught the still small whisper, higher
Than storm, than earthquake, or than fire.

2 O Master, it is good to be
With Thee and with Thy faithful three:
Here, where the apostle's heart of rock
Is nerved against temptation's shock;
Here, where the Son of Thunder learns
The thought that breathes, the word that burns;
Here, where on eagle's wings we move
With him whose last, best creed is love.

3 O Master, it is good to be
Entranced, enwrapt, alone with Thee;
Watching the glistering raiment glow,
Whiter than Hermon's whitest snow,
The human lineaments that shine
Irradiant with a light divine:
Till we too change from grace to grace,
Gazing on that transfigured face.

4 O Master, it is good to be
Here on the holy mount with Thee;
When darkling in the depths of night,
When dazzled with excess of light,
We bow before the heavenly voice
That bids bewildered souls rejoice,
Though love wax cold and faith be dim,
'This is My Son! O hear ye Him!'

ARTHUR PENRHYN STANLEY, 1815–81.

89 DAS WALT' GOTT VATER. (L.M.)

DANIEL VETTER, *c.* 1713.
Arranged by JOHANN SEBASTIAN BACH, 1685–1750.

Doh = E♭. *Slow.*

:d |m :s |s :m |d :r |m ‖ d |s :s |l :t |d'.t :l |s ‖
:s, |d :d |t, :t, |t,.l, :s, |s, ‖ s, |d :r |m.fe :s |s :-.fe |r ‖
:m |s :s |r :m |m :r |d ‖ m |m :s |d' :t |m' m} :l |t ‖
:d |d :m,.f, |s, :se, |l, :t, |d ‖ d |d :-.t, |l, :m.r |d :r |s, ‖

:s |m :s |l :s |f :m |r ‖ s |m.f :s |f :m.r |d :r |d ‖ d |d ‖
:r |r.d,t, :d |d :d |r.s, :s,.d |d.t, ‖ r |d :d |d :t, |l,.d :-.t, |d ‖ l, |s, ‖
:s |s :s |s.f :f.m |r :m.,f |s ‖ s |s :s |l :s.f |m :s.,f |m ‖ f |m ‖
:t, |d :m.d |l, :d |d.t, :d |s, ‖ t, |d :m, |f, :s, |l, :s, |d ‖ f, |d ‖

A-men.

Caelestis formam gloriae.

O WONDROUS type, O vision fair
Of glory that the Church shall share,
Which Christ upon the mountain shows,
Where brighter than the sun He glows!

2 With shining face and bright array,
Christ deigns to manifest to-day
What glory shall be theirs, above,
Who joy in God with perfect love.

3 And faithful hearts are raised on high
By this great vision's mystery,
For which, in joyful strains, we raise
The voice of prayer, the hymn of praise.

4 O Father, with the eternal Son
And Holy Spirit ever One,
Vouchsafe to bring us, by Thy grace,
To see Thy glory face to face.

15th century; *tr.* by JOHN MASON NEALE, 1818–66.

90 ST. FRANCES. (C.M.)

Doh = E♭. *In moderate time.* George Augustus Löhr, 1821–97.

:d	f :m	r :d	s :f	m :m	r :s	l :l	s :—	—
:s_1	d :d	t_1 :d	r :r	d :d	r :t_1	m :r.d	t_1 :—	—
:m	l :s	f :m	s :s	s :s	s :r	m :fe	s :—	—
:d	d :d	s_1 :l_1	t_1 :t_1	d :d	t_1 :s_1	d :r	s_1 :—	—

:s	d' :m	f :l	s :f	m :m	f :r	d :t_1	d :—	—	d	d
:r	d :ta_1	l_1 :d	t_1 :t_1	d :ta_1	l_1 :l_1	s_1 :s_1	s_1 :—	—	l_1	s_1
:f	m :s	f :f	r :s	s :s	f :f	m :r	m :—	—	f	m
:t_1	d :d	f_1 :f_1	s_1 :s_1	d :d	f_1 :f_1	s_1 :s_1	d :—	—	f_1	d

A-men.

LORD, as to Thy dear Cross we flee,
And plead to be forgiven,
So let Thy life our pattern be,
And form our souls for heaven.

2 Help us, through good report and ill,
Our daily cross to bear,
Like Thee, to do our Father's will,
Our brethren's griefs to share.

3 Let grace our selfishness expel,
Our earthliness refine,
And kindness in our bosoms dwell,
As free and true as Thine.

4 If joy shall at Thy bidding fly,
And grief's dark day ccme on,
We, in our turn, would meekly cry,
'Father, Thy will be done.'

5 Should friends misjudge, or foes defame,
Or brethren faithless prove,
Then, like Thine own, be all our aim
To conquer them by love.

6 Kept peaceful in the midst of strife,
Forgiving and forgiven,
O may we lead the pilgrim's life,
And follow Thee to heaven.

John Hampden Gurney, 1802–62.

91 ST. THEODULPH. (76. 76. D.)

MELCHIOR TESCHNER, *c.* 1615.

Doh = C. *Slow and majestic.* *D.C.* FINE.

```
:d  |s  :s  |l  :t  |d' :— |d' :m' |r' :d' |d' :t  |d' :— |— ||
:d  |r  :m  |f  :f  |m  :— |m  :m  |l  :f  |m  :r  |m  :— |— ||
:m  |s  :d' |d' :r' |d' :— |d' :d' |l  :l  |s  :s  |s  :— |— ||
:d  |t, :d  |f  :r  |l  :— |l, :l  |f  :r  |s  :s, |d  :— |— ||

:d' |m'      :m'  |r' :d' |t  :— |s  :t  |d' :t  |l  :l     |s  :— |— ||
:m  |s       :l   |l  :fe |s  :— |r  :s  |m  :s  |s  :fe    |s  :— |— ||
:s  |d'      :d'  |r' :r' |r' :— |t  :m' |d' :r' |m' :r'.d' |t  :— |— ||
:d  |d'.t    :l.s |fe :r  |s  :— |s  :m  |l, :t, |d  :r     |s, :— |— ||

:s  |m  :s  |l  :s  |s  :f  |m  :s  |f  :m  |r  :r  |d  :— |— ||d' |d' ||
:r  |d  :r  |m  :d  |d  :r  |s, :d  |l, :d  |d  :t, |d  :— |— ||f  |m  ||
:s  |m' :r' |d' :s  |l  :t  |d' :m  |f  :s  |l  :s  |m  :— |— ||l  |s  ||
:t, |d  :t, |l, :m  |r  :s, |d  :d  |r  :m  |f  :s  |d  :— |— ||f  |d  ||
                                                               A-men.
```

Gloria, laus et honor.

ALL glory, laud, and honour
To Thee, Redeemer King,
To whom the lips of children
Made sweet hosannas ring!
Thou art the King of Israel,
Thou David's royal Son,
Who in the Lord's Name comest,
The King and Blessèd One.

2 *All glory, etc.*
The company of angels
Are praising Thee on high,
And mortal men and all things
Created make reply.

3 *All glory, etc.*
The people of the Hebrews
With palms before Thee went;
Our praise and prayer and anthems
Before Thee we present.

4 *All glory, etc.*
To Thee before Thy passion
They sang their hymns of praise;
To Thee now high exalted
Our melody we raise.

5 *All glory, etc.*
Thou didst accept their praises;
Accept the prayers we bring,
Who in all good delightest,
Thou good and gracious King.

All glory, laud, and honour
To Thee, Redeemer King,
To whom the lips of children
Made sweet hosannas ring!

ST. THEODULPH OF ORLEANS, *c.* 821; *tr.* by JOHN MASON NEALE, 1818–66.

92 CRASSELIUS. (L.M.)

Musikalisch Hand-Buch, Hamburg, 1690.

Doh = B♭. *Slow and dignified.*

```
:s,  |d :s,   |l, :l,     |s, :f,   |m, :m, |f, :m,      |r, :s,  |s,  :fe, |s,
:m,  |s, :m,  |f, :f,.m,  |r, :t,,  |d, :d, |d, :d,      |r, :m,  |m,  :r,  |r,
:d   |d :d    |d :f,      |s, :s,   |s, :s, |l, :s,.l,   |t, :t,  |d.t,:l,  |t,
:d,  |m, :d,  |f, :r,.d,  |t,, :s,, |d, :d, |l,, :d,     |s,, :m, |d,  :r,  |s,,

:s,    |d :r     |m :d      |f :m       |r :m    |d :l,  |s, :d  |d :t,  |d  || d  |d
:s,    |s, :f,   |m, :l,.s, |f, :s,     |s, :s,  |s, :f, |s, :m, |l, :s, |s, || l, |s,
:t,    |d :l,.t, |d :d      |d.t, :d    |t, :d   |d :d   |d :d   |r :r   |m  || f  |m
:s,.f, |m, :r,   |d, :f,.m, |r, :m,.f,  |s, :d,  |m, :f, |m, :l, |f, :s, |d, || f, |d,
                                                                                 A-men.
```

OBER AMMERGAU. (L.M. and refrain.)

Adapted from Triumphal Entry Music by Robert Alexander Stewart Macalister, 1870–

Doh = E♭. *Moderately slow.*

```
:m  |s :s       |d' :m  |s :s         |d' :—  |— :s   |d' :t
:d  |r :r       |d :d   |m.r :d.r     |m :—   |— :r   |d :r
:s  |s :t       |d' :d' |d'.t :l.t    |d' :—  |— :r   |m :r
:d  |t,.r :s.f  |m :l   |s :s         |d :—   |— :t,  |l, :t,

                           f.A♭.
|l :s  |s :fe  |s :—   |—  ||r l,    |l, :t,  |d :r    |m :r
|m :m  |r :r   |t, :—  |—  ||ta,f,   |m, :se, |l, :l,  |se, :t,
|l :l  |t :l   |s :—   |—  ||s r     |m :r    |d :l,   |t, :m
|d :d  |r :r   |s, :—  |—  ||s r     |d :t,   |l, :f,  |m, :se,

E♭.t.
|d f :—   |— :s   |m :r    |d :r    |m :re       |m :—   |—  ||
|l, r :—  |— :r   |d :t,   |l, :d   |t, :t,.l,   |se, :— |—  ||
|m l :—   |— :s   |s :s.f  |m :fe   |s :fe       |m :—   |—  ||
|l, r :—  |— :t,  |d :s,   |l, :l,  |s,.l, :t,   |m :—   |—  ||
```

:m	m :f	s :- .f	m :r	d :—	—	d	d
:r	d :r	m :- .r	d :t_1	d :—	—	l_1	s_1
Ride	on, ride	on, in	ma - jes -	ty.		A -	men.
:se	l :l .t	d' :- .l	s :s	m :—	—	f	m
:m	l :f	m :- .f	s :s_1	d :—	—	f_1	d

RIDE on! ride on in majesty!
Hark! all the tribes 'Hosanna!' cry;
O Saviour meek, pursue Thy road
With palms and scattered garments strowed.

2 Ride on! ride on in majesty!
In lowly pomp ride on to die;
O Christ, Thy triumphs now begin
O'er captive death and conquered sin.

3 Ride on! ride on in majesty!
The wingèd squadrons of the sky
Look down with sad and wondering eyes
To see the approaching sacrifice.

4 Ride on! ride on in majesty!
Thy last and fiercest strife is nigh;
The Father on His sapphire throne
Awaits His own anointed Son.

5 Ride on! ride on in majesty!
In lowly pomp ride on to die;
Bow Thy meek head to mortal pain,
Then take, O God, Thy power, and reign.

HENRY HART MILMAN, 1791-1868.

93

ELLACOMBE. (76. 76. D.)

Doh = B♭. *Brightly.* *Mainz Gesangbuch, c.* 1833.

```
:s, |d :t,.l, |s, :d   |m, :f, |s, :s, |l,.t, :d |r :r   |m :— |—  ||
:s, |d :t,.l, |s, :s,  |d, :—  |r, :m, |f,  :s,   |l, :s, |s, :— |— ||
:s, |d :t,.l, |s, :d   |d  :—  |t, :d  |d   :d    |d :t,  |d :— |—  ||
:s, |d :t,.l, |s, :m,  |l, :—  |s, :d, |f,  :m,   |f, :s, |d, :— |— ||
```

```
:s, |d :t,.l, |s, :d   |m, :f, |s, :s, |l,.t, :d   |d :t,  |d :— |—  ||
:s, |d :t,.l, |s, :s,  |d, :—  |r, :m, |f,  :m,.f,  |s, :s, |s, :— |— ||
:s, |d :t,.l, |s, :d   |d  :—  |t, :d  |d   :d      |r :r   |m :— |—  ||
:s, |d :t,.l, |s, :m,  |l, :—  |s, :d, |f,  :l,     |s, :s, |d, :— |— ||
```

```
:d .r   |m  :r  |m  :f  |r  :t,.d  |r  :d .r   |m :r  |m :f  |r  :— |— ||
:m,.f,  |s, :s, |s, :l, |s, :—     |s, :d .s,  |s, :s,|s, :l,|s, :— |— ||
:d      |d  :r  |d  :d  |t, :s,.l, |t, :m .r   |d :r  |d :d  |t, :— |— ||
:d,     |d  :t, |d  :f, |s, :—     |s, :l,.t,  |d :t, |d :f, |s, :— |— ||
```

```
:s, |d :t,.l, |s, :d  |m, :f, |s, :s, |l,.t, :d  |d :t,  |d :—  |— || d  | d  ||
:s, |d :t,.l, |s, :s, |d, :—  |r, :m, |f, :m,.f, |s, :s, |s, :— |— || f, | m, ||
:s, |d :t,.l, |s, :d  |d  :—  |t, :d  |d  :d     |r :r   |m :—  |— || l, | s, ||
:s, |d :t,.l, |s, :m, |l, :—  |s, :d, |f, :l,    |s, :s, |d, :— |— || f, | d, ||
```

A-men.

HOSANNA, loud hosanna,
The little children sang;
Through pillared court and temple
The joyful anthem rang;
To Jesus, who had blessed them
Close folded to His breast,
The children sang their praises,
The simplest and the best.

2 From Olivet they followed,
'Mid an exultant crowd,
The victor palm-branch waving,
And chanting clear and loud;
Bright angels joined the chorus,
Beyond the cloudless sky,—
'Hosanna in the highest!
Glory to God on high!'

3 Fair leaves of silvery olive
They strowed upon the ground,
While Salem's circling mountains
Echoed the joyful sound;
The Lord of men and angels
Rode on in lowly state,
Nor scorned that little children
Should on His bidding wait.

4 'Hosanna in the highest!'
That ancient song we sing,
For Christ is our Redeemer,
The Lord of heaven our King.
O may we ever praise Him
With heart and life and voice,
And in His blissful presence
Eternally rejoice.

JENNETTE THRELFALL, 1821–80.

Also the following:

141 Immortal Love, for ever full
510 Teach me, O Lord, to follow Him who trod
513 O Lord and Master of us all
514 Through good report and evil, Lord
659 When mothers of Salem

94

CROWLE. (C.M.)

Lah = F. Doh = A♭. *Moderately slow.* *Green's Book of Psalmody*, 1724.

```
:l,  | m   :r   :d   | t,  :—   :d   | t,  :l,  :se, | l,  :—   :d
:l,  | t,  :—   :l,  | se, :—   :l,  | f,  :—   :m,  | m,  :—   :m,
:d   | m   :—   :m   | m   :—   :m   | r   :d   :t,  | d   :—   :d
:l,  | se, :—   :l,  | m,  :—   :l,  | r,  :—   :m,  | l,  :—   :l,

t,  :l,  :t,  | d   :—  :r   || m   :—  || m   | t,  :d   :r   | m   :—  :t,
m,  :—   :m,  | l,  :—  :l,  || se, :—  || s,  | s,  :—   :s,  | s,  :—  :se,
m   :—   :m   | m   :—  :r   || t,  :—  || d   | r   :d   :s   | s   :—  :r
se, :ba, :se, | l,  :—  :f,  || m,  :—  || d,  | s,  :l,  :t,  | d   :—  :t,

d   :t,  :l,    | se, :—  :d   | m   :—  :d   | t,  :-.l, :se, | l,  :—  || l,  | l,
l,  :m,  :m,.r, | m,  :—  :m,  | m,  :—  :m,  | f,  :—    :m,  | m,  :—  || f,  | m,
m   :—   :l,    | t,  :—  :d   | t,  :—  :d   | r   :-.d  :t,  | d   :—  || r   | de
l,  :s,  :f,    | m,  :—  :l,  | se, :—  :l,  | r,  :—    :m,  | l,  :—  || r,  | l,
                                                                          A-men.
```

WEEP not for Him who onward bears
His Cross to Calvary;
He does not ask man's pitying tears,
Who wills for man to die.

2 The awful sorrow of His face,
The bowing of His frame,
Come not from torture nor disgrace:
He fears not cross nor shame.

3 There is a deeper pang of grief,
An agony unknown,
In which His love finds no relief—
He bears it all alone.

4 He sees the souls for whom He dies
Yet clinging to their sin,
And heirs of mansions in the skies
Who will not enter in.

5 O may I in Thy sorrow share,
And mourn that sins of mine
Should ever wound with grief or care
That loving heart of Thine.

THOMAS BENSON POLLOCK, 1836–96.

95

PSALM 110 (L'OMNIPOTENT). (11 10. 11 10.) *French Psalter*, 1551.

Composed or arranged by LOUIS BOURGEOIS, 1510– ?.

Lah = G. Doh = B♭. *Moderately slow.*

```
l,  :—  |s,  :l,  |t,  :—  |d   :—  |r   :m   |r   :d    |t,  :—  |l,  :—  ||
m,  :—  |m,  :m,  |s,  :—  |—   :l, |t,  :d   |t,  :l,   |se, :—  |l,  :—  ||
d   :—  |t,  :d   |r   :—  |m   :—  |f   :s   |f   :—.m  |r   :—  |d   :—  ||
l,  :—  |m,  :l,  |s,  :f, |m,  :—  |r,  :d,  |r,  :r,   |m,  :—  |f,  :—  ||

d   :—  |t,  :l,  |s,  :—  |l,  :—  |t,  :l,  |l,  :se,  |l,  :—  |—   :—  ||
s,  :—  |s,  :f,  |m,  :—  |fe, :—  |s,  :fe, |m,  :m,   |m,  :—  |—   :—  ||
m   :—  |d   :d   |d   :—  |d   :—  |t,  :r.d |t,  :t,   |d   :—  |—   :—  ||
d,  :—  |m,  :f,  |d,  :t,,|l,, :—  |s,, :r,  |m,  :m,   |l,, :—  |—   :—  ||

m,  :—  |l,  :l,  |s,  :—  |l,  :—  |d   :t,  |l,  :s,   |f,  :—  |m,  :—  ||  :s, |l,  :t,
d,  :—  |f,  :f,  |m,  :—  |f,  :—  |m,  :s,  |f,  :m,   |r,  :—  |m,  :—  ||  :r, |f,  :f,
d   :—  |d   :r   |m   :r  |d   :—  |d   :m   |d   :d    |d   :t, |s,  :—  ||  :t, |d   :r
l,, :—  |l,, :t,, |d,  :—  |f,  :—  |l,  :m,  |f,  :d,   |r,  :—  |d,  :—  ||  :s, |f,  :r,

d   :—  |d   :—   |r   :l, |d   :—  |t,  :—   |l,  :—    |—   :—  || l,  |l,  ||
m,  :—  |f,  :—   |f,  :r, |m,  :ba,|se, :—   |l,  :—    |—   :—  || f,  |m,  ||
d   :ta,|l,  :—   |l,  :l, |m   :—  |—   :r   |d   :—    |—   :—  || r   |de  ||
l,  :s, |f,  :—   |r,  :f, |d,  :r, |m,  :—   |l,  :—    |—   :—  || r,  |l,, ||
```

A-men.

Est-ce vous que je vois?

MY Lord, my Master, at Thy feet adoring,
  I see Thee bowed beneath Thy load of woe:
For me, a sinner, is Thy life-blood pouring;
  For Thee, my Saviour, scarce my tears will flow.

2 Thine own disciple to the Jews has sold Thee;
  With friendship's kiss and loyal word he came:
How oft of faithful love my lips have told Thee,
  While Thou hast seen my falsehood and my shame!

3 With taunts and scoffs they mock what seems Thy weakness,
  With blows and outrage adding pain to pain:
Thou art unmoved and steadfast in Thy meekness;
  When I am wronged, how quickly I complain!

4 My Lord, my Saviour, when I see Thee wearing
Upon Thy bleeding brow the crown of thorn,
Shall I for pleasure live, or shrink from bearing
Whate'er my lot may be of pain or scorn?

5 O victim of Thy love! O pangs most healing!
O saving death! O fruitful agonies!
I pray Thee, Christ, before Thee humbly kneeling,
For ever keep Thy Cross before mine eyes.

JACQUES BRIDAINE, 1701–67; *tr.* by THOMAS BENSON POLLOCK, 1836–96.

96

ST. CROSS. (L.M.)

Lah = D. Doh = F. *Slow.* JOHN BACCHUS DYKES, 1823–76.

|d :— |d :r |m :— |— :l |s :— |f :— |m :— |— :— |m :— |m :f |s :—
|l, :— |l, :t, |d :— |— :d |d :s, |l, :t, |d :— |— :— |d :— |t, :l, |s, :—
|m :— |m :s |s :— |— :f |m :— |— :r |m :— |— :— |d :— |d :d |d :r
|l, :— |l, :s, |d :— |— :f, |s, :— |s, :— |d :— |— :— |l, :— |s, :f, |m, :—

|d :— |m :— |r :— |d :— |— ||m |m :— |— :m |r :— |m :— |d :— |r :—
|d :— |d :— |t, :— |d :— |— ||s, |s, :— |— :l, |l, :— |se, :— |l, :— |t, :l,
|m :f |s :— |— :f |m :— |— ||m |m :— |— :m |f :— |m :— |m :— |f :—
|l, :— |s, :— |s, :— |d, :— |— ||d |d :— |— :d |t, :— |m, :— |l, :— |r, :—

t, :—	— :—	l, :—	l, :l,	m :—	— :r	d :—	t, :—	l, :—	— :—		l,	l,	
se, :—	— :—	l, :—	l, :l,	m :—	— :l,	l, :—	se, :—	l, :—	— :—		f,	m,	
m :—	— :—	l, :—	l, :l,	m :—	— :f	m :—	r :—	d :—	— :—		r	de	
m, :—	— :—	l, :—	l, :l,	m :—	— :r,	m, :—	m, :—	l, :—	— :—		r,	l,	

A-men.

O COME and mourn with me awhile;
O come ye to the Saviour's side;
O come, together let us mourn:
Jesus, our Lord, is crucified!

2 Have we no tears to shed for Him,
While soldiers scoff and Jews deride?
Ah! look how patiently He hangs:
Jesus, our Lord, is crucified!

3 Seven times He spake, seven words of love;
And all three hours His silence cried
For mercy on the souls of men:
Jesus, our Lord, is crucified!

4 O break, O break, hard heart of mine!
Thy weak self-love and guilty pride
His Pilate and His Judas were:
Jesus, our Lord, is crucified!

5 A broken heart, a fount of tears,
Ask, and they will not be denied;
A broken heart love's cradle is:
Jesus, our Lord, is crucified!

6 O love of God! O sin of man!
In this dread act your strength is tried,
And victory remains with love:
Jesus, our Lord, is crucified!

FREDERICK WILLIAM FABER, 1814–63.

97

PSALM 80. (11 10. 11 10.) *Scottish Psalter*, 1564. Adapted by JAMES SMITH ANDERSON, 1853-

Lah = D. Doh = F. *Moderately slow.*

```
l,  :—  |m  :m   |r  :m   |l,  :d   |r  :—  |—  :d   |t,  :—  |l,  :—
l,  :—  |t, :s,  |s, :s,  |f,  :s,  |s, :—  |—  :m,  |s,  :—  |f,  :—
d   :—  |m  :m   |t, :d   |d   :d   |t, :—  |—  :d   |m   :—  |d   :—
l,  :—  |s, :m,  |s, :d,  |f,  :m,  |s, :—  |—  :l,  |m,  :—  |f,  :—

l,  :—  |r  :d   |l, :d   |r   :m   |r  :—  |—  :d   |t,  :—  |—  :—
f,  :—  |l, :s,  |f, :d   |t,  :d   |t, :—  |—  :l,  |se, :—  |—  :—
d   :—  |f  :m   |r  :m   |s   :s   |s  :—  |—  :m   |m   :—  |—  :—
f,  :—  |r, :m,  |f, :l,  |s,  :d   |s, :—  |—  :l,  |m,  :—  |—  :—

l,  :—  |d  :r   |d  :l,  |d   :r   |m  :—  |—  :r   |r   :—  |d   :—
l,  :—  |l, :t,  |l, :l,  |l,  :t,  |d  :—  |—  :t,  |t,  :—  |d   :—
m   :—  |m  :s   |m  :m   |m   :s   |s  :—  |—  :s   |s   :—  |m   :—
d   :—  |l, :s,  |l, :d   |l,  :s,  |d  :—  |—  :s,  |s,  :—  |l,  :—

s   :—  |l  :s   |m  :d   |r   :m   |r  :—  |t, :—   |l,  :—  |—  :—  ||r   de
d   :—  |d  :d   |d  :s,  |t,  :d   |l, :—  |—  :se, |l,  :—  |—  :—  ||l,  l,
s   :—  |f  :s   |s  :m   |s   :s   |f  :—  |m  :—   |d   :—  |—  :—  ||f   m
m   :—  |f  :m   |d  :d   |s,  :d,  |r, :—  |m, :—   |l,  :—  |—  :—  ||r,  l,
                                                                        A - men.
```

'Father, forgive them ; for they know not what they do.'

O WORD of pity, for our pardon pleading,
Breathed in the hour of loneliness and pain ;
O voice, which, through the ages interceding,
Calls us to fellowship with God again.

2 O word of comfort, through the silence stealing,
As the dread act of sacrifice began ;
O infinite compassion, still revealing
The infinite forgiveness won for man.

3 O word of hope, to raise us nearer heaven,
When courage fails us, and when faith is dim ;
The souls for whom Christ prays to Christ are given,
To find their pardon and their joy in Him.

4 O Intercessor, who art ever living
To plead for dying souls that they may live,
Teach us to know our sin which needs forgiving,
Teach us to know the love which can forgive.

ADA RUNDALL GREENAWAY, 1861-

[May be sung to INTERCESSOR, No. 485.]

98

CONGLETON. (10 10. 10 10.)

Lah = G. Doh = B♭. *Moderately slow.* MICHAEL WISE, *c.* 1648–87.

```
|l,  :d    |— :t,   |d  :l,  |se, :l,  |s, :-.f, |m, :— |— ||s, |s,  :m,
|m,  :m,   |— :m,   |m, :r,  |m,  :d,  |r, :r,   |m, :— |— ||m, |r,  :d,
|d   :l,   |— :t,   |l, :l,  |t,  :l,  |l, :t,   |d  :— |— ||s, |s,  :s,
|l,2 :l,   |— :se,  |l, :f,  |m,  :f,  |r, :r,   |d, :— |— ||d, |t,2 :d,

|l,  :-.t,  |d  :-.t, |l, :l, |se :— |— ||t,  |t,  :t,  |d  :r  |m  :m  |r  :r
|d,  :-.m,  |m, :m,   |m, :r, |m, :— |— ||m,  |m,  :m,  |m, :s, |s, :s, |s, :s,.f,
|l,  :-.se, |l, :-.t, |d  :l, |t, :— |— ||se, |se, :se, |l, :t, |t, :d  |d  :t,
|l,2 :-.m,  |l, :s,   |f, :f, |m, :— |— ||m,  |m,  :m,  |l, :s, |m, :d, |s, :s,

|d  :— |— ||m, |ba, :ba,  |se, :se, |l, :t, |se, :-.se, |l,  :— ||l, |l,  ||
|m, :— |— ||m, |m,  :r,   |m,  :m,  |m, :f, |m,  :-.m,  |m,  :— ||f, |m,  ||
|d  :— |— ||d  |l,  :t,   |t,  :t,  |d  :t, |t,  :-.t,  |d   :— ||r  |de  ||
|d, :— |— ||d, |r,  :t,2  |m,  :r,  |d, :r, |m,  :-.m,  |l,2 :— ||r, |l,2 ||
                                                                 A-men.
```

'Verily I say unto thee, To-day thou shalt be with Me in Paradise.'

'LORD, when Thy Kingdom comes, remember me!'
Thus spake the dying lips to dying ears.
O faith, which in that darkest hour could see
The promised glory of the far-off years!

2 No kingly sign declares that glory now;
No ray of hope lights up that awful hour;
A thorny crown surrounds the bleeding brow;
The hands are stretched in weakness, not in power.

3 Hark! through the gloom the dying Saviour saith,
'Thou too shalt rest in Paradise to-day';
O words of love to answer words of faith!
O words of hope for those who live to pray!

4 Lord, when with dying lips my prayer is said,
Grant that in faith Thy Kingdom I may see,
And, thinking on Thy Cross and bleeding head,
May breathe my parting words, 'Remember me.'

5 Remember me, but not my shame or sin;
Thy cleansing blood hath washed them all away;
Thy precious death for me did pardon win;
Thy blood redeemed me in that awful day.

6 Remember me; and, ere I pass away,
Speak Thou the assuring word that sets us free,
And make Thy promise to my heart, 'To-day
Thou too shalt rest in Paradise with Me.'

WILLIAM DALRYMPLE MACLAGAN, 1826–1910.

99

STABAT MATER. (8 8 7. D.)

Doh = F. *Very slow and solemn.* French Church Melody.

```
d  :r  |m  :r  |m  :s  |f    :m ||m  :r  |l,  :t,
s, :t, |d  :r  |d  :s, |l,.t, :d ||d  :t, |l,  :s,
m  :s  |s  :s  |s  :m  |f    :s ||s  :s  |m   :r
d  :s, |d  :t, |d  :m  |r    :d ||d  :s, |l,  :t,.d
```

D.C.

```
l,  :t, |l,   :s, ||r  :d  |r  :m  |r  :-.d  |d  :— ||d  |d
fe, :s, |fe,  :s, ||l, :l, |t, :d  |d  :t,.d |s, :— ||l, |s,
r   :r  |r.d  :t, ||r  :m  |s  :s  |s  :s    |m  :— ||f  |m
r   :s, |r,   :s, ||f, :l, |s, :m, |s, :s,   |d  :— ||f, |d,
                                                        A-men.
```

Stabat mater dolorosa.

'Woman, behold thy son . . . Behold thy mother.'

AT the Cross, her station keeping,
Stood the mournful mother weeping,
Where He hung, the dying Lord;
For her soul, of joy bereavèd,
Bowed with anguish, deeply grievèd,
Felt the sharp and piercing sword.

2 O, how sad and sore distressèd
Now was she, that mother blessèd
Of the sole-begotten One;
Deep the woe of her affliction,
When she saw the crucifixion
Of her ever-glorious Son.

3 Who, on Christ's dear mother gazing,
Pierced by anguish so amazing,
Born of woman, would not weep?
Who, on Christ's dear mother thinking,
Such a cup of sorrow drinking,
Would not share her sorrows deep?

4 For His people's sins chastisèd,
She beheld her Son despisèd,
Scourged, and crowned with thorns entwined;
Saw Him then from judgment taken,
And in death by all forsaken,
Till His spirit He resigned.

5 Jesus, may her deep devotion
Stir in me the same emotion,
Fount of love, Redeemer kind,
That my heart, fresh ardour gaining,
And a purer love attaining,
May with Thee acceptance find.

13th century; *tr.* by EDWARD CASWALL, 1814–78, and others.

100 ARFON. (7 7. 7 7. 7 7.)

Lah = G. Doh = B♭. *Slow.* Welsh Hymn Melody.

m_1 :l_1 | l_1.se_1 :ba_1.m_1 | l_1 :t_1 | d :— | r :d | t_1 :l_1 | d.t_1 :l_1.se_1 | l_1 :— ‖
m_1 :l_1 | l_1.se_1 :ba_1.m_1 | m_1 :m_1 | m_1 :— | m_1 :m_1 | m_1 :d_1 | f_1 :m_1 | d_1 :— ‖
m_1 :l_1 | l_1.se_1 :ba_1.m_1 | l_1 :se_1 | l_1 :— | t_1 :l_1 | se_1 :l_1 | l_1.t_1 :d.t_1 | l_1 :— ‖
m_1 :l_1 | l_1.se_1 :ba_1.m_1 | d_1 :m_1 | l_1 :— | se_1 :l_1 | m_1 :f_1 | r_1 :m_1 | l_2 :— ‖

m :m.r | d :m | r :d | t_1 :— | m :m.r | d :m | r :d | d :t_1 ‖
m_1 :m_1 | l_1 :l_1 | l_1.se_1 :l_1 | se_1 :— | l_1 :l_1.se_1 | l_1 :l_1 | l_1 :f_1 | m_1 :— ‖
d :t_1 | m :d | r :m | m :— | m :d.r | m :d | l_1 :l_1 | l_1 :se_1 ‖
l_1 :se_1 | l_1 :d | t_1 :l_1 | m_1 :— | d :d.t_1 | l_1 :s_1 | f_1 :r_1 | m_1 :— ‖

m_1 :l_1 | l_1.se_1 :ba_1.m_1 | l_1 :t_1 | d :— | r :d | t_1 :l_1 | d.t_1 :l_1.se_1 | l_1 :— ‖ l_1 | l_1 ‖
t_2 :m_1 | r_1 :t_2 | m_1 :m_1 | m_1 :— | m_1 :m_1 | m_1 :d_1 | f_1 :m_1 | m_1 :— ‖ f_1 | m ‖
se_1 :l_1 | m_1 :ba_1.se_1 | l_1 :se_1 | l_1 :— | t_1 :l_1 | se_1 :l_1 | l_1.t_1 :d.r | d :— ‖ r | de ‖
r_1 :d_1 | t_2 :r_1 | d_1 :m_1 | l_1 :— | se_1 :l_1 | m_1 :f_1 | r_1 :m_1 | l_2 :— ‖ r_1 | l_1 ‖

A-men.

'My God, My God, why hast Thou forsaken Me?'

THRONED upon the awful Tree,
King of grief, I watch with Thee.
Darkness veils Thine anguished face:
None its lines of woe can trace:
None can tell what pangs unknown
Hold Thee silent and alone,—

2 Silent through those three dread hours,
Wrestling with the evil powers,
Left alone with human sin,
Gloom around Thee and within,
Till the appointed time is nigh,
Till the Lamb of God may die.

3 Hark, that cry that peals aloud
Upward through the whelming cloud!
Thou, the Father's only Son,
Thou, His own anointed One,
Thou dost ask Him—can it be?—
'Why hast Thou forsaken Me?'

4 Lord, should fear and anguish roll
Darkly o'er my sinful soul,
Thou, who once wast thus bereft
That Thine own might ne'er be left,
Teach me by that bitter cry
In the gloom to know Thee nigh.

JOHN ELLERTON, 1826–93.

101 ISLEWORTH. (8 8. 8 6.)

Lah = D. Doh = F. *Moderately slow.* SAMUEL HOWARD, 1710–82.

:m |l :m |f :r |d :t, |l, :t, |d :r |m :l
:l, |l,.t, :d |l, :l, |l, :se, |m, :s, |s, :l,.t, |d .t, :d .r
:d .r |m :m |r :l,.t, |d .r :m |d :r |d :f |m :d'
:l,.t, |d :l, |r, :f, |m, :m, |l, :s,.f, |m, :r, |l, :l,

|s :fe |m ||m |r :d |s :d |r :d .t, |d :d
|m :re |m ||d .t, |l,.t, :d |t, :l, |l, :s, |s, :l,
|t :t .l |s ||s |f :m .fe |s :m |f .m :r |m :f
|t, :t, |m, ||d |r :l, |m, :l,.s, |f, :s, |d :f,

m :r	d :t,	l, :—	—		l,	l,	
d :– .t,	l, :se,	l, :—	—		f,	m,	
s :f	m :m .r	d :—	—		r	de	
d, :r,	m, :m,	l, :—	—		r,	l,	

A-men.

'I thirst.'

HIS are the thousand sparkling rills
That from a thousand fountains burst,
And fill with music all the hills;
And yet He saith, 'I thirst.'

2 All fiery pangs on battle-fields,
On fever beds where sick men toss,
Are in that human cry He yields
To anguish on the Cross.

3 But more than pains that racked Him then
Was the deep longing thirst divine
That thirsted for the souls of men;
Dear Lord! and one was mine.

4 O Love most patient, give me grace;
Make all my soul athirst for Thee;
That parched dry lip, that fading face,
That thirst, were all for me.

CECIL FRANCES ALEXANDER, 1823–95.

102 NEWLAND. (S.M.)

Doh = F. *Moderately slow.* HENRY JOHN GAUNTLETT, 1805–76.

```
:s |d :m |r :r  |m :— |— :m |f  :l  |s :m |r  :— |—
:d |d :d |d :t, |d :— |— :d |d  :d  |d :d |t, :— |—
:m |s :s |s :s  |s :— |— :s |f  :f  |m :s |s  :— |—
:d |m :d |s, :s,|d :— |— :d |l, :f, |d :d |s, :— |—

:m |m :r  |d :d |f :m |r  :r  |s :f.m |m :r  |d :— |— || d  | d  ||
:d |d :t, |d :d |d :d |t, :t, |d :d   |d :t, |d :— |— || l, | s, ||
:s |s :s  |s :s |l :l |t  :s  |s :l   |s :s  |m :— |— || f  | m  ||
:d |s :f  |m :m |r :r |s  :f  |m :f   |s :s, |d :— |— || f, | d  ||
                                                          A - men.
```

SOUTHWELL. (S.M.)

Lah = E. Doh = G. *Moderately slow.* *Damon's Psalmes*, 1579.

```
|l, :— |d  :d  |t, :t,  |l, :— ||l, :— |d  :d  |r  :r  |m :— ||
|m, :— |m, :l, |l, :se, |l, :— ||m, :— |l, :d  |d  :t, |d :— ||
|d  :— |d  :d  |f  :m   |d  :— ||d  :— |m  :m  |l  :s  |s :— ||
|l, :— |l, :f, |r, :m,  |l, :— ||l, :— |l, :s, |f, :s, |d :— ||

|m :— |s  :s  |f  :f  |m  :m  |r  :— ||m  :— |r  :d  |t, :t,  |l, :— || l, | l, ||
|d :— |d  :t, |l, :s, |s, :d  |t, :— ||d  :— |t, :l, |l, :se, |l, :— || f, | m, ||
|m :— |r  :r  |d  :r  |m  :s  |s  :— ||s  :— |s  :m  |f  :m   |d  :— || r  | de ||
|d :— |s, :s, |l, :t, |d  :m, |s, :— ||d, :— |s, :l, |r, :m,  |l, :— || r, | l, ||
                                                                          A-men.
```

'It is finished.'

O PERFECT life of love!
 All, all is finished now,
All that He left His throne above
 To do for us below.

2 No work is left undone
 Of all the Father willed;
His toils and sorrows, one by one,
 The Scripture have fulfilled.

3 No pain that we can share
 But He has felt its smart;
All forms of human grief and care
 Have pierced that tender heart.

4 And on His thorn-crowned head,
 And on His sinless soul,
Our sins in all their guilt were laid,
 That He might make us whole.

5 In perfect love He dies;
 For me He dies, for me!
O all-atoning Sacrifice,
 I cling by faith to Thee.

6 In every time of need,
 Before the judgment throne,
Thy work, O Lamb of God, I'll plead,
 Thy merits, not my own.

7 Yet work, O Lord, in me,
 As Thou for me hast wrought;
And let my love the answer be
 To grace Thy love has brought.

HENRY WILLIAMS BAKER, 1821–77.

103

ZU MEINEM HERRN. (11 10. 11 10.)

Doh = A♭. *Moderately slow.* JOHANN GOTTFRIED SCHICHT, 1753–1823.

```
|s, :—  |l, :t, |d  :t,    |m, :l,  ...
```

```
|s,  :—  |l,  :t,  |d  :t,     |d  :d     |r  :r   |m  :d   ‖m  :—  |r  :d
|m,  :—  |f,  :f,  |s, :s,.f,  |m, :l,    |l, :s,  |s, :m,  ‖s, :—  |s, :l,
|d   :—  |d   :r   |s, :r      |d  :m     |r  :t,  |d  :d   ‖d  :—  |r  :m.fe
|d,  :—  |f,  :r,  |m, :s,     |l, :-.s,  |f, :s,  |d  :d,  ‖d  :—  |t, :l,

|t,  :s,     |d  :t,  |l,  :l,   |s, :—  ‖r  :—  |r  :d   |t, :t,  |m  :r   |d  :t,
|r,  :r,     |s, :s,  |s,  :fe,  |s, :—  ‖f, :—  |s, :l,  |t, :t,  |d  :t,  |l, :se,
|s   :t,     |d  :r   |m   :r.d  |t, :—  ‖f  :—  |m  :m   |r  :s   |s  :f   |m  :m
|s,  :-.fe,  |m, :r,  |d,  :r,   |s, :—  ‖r, :—  |m, :f,  |s, :s,  |d, :r,  |m, :m,

|d  :l,  |—  ‖r   |r  :m    |f  :m    |r  :d   |l, :t,  |d  :—  ‖d  |d  ‖
|l, :m,  |—  ‖s,  |l, :s,   |f, :l,   |l, :s,  |f, :f,  |m, :—  ‖f, |m, ‖
|m  :d   |—  ‖ta, |l, :de   |r  :m    |f  :m   |m  :r   |d  :—  ‖l, |s, ‖
|l, :l,  |—  ‖s,  |f, :m,   |r, :de,  |r, :m,  |f, :s,  |d, :—  ‖f, |d, ‖
```

A-men.

'Father, into Thy hands I commend My spirit.'

AND now, belovèd Lord, Thy soul resigning
Into Thy Father's arms with conscious will,
Calmly, with reverend grace, Thy head inclining,
The throbbing brow and labouring breast grow still.

2 Freely Thy life Thou yieldest, meekly bending
Even to the last beneath our sorrows' load,
Yet strong in death, in perfect peace commending
Thy spirit to Thy Father and Thy God.

3 My Saviour, in mine hour of mortal anguish,
When earth grows dim, and round me falls the night,
O breathe Thy peace, as flesh and spirit languish;
At that dread eventide let there be light.

4 To Thy dear Cross turn Thou mine eyes in dying;
Lay but my fainting head upon Thy breast;
Thine outstretched arms receive my latest sighing;
And then, O then, Thine everlasting rest!

ELIZA SIBBALD ALDERSON, 1818–89.

104

SHILOH. (8 8 7. D.) — 18th cent. Hymn-tune. Adapted by JAMES SMITH ANDERSON, 1853-

Lah = D. Doh = F. *Moderately slow.*

```
|m  :r     |d     :t,   |l,  :se,  |t,  :l,  |d   :t,     |l,  :t,  |d    :r    |f  :m
|d  :t,.l, |s,    :s,   |m,  :m,   |se, :l,  |s,  :f,.s,  |l,  :f,  |s,   :s,   |l, :s,
|s  :f     |m     :r    |d   :r    |m   :m   |m   :r      |d   :f   |m    :t,   |d  :d
|d, :r,    |m,.f, :s,   |l,  :t,   |d   :d   |d,  :r,.m,  |f,  :r,  |m,   :s,   |d  :d

|m   :r.d  |r.m,f :m.r  |d   :t,   |l,  :—  ||l   :se  |l   :m   |f.r  :s.f  |f  :m
|t,  :l,   |l,    :-.t, |l,  :se,  |l,  :—  ||m   :r   |d   :t,  |l,   :t,   |t, :d
|t,  :m    |r     :f    |m   :m.r  |d   :—  ||d   :r   |m   :m   |d    :r    |r  :d
|se, :l,   |f,    :r,   |m,  :m,   |l,  :—  ||d   :t,  |l,  :s,  |f,   :r,   |l, :l,

|l   :se   |l  :t   |d'.t :l .se |l :l  |d  :s.f |m.,f :m.r |d :t,   |l, :— ||r  |de
|d.r :m.f  |m  :r   |d    :m .r  |d :r  |s, :r   |d    :-.t, |l, :se, |l, :— ||l, |l,
|l   :t    |m  :se  |l    :t     |l :f  |s  :s   |s    :-.f |m :m.r  |d  :— ||f  |m
|f   :m.r  |d  :t,  |l,   :m     |f :r  |m  :t,  |d    :-.r |m :m,   |l, :— ||r, |l,
                                                                          A-men.
```

BY the Cross of Jesus standing,
Love our straitened souls expanding,
  Taste we now the peace and grace!
Health from yonder Tree is flowing,
Heavenly light is on it glowing,
  From the blessèd Sufferer's face.

2 Here is pardon's pledge and token,
Guilt's strong chain for ever broken,
  Righteous peace securely made;
Brightens now the brow once shaded,
Freshens now the face once faded,
  Peace with God now makes us glad.

3 All the love of God is yonder,
Love above all thought and wonder,
  Perfect love that casts out fear!
Strength, like dew, is here distilling,
Glorious life our souls is filling—
  Life eternal, only here!

4 Here the living water welleth;
Here the Rock, now smitten, telleth
  Of salvation freely given:
This the fount of love and pity,
This the pathway to the city,
  This the very gate of heaven.

HORATIUS BONAR, 1808-89.

[May be sung to EVENING HYMN, No. 283.]

105 HORSLEY. (C.M.)

Doh = E♭. *In moderate time.* William Horsley, 1774–1858.

```
:d  | r  :m  | f  :m  | s  :f.m | r  :s  | m  :d' | t  :l  | s  :— | — ||
:d  | t, :d  | d  :d  | d  :d   | t, :s, | d  :d  | r  :r  | t, :— | — ||
:m  | s  :s  | f  :s  | s  :l   | r  :r  | s  :l  | s  :fe | s  :— | — ||
:d  | s, :d  | l, :d  | m, :f,  | s, :t, | d  :l, | r  :r  | s, :— | — ||

:r.m | f  :f  | f  :m  | l  :l  | se :se | l  :f  | m  :r   | d :— | — || d  | d  ||
:t,  | d  :d  | r  :m  | m  :r  | m  :m  | d  :r  | d  :t,  | d :— | — || l, | s, ||
:s   | f  :l  | s  :s  | l  :l  | t  :t  | l  :l  | s  :-.f | m :— | — || f  | m  ||
:s,  | l, :l, | t, :d  | f  :f  | m  :m  | f  :f, | s, :s,  | d :— | — || f, | d  ||
                                                                      A - men.
```

THERE is a green hill far away,
Without a city wall,
Where the dear Lord was crucified,
Who died to save us all.

2 We may not know, we cannot tell
What pains He had to bear;
But we believe it was for us
He hung and suffered there.

3 He died that we might be forgiven,
He died to make us good,
That we might go at last to heaven,
Saved by His precious blood.

4 There was no other good enough
To pay the price of sin;
He only could unlock the gate
Of heaven, and let us in.

5 O dearly, dearly has He loved,
And we must love Him too,
And trust in His redeeming blood,
And try His works to do.

Cecil Frances Alexander, 1823–95

106 ROCKINGHAM (COMMUNION). (L.M.)

Doh = E♭. *Moderately slow.* Adapted by Edward Miller, 1731–1807.

```
:d | m  :f  :r   | d :— :m | s :— :l | s :— :s  | d' :— :t  | l  :— :s
:d | d  :—  :t,  | d :— :d | d :— :d | d :— :r  | d  :— :d  | d  :r :m
:m | s  :l  :s.f | m :— :s | s :— :f | m :— :s  | m  :f  :s  | l  :t :d'
:d | d  :f, :s,  | d :— :d | m :— :f | d :— :t, | l, :— :s, | f, :f :m

| s  :f  :m | m  :r  | r  | s  :— :l  | t :— :s   | d' :m  :fe
| m  :r  :d | d  :t, | t, | r  :— :r  | r :— :t,  | d  :m  :r.d
| d' :s  :s | s  :—  | s  | s  :— :fe | s :— :s.f | m  :d' :l
| l, :t, :d | s, :—  | s, | t, :— :r  | s :— :s,  | l, :—  :r
```

```
s  :— :d  | f  :— :m  | r  :— :d  | d.r:m :r  | d :— || d  | d
t, :— :d  | d  :r :d  | l, :t, :d | d  :— :t, | d :— || l, | s,
s  :— :s  | l  :— :s  | f  :— :m  | m.f:s :f  | m :— || f  | m
s, :— :m  | l, :t, :d | f, :s, :l,| s, :— :s, | d :— || f, | d
                                                        A-men.
```

FAUX-BOURDON SETTING.

Doh = E♭. GEOFFREY TURTON SHAW, 1879–

```
:m  | s :l :f   | f  :m :s  | d' :m :fe  | s  :— :s   | m  :ba:se | l  :d' :t
:s, | d :— :t,  | s, :— :d  | d  :m :r.d | t, :d :r   | m  :— :r  | d  :-.r:m
:d  | m :f :r   | d  :— :m  | s  :— :l   | s  :— :s   | d' :— :t  | l  :— :s
:d  | d :f, :s, | d  :— :d  | l, :— :r   | s, :l, :t, | d  :r :m  | l, :— :m,
```

```
l  :— :m  | s  :—  || r  | m :— :fe | fe :s :t  | l  :-.t:d'
m  :r :d  | d  :t, || r  | r :d :r  | r  :— :t, | m  :d :r
s  :f :m  | m  :r  || r  | s :— :l  | t  :— :s  | d' :m :fe
f, :— :l, | s, :—  || t, | d :— :d  | t, :— :m  | d  :l, :r
```

```
d' :t :d'.t    | l  :— :m   | s    :f :m  | l    :d :t,    | d     :—
r  :s :s,      | l, :t, :de | r.l, :t, :d | l,   :s, :-.f, | m,    :—
s  :— :d       | f  :— :m   | r    :— :d  | d.r  :m :r     | d     :—
s, :-.f, :m,   | f, :s, :l, | r,   :— :m, | f,   :s, :s,   | d/d,  :—
```

WHEN I survey the wondrous Cross
On which the Prince of Glory died,
My richest gain I count but loss,
And pour contempt on all my pride.

2 Forbid it, Lord, that I should boast,
Save in the death of Christ, my God;
All the vain things that charm me most,
I sacrifice them to His blood.

3 See! from His head, His hands, His feet,
Sorrow and love flow mingled down;
Did e'er such love and sorrow meet,
Or thorns compose so rich a crown?

4 Were the whole realm of Nature mine,
That were an offering far too small;
Love so amazing, so divine,
Demands my soul, my life, my all.

ISAAC WATTS, 1674–1748.

107

PASSION CHORALE. (76. 76. D.) HANS LEO HASSLER, 1564–1612.
Arranged by JOHANN SEBASTIAN BACH, 1685–1750.

Doh = C. *Slow.*

:m |l :s |f :m |r :— |m ||t |d' :d' |t .l :t
:d |d :d |d .r :r .d |d :t, |d ||r |d .r :m |m :m .r
:s |f :s |l .s :s |l :s |s ||se |m :l |l :se
:d |f :m |l,.t, :d |f, :s, |d ||t, |l,.t, :d .r |m :m (m,)

D.C.

l :— |— ||d' |t .l :s |l :t |d' :— |d' ||s
d :— |— ||l .s |f :m.r |d :f |f :m .r |m ||m
l :— |— ||m' |r'.d' :t |l .s :f .s |l :s .f |s ||d'
l, :— |— ||l |r :m |f .m :r |d :— |d ||d

G.t.

l :s |f :f |m :— |— ||d'f |m .f :s |f :m
f :m |m :r |de :— |— ||r s, |s, :s, |l, :s,
d' :d'.t |l :l |l :— |— ||l r |d :d .t, |d .r :m .d
f :d |r .m :f .s |l :— |— ||fe t, |d :m, |l, .t, :d

f.C.

r :— |m t ||m |f :m |r :s |m :— |— ||f |m ||
l, :s, |s r ||d |d .t, :d |d :t, |d :— |— ||d |d ||
l,.r :t, |d s ||s |f :s |l :r .s |s :— |— ||l |s ||
f, :s, |d s, ||d .t, |l, :s, |f, :s, |d :— |— ||f, |d ||

A - men.

O Haupt voll Blut und Wunden.

O SACRED Head, sore wounded,
With grief and shame weighed down!
O Kingly Head, surrounded
With thorns, Thine only crown!
How pale art Thou with anguish,
With sore abuse and scorn!
How does that visage languish,
Which once was bright as morn!

2 O Lord of life and glory,
What bliss till now was Thine!
I read the wondrous story;
I joy to call Thee mine.
Thy grief and bitter passion
Were all for sinners' gain;
Mine, mine was the transgression,
But Thine the deadly pain.

ALTERNATIVE VERSION.

Harmonized by JOHANN SEBASTIAN BACH, 1685–1750.
In *The Passion according to St. Matthew.*

Lah = A. Doh = C. *Slow.*

```
:m   |l    :s  |f     :m  |r   :–  |m  ‖ t   |d'  :t.d',r' |d'  :t.l
:d   |d.r  :m  |l,.t, :d  |d   :t, |d  ‖ m   |m   :f       |m   :r.d
:l   |l.t  :d' |r'    :s  |l   :s  |s  ‖ t   |l   :l       |l   :se
:l.s |f    :m  |r     :d  |fe, :s, |d  ‖ se, |l,  :r       |m   :m
```

D.C.

```
l  :– |– ‖ d'  |t.l :s |l  :t  |d'.ta :–.la |d' ‖ s
d  :– |– ‖ m   |fe  :m |f  :f  |s     :f    |m  ‖ m
m  :– |– ‖ l.s |fe  :t |d' :r' |d'.ta :–.la |s  ‖ d'.ta
l, :– |– ‖ l   |re  :m |ma :r  |m     :f    |d  ‖ d
```

G.t.

```
l   :s    |l.s :f   |m  :–  |– ‖ ᵈf   |m.f :s      |f     :m
m.r :de.r |m   :m.r |r  :de |– ‖ ˡr   |d   :d      |d.r   :m.d
l   :ta   |l   :l   |l  :–  |– ‖ ʳ's  |s   :s.l,ta |l     :s
f   :m.r  |de  :r   |l, :–  |– ‖ ᶠᵉt, |d.r :m      |l,.t, :d
```

f.C.

```
r   :–  |ᵐt   ‖ m |f  :m |r      :s.f |m   :–  |–  ‖ f |m ‖
d   :t, |ᵈs   ‖ d |r  :d |r      :m.r |r   :d  |t, ‖ r |t, ‖
l   :s  |ˢr'  ‖ s |s  :s |s.l    :ta  |t   :l  |se ‖ l |se ‖
fe, :s, |ᵈs,  ‖ d |t, :d |ta,.l, :s,  |se, :l, |m  ‖ r |m ‖
```

A-men.

3 What language shall I borrow
To praise Thee, heavenly Friend,
For this Thy dying sorrow,
Thy pity without end?
O make me Thine for ever,
And, should I fainting be,
Lord, let me never, never
Outlive my love to Thee.

4 Be near me, Lord, when dying;
O show Thy Cross to me;
And, for my succour flying,
Come, Lord, to set me free;
These eyes, new faith receiving,
From Thee shall never move;
For he who dies believing
Dies safely through Thy love.

PAUL GERHARDT, 1607–76; *tr.* by JAMES WADDELL ALEXANDER, 1804–59.

108 PANGE LINGUA.

Doh = C. *Unison.* *In free rhythm.* Plainsong Melody. Mode iii.

m :m :m :r :s :s :l :d' :d' | d' :r' :d' :d' :d' :l :d' :t :l :s

s :l :d' :t :l :s :l :l | l :t :s :fe :m :l :l :r

s :s :s :m :s :l :l :s | l :t :s :l :s :f :r :m || m :f :m :r :m ||

A - men.

ARDUDWY. (8 7. 8 7. 8 7.)

Lah = C. Doh = E♭. *In moderate time.* JOHN ROBERTS (IEUAN GWYLLT), 1822–77.

m :-.m	m :r	d :r	d :l,	s :-.s	s :fe	m :re	m :—	
d :-.t,	l, :se,	l, :l,	l, :l,	t, :-.t,	d :d	t, :t,	t, :—	
m :-.r	d :t,	l, :f	m :m	m :-.f	m :re	m :l	s :—	
l, :-.se,	l, :m,	f, :r,	l, :d	m :-.r	d :l,	s, :fe,	m, :—	

l :-.se	l :m.fe	s :l	s :m	m :-.m	m :r	d.,r :m.,fe	s :—	
m :-.r	d :d	t, :r	r :d	d :-.d	d :t,	d :d	t, :—	
m :-.m	m :l	s :s.fe	s :s	s :-.s	s :f	m :d	r :—	
d :-.t,	l,.t, :d.r	m :r.d	t, :d	d :-.d	d :s,	l, :l,	s, :—	

m :-.m	m :d	s :-.s	s :m	d' :-.t	l :m.r	d :t,	l, :—		r	de	
l, :-.se,	l, :l,	d :-.t,	d :d	m :-.r	d :d.t,	l, :se,	l, :—		l,	l,	
m :-.r	d :m	m :-.f	m :s	l :-.se	l.m :m.f	m :r	d :—		f	m	
d :-.t,	l, :l,	m :-.r	d :d	l, :-.t,	d :d.r	m :m,	l, :—		r,	l,	

A-men.

Pange lingua gloriosi proelium certaminis.

SING, my tongue, how glorious battle
 Glorious victory became ;
And above the Cross, His trophy,
 Tell the triumph and the fame :
Tell how He, the earth's Redeemer,
 By His death for man o'ercame.

2 Thirty years fulfilled among us—
 Perfect life in low estate—
Born for this, and self-surrendered,
 To His passion dedicate,
On the Cross the Lamb is lifted,
 For His people immolate.

3 His the nails, the spear, the spitting,
 Reed and vinegar and gall ;
From His patient body piercèd
 Blood and water streaming fall :
Earth and sea and stars and mankind
 By that stream are cleansèd all.

4 Faithful Cross, above all other,
 One and only noble Tree,
None in foliage, none in blossom,
 None in fruit compares with thee :
Sweet the wood and sweet the iron,
 And thy Load how sweet is He.

5 Unto God be laud and honour :
 To the Father, to the Son,
To the mighty Spirit, glory—
 Ever Three and ever One :
Power and glory in the highest
 While eternal ages run.

VENANTIUS HONORIUS CLEMENTIANUS FORTUNATUS, *c.* 530–609 ; *tr.* by WILLIAM MAIR, 1830–1920 ; and ARTHUR WELLESLEY WOTHERSPOON, 1853– and *v.* 4 JOHN MASON NEALE, 1818–66.

109 WALTON. (L.M.)

Doh = B♭. *In moderate time.* WILLIAM GARDINER'S *Sacred Melodies*, 1815.

F.t.

:s, |d :— :t, |d :— :r |s, :l, :t, |d :— :[d]f |f :m :r
:s, |s, :— :s, |s, :— :l, |s, :— :f, |m, :— :[m]l, |t, :— :t,
:m |m :— :f |m :— :r |m :— :r |d :— :[d]f |s :— :s
:d, |d, :— :r, |m, :— :f, |s, :— :s, |d, :— :[l]r |s, :— :f,

f.B♭.

|s :— :m |m.r:d :t, |d :— ||[d]s, |s, :— :d |d :t, :l,
|d :— :d.t, |l, :s, :f, |m, :— ||[s]r, |m, :— :m, |f, :— :f,
|s :— :d |f :m :r |d :— ||[m]t, |d :— :s, |s, :— :l,.t,
|m, :— :l, |f, :s, :s, |d :— ||[d]s, |d, :— :d, |r, :— :r,

|s, :— :m |m :r :d |t, :— :f |f :m :r |d :r :t, |d :— ||d |d
|s, :— :s, |l, :— :l, |s, :— :t, |d :— :l, |s, :— :f, |m, :— ||f, |m,
|d :— :d |l, :— :r |r :— :r |d :— :r |m :f :r |d :— ||l, |s,
|m, :— :m, |f, :— :f, |s, :— :s, |l, :— :f, |s, :— :s, |d, :— ||f, |d,

A-men.

WE sing the praise of Him who died,
Of Him who died upon the Cross;
The sinner's hope let men deride,
For this we count the world but loss.

2 Inscribed upon the Cross we see,
In shining letters, 'God is love';
He bears our sins upon the Tree;
He brings us mercy from above.

3 The Cross! it takes our guilt away;
It holds the fainting spirit up;
It cheers with hope the gloomy day,
And sweetens every bitter cup;

4 It makes the coward spirit brave,
And nerves the feeble arm for fight;
It takes its terror from the grave,
And gilds the bed of death with light;

5 The balm of life, the cure of woe,
The measure and the pledge of love,
The sinner's refuge here below,
The angels' theme in heaven above.

THOMAS KELLY, 1769–1854.

110 ISRAEL. (88. 88. 88.)

Doh = E. *In moderate time.* GEORGE CLEMENT MARTIN, 1844–1916.

|s :s :s |s :— :f |m :— :r |d :— :— |l :l :l |l :— :s
|d :t, :d |m :— :r |d :— :t, |d :— :t, |l, :t, :de |r :t, :d
|m :f :s |l :— :l |s :— :f |m :— :d |d :r :m |f :— :s
|d :r :m |f :— :r |s :— :s, |l, :— :s, |f, :f, :m, |r, :— :m,

B.t.

f.E.

A-men.

AND can it be, that I should gain
An interest in the Saviour's blood ?
Died He for me, who caused His pain—
For me, who Him to death pursued ?
Amazing love ! how can it be
That Thou, my God, shouldst die for me ?

2 'Tis mystery all ! The Immortal dies :
Who can explore His strange design ?
In vain the first-born seraph tries
To sound the depths of love divine.
'Tis mercy all ! let earth adore,
Let angel minds inquire no more.

3 He left His Father's throne above,—
So free, so infinite His grace—
Emptied Himself of all but love,
And bled for Adam's helpless race :
'Tis mercy all, immense and free ;
For, O my God, it found out me !

4 Long my imprisoned spirit lay
Fast bound in sin and nature's night ;
Thine eye diffused a quickening ray,—
I woke, the dungeon flamed with light ;
My chains fell off, my heart was free,
I rose, went forth, and followed Thee.

5 No condemnation now I dread ;
Jesus, and all in Him, is mine !
Alive in Him, my living Head,
And clothed in righteousness divine,
Bold I approach the eternal throne,
And claim the crown, through Christ my own.

CHARLES WESLEY, 1707–88.

111 HAMMERSMITH. (86. 886.)

Doh = F. *In moderate time.* WILLIAM HENRY GLADSTONE, 1840–91.

:m |s :m.r |d :l, |m :d.t, |l, :r |d :l, |f :f
:d |d :t, |l, :l, |l, :se, |l, :l, |l, :l, |l, :t,.l,
:d |r :s.f |m :d |d :m.r |d :r |m :d |r :r.d
:d |s, :s, |l, :l, |m, :m, |f, :f, |m, :m, |r, :r,

C.t.
m :— |— ||m |l :s.f |m :l, |f :m.r |d :ml
se, :— |— ||l, |d :t, |s, :l, |l, :se, |l, :l,r
t, :— |— ||d |f :r |d :m |r :m |m :df
m, :— |— ||l, |f, :s, |d :d |t, :m, |l, :l,r

f.F.
l :se |d' :t |l :t |ds :s |d :d |m :r |d :— |— ||d |d ||
d :t, |l, :-.t, |d :m |mt, :t, |d :l, |s, :-.f, |m, :— |— ||f, |m, ||
m :m |m :f |m :se |l,m :f |m :d |d :t, |d :— |— ||l, |s, ||
m :m.r |d :r |m :m |l,m :r |d :f, |s, :s, |d, :— |— ||f, |d, ||

A - men.

O SAVIOUR, where shall guilty man
Find rest, except in Thee?
Thine was the warfare with his foe,
The Cross of pain, the cup of woe,
And Thine the victory.

2 How came the everlasting Son,
The Lord of Life, to die?
Why didst Thou meet the tempter's power?
Why, Jesus, in Thy dying hour,
Endure such agony?

3 To save us by Thy precious blood,
To make us one in Thee,
That ours might be Thy perfect life,
Thy thorny crown, Thy Cross, Thy strife,
And ours the victory.

4 O make us worthy, gracious Lord,
Of all Thy love to be;
To Thy blest will our wills incline,
That unto death we may be Thine,
And ever live in Thee.

CAROLINE ELIZABETH MAY, 1808–73.

[May be sung to NEWCASTLE, No. 36.]

112

PRESSBURG. (77. 77. 77.)

Lah = A. Doh = C. *Slow and solemn.* *Freylinghausen's Gesangbuch*, Halle, 1714.

```
| l  :se  | l  :m    | d'   :t.l   | se :— | s   :l.m  | f   :s.r  | m   :-.r | m  :— ||
| m  :r   | m  :m.r  | d    :f     | m  :— | m   :m    | r   :r    | r.d :l,  | t, :— ||
| d' :t   | l  :se   | l.m' :r'.d' | t  :— | d'  :d'   | l   :s    | s   :l   | se :— ||
| l, :t,  | d  :t,   | l,   :r     | m  :— | d.t,:l,   | r.d :t,   | d   :f   | m  :— ||

| m' :t     | d' :s     | l   :s.f  | m  :— | s  :s    | l.t :d'  | m :r   | d :— ||
| m  :se    | l  :s     | f.m :r    | d  :— | r  :m    | d.f :m.r | d :t,  | d :— ||
| t  :m'.r' | d' :r'.m' | d'  :-.t  | d' :— | s  :d'.t | l   :s.l | s :s.f | m :— ||
| se :m     | l  :t.d'  | f   :s    | d  :— | t, :d    | f.r :m.f | s :s,  | d :— ||

| m':m' | r':m'.t | d'   :t.l   | se:— | t.d':r'    | d'.r':m' | d':t   | l :— || l | l  ||
| s :l  | f :m    | m    :f     | m :— | m   :m     | m    :m  | m :m.r | d :— || r | de ||
| d':d' | t :t    | l.m' :r'.d' | t :— | t   :l.t   | d'   :l  | l :se  | l :— || f | m  ||
| d':l  | l :se   | l    :r     | m :— | se  :ba.se | l    :d.r| m :m   | l,:— || r | l, ||
                                                                                  A-men.
```

DARK the day on Calvary's Cross
Where in pain Thou diedst for me,
Choosing bitterness and loss,
From my sins to set me free.
Help me, every passing hour,
By Love's power
To live for Thee.

2 Faith and Hope through fear did fail—
Heaven's high stars they could not see;
Yet even Death could not prevail,
Sealing Thy captivity:
Thou didst leave its darksome place:
Give me grace
To live in Thee.

3 Often we have weary feet,
Many a heavy cross have we;
Yet Thy sacrifice complete
Gives us faith that Thine we be:
Through the dark day's dragging length
Give me strength
To live to Thee.

4 Saviour, who didst win Love's crown,
Just to pass it on to me,
Help me, those in sin bowed down
To uplift and bring to Thee,
That together we may climb
Up through Time
To live with Thee.

LAUCHLAN MACLEAN WATT, 1867–

113

STUTTGART. (8 7. 8 7.) — CHRISTIAN FRIEDRICH WITT, *c.* 1660–1716. *Psalmodia Sacra*, Gotha, 1715.

Doh = G. *In moderate time.*

|s, :s, |d :d |r :r |m :d |s :s |l :f |r :s |m :— ||

|s, :s, |m, :s, |l, :s, |s, :s, |s, :d |d :d |d :t, |d :— ||

|m :r |d :d |d :t, |d :m |r :m |f :l |s :s |s :— ||

|d :t, |l, :m, |f, :s, |d, :d |t, :d |f, :f, |s, :s, |d :— ||

|m :m |r :m |d :r |t, :t, |l, :l, |s, :d |d :t, |d :— || d | d ||

|s, :s, |s, :s, |m, :l, |l, :se, |l, :f, |f, :m, |l, :s, |s, :— || l, | s, ||

|d :d |t, :t, |d :f |m :m |d :r |t, :d |r :r |m :— || f | m ||

|d, :m, |s, :m, |l, :r, |m, :m, |f, :r, |s, :l, |f, :s, |d, :— || f, | d, ||

A - men.

IN the Cross of Christ I glory,
Towering o'er the wrecks of Time;
All the light of sacred story
Gathers round its head sublime.

2 When the woes of life o'ertake me,
Hopes deceive and fears annoy,
Never shall the Cross forsake me;
Lo! it glows with peace and joy.

3 When the sun of bliss is beaming
Light and love upon my way,
From the Cross the radiance streaming
Adds more lustre to the day.

4 Bane and blessing, pain and pleasure,
By the Cross are sanctified;
Peace is there that knows no measure,
Joys that through all time abide.

5 In the Cross of Christ I glory,
Towering o'er the wrecks of Time;
All the light of sacred story
Gathers round its head sublime.

JOHN BOWRING, 1792–1872.

114 O MENSCH SIEH. (888.)

Doh = F. *Slow.* Bohemian Brethren's *Gesangbuch*, 1566.

:m |m :m |r :— |— :d |r :f |m :— |—
:d |d :d |t_1 :— |— :l_1 |t_1 :d |d :— |—
:s |s :s |s :— |— :m |s :l |s :— |—
:d |m :d |s_1 :— |— :l_1 |s_1 :f_1 |d :— |—

:s |l :m |s :— |— :m |r :m |d :— |—
:d |d :d |t_1 :— |— :d |l_1 :t_1 |t_1 :— |l_1
:m |f :d |m :— |— :m |l :s |m :— |—
:d |f_1 :l_1 |m_1 :— |— :l_1 |f_1 :s_1 |l_1 :— |—

:m |m :m |r :— |— :d |l_1 :t_1 |l_1 :— |— ‖ r |de
:s_1 |s_1 :l_1 |l_1 :— |s_1 :— |l_1 :se_1 |l_1 :— |— ‖ l_1 |l_1
:m |t_1 :d |f :— |m :— |d :m |l_1 :— |— ‖ f |m
:d_1 |m_1 :l_1 |r_1 :— |m_1 :— |f_1 :m_1 |l_1 :— |— ‖ r_1 |l_1

A-men.

BY Jesus' grave on either hand,
While night is brooding o'er the land,
The sad and silent mourners stand.

2 At last the weary life is o'er,
The agony and conflict sore
Of Him who all our suffering bore.

3 Deep in the rock's sepulchral shade
The Lord, by whom the worlds were made,
The Saviour of mankind, is laid.

4 O hearts bereaved and sore distressed,
Here is for you a place of rest;
Here leave your griefs on Jesus' breast.

5 So, when the dayspring from on high
Shall chase the night and fill the sky,
Then shall the Lord again draw nigh.

ISAAC GREGORY SMITH, 1826–1920.

Also the following:

32 Praise to the Holiest in the height
413 Rock of Ages, cleft for me
690 Thou who didst on Calvary bleed
692 There is a fountain filled with blood

HIS RESURRECTION

115 FORTUNATUS. (11 11. 11 11. and refrain.)

Doh = G. *Brightly.* ARTHUR SEYMOUR SULLIVAN, 1842–1900.

```
|d .t, :d  |r  :m  |f  :m  |r  :d  |d  :— |t, :— |d  :— |— :— ||
|s,    :s, |t, :d  |d  :d  |l, :s, |l, :— |s, :— |s, :— |— :— ||
|m .r  :m  |s  :s  |l  :s  |f  :m  |r  :— |r  :— |m  :— |— :— ||
|d     :d  |s, :d  |f, :d, |r, :m, |f, :— |s, :— |d, :— |— :— ||

                                    D.t.
|m .f  :s  |l  :s  |f  :m  |r  :m  |(r)s   :— |t  :— |d' :— |— :— ||
|d     :d  |d  :d  |t, :d  |r  :d  |(t,)m  :— |f  :— |m  :— |— :— ||
|s     :s  |f  :s  |s  :s  |s  :s  |(s)d'  :— |s  :— |s  :— |— :— ||
|d .r  :m  |f  :m  |r  :d  |t, :d  |(r)s   :— |s, :— |d  :— |— :— ||

|d'    :d' |t  :t  |l  :— |m  :— |l  :l  |s  :f  |m  :— |— :— ||
|m     :m  |m  :r  |d  :— |d  :— |f  :f  |m  :r  |d  :— |— :— ||
|l     :l  |se :se |l  :— |l  :— |l  :l  |l  :l  |l  :— |— :— ||
|l,    :d  |m  :m, |l, :— |l, :— |l, :l, |r  :f  |l  :— |— :— ||

                                                 f.G.
|f     :f  |m  :r  |s  :f  |m  :d  |m  :— |r  :— |(d)s, :— |— :— ||
|d     :d  |t, :t, |d  :r  |d  :d  |d  :— |t, :— |(d)s, :— |— :— ||
|l     :l  |s  :s  |s  :s  |s  :l  |s  :— |f  :— |(m)t, :— |— :— ||
|r     :r  |s  :f  |m  :t, |d  :f, |s, :— |s, :— |(d)s, :— |— :— ||

REFRAIN.
|m .f :s |l :s |m :r  |d  :f  |m  :— |r  :— |d  :— |— :— || d  |d  ||
|d    :d |d :d |d :t, |d  :r  |d  :— |t, :— |s, :— |— :— || l, |s, ||
|s    :s |f :s |s :f  |m  :l  |s  :— |— :f  |m  :— |— :— || f  |m  ||
|d .r :m |f :m |d :s, |l, :f, |s, :— |s, :— |d, :— |— :— || f, |d, ||
                                                           A - men.
```

[*By permission of Novello & Co., Ltd.*]

Salve, festa dies.

'WELCOME, happy morning!'—age to age shall say:
'Hell to-day is vanquished, heaven is won to-day.'
Lo! the Dead is living, God for evermore:
Him, their true Creator, all His works adore.
'*Welcome, happy morning!'—age to age shall say.*

2 Earth with joy confesses, clothing her for spring,
All good gifts return with her returning King :
Bloom in every meadow, leaves on every bough,
Speak His sorrows ended, hail His triumph now.

3 Thou, of life the Author, death didst undergo,
Tread the path of darkness, saving strength to show.
Come then, True and Faithful, now fulfil Thy word ;
'Tis Thine own third morning : rise, O buried Lord !

4 Loose the souls long prisoned, bound with Satan's chain :
All that now is fallen raise to life again :
Show Thy face in brightness, bid the nations see :
Bring again our daylight : day returns with Thee.

VENANTIUS HONORIUS CLEMENTIANUS FORTUNATUS, *c.* 530–609 ;
tr. by JOHN ELLERTON, 1826–93.

116 LANCASTER. (C.M.)

Doh = A. *In moderate time.* SAMUEL HOWARD, 1710–82.

:s, |d :r |m :d |f :m |r :r |m :d |t, :l, |s, :— |— ||
:m, |s, :s, |s, :l, |l, :s, |s, :s, |s, :s, |s, :fe, |s, :— |— ||
:d |d :t, |d :d |l,.t, :d |t, :r |d :s, |r :r.d |t, :— |— ||
:d, |m, :s, |d :l, |r, :m,.f, |s, :t,, |d, :m, |r, :r, |s, :— |— ||

Harmony.

:s, |l, :t, |d :t, |d :r |m :m |s :f |m :r |d :— |— || d | d ||
:s, |s, :f, |m, :s, |d :t, |d :d |s, :l, |s, :s,.f, |m, :— |— || f, | m, ||
:d |d :r |d :r |s :f |m :d |d :d |d :t, |d :— |— || l, | s, ||
:m, |f, :r, |l, :s,.f, |m, :r, |d, :l, |m, :f, |s, :s, |d, :— |— || f, | d, ||

BLEST morning, whose first dawning rays
Beheld the Son of God
Arise triumphant from the grave,
And leave His dark abode !

2 Wrapt in the silence of the tomb
The great Redeemer lay,
Till the revolving skies had brought
The third, the appointed day.

3 Hell and the grave combined their force
To hold our Lord, in vain ;
Sudden the Conqueror arose,
And burst their feeble chain.

Unison.
4 To Thy great Name, Almighty [Lord,
We sacred honours pay,
And loud hosannas shall proclaim
The triumphs of the day.

Harmony.
5 Salvation and immortal praise
To our victorious King !
Let heaven and earth, and rocks and seas,
With glad hosannas ring.

Unison.
6 To Father, Son, and Holy Ghost,
The God whom we adore,
Be glory, as it was, and is,
And shall be evermore.

ISAAC WATTS, 1674–1748.

[May be sung to CREDITON, No. 40.]

117

WATERSTOCK. (66. 66. and refrain.)

Doh = E♭. *Brightly.* JOHN GOSS, 1800–80.

```
:s  |m   :-.f  |s  :d'  |s   :—    |—  :s   |m   :-.f  |s   :l
:t, |d   :-.t, |d  :m   |r   :—    |—  :t,  |d   :-.d  |d   :d
:s  |s   :-.s  |s  :s   |s   :—    |—  :s   |d   :-.r  |m   :r.d
:s, |d   :-.r  |m  :d   |t,  :—    |—  :s,  |l,  :-.l, |m,  :f,

                              B♭.t.
r   :—  |—  :r  |m  :m  |d'f  :-.m  |r   :—  |—  :r
t,  :—  |—  :t, |d  :d  |ml,  :-.l, |r,  :—  |—  :s,
s   :—  |—  :s  |s  :s  |lr   :-.d  |t,  :—  |—  :t,
s,  :—  |—  :s, |d  :d  |l,r, :-.r, |s,  :—  |—  :s,.f,

                f.E♭.                 REFRAIN.
s   :d.r      |m   :r   |ds   :—  |— ||s   s  :d' |l  :s.f
s,  :m,.fe,   |s,  :f,  |mt,  :—  |— ||t,  d  :d  |d  :r
d   :d        |d   :t,  |ds   :—  |— ||s   s  :m  |f  :r.s
m,  :l,       |s,  :s,  |d,s, :—  |— ||s   m  :d  |f  :t,

m  :-.f  |s  :l   |s.f  :m.r  |d   :f   |m   :—  |r   :—  |d  :—  |— ||d  |d
d  :-.t, |d  :f   |m.r  :d.t, |d   :r   |d   :—  |t,  :—  |d  :—  |— ||l, |s,
s  :-.f  |m  :d'  |d'   :s.f  |m   :l   |s   :—  |f   :—  |m  :—  |— ||f  |m
d  :-.r  |m  :f   |s    :s,   |l,  :f,  |s,  :—  |s,  :—  |d  :—  |— ||f, |d
                                                                     A-men.
```

ON wings of living light,
At earliest dawn of day,
Came down the angel bright,
And rolled the stone away.
Your voices raise
With one accord,
To bless and praise
Your risen Lord.

2 The keepers watching near,
At that dread sight and sound,
Fell down with sudden fear,
Like dead men, to the ground.

3 Then rose from death's dark gloom,
Unseen by mortal eye,
Triumphant o'er the tomb,
The Lord of earth and sky.

4 Ye children of the light,
Arise with Him, arise;
See how the Daystar bright
Is burning in the skies!

5 Leave in the grave beneath
The old things passed away;
Buried with Him in death,
O live with Him to-day.

6 We sing Thee, Lord Divine,
With all our hearts and powers;
For we are ever Thine,
And Thou art ever ours.

WILLIAM WALSHAM HOW, 1823–97.

118 ST. GEORGE'S, WINDSOR. (77. 77. D.)

Doh = G. *Brightly.* George Job Elvey, 1816–93.

```
|m  :-.m |s  :m  |d  :r  |m  :—  |m  :-.m |s  :m  |d  :r  |m   :—  ||
|s, :-.s,|s, :s, |l, :t, |d  :—  |s, :-.s,|s, :s, |l, :l, |se, :—  ||
|d  :-.d |r  :m  |m  :s  |s  :—  |d  :-.d |r  :d  |m  :f  |t,  :—  ||
|d  :-.d |t, :d  |l, :s, |d  :—  |d  :-.d |t, :d  |l, :f, |m,  :—  ||

                                  D.t.                      f.G.
|m  :-.m |f  :f  |r  :-.r |m  :— |ml :t   |d' :f  |m  :r    |ds, :— ||
|l, :-.l,|l, :l, |s, :s,  |s, :— |sd :r   |d  :r  |d  :t,   |ds, :— ||
|d  :-.d |r  :r  |t, :t,  |d  :— |df :f   |s  :l  |s  :-.f  |mt, :— ||
|l, :-.l,|r, :r, |s, :s,  |d, :— |df :r   |m  :f  |s  :s,   |ds, :— ||

                                  f.C.
|t, :-.t,|r  :t, |d  :r   |m  :— |mt  :-.t |r' :t  |d' :r'  |m' :—  ||
|s, :-.s,|s, :s, |s, :f,  |m, :— |s,r :-.r |s  :s  |s  :f   |m  :—  ||
|r  :r   |t, :r  |d  :-.t,|d  :— |ds  :-.s |t  :r' |d' :-.t |d' :—  ||
|s, :-.s,|s, :f, |m, :r,  |d, :— |ds  :-.s |s  :f  |m  :r   |d  :—  ||

        G.t.
|m' :-.m'|d'f :r   |s  :-.s |m :— |f  :l  |s  :d  |m  :r   |d  :— ||d  |d  ||
|m  :se  |lr  :l,  |s, :t,  |d :— |d  :d  |d  :d  |d  :t,  |d  :— ||l, |s, ||
|t  :m'  |m'l :f   |r  :s   |s :— |f  :f  |s  :m  |s  :-.f |m  :— ||f  |m  ||
|se :m   |lr  :-.r |t, :s,  |d :— |l, :f, |m, :l, |s, :s,  |d, :— ||f, |d, ||
                                                                      A-men.
```

'Christ the Lord is risen to-day,'
Sons of men and angels say;
Raise your joys and triumphs high;
Sing, ye heavens, and, earth, reply.
Love's redeeming work is done,
Fought the fight, the battle won;
Lo! our Sun's eclipse is o'er;
Lo! He sets in blood no more.

2 Vain the stone, the watch, the seal;
Christ has burst the gates of hell:
Death in vain forbids His rise;
Christ has opened Paradise.
Lives again our glorious King;
Where, O Death, is now thy sting?
Once He died, our souls to save;
Where thy victory, O grave?

3 Soar we now where Christ has led,
Following our exalted Head;
Made like Him, like Him we rise;
Ours the Cross, the grave, the skies.
Hail, the Lord of earth and heaven
Praise to Thee by both be given;
Thee we greet triumphant now;
Hail, the Resurrection Thou!

Charles Wesley, 1707–88.

119 EASTER HYMN. (77. 77. and Hallelujahs.)

Doh = C. *Moderately quick.* *Lyra Davidica*, 1708.

d :m	s :d	f :l	l :s	m.f:s.d	f :m.f	m :r	d :—
d :d	r :d	d :f	f :m	d :—	—.t,:d	d :t,	d :—
m :s	s :m	d' :d'	d' :—	s :—	— :s.f	s :—.f	m :—
d :d	t, :d	l :f	d :—	d.r:m	r :d.l,	s, :—	d :—

f :s	l :s	f :m	m :r	m.f:s.d	f :m.f	m :r	d :—
d :d	d :d	d.t,:d	d :t,	d :—	—.t,:d	d :t,	d :—
f :m	f :s	l.f :s	s :—	s :—	— :s.f	s :—.f	m :—
l, :d	f :m	r :m.f	s :—	d.r:m	r :d.l,	s, :—	d :—

				G.t.			f.C.
t :d'	r' :s	d' :r'	m' :—	(t)m.f:s.d	f :m.f	m :r	(d)s :—
s :—.fe	s :s	s :f	m :—	(s)d :—	—.t,:d	d :t,	(d)s :—
r' :d'	t :t	d' :—.t	d' :—	(r')s :—	— :s.f	s :—.f	(m)t :—
s :l	t :s.f	m :r	d :—	(s)d.r:m	r :d.l,	s, :—	(d)s, :—

s.l:t.s	d' :m	f :l	l :s	d'.t:d'.s	l.t:d'.r'	d' :t	d' :—	d'	d'
t,.d:r.t,	d :d	d :f	f :m	m.f:s.m	f :m.f	m :s.f	m :—	f	m
s :s	s :d'	d' :d'	d' :—	d'.s:d'	—.s:d'.l	s :r'	d' :—	l	s
s :f	m :d'.t	l :f	d :—	d.r:m.d	f.s:l.f	s :—	d :—	f	d

A-men.

JESUS CHRIST is risen to-day, *Hallelujah!*
Our triumphant holy day, *Hallelujah!*
Who did once, upon the Cross, *Hallelujah!*
Suffer to redeem our loss. *Hallelujah!*

2 Hymns of praise, then, let us sing *Hallelujah!*
Unto Christ, our heavenly King, *Hallelujah!*
Who endured the Cross and grave, *Hallelujah!*
Sinners to redeem and save. *Hallelujah!*

HIS RESURRECTION

LLANFAIR. (77. 77. and Hallelujahs.)

Doh = G. *Moderately quick time.* ROBERT WILLIAMS, *c.* 1781–1821.

D.C.

```
d  :d  |m  :m  |s   :f.m  |r  :— |s  :-.f   |m :f.m   |r   :—   |d  :—
s, :s, |d  :d  |d   :r.d  |t, :— |s, :l,.t, |d :d     |d   :t,  |d  :—
m  :m  |d  :d  |s   :l    |r  :— |m  :-.f   |s :f.s   |l   :s   |m  :—
d  :d  |l, :l, |m,  :f,   |s, :— |m  :-.r   |d :l,.s, |f,  :s,  |d  :—

m  :m  |s  :s  |l.s :f.m  |r  :— |m  :-.r   |m :fe    |s   :—   |s  :—
s, :l, |s, :d  |l,  :t,.d |t, :— |d  :-.r   |d :d     |t,  :-.d |t, :—
m  :d  |r  :m  |f   :s    |s  :— |s  :—     |— :d     |r   :-.m |r  :—
d  :l, |t, :d  |f.m :r.d  |s, :— |d  :-.t,  |d :l,    |s,  :—   |s, :—

d  :d   |m  :m  |s  :f.m |r  :— |s  :-.f   |m :f.m   |r  :—  |d  :—
d  :s,  |s, :d  |d  :r.d |t, :— |s, :l,.t, |d :d     |d  :t, |d  :—
m  :s.f |m  :d  |s  :l   |r  :— |m  :-.f   |s :f.s   |l  :s  |m  :—
d  :m.r |d  :l, |m, :f,  |s, :— |m  :-.r   |d :l,.s, |f, :s, |d, :—
```

3 But the anguish He endured *Hallelujah !*
Our salvation hath procured ; *Hallelujah !*
Now above the sky He 's King, *Hallelujah !*
Where the angels ever sing. *Hallelujah !*

4 Sing we to our God above *Hallelujah !*
Praise eternal as His love ; *Hallelujah !*
Praise Him, all ye heavenly host, *Hallelujah !*
Father, Son, and Holy Ghost. *Hallelujah !*

Lyra Davidica, 1708.

```
f  :— |l  :—  |s :— |— :—
d  :— |l, :t, |d :— |— :—
f  :— |d  :r  |m :— |— :—
l, :— |f, :—  |d :— |— :—
A  -     -     men.
```

120

OLD 134TH (ST. MICHAEL). (S.M.)

French Psalter, 1551.
Composed or arranged by Louis Bourgeois, 1510– ?

Doh = A♭. *In moderate time.*

s, :—	d :m	r :r	m :—		s :—	f :m	r :r	d :—	
m, :—	m, :s,	l, :s,	s, :—		s, :—	d :d	d :t,	d :—	
d :—	d :d	d :t,	d :—		r :—	f :s	s :-.f	m :—	
d :—	l, :m,	f, :s,	d :—		t, :—	l, :d	s, :s,	d, :—	

d :—	t, :l,	s, :d	d :r	m :—		m :—	r :d	d :t,	d :—		d	d	
l, :—	s, :f,	m, :s,	l, :l,	se, :—		s, :—	f, :s,	l, :s,	s, :—		l,	s,	
m :—	m :d	d :d	m :r	t, :—		d :—	l,.t, :d	f :r	m :—		f	m	
l, :—	m, :f,	d, :m,	l, :f,	m, :—		d, :—	r, :m,	f, :s,	d, :—		f,	d,	

A-men.

QUINTA. (S.M.)

'University of Wales' (*Students' Hymnal*), 1923.

Doh = C. *In moderate time.*

d :—	m :s	d' :-.s	m' :—	— :d'	s :l	s :-.f	m :—	—	
s, :—	d :m	s :-.s	s :—	— :d	d :f	r :-.t,	d :—	—	
m :—	s :d'	d' :-.r'	m' :—	— :m'	d' :d'	t :-.s	s :—	—	
d :—	d :d	m :-.s	d' :—	— :l	m :f	s :-.s	d :—	—	

G.t. f.C.

:s |m :r |d :[d]f |m :-.r |d :r.m |[f]d' :m' |m' :r' |d' :— ||d' |d' ||
:m |d :t, |d :[m]l, |se, :l,.t, |d :ta, |[l]m :s |s :s |s :— ||f |m ||
:d' |s :s.f |m :[l]r |t, :m |m :s |[d]s :d' |d' :r' t |m' :— ||l |s ||
:d |d :s, |l, :[l]r, |m, :ba,se, |l, :s, |[f]d :d.m |s :s |d :— ||f |d ||

A-men.

'THE Lord is risen indeed';
Now is His work performed;
Now is the mighty Captive freed,
And Death's strong castle stormed.

2 'The Lord is risen indeed':
The grave has lost his prey;
With Him is risen the ransomed seed,
To reign in endless day.

3 'The Lord is risen indeed';
He lives, to die no more;
He lives, the sinner's cause to plead,
Whose curse and shame He bore.

4 Then, angels, tune your lyres,
And strike each cheerful chord;
Join, all ye bright celestial choirs,
To sing our risen Lord!

Thomas Kelly, 1769–1854.

121

CHRIST IST ERSTANDEN (78. 78. and Hallelujah.)

German traditional melody, about 13th century.

Lah = D. Doh = F. *Unison.* *Moderately slow, very dignified.*

| m :m | r :m | s :— | l :— | m :— | — :— | m :r | m :d | t, :— | d :— |

| l, :— | l, :— (pause) || r :r | l, :s, | d :— | r :— | m :— | — :— || m :r | m :d |

| t, :— | d :— | l, :— | t, :— || : | s, :l, | t, :— | l, :— (pause) || l, | l, ||
A - men.

Note.—The above tune is appropriate to this hymn, being anciently connected with Eastertide.

ST. ALBINUS. (78. 78. and Hallelujah.)

Doh = C. *In moderate time.* HENRY JOHN GAUNTLETT, 1805–76.

m :d	s :-.m	l :l	s :—	m' :r'	d' :t	l :d'
m :d	s :-.m	l :l	s :—	s :s	m :m	d :d.r
m :d	s :-.m	l :l	s :—	d' :t	l :s	l :l.t
m :d	s :-.m	l :l	s :—	d' :s	l :m	f :f

d' :—	s :—		d' :s	l :m	s :f	m :—	m' :t	d' :s
m :—	m :—		m :m	d :d	d :d.t,	d :—	s :s	m :s
d' :—	d' :—		d' :d'	l :l	s :s	s :—	m' :r'	d' :d'
d :—	d :—		l, :d	f :l	m :s	d :—	d' :s	l :m

l :d'	r' :—	d' :—		d' :d'	f' :—	m' :—		r'	d'	
s :f	f :—	m :—		m :m	l :—	s :—		s	m	
d' :d'	t :—	d' :—		d' :d'	d' :—	d' :—		t	d'	
f :l	s :—	d :—		d' :l	f :—	d :—		s	d	
A-men.

Jesus lebt, mit ihm auch ich.

JESUS lives! thy terrors now
Can, O Death, no more appal us;
Jesus lives: by this we know
Thou, O grave, canst not enthral us. *Hallelujah!*

2 Jesus lives! henceforth is death
But the gate of life immortal;
This shall calm our trembling breath
When we pass its gloomy portal. *Hallelujah!*

3 Jesus lives! for us He died;
Then, alone to Jesus living,
Pure in heart may we abide,
Glory to our Saviour giving. *Hallelujah!*

4 Jesus lives! our hearts know well
Nought from us His love shall sever;
Life, nor death, nor powers of hell
Part us from His keeping ever. *Hallelujah!*

5 Jesus lives! to Him the throne
High o'er heaven and earth is given;
May we go where He is gone,
Rest and reign with Him in heaven. *Hallelujah!*

CHRISTIAN FÜRCHTEGOTT GELLERT, 1715–69; *tr.* by FRANCES ELIZABETH COX, 1812–97.

122

VICTORY. (888. and Alleluias.)

From GIOVANNI PIERLUIGI DA PALESTRINA, 1525–94. Adapted by WILLIAM HENRY MONK, 1823–89.

Doh = D. *Slow and dignified.*

```
   :m :m | f  :— :— | m :s  :s  | l  :— :— | s :s  :d' | t  :— :— | d' :— :—
   :d :d | d  :— :— | d :d  :m  | m  :— :— | m :d  :m  | s  :— :— | m  :— :—
   Al-le-| lu  -  - | ia, Al-le-| lu  -  - | ia, Al-le-| lu  -  - | ia!
   :s :s | l  :— :— | s :m  :s  | d' :— :— | t :d' :d' | r' :— :— | d' :— :—
d, :d :d | f, :— :— | d :d  :d  | l, :— :— | m :m  :d  | s  :— :— | d  :— :—

S.
s  :s  :s  | l  :— :s  | s :f  :m  | s :— :— | m :m :m
m  :m  :m  | f  :— :m  | m :l, :d  | r :— :— | d :d :d
d' :d' :d' | d' :— :d' | t :r' :d' | t :— :— | s :s :s
d  :d  :d  | f  :— :d  | m :r  :l  | s :— :— | d :d :d

m  :— :m  | m :r  :d  | r  :— :— | s  :s  :s | l  :— :s
d  :— :t, | d :l, :d  | t, :— :— | t, :m  :r | d  :— :m
l  :— :s  | s :f  :m  | s  :— :— | s  :d' :t | l  :— :d'
l, :— :m  | d :r  :l, | s, :— :— | m  :d  :d | f  :— :d

                                                   D.S.
s :f  :m  | s :— :— | :s  :d' | t  :— :— | d' :— :— | l  | s
m :l, :d  | r :— :— | :s  :m  | r  :— :— | m  :— :— | d  | d
                      Al-le-    lu  -  -   ia!        A- | men.
t :r' :d' | t :— :— | :d' :s  | s  :— :— | s  :— :— | f  | m
m :r  :l  | s :— :— | :m  :d  | s, :— :— | d  :— :— | f, | d
```

Finita iam sunt proelia.

ALLELUIA! ALLELUIA! ALLELUIA!

THE strife is o'er, the battle done;
Now is the Victor's triumph won;
Now be the song of praise begun,—
'Alleluia!'

2 The powers of death have done their worst,
But Christ their legions hath dispersed;
Let shouts of holy joy outburst,—
'Alleluia!'

3 The three sad days have quickly sped;
He rises glorious from the dead;
All glory to our risen Head!
Alleluia!

4 He brake the age-bound chains of hell;
The bars from heaven's high portals fell;
Let hymns of praise His triumph tell.
Alleluia!

5 Lord, by the stripes which wounded Thee,
From death's dread sting Thy servants free,
That we may live, and sing to Thee,
'Alleluia!'

Tr. by FRANCIS POTT, 1832–1909.

123 LANCASHIRE. (76. 76. D.)

Doh = D. *Brightly.* HENRY SMART, 1813–79.

```
:s  |s  :m  |f  :l  |s  :—  |m  :d' |d' :f  |s  :l  |r  :—  |—  ||
:d  |d  :d  |d  :d  |d  :—  |d  :m  |f  :d  |d  :d  |t, :—  |—  ||
:m  |m  :s  |l  :f  |m  :—  |s  :s  |l  :d' |t  :l  |s  :—  |—  ||
:d  |d  :d  |d  :d  |d  :—  |d  :ta,|l, :l, |s, :f, |s, :—  |—  ||

:s  |s  :m  |f  :l  |s  :—  |m  :m  |r  :t  |l  :fe |s  :—  |—  ||
:t, |d  :d  |d  :d  |d  :—  |d  :d  |t, :r  |d  :d  |t, :—  |—  ||
:f  |m  :ta |l  :f  |m  :—  |s  :s  |s  :s  |fe :l  |s  :—  |—  ||
:s, |d  :d  |d  :d  |d  :—  |d  :d  |r  :r  |r  :r  |s, :—  |—  ||

           f.G.                           A.t.m.                f.D.
:s  |s  :(m)t,  |s, :s  |s  :—.m |d  :m   |(m)r   :t, |s, :s  |(s)r' :— |t  ||
:t, |d  :(d)s,  |r, :t, |d  :—   |s, :se, |(l)s,  :s, |r, :t, |(d)s  :— |—  ||
:f  |m  :(ta)f  |f  :f  |m  :—.s |m  :r   |(de)t, :f  |f  :f  |(m)t  :— |r' ||
:s, |d  :(s)r   |t, :s, |d, :—   |d  :t,  |(l)s,  :r  |t, :s, |(d)s, :— |s  ||

:s  |d' :d' |d' :d' |d' :—  |t  :l  |s  :m  |r  :t, |d  :—  |—  || f  |m  ||
:r  |s, :d  |r  :m  |f  :—  |d  :d  |d  :d  |s, :s, |s, :—  |—  || d  |d  ||
:t  |d' :s  |l  :ta |l  :—  |d' :f  |m  :s  |f  :r  |m  :—  |—  || l  |s  ||
:f  |m  :m  |f  :s  |l  :—  |f  :f, |s, :s, |s, :s, |d  :—  |—  || f, |d  ||
                                                              A - men.
```

Ἀναστάσεως ἡμέρα.

THE day of resurrection!
Earth, tell it out abroad;
The passover of gladness,
The passover of God!
From death to life eternal,
From earth unto the sky,
Our Christ hath brought us over
With hymns of victory.

2 Our hearts be pure from evil,
That we may see aright
The Lord in rays eternal
Of resurrection light,
And, listening to His accents,
May hear, so calm and plain,
His own 'All hail!' and, hearing,
May raise the victor strain.

3 Now let the heavens be joyful;
Let earth her song begin;
Let the round world keep triumph,
And all that is therein;
Let all things seen and unseen
Their notes of gladness blend,
For Christ the Lord hath risen,
Our Joy that hath no end.

ST. JOHN OF DAMASCUS, 8th century; *tr.* by JOHN MASON NEALE, 1818–66.

124 O FILII ET FILIAE. (888. and Alleluias.) Proper melody harmonized by EDMUND WILLIAM GOLDSMITH, 1860–

𝄋 Lah = G. *Unison.* *Fine.*

:l, | l, :— :t, | l, :s, :l, | d :t, :l, | m, :— | t, :d | t, :— | l, :—
:l, | m, :— :m, | m, :— :fe, | s, :— :f, | m, :— | r, :m, | m, :— | m, :—
| | | | | t₂ :— | de, :—
Al- | le - lu- | ia, Al- | le - lu- | ia, | Al - le - | lu - | ia
:l, | d :— :t, | t, :— :r | m :r :— | d :— | s, :-.l, | l, :se, | l, :—
| | | s, | | | | m,
:l₂ | l, :— :s, | m, :— :r, | d, :s, :r, | l, :— | s, :d, | m, :— | l₂ :—

l, .t, .l, | l, :— || l, | d :— :r | m :r :d | r :d :t, | l, :—
r, :— | de, :— || m, | m, :— :s, | m, :— :l, | f, :— :f, | m, :—
A - | men.
f, :— | m, :— || l, | l, :— :t, | s, :— :l, | l, :d :r | d :—
r, :— | l₂ :— || l, | l, :— :s, | d, :— :f, | r, :— :r, | l₂ :—

Ray = G.

:l, r | f :— :s | l :s :f | s :f :m | r :—
:fe, t, | l, :d :— | d :— :l, | t, :l, :s, .l, | t, :—
:r s | d :— :m | f :m :f | r :d :d | r :—
:r, s, | f, :l, :d | f :d :r | s, :l, :d | s, :—

Lah = G. *dal* 𝄋.

:r l, | l, :— :t, | l, :s, :l, | d :t, :l, | m, :— | t, :d | t, :— | l, :—
:ta f, | m, :— :t₂ | r, :m, :f, | l, :t, :m, | m, :— | r, :s, | — :s, | m, :—
| | | | | Al - le - | lu - | ia.
:s r | l, :d :f, | l, :t, :r | m :— :d | t, :— | s, :s, | r :— | d :—
:s, r, | d, :— :r, | f, :m, :r, | l₂ :t₂ :d, .r, | m, :— | s, :m, | s, :— | l, :—

Note.—The successive verses of the hymn may be varied by being sung occasionally in harmony or in other ways at the discretion of the choirmaster. The Alleluias at the opening of each verse should always be in unison.

O filii et filiae.

ALLELUIA! ALLELUIA! ALLELUIA!

O SONS and daughters, let us sing!
The King of heaven, the glorious King,
O'er death to-day rose triumphing. *Alleluia!*

2 That Easter morn, at break of day,
The faithful women went their way
To seek the tomb where Jesus lay.

3 An angel clad in white they see,
Who sat, and spake unto the three,
'Your Lord doth go to Galilee.'

4 That night the apostles met in fear;
Amidst them came their Lord most dear,
And said, 'My peace be on all here.'

ALTERNATIVE VERSION.

Slightly altered from *An Essay on the Church Plain Chant*, 1782.

Lah = G. Doh = B♭. *Unison. Moderately fast.*

Al- le - lu- ia, Al - le - lu - ia, Al - - - le- lu - - ia.

A-men.

5 When Thomas first the tidings heard,
He doubted if it were their Lord,
Until He came and spake the word :

6 ' My piercèd side, O Thomas, see ;
Behold My hands, My feet,' said He,
' Not faithless, but believing be.'

7 No longer Thomas then denied ;
He saw the feet, the hands, the side ;
' Thou art my Lord and God,' he cried.

8 How blest are they who have not seen,
And yet whose faith hath constant been,
For they eternal life shall win.

9 On this most holy day of days,
To God your hearts and voices raise
In laud and jubilee and praise.

JEAN TISSERAND, ? -1494 ; *tr.* by JOHN MASON NEALE, 1818-66.

125 KIRN. (11 11. 12 11 11.)

Doh = A. *Moderately fast.* JOHN PRENTICE TAYLOR, 1871–

1. Our Lord Christ hath risen! The tempter is foiled;
His legions are scattered, His strongholds are spoiled.
O sing Hallelujah! O sing Hallelujah!
O sing Hallelujah! Be joyful and sing,
Our great foe is baffled—Christ Jesus is King!

2. O death, we defy thee! A stronger than thou
Hath entered thy palace; We fear thee not now!
O sing Hallelujah! O sing Hallelujah!
O sing Hallelujah! Be joyful and sing,
Death cannot affright us—Christ Jesus is King!

3. O sin, thou art vanquished, Thy long reign is o'er;
Though still thou dost vex us, We dread thee no more.
O sing Hallelujah! O sing Hallelujah!
O sing Hallelujah! Be joyful and sing,
Who now can condemn us? Christ Jesus is King!

4. Our Lord Christ hath risen! Day breaketh at last;
The long night of weeping Is now well-nigh past.
O sing Hallelujah! O sing Hallelujah!
O sing Hallelujah! Be joyful and sing,
Our foes are all conquered—Christ Jesus is King!

Amen.

[*Copyright*, 1927, *by Oxford University Press.*]

WILLIAM CONYNGHAM PLUNKET, 1828–97.

126 LUX EOI. (8 7. 8 7. D.)

Doh = C. *Brightly.* ARTHUR SEYMOUR SULLIVAN, 1842–1900.

s :-.s |d' :s |s :f |f :m |l :l |s :m |r :d |r :— ||
d :-.d |d :d |m :r |r :d |d :r |m :s, |l, :l, |t, :— ||
m :-.m |m :s |d' :t |t :d' |l :t |d' :m |fe :fe |s :— ||
d :-.d |d :m |s :s, |s, :d |f :f |m :d |l, :r |s, :— ||

G.t. f.C.

s :-.s |d' :(d)f |m :r |s :d |t, :l, |s, :d |d :t, |(d)s :— ||
t, :-.t, |d :(d)f, |s, :s, |s, :s, |s, :f, |m, :l,.s, |f, :f, |(m)t, :— ||
s :-.s |s :(s)d |d :t, |d :d |d :r |m :f.m |r :s, |(s,)r :— ||
s :-.f |m :(m)l, |s, :f, |m, :m, |f, :f, |s, :s, |s, :s, |(d,)s, :— ||

f :f |m :m |l :-.l |l :se |l :t |d' :t |m :se |l :— ||
d :d |t, :t, |d :r |m :m |m :m |m :f |m :m |m :— ||
f :f |s :s |l :l |t :t |l :se |l :l.t |d' :t |d' :— ||
l, :l, |s, :s, |f, :f |m :m |d :t, |l, :r |m :m |l :— ||

s :d' |m' :r' |d' :t |l :s |fe :f |m :l |d :r |d :— || f |m ||
f :m |s :s |s :s |f :m |ma :r |d :d |s, :t, |d :— || d |d ||
r' :d' |d' :t |d' :d' |d' :d' |d' :s |d :r |m :f |m :— || l |s ||
t :d' |s :f |m :m |f :d |l, :t, |d :f, |s, :s, |d :— || f, |d ||

A - men.

[*By permission of Novello & Co., Ltd.*]

HALLELUJAH ! hallelujah !
Hearts to heaven and voices raise ;
Sing to God a hymn of gladness,
Sing to God a hymn of praise ;
He who on the Cross a victim
For the world's salvation bled,
Jesus Christ, the King of Glory,
Now is risen from the dead.

2 Christ is risen ; we are risen ;
Shed upon us heavenly grace,
Rain and dew, and gleams of glory
From the brightness of Thy face,
That we, with our hearts in heaven,
Here on earth may fruitful be,
And by angel hands be gathered,
And be ever, Lord, with Thee.

3 Hallelujah ! hallelujah !
Glory be to God on high ;
Hallelujah to the Saviour,
Who has gained the victory ;
Hallelujah to the Spirit,
Fount of love and sanctity :
Hallelujah ! hallelujah
To the Triune Majesty !

CHRISTOPHER WORDSWORTH, 1807–85.

127

KIRKLAND. (6 5. 6 5. D.)

Doh = E♭. *In moderate time.* David Evans, 1874–

d.r :m :s	l :—:s	m.d :r :m	l_1 :—:—	d.r :m :s	l :—:s
d.t_1:d :r	m :—:r	s_1.d :d :t_1	l_1 :—:—	s_1.s_1:s_1 :r	d :—:t_1
s.f :m :r	d :—:r	m.s :l :s	d :—:—	s.f :m :r	m :—:s
m.r :d :t_1	l_1 :—:t_1	d.m_1:f_1 :s_1	l_1 :—:—	m.r :d :t_1	l_1 :—:m

m.s :d' :l	t :—:—	d' :t :l.m	s :r :—	f.f :m :d	t_1 :—:—
d.r :m :r	r :—:—	m :r :d.d	m :t_1 :—	l_1.l_1 :s_1 :l_1	t_1 :—:—
s.s :s :fe	s :—:—	s :f.s :l.d'	t :s :—	d.r :m :ba	se :—:—
d.t_1 :l_1 :r	s_1 :—:—	d :r.m :f.l	m :s :—	l_1.t_1 :d :l_1	m_1 :—:—

d.r :m :s	l :—:s	m.d :r :m	d :—:—	f	m
l_1.t_1 :d :r	d :—:r	d.s_1 :d :t_1	d :—:—	d	d
m.s :s :r	m :—:s	s.m :l :s	m :—:—	l	s
l_1.s_1 :d :t_1	l_1 :—:t_1	d.m :f :s	d :—:—	f_1	d

A-men.

[*Copyright*, 1927, *by David Evans.*]

JESUS, Lord, Redeemer,
Once for sinners slain,
Crucified in weakness,
Raised in power, to reign,
Dwelling with the Father,
Endless in Thy days,
Unto Thee be glory,
Honour, blessing, praise.

2 Faithful ones, communing,
Towards the close of day,
Desolate and weary,
Met Thee in the way.
So, when sun is setting,
Come to us, and show
All the truth; and in us
Make our hearts to glow.

3 In the upper chamber,
Where the ten, in fear,
Gathered sad and troubled,
There Thou didst appear.
So, O Lord, this evening,
Bid our sorrows cease;
Breathing on us, Saviour,
Say, 'I give you peace.'

Patrick Miller Kirkland, 1857–

[May be sung to Urswicke, No. 696.]

Also the following:

237 Again the morn of gladness
248 Jesus, stand among us
266 Hail, thou bright and sacred morn
267 This is the day of light
268 O day of rest and gladness
481 Father of peace, and God of love

128 CANTATE DOMINO. (D.L.M.)

JOSEPH BARNBY, 1838–96.

```
Doh = Eb. Brightly.                 Bb.t.                                   f.Eb.
:m | s :l | s :m.r | d :r | m :(s)d | l, :t, | d :r.m | r :r | (d)s ||
:d | d :d | d :t, | d :t, | d :(r)s, | l, :f, | m, :f,.s, | l, :s,.f, | (m)t, ||
:s | m :f | r :s.f | m :s | s :(s)d | d :r | d :d | d :t, | (d)s ||
:d | d :f, | s, :s, | l, :s, | d :(t)m, | f, :r, | l, :s, | f, :s, | (d)s, ||

                                    Bb.t.                                   f.Eb.
:s | m :l | s :m.r | d :r | m :(fe)t, | d :r | m :f.m | r :r | (d)s ||
:r | d :d | r :t, | d :s, | m :(d)f, | m, :s, | s, :f,.s, | l, :s,.f, | (m)t, ||
:s | s :f | f.r :s.f | m :s | s :(l)r | d :t, | d :d | d :t, | (d)s ||
:t, | d :l, | t, :s, | l, :t, | d :(l)r, | l, :s, | d.t, :l,.s, | f, :s, | (d)s ||

                                                   Bb.t.                     f.Eb.
:s | d' :d' | t :d'.t | l :l | s :d | f :f | (m)l, :t,.d | r :d.t, | (d)s ||
:s | d' :d' | t :d'.t | l :l | s :d | d :t, | (m)l, :l, | l, :se, | (l)m ||
:s | d' :d' | t :d'.t | l :l | s :s | l :s | (s)d :f.m | r :r | (d)s ||
:s | d' :d' | t :d'.t | l :l | s :m | r :s, | (d)f,.m, :r,.d, | t,, :m, | (l)m ||

:s | d' :d' | t :d'.t | l :l | s :d | f :m | r :d | t, :d | r :— | d :— | — || f | m ||
:s | d' :d' | t :d'.t | l :l | s :d | d :de | r :l, | s, :d | t, :— | d :— | — || d | d ||
:s | d' :d' | t :d'.t | l :l | s :m | f :s | f :m | r :m | f :— | m :— | — || l | s ||
:s | d' :d' | t :d'.t | l :l | s :d | l, :l, | r :f, | s, :— | s, :— | d :— | — || f, | d ||
                                                                              A-men.
```

[*By permission of Novello & Co., Ltd.*]

OUR Lord is risen from the dead,
Our Jesus is gone up on high!
The powers of hell are captive led,
Dragged to the portals of the sky.
There His triumphal chariot waits,
And angels chant the solemn lay:
'Lift up your heads, ye heavenly gates,
Ye everlasting doors, give way!'

2 Loose all your bars of massy light,
And wide unfold the ethereal scene:
He claims these mansions as His right;
Receive the King of Glory in!
Who is this King of Glory? Who?
The Lord, that all our foes o'ercame,
The world, sin, death and hell o'erthrew;
And Jesus is the Conqueror's name.

3 Lo! His triumphal chariot waits,
And angels chant the solemn lay:
'Lift up your heads, ye heavenly gates;
Ye everlasting doors, give way!'
Who is this King of Glory? Who?
The Lord, of glorious power possessed,
The King of saints, and angels too,
God over all, for ever blest!

CHARLES WESLEY, 1707–88.

129

ALLE MENSCHEN MÜSSEN STERBEN (SCHÖNBERG). (77. 77. D.)

JAKOB HINTZE, 1622–1702.
Arranged by JOHANN SEBASTIAN BACH, 1685–1750.

Doh = D. *Moderately slow, dignified.*

|s :d' |s :l |s :-.f |m :m |s :s |f :m |r :r |d :— ||

|d :d |d :d |d :t, |d :d |d :d.t, |l,.t,:d |d :t, |d :— ||

|m :m.f |s :f.m |r.d :r |d :d |m :m |f :s |l :s |m :— ||

|d :l, |m, :f, |s, :s, |d :d |d :d |r :m |f.r:s |d :— ||

|s :d' |s :l |s :-.f |m :m |s :s |f :m |r :r |d :— ||

|d :d |d :d |d :t, |d :d |d :d.t, |l,.t,:d |d :t, |d :— ||

|m :m.f |s :f.m |r.d :r |d :d |m :m |f :s |l :s |m :— ||

|d :l, |m, :f, |s, :s, |d :d |d :d |r :m |f.r:s |d :— ||

|r :r |m.fe:s |s :fe |s :— |l :-.t |d' :d' |t :t |l :— ||

|t, :t, |d :t, |m :r.d |t, :— |r.m:f |m :m |m :m.r |d :— ||

|s :s |s :s |l :l |s :— |f :-.s |l :l |l :se |l :— ||

|s, :s, |d :m.r |d :r |s, :— |r :r |l,.t,:d.r |m :m |l, :— ||

|m :m |l :s |s :fe |s :— |l :s |f :m |r :r |d :— || d |d ||

|d :d |d :t, |d :d |t, :— |d :d.t, |l,.t,:d |d :t, |d :— || l, |s, ||

|s :s |f.m:r |d.m:r.d |r :— |f :m |f :s |l :s.f |m :— || f |m ||

|d :d |f, :s, |l, :l, |s, :— |f, :d |r :m |f.r:s |d :— || f, |d ||

A-men.

HE is gone—beyond the skies!
A cloud receives Him from our eyes:
Gone beyond the highest height
Of mortal gaze or angel's flight,
Through the veils of time and space
Passed into the holiest place,—
All the toil, the sorrow done,
All the battle fought and won.

2 He is gone: and we remain
In this world of sin and pain;
In the void which He has left
On this earth, of Him bereft,
We have still His work to do,
We can still His path pursue,
Seek Him both in friend and foe,
In ourselves His image show.

3 He is gone : we heard Him say,
‘ Good that I should go away.’
Gone is that dear form and face,
But not gone His present grace ;
Though Himself no more we see,
Comfortless we cannot be :
No ! His Spirit still is ours,
Quickening, freshening all our
powers.

4 He is gone : but we once more
Shall behold Him as before,
In the heaven of heavens the
same
As on earth He went and came :
In the many mansions there
Place for us He will prepare ;
In that world unseen, unknown,
He and we shall yet be one.

Arthur Penrhyn Stanley, 1815–81.

130

PRAETORIUS. (C.M.)

Doh = F. *In moderate time, with dignity.* *Görlitz Gesangbuch*, 1599.

:d | s :s | l :s | s :-.f | m :d | r :m | f :f | m :— | —
:s_1 | s_1 :d | d :d | t_1 :-.t_1 | d :m_1 | s_1 :s_1 | l_1 :s_1 | s_1 :— | —
:m | r :m | f :s | r :-.s | s :d | t_1 :d | d :t_1 | d :— | —
:d | t_1 :d | f_1 :m_1.f_1 | s_1 :-.s_1 | d :l_1 | s_1.f_1 :m_1 | r_1 :s_1 | d_1 :— | —

Harmony.

:m | m :s | f :r | m :d | t_1 :s_1 | l_1 :d | d :t_1 | d :— | — | d | d
:s_1 | d :s_1 | l_1 :s_1 | s_1 :fe_1 | s_1 :s_1 | f_1 :m_1 | s_1 :s_1 | s_1 :— | — | l_1 | s_1
:d | d :d | d :t_1 | d :d | r :d | d :d | r :r | m :— | — | f | m
:d | l_1 :m_1 | f_1 :s_1 | d :l_1 | s_1 :m_1 | f_1 :l_1 | s_1 :s_1 | d_1 :— | — | f_1 | d_1

A-men.

THE golden gates are lifted up,
The doors are opened wide ;
The King of Glory is gone in
Unto His Father's side.

2 Thou art gone up before us, Lord,
To make for us a place,
That we may be where now Thou
art,
And look upon God's face.

3 And ever on our earthly path
A gleam of glory lies ;
A light still breaks behind the cloud
That veiled Thee from our eyes.

Unison.
4 Lift up our hearts, lift up our minds ;
Let Thy dear grace be given,
That, while we wander here below,
Our treasure be in heaven ;

5 That where Thou art, at God's right hand,
Our hope, our love may be.
Dwell Thou in us, that we may dwell
For evermore in Thee.

Cecil Frances Alexander, 1823–95.

131 ST. MAGNUS (NOTTINGHAM). (C.M.)

Doh = G. *Moderately slow.* JEREMIAH CLARK, 1670–1707.

:s, |d :r |t, :s, |d :r |m :r |m :d |m :fe |s :— |— ||

:s, |l, :l, |s, :s, |s, :l,.t, |d :t, |d :s, |s, :d |t, :— |— ||

:m |m :f |r :t, |d :f |m :s |s :s.f |m.r :d |r :— |— ||

:d |l, :f, |s, :s,.f, |m, :r, |d, :s, |d :m.r |d.t, :l, |s, :— |— ||

:r |m :r |d :t, |l, :r |t, :s, |s :s.f |m :r |d :— |— || d |d ||

:t, |d :t, |l, :s, |f, :l, |s, :s, |d :d |d :t, |d :— |— || l, |s, ||

:s |s :s |m :m.r |d :f |r :t, |d :l |s :-.f |m :— |— || d |m ||

:s, |d :s, |l, :m, |f, :r, |s, :s,.f, |m, :f, |s, :s, |d :— |— || f, |d ||

A-men.

FAUX-BOURDON SETTING.

Doh = G. GEOFFREY TURTON SHAW, 1879– .

:s, |d :r |t, :s, |d :l |s :-.f |m.r :m.fe |s :l |t :— |— ||

:s, |d :r |t, :s, |d :-.t, |d :t, |s, :s, |r :d |t, :— |— ||

:s, |d :r |t, :s, |d :r |m :r |m :d |m :fe |s :— |— ||

:s, |d :r |t, :s, |l, :f, |d :s, |d, :d |t, :l, |s, :— |— ||

:l |se :l.t |m :-.r |r.d :t,.l, |s, :m.f |s :l |d :-.t, |d :— |— ||

:r |t, :m, |m,.ba, :se |l, :f, |s, :t, |de :r.l, |s, :s, |m, :— |— ||

:r |m :r |d :t, |l, :r |t, :s, |s :s.f |m :r |d :— |— ||

:f, |m, :ba,.se, |l, :m, |f, :r, |s, :s,.f, |m, :r, |s, :s, |d, :— |— ||

THE Head that once was crowned with thorns
Is crowned with glory now;
A royal diadem adorns
The mighty Victor's brow.

2 The highest place that heaven affords
Is His, is His by right,
The King of kings, and Lord of lords,
And heaven's eternal Light,

3 The joy of all who dwell above,
The joy of all below
To whom He manifests His love,
And grants His Name to know.

4 To them the Cross, with all its shame,
With all its grace, is given,
Their name an everlasting name,
Their joy the joy of heaven.

5 They suffer with their Lord below,
They reign with Him above,
Their profit and their joy to know
The mystery of His love.

6 The Cross He bore is life and health,
Though shame and death to Him,
His people's hope, His people's wealth,
Their everlasting theme.

THOMAS KELLY, 1769–1854.

132 ASCENDIT DEUS. (887. 887.)

Doh = A♭. *In moderate time, with dignity.* JOHANN GOTTFRIED SCHICHT, 1753–1823.

```
:s, |l, :t, |d :t,    |d :r      |m :m  |s :f      |m :d  |f :m      |r :r
:m, |f, :f, |s, :s,   |s, :l,.t, |d :d  |t, :l,    |s, :d |l, :d     |t, :t,
:d  |d :r   |d :r     |m :f      |s :m  |r :d.r    |m :m  |l :s      |s :s
:d, |f, :r, |m, :s,.f,|m, :r,    |d, :d |s, :l,.t, |d :l, |r, :m,.f, |s, :s,

|m :fe |s :d      |t, :l,  |s, ||s,   |d :s,        |l, :f,    |r :d      |t, :t,
|d :d  |t,.l, :s, |s, :fe, |s, ||r,   |s,.f, :m,.r, |d, :f,    |l, :s,    |s, :fe,
|s :l  |r :m      |r :-.d  |t, ||t,   |d :d.t,      |l, :l,    |f :m      |r :re
|d :l, |t, :d     |r :r,   |s, ||s,.f,|m, :d,       |f, :f,.m, |r, :m,.f, |s, :t,.l,

|m :t,   |d :l,     |f :m      |r :r   |m :d       |s :f.m |r :—   |d  ||d  |d
|t, :se, |l, :m,    |l, :d     |t, :t, |d :s,      |s, :d  |d :t,  |s, ||l, |s,
|m :m    |m :d      |d.r :m.f  |s :s   |s.f :m.r   |d :l   |r :s.f |m  ||f  |m
|se, :m, |l, :l,.s, |f, :d     |s, :s, |d :d,      |m, :f, |s, :—  |d, ||f, |d,
                                                                          A- men.
```

THE Lord ascendeth up on high,
The Lord hath triumphed gloriously,
In power and might excelling;
The grave and hell are captive led,
Lo! He returns, our glorious Head,
To His eternal dwelling.

2 The heavens with joy receive their Lord,
By saints, by angel hosts adored;
O day of exultation!
O earth, adore thy glorious King!
His rising, His ascension sing
With grateful adoration!

3 Our great High Priest hath gone before,
Now on His Church His grace to pour,
And still His love He giveth:
O may our hearts to Him ascend;
May all within us upward tend
To Him who ever liveth!

ARTHUR TOZER RUSSELL, 1806–74.

133 HERMAS. (65. 65. D. and refrain.)

Doh = A. *Brightly.* FRANCES RIDLEY HAVERGAL, 1836–79.

m :-.m |m :r |d :— |l, :— |f :-.m |r :d |t, :— |— :— ||
s, :-.s, |se, :t, |l, :— |m, :— |l, :-.s, |l, :l, |s, :— |— :— ||
d :-.d |t, :m |m :— |d :— |r :-.s |f :m |r :— |— :— ||
d :d, |m, :se, |l, :— |l, :— |r, :-.m, |f, :fe, |s, :— |— :— ||

s :r |m :f |m :— |d :— |r :-.d |t, :l, |s, :— |— :— ||
s, :s, |s, :s, |s, :— |s, :— |s, :-.l, |s, :fe, |s, :— |— :— ||
t, :t, |d :t, |d :— |m :— |r :-.m |r :d |t, :— |— :— ||
s, :f, |m, :r, |d, :— |d, :— |t_2 :-.d, |r, :r, |s, :— |— :— ||

s, :s, |l, :t, |r :— |d :— |d :d |f :f |m :— |— :— ||
m, :s, |f, :f, |s, :— |s, :— |l, :s, |l, :s, |s, :— |— :— ||
d :d |d :r |f :— |m :— |d :d |d :t, |d :— |— :— ||
d, :m, |f, :r, |t_2 :— |d, :— |f, :m, |r, :s, |d, :— |— :— ||

d :r |m :f |s :— |s, :— |l, :f |m :r |d :— |— :— ||
s, :s, |s, :l, |s, :— |s, :— |f, :l, |s, :-.f, |m, :— |— :— ||
m :r |d :d |d :— |d :— |d :d |d :t, |d :— |— :— ||
d :t, |d :l, |m, :— |m, :— |f, :r, |s, :s, |d, :— |— :— ||

REFRAIN.

m :-.m |m :r |d :— |l, :— |f :-.m |r :d |t, :— |— :— ||
s, :-.s, |se, :t, |l, :— |m, :— |l, :-.s, |l, :l, |s, :— |— :— ||
d :-.d |t, :m |m :— |d :— |r :-.s |f :m |r :— |— :— ||
d :d, |m, :se, |l, :— |l, :— |r, :-.m, |f, :fe, |s, :— |— :— ||

d :r |m :f |s :— |s, :— |l, :f |m :r |d :— |— :— || d |d ||
s, :t, |d :d |s, :— |s, :— |f, :l, |s, :-.f, |m, :— |— :— || f, |m, ||
s :f |s :d |d :— |d :— |d :d |d :t, |d :— |— :— || l, |s, ||
m :r |d :l, |m, :— |m, :— |f, :r, |s, :s, |d, :— |— :— || f, |d, ||

A-men.

GOLDEN harps are sounding,
Angel voices ring,
Pearly gates are opened,
Opened for the King.
Christ, the King of Glory,
Jesus, King of Love,
Is gone up in triumph
To His throne above.
'All His work is ended,'
Joyfully we sing:
'Jesus hath ascended!
Glory to our King!'

2 He who came to save us,
He who bled and died,
Now is crowned with glory
At His Father's side.
Never more to suffer,
Never more to die,
Jesus, King of Glory,
Is gone up on high.

3 Praying for His children,
In that blessèd place,
Calling them to glory,
Sending them His grace,
His bright home preparing,
Faithful ones, for you,
Jesus ever liveth,
Ever loveth too.

FRANCES RIDLEY HAVERGAL, 1836–79.

134 TRIUMPH. (87. 87. 87.)

Doh = B♭. *In moderate time.* HENRY JOHN GAUNTLETT, 1805–76.

$d_1 :m_1 | s_1 :-.s_1 | s_1 :l_1 | s_1 :m_1 | s_1 :s_1 | d :t_1 | l_1 :l_1 | s_1 :—$
$d_1 :m_1 | s_1 :-.s_1 | s_1 :l_1 | s_1 :m_1 | m_1 :s_1 | fe_1 :s_1 | s_1 :fe_1 | s_1 :—$
$d_1 :m_1 | s_1 :-.s_1 | s_1 :l_1 | s_1 :m_1 | m :r | d :r | r :d | t_1 :—$
$d_1 :m_1 | s_1 :-.s_1 | s_1 :l_1 | s_1 :m_1 | d :t_1 | l_1 :s_1 | r_1 :r_1 | s_1 :—$

$m_1 :s_1 | d :-.d | d :t_1 | r :d | d :l_1 | s_1 :m | r :-.r | d :—$
$m_1 :s_1 | d :-.d | d :t_1 | r :d | l_1 :f_1 | s_1 :s_1 | s_1 :-.f_1 | m_1 :—$
$m_1 :s_1 | d :-.d | d :t_1 | r :d | d :d | d :d | d :-.t_1 | d :—$
$m_1 :s_1 | d :-.d | d :t_1 | r :d | f_1 :f_1 | m_1 :d_1 | s_1 :-.s_1 | d_1 :—$

://:

$m_1 :s_1 | l_1 :fe_1 | s_1 :d | d :t_1 | d :f | f :m | r :-.r | d :— \| d | d$
$d_1 :r_1 | m_1 :r_1 | r_1 :s_1 | f_1 :f_1 | m_1 :f_1 | s_1 :s_1 | s_1 :-.f_1 | m_1 :— \| f_1 | m_1$
$s_1 :t_1 | d :l_1 | r :d | r :r | d :d | r :d | d :-.t_1 | d :— \| l_1 | s_1$
$d_1 :t_2 | l_2 :r_1 | t_2 :m_1 | r_1 :s_1 | l_1 :l_1 | t_1 :d | s_1 :-.s_1 | d_1 :— \| f_1 | d_1$

A-men.

LOOK, ye saints! the sight is glorious;
See the Man of Sorrows now;
From the fight returned victorious,
Every knee to Him shall bow:
Crown Him! crown Him!
Crowns become the Victor's brow.

2 Crown the Saviour! angels, crown Him!
Rich the trophies Jesus brings;
In the seat of power enthrone Him,
While the vault of heaven rings:
Crown Him! crown Him!
Crown the Saviour King of kings!

3 Sinners in derision crowned Him,
Mocking thus the Saviour's claim;
Saints and angels crowd around Him,
Own His title, praise His Name
Crown Him! crown Him!
Spread abroad the Victor's fame.

4 Hark, those bursts of acclamation!
Hark, those loud triumphant chords!
Jesus takes the highest station:
O what joy the sight affords!
Crown Him! crown Him
King of kings, and Lord of lords!

THOMAS KELLY, 1769–1854.

135 DARWALL. (66. 66. 88.)

Doh = D. *Brightly.* JOHN DARWALL, 1731–89.

:d |m :d |s :m |d' :— |— :t |l :s |f :m |r :— |— ||
:d |d :d |r :m |m :— |— :m |f :d |t, :d |t, :— |— ||
:m |s :m |s :s |l :— |— :t |d' :s |s :s |s :— |— ||
:d |d :d |t, :d |l :— |— :s |f :m |r :d |s, :— |— ||

:r |m :d |l :s |fe :r |r' :d' |t :— |l :— |s :— |— ||
:t, |d :d |m :r |r :r |r :m |r :— |r :d |t, :— |— ||
:s |s :s |d' :t |l :fe |s :s |s :— |fe :— |s :— |— ||
:s, |d :m |l, :t,.d |r :r.d |t, :d |r :— |r :— |s, :— |— ||

:s |l :— |t :— |d' :— |— :d |r :m |f :s |l :t |d' :r' |d' :— |t :— |d' :— |— || d' |d' ||
:d |d :— |f :— |m :— |— :d |t, :d |d :d |d :f |m :r |m :— |r :f |m :— |— || f |m ||
:m |f :— |f :— |l :— |— :s |s :s |f :m |f :f |s :l |s :— |s :— |s :— |— || l |s ||
:d |f :— |r :— |l, :— |— :m |r :d |l, :d |f :r |m :f |s :— |s, :— |d :— |— || f |d ||

A-men.

GOPSAL. (66. 66. 88.)

Doh = C. *In moderate time.* GEORGE FREDERICK HANDEL, 1685–1759.

:s |l :s |m :-.fe |s :— |— :d |f :m.r |r :-.d |d :— |— ||
:m |f :r |d :-.d |r :— |— :d |t, :d |d :t, |d :— |— ||
:d' |d' :t |l :-.l |t :— |— :s |f :s |s :s |m :— |— ||
:d |f, :s, |l, :-.l, |s, :s |f :m |r :d |s :s, |d :— |— ||

:s |s :m |l :t |d' :— |— :m' |r' :s.l |fe :-.s |s :— |— ||
:m |r :d |d :f |m :— |— :s |r :r |r :r |t, :— |— ||
:d' |s :s |l :r' |d' :— |— :d' |l :t.d' |l :l |s :— |— ||
:d |t, :d |f :r |l :— |— :m |fe :s |r :r |s, :— |— ||

:s | d' :m | l :s | f :-.f | m :— ‖ :s | l :-.d' | r :m.f | r :- .d | d :— | — ‖ f | m ‖
:s | m :d | d :m | r :-.r | d :— ‖ :d | d :-.d | d :d | d :t,.d | s, :— | — ‖ d | d ‖
:t | d :s | f :l | l :l | l :— ‖ :s | d' :-.s | l :l | s :s | m :— | — ‖ l | s ‖
:s, | l,.,t, :d | f :de | r :r | l, :— ‖ :m | f :-.m | f :r | s :s, | d :— | — ‖ f, | d ‖

A-men.

REJOICE, the Lord is King ;
Your Lord and King adore ;
Mortals, give thanks and sing
And triumph evermore :
Lift up your heart, lift up your voice ;
Rejoice ; again I say, ‘ Rejoice.’

2 Jesus, the Saviour, reigns,
The God of truth and love ;
When He had purged our stains,
He took His seat above :
Lift up your heart, lift up your voice ;
Rejoice ; again I say, ‘ Rejoice.’

3 His Kingdom cannot fail ;
He rules o'er earth and heaven ;
The keys of death and hell
Are to our Jesus given :
Lift up your heart, lift up your voice ;
Rejoice ; again I say, ‘ Rejoice.’

4 He sits at God's right hand
Till all His foes submit,
And bow to His command,
And fall beneath His feet :
Lift up your heart, lift up your voice ;
Rejoice ; again I say, ‘ Rejoice.’

5 Rejoice in glorious hope ;
Jesus, the Judge, shall come,
And take His servants up
To their eternal home ;
We soon shall hear the archangel's voice ;
The trump of God shall sound, ‘ Rejoice.’

CHARLES WESLEY, 1707–88.

136 DIADEMATA. (D.S.M.)

Doh = E. *Brightly.* GEORGE JOB ELVEY, 1816–93.

```
d  :d .d |m  :m  |l  :—  |—  :l  |s  :d  |f  :m  |r  :—  |—
s, :s,.s,|d  :d  |d  :—  |—  :d  |d  :d  |t, :d  |t, :—  |—
m  :m .m |m  :m  |f  :—  |—  :f  |s  :l  |f  :s  |s  :—  |—
d  :d .d |l, :l, |f, :—  |—  :f  |m  :f  |r  :d  |s, :—  |—

          B.t.                                          f.E.
:r  |m :(s)d  |r  :d  |t, :l,.s, |d  :f  |m  :f  |r  :r  |(d)s   :— |—
:t, |d :(r)s, |f, :f, |r, :r,    |s, :f, |s, :l, |r, :s, |(m)t,  :— |—
:s  |s :(s)d  |l, :l, |t, :t,    |d  :t, |d  :d  |d  :t, |(d)s   :— |—
:s, |d :(t)m, |r, :f, |s, :f,    |m, :r, |d, :f, |s, :s, |(d)s,  :— |—

                                   B.t.                  f.E.
:s  |s :m |r  :d |l :— |— :(l)r    |r  :t, |l, :s, |(m)t :— |—
:t, |d :d |t, :d |d :— |— :(de)fe, |s, :s, |f, :s, |(s)r :— |—
:s  |s :s |f  :s |l :— |— :(s)d    |t, :r  |d  :r  |(d)s :— |—
:f  |m :d |r  :m |f :— |— :(m)l,   |s, :s, |l, :t, |(d)s :— |—

:t |d' :-.t |l :s |f :r  |m :s  |f  :m |r  :r   |d :— |— :— || f  |m
:r |d  :d   |d :d |d :t, |d :d  |d  :d |d  :t,  |d :— |— :— || d  |d
:s |s  :s   |f :s |l :s  |s :s  |l  :s |s  :-.f |m :— |— :— || l  |s
:f |m  :m   |f :m |r :s  |d :m, |f, :d |s, :s,  |d :— |— :— || f, |d
                                                                A-men.
```

CROWN Him with many crowns,
The Lamb upon His throne:
Hark how the heavenly anthem drowns
All music but its own.
Awake, my soul, and sing
Of Him who died for thee,
And hail Him as thy matchless King
Through all eternity.

2 Crown Him the Lord of life,
Who triumphed o'er the grave,
And rose victorious in the strife
For those He came to save.
His glories now we sing
Who died and rose on high,
Who died eternal life to bring,
And lives that death may die.

3 Crown Him the Lord of peace,
Whose power a sceptre sways
From pole to pole, that wars may cease,
Absorbed in prayer and praise.
His reign shall know no end;
And round His piercèd feet
Fair flowers of Paradise extend
Their fragrance ever sweet.

4 Crown Him the Lord of love;
Behold His hands and side,
Rich wounds yet visible above,
In beauty glorified.
All hail, Redeemer, hail!
For Thou hast died for me:
Thy praise shall never, never fail
Throughout eternity.

MATTHEW BRIDGES, 1800–94; and GODFREY THRING, 1823–1903.

137 BISHOPTHORPE. (C.M.)

Doh = G. *In moderate time.* JEREMIAH CLARK, 1670–1707.

:s.,f | m :- .r :d | t, :l, :f | m :d :t, | d :— :r
:d | s, :— :s, | f, :— :f, | s, :— :s, | s, :— :t,
:m.,r | d :— :d | d :— :d | d :m :r | d :— :f
:d | d :— :m, | f, :— :l, | s, :— :f, | m, :— :r,

| m :- .f :s | s :f :m | m :r (pause) || s | s :f :m | f :— :f
| d :- .r :m | m :r :d | d :t, || r | de :r :l, | l, :— :l,
| m :— :d | d :s :s | s :— || s | m :r :de | r :— :r
| d, :— :d | l, :t, :d | s, :— || ta, | l, :— :l, | r, :— :r,

f :m :r	m :— :s .,f	m :- .r :d	l, .,r :d :t,	d :—		d	d	
t, :d :s,	s, :— :r	d :— :s,	l, :s, :s,	s, :—		l,	s,	
r :d :t,	d :— :r	s :— :s	f :m :r	m :—		f	m	
s, :— :s,	d :— :t,	d :— :m,	f, :s, :s,	d, :—		f,	d,	

A-men.

From 1 St. Peter i. 3–5.

BLEST be the everlasting God,
The Father of our Lord!
Be His abounding mercy praised,
His majesty adored!

2 When from the dead He raised His Son,
And called Him to the sky,
He gave our souls a lively hope
That they should never die.

3 To an inheritance divine
He taught our hearts to rise;
'Tis uncorrupted, undefiled,
Unfading in the skies.

4 Saints by the power of God are kept,
Till the salvation come:
We walk by faith as strangers here:
But Christ shall call us home.

ISAAC WATTS, 1674–1748, and WILLIAM CAMERON, 1751–1811, as in *Scottish Paraphrases*, 1781.

138 ALLELUIA. (8 7. 8 7. D.)

Doh = F. *In moderate time.* SAMUEL SEBASTIAN WESLEY, 1810–76.

d :d |t, :d |l, :s, |l, :t, |d :r |m :s |l :l |s :— ||
s, :s, |r, :s, |f, :s, |fe, :f, |m, :s, |d :d |d :d |d :— ||
m :m |f :m |d :d |d :s, |d :s |s :s |s :f |m :— ||
d :d |d :d |f, :m, |r, :s, |l, :t, |d :m, |f, :l, |d :— ||

C.t.

s :m.r |d :r |m :f |m :r |(t)m :s |d' :r' |m' :r' |d' :— ||
d :t, |d :s, |d :d |d :t, |(t)m :r |s :fe |s :s.f |m :— ||
s :s.f |m :s |s :l |s :s |(s)d' :t |d' :d' |d' :t |s :— ||
m, :s, |l, :t, |d :f |s :s |(s)d' :s.f |m :l |s :s, |d :— ||

f.F. A.t m.l.r. >>> r.s.d.f.F.

(f)d :d |t, :d |l, :s, |l, :t, |d :r |(m)d :s, |s, :s, |(s)t, :— |
(d)s, :s, |s, :m, |f, :s, |fe, :f, |m, :l, |(se)m, :d, |r, :r, |(m)se, :— |
(l)m :m |r :d |d :d |d :s, |d :t,.l, |(t)s, :d |d :t, |(d)m :— |
(f)d :d |s, :l, |f, :m, |r, :s, |l, :f, |(m)d, :m, |s, :s, |(d)m, :— |

s :m |r :m |f :f.m |m :r |{d'* s} :l |f :m |r :r |d :— || d |d
s, :t, |l, :l, |l, :r.d |d :t, |d :m |l,.t, :d |d :t, |d :— || l, |s,
t, :m |f :de |r :l |s :s |s :m |l :l |l :s.f |m :— || f |m
m, :s, |l, :l, |r :f |s :s |m :d |r :l,.s, |f, :s, |d :— || f, |d,

A-men.

* *Treble* s *or* d'.

ALLELUIA! sing to Jesus!
His the sceptre, His the throne;
Alleluia! His the triumph,
His the victory alone.
Hark! the songs of peaceful Zion
Thunder like a mighty flood:
'Jesus, out of every nation,
Hath redeemed us by His blood.'

2 Alleluia! not as orphans
Are we left in sorrow now;
Alleluia! He is near us,
Faith believes, nor questions how.
Though the cloud from sight received Him
When the forty days were o'er,
Shall our hearts forget His promise,
'I am with you evermore'?

3 Alleluia! Bread of angels,
Thou on earth our Food, our Stay;
Alleluia! here the sinful
Flee to Thee from day to day.
Intercessor, Friend of sinners,
Earth's Redeemer, plead for me,
Where the songs of all the sinless
Sweep across the crystal sea.

4 Alleluia! sing to Jesus!
His the sceptre, His the throne;
Alleluia! His the triumph,
His the victory alone.
Hark! the songs of peaceful Zion
Thunder like a mighty flood:
'Jesus, out of every nation,
Hath redeemed us by His blood.'

WILLIAM CHATTERTON DIX, 1837–98.

139

MILES LANE. (C.M.) FIRST TUNE.

Doh = A. *In moderate time.* WILLIAM SHRUBSOLE, 1760–1806.

```
:s, |d  :d  |d  :r  |m   :r.d |r  :s, |l, :s,.f, |m, :r,  |d, :— |— ||
:m, |s, :l, |s, :s, |s,  :fe, |s, :s, |f, :d,    |d, :t,, |d, :— |— ||
:d  |m  :d  |d  :t, |d   :d   |t, :d  |d  :s,.l, |s, :s,  |m, :— |— ||
:d, |d, :f, |m, :s, |d   :l,  |s, :m, |f, :m,.f, |s, :s,  |d, :— |— ||

:s, |d  :d  |d  :r  |m    :r.d |r  :s, |d  :— |d  :— |m  :— |m  :—
:m, |m, :f, |s, :s, |s,   :fe, |s, :f, |m, :— |m, :— |l, :— |l, :—
                                        crown   Him,   crown  Him,
:s, |s, :l, |s, :t, |d.t, :l,  |t, :t, |d  :— |d  :— |d  :— |d  :—
:d, |d, :f, |m, :s, |d,   :r,  |s, :s, |d, :— |d, :— |l, :— |l, :—

s  :— |s  :— |m  :— |f  :— |m  :— |r  :— |d  :— |— || d  | d
t, :— |t, :— |s, :— |l, :— |s, :— |t, :— |d  :— |— || l, | s,
crown  Him,   crown  Him    Lord   of     all.       A - men.
r  :— |r  :— |d  :— |d  :— |d  :— |f  :— |m  :— |— || f  | m
s, :— |s, :— |d  :— |f, :— |s, :— |s, :— |d  :— |— || f, | d,
```

ALL hail, the power of Jesus' Name!
Let angels prostrate fall;
Bring forth the royal diadem,
To crown Him Lord of all.

2 Crown Him, ye martyrs of your God,
Who from His altar call;
Extol Him in whose path ye trod,
And crown Him Lord of all.

3 Ye seed of Israel's chosen race,
Ye ransomed of the fall,
Hail Him who saves you by His grace,
And crown Him Lord of all.

4 Sinners, whose love can ne'er forget
The wormwood and the gall,
Go, spread your trophies at His feet,
And crown Him Lord of all.

5 Let every tongue and every tribe,
Responsive to the call,
To Him all majesty ascribe,
And crown Him Lord of all.

6 O that, with yonder sacred throng,
We at His feet may fall,
Join in the everlasting song,
And crown Him Lord of all!

EDWARD PERRONET, 1726–92.

139 LADYWELL. (C.M.) SECOND TUNE

WILLIAM HAROLD FERGUSON, 1874–

Doh = A♭. vv. 1, 2, 5, 6 in *Unison*, 3, 4 in *Harmony*. *Stately.*

```
:s, |d :r |m :s |f :m |r :d.r |m.r :d |s, :f, |m, :— |— :s,
:m, |m,.t, :l, |s, :ta, |l,.t, :d |d.t, :s, |s, :s,.l, |m, :r, |d, :— |— :m,
:d |d :d.t, |d :m |f :s.l |r :l,.t, |d.t, :d |d :d.t, |d :— |— :d
:d.t, |l,.s, :f, |m, :de, |r, :m,.fe, |s, :m,.r, |d,.r, :m,.f, |s, :s, |s,/d, :— |— :d.t,

C.t.m.l.r.  r.s.d.f.Ab.
|d :r |(m)d' :s |m :r |m :(d)m, |l, :l,.t, |d :r |r :— |— :s,
|m,.t, :l, |(se)m :d |d :d.t, |d :(d)m, |m,.f, :m,.se, |l,.s, :fe, |s, :— |— :f,
|d :d.l, |(t,)s :s |s :s |s :(d')m |m.r :m |m :r.d |t, :— |— :t,
|l,.s, :f, |(m,)d.r :m |s :s, |d :(d')m.r |d.r :d.t, |l, :r, |s, :— |— :s,

f.Db.  Ab.t.
|m :m |m :d.r |m :r.d |r :(r)l.t |d' :t |l :se |l :— |— :(r)s,
|s,/m, :se, |l,.d :t,.l, |d.t, :l, |t, :(ta,)f |l :f |m :m |m :— |— :(l,)r,
|d :r |d :m.f |s :f.m |s :(s)r' |m' :r' |d' :t.r' |d' :— |— :(fe)t,
|d, :t, |l, :s,.f, |m, :f,.l, |s, :(s,)r |l, :r |m :m |l, :— |— :(r)s,.f,

cres.  < >
|d :r |m :s.f |m :r.m |d :l,.s, |d :s.f |m :r |d :— |— ||
|s, :f, |m, :ta,.l, |se, :l,.t, |l, :f, |s, :d |d :t, |s, :— |— ||
|d.s, :l,.t, |d :m.r |d.t, :l,.m |m :t, |d :d.r |m.f :s.f |m :— |— ||
|m, :r, |d, :de,.r, |m, :ba,.se, |l, :r, |m, :l, |s, :s, |d, :— |— ||
```

ALL hail, the power of Jesus' Name!
Let angels prostrate fall;
Bring forth the royal diadem,
To crown Him Lord of all.

2 Crown Him, ye martyrs of your God,
Who from His altar call;
Extol Him in whose path ye trod,
And crown Him Lord of all.

3 Ye seed of Israel's chosen race,
Ye ransomed of the fall,
Hail Him who saves you by His grace,
And crown Him Lord of all.

4 Sinners, whose love can ne'er forget
The wormwood and the gall,
Go, spread your trophies at His feet,
And crown Him Lord of all.

5 Let every tongue and every tribe,
Responsive to the call,
To Him all majesty ascribe,
And crown Him Lord of all.

6 O that, with yonder sacred throng,
We at His feet may fall,
Join in the everlasting song,
And crown Him Lord of all!

EDWARD PERRONET, 1726–92.

```
|f :— |d :r |m :— |— :— ||
 A   -   -   men.
```

[May be sung to UNIVERSITY, No. 498.]

Also the following:

147 Thou who didst stoop below | 169 Blessing and honour and glory and power

140

SOLDAU. (L.M.)

Doh = G. *Moderately slow.* *Wittenberg Gesangbuch*, 1524.

:d | r :r | d :l, | s, :l, | d :m | s :l | s :m | d :l, | d ||
:m, | l, :s, | m, :f, | s, :f, | m, :d | t, :r | r :t, | l, :l, | s, ||
:d | d :t, | d :d | d :d | d :s | m :fe | s :s | m :f | m ||
:d | f, :s, | l, :f, | m, :f, | d, :d | m :r.d | t, :s, | l, :f, | d, ||

:m | m :r | m :d | r :r | m :d | l, :s, | l, :-.t, | d :d | d || t, | d ||
:d | d :t, | t, :d | d :t, | d :s, | f, :r, | f, :-.f, | s, :l, | s, || s, | s, ||
:s | s :s | s :m | l :s | s :d | d :t, | d :-.r | m :f | m || r | m ||
:d | d :s, | m, :l, | f, :s, | d, :m, | f, :s, | f, :-.r, | d, :f, | d, || s, | d, ||

A-men.

From Heb. iv. 14–16.

WHERE high the heavenly temple stands,
The house of God not made with hands,
A great High Priest our nature wears,
The Guardian of mankind appears.

2 He who for men their surety stood,
And poured on earth His precious blood,
Pursues in heaven His mighty plan,
The Saviour and the Friend of man.

3 Though now ascended up on high,
He bends on earth a brother's eye;
Partaker of the human name,
He knows the frailty of our frame.

4 Our fellow-sufferer yet retains
A fellow-feeling of our pains;
And still remembers in the skies
His tears, His agonies, and cries.

5 In every pang that rends the heart
The Man of Sorrows had a part;
He sympathizes with our grief,
And to the sufferer sends relief.

6 With boldness, therefore, at the throne,
Let us make all our sorrows known;
And ask the aids of heavenly power
To help us in the evil hour.

Scottish Paraphrases, 1781.

[May be sung to WAREHAM, No. 253.]

141 FINGAL. (C.M.)

Doh = E♭. *In moderate time.* JAMES SMITH ANDERSON, 1853–

:m	f :m	r :d	d :t,	d :s	d :d	f :f	m :—	—
:d	d :d	t, :d	s, :s,	s, :d	d :d	r :r	t, :—	—
:s	l :s	f :m	m :r	m :ta	l :l	l :l	se :—	—
:d	d :d	s, :l,	s, :s,	d :m	f :f	r :r	m :—	—

:m	d' :t	l :m	l :s	f :r	s :d	d :t,	d :—	—	d	d
:r	d :r	m :m	m :de	r :t,	d :s,	s, :s,	s, :—	—	l,	s,
:se	l :se	l :l	m :l	l :s	s :m	r :r	m :—	—	f	m
:m	l, :t,	d :d	de :l,	r :f	m :m,	s, :s,	d :—	—	f,	d

A-men.

IMMORTAL Love, for ever full,
For ever flowing free,
For ever shared, for ever whole,
A never-ebbing sea!

Unison. 2 Blow, winds of God, awake and blow
The mists of earth away:
Shine out, O Light Divine, and show
How wide and far we stray.

Harmony. 3 We may not climb the heavenly steeps
To bring the Lord Christ down;
In vain we search the lowest deeps,
For Him no depths can drown.

4 And not for signs in heaven above,
Or earth below, they look
Who know with John His smile of love,
With Peter His rebuke.

5 In joy of inward peace, or sense
Of sorrow over sin,
He is His own best evidence;
His witness is within.

6 And, warm, sweet, tender, even yet
A present help is He;
And faith has still its Olivet,
And love its Galilee.

7 The healing of His seamless dress
Is by our beds of pain;
We touch Him in life's throng and press,
And we are whole again.

JOHN GREENLEAF WHITTIER, 1807–92.

142 ST. VENANTIUS. (L.M.)

Doh = E. *Unison.* *In moderate time.* Rouen Church Melody.

:d | m :s :f | m :r :m | d :—:r | m :— || s | l :s :f | m :f :s

| s :f :m | r :— || r | f :m :r | d :l_1 :t_1 | d :t_1 :-.l_1 | s_1 :— ||

:r | m :d :f | m :r :d | t_1 :—:d | d :— || d :r :d | t_1 :d ||
A - - men.

STRONG Son of God, immortal Love,
Whom we, that have not seen Thy face,
By faith, and faith alone, embrace,
Believing where we cannot prove;

2 Thou wilt not leave us in the dust;
Thou madest man, he knows not why;
He thinks he was not made to die:
And Thou hast made him; Thou art just.

3 Thou seemest human and divine,
The highest, holiest manhood, Thou:
Our wills are ours, we know not how:
Our wills are ours, to make them Thine.

4 Our little systems have their day;
They have their day and cease to be:
They are but broken lights of Thee,
And Thou, O Lord, art more than they.

5 We have but faith: we cannot know;
For knowledge is of things we see;
And yet we trust it comes from Thee,
A beam in darkness: let it grow.

6 Let knowledge grow from more to more,
But more of reverence in us dwell;
That mind and soul, according well,
May make one music as before,

7 But vaster: we are fools and slight,
We mock Thee when we do not fear:
But help Thy foolish ones to bear;
Help Thy vain worlds to bear Thy light.

ALFRED TENNYSON, 1809–92.

143 O AMOR QUAM EXSTATICUS. (L.M.) Old French Melody. Mode i.

Lah = D. Doh = F. *Unison.* *In free time.* Set by BASIL HARWOOD, 1859–

|l, :— |m :— :— :— :r :— |d :— :— :t, :l, :— |d :— :— :— :r :—

|m :— :— :— ||m :— |l :— :— :— :s :— |f :— :m :— :r :—

|m :— :r :— :d |d :— :— :— ||m :— |s :— :— :— s :—

|l :— :— :— :m :— |r :— :d :— :r |m :— :— :— ||d :— |f :— :m :—

:r :— |m :— :r :— :d :— |t, :— :— :— :l, :— |l, :— :— :— ||

||l, :— :— :— |— :— :t, :— |de :— :— :— ||
A - - men.

O LOVE Divine! that stooped to share
Our sharpest pang, our bitterest tear,
On Thee we cast each earth-born care,
We smile at pain while Thou art near.

2 Though long the weary way we tread,
And sorrow crown each lingering year,
No path we shun, no darkness dread,
Our hearts still whispering, 'Thou art near.'

3 When drooping pleasure turns to grief,
And trembling faith is changed to fear,
The murmuring wind, the quivering leaf,
Shall softly tell us Thou art near.

4 On Thee we fling our burdening woe,
O Love Divine, for ever dear;
Content to suffer, while we know,
Living and dying, Thou art near!

OLIVER WENDELL HOLMES, 1809–94.

144 TEMPLE BRYAN. (10 10. 10 6.)

ROBERT ALEXANDER STEWART MACALISTER, 1870–

Doh = C. *In moderate time.* G.t.

|m :— |s :l |t :d' |d' :-.m |m :r |m :— |(s)d :— |r :m
|d :— |m :m |f :s |l :l, |d :t, |d :— |(r)s, :— |d :d
|s :— |d' :d' |r' :m' |d' :d' |l :l |s :— |(s)d :— |l :l
|d :— |d :d |d' :d' |l :l |f :f |d :— |(t,)m, :— |f, :f,

d.f.F.

|f :l |s :d |d :-.t, |d :— ||d :— |(r)m :m |ba :se |t :l
|d :t, |d :l, |s, :s, |s, :— ||s, :— |(s,)l, :r |d :r |m :m
|l :f |s :r |m :r |m :— ||m :— |(s)l :se |l :m |m :d'
|r, :r, |m, :f, |s, :s, |d :— ||d :— |(ta,)d :t, |l, :t, |d :d

C.t.

s :f	m :—	— :—	(d)f :—	m :r	r :d	r :—	m :—		f	m	
r :-.d	t, :—	— :—	(l,)r :—	d :d	t, :l,	t, :—	d :—		d	d	
t :l	se :—	— :—	(l)r' :l	s :l	s :—	s :—	s :—		l	s	
r :r	m :—	— :—	(l,)r :—	m :f	s :—	s, :—	d :—		f,	d	

A-men.

[*Copyright*, 1927, *by Oxford University Press.*]

AND didst Thou love the race that loved not Thee?
And didst Thou take to heaven a human brow?
Dost plead with man's voice by the marvellous sea?
Art Thou his kinsman now?

2 O God, O Kinsman loved, but not enough,
O Man, with eyes majestic after death,
Whose feet have toiled along our pathways rough,
Whose lips drawn human breath!—

3 By that one likeness which is ours and Thine,
By that one nature which doth hold us kin,
By that high heaven where, sinless, Thou dost shine
To draw us sinners in;

4 By Thy last silence in the judgment hall,
By long foreknowledge of the deadly Tree,
By darkness, by the wormwood and the gall,
I pray Thee visit me.

5 Come, lest this heart should, cold and cast away,
Die ere the Guest adored she entertain—
Lest eyes which never saw Thine earthly day
Should miss Thy heavenly reign.

JEAN INGELOW, 1820–97.

145 GODESBERG. (8 7. 8 7. 7 7.)

Doh = G. *In moderate time.* HEINRICH ALBERT, 1604–51.

d :— :r	m :s :f	m :d :t,	l, :— :s,	l, :— :t,	d :— :r
s, :— :s,	s, :— :l,	s, :m, :s,	f, :— :m,	f, :— :f,	s, :— :l,
m :— :r	d :— :d	d :— :d	d :— :d	d :— :r	d :— :d
d :— :t,	d :m, :f,	d, :— :m,	f, :— :d,	f, :— :r,	m, :— :f,

m :r :—	d :— :—		d :— :r	m :s :f	m :d :t,	l, :— :s,
s, :— :f,	m, :— :—		s, :— :s,	s, :— :l,	s, :m, :s,	f, :— :m,
d :— :t,	d :— :—		d :— :t,	d :— :d	d :— :d	d :— :d
s, :— :s,	d, :— :—		m, :— :s,	d :m, :f,	d, :— :m,	f, :— :d,

l, :— :t,	d :— :r	m :r :—	d :— :—		m :— :t,	d :m :r
f, :— :f,	s, :— :l,	s, :— :f,	m, :— :—		m, :— :m,	m, :fe, :s,
d :— :r	d :— :d	d :— :t,	d :— :—		d :— :r	d :— :r
f, :— :r,	m, :— :f,	s, :— :s,	d, :— :—		l, :— :se,	l, :— :t,

d :t, :l,	t, :— :—	d :— :r	m :f :m	r :d :r	d :— :—		d	d	
l, :s, :fe,	s, :— :—	m, :— :s,	s, :l, :s,	l, :s, :f,	m, :— :—		f,	m,	
m :r :r	r :— :—	d :— :t,	d :— :d	f :m :t,	d :— :—		l,	s,	
d :r :r,	s, :— :—	l, :— :s,	d :— :d	f, :s, :s,	d, :— :—		f,	d,	

A-men.

ONE there is, above all others,
Well deserves the name of Friend;
His is love beyond a brother's,
Costly, free, and knows no end:
They who once His kindness prove
Find it everlasting love.

2 When He lived on earth abasèd,
Friend of sinners was His name;
Now, above all glory raisèd,
He rejoices in the same;
Still He calls them brethren, friends,
And to all their wants attends.

3 Could we bear from one another
What He daily bears from us?
Yet this glorious Friend and Brother
Loves us though we treat Him thus;
Though for good we render ill,
He accounts us brethren still.

4 O for grace our hearts to soften!
Teach us, Lord, at length to love
We, alas! forget too often
What a Friend we have above;
But, when home our souls are brought,
We will love Thee as we ought.

JOHN NEWTON, 1725–1807.

146 CHARTERHOUSE. (11 10. 11 10.)

Doh = F. *Unison.* *In moderate time.* DAVID EVANS, 1874–

{ | d, :s, | d :r | m :— | — :d | f :m | r :m | d :— | l, :— | — }

{ :d | t, :l, | s, :s, | d :m | s :— | m :— | r :— | — :— | — }

{ :r | r :r | f :— | m :— | l, :t, | d :r | m :— | s :— | — }

{ :t, | d :r | m :s | l :s | m :d | r :m | d :— | — :— || d d / l, s, / f m / f, d, ||

A-men.

[*Copyright*, 1927, *by David Evans.*]

O SON of Man, our Hero strong and tender,
   Whose servants are the brave in all the earth,
Our living sacrifice to Thee we render,
   Who sharest all our sorrows, all our mirth.

2 O feet so strong to climb the path of duty,
   O lips divine that taught the words of truth,
Kind eyes that marked the lilies in their beauty,
   And heart that kindled at the zeal of youth ;

3 Lover of children, boyhood's inspiration,
   Of all mankind the Servant and the King ;
O Lord of joy and hope and consolation,
   To Thee our fears and joys and hopes we bring.

4 Not in our failures only and our sadness
   We seek Thy presence, Comforter and Friend ;
O rich man's Guest, be with us in our gladness,
   O poor man's Mate, our lowliest tasks attend.

FRANK FLETCHER, 1870–

147 ELVEY. (6 6 10. 6 6 10.)

Doh = E. *Moderately slow.* GEORGE JOB ELVEY, 1816–93.

:d |m :s |f :m |r :— |— :s |l :d' |t :l |s :— |— ‖
:d |d :r |d :d |t, :— |— :t, |d :d |r :d |t, :— |— ‖
:m |s :s |l :s |s :— |— :s |m :l |s :fe |s :— |— ‖
:d |d :t, |l, :d |s, :— |— :m |d :l, |r :r |s, :— |— ‖

:s |d :— |r :— |m :fe |s :d' |t :— |l :— |s :— |— ‖
:t, |d :— |— :t, |d :d |t, :m |r :— |r :d |t, :— |— ‖
:s |m :— |s :— |s :l |s :s |s :— |fe :— |s :— |— ‖
:m, |l, :— |s, :— |d :l, |m :d |r :— |r :— |s, :— |— ‖

:s |s :m |l :s |f :— |— :f |f :r |s :f |m :— |— ‖
:t, |de :m |r :de |r :— |— :l, |t, :r |d :t, |d :— |— ‖
:s |m :s |f :m |r :— |— :r |r :f |m :r |d :— |— ‖
:m, |l, :l, |l, :l, |r :— |— :r, |s, :s, |s, :s, |d :— |— ‖

:d |l :— |— :s |f :s |m :f |m :— |r :— |d :— |— ‖d |d ‖
:d |d :r |m :— |r :r |d :d |d :— |t, :— |d :— |— ‖l, |s, ‖
:s |l :— |l :— |l :s |s :l |s :— |s :f |m :— |— ‖f |m ‖
:m |f :— |de :— |r :t, |d :f, |s, :— |s, :— |d :— |— ‖f, |d ‖

A-men.

THOU who didst stoop below
To drain the cup of woe,
Wearing the form of frail mortality,
Thy blessèd labours done,
Thy crown of victory won,
Hast passed from earth, passed to Thy home on high.

2 Our eyes behold Thee not,
Yet hast Thou not forgot
Those who have placed their hope, their trust in Thee;
Before Thy Father's face
Thou hast prepared a place,
That, where Thou art, there they may also be.

3 O Thou who art our life,
Be with us through the strife:
Thy holy head by earth's fierce storms was bowed;
Raise Thou our eyes above,
To see a Father's love
Beam, like the bow of promise, through the cloud.

4 And O, if thoughts of gloom
Should hover o'er the tomb,
That light of love our guiding star shall be;
Our spirits shall not dread
The shadowy way to tread,
Friend, Guardian, Saviour, which doth lead to Thee.

SARAH ELIZABETH MILES, 1807–77.

148 WALSALL. (C.M.)

Lah = F. Doh = A♭. *Slow.* *Anchors' Collection of Psalm Tunes*, c. 1721.

```
:l, |d  :t,.l, |m,  :m  |r .d:t, |l, :d  |l,  :se, |l,.t,:d .r |m  :— |—  ||
:m, |m, :m,    |m,  :l, |f,  :r, |d, :l, |m,  :r,  |m,   :l,   |se,:— |—  ||
:d  |l, :l,    |se, :d  |l,  :se,|l, :m  |d   :r   |d    :l,   |t, :— |—  ||
:l2 |l, :d,    |m,  :l2 |r,  :m, |l, :l, |d   :t,  |l,   :f,   |m, :— |—  ||

:m  |m :m  |r :d .t, |l,:r .d|t,:m  |l,.se,:l,.t, |d .r :t,.,l, |l, :— |— || l, |l,  ||
:s, |s,:s, |s,:s,    |f,:l,  |s,:s, |f,    :l,    |l,   :se,    |l, :— |— || f, |m,  ||
:d  |d :d  |t,:d     |d :f   |r :d  |d     :f     |m .f :r      |d  :— |— || r  |de  ||
:d, |m,:d, |s,:m,    |f,:r,  |s,:d, |f,    :r,    |m,.r,:m,     |l2 :— |— || r, |l2  ||
                                                                          A-men.
```

THERE is no sorrow, Lord, too light
To bring in prayer to Thee;
There is no anxious care too slight
To wake Thy sympathy.

2 Thou, who hast trod the thorny road,
Wilt share each small distress;
The love which bore the greater load
Will not refuse the less.

3 There is no secret sigh we breathe
But meets Thine ear divine;
And every cross grows light beneath
The shadow, Lord, of Thine.

4 Life's ills without, sin's strife within,
The heart would overflow,
But for that love which died for sin,
That love which wept with woe.

JANE CREWDSON, 1809–63.

[May be sung to EVAN, No. 692.]

Also the following:

86 Thine arm, O Lord, in days of old
174 Rest of the weary
277 At even, when the sun was set
329 When our heads are bowed with woe
352 Thou to whom the sick and dying
556 Be still, my soul: the Lord is on thy side

149

VENI IMMANUEL. (88. 88. and refrain.) *The Hymnal Noted*, 1854.

Lah = E. Doh = G. *Unison. In free rhythm.* Adapted by THOMAS HELMORE, 1811–90.

:l, :d :m :m :m :r :f :m :r :d
1. O come, O come, Im - man - - u - el,

:r :m :d :l, :d :r :t, :l, :s, :l, :— :—
And ran - som cap - tive Is - - ra - el,

:r :r :l, :l, :t, :d :— :t, :l, :s, :— :—
That mourns in lone - ly ex - - ile here

:d :r :m :m :m :r :f :m :r :d :— :—
Un - til the Son of God - ap - pear.

REFRAIN.

:s :s :— : :m :m :— : :m :r :f :m :r :d
Re - joice! re - joice! Im - man - - - u - el

:r :m :d :l, :d :r :t, :l, :s, :l, :— :—
Shall come to thee, O Is - - - - ra - el.

s, l,
m, m,
t, d
m, l,
A-men.

Veni Immanuel.

O COME, O come, Immanuel,
And ransom captive Israel,
That mourns in lonely exile here
Until the Son of God appear.
Rejoice! rejoice! Immanuel
Shall come to thee, O Israel.

2 O come, O come, Thou Lord of might,
Who to Thy tribes, on Sinai's height,
In ancient times didst give the law
In cloud and majesty and awe.

3 O come, Thou Rod of Jesse, free
Thine own from Satan's tyranny;
From depths of hell Thy people save,
And give them victory o'er the grave.

4 O come, Thou Dayspring, come and cheer
Our spirits by Thine advent here;
Disperse the gloomy clouds of night,
And death's dark shadows put to flight.

5 O come, Thou Key of David, come,
And open wide our heavenly home;
Make safe the way that leads on high,
And close the path to misery.

12th century; *tr.* by JOHN MASON NEALE, 1818–66.

150

ST. NICOLAS. (87. 87.)

Doh = E♭. *In moderate time.* RICHARD REDHEAD, 1820–1901.

s :l	l :s	f :m	m :r	d :r	m :s	d' :l	s :—	
d :d	d :d	r :d	d :t_1	d :t_1	d :r	m :r.d	t_1 :—	
m :f	f :m	s :s	s :s	s :s	s :s	s :fe	s :f	
d :d	d :d	t_1 :d	s :f	m :r	d :t_1	l_1 :r	s_1 :—	

s :d'	t :l	s :-.l	s :f	f :m	m :r	d :r	d :—		d	d	
d :d	f :f	f :m	r :r	r :d	l_1 :l_1	s_1 :t_1	d :—		l_1	s_1	
m :m	f :l	r' :d'	t :l	s :s	s :f	m :f	m :—		f	m	
d :l_1	r :d	t_1 :d	r :r.d	t_1 :d	f_1 :f_1	s_1 :s_1	d :—		f_1	d	

A - men.

COME, Thou long-expected Jesus,
  Born to set Thy people free ;
From our fears and sins release us ;
  Let us find our rest in Thee.

2 Israel's Strength and Consolation,
  Hope of all the earth Thou art,
Dear Desire of every nation,
  Joy of every longing heart.

3 Born Thy people to deliver,
  Born a Child and yet a King,
Born to reign in us for ever,
  Now Thy gracious Kingdom bring.

4 By Thine own eternal Spirit
  Rule in all our hearts alone ;
By Thine all-sufficient merit
  Raise us to Thy glorious throne.

CHARLES WESLEY, 1707–88.

151 PSALM 107. (D.C.M.) *French Psalter*, 1543.

Lah = D. Doh = F. *Slow.* Composed or arranged by Louis Bourgeois, 1510- ? .

```
:l,     |l,     :m       :l .l    |s .s   :m     :m     |f .m   :d     :r      |d   :—   ||
:m,     |l,     :l, .t,  :l, .t,  |d .d   :t,    :l,    |f, .s, :m,    :s, .f, |m,  :—   ||
:d .r   |m .r   :d .m    :m .r    |m .m   :s     :d     |r .d   :d     :t,     |d   :—   ||
:l, .t, |d .t,  :l, .s,  :f, .f,  |d, .d, :m,    :l,    |r, .m, :l,    :s,     |d,  :—   ||

:l,     |l,     :m       :l .l    |s .s   :m     :d     |r .m   :d     :t,     |l,  :—  :—  ||
:m,     |l,     :l,      :t, .t,  |t, .t, :l,    :s,    |s, .s, :fe,   :se,    |l,  :—  :—  ||
:d      |r      :— .d    :f .f    |m .m   :d     :m     |s .m   :fe    :t,     |d   :—  :—  ||
:l, .s, |f,     :m,      :r, .r,  |m, .m, :l,    :d     |t, .d  :r,    :m,     |l,  :—  :—  ||
```

Unison.

```
|l       :m .fe  :s .l    |s       :fe      |m    :—  |l    :t .l    |m    :fe      |m    :—  ||
|l,      :l, .d  :t, .d   |t,      :t, .l,  |se,  :—  |l,   :m .d    |s,   :t, .l,  |se,  :—  ||
|d .r    :m .l   :s .m    |m       :re      |m    :—  |m    :s .m    |m    :re      |m    :—  ||
|l, .t,  :d .r   :m .l,   |m, .s,  :t,      |m,   :—  |d    :s, .l,  |d    :t,      |m,   :—  ||
```

Harmony.

```
|m       :s .fe   :m .m   |r .r    :d       :d        |r .m    :r          :t,        |l,  :—  ||l,  |l,  ||
|l, .d   :t, .r   :r .d   |d .t,   :l,      :l, .s,   |f, .m,  :fe, .l,    :— .se,    |l,  :—  ||f,  |m,  ||
|d .l    :s .t    :s .s   |s .f    :m       :f .d     |l, .l,  :r .fe      :m .r      |d   :—  ||r   |de  ||
|l,      :m .t,   :d .d   |s, .s,  :l, .s,  :f, .m,   |r, .d,  :r,         :m,        |l,  :—  ||r,  |l,  ||
                                                                                                 A - men.
```

From Psalms lxxxv, lxxxii, lxxxvi.

THE Lord will come and not be slow,
His footsteps cannot err ;
Before Him righteousness shall go,
His royal harbinger.
Truth from the earth, like to a flower,
Shall bud and blossom then ;
And justice, from her heavenly bower,
Look down on mortal men.

2 Surely to such as do Him fear
Salvation is at hand !
And glory shall ere long appear
To dwell within our land.
Rise, God, judge Thou the earth in might,
This wicked earth redress ;
For Thou art He who shall by right
The nations all possess.

3 The nations all whom Thou hast made
  Shall come, and all shall frame
To bow them low before Thee, Lord,
  And glorify Thy Name.
For great Thou art, and wonders great
  By Thy strong hand are done :
Thou in Thy everlasting seat
  Remainest God alone.

JOHN MILTON, 1608–74.

152 ST. CECILIA. (6 6. 6 6.)

Doh = G. *In moderate time.* LEIGHTON GEORGE HAYNE, 1836–83.

```
:s  | f  :m  | m  :r  | d  :—  | — :m   | r  :t,  | t,  :l,  | s,  :— | — ||
:d  | d  :d  | d  :t, | d  :—  | — :fe, | s, :s,  | s,  :fe, | s,  :— | — ||
:m  | f  :s  | s  :f  | m  :—  | — :d   | r  :r   | r   :d   | t,  :— | — ||
:d  | l, :d  | s, :s, | l, :—  | — :l,  | t, :s,  | r,  :r,  | s,  :— | — ||

:r  | r  :m  | f  :s  | m  :—  | — :d   | l, :d   | r   :r   | d   :— | — || d  | d  ||
:t, | t, :d  | d  :t, | d  :—  | — :s,  | f, :d   | d   :t,  | d   :— | — || l, | s, ||
:s  | s  :s  | l  :s  | s  :—  | — :d   | d  :s   | s   :f   | m   :— | — || f  | m  ||
:s, | f  :m  | r  :s, | d  :—  | — :m,  | f, :m,  | s,  :s,  | d,  :— | — || f, | d, ||
```

A-men.

THY Kingdom come, O God ;
  Thy rule, O Christ, begin ;
Break with Thine iron rod
  The tyrannies of sin.

2 Where is Thy reign of peace
  And purity and love ?
When shall all hatred cease,
  As in the realms above ?

3 When comes the promised time
  That war shall be no more,
And lust, oppression, crime,
  Shall flee Thy face before ?

Unison.

4 We pray Thee, Lord, arise,
  And come in Thy great might ;
Revive our longing eyes,
  Which languish for Thy sight.

Harmony.

5 Men scorn Thy sacred Name,
  And wolves devour Thy fold ;
By many deeds of shame
  We learn that love grows cold.

6 O'er heathen lands afar
  Thick darkness broodeth yet ;
Arise, O Morning Star,
  Arise, and never set.

LEWIS HENSLEY, 1824–1905.

153 IRISH. (C.M.)

Doh = E. *In moderate time.* *Hymns and Sacred Poems*, Dublin, 1749.

:d | d :— :s, | d :r :m | f :m :r | m :— :s
:s, | s, :— :s, | l, :t, :d | d :— :t, | d :— :r
:m | m :— :r | m :s :s | l :s :s | s :— :s
:d | d :— :t, | l, :s, :d | f, :s, :s, | d :— :t,

m :f :s	d :r :t,	d :—		s	d' :s :l	s :f :m
d :— :d	l, :— :s,	s, :—		d	d :m :d	d :t, :d
s :l :s	m :f :r	m :—		m.f	s :— :f	s :— :s
d :l, :m,	l, :f, :s,	d :—		d.r	m :d :f	m :r :d

l.,s:f :m	r :— :s	d'.,t:l :s	f :m :r	d :—		d	d	
d :r :s,	s, :— :t,	d :— :d	r :d :t,	d :—		l,	s,	
f.,s:l.t :d'	t :— :s.f	m :f :s	l :s :f	m :—		f	m	
f.,m:r :d	s, :— :s,	l, :f, :m,	f, :s, :s,	d :—		f,	d	

A-men.

'THY Kingdom come! '—on bended knee
The passing ages pray;
And faithful souls have yearned to see
On earth that Kingdom's day.

2 But the slow watches of the night
Not less to God belong;
And for the everlasting right
The silent stars are strong.

3 And lo! already on the hills
The flags of dawn appear;
Gird up your loins, ye prophet souls,
Proclaim the day is near:

4 The day in whose clear-shining light
All wrong shall stand revealed,
When justice shall be throned with might,
And every hurt be healed:

5 When knowledge, hand in hand with peace,
Shall walk the earth abroad,—
The day of perfect righteousness,
The promised day of God.

FREDERICK LUCIAN HOSMER, 1840–

154 CRÜGER. (76. 76. D.)

JOHANN CRÜGER, 1598–1662.

Doh = G. *Moderately slow.* *D.C.*

```
:s  |l  :s  |f  :m  |r  :—  |m  :m  |d  :d  |r  :s  |m  :—  |—  ||
:d  |d  :d  |d  :d  |d  :t, |d  :d  |s, :d  |d  :t, |d  :—  |—  ||
:m  |f  :s  |l  :s  |s  :—  |s  :s  |m  :m  |s  :s  |s  :—  |—  ||
:d  |f, :m, |f, :d, |s, :—  |d  :d  |m  :l, |s, :s, |d  :—  |—  ||

:m  |f  :m  |r  :d  |t, :—  |d  :m  |r  :r  |m  :d  |t, :—  |—  ||
:d  |d  :d  |t, :l, |l, :se,|l, :d  |t, :l, |se,:l, |se,:—  |—  ||
:s  |f  :s  |s  :m  |m  :—  |m  :s  |s  :r  |t, :d.r|m  :—  |—  ||
:d  |l, :d  |s, :l, |m, :—  |l, :d, |s, :f, |m, :l, |m, :—  |—  ||

:m  |m  :r  |m  :l  |s  :—  |m  :s  |f  :m  |r  :r  |d  :—  |—  ||d  |d  ||
:s, |d  :t, |d  :d  |t, :—  |d  :d  |d  :d  |d  :t, |d  :—  |—  ||l, |s, ||
:m  |s  :s  |s  :f  |r  :s  |s  :s  |l  :s  |s  :s  |m  :—  |—  ||f  |m  ||
:d  |d  :s, |d  :f, |s, :—  |d  :m, |f, :d, |s, :s, |d  :—  |—  ||f, |d  ||
                                                               A-men.
```

From Psalm lxxii.

HAIL to the Lord's Anointed,
  Great David's greater Son!
Hail, in the time appointed,
  His reign on earth begun!
He comes to break oppression,
  To let the captive free,
To take away transgression,
  And rule in equity.

2 He comes with succour speedy
  To those who suffer wrong,
To help the poor and needy,
  And bid the weak be strong,
To give them songs for sighing,
  Their darkness turn to light
Whose souls, condemned and dying,
  Were precious in His sight.

3 He shall come down like showers
  Upon the fruitful earth,
And love, joy, hope, like flowers,
  Spring in His path to birth.
Before Him, on the mountains,
  Shall peace, the herald, go;
And righteousness in fountains
  From hill to valley flow.

4 For Him shall prayer unceasing
  And daily vows ascend,
His Kingdom still increasing,
  A Kingdom without end.
The mountain dews shall nourish
  A seed, in weakness sown,
Whose fruit shall spread and flourish
  And shake like Lebanon.

5 O'er every foe victorious,
  He on His throne shall rest,
From age to age more glorious,
  All blessing and all-blest.
The tide of time shall never
  His covenant remove;
His Name shall stand for ever;
  That Name to us is Love.

JAMES MONTGOMERY, 1771–1854.

155 VISION. (Irr.)

Doh = C. *Unison.* *Fervently.* HENRY WALFORD DAVIES, 1869-

|d :r |m :-.r |m :s |l :s |m :d |r :m |f :-.m |m :— ||

1. Mine eyes have seen the glo - ry of the com - ing of the Lord:
2. He hath sound - ed forth the trum - pet that shall nev - er call re - treat;

|d :r |m :-.r |m :s |l :s |l :t |r' :d' |t :l |s :— ||

He is tramp-ling out the vin - tage where the grapes of wrath are stored;
He is sift - ing out the hearts of men be - fore His judg - ment-seat:

|s :s |m' :-.r' |d' :l |d' :s |s :s |m' :-.r' |d' :l |d' :— ||

He hath loosed the fa - tal light-ning of His ter - ri - ble swift sword:
O, be swift, my soul, to an - swer Him; be ju - bi - lant, my feet!

|d :r |m :— |l :— |t :— |— :l |d' :— |— :— |— :— |— :— |— :— |— :— ||

His truth is march - ing on.
Our God is march - ing on.

Harmony.

|d :r |m :-.r |m :s |l :s |m :d |r :m |f :-.m |m :— ||
|d :r |m :-.r |m :s |l :s |m :d |r :s, |t, :-.d |d :— ||

3. In the beau - ty of the li - lies Christ was born a - cross the sea,
4. He is com - ing like the glo - ry of the morn - ing on the wave;

|d :r |m :-.r |m :s |l :s |m :d |l :d' |s :-.s |s :— ||
|d :r |m :-.r |m :s |l :s |m :d |f :m |r :-.d |d :— ||

G.t. f.C.

|d :r |m :-.r |m :s |l :s |[l]r :m |s :f |m :r |[d]s :— ||
|d :r |m :-.r |m :s |l :s |[l]r :d |t, :l, |se, :-.se, |[l]m :— ||

With a glo - ry in His bo - som that trans - fi - gures you and me:
He is wis - dom to the migh - ty; He is suc - cour to the brave;

|d :r |m :-.r |m :s |l :s |[m]l :s |f :r |m :-.m |[m]t :— ||
|d :r |m :-.r |m :s |l :s |[d]f :m |r :t, |m :-.m |[l]m :— ||

|s :s |m' :-.r' |d' :l |d' :s |s :s |m' :-.r' |d' :l |d' :— ||
|r :f |m :-.f |s :l |s :m |s :f |m :-.f |s :l |m :— ||

As He died to make men ho - ly, let us live to make men free,
So the world shall be His foot - stool, and the soul of time His slave:

|t :r' |d' :-.t |d' :d' |d'.r' :m' |d' :s |s' :-.f' |m' :f' |s' :— ||
|s :s |d :-.r |m :f |m :d |m :s |d' :-.r' |m' :r' |d' :— ||

While God is marching on. (marching on.)
Our God is marching on! (marching on.)

Julia Ward Howe, 1819–1910, and others.

BATTLE SONG. (Irr.)
Lah = D. Doh = F. *With life.*

Martin Shaw, 1876–

7 bars Instrumental

1. Mine eyes have seen the glory of the coming of the Lord: He is trampling out the vintage where the grapes of wrath are stored; He hath loosed the fatal lightning of His terrible swift sword: His truth is marching on.

2. He hath sounded forth the trumpet that shall never call retreat; He is sifting out the hearts of men before His judgment-seat: O, be swift, my soul, to answer Him; be jubilant, my feet! Our God is marching on.

3. In the beauty of the lilies Christ was born across the sea, With a glory in His bosom that transfigures you and me: As He died to make men holy, let us live to make men free, While God is marching on.

4. He is coming like the glory of the morning on the wave; He is wisdom to the mighty; He is succour to the brave; So the world shall be His footstool, and the soul of time His slave: Our God is marching on!

1st time. *D.C.* || *Last time.*

[*Copyright*, 1915, *by J. Curwen & Sons, Ltd.*]

Julia Ward Howe, 1819–1910, and others.

156

OLD 134TH (ST. MICHAEL). (S.M.) *French Psalter*, 1551. Composed or arranged by LOUIS BOURGEOIS, 1510– ?

Doh = A♭. *In moderate time.*

```
|s,  :—  |d   :m   |r   :r   |m   :—  ||s   :—  |f   :m   |r   :r   |d   :—  ||
|m,  :—  |m,  :s,  |l,  :s,  |s,  :—  ||s,  :—  |d   :d   |d   :t,  |d   :—  ||
|d   :—  |d   :d   |d   :t,  |d   :—  ||r   :—  |f   :s   |s   :-.f |m   :—  ||
|d   :—  |l,  :m,  |f,  :s,  |d   :—  ||t,  :—  |l,  :d   |s,  :s,  |d,  :—  ||
```

```
|d  :—  |t, :l, |s, :d  |d  :r  |m  :—  ||m  :—  |r    :d  |d  :t, |d  :—  ||d  |d  ||
|l, :—  |s, :f, |m, :s, |l, :l, |se,:—  ||s, :—  |f,   :s, |l, :s, |s, :—  ||l, |s, ||
|m  :—  |m  :d  |d  :d  |m  :r  |t, :—  ||d  :—  |l,.t,:d  |f  :r  |m  :—  ||f  |m  ||
|l, :—  |m, :f, |d, :m, |l, :f, |m, :—  ||d, :—  |r,   :m, |f, :s, |d, :—  ||f, |d, ||
```

A-men.

YE servants of the Lord,
Each in his office wait,
Observant of His heavenly word,
And watchful at His gate.

2 Let all your lamps be bright,
And trim the golden flame;
Gird up your loins, as in His sight,
For awful is His Name.

3 Watch: 'tis your Lord's command,
And while we speak He 's near;
Mark the first signal of His hand,
And ready all appear.

4 O happy servant he,
In such a posture found!
He shall his Lord with rapture see,
And be with honour crowned.

5 Christ shall the banquet spread
With His own royal hand,
And raise that faithful servant's head
Amid the angelic band.

PHILIP DODDRIDGE, 1702–51.

157

BEVERLEY. (8 7. 8 8 7. 7 7. 7 7.)

Doh = C. *Moderately quick.* WILLIAM HENRY MONK, 1823–89.

```
|s  :s  |d' :s  |f  :m  |r  :d  |s  :f  |m  :m  |r  :d    |s  :—  ||
|s  :s  |d  :d  |t, :d  |t, :d  |r  :r  |d  :d  |r  :l,   |t, :—  ||
|s  :s  |s  :m  |f  :s  |f  :m  |s  :s  |s  :s  |s  :-.fe |s  :—  ||
|s  :f  |m  :m  |r  :d  |s, :l, |t, :t, |d  :d  |t, :l,   |s, :—  ||
```

```
|s  :s  |d'  :s    |d' :r' |m' :d' |m  :m  |l  :m    |l  :t
|s  :t, |d   :s    |s  :f  |m  :s  |m  :m  |m  :m    |m  :m
|s  :s  |s   :s.l  |s  :t  |d' :d' |m  :se |l  :se   |l  :se
|s  :f  |m   :m.f  |m  :r  |d  :m  |m  :r  |d  :m.r  |d  :t,
```

```
d' :l  |t  :d' |t  :s  |l  :t  |s  :—  ||s  :-.s |l  :s
m  :m  |r  :d  |r  :t, |m  :d  |t, :—  ||t, :-.r |f  :d
l  :l  |se :l  |s  :s  |s  :fe |s  :—  ||s  :-.t |d' :s
l, :d  |m  :l, |t, :m  |d  :r  |s, :—  ||s  :-.s |f  :m

                f.F.                                   C.t.
l  :t  |d' :—  |[d']s :-.s  |s  :s  |s  :f  |m  :—  ||[m]l   :l
f  :f  |m  :—  |[m]t, :-.t, |d  :t, |d  :t, |d  :—  ||[s]d   :d
f  :f  |s  :—  |[d']s :-.s  |s  :s  |s  :s  |s  :—  ||[s]d'  :l
r  :r  |d  :—  |[d]s  :-.f  |m  :f  |m  :r  |d  :—  ||[d]f   :f

s  :d'  |m' :r' |d' :— |t  :l  |s  :d' |l  :t  |d' :— ||d' |d'
r  :s   |s  :f  |m  :— |s  :f  |m  :s  |f  :f  |m  :— ||f  |m
t  :d'  |d' :t  |d' :— |d' :d' |d' :m' |r' :r' |d' :— ||l  |s
f  :m.f |s  :se |l  :— |m  :f  |s  :s  |s  :s  |d  :— ||f  |d
                                                        A-men.
```

THOU art coming, O my Saviour,
Thou art coming, O my King,
In Thy beauty all-resplendent,
In Thy glory all-transcendent;
Well may we rejoice and sing.
Coming! in the opening east
Herald brightness slowly swells;
Coming! O my glorious Priest,
Hear we not Thy golden bells?

2 Thou art coming, Thou art coming;
We shall meet Thee on Thy way,
We shall see Thee, we shall know Thee,
We shall bless Thee, we shall show Thee
All our hearts could never say.
What an anthem that will be,
Ringing out our love to Thee,
Pouring out our rapture sweet
At Thine own all-glorious feet!

3 Thou art coming; at Thy table
We are witnesses for this,
While remembering hearts Thou meetest
In communion clearest, sweetest,
Earnest of our coming bliss;
Showing not Thy death alone
And Thy love exceeding great,
But Thy coming and Thy throne,
All for which we long and wait.

4 O the joy to see Thee reigning,
Thee, my own belovèd Lord!
Every tongue Thy name confessing,
Worship, honour, glory, blessing
Brought to Thee with glad accord,—
Thee, my Master and my Friend,
Vindicated and enthroned,
Unto earth's remotest end
Glorified, adored, and owned.

FRANCES RIDLEY HAVERGAL, 1836–79.

158 WHEN HE COMETH. (8 6. 8 5. and refrain.)

Doh = E. *Brightly.* GEORGE FREDERICK ROOT, 1820–95.

:d.r	m :m :m.f	s :s :l	m :m :r	d :d	‖ d.r	m :m :m.f
:d.d	d :s, :m.d	r :s, :d	d :l, :t,	d :d	‖ d.t,	d :s, :m.d
:m.f	s :d' :s.l	r :m :d.r	m.f :s :f	m :m	‖ m.f	s :d' :s.l
:d.d	d :d :d.d	t, :d :f,	s, :s, :s,	d :d	‖ m.r	d :d :d.d

REFRAIN.

s :s :l	m :m :r	d :—	‖ d'.t	l :l :d'	s :s :l.s	d :d :r
r :s, :d	d :l, :t,	d :—	‖ d.d	d :d :d	d :s, :r	d :d :t,
r :m :d.r	m.f :s :f	m :—	‖ s.s	l :l :s.f	s :m :r	m :s :s.f
t, :d :f,	s, :s, :s,	d :—	‖ m.m	f :f :m.r	m :d :t,	l, :m, :s,

m :s	‖ d'.t	l :l :d'	s :s :l	s :d :r	d :—	‖ d | d
d :r	‖ d.r	m.r :d :d	r :s, :d	d :l, :t,	d :—	‖ l, | s,
m :r	‖ m.s	d'.t :l.s :f.m	r :m :d.r	m :m :f	m :—	‖ f | m
d :t,	‖ l,.t,	d :f.m :r.d	t, :d :f,	s, :l, :s,	d :—	‖ f, | d

A-men.

NESTA. (8 6. 8 5. and refrain.)

LEWIS JONES ROBERTS, 1866–

Doh = C. *In moderate time.* G.t.

:d.m	s :f :m.s	d' :t :l.t	d' :s :f	f :m	^{d}f,.l,	d :t, :l,.d
:d.d	m :r :d.d	m :r :r	d :m :t,	r :d	^{d}f,.f,	l, :se, :l,.l,
:m.s	d' :s :s.s	s :s :l.s	s :s :s	s :s	^{m}l,.d	m :m :d.m
:d.d	d :d :d.m	s :s :f	m :d :s,	d :d	^{d}f,.f,	m, :m, :l,.l,

f.C. REFRAIN.

m :r :d.m	s :-.f :r.m	^{d}s :—	‖ s.s	l :l :l	t :t :t
d :t, :d	d :— :d.t,	^{d}s :—	‖ d.d	d :d :r	r :r :m
s :s :s	l :— :f.s	^{m}t :—	‖ s.m	f :f :fe	s :s :se
s, :f, :m,	f, :— :s,.s,	^{d}s :—	‖ m.d	f :f :r	s :s :m

```
| d' :-.l  :t.d'  | r' :r'  || s.s | m' :— :r'.d' | t  :l  :s  | l  :d' :t  | d' :— || d' | d' ||
| m  :—    :s.s   | s  :fe  || s.s | s  :— :f .m  | r  :d  :m  | f  :l  :s  | s  :— || f  | m  ||
| l  :-.d' :r'.s  | l  :l   || t.t | d' :— :l .l  | se :l  :d' | d' :f' :r' | m' :— || l  | s  ||
| l  :-.s  :f.m   | r  :r   || s.s | d  :— :r .r  | m  :f  :d  | f  :r  :s  | d  :— || f  | d  ||
```

A-men.

WHEN He cometh, when He cometh
To make up His jewels,
All His jewels, precious jewels,
His loved and His own,
Like the stars of the morning,
His bright crown adorning,
They shall shine in their beauty,
Bright gems for His crown.

2 He will gather, He will gather
The gems for His Kingdom,
All the pure ones, all the bright ones,
His loved and His own.

3 Little children, little children
Who love their Redeemer,
Are the jewels, precious jewels,
His loved and His own.

WILLIAM ORCUTT CUSHING, 1823–1903.

159

ST. HILD. (77. 75.)

Doh = G. *In moderate time.* WILLIAM ELLIS, 1868-

```
| m  :s,  | l,  :t,  | d  :r    | m  :— | f  :l,  | r  :d   | t, :d      | r  :— ||
| m, :s,  | f,  :s,  | m, :s,   | s, :— | f, :s,  | l, :l,  | s, :m,.fe, | s, :— ||
| s, :d   | f.m :r   | d  :d .t,| d  :— | l, :de  | r  :f.m | r  :d      | t, :— ||
| d, :m,  | r,  :s,  | l, :s,   | d  :— | r, :m,  | f, :r,  | s, :l,     | s, :— ||

| s  :f.m | f   :r   | m  :d    | t, :— | d  :l,  | r  :t,  | d  :— | — :— || d  | d  ||
| s, :l,  | l,  :t,  | d  :l,   | s, :— | s, :l,  | l, :s,  | s, :— | — :— || l, | s, ||
| t, :de  | r.m :f   | s  :f.m  | r  :— | d  :l.s | f  :r   | m  :— | — :— || f  | m  ||
| m, :l,  | r,  :s,  | d, :f,   | s, :— | m, :f,  | r, :s,  | d, :— | — :— || f, | d, ||
```

A-men.

LORD of mercy and of might,
Of mankind the Life and Light,
Maker, Teacher infinite,
Jesus, hear and save.

2 Strong Creator, Saviour mild,
Humbled to a mortal child,
Captive, beaten, bound, reviled,
Jesus, hear and save.

3 Throned above celestial things,
Borne aloft on angels' wings,
Lord of lords and King of kings,
Jesus, hear and save.

4 Soon to come to earth again,
Judge of angels and of men,
Hear us now, and hear us then,
Jesus, hear and save.

REGINALD HEBER, 1783–1826.

160 HELMSLEY. (87. 87. 47.)

Lock Hospital Collection. 1769.

Doh = G. *Two beats in a measure. Moderately slow, very dignified.*

```
|d  :—  |m  :s  |d  :t,  |l,  :s,  |l,  :-.t, |d  :t,.l, |s,  :-.f, |m,  :—  ||
|s, :—  |s, :—  |m, :s,  |f,  :s,  |f,  :-.s, |l,  :s,.f, |r,  :—    |d,  :—  ||
|m  :—  |m  :r  |d  :m   |d.r :m   |d   :—    |—   :d     |t,  :—    |d   :—  ||
|d  :—  |d  :t, |l, :m,  |f,  :d,  |f,  :—    |—   :f,    |s,  :—    |d,  :—  ||

                                                      D.C.
|s, :—  |— :s,  |d  :—  |r  :—  |m  :s  |f  :m  |m  :—  |r  :   ||r  :-.m |r  :m
|r, :—  |— :s,  |s, :—  |l, :t, |d  :m  |r  :d  |d  :—  |t, :   ||t, :-.d |t, :s,
|t, :d  |t, :t, |d  :—  |f  :—  |m  :—  |l  :—  |s  :—  |—  :   ||s  :—   |—  :s
|s, :l, |s, :f, |m, :—  |r, :—  |d, :—  |f, :—  |s, :—  |—  :   ||s, :—   |—  :m,

              ://                                    ://
|f  :—  |m  :—  |d  :-.r |d  :f  |m      :r    |d  :—  |m  :-.f |m  :s  |f  :m   |r  :—  ||
|l, :t, |d  :—  |s, :—   |l, :l, |d      :t,   |l, :—  |l, :—   |—  :s, |t, :d   |d  :t, ||
|f  :—  |s  :—  |m  :-.r |m  :f  |s      :-.f  |m  :—  |d  :-.r |d  :d  |r  :m.f |s  :—  ||
|r, :—  |d, :—  |d  :-.t,|l, :r, |m,.f,  :s,   |l, :—  |l, :—   |—  :m, |r, :d,  |s, :—  ||

|d  :—  |—  :r.m |s, :—  |f  :—  |m  :—  |r  :—  |d  :—  |—  :—  ||d  |d  ||
|s, :—  |—  :s,  |s, :—  |d  :—  |d  :—  |t, :—  |d  :—  |—  :—  ||l, |s, ||
|m  :—  |—  :m   |r  :—  |d  :r  |m  :f  |s  :f  |m  :—  |—  :—  ||f  |m  ||
|d  :—  |—  :d   |t, :—  |l, :—  |s, :—  |s, :—  |d, :—  |—  :—  ||f, |d, ||
                                                                    A-men.
```

LO! He comes, with clouds descending,
Once for favoured sinners slain;
Thousand thousand saints attending
Swell the triumph of His train;
Hallelujah!
God appears on earth to reign.

2 Every eye shall now behold Him,
Robed in dreadful majesty;
Those who set at nought and sold Him,
Pierced, and nailed Him to the Tree,
Deeply wailing,
Shall the true Messiah see.

3 Now redemption, long expected,
See in solemn pomp appear;
All His saints, by man rejected,
Now shall meet Him in the air;
Hallelujah!
See the day of God appear!

4 Yea, Amen! let all adore Thee,
High on Thine eternal throne;
Saviour, take the power and glory,
Claim the kingdom for Thine own:
O come quickly;
Hallelujah! come, Lord, come!

John Cennick, 1718–55; Charles Wesley, 1707–88; Martin Madan, 1726–90.

[May be sung to Holywood, No. 299.]

161 LLEF. (L.M.)

Griffith H. Jones (Gutyn Arfon), 1849–1919.

Lah = E. Doh = G. *Moderately slow.*

l, :l,.l, |d :-.r |d :t, |l, :— |d :r .r |m :-.m |r :d |t, :—
l, :l,.l, |l, :-.l, |l, :se, |l, :— |l, :t,.t, |d :-.l, |se, :l, |se, :—
l, :l,.l, |m :-.f |m :r |d :— |m :s .s |s :-.d |r :re |m :—
l, :l,.l, |l, :-.r, |m, :m, |l, :— |l, :s,.s, |d :-.d |t, :l, |m, :—

D.t. f.G.

(m)l :l.l |d' :-.r' |d' :t |l :— |(l)m :r .r |d :-.r |d :t, |l, :— || l, | l, ||
(m)l :l.l |m :-.f |m :se |l :— |(r)l, :se,.se, |l, :-.l, |l, :se, |l, :— || f, | m, ||
(m)l :l.l |l :-.l |l :r' |d' :— |(l)m :m .m |m :-.f |m :r |d :— || r | de ||
(m)l :l.l |l :-.r |m :m |l :— |(f)d :t,.t, |l, :-.r, |m, :m, |l, :— || r, | l, ||

A-men.

Dies irae, dies illa.

THAT day of wrath, that dreadful day,
When heaven and earth shall pass away,
What power shall be the sinner's stay?
How shall he meet that dreadful day?

2 When, shrivelling like a parchèd scroll,
The flaming heavens together roll;
When, louder yet, and yet more dread,
Swells the high trump that wakes the dead;

3 O, on that day, that wrathful day,
When man to judgment wakes from clay,
Be Thou the trembling sinner's stay,
Though heaven and earth shall pass away!

Walter Scott, 1771–1832.

162

WACHET AUF (NICOLAI). (8 9 8. D. 6 6 4. 8 8.)

Doh = C. *Slow.*

PHILIPP NICOLAI, 1556–1608.

```
| d      :m    | s     :s      | s     .r   :s       | l     :—       | s  ||
| s,     :d    | r     :r      | d     .r   :m       | m     :r       | m  ||
| m      :l    | t     :t      | m'    .r'  :d' .t   | l     :— .t    | d' ||
| d      :l,   | s,    :f      | m          :m       | f     :—       | d  ||

:s      | d'    :s     | d'     :m'      | r'    :d'  | r'     :—    | s ||
:m      | m     :s     | s      :s       | fe    :s   | s      :fe   | s ||
:d'     | d'    :t     | d'     :d' .t   | l     :s   | l .t   :d'   | t ||
:d' .t  | l     :s .f  | m .r   :d       | r     :m   | r      :—    | s ||

:s      | d'      :s      | l     :m        | f .m    :r        | d  :—   D.C.
:m .r   | m .f    :s      | d     :d .ta,   | l, .d   :— .t,    | d  :—
:d' .r' | d'      :d' .t  | l     :s        | f .s    :l .s     | m  :—
:d .t,  | l,      :s,     | f,    :d        | r .m    :f .s     | d  :—

:s      | s  :f     | m   :r        | d  || s   | s  :f     | m  :r      | d   :—
:m      | m  :r.d   | t,  :l, .t,   | d  || t   | m  :r .d  | d  :t,     | d   :—
:d' .t  | l  :t.l   | se  :ba.se    | l  || s   | l  :l     | l  :—.se   | l   :—
:d      | r  :r     | m   :m        | l, || m.r | d  :r     | m  :m      | l,  :—

| r  :m   | f   :—  | m || s  | l  :t  | d'  :d' | m'    :r'   | d'  :— | — ||
| l, :d   | d   :—  | d || m  | m  :r  | d   :f  | s     :s    | s   :— | — ||
| f  :l   | l   :—  | s || d' | l  :f  | l   :l  | d'    :t.f' | m'  :— | — ||
| r  :l,  | f,  :—  | d || d  | f  :r  | l   :f  | m .f  :s    | d   :— | — ||

:s      | d'  :s       | l      :m    | f       :r       | d  :—  || d  | d  ||
:m      | m   :s       | d .r   :m    | l, .d   :— .t,   | d  :—  || l, | s, ||
:d'     | d'  :d' .ta  | l      :se   | l       :s       | m  :—  || f  | m  ||
:d' .t  | l   :m       | f      :m    | r       :s       | d  :—  || f, | d  ||
                                                                      A-men.
```

Wachet auf! ruft uns die Stimme.

'Wake, awake! for night is flying,'
The watchmen on the heights are crying,
'Awake, Jerusalem, at last!'
Midnight hears the welcome voices,
And at the thrilling cry rejoices:
'Come forth, ye virgins, night is past!
The Bridegroom comes; awake,
Your lamps with gladness take;
Hallelujah!
And for His marriage feast prepare,
For ye must go to meet Him there.'

2 Zion hears the watchmen singing,
And all her heart with joy is springing;
She wakes, she rises from her gloom;
For her Lord comes down all-glorious,
The strong in grace, in truth victorious;
Her Star is risen, her Light is come!
Ah come, Thou blessèd One,
God's own belovèd Son;
Hallelujah!
We follow till the halls we see
Where Thou hast bid us sup with Thee.

3 Now let all the heavens adore Thee,
And men and angels sing before Thee,
With harp and cymbal's clearest tone;
Of one pearl each shining portal,
Where we are with the choir immortal
Of angels round Thy dazzling throne;
Nor eye hath seen, nor ear
Hath yet attained to hear
What there is ours;
But we rejoice, and sing to Thee
Our hymn of joy eternally.

Philipp Nicolai, 1556–1608; *tr.* by Catherine Winkworth, 1829–78.

163

NEANDER. (87. 87. 87.)

Doh = C. *In moderate time.*

JOACHIM NEANDER, 1650–80.

```
d  :-.r |m  :d  |m  :f  |s  :s  |d'  :t.l  |s  :m' |r' :r' |d' :—  ‖
d  :-.d |d  :d  |d  :d  |r  :r  |d   :d    |d  :s  |l  :s  |m  :—  ‖
m  :-.f |s  :s  |s  :l  |t  :t  |s   :f    |s  :d' |d' :t  |d' :—  ‖
d  :-.d |d  :m  |d  :l, |s, :s  |m   :f    |m  :d  |f  :s  |d  :—  ‖

d  :-.r |m  :d  |m  :f  |s  :s  |d'  :t.l  |s  :m' |r' :r' |d' :—  ‖
d  :-.d |d  :d  |d  :d  |r  :r  |d.r :m.f  |s  :s  |l  :s  |m  :—  ‖
m  :-.f |s  :s  |s  :l  |t  :t  |d'  :d'   |d' :d' |d' :t  |d' :—  ‖
d  :-.d |d  :m  |d  :l, |s, :s  |l   :s.f  |m  :d  |f  :s  |d  :—  ‖

                  ://:
m' :-.m'|r' :r' |d' :-.d'|t :t  |l   :-.l  |s  :d' |r' :t  |d' :—  ‖d' |d' ‖
s  :s   |s  :s  |m  :m   |m :m  |d   :f    |m  :m  |r  :r  |m  :—  ‖f  |m  ‖
d' :d'  |d' :t  |l  :l   |l :se |l.t :d'.r'|m' :d' |l  :s  |s  :—  ‖l  |s  ‖
d  :m.f |s  :s  |l  :d.r |m :m  |f.s :l.t  |d' :l  |f  :s  |d  :—  ‖f  |d  ‖
                                                                    A-men.
```

CHRIST is coming! let creation
From her groans and travail cease;
Let the glorious proclamation
Hope restore and faith increase:
Christ is coming!
Come, Thou blessèd Prince of Peace.

2 Earth can now but tell the story
Of Thy bitter Cross and pain;
She shall yet behold Thy glory,
When Thou comest back to reign:
Christ is coming!
Let each heart repeat the strain.

3 Long Thine exiles have been pining,
Far from rest, and home, and Thee:
But, in heavenly vestures shining,
They their loving Lord shall see:
Christ is coming!
Haste the joyous jubilee.

4 With that blessèd hope before us,
Let no harp remain unstrung;
Let the mighty advent chorus
Onward roll from tongue to tongue:
'Christ is coming!
Come, Lord Jesus, quickly come!'

JOHN ROSS MACDUFF, 1818–95.

Also the following:

40 Hark, the glad sound! the Saviour comes
78 On Jordan's bank the Baptist's cry
321 'Till He come!' O let the words
364–89 *Hymns of Missions*
479 Love Divine, all loves excelling

164 ORIEL. (87. 87. 87.)

Doh = A. *In moderate time.* E.t. *Caspar Ett's Cantica Sacra,* 1840.

d :d	d :d	r :m	f :m	[m]l :l	s :f	m :r	d :—	
m, :l,	s, :m,	s, :s,	l,.s, :s,	[s,]d :r	m :r	d :t,	d :—	
d :d	d :d	t, :d	d.t, :d	[m]l :t	d' :l	s :-.f	m :—	
d, :f,	m, :l,	s, :m,	r, :d,	[d]f :f	m :f	s :s,	d :—	

f.A. E.t.

[f]d :d	d :d	r :m	f :m	[m]l :l	s :f	m :r	d :—	
[d]s, :l,	s, :m,	s, :s,	l, :s,	[s,]d :d.r	m :r	d :t,	d :—	
[f]d :d	d :d	t, :d	d :d	[d]f.s :l.t	d' :l	s :-.f	m :—	
[l,]m, :f,	m, :l,	s, :d	f, :d,	[d]f :f	m :f	s :s,	d :—	

f.A.

m :m	l :m	[m]t, :d	r :d	f :f	m :r	d :t,	d :—		d	d	
s, :se,	l, :t,	[d]s, :m,	s,.f, :m,	l, :l,	s, :l,	s, :s,	s, :—		l,	s,	
m :r	d :m	[l,]m :d	t, :d	l,.t, :d.r	m :f	m :r	m :—		f	m	
d :t,	l, :se,	[l,]m, :l,	s, :l,	f,.s, :l,.t,	d :f,	s, :s,	d, :—		f,	d,	

A-men.

Gloriosi Salvatoris.

TO the Name of our Salvation
Laud and honour let us pay,
Which for many a generation
Hid in God's foreknowledge lay,
But with holy exultation
We may sing aloud to-day.

2 Jesus is the Name we treasure,
Name beyond what words can tell,
Name of gladness, Name of pleasure,
Ear and heart delighting well;
Name of sweetness passing measure,
Saving us from sin and hell.

3 'Tis the Name that whoso preacheth
Speaks like music to the ear;
Who in prayer this Name beseecheth
Sweetest comfort findeth near;
Who its perfect wisdom reacheth
Heavenly joy possesseth here.

4 Jesus is the Name exalted
Over every other name;
In this Name, whene'er assaulted,
We can put our foes to shame;
Strength to them who else had halted,
Eyes to blind, and feet to lame.

5 Therefore we, in love adoring,
This most blessèd Name revere,
Holy Jesus, Thee imploring
So to write it in us here
That hereafter, heavenward soaring,
We may sing with angels there.

15th century; *tr.* by JOHN MASON NEALE, 1818–66.

165 WARSAW. (66. 66. 88.)

Doh = C. *In free time.* THOMAS CLARK, 1775–1859.

```
d' :—  |s  :-.f  |m  :—  |d  :—  |s  :—  |—  :m  |f :s  |l :t
m  :—  |r  :-.r  |d  :—  |d  :—  |t, :—  |—  :d  |d :—  |d :r
s  :—  |s  :-.s  |s  :—  |fe :—  |s  :—  |—  :s  |l :s  |f :—
d  :—  |t, :-.t, |d  :—  |l, :—  |s, :—  |—  :d  |f :m  |f :r

d' :—  |r' :-.d' |d' :t  |—  ||s   |d' :—  |t :l  |s :—  |l :—
d  :—  |f  :-.m  |m  :r  |—  ||t,  |d  :m  |f :—  |m :d  |d :—
s  :—  |l  :—    |s  :—  |—  ||s   |s  :—  |f :—  |s :—  |f :l
m  :—  |f  :—    |s  :—  |—  ||s.f |m  :d  |r :—  |m :—  |f :—

r  :—  |—  :m  |f  :l  |s  :f  |m  :—  |r  :—  |d  :—  |—
t, :—  |—  :d  |d  :—  |—  :r  |d  :—  |t, :—  |d  :—  |—
s  :—  |—  :s  |l  :f  |s  :l  |s  :—  |s  :—  |m  :—  |—
s  :—  |—  :d  |f  :—  |m  :f  |s  :—  |s, :—  |d  :—  |—

:s  |s  :—  |f  :—  |m  :—  |—  :s  |d' :—  |l  :—  |s  :—  |—  :s
:d  |r  :—  |t, :—  |d  :—  |—  :r  |m  :—  |r  :d  |t, :—  |—  :r
:m  |s  :—  |s  :—  |s  :—  |—  :s  |s  :—  |fe :—  |s  :—  |—  :t
:d  |t, :—  |s, :—  |d  :—  |—  :t, |l, :—  |r  :—  |s, :—  |—  :s.f

d' :—  |r' :—  |m' :d' |s  :f  |m  :—  |r  :—  |d  :—  |—  :—  ||d  |d
s  :—  |s  :—  |s  :—  |d  :r  |d  :—  |t, :—  |d  :—  |—  :—  ||l, |s,
d' :—  |t  :—  |d' :m' |s  :l  |s  :—  |s  :—  |m  :—  |—  :—  ||f  |m
m  :—  |r  :—  |d  :—  |m  :f  |s  :—  |s, :—  |d  :—  |—  :—  ||f, |d
                                                               A-men.
```

JOIN all the glorious names
  Of wisdom, love, and power,
That ever mortals knew,
  That angels ever bore:
All are too mean to speak His worth,
Too mean to set my Saviour forth.

2 Great Prophet of my God,
  My tongue would bless Thy Name;
By Thee the joyful news
  Of our salvation came,—
The joyful news of sins forgiven,
Of hell subdued, and peace with heaven.

3 Jesus, my great High Priest,
  Offered His blood and died;
My guilty conscience seeks
  No sacrifice beside:
His powerful blood did once atone,
And now it pleads before the throne.

4 My dear Almighty Lord,
My Conqueror and my King,
Thy sceptre and Thy sword,
Thy reigning grace, I sing :
Thine is the power : behold, I sit
In willing bonds before Thy feet.

5 Now let my soul arise,
And tread the tempter down :
My Captain leads me forth
To conquest and a crown :
A feeble saint shall win the day,
Though death and hell obstruct the way.

Isaac Watts, 1674–1748.

166 SOUTHWARK. (C.M.)

Doh = A. *In moderate time.* Adapted from Christopher Tye, *c.* 1508–72.

:s, |d :r |m :f |s :-.f |m :f |m :-.r |d :d |t, :— |—
:s, |s, :s, |s, :l, |t, :-.t, |d :l, |s, :-.f, |m, :l, |s, :— |—
:m |m :r |d :d |r :-.r |d :d |d :-.t, |d :f |r :— |—
:d |d :t, |d :l, |s, :-.s, |d :f, |d :-.s, |l, :f, |s, :— |—

:r |r :de |r :d |d :t, |d :m |r :s |f :r |d :— |— || d |d
:ta, |l, :s, |f, :l, |s, :f, |m, :d |t, :d |l, :t, |d :— |— || l, |s,
:s |m :m |f :f |r :r |d :s |s :-.d |r :f |m :— |— || f |m
:s, |l, :l, |r, :f, |s, :s, |d, :d, |s, :m, |f, :s, |d :— |— || f, |d,

A-men.

O FOR a thousand tongues, to sing
My great Redeemer's praise,
The glories of my God and King,
The triumphs of His grace !

2 My gracious Master and my God,
Assist me to proclaim,
To spread through all the earth abroad
The honours of Thy Name.

3 Jesus ! the Name that charms our fears,
That bids our sorrows cease ;
'Tis music in the sinner's ears,
'Tis life, and health, and peace.

4 He breaks the power of cancelled sin,
He sets the prisoner free ;
His blood can make the foulest clean,
His blood availed for me.

5 He speaks, and, listening to His voice,
New life the dead receive,
The mournful, broken hearts rejoice,
The humble poor believe.

6 Hear Him, ye deaf ; His praise, ye dumb,
Your loosened tongues employ ;
Ye blind, behold your Saviour come ;
And leap, ye lame, for joy !

7 Glory to God, and praise, and love
Be ever, ever given
By saints below and saints above,
The Church in earth and heaven.

Charles Wesley, 1707–88.

167 PSALM 3 (O SEIGNEUR). (6 6 7. 6 6 7. D.) *French Psalter*, 1551.
Composed or arranged by LOUIS BOURGEOIS, 1510– ?

Doh = E♭. *With vigour.*

```
|d :— |s :— |s :— |l :t |d' :— |d' :— |t :l |s :f |s :— |m :—
|d :— |d :— |d :— |d :r |m :— |m :f |s :d |d :d |t, :— |d :—
                                                             May
|m :f |s :f |s :m |f :f |s :— |l :— |s :f |m :d |r :— |m :—
|d :r |m :r |m :d |f :r |d :— |l, :— |m :f |d :l, |s, :— |d :—
```

```
|m :d |f :m |r :— |d :— ||s :— |s :l |s :f |m :— |m :—
|d :s, |d :d |d :t, |d :— ||r :— |m :m |m :r |t, :— |d :—
 Je-sus Christ be prais - ed!
|s :m |d :s |l :s |m :— ||s :— |s :d' |d' :l |se :— |l :—
|d :t, |l, :s, |f, :s, |d :— ||t, :— |d :l, |d :r |m :— |l, :—
```

```
|s :s |f :m |r :— |m :— |f :m |d :m |r :— |d :— ||
|r :m |r :d |t, :— |t, :— |d :d |d :d |d :t, |d :— ||
                    May    Je - sus Christ be prais - ed!
|s :m |l :s |s :— |m :— |d :s |l :s |s :— |m :— ||
|t, :de |r :m.f |s :s, |se, :— |l, :d |f :m.f |s :— |d :— ||
```

```
|d :— |d :r |m :f |s :— |s :— |l :t |d' :l |s :—
|s, :— |d :d |d :d |d :t, |d :f |m :r |d :d |t, :r
|m :— |m :f |s :l |s :— |s :t |d' :s |s :fe |s :—
|d :t, |l, :l |s :f |m :f |m :r |d :t, |l, :r |s :f
```

```
        f.A♭.                              E♭.t.
|s :— |sr :r |m :r |d :— |t, :— |s,d :— |m :s |s :fe |s :—
|d :t, |mt, :l, |se, :t, |t, :l, |se, :— |m,l, :— |s, :d |d :d |d :t,
 May   Je - sus Christ be prais - ed!
|s :— |sr :r |t, :m |m :re |m :— |tm :— |m :m |m :r |r' :—
|m :r |ds, :f, |m, :ba,.se, |l, :— |m, :— |m,l, :t, |d :t, |l, :r |s, :—
```

```
|s :— |l :d' |d' :t |d' :— |d' :— |l :s |f :m |r :— |d :— || d | d ||
|d :— |d :f |f :r |m :— |m :— |f :m |d :d |d :t, |d :— || l, | s, ||
                         May    Je-sus Christ be prais - ed!  A- men.
|d' :t |l :l |l :s |d' :— |d' :— |d' :t |l :l |r :s |m :— || f | m ||
|m :— |f :m |r :s |d' :t |l :s |f :s |l :f |s :s, |d :— || f, | d ||
```

167 LAUDES DOMINI. (666. 666.)

Doh = C. *Moderately quick.* JOSEPH BARNBY, 1838–96.

```
                                                G.t.
:m  |f  :s  |l  :d' |t  :—  |l  :s  |l  :t  |d' :m'l |s  :— |—
:d  |d  :d  |d  :f  |f  :—  |—  :f  |m  :s  |s  :s d |t, :— |d
:s  |s  :s  |f  :l  |t  :—  |d' :r' |d' :r' |d' :d'f |f  :— |m
:d  |r  :m  |f  :r  |s  :—  |l  :t  |d' :t  |l  :l r |s, :— |l,
```

```
                   f.C.
:f  |m  :f  |r  :-.d  |d s  :— |— || s |s  :d' |t  :d' |s  :—  |—
:s, |s, :l, |f, :-.m, |m t, :— |— || r |d  :d  |f  :f  |f  :—  |m
:r  |d  :d  |d  :t,   |d s  :— |— || t |d' :s  |t  :l  |r' :d' |t
:t, |d  :f, |s, :s,   |d,s, :— |— || f |m  :m  |r  :d  |t, :l, |s,
```

```
:s |s :d' |t :d'  |s :— |— :s |s :—  |d':— |d':— |r':— |d':— |— || d' |d'
:r |d :m  |fe:fe  |s :r |m :f |m :f  |s :— |f :— |f :— |m :— |— || f  |m
:t |d':s  |r':d'  |t :— |— :t |d':r' |m':— |d':— |— :t |d':— |— || l  |s
:f |m :d  |r :r   |s :f |m :r |d :—  |ta:— |l :— |s :— |d :— |— || f  |d
                                                                A-men.
```

Beim frühen Morgenlicht.

WHEN morning gilds the skies,
My heart awaking cries,
'May Jesus Christ be praised!'
Alike at work and prayer
To Jesus I repair:
'May Jesus Christ be praised!'

2 Whene'er the sweet church bell
Peals over hill and dell,
'May Jesus Christ be praised!'
O hark to what it sings,
As joyously it rings,
'May Jesus Christ be praised!'

3 When sleep her balm denies,
My silent spirit sighs,
'May Jesus Christ be praised!'
When evil thoughts molest,
With this I shield my breast,
'May Jesus Christ be praised!'

4 Does sadness fill my mind?
A solace here I find,
'May Jesus Christ be praised!'
Or fades my earthly bliss?
My comfort still is this,
'May Jesus Christ be praised!'

5 Let earth's wide circle round
In joyful notes resound,
'May Jesus Christ be praised!'
Let air and sea and sky,
From depth to height, reply,
'May Jesus Christ be praised!'

6 Be this, while life is mine,
My canticle divine,
'May Jesus Christ be praised!'
Be this the eternal song
Through all the ages long,
'May Jesus Christ be praised!'

Tr. by EDWARD CASWALL, 1814–78.

168

LAUDATE DOMINUM. (10 10. 11 11.)

Doh = B♭. *With vigour.* (Verse 4 *Unison.*)

Charles Hubert Hastings Parry, 1848–1918.

:s, |m :d :r |s, :— :d |l, :s, :f, |m, :— :s,
:s, |s, :s, :l, |s, :— :s, |d, :m, :r, |d, :— :s,
:s, |d :m :r.d |t, :— :s, |l, :l, :t, |d :— :m
:s, |d :m, :f, |s, :— :m, |f, :r, :s, |d, :— :d

|m :r :s, |d :— :t, |r :d :l, |s, :— ||s, |d :d :d
|d :t, :s, |s, :l, :s, |se, :l, :fe, |s, :— ||r, |d, :f, :s,
|fe :s :r |m :r :r |f :m :d |t, :— ||t, |d :d :ta,
|l, :t, :t,, |m, :fe, :s, |t,, :d, :r, |s, :— ||f, |m, :r, :m,

|d :t,.l, :t,.d |r :d :r |s, :— :t, |m :m :m |d.t, :l, :f
|l, :f, :s, |l, :s, :l, |s, :— :s, |se, :l, :t, |l, :l, :l,
|l, :d :d |f :m :r.d |t, :— :r |r :d :t, |m.r :d :d
|f, :f, :m, |r, :m, :f, |s, :— :f, |m, :ba, :se, |l, :l, :r,

|m :d :r |d :— |s :— :f |-. :r :— |d :— :— ||
|s, :-.l, :t, |d :— |d :t, :l, |-. :s,.l, :t, |d :— :— ||
A - men, A - men.
|d :m :f |m :— |s :— :d |-. :t, :f |m :— :— ||
|s, :s, :s, |d, :— |m, :— :f, |-. :s, :— |d, :— :— ||

[*Copyright*, 1915, *by Novello & Co., Ltd.*]

YE servants of God, your Master proclaim,
And publish abroad His wonderful Name;
The Name all-victorious of Jesus extol;
His Kingdom is glorious, and rules over all.

HOUGHTON. (10 10. 11 11.)

Doh = G. *With vigour.* HENRY JOHN GAUNTLETT, 1805–76.

```
:s,  | m   :d   :l,  | s,  :—  :s,  | m   :d   :l,  | s,  :—  :d   | f   :f   :r
:s,  | s,  :s,  :f,  | m,  :—  :s,  | s,  :s,  :f,  | m,  :—  :d   | d   :d   :t,
:m   | m   :s   :d   | m   :—  :m   | m   :s   :d   | m   :—  :m   | l   :l   :s
:d   | d   :m,  :f,  | d   :—  :d   | d   :m,  :f,  | d   :—  :l,  | r,  :r,  :s,

| s   :—  :m   | r   :t,  :l,  | s,  :—  || r   | t,  :d   :m   | m   :r   :m
| d   :—  :d   | t,  :s,  :fe, | s,  :—  || s,  | s,  :s,  :d   | d   :t,  :d
| s   :—  :s   | s   :r   :d   | t,  :—  || t,  | r   :m   :s   | s   :s   :s
| m,  :—  :d,  | r,  :r,  :r,  | s,  :—  || s,  | s,  :m,  :d,  | s,  :s,  :d

| f   :s   :l   | s   :—  :s   | s   :f   :f   | f   :m   :m   | r   :d   :t,  | d   :—  || d   | d   ||
| d   :d   :d   | d   :—  :ta, | l,  :l,  :l,  | s,  :s,  :s,  | l,  :s,  :s,  | s,  :—  || l,  | s,  ||
| f   :m   :f   | m   :—  :m   | m   :r   :r   | r   :d   :s   | f   :m   :r   | m   :—  || f   | m   ||
| l,  :s,  :f,  | d   :—  :d   | de  :r   :d   | t,  :d   :d,  | f,  :s,  :s,  | d,  :—  || f,  | d,  ||
                                                                                        A-men.
```

2 God ruleth on high, almighty to save ;
And still He is nigh, His presence we have ;
The great congregation His triumph shall sing,
Ascribing salvation to Jesus our King.

3 Salvation to God, who sits on the throne !
Let all cry aloud, and honour the Son :
The praises of Jesus the angels proclaim,
Fall down on their faces, and worship the Lamb.

4 Then let us adore, and give Him His right,
All glory and power, all wisdom and might,
All honour and blessing, with angels above,
And thanks never-ceasing, and infinite love.

CHARLES WESLEY, 1707–88.

169

TRISAGION. (10 10. 10 10. Dactylic.)

Doh = G. *In moderate time.* HENRY SMART, 1813–79.

s :s :l | s :m :r | d :r :r | m :— :— || m :r :d
d :d :d | d :d :t_1 | d :d :t_1 | d :— :— || d :t_1 :d
m :m :f | m :s :f | m :l :s | s :— :— || s :f :m
d :d :f_1 | d :d :s_1 | l_1 :f_1 :s_1 | d :— :— || d :s_1 :l_1

s :-.f:m | r :m :d | m :r :— || s_1 :d :m | s :m :r
r :t_1 :d | l_1 :s_1 :m_1.fe_1 | s_1 :— :— || s_1 :s_1 :s_1 | s_1 :s_1 :s_1
r :r :d | d :d :d | d :t_1 :— || d :d :d | d :d :r.m
t_1 :s_1 :d | f_1 :s_1 :l_1 | s_1 :— :f_1 || m_1 :m_1 :d_1 | m_1 :s_1 :ta_1

d :f :s | l :—:— || l :l :s | d :f :m | r :d :t_1 | d :—:— || d | d
l_1 :l_1 :d | d :—:— || d :d :t_1 | d :r :d | l_1 :s_1 :s_1 | s_1 :—:— || l_1 | s_1
f :f :m | f :—:— || f :f :r | d :s :s | f :m :r | m :—:— || f | m
l_1 :r :d | f_1 :—:— || f_1 :f_1 :s_1 | l_1 :t_1 :d | f_1 :s_1 :s_1 | d/d_1 :—:— || f_1 | d_1

A-men.

BLESSING and honour and glory and power,
Wisdom and riches and strength evermore
Give ye to Him who our battle hath won,
Whose are the Kingdom, the crown, and the throne.

2 Into the heaven of the heavens hath He gone;
Sitteth He now in the joy of the throne;
Weareth He now of the Kingdom the crown;
Singeth He now the new song with His own.

3 Soundeth the heaven of the heavens with His Name;
Ringeth the earth with His glory and fame;
Ocean and mountain, stream, forest, and flower
Echo His praises and tell of His power.

4 Ever ascendeth the song and the joy;
Ever descendeth the love from on high;
Blessing and honour and glory and praise,—
This is the theme of the hymns that we raise.

5 Give we the glory and praise to the Lamb;
Take we the robe and the harp and the palm;
Sing we the song of the Lamb that was slain,
Dying in weakness, but rising to reign.

HORATIUS BONAR, 1808–89.

[May be sung to O QUANTA QUALIA, No. 224.]

170

LÜBECK. (77. 77.)

Doh = D. *In moderate time.* *Freylinghausen's Gesangbuch*, 1704.

d :m	s :s	l :t	d' :—	t :d'	r' :t	l :l	s :—
d :d	r :m	d :r	m :—	r :m	r :m	m :r	t, :—
m :l	t :d'	l :f	s :—	s :s	s :s	s :fe	s :—
d :l,	s, :d	f :r	d :—	s :m	t, :m	d :r	s, :—

m :f	s :s	r :m	f :—	m :f	s :m	r :r	d :—	f	m
d :d	t, :d	r :de	r :—	d :r	r :d	d :t,	d :—	d	d
s :f	r :m	l :s	f :—	l :l	s :s	s :-.f	m :—	l	s
d :l,	s, :d	f :m	r :—	l, :r	t, :d	s, :s,	d :—	f,	d

A-men.

BONN (FESTUS). (77. 77.)

Doh = D. *In moderate time.* *Freylinghausen's Gesangbuch*, 1714.

				A.t.			f.D.
d' :t.l	s :l	r :f	m :—	(r)s, :d	l,.t, :d	r :f	(m)t :—
m :f	m :d	d :t,	d :—	(t,)m, :s,	f, :s,	l, :t,	(d)s :—
s :t	d' :l	s :s	s :—	(s)d :d	d :m	f :s	(s)r' :—
d :r	m :f	s :s,	d :—	(s,)d, :m,	f, :m,	r, :s,	(d,)s, :—

d' :s.f	m :s	d' :r'.d'	t :—	d' :s	l.t :d'	m :r	d :—	f	m
d :r	m :r	d :f	r :—	d :m	f :d	d :t,	d :—	d	d
s :s	d' :t	s :l	s :—	s :d'	d' :s.l	s :s.f	m :—	l	s
m :t,	d :r	m :f	s :—	m :d	f :m.f	s :s,	d :—	f,	d

A-men.

SWEETER sounds than music knows
Charm me in Immanuel's Name ;
All her hopes my spirit owes
To His birth, and Cross, and shame.

2 When He came, the angels sung
'Glory be to God on high !'
Lord, unloose my stammering tongue :
Who should louder sing than I ?

3 Did the Lord a man become,
That He might the law fulfil,
Bleed and suffer in my room,—
And canst thou, my tongue, be still ?

4 No ! I must my praises bring,
Though they worthless are, and weak ;
For, should I refuse to sing,
Sure the very stones would speak.

5 O my Saviour, Shield, and Sun,
Shepherd, Brother, Husband, Friend—
Every precious name in one—
I will love Thee without end.

JOHN NEWTON, 1725–1807.

171

WILTON. (11 6. 11 6.)

Doh = E♭. *In moderate time.* ARTHUR HENRY MANN, 1850-

| s :— | m :r | d :— | r :— | m :s | f :l | l :— | s :s |

| s, :— | d :t, | l, :— | t, :— | d :d | d :d | d :— | d :r |

| m :— | s :f | m :— | s :— | s :m | f :f | f :— | m :s |

| d :— | d :s, | l, :— | s, :— | d :ta, | l, :f, | d :— | d :t, |

| d' :— | t :l | s :— | — :fe | s :— | — :s | s :— | m :r | d :— | m :— |

| d :— | r :m | r :— | d :— | t, :— | — :t, | d :— | d :t, | l, :— | l, :t, |

v. 2. past All that thou wast

v. 4. a - way Ban - ish

| l :— | se :l | t :— | l :— | s :— | — :f | m :— | s :f | m :— | m :se |

| l, :— | t, :d | r :— | — :r | s, :— | — :s, | d :— | s, :s, | l, :— | d :t, |

| d' :t | l :se | se :— | l :t | d' :— | s :f | m :— | — :r | d :— | — :— || f | m ||

| d :r | m :m | r :— | d :r | d :— | d :r | d :— | t, :— | d :— | — :— || d | d ||

v. 2. ev - er Bright-ness from

| l :se | l :t | t :— | l :la | s :— | ta :l | s :— | — :f | m :— | — :— || l | s ||

| l, :t, | d :m | f :— | f :f | m :— | m :f | s :— | s, :— | d :— | — :— || f, | d ||

A-men.

LIGHT of the world! for ever, ever shining,
There is no change in Thee;
True Light of Life, all joy and health enshrining,
Thou canst not fade nor flee.

2 Thou hast arisen, but Thou descendest never;
To-day shines as the past;
All that Thou wast Thou art, and shalt be ever,
Brightness from first to last.

3 Night visits not Thy sky, nor storm, nor sadness;
Day fills up all its blue,—
Unfailing beauty, and unfaltering gladness,
And love for ever new.

4 Light of the world, undimming and unsetting!
O shine each mist away;
Banish the fear, the falsehood, and the fretting;
Be our unchanging Day.

HORATIUS BONAR, 1808-89.

172

SURREY. (88. 88. 88.)

Doh = F. *Moderately slow.* HENRY CAREY, 1692-1743.

| :s | f :m :l | d :t, :d | f :m :r | m :— :m | r :— :fe |

| :d | d :— :l, | s, :— :m, | l, :s, :s, | s, :— :d | r :— :d |

| :m | l :s :f | m :r :d | d :— :t, | d :— :s | s :— :d |

| :d | d :— :f, | s, :— :l, | f, :s, :s, | d, :— :d | t, :— :l, |

D.C.

s :— :s,	d :t, :l,	s, :—		s	l :— :s.f	s :— :f.m
t, :— :s,	l, :s, :fe,	s, :—		d	d :— :d	d :— :r.d
r :— :r	m :r :r.d	t, :—		s	f :— :s.l	s :— :l
s, :—.l, :t,	d :r :r,	s, :—		m	f :— :m.r	m :— :l,

f :— :m.r	m :— :m	r :— :f	m :r :d	r :d :t,	d, :—		d	d	
r :l, :d.t,	d :— :d	d :t, :r	d :t, :d	l, :s, :s,	s, :—		l,	s,	
l :f :s	s :— :s	s :— :l	s :—.f :m	f :m :r	m :—		f	m	
r :— :s,	d :— :d,	s, :— :r,	m, :s, :l,	f, :s, :s,	d :—		f,	d	

A-men.

O LIGHT, whose beams illumine all
From twilight dawn to perfect day,
Shine Thou before the shadows fall
That lead our wandering feet astray:
At morn and eve Thy radiance pour,
That youth may love, and age adore.

2 O Way, through whom our souls draw near
To yon eternal home of peace,
Where perfect love shall cast out fear,
And earth's vain toil and wandering cease,
In strength or weakness may we see
Our heavenward path, O Lord, through Thee.

3 O Truth, before whose shrine we bow,
Thou priceless pearl for all who seek,
To Thee our earliest strength we vow;
Thy love will bless the pure and meek;
When dreams or mists beguile our sight,
Turn Thou our darkness into light.

4 O Life, the well that ever flows
To slake the thirst of those that faint,
Thy power to bless, what seraph knows?
Thy joy supreme, what words can paint?
In earth's last hour of fleeting breath,
Be Thou our Conqueror over death.

5 O Light, O Way, O Truth, O Life,
O Jesus, born mankind to save,
Give Thou Thy peace in deadliest strife,
Shed Thou Thy calm on stormiest wave;
Be Thou our hope, our joy, our dread,
Lord of the living and the dead.

EDWARD HAYES PLUMPTRE, 1821–91.

173 ST. JAMES. (C.M.)

Doh = A. *In moderate time.* RAPHAEL COURTEVILLE, ? –1772.

```
:s, |d  :r  |m  :d  |r  :f  |m  :m  |l,  :t, |d  :l,   |s, :— |— ||
:m, |s, :s, |s, :s, |l, :s, |s, :s, |fe, :s, |s, :fe   |s, :— |— ||
:d  |d  :t, |d  :d  |d  :t, |d  :m  |r   :r  |m  :r.d  |t, :— |— ||
:d, |m, :s, |d  :m, |f, :s, |d, :d, |r,  :s, |d, :r,   |s, :— |— ||
```

```
:r  |m  :d  |f  :m  |l, :r  |t, :s,    |d  :m  |f  :r     |d  :— |— || d  |d  ||
:s, |s, :s, |f, :s, |l, :l, |s, :r,    |s, :m, |l, :s,.f, |m, :— |— || f, |m, ||
:t, |d  :d  |t, :d  |d  :f  |r  :t,    |d  :d  |d  :t,    |d  :— |— || l, |s, ||
:s, |d, :m, |r, :d, |f, :r, |s, :s,.f, |m, :d, |r, :s,    |d, :— |— || f, |d, ||
```

A-men.

THOU art the Way : to Thee alone
From sin and death we flee ;
And he who would the Father seek
Must seek Him, Lord, by Thee.

2 Thou art the Truth : Thy word alone
True wisdom can impart ;
Thou only canst inform the mind,
And purify the heart.

3 Thou art the Life : the rending tomb
Proclaims Thy conquering arm ;
And those who put their trust in Thee
Nor death nor hell shall harm.

4 Thou art the Way, the Truth, the Life :
Grant us that way to know,
That truth to keep, that life to win,
Whose joys eternal flow.

GEORGE WASHINGTON DOANE, 1799–1859.

174

FIRST TUNE.

THEODORA. (5 4. 5 4. D.)

Doh = E. *In moderate time.* ALFRED LEGGE, 1843–1919.

d :r :m	f :— :m	r :m :f	m :— :—	s :s :d
d :d :d	d :— :d	d :d :t,	d :— :—	d :t, :d
m :f :s	l :— :s	l :s :s	s :— :—	m :f :s
d :d :d	d :— :d	f, :s, :s,	d :— :—	d :r :m

l :— :s	t :l :r	s :— :— ‖	r :m :r	r :— :d	f :m :r
d :— :d	r :r :d	t, :— :— ‖	t, :t, :t,	t, :— :d	d :d :t,
f :— :s	s :fe :fe	s :— :— ‖	f :s :f	f :— :m	f :s :s
f :— :m	r :r :r	s, :— :— ‖	s, :s, :s,	d :— :d	l, :s, :f,

s :— :—	d' :t :l	s :f :m	r :d :t,	d :— :— ‖	d	d ‖
d :— :—	d :d :d	d :-.t, :d	l, :s, :s,	s, :— :— ‖	l,	s, ‖
s :— :—	s :s :f	s :— :s	f :m :r	m :— :— ‖	f	m ‖
m, :— :—	m :m :f	m :r :d	f, :s, :s,	d :— :— ‖	f,	d ‖

A-men.

REST of the weary,
Joy of the sad,
Hope of the dreary,
Light of the glad,
Home of the stranger,
Strength to the end,
Refuge from danger,
Saviour and Friend!

2 Pillow where, lying,
Love rests its head,
Peace of the dying,
Life of the dead,
Path of the lowly,
Prize at the end,
Breath of the holy,
Saviour and Friend!

3 When my feet stumble,
I to Thee cry,
Crown of the humble,
Cross of the high;
When my steps wander,
Over me bend,
Truer and fonder,
Saviour and Friend.

4 Ever confessing
Thee, I will raise
Unto Thee blessing,
Glory, and praise,—
All my endeavour,
World without end,
Thine to be ever,
Saviour and Friend.

JOHN SAMUEL BEWLEY MONSELL, 1811–75.

174

SECOND TUNE.

FORTUNE. (54. 54. D.)

Lah = E. Doh = G. *Slow.* Old English Melody.

```
l, :—  |l, :-.t,  |d  :—  |— :t,  |l, :m  |r  :d  |t,  :— |— :— ||
m, :—  |m, :-.m,  |m, :—  |— :se, |l, :d  |t, :l, |se, :— |— :— ||
d  :—  |d  :-.m   |m  :—  |— :r   |m  :—  |f  :f  |t,  :— |— :— ||
l, :—  |l, :-.se, |l, :—  |— :t,  |d  :d, |r, :r, |m,  :— |— :— ||

l, :—  |l, :-.t,  |d  :—  |— :t,  |l, :m  |r  :d  |t,  :— |— :— ||
l, :—  |m, :-.se, |l, :—  |— :se, |l, :d  |t, :l, |se, :— |— :— ||
d  :—  |m  :-.m   |m  :—  |— :r   |m  :—  |f  :f  |t,  :— |— :— ||
l, :—  |d, :-.m,  |l, :—  |— :t,  |d  :d, |r, :r, |m,  :— |— :— ||

m  :—  |m  :-.m   |m  :—  |— :m   |m  :s  |f  :m  |r   :— |— :— ||
s, :—  |s, :-.s,  |s, :—  |— :s,  |l, :—  |l, :l, |t,  :— |— :— ||
d  :—  |d  :-.d   |d  :—  |— :d   |d  :m  |r  :d  |s   :— |— :— ||
d, :—  |d  :-.d   |d  :—  |— :d   |l, :—  |f, :f, |s,  :— |— :— ||

r  :—  |s  :-.f   |m  :—  |r  :d  |t, :l, |l, :se, |l, :— |— :— || l, | l, ||
t, :—  |d  :-.r   |d  :—  |s, :l, |f, :—  |m, :m,  |m, :— |— :— || f, | m, ||
s  :—  |s  :-.s   |s  :—  |r  :m  |r  :d  |t, :t,  |d  :— |— :— || r  | de ||
s, :—  |l, :-.t,  |d  :—  |t, :l, |r, :—  |m, :m,  |l, :— |— :— || r, | l, ||
                                                                   A-men.
```

REST of the weary,
  Joy of the sad,
Hope of the dreary,
  Light of the glad,
Home of the stranger,
  Strength to the end,
Refuge from danger,
  Saviour and Friend!

2 Pillow where lying,
  Love rests its head,
Peace of the dying,
  Life of the dead,
Path of the lowly,
  Prize at the end,
Breath of the holy,
  Saviour and Friend!

3 When my feet stumble,
  I to Thee cry,
Crown of the humble,
  Cross of the high;
When my steps wander,
  Over me bend,
Truer and fonder,
  Saviour and Friend!

4 Ever confessing
  Thee, I will raise
Unto Thee blessing,
  Glory, and praise,—
All my endeavour,
  World without end,
Thine to be ever,
  Saviour and Friend.

JOHN SAMUEL BEWLEY MONSELL, 1811–75.

175 HEBDOMADAL. (C.M.)

Doh = D. *With vigour.* THOMAS BANKS STRONG, 1861-

d' :— | s :m | d :— | —:d | l :— | —:l | s :— | —:(s) | d' :— | t :s
m :— | r :t, | l, :— | t, :l, | d :-.t, | d :r | m :— | —:(m) | d :— | r :t,
v. 3 Hon - our
s :— | s :s | m :— | —:f | l :-.s | l :t | d' :— | —:(t) | l :— | s :s
d :— | t, :s, | l, :— | s, :f, | f :— | —:f | d :— | —:(m) | l, :— | t, :m

f.G. D.t.

l :— | —:l | s :— | —:— || mt, :— | l, :s, | m :— | s :— | sd' :— | —:r
m :— | r :d | t, :— | —:— || ds, :— | f, :f, | s, :— | l, :— | lr :— | —:d
m :— | fe :fe | s :— | —:— || sr :— | d :r | m :— | d :— | ml :— | —:l
d :— | r :r | s, :— | —:— || ds, :— | l, :t, | d :— | l, :— | df, :— | —:f,

r :— | l :— | s :— | d :— | d :— | r :— | d :— | —:— || d | d
t, :— | d :r | m :— | d :— | s, :— | t, :— | d :— | —:— || l, | s,
s :— | l :t | d' :— | m :f | m :— | f :— | m :— | —:— || f | m
s, :— | f :— | m :— | l, :— | s, :— | s, :— | d :— | —:— || f, | d

A-men.

COME, let us join our cheerful songs
With angels round the throne;
Ten thousand thousand are their tongues,
But all their joys are one.

2 'Worthy the Lamb that died,' they cry,
'To be exalted thus';
'Worthy the Lamb,' our lips reply,
'For He was slain for us.'

3 Jesus is worthy to receive
Honour and power divine;
And blessings, more than we can give,
Be, Lord, for ever Thine.

4 The whole creation join in one
To bless the sacred Name
Of Him that sits upon the throne,
And to adore the Lamb.

ISAAC WATTS, 1674–1748.

[May be sung to NATIVITY, No. 617.]

176

KOMM, SEELE. (7 6. 7 6. D.)

Doh = E♭. *Brightly.* JOHANN WOLFGANG FRANCK, 1641–88 (?).

:s |d' :s |l :s.f |m :— |m :s |f :m.r |r :-.d |d :— |— ||
:d |d :m.r |d :r |m :— |m :d |l,.t, :d |d :t, |d :— |— ||
:m |s :d'.t |l :t |d' :— |d' :m |f :s |l :s |m :— |— ||
:d |m :d |f :r |l :— |l, :m |r :m |f :s |d :— |— ||

B♭.t.

:(m)l, |s, :d |r.m :f.r |m :-.r |d :m |l,.t, :d |d :t, |d :— |— ||
:(d)f, |s, :m, |l, :s, |s, :— |s, :s, |f, :s, |l, :s, |s, :— |— ||
:(s)d |d :d |d :t, |d :-.r |m :d |d :d |f :r |m :— |— ||
:(d)f, |m, :l, |f, :s, |d :— |d :m, |f, :m, |r, :s, |d, :— |— ||

d.f.A♭.

:(s,)l, |l, :l, |t, :t, |d :— |d :m.r |d.t, :d.r |d :t, |l, :— |— ||
:(s,)l, |l, :l, |l, :se, |l, :— |m, :m, |m, :l, |l, :se, |l, :— |— ||
:(ma)f |f :m |r :m |m :— |d :t, |d :l, |m :r |d :— |— ||
:(d,)r, |r :d |t, :m, |l, :— |l, :se, |l, :f, |m, :m, |l, :— |— ||

E♭.t.

:(l)r |s :r |f.m :f.s |m :— |m :d'.t |l.s :f.m |m :r |d :— |— || d |d ||
:(m,)l, |r :t, |d :r |s, :l, |t, :d |d :r.d |d :t, |d :— |— || l, |s, ||
:(d)f |s :s |f :r |m :d |s :s |l :l |s :s.f |m :— |— || f |m ||
:(s,)d |t, :s, |l, :t, |d :l, |m, :m |f :r |s :s, |d :— |— || f, |d ||

A-men.

O JESUS, ever present,
  O Shepherd, ever kind,
Thy very Name is music
  To ear, and heart, and mind.
It woke our wondering childhood
  To muse on things above;
It drew our harder manhood
  With cords of mighty love.

2 How oft to sure destruction
  Our feet had gone astray,
Hadst Thou not, patient Shepherd,
  Been Guardian of our way.
How oft, in darkness fallen,
  And wounded sore by sin,
Thy hand has gently raised us,
  And healing balm poured in.

3 O Shepherd good! we follow
  Wherever Thou wilt lead:
No matter where the pasture,
  With Thee at hand to feed.
Thy voice, in life so mighty,
  In death shall make us bold:
O bring our ransomed spirits
  To Thine eternal fold.

LAWRENCE TUTTIETT, 1825–97.

177 MADRID. (66. 66. D.)

Source unknown.

Doh = A. *Brightly.* *D.C.*

d :—	t, :d	l, :d	s, :—	m :d	f :r	d :t,	d :—	
s, :—	s, :s,	f, :f,	m, :—	s, :s,	l, :l,	s, :f,	m, :—	
m :—	r :d	d :d	d :—	d :m	r :f	m :r	d :—	
d, :—	s, :m,	f, :l,	d :—	d :d	f, :f,	s, :—	d, :—	

m :—	r :m	f :m	r :—	m :—	r :m	f :m	r :—	
s, :—	s, :s,	l, :s,	s, :—	s, :—	s, :s,	f, :s,	s, :—	
d :—	f :m	d :d	t, :—	d :—	t, :d	l, :d	t, :—	
d :—	t, :d	l, :d	s, :—	d, :—	s,.f, :m,	r, :m,.f,	s, :—	

d :—	t, :d	l, :d	s, :—	m :d	f :r	d :t,	d :—		d	d	
s, :d,	r, :s,	l, :f,	s, :—	s, :l,	l, :l,	s, :f,	m, :—		f,	m,	
m :s	f :m	d :d	r :t,	d :m	r :f	m :r	d :—		l,	s,	
d, :m,	r, :d,	f, :l,	t, :s,	d :l,	f, :f,	s, :—	d, :—		f,	d,	

A-men.

COME, children, join to sing—
Hallelujah! Amen!—
Loud praise to Christ our King;
Hallelujah! Amen!
Let all, with heart and voice,
Before His throne rejoice;
Praise is His gracious choice:
Hallelujah! Amen!

2 Come, lift your hearts on high;
Hallelujah! Amen!
Let praises fill the sky;
Hallelujah! Amen!
He is our Guide and Friend;
To us He'll condescend;
His love shall never end:
Hallelujah! Amen!

3 Praise yet the Lord again;
Hallelujah! Amen!
Life shall not end the strain;
Hallelujah! Amen!
On heaven's blissful shore
His goodness we'll adore,
Singing for evermore,
'Hallelujah! Amen!'

CHRISTIAN HENRY BATEMAN, 1813–89.

178 CUDDESDON. (6 5. 6 5. D.)

Doh = A♭. *Unison.* *With great dignity.* WILLIAM HAROLD FERGUSON, 1874–

| s, :l, | t, :d | f :— | f :— | m :r | d :r | m :— | — :— ||

Eb.t. f.Ab.

| s,d :r | m :f | l :t | s :— | m :r | d :r | m t, :— | — :— ||

| s, :d | r :m | s :— | f :m | f :m | r :m | f :— | — :— ||

| f :f | m :r | s :s, | l, :d | m :— | r :— | d :— | — :— ||

| d :— | r :— | m :— | — :— ||
A - - men.

EVELYNS. (6 5. 6 5. D.)

Doh = E. *In moderate time.* WILLIAM HENRY MONK, 1823–89.

m :s	l :s	d' :—	s :—	f :m	r :-.d	d :—	— :—	
d :d	d :d	d :—	d :r	d :d	d :t,	d :—	— :—	
s :m	f :s	s :f	m :s	d :m	l :s	m :—	— :—	
d :d	f :m	l, :—	d :t,	l, :s,	f, :s,	d :—	— :—	

d :m	f :m	r :m	d :—	l :s	m :d	m :—	r :—	
d :l,	l, :l,	t, :—	d :t,	l, :d	t, :d	d :—	t, :—	
m :d	r :d	f :m	m :—	f :m	m :m.f	s :—	— :—	
l, :l,	r :l,	l, :se,	l, :s,	f, :d	s, :l,	s, :—	— :—	

s :s	l :s	d' :—	t :—	l :s	t :l	s :—	— :—	
t, :t,	t, :t,	d :—	r :—	m :r	r :d	t, :—	— :—	
s :s	s :s	s :fe	s :—	m.fe :s	s :fe	s :—	f :—	
s :s	f :f	m :l,	s, :t,	d :t,.d	r :r	s, :—	— :—	

d :s	f :m	l :—	r :—	s :d	m :r	d :—	— :—		d	d	
d :d	d :d	d :—	d :t,	d :d	d :t,	d :—	— :—		l,	s,	
m :m	f :s	r :—	r :—	m :m	s :f	m :—	— :—		f	m	
l, :ta,	l, :s,	fe, :—	s, :—	m, :l,	s, :s,	d :—	— :—		f,	d	

A-men.

IN the Name of Jesus
Every knee shall bow,
Every tongue confess Him
King of Glory now ;
'Tis the Father's pleasure
We should call Him Lord,
Who from the beginning
Was the mighty Word.

2 Humbled for a season,
To receive a name
From the lips of sinners,
Unto whom He came,
Faithfully He bore it
Spotless to the last ;
Brought it back victorious,
When from death He passed.

3 Name Him, brothers, name Him
With love strong as death,
But with awe and wonder
And with bated breath !
He is God the Saviour,
He is Christ the Lord,
Ever to be worshipped,
Trusted, and adored.

4 In your hearts enthrone Him ;
There let Him subdue
All that is not holy,
All that is not true :
Crown Him as your Captain
In temptation's hour ;
Let His will enfold you
In its light and power.

5 Brothers, this Lord Jesus
Shall return again,
With His Father's glory,
With His angel train ;
For all wreaths of empire
Meet upon His brow,
And our hearts confess Him
King of Glory now.

CAROLINE MARIA NOEL, 1817–77

For v. 3.

m :s	l :s	d' :—	s :s	f :m	r :-.d	d :—	— :—
d :d	d :d	d :—	d :r	d :—	d :t_1	d :—	— :—
Name Him, bro -	thers,	name	Him With	love	strong as	death,	
s :m	f :s	s :f	m :s	d :m	l :s	m :—	— :—
d :d	f :m	l_1 :—	d :t_1	l_1 :s_1	f_1 :s_1	d :—	— :—

179

MOVILLE. (76. 76. D.)

(*a*) Lah = D. Doh = F. *In moderate time.* Irish Traditional Melody.

l, :l,.s,	l, :l,.t,	d :—	d :t,.d	r :—	— :f
m, :m,.m,	m, :f,	s, :f,	m, :s,	l, :s,	f, :l,.t,
d :d.t,	d :d	d :—	d :s,	r :—	— :r
l, :l,.m,	l, :f,	m, :r,	d, :m,	f, :m,	r, :r,

m :-.r	d		r	m :-.r	d.r :m.s	l :—	s :-.d
d :t,	s,		t,	d :t,	l, :t,	l, :t,	d :s,
s :s	m		s	s :s	m :m	d :r	m :d
m,.f, :s,	d		s,	d :s,	l, :s,	f, :—	d :m,

(*b*)

d :-.d	t, :-.l,	l, :—	—		m	l :-.s	l :t	d' :—	t :d'.t
l, :-.l,	l, :se,	l, :—	—		m	d :-.m	m :s	m :—	r :m
d :m	f :m	d :—	—		m	l :-.t	d' :r'	d' :—	r' :d'
f, :m,	r, :m,	l, :—	—		m	l, :-.m	l :s	d :m	s :d

l :-.s	m :r	d :t,	l,		d.r	m :-.r	d.r :m.s
d :—	— :t,	l, :s,	f,		l,	s, :-.f,	m, :t,
d' :—	s :s	m :m	d		d	d :t,	d :t,
f :m	d :s,	l, :m,	f,		f,	d, :s,	l, :s,

l :—	s :d	d :-.d	t, :-.l,	l, :—	— :—		l,	l,	
l, :—	t, :l,	l, :-.l,	l, :se,	m, :—	— :—		f,	m,	
d :f.m	r :d	d :m	f :m	d :—	— :—		r	de	
f, :—	s, :l,	f, :m,	r, :m,	l, :—	— :—		r,	l,	

A-men.

HIS PRAISE

Christus Redemptor gentium.

CHRIST is the world's Redeemer,
The lover of the pure,
The fount of heavenly wisdom,
Our trust and hope secure;
The armour of His soldiers,
The Lord of earth and sky;
Our health while we are living,
Our life when we shall die.

2 Christ hath our host surrounded
With clouds of martyrs bright,
Who wave their palms in triumph,
And fire us for the fight.
Christ the red Cross ascended
To save a world undone,
And, suffering for the sinful,
Our full redemption won.

3 Down in the realm of darkness
He lay a captive bound,
But at the hour appointed
He rose, a victor crowned;
And now, to heaven ascended,
He sits upon the throne,
In glorious dominion,
His Father's and His own.

4 All glory to the Father,
The unbegotten One;
All honour be to Jesus,
His sole-begotten Son;
And to the Holy Spirit—
The Perfect Trinity.
Let all the worlds give answer,
'Amen—so let it be.'

ST. COLUMBA, 521–97; *tr.* by DUNCAN MACGREGOR, 1854–1923.

(*a*) v. 4.

:l,	l,	:-.s,
:m,	m,	:-.m,
All	glo -	ry
:d	d	:-.t,
:l,	l,	:-.m,

(*b*) v. 2.

l,	:—	—	:—	l	:l .s	l	:t
l,	:—	—	:—	d	:d .m	m	:s
fight.				Christ the red Cross as-			
d	:—	—	:—	l	:l .t	d'	:r'
l,	:—	—	:—	l,	:l, .m	l	:s

Also the following:

32 Praise to the Holiest in the height
60 Of the Father's love begotten
62 'Jesus!' Name of wondrous love
91 All glory, laud, and honour
93 Hosanna, loud hosanna
108 Sing, my tongue, how glorious battle
128–39 *Hymns of our Lord's Ascension and Exaltation*
416–37 *Hymns of Love and Gratitude*

180

ESSEX. (86. 84.)

Doh = D. *In moderate time.* GUSTAV HOLST, 1874-

:s |l :d' |t :s |l :l |l :s |m :s |m :r |m :— ||
:m |m :f |r :m |m :f |m :r |d :t, |d :r |d :— ||
:d' |d' :l |s :s |d' :l.t |d' :s |s :s |l :l |s :— ||
:d |l, :f, |s, :d |l, :r |l, :t, |d :m |l :f |d :— ||

:d |r :f |s :-.s |s :l |d' :— |d :r |m :f |s :— || l |s ||
:d |r :f |r :-.r |m :m |f :— |l, :— |t, :r |m :— || f |m ||
:d' |r' :d' |t :-.t |t :d' |l :— |f :— |s :l |d' :— || d' |d' ||
:d' |ta :l |s :-.s |m :l |f :— |f :— |m :r |d :— || f, |d ||

A-men.

ST. CUTHBERT. (86. 84.)

Doh = E♭. *In moderate time.* JOHN BACCHUS DYKES, 1823–76.

:d |d :-.d |r :m |f :-.f |m :s |d' :m |m :fe |s :— |— ||
:s, |s, :-.d |d :d |d :-.d |d :d.t, |d :d |d :d |t, :— |— ||
:m |m :-.m |f :s |l :l |s :m.f |s :s |s :l |s :— |— ||
:d |d :-.d |d :d |f, :f, |d :d.r |m :d |l, :r |s, :— |— ||

:f |m :-.m |f :s |l :l |s :m |s :— |— :f |m :— |— || f |m ||
:t, |d :-.d |d :ta, |l, :t, |d :d |d :— |t, :— |d :— |— || d |d ||
:s |s :-.s |l :m |f :f |s :s |m :— |r :s |s :— |— || l |s ||
:s, |d :-.d |d :d |f :r |m :d |s, :— |s, :— |d :— |— || f, |d ||

A-men.

OUR blest Redeemer, ere He breathed
His tender last farewell,
A Guide, a Comforter bequeathed,
With us to dwell.

2 He came in tongues of living flame,
To teach, convince, subdue ;
All-powerful as the wind He came,
As viewless too.

3 He came sweet influence to impart,
A gracious, willing Guest,
While He can find one humble heart
Wherein to rest.

4 And His that gentle voice we hear,
Soft as the breath of even,
That checks each fault, that calms each fear,
And speaks of heaven.

5 And every virtue we possess,
And every victory won,
And every thought of holiness,
Are His alone.

6 Spirit of purity and grace,
Our weakness, pitying, see ;
O make our hearts Thy dwelling-place,
And worthier Thee.

HARRIET AUBER, 1773–1862.

181 WINCHESTER. (C.M.)

Doh = F. *In moderate time.* *Este's Psalter*, 1592.

d :—	m :-.m	r :d	f :f	m :—		r :—	m :s	s :fe	s :—	
s_1 :—	d :-.d	t_1 :l_1	l_1 :d	d :—		t_1 :—	d :t_1	r :r	t_1 :—	
m :—	s :-.s	s :m	f :l	s :—		s :—	s :s	l :l	s :—	
d :—	d :-.d	s_1 :l_1	f_1 :f_1	d :—		s_1 :—	d :m	r :r	s_1 :—	

m :—	l :-.s	f :m	r :d	t_1 :—		m :—	r :d	d :t_1	d :—		d	d	
d :—	d :-.d	d :d	t_1 :l_1	se_1 :—		s_1 :—	t_1 :l_1	l_1 :s_1	s_1 :—		l_1	s_1	
s :—	f :-.m	f :s	s :m	m :—		m :—	s :m	f :r	m :—		f	m	
d :—	f :-.d	l_1 :d	s_1 :l_1	m_1 :—		d :—	s_1 :l_1	f_1 :s_1	d :—		f_1	d_1	

A-men.

WHEN God of old came down from heaven,
In power and wrath He came;
Before His feet the clouds were riven,
Half darkness and half flame.

2 But, when He came the second time,
He came in power and love;
Softer than gale at morning prime
Hovered His holy Dove.

3 The fires that rushed on Sinai down
In sudden torrents dread,
Now gently light, a glorious crown,
On every sainted head.

4 And, as on Israel's awe-struck ear
The voice exceeding loud,
The trump that angels quake to hear,
Thrilled from the deep, dark cloud,

Unison.

5 So, when the Spirit of our God
Came down His flock to find,
A voice from heaven was heard abroad,
A rushing mighty wind.

6 It fills the Church of God; it fills
The sinful world around;
Only in stubborn hearts and wills
No place for it is found.

Harmony.

7 Come, Lord; come, Wisdom, Love, and Power;
Open our ears to hear;
Let us not miss the accepted hour;
Save, Lord, by love or fear.

JOHN KEBLE, 1792–1866.

182 VENI CREATOR. (L.M.)

Veni, Creator Spiritus.

Plainsong Melody from *Vesperale Romanorum*, Mechlin. Mode viii.

Doh = B♭. *Unison. In free rhythm.*

s, :l, :s, :f, :s, :l, :s, :d :r :-.r :d :— :—

1. Come, Ho - ly Ghost, our souls in - spire
2. Thy bless - ed unc - tion from a - bove
3. A - noint and cheer our soil - ed face
4. Teach us to know the Fa - ther, Son,

d :s, :l, :d :r :d :r :m :- .m :r :—

And light - en with ce - les - - tial fire;
Is com - fort, life, and fire of love;
With the a - bun - dance of Thy grace;
And Thee of Both, to be but One,

d :r :m :d :t, :l, :s, :r :l, :t, :d :— :—

Thou the a - noint - ing Spi - rit art,
En - a - ble with per - pe - tual light
Keep far our foes; give peace at home:
That through the a - ges all a - long

t, :d :l, :s, :f, :l, :d :t, :- .l, :s, :—

Who dost Thy seven - fold gifts im - part.
The dul - ness of our blind - ed sight;
Where Thou art Guide no ill can come.
This may be our end - less song,

After 4th verse.

d :r :m :d :t, :l, :s, :r :l, :t, :d :d :—

Praise . . to Thine e - ter - nal me - rit,

t, :d :l, :s, :f, :l, :d :t, :-.l, :s, :s :—

Fa - ther, Son, and Ho - - ly Spi - rit.

s, :l, :s, :s, :—

A - - men.

9th century; *tr.* by JOHN COSIN, 1594–1672.

183 ABERGELE. (C.M.)

Doh = B♭. *In moderate time.* JOHN AMBROSE LLOYD, 1815–74.

```
| s,  :l,  :t,  | d   :—  :d   | m   :—  :r   | d   :—  :—  | d   :t,  :d   |
| m,  :f,  :s,  | s,  :—  :m,  | s,  :—  :f,  | m,  :—  :—  | m,  :m,  :m,  |
| d   :d   :r   | d   :—  :d   | d   :—  :t,  | d   :—  :—  | l,  :se, :l,  |
| d,  :f,  :f,  | m,  :—  :d,  | s,  :—  :s,  | l,  :—  :—  | l,  :m,  :l,  |

| r   :—  :r   | m   :—  || m   | m   :f   :m   | m   :r   :d   | d   :t,  :l,  |
| l,  :—  :l,  | se, :—  || s,  | s,  :—  :s,  | s,  :f,  :m,  | s,  :—  :f,  |
| l,  :—  :l,  | t,  :—  || d   | d   :r   :d   | d   :t,  :d   | d   :—  :d   |
| f,  :—  :f,  | m,  :—  || d   | d   :t,  :d   | s,  :—  :l,  | m,  :—  :f,  |

| s,  :—  :s,  | s,  :—  :s,  | l,  :—  :s,  | s,  :—  :—  || d   | d   ||
| m,  :—  :m,  | m,  :—  :m,  | f,  :—  :f,  | m,  :—  :—  || f,  | m,  ||
| d   :—  :d   | d   :—  :m   | r   :—  :r   | d   :—  :—  || l,  | s,  ||
| d,  :—  :d,  | d,  :—  :d,  | t,, :—  :t,, | d,  :—  :—  || d,  | d,  ||
                                                             A-men.
```

SPIRIT Divine, attend our prayers,
  And make this house Thy home;
Descend with all Thy gracious powers;
  O come, great Spirit, come!

2 Come as the light: to us reveal
  Our emptiness and woe;
And lead us in those paths of life
  Where all the righteous go.

3 Come as the fire: and purge our hearts
  Like sacrificial flame;
Let our whole soul an offering be
  To our Redeemer's Name.

4 Come as the dew: and sweetly bless
  This consecrated hour;
May barrenness rejoice to own
  Thy fertilizing power.

5 Come as the dove: and spread Thy wings,
  The wings of peaceful love;
And let Thy Church on earth become
  Blest as the Church above.

6 Come as the wind, with rushing sound
  And Pentecostal grace,
That all of woman born may see
  The glory of Thy face.

7 Spirit Divine, attend our prayers;
  Make a lost world Thy home;
Descend with all Thy gracious powers;
  O come, great Spirit, come! ANDREW REED, 1787–1862.

[May be sung to EVAN, No. 692.]

184 ATTWOOD. (88. 88. 88.)

THOMAS ATTWOOD, 1765–1838.

Doh = D. *Moderately slow.*

```
                                                A.t.
:s  |s :d' :t.l |s :— :m  |d :— :r  |m :— :[m]l, |s, :d :r   |m :s :—
:d  |d :— :d    |d :— :t, |d :— :t, |d :— :[d]f, |m, :s, :s, |s, :s, :—
:m  |m :— :f    |m :— :s  |l :— :s  |s :— :[s]d  |d :— :t,   |d :d :—
:d  |d :— :d    |d :— :m  |l :— :s  |d :— :[d]f, |d, :m, :s, |d :m, :—

                       f.D.
|d.r :m :m.r     |d :—  ‖[d]s  |s :m :f  |r :— :r   |s :m :l   |r :— :—
|m,.fe, :s, :f,  |m, :— ‖[m]t, |d :— :d  |d :t, :t, |d :— :d   |t, :— :—
|d :— :t,        |d :—  ‖[d]s  |m :s :f  |s :— :s   |s :l :l   |s :— :—
|l, :s, :s,      |d, :— ‖[d]s, |m :d :l, |s, :— :f  |m :l :f   |s :— :—

f.G.                                             D.t.
|[r]l, :d :t,    |l, :d :t,   |l, :l, :—   |[l]r :— :—   ‖s :s :s     |s :d' :m
|[l]m, :l, :se,  |l, :m, :r,  |de, :m, :s, |[fe]t, :— :— ‖r :m :r     |r :d :d
|[f]d :m :r      |d :l, :se,  |l, :de :—   |[r]s :— :—   ‖f :f :f     |m :— :m
|[r]l, :m, :m,   |f, :d, :m,  |l, :— :l,   |[r]s, :— :—  ‖s, :s, :s,  |s, :— :s,

|r :l :s     |f :m :m     |f :s :l     |s :t, :d    |f :— :r   |r :m  ‖
|d :t, :t,   |d :— :d     |d :ta, :l,  |t, :s, :s,  |r :— :t,  |t, :d ‖
|f :— :r     |d :— :s     |d' :— :d'   |s :— :s     |l :— :s   |s :—  ‖
|s, :— :s,   |l, :— :ta,  |l, :s, :f,  |f, :f :m    |r :— :s,  |d :—  ‖

://:
:s   |d' :t :l      |s :t, :d     |f :— :r    |d :—  ‖d  d  ‖
:r   |m :— :d       |t, :— :l,    |r :— :t,   |d :—  ‖l, s, ‖
:s   |m.l :s :f     |r :f :m      |l :— :f    |m :—  ‖f  m  ‖
:t,  |l, :m, :f,    |s, :se, :l,  |f, :— :s,  |d :—  ‖f, d  ‖
                                                        A-men.
```

Veni, Creator Spiritus.

CREATOR Spirit ! by whose aid
The world's foundations first were laid,
Come, visit every pious mind,
Come, pour Thy joys on human kind ;
From sin and sorrow set us free,
And make Thy temples worthy Thee.

2 O Source of uncreated light,
The Father's promised Paraclete,
Thrice holy Fount, thrice holy Fire,
Our hearts with heavenly love inspire;
Come, and Thy sacred unction bring
To sanctify us while we sing.

3 Plenteous of grace, descend from high,
Rich in Thy sevenfold energy;
Thou Strength of His almighty hand
Whose power does heaven and earth command,
Give us Thyself, that we may see
The Father and the Son by Thee.

4 Immortal honour, endless fame
Attend the Almighty Father's Name;
The Saviour Son be glorified,
Who for lost man's redemption died;
And equal adoration be,
Eternal Paraclete, to Thee.

9th century; *tr.* by John Dryden, 1631–1700.

185 SOLDAU. (L.M.)

Wittenberg Gesangbuch, 1524.

Doh = G. *Moderately slow.*

:d |r :r |d :l, |s, :l, |d :m |s :l |s :m |d :l, |d ||
:m, |l, :s, |m, :f, |s, :f, |m, :d |t, :r |r :t, |l, :l, |s, ||
:d |d :t, |d :d |d :d |d :s |m :fe |s :s |m :f |m ||
:d |f, :s, |l, :f, |m, :f, |d, :d |m :r.d |t, :s, |l, :f, |d, ||

:m |m :r |m :d |r :r |m :d |l, :s, |l, :-.t, |d :d |d || t, |d ||
:d |d :t, |t, :d |d :t, |d :s, |f, :r, |f, :-.f, |s, :l, |s, || s, |s, ||
:s |s :s |s :m |l :s |s :d |d :t, |d :-.r |m :f |m || r |m ||
:d |d :s, |m, :l, |f, :s, |d, :m, |f, :s, |f, :-.r, |d, :f, |d, || s, |d, ||

A-men.

SPIRIT of God, that moved of old
Upon the waters' darkened face,
Come, when our faithless hearts are cold,
And stir them with an inward grace.

2 Thou that art power and peace combined,
All highest strength, all purest love,
The rushing of the mighty wind,
The brooding of the gentle dove,

3 Come, give us still Thy powerful aid,
And urge us on, and keep us Thine;
Nor leave the hearts that once were made
Fit temples for Thy grace divine;

4 Nor let us quench Thy sevenfold light;
But still with softest breathings stir
Our wayward souls, and lead us right,
O Holy Ghost, the Comforter.

Cecil Frances Alexander, 1823–95.

186

ST. PHILIP. (777.)

Doh = E♭. *Moderately slow.* WILLIAM HENRY MONK, 1823–89.

```
d  :— :d  | r  :— :m | f  :m  :r  | d :— :— || d  :— :f  | s  :— :s
s, :— :l, | t, :— :d | d  :—  :t, | d :— :— || s, :— :d  | t, :— :d
m  :— :m  | s  :— :s | l  :s  :f  | m :— :— || d  :— :d  | r  :— :s
d  :— :l, | s, :— :d | f, :s, :s, | d :— :— || d  :— :l, | s, :— :m,
```

```
l  :s  :f  | m :— :— || m :— :r  | f  :— :m  | r  :— :r  | d :— :— || f  | m ||
d  :—  :t, | d :— :— || d :— :s, | d  :— :d  | d  :— :t, | d :— :— || d  | d ||
f  :d  :r  | d :— :— || s :— :s  | f  :— :s  | l  :— :s  | m :— :— || l  | s ||
f, :m, :s, | d :— :— || d :— :t, | l, :— :m, | f, :— :s, | d :— :— || f, | d ||
```

A-men.

VENI SANCTE SPIRITUS. (777. 777.)

Doh = F. *Moderately slow.* SAMUEL WEBBE, 1740–1816.

```
d :d  | d  :r  | m  :-.r | d :— | r  :m | r  :s  | s :fe  | s  :— ||
d :d  | d  :d  | d  :t,  | d :— | s, :d | r  :r  | r :r.d | t, :— ||
m :l  | s  :l  | s  :f   | m :— | s  :s | s  :t  | l :l   | s  :— ||
d :f, | m, :f, | s, :s,  | d :— | t, :d | t, :s, | r :r   | s, :— ||
```

f.B♭.

```
l :s | f    :m | r  :-.d | d  :— | (d)s, :d  | t, :d.r | m  :r  | d  :— ||
d :d | d.t, :d | d  :t,  | d  :— | (d)s, :s, | f, :s,  | s, :f, | m, :— ||
f :s | l.f  :s | s  :f   | m  :— | (f)d  :d  | r  :m.r | d  :t, | d  :— ||
f :m | r    :d | s, :s,  | d, :— | (l)m, :m, | r, :d,  | s, :s, | d, :— ||
```

F.t.

```
(t)m :s  | f      :m | r  :d  | t, :— | r  :f      | m :r  | d  :t,   | d  :— || d  | d  ||
(s)d :s, | l,.t,  :d | l, :l, | s, :— | t, :d.r    | d :l, | s, :-.f, | m, :— || f, | m, ||
(r)s :m  | f      :s | l  :f  | r  :— | r  :l.s    | s :f  | m  :r    | d  :— || l, | s, ||
(s)d :m  | r      :d | f, :r, | s, :— | s, :l,.t,  | d :f, | s, :s,   | d, :— || f, | d, ||
```

A-men.

Veni, sancte Spiritus.

COME, Thou Holy Paraclete,
And from Thy celestial seat
Send Thy light and brilliancy.

2 Father of the poor, draw near;
Giver of all gifts, be here;
Come, the soul's true radiancy.

3 Come, of comforters the best,
Of the soul the sweetest guest,
Come in toil refreshingly.

4 Thou in labour rest most sweet,
Thou art shadow from the heat,
Comfort in adversity.

5 O Thou Light, most pure and blest,
Shine within the inmost breast
Of Thy faithful company.

6 Where Thou art not, man hath nought;
Every holy deed and thought
Comes from Thy Divinity.

7 What is soilèd make Thou pure;
What is wounded, work its cure;
What is parchèd fructify;

8 What is rigid gently bend;
What is frozen warmly tend;
Straighten what goes erringly.

9 Fill Thy faithful, who confide
In Thy power to guard and guide,
With Thy sevenfold mystery.

10 Here Thy grace and virtue send;
Grant salvation in the end,
And in heaven felicity.

13th century; *tr.* by John Mason Neale, 1818–66.

187 CASSEL. (77. 77. 77.)

Doh = G. *Moderately slow.* *Thommen's Gesangbuch*, Basle, 1745.

d :r |m :s |f :m |r :— |m :r |d :r |d :t, |d :—
s, :s, |s, :t, |l, :s, |s, :— |s, :s, |m, :l, |s, :s, |s, :—
m :r |d :r |d :d |t, :— |d :t, |d :f |m :r |m :—
d :t, |d :s, |l, :d |s, :— |d :s, |l, :f, |s, :s, |d, :—

t, :d |r :r |d :t, |l, :— |t, :d |r :m |f :m |r :—
s, :s, |fe, :s, |fe, :s, |fe, :— |s, :s, |s, :s, |l, :s, |s, :—
r :s, |l, :t, |d :r |r :— |r :d |t, :d |d :d |t, :—
s, :m, |r, :s, |l, :s, |r, :— |s, :m, |s, :d |f, :d |s, :—

d :r |m :s |f :m |r :— |m :r |d :r |d :t, |d :— || d |d
s, :t, |d :t, |l, :s, |s, :— |s, :s, |m, :l, |s, :s, |s, :— || l, |s,
s :f |m :r |d :d |t, :— |d :t, |d :f |m :r |m :— || f |m
m :r |d :s, |l, :d |s, :— |d :s, |l, :f, |s, :s, |d, :— || f, |d,

A-men.

GRACIOUS Spirit, dwell with me!
I myself would gracious be;
And, with words that help and heal,
Would Thy life in mine reveal;
And, with actions bold and meek,
Would for Christ, my Saviour, speak.

2 Truthful Spirit, dwell with me!
I myself would truthful be;
And, with wisdom kind and clear,
Let Thy life in mine appear;
And, with actions brotherly,
Speak my Lord's sincerity.

3 Tender Spirit, dwell with me!
I myself would tender be;
Shut my heart up like a flower
In temptation's darksome hour;
Open it when shines the sun,
And His love by fragrance own.

4 Holy Spirit, dwell with me!
I myself would holy be;
Separate from sin, I would
Choose and cherish all things good,
And whatever I can be
Give to Him who gave me Thee.

Thomas Toke Lynch, 1818–71.

188

VERBUM SUPERNUM. (L.M.)

Doh = C. *Unison.* *In free rhythm.*

Antiphonarium Romanum, Mechlin. Mode viii.

s :l :s :l :d' :t :l :s :m :f :s :— || s :t :d'

:r' :d' :t :s :l :d' :— || l :d' :t :d' :s :l :s :f :s :— ||

:s :l :s :l :d' :t :l :s :m :-.f :s :— || s :l :s :f :s :— ||

A - - men.

LUDBOROUGH. (L.M.)

Doh = E♭. *In moderate time.*

TIMOTHY RICHARD MATTHEWS, 1826–1910.

:d |m :f |s :l |s :f |m :m |m :r |d :d' |t :l |s ||

:d |d :d |d :d |d :t, |d :d |t, :t, |d :d |r :-.d |t, ||

:m |s :l |s :f.m |r :s |s :s |s :f |m :l |s :fe |s ||

:d |d :l, |m, :f, |s, :s, |d :d |s, :s, |l, :l, |r :r |s, ||

:s |r :m |f :m.r |m :f |s :l |d :r |m :s.f |m :r |d || d |d ||

:t, |t, :d |d :t, |d :-.t, |d :d |l, :t, |d :d |d :t, |d || l, |s, ||

:s |s :s |l :s |s :l |s :f |m :s |s :s.l |s :-.f |m || f |m ||

:s |f :m |r :s, |d :l, |m, :f, |l, :s, |d :m,.f, |s, :s, |d || f, |d ||

A-men.

[*By permission of Novello & Co., Ltd.*]

COME, gracious Spirit, heavenly Dove,
With light and comfort from above;
Be Thou our Guardian, Thou our Guide;
O'er every thought and step preside.

2 The light of truth to us display,
And make us know and choose Thy way;
Plant holy fear in every heart,
That we from God may ne'er depart.

3 Lead us to Christ, the living Way;
Nor let us from His pastures stray:
Lead us to holiness, the road
That we must take to dwell with God.

4 Lead us to heaven, that we may share
Fulness of joy for ever there;
Lead us to God, our final rest,
To be with Him for ever blest.

SIMON BROWNE, 1680–1732.

189 ERNSTEIN. (6 5. 6 5.)

Doh = G. *In moderate time.* JAMES FREDERICK SWIFT, 1847–

```
s, :m  |m  :r   |d  :—  |s, :—  |l, :f  |f  :m     |r  :—  |— :—
m, :s, |s, :f,  |m, :f, |s, :—  |f, :l, |l, :d     |t, :—  |— :—
d  :d  |d  :t,  |d  :—  |d  :—  |d  :d  |r  :s     |s  :—  |— :—
d, :d, |d  :s,  |l, :—  |m, :—  |f, :f, |r, :m,.f, |s, :—  |— :—

s  :d  |r  :m    |f  :—  |l, :—  |d  :t, |m  :r  |d  :—  |— :— ||d  |d
s, :d  |t, :d    |f, :—  |f, :—  |s, :s, |s, :f, |m, :—  |— :— ||f, |m,
d  :s  |f  :m    |d  :—  |d  :r  |m  :r  |d  :t, |d  :—  |— :— ||l, |s,
m, :m  |r  :d.ta, |l, :s, |f, :r, |s, :s, |s, :s, |d, :—  |— :— ||f, |d,
                                                                  A-men.
```

[*By permission of the Wesleyan Methodist Sunday School Department.*]

HOLY Spirit, hear us;
Help us while we sing;
Breathe into the music
Of the praise we bring.

2 Holy Spirit, prompt us
When we kneel to pray;
Nearer come, and teach us
What we ought to say.

3 Holy Spirit, shine Thou
On the book we read;
Gild its holy pages
With the light we need.

4 Holy Spirit, give us
Each a lowly mind;
Make us more like Jesus,
Gentle, pure, and kind.

5 Holy Spirit, brighten
Little deeds of toil;
And our playful pastimes
Let no folly spoil.

6 Holy Spirit, help us
Daily, by Thy might,
What is wrong to conquer,
And to choose the right.

WILLIAM HENRY PARKER, 1845–

190

FRANCONIA. (S.M.)

Doh = E♭. *In moderate time.* *König's Choralbuch*, 1738.

```
:d  |r  :m  |f  :s  |m  :—  |—  :s  |l  :d' |f  :m  |r  :—  |—  ||
:s, |t, :d  |d  :t, |d  :—  |—  :d  |d  :d  |t, :d  |t, :—  |—  ||
:m  |s  :s  |f  :r  |m  :—  |—  :m  |f  :s  |f  :s  |s  :—  |—  ||
:d  |s, :d  |l, :s, |d  :—  |—  :d  |f  :m  |r  :d  |s, :—  |—  ||
```

```
:s  |d' :t  |l  :s   |l   :l   |s  :s  |d  :m  |r  :r   |d :—|—||d |d ||
:r  |d  :r  |m  :m   |m   :r.d |t, :t, |d  :d  |d  :t,  |d :—|—||l,|s,||
:t  |s  :s  |d' :t   |l.s :fe  |s  :s  |m  :s  |l  :s.f |m :—|—||f |m ||
:s  |m  :s  |d  :m.r |d   :r   |s, :s, |l, :m, |f, :s,  |d :—|—||f,|d ||
```

A-men.

DOLE. (S.M.)

Lah = D. Doh = F. *In moderate time.* JOHN THOMAS REES, 1858–

```
:m |r :d |t, :-.d |l, :— |— :d  |t, :m  |m  :re |m   :— |— ||
:m |r :d |t, :-.d |l, :— |— :l, |t, :t, |t, :l, |se, :— |— ||
:m |r :d |t, :-.d |l, :— |— :m  |m  :s  |fe :fe |m   :— |— ||
:m |r :d |t, :-.d |l, :— |— :l, |s, :m, |t, :t, |m,  :— |— ||
```

```
:m |f :m |r :d |t, :l, |l  :l,     |r  :d    |t,   :-.d |l, :—|—||r |de||
:m |f :m |r :d |t, :l, |d  :l,     |l, :l,   |l,   :se, |l, :—|—||l,|l,||
:m |f :m |r :d |t, :l, |f  :d      |f  :m    |r.t, :m.r |d  :—|—||f |m ||
:m |f :m |r :d |t, :l, |f, :f,.m,  |r, :-.r, |m,   :m,  |l, :—|—||r,|l,||
```

A-men.

COME, Holy Spirit, come;
Let Thy bright beams arise;
Dispel the darkness from our minds,
And open all our eyes.

2 Cheer our desponding hearts,
Thou heavenly Paraclete;
Give us to lie with humble hope
At our Redeemer's feet.

3 Revive our drooping faith;
Our doubts and fears remove;
And kindle in our breasts the flame
Of never-dying love.

4 Convince us of our sin;
Then lead to Jesus' blood,
And to our wondering view reveal
The secret love of God.

5 'Tis Thine to cleanse the heart,
To sanctify the soul,
To pour fresh life on every part,
And new create the whole.

6 Dwell, therefore, in our hearts;
Our minds from bondage free;
Then shall we know and praise and love
The Father, Son, and Thee.

JOSEPH HART, 1712–68.

191 DOWN AMPNEY. (66. 11. D.)

Doh = D. *Moderately slow.* RALPH VAUGHAN WILLIAMS, 1872–

d :—	r :m	s :—	l :—	s :—	— :—	s :—	l :s	d' :t
s, :—	s, :d	d :t,	l, :t,	d :—	— :—	m :—	m :r	d :r
m :—	s :d	r :—	f :r	m :—	— :—	s :—	d :r	m :s
d :—	t, :d	s, :—	f, :—	d :—	— :—	d :—	d :t,	l, :t,

l :—	s :—	s :—	l :s	f :m	r :d	r :m.f	r :—	d :—	
d :—	t, :—	d :—	d :t,	d :d	l, :d	d :d	d :t,	d :—	
s :fe	s :—	m :—	f :r	f :s	f :s	l :l	s :—.f	m :—	
r :—	s, :—	d :—	f, :s,	l, :d	f :m	f :r	s, :—	d :—	

d' :—	t :l	s :—	l :—	s :—	— :—	ta :—	l :s	f :—
m :—	m :d	m :—	r :d	t, :—	— :—	r :—	d :d	l, :t,
l :—	s :l	d' :t	l :—	t :—	— :—	f :s	l :m	f :—
l :—	m :f	d :m	fe :—	s :—	— :—	r :m	f :d	r :—

m :—	r :—	r :—	s :l	s :f	m :d	r :m.f	r :—	d :—		d	d	
d :—	s, :—	t, :—	d :d	t, :d.r	s, :d	d :d	d :t,	d :—		l,	s,	
s :l	t :—	s :—	s :f	r :l	s :s	l :f	s :—.f	m :—		f	m	
m :f	s :—	s, :f,	m, :f,	s, :l,.t,	d :m	f :r	s, :—	d :—		f,	d	

A-men.

Discendi, Amor santo.

COME down, O Love Divine,
Seek Thou this soul of mine,
And visit it with Thine own ardour glowing;
O Comforter, draw near,
Within my heart appear,
And kindle it, Thy holy flame bestowing.

2 O let it freely burn,
Till earthly passions turn
To dust and ashes, in its heat consuming;
And let Thy glorious light
Shine ever on my sight,
And clothe me round, the while my path illuming.

3 Let holy charity
Mine outward vesture be,
And lowliness become mine inner clothing;
True lowliness of heart,
Which takes the humbler part,
And o'er its own shortcomings weeps with loathing.

4 And so the yearning strong,
With which the soul will long,
Shall far outpass the power of human telling;
For none can guess its grace,
Till he become the place
Wherein the Holy Spirit makes His dwelling.

BIANCO DA SIENA, ? –1434; *tr.* by RICHARD FREDERICK LITTLEDALE, 1833–90.

192 LLANSAMLET. (88. 88. 88.)

Doh = F. *In moderate time.* EDWARD ARTHUR, 1874–

```
| m    :s    :d    | r    :—    :s,   | l,.,t,:d  :r    | m  :—  :d   | f   :—  :m   |
| s,   :s,   :l,   | t,   :s,   :s,   | f,.,s,:l, :t,   | d  :—  :d   | d   :r   :d  |
| d    :r    :m    | s    :t,   :d    | f     :—  :f    | m  :—  :m   | l   :—  :s   |
| d    :t,   :l,   | s,   :-.f, :m,   | r,    :—  :s,   | d, :—  :d   | l,  :t,  :l  |

| r    :s    :m    | r.,d  :t,  :l,   | s,  :—  || s,  | m.,r:d  :r      | m  :s   :f    |
| t,   :—    :s,   | s,.,l,:s,  :fe,  | s,  :—  || s,  | s,  :—  :l,.t,  | d  :r   :d    |
| s    :—    :d    | r.,m  :r   :r.d  | t,  :—  || s,  | s.,f:m  :f      | s  :—   :d.r  |
| s,   :—    :d    | t,.,d :r   :r,   | s,  :—  || s,  | d.,r:m  :r      | d  :t,  :l,   |

| m.,r:d  :r    | m   :—  :d     | r.,m:f    :l    | s   :m   :d   | m.,r:d   :t,  |
| t,  :d  :l,   | t,  :—  :d.t,  | l,  :—    :t,   | d   :t,  :l,  | l,   :s, :s,  |
| m   :—  :l    | se  :—  :m     | l   :-.s  :f    | s   :—   :m   | s.,f:m   :r   |
| se, :l, :f,   | m,  :—  :l,    | f,  :-.m, :r,   | m,  :s,  :l,  | f,   :s, :s,  |

| d  :—  :—  || r   :m   :f    | m    :—  :d   | r     :m  :f    | s   :—  :m  |
| s, :—  :—  || s,  :s,  :d    | t,   :—  :d   | l,.t, :d  :l,   | s,  :—  :d  |
| m  :—  :—  || r   :d   :d.r  | m    :—  :m   | l     :s  :f.m  | r   :—  :s  |
| d  :—  :—  || t,  :d   :l,   | se,  :—  :l,  | f     :m  :r.d  | t,  :—  :d  |
                                                                  v. 1. gloom

| l   :s   :f      | m.,f:s   :d     | r   :d   :t,  | d     :—  :—  || d   | d   ||
| d   :t,  :d.r    | d   :—   :d.t,  | l,  :s,  :s,  | s,    :—  :—  || l,  | s,  ||
| f   :r   :l      | s   :—   :m     | f   :m   :r   | m     :—  :—  || f   | m   ||
| f,  :s,  :l,.t,  | d   :m,  :l,    | f,  :s,  :s,  | d/d,} :—  :—  || f,  | d,  ||
Wil - dered.                                                          A - men.
```

O Gott! O Geist! O Licht des Lebens.

SPIRIT of Grace, Thou Light of Life
Amidst the darkness of the dead!
Bright Star, whereby through worldly strife
The patient pilgrim still is led;
Thou Dayspring in the deepest gloom,
Wildered and dark, to Thee I come!

2 Pure Fire of God, burn out my sin,
Cleanse all the earthly dross from me;
Refine my secret heart within,
The golden streams of love set free!
Live Thou in me, O Life divine,
Until my deepest love be Thine.

3 O Breath from far Eternity,
Breathe o'er my soul's unfertile land;
So shall the pine and myrtle-tree
Spring up amidst the desert sand;
And where Thy living water flows,
My heart shall blossom as the rose.

GERHARD TERSTEEGEN, 1697–1769; *tr.* by EMMA FRANCES BEVAN, 1827–1909, and BENJAMIN HALL KENNEDY, 1804–89.

193 BUCKLAND. (77. 77.)

Doh = D. *Moderately slow.* LEIGHTON GEORGE HAYNE, 1836–83.

```
|s  :m  |r  :d  |r  :r  |m  :—  |s  :d' |t  :s  |s  :fe |s  :—  ||
|m  :d  |t, :d  |d  :t, |d  :—  |m  :d  |r  :r  |m  :r  |r  :—  ||
|s  :s  |s  :s  |l  :s  |s  :—  |s  :fe |s  :r' |l  :l  |t  :—  ||
|d  :m  |f  :m  |f  :s  |d  :—  |d  :l, |s, :t, |d  :r  |s  :—  ||

|d' :s  |f  :m  |r  :m  |f  :—  |f  :s  |m  :d  |d  :t, |d  :—  ||d  |d  ||
|m  :d  |d  :d  |l, :de |r  :—  |r  :r  |d  :d  |s, :s, |s, :—  ||l, |s, ||
|s  :s  |l  :s  |f  :l  |l  :—  |l  :s  |s  :s  |r  :r  |m  :—  ||f  |m  ||
|d  :m  |f  :d  |r  :l, |r  :—  |r  :t, |d  :m, |s, :s, |d  :—  ||f, |d  ||
                                                                 A-men.
```

HOLY Spirit, Truth Divine,
Dawn upon this soul of mine;
Word of God, and inward Light,
Wake my spirit, clear my sight.

2 Holy Spirit, Love Divine,
Glow within this heart of mine;
Kindle every high desire;
Perish self in Thy pure fire.

3 Holy Spirit, Power Divine,
Fill and nerve this will of mine;
By Thee may I strongly live,
Bravely bear, and nobly strive.

4 Holy Spirit, Right Divine,
King within my conscience reign;
Be my law, and I shall be
Firmly bound, for ever free.

5 Holy Spirit, Peace Divine,
Still this restless heart of mine;
Speak to calm this tossing sea,
Stayed in Thy tranquillity.

6 Holy Spirit, Joy Divine,
Gladden Thou this heart of mine;
In the desert ways I sing,
'Spring, O Well, for ever spring!'

SAMUEL LONGFELLOW, 1819–92.

194 VENI SPIRITUS. (S.M.)

Doh = E♭. *Slow.* JOHN STAINER, 1840–1901.

B♭.t. f.E♭.

m :r :d	d :— :r	m :— :—	[l]r :d :t,	l, :— :se,	[l,]m :—		m
d :t, :d	l, :— :t,	t, :— :—	[m]l, :s, :f,	m, :— :m,	[m]t, :m		r
m :f :s	l :— :l	se :— :—	[d']f :m :r	d :— :t,	[de]se :l		t
d :r :m	f :— :f	m :— :—	[l,]r, :r, :r,	m, :— :m,	[l,]m :ba		se

d' :— :d'	t :l :se	l :d :r	m :— :m	m :— :f	s :— :s	s :— :—		f	m	
d :r :m	r :d :t,	l, :— :l,	t, :— :t,	m :r :d	d :— :t,	d :— :—		d	d	
l :t :d'	se :l :r'	d' :— :l	se :— :se	l :t :d'	r :m :f	m :— :—		l	s	
l :— :l	m :— :m	f :— :f	m :— :r	d :t, :l,	s, :— :s,	d :— :—		f,	d	

A-men.

[*By permission of Novello & Co., Ltd.*]

WIRKSWORTH. (S.M.)

Lah = F♯. Doh = A. *Slow.* *Chetham's Psalmody*, 1718.

l, :m .r	d :t,	l, :—	m :s .f	m :r	m :—	
l, :l, .l,	l, :se,	l, :—	l, :s, .l,	s, :s,	s, :—	
d :m .f	m :m .r	d :—	d :d .d	d :t,	d :—	
l, :d, .r,	m, :m,	l, :—	l, :m, .f,	s, :s,	d, :—	

:d | t, .l, :m :d | r .d :t, :t, | m .r :d :t, | l, :— || l, | l, ||
:m, | m, .m, :se, :l, | l, .l, :se, :se, | l, .l, :l, :se, | l, :— || f, | m, ||
:d | r .d :t, :d | f .m :m :m | m .f :m :m .r | d :— || r | de ||
:l, | se, .l, :m, :l, | r, .l, :m, :m, .r, | d, .r, :m, :m, | l, :— || r, | l₂ ||

A-men.

BREATHE on me, Breath of God;
Fill me with life anew,
That I may love what Thou dost love,
And do what Thou wouldst do.

2 Breathe on me, Breath of God,
Until my heart is pure,
Until with Thee I will one will,
To do and to endure.

3 Breathe on me, Breath of God,
Till I am wholly Thine,
Until this earthly part of me
Glows with Thy fire divine.

4 Breathe on me, Breath of God;
So shall I never die,
But live with Thee the perfect life
Of Thine eternity.

EDWIN HATCH, 1835–89.

195

SONG 22. (10. 10. 10. 10.)

Doh = F. *In moderate time.* ORLANDO GIBBONS, 1583–1625.

```
s  :—  |s  :m  |l  :—  |s  :—  |s  :f      |m  :s  |r  :—  ||
d  :—  |r  :m  |d  :—  |d  :—  |d  :l,.t,  |d  :d  |t, :—  ||
m  :—  |s  :s  |f  :—  |m  :—  |m  :f      |s  :m  |s  :—  ||
d  :—  |t, :d  |f, :—  |d  :—  |d  :r      |m  :d  |s  :—  ||

   :r  |m  :d  |f  :—  |r  :—  |s  :d  |m  :r   |d  :—  |—  ||
   :t, |d  :l, |l, :—  |t, :—  |d  :d  |d  :t,  |d  :—  |—  ||
   :s  |s  :f  |f  :—  |s  :—  |s  :l  |s  :-.f |m  :—  |—  ||
   :s, |d  :f  |r  :—  |s, :—  |m  :f  |s  :s,  |d  :—  |—  ||

f.B♭.                        f.E♭.                      F.t.m.
:(m)t, |d  :r      |m      :(m)t, |m  :l  |l  :se  |(l)s,  :—  |—  ||
:(d)s, |s, :f,     |m,.f,  :(s)r  |m  :f  |t, :t,  |(de)t, :—  |—  ||
:(s)r  |s, :l,.t,  |d .r   :(m)t  |t  :l  |m  :m   |(m)r   :—  |—  ||
:(d)s, |m, :r,     |d,     :(d)s, |d  :r  |m  :m,  |(l)s,  :—  |—  ||

:t,  |d  :r      |m  :-.f    |s  :l    |r  :r   |d  :—  |—  :—  || d  |d  ||
:s,  |s, :l,.t,  |d  :t,.l,  |s, :d    |d  :t,  |d  :—  |—  :—  || l, |s, ||
:r   |m  :f      |s  :-.r    |s  :f.m  |r  :r   |m  :—  |—  :—  || f  |m  ||
:s,  |m, :r,     |d, :-.r,   |m, :f,   |s, :s,  |d  :—  |—  :—  || f, |d, ||
                                                                  A-men.
```

SPIRIT of God, descend upon my heart;
 Wean it from earth; through all its pulses move;
Stoop to my weakness, mighty as Thou art,
 And make me love Thee as I ought to love.

2 I ask no dream, no prophet-ecstasies,
 No sudden rending of the veil of clay,
No angel-visitant, no opening skies;
 But take the dimness of my soul away.

3 Hast Thou not bid me love Thee, God and King—
 All, all Thine own, soul, heart, and strength, and mind?
I see Thy Cross—there teach my heart to cling:
 O let me seek Thee, and O let me find!

4 Teach me to feel that Thou art always nigh;
 Teach me the struggles of the soul to bear,
To check the rising doubt, the rebel sigh;
 Teach me the patience of unanswered prayer.

5 Teach me to love Thee as Thine angels love,
 One holy passion filling all my frame—
The baptism of the heaven-descended Dove,
 My heart an altar, and Thy love the flame.

GEORGE CROLY, 1780–1860

196 ST. COLUMBA (ERIN). (C.M.)

Doh = E♭. *Moderately slow.* Old Irish Hymn Melody.

:d .r | m :— :f | s :— :f .s | m :— :r | d :— ‖
:s, | d :— :d | t, :— :d .r | r :d :t, | l, :— ‖
:m .f | s :— :f | r :— :d .s | s :— :s | m :— ‖
:d | d :t, :l, | s, :— :l, .t, | d :— :s, | l, :— ‖

:d .r | m :— :f | s :— :f.s.l | s :— ‖ s | d' :— :l | s :— :f
:l, .t, | d :— :d | d :— :l, | d :— ‖ t, | d :— :d | d :— :r
:f | s :— :l | s :— :d | m :— ‖ s.f | m :— :f | s :— :l
:f, | d :t, :l, | m, :— :f, | d :— ‖ s, | l, :s, :f, | f, :m, :r,

m :— :r | d :— ‖ m | s :— :f | m :— :r | d :— ‖ d | d ‖
r :d :t, | d :— ‖ d | d :— :d | d :— :t, | d :— ‖ l, | s, ‖
s :— :f | m :— ‖ m | d' :t :l | s :— :s.f | m :— ‖ f | m ‖
m, :-.f, :s, | l, :— ‖ l, | m, :— :f, | s, :— :s, | d :— ‖ f, | d ‖

A-men.

COME, Holy Ghost, our hearts inspire;
Let us Thine influence prove,
Source of the old prophetic fire,
Fountain of life and love.

2 Come, Holy Ghost, for moved by Thee
The prophets wrote and spoke;
Unlock the truth, Thyself the key;
Unseal the sacred book.

3 Expand Thy wings, celestial Dove;
Brood o'er our nature's night;
On our disordered spirits move,
And let there now be light.

4 God through Himself we then shall know,
If Thou within us shine,
And sound, with all Thy saints below,
The depths of love divine.

CHARLES WESLEY, 1707–88.

Also the following:

386 O Spirit of the living God
457 O for a closer walk with God
483 Behold the amazing gift of love
484 Gracious Spirit, Holy Ghost
608 The glory of the spring how sweet!

197 CASTLEFORD. (C.M.)

Sacred Harmony, Leeds, *c.*1720.
Arranged by SAMUEL SEBASTIAN WESLEY, 1810–76.

Doh = E. *In moderate time.*

```
:d  |m  :r    |d  :l   |s  :f    |m  :m  |s  :d'  |t  :l    |s  :— |— ||
:d  |d  :t,   |d  :d   |d  :-.t, |d  :d  |r  :m   |r  :-.d  |t, :— |— ||
:m  |s  :-.f  |m  :f   |r  :s    |s  :s  |s  :s   |s  :fe   |s  :— |— ||
:d  |d  :s,   |l, :f,  |s, :s,   |d  :d  |t, :l,  |r  :r    |s, :— |— ||

:s  |m  :d  |l  :s  |l.t :d'  |t  :s    |d' :d.f |m  :r    |d  :— |— ||d  |d  ||
:r  |d  :d  |d  :d  |f   :m   |r  :t,   |d  :d   |d  :t,   |d  :— |— ||l, |s, ||
:s  |s  :s  |l  :m  |f   :s   |s  :s.f  |m  :l   |s  :-.f  |m  :— |— ||f  |m  ||
:t, |d  :m  |f  :m  |r   :d   |s, :s,   |l, :f,  |s, :s,   |d  :— |— ||f, |d  ||
```

A-men.

THE Spirit breathes upon the word,
And brings the truth to sight ;
Precepts and promises afford
A sanctifying light.

2 A glory gilds the sacred page,
Majestic, like the sun :
It gives a light to every age ;
It gives, but borrows none.

3 The hand that gave it still supplies
The gracious light and heat ;
His truths upon the nations rise ;
They rise, but never set.

4 Let everlasting thanks be Thine,
For such a bright display
As makes a world of darkness shine
With beams of heavenly day.

5 My soul rejoices to pursue
The steps of Him I love,
Till glory breaks upon my view
In brighter worlds above.

WILLIAM COWPER, 1731–1800.

198 CHEBAR. (76. 76. D.)

Doh = E♭. *In moderate time.* HENRY SMART, 1813–79.

:s |m :d |f :m |l :— |s :d |f :f |m :r |m :— |— ||
:d |d :s, |d :d |d :— |d :d |l, :r |d :t, |d :— |— ||
:m |s :m |f :s |f :— |m :m |r :l |s :s |s :— |— ||
:d |d :m |l, :d |f, :— |d :l, |f, :f, |s, :s, |d :— |— ||

:s |m :d |f :m |l :— |s :s |d' :l |s :fe |s :— |— ||
:t, |d :s, |d :d |d :r |m :f |m :m |r :d |t, :— |— ||
:s |s :m |f :s |l :t |d' :t |s :d' |t :l |s :— |— ||
:s, |d :-.t, |l, :s, |f, :f |m :r |d :d |r :r |s, :— |— ||

:r |m :r |m :f |l :— |s :s |l :s |l :t |d' :— ||
:t, |d :t, |d :t, |r :— |s, :d |d :d |d :f |m :— ||
:s |s :s |s :t |t :— |d' :m |f :m |f :r' |d' :— ||
:s, |d :s, |d :r |f :— |m :d |f :d |f :r |l :— ||

d' :—	t :l	s :l	f :—	m :s	d :f	m :r	d :—	—		d	d	
fe :—	s :r	m :m	l, :t,	d :d	d :d	d :t,	s, :—	—		l,	s,	
l :r'	r' :t	d' :m	f :s	s :ta	l :l	s :f	m :—	—		f	m	
r :—	s :f	m :d	r :s,	d :m	f :r	s :s,	d :—	—		f,	d	

A-men.

O WORD of God Incarnate,
O Wisdom from on high,
O Truth unchanged, unchanging,
O Light of our dark sky,
We praise Thee for the radiance
That from the hallowed page,
A lantern to our footsteps,
Shines on from age to age.

2 The Church from her dear Master
Received the gift divine,
And still that light she lifteth,
O'er all the earth to shine ;
It is the golden casket
Where gems of truth are stored ;
It is the heaven-drawn picture
Of Christ, the living Word ;

3 It floateth like a banner
Before God's host unfurled ;
It shineth like a beacon,
Above the darkling world ;
It is the chart and compass
That, o'er life's surging sea,
'Mid mists and rocks and quicksands,
Still guides, O Christ, to Thee.

4 O make Thy Church, dear Saviour,
A lamp of purest gold,
To bear before the nations
Thy true light, as of old ;
O teach Thy wandering pilgrims
By this their path to trace,
Till, clouds and darkness ended,
They see Thee face to face.

William Walsham How, 1823–97

199

RAVENSHAW. (6 6. 6 6. Trochaic.)

Doh = E♭. *Moderately slow.* *Weisse's Gesangbuch*, 1531.

d :d |m :f |s :— |s :— |l :t |d' :s |m :fe |s :— ‖
s, :s, |d :d |d :t, |d :— |d :r |m :r |d :— |t, :— ‖
m :m |s :f |r :— |m :— |f :f |s :s |s :l |r :— ‖
d :d |d :l, |s, :— |d :— |f :r |d :t, |d :l, |s, :— ‖

f :r |m :f |m :r |d :— |t, :d |r :m |r :— |d :— ‖ d |d ‖
d :r |d :d |d :t, |d :— |s, :s, |t, :d |d :t, |d :— ‖ l, |s, ‖
d :s |s :l |s :— |m :— |s :s |f :m |s :— |m :— ‖ f |m ‖
l, :t, |d :f, |s, :— |l, :— |s, :m |r :d |s, :— |d :— ‖ f, |d ‖
:m, |r, :d,

A - men.

LORD, Thy word abideth,
And our footsteps guideth:
Who its truth believeth
Light and joy receiveth.

2 When our foes are near us,
Then Thy word doth cheer us,
Word of consolation,
Message of salvation.

3 When the storms are o'er us,
And dark clouds before us,
Then its light directeth,
And our way protecteth.

4 Who can tell the pleasure,
Who recount the treasure,
By Thy word imparted
To the simple-hearted?

5 Word of mercy, giving
Succour to the living;
Word of life, supplying
Comfort to the dying!

6 O that we, discerning
Its most holy learning,
Lord, may love and fear Thee,
Evermore be near Thee!

HENRY WILLIAMS BAKER, 1821–77.

200 ROTHLEY. (86. 84.)

Doh = A♭. *In moderate time.* JOHN GOSS, 1800–80.

```
:s, |d  :m  |s  :-.f  |m  :r  |d  :t,  |l, :d  |t, :l,  |s, :— |— ||
:m, |s, :s, |s, :-.s, |s, :t, |l, :se, |l, :l, |s, :fe, |s, :— |— ||
:d  |m  :d  |r  :-.r  |d  :f  |m  :r   |m  :m  |r  :d   |t, :— |— ||
:d, |d, :d  |t, :-.t, |d  :se,|l, :t,  |d  :l, |r  :r,  |s, :— |— ||

:d  |l, :-.l, |f  :r  |d  :t, |s  :d  |m  :— |— :r |d  :— |— ||d :— |d :— ||
:s, |f, :-.f, |l, :l, |s, :s, |s, :m, |s, :— |f, :— |m, :— |— ||l,:— |s,:— ||
:d  |d  :-.d  |r  :f  |m  :r  |d  :d  |d  :— |t, :— |d  :— |— ||d :r |m :— ||
:m, |f, :-.f, |r, :r, |s, :f, |m, :l, |s, :— |s, :— |d, :— |— ||f,:— |d,:— ||
                                                                  A  -  men.
```

[*By permission of Novello & Co., Ltd.*]

TO Thee, O God, we render thanks,
That Thou to us hast given
A light that shineth on our path,
A light from heaven :

2 That Thou into the hearts of men
Didst breathe Thy Breath Divine,
And mad'st their lips the source from whence
Flowed words of Thine :

3 The words that speak of lives that live,
And life beyond the grave,
Of Him who came that life to give,
Those lives to save :

4 Of Him who lowly came as man,
To come as man again
On clouds of glory throned on high,
As Judge of men :

5 Who lived on earth, on earth who died,
To set His servants free,
And left this message as their guide,
'Remember Me.'

6 Then teach us humbly so to tread
The path that Saviour trod,
That we may ever stand prepared
To meet our God.

GODFREY THRING, 1823–1903.

201 ELVET. (C.M.)

Doh = E♭. *In moderate time.* JOHN BACCHUS DYKES, 1823–76.

```
| m :f .f | s  :d    | d  :l   | s  :d'   | t  :l | s  :fe | s :— | — :— ||
| d :d .d | d  :d .t,| l,.t,:d .r | m :m  | r  :m | r  :r  | r :— | — :— ||
| s :f .f | m  :m    | f .s :l .t | d' :m.fe | s :d' | t :l | t :— | — :— ||
| d :l,.l,| s, :l,.s,| f, :f   | d  :l,   | t, :d | r  :r  | s :— | — :— ||

| m :f .s  | l  :r    | r  :m .f | s :s  | f :r  | d  :t, | d  :— | — :— || d  | d  ||
| d :d .m  | f .m:r.d | t, :t,   | d :d  | d :l, | s, :s, | s, :— | — :— || l, | s, ||
| l :d'.d' | d' :l    | t .l :s  | s :ta | l :f  | m  :r  | m  :— | — :— || f  | m  ||
| l :l .s  | f  :f    | f  :s .f | m :m  | f :f, | s, :s, | d  :— | — :— || f, | d  ||
```

A-men.

LAMP of our feet, whereby we trace
Our path when wont to stray;
Stream from the fount of heavenly grace,
Brook by the traveller's way;

2 Bread of our souls, whereon we feed,
True manna from on high;
Our guide and chart, wherein we read
Of realms beyond the sky;

Unison.

3 Pillar of fire through watches dark
Or radiant cloud by day;
When waves would whelm our tossing bark,
Our anchor and our stay;

Harmony.

4 Word of the ever-living God,
Will of His glorious Son,—
Without thee how could earth be trod,
Or heaven itself be won?

5 Lord, grant that we aright may learn
The wisdom it imparts,
And to its heavenly teaching turn
With simple, childlike hearts.

BERNARD BARTON, 1784–1849.

[May be sung to NOX PRAECESSIT, No. 482.]

202 ALL SOULS. (10 10. 10 10.)

Doh = D. *In moderate time.* JOHN YOAKLEY, 1860–

```
| m :— | r  :d  | f  :—  | m :— | l  :l  | s  :r  | m :— | — ||
| d :— | t, :d  | d  :—  | d :— | d  :d  | d  :t, | d :— | — ||
| s :— | s  :m  | l  :—  | s :— | f  :m  | r  :s  | s :— | — ||
| d :— | s, :l, | f, :l, | d :— | f, :f, | s, :s, | d :— | — ||

:m  | fe :— | s  :— | d' :t | l  :s | s :— | fe :— | s  :— | — ||
:d  | d  :— | t, :m | r  :r | m  :m | r :— | r  :d | t, :— | — ||
:l  | l  :— | s  :— | l  :t | d' :t | l :— | l  :— | s  :— | — ||
:l, | r  :— | m  :— | fe :s | d  :d | r :— | r  :— | s, :— | — ||
```

```
:s   |s   :—  |f   :—  |m   :m   |r   :d   |l   :—  |l   :—  |se  :—  |—  ||
:r   |d   :—  |r   :—  |d   :d   |t,  :d   |d   :—  |r   :—  |m   :—  |—  ||
:t   |d'  :—  |s   :—  |s   :s   |f   :s   |f   :—  |l   :—  |t   :—  |—  ||
:s,  |l,  :—  |t,  :—  |d   :d   |r   :m   |f   :—  |f   :—  |m   :—  |—  ||

:m   |l   :—  |t   :—  |d'  :l   |f   :m   |r   :—  |r   :—  |d   :—  |—  :—  ||d   |d   ||
:m   |m   :—  |m   :r  |d   :d   |d   :d   |d   :—  |t,  :—  |d   :—  |—  :—  ||l,  |s,  ||
:se  |l   :—  |se  :—  |l   :m   |f   :s   |l   :—  |s   :f  |m   :—  |—  :—  ||f   |m   ||
:r   |d   :—  |m   :—  |l,  :l,  |l,  :s,  |f,  :—  |s,  :—  |d   :—  |—  :—  ||f,  |d   ||
```

A-men.

CONGLETON. (10 10. 10 10.)

Lah = G. Doh = B♭. *Moderately slow.*

MICHAEL WISE, *c.* 1648–87.

```
|l,   :d    |—  :t,   |d   :l,   |se,  :l,  |s,  :-.f,  |m,  :—  |—  ||s,  |s,  :m,
|m,   :m,   |—  :m,   |m,  :r,   |m,   :d,  |r,  :r,    |m,  :—  |—  ||m,  |r,  :d,
|d    :l,   |—  :t,   |l,  :l,   |t,   :l,  |l,  :t,    |d   :—  |—  ||s,  |s,  :s,
|l,,  :l,   |—  :se,  |l,  :f,   |m,   :f,  |r,  :r,    |d,  :—  |—  ||d,  |t,, :d,

|l,   :-.t,   |d   :-.t,  |l,  :l,  |se  :—  |—  ||t,   |t,   :t,   |d   :r   |m   :m   |r   :r
|d,   :-.m,   |m,  :m,    |m,  :r,  |m,  :—  |—  ||m,   |m,   :m,   |m,  :s,  |s,  :s,  |s,  :s,.f,
|l,   :-.se,  |l,  :-.t,  |d   :l,  |t,  :—  |—  ||se,  |se,  :se,  |l,  :t,  |t,  :d   |d   :t,
|l,,  :-.m,   |l,  :s,    |f,  :f,  |m,  :—  |—  ||m,   |m,   :m,   |l,  :s,  |m,  :d,  |s,  :s,

|d   :—  |—  ||m,  |ba,  :ba,  |se,  :se,  |l,  :t,  |se,  :-.se,  |l,   :—  ||l,  |l,   ||
|m,  :—  |—  ||m,  |m,   :r,   |m,   :m,   |m,  :f,  |m,   :-.m,   |m,   :—  ||f,  |m,   ||
|d   :—  |—  ||d   |l,   :t,   |t,   :t,   |d   :t,  |t,   :-.t,   |d    :—  ||r   |de   ||
|d,  :—  |—  ||d,  |r,   :t,,  |m,   :r,   |d,  :r,  |m,   :-.m,   |l,,  :—  ||r,  |l,,  ||
```

A-men.

BREAK Thou the bread of life
  Dear Lord, to me,
As Thou didst break the loaves
  Beside the sea ;
Beyond the sacred page
  I seek Thee, Lord ;
My spirit pants for Thee,
  O living Word.

2 Bless Thou the truth, dear Lord,
  To me, to me,
As Thou didst bless the bread
  By Galilee ;
Then shall all bondage cease,
  All fetters fall ;
And I shall find my peace.
  My all in all.

MARY ARTEMISIA LATHBURY, 1841–1913.

203

LIEBSTER JESU. (78. 78. 88.) JOHANN RODOLPH AHLE, 1625–73.
Arranged by JOHANN SEBASTIAN BACH, 1685–1750.

Doh = G. *Slow.*

m :r.d | r :s | m :d | r :— ‖ d :d | d :d | r :m
s, :s, | s, :t, | s, :s,.l, | t, :— ‖ l, :ta, | l, :s, | l,.t, :d
d.r :m | r :r | m.f :s | s :— ‖ m :m | f :d | f :s
d, :d | t, :s, | d.r :m.d | s, :— ‖ l, :s, | f, :m, | r, :d,.m,

D.C.

r :— | d :— | — :— ‖ s, :s, | l, :t, | d :r.d | t,.l, :s,
d :t, | d :— | — :— ‖ m, :r, | m,.fe, :s, | l, :l, | s, :r,
l :s.f | m :— | — :— ‖ d :r | d :r | m :r | r.d :t,
f, :s, | d, :— | — :— ‖ d :t, | l, :s, | s, :fe, | s, :s,

d :d | d :d | r :m | r :— | d :— | — :— ‖ d | d
l, :ta, | l, :s, | l,.t, :d | d :t, | d :— | — :— ‖ l, | s,
m :m | f :d | f :s | s :-.f | m :— | — :— ‖ f | m
l, :s, | f, :m, | r, :d, | s, :— | d, :— | — :— ‖ f, | d,

A-men.

Liebster Jesu, wir sind hier.

LOOK upon us, blessèd Lord,
Take our wandering thoughts and guide us:
We have come to hear Thy word:
With Thy teaching now provide us,
That, from earth's distractions turning,
We Thy message may be learning.

2 For Thy Spirit's radiance bright
We, assembled here, are hoping:
If Thou shouldst withhold the light,
In the dark our souls were groping:
In word, deed, and thought direct us:
Thou, none other, canst correct us.

3 Brightness of the Father's face,
Light of Light, from God proceeding,
Make us ready in this place:
Ear and heart await Thy leading.
In our study, prayers, and praising,
May our souls find their upraising.

TOBIAS CLAUSNITZER, 1619–84;
tr. by ROBERT ALEXANDER STEWART MACALISTER, 1870–

204 ILLUMINATIO. (77. 77. 77.)

Doh = A. *In moderate time.* GEORGE JOB ELVEY, 1816–93.

| m :m | f :m | m :r | d :— | r :l_1 | t_1 :s_1 | d :m | r :— ||

| s_1 :s_1 | s_1 :s_1 | s_1 :f_1 | m_1 :— | fe_1 :fe_1 | s_1 :s_1 | s_1 :s_1 | s_1 :— ||

| d :d | r :d | t_1 :t_1 | d :— | l_1 :r | r :t_1 | d :d | t_1 :— ||

| d :d | t_1 :d | s_1 :s_1 | l_1 :— | r_1 :r_1 | s_1 :f_1 | m_1 :d_1 | s_1 :— ||

| m :m | f :m | m :r | d :— | d :d | r :d | d :t_1 | l_1 :— ||

| s_1 :s_1 | s_1 :s_1 | m_1 :m_1 | m_1 :— | l_1 :l_1 | t_1 :l_1 | se_1 :se_1 | l_1 :— ||

| d :d | r :d | t_1 :t_1 | d :— | m :m | m :m | m :r | d :— ||

| d :d | t_1 :d | se_1 :se_1 | l_1 :— | l_1 :l_1 | se_1 :l_1 | m_1 :m_1 | f_1 :— ||

| l_1 :l_1 | s_1 :s_1 | d :d | t_1 :— | d :s | f :m.r | d :t_1 | d :— || d | d ||

| f_1 :f_1 | f_1 :m_1 | m_1 :fe_1 | s_1 :— | s_1 :ta_1 | l_1 :l_1 | s_1 :s_1 | s_1 :— || l_1 | s_1 ||

| r :r | r :d | d :r | r :— | d :d | d :f | m :r | m :— || f | m ||

| r_1 :d_1 | t_2 :d_1 | l_2 :r_1 | s_1 :f_1 | m_1 :m_1 | f_1 :f_1 | s_1 :s_1 | d_1 :— || f_1 | d_1 ||

A-men.

HOLY Father, Thou hast given
Holy truth from highest heaven ;
Words of counsel wise and pure,
Words of promise bright and sure ;
Light that guides us back to Thee,
Back to peace and purity.

2 Clearer than the sun at noon,
Fairer than the silver moon,
Through the clouds and through the night
Shineth aye this heavenly light ;
Help us, Lord, to lift our eyes,
Take its guidance, and be wise.

3 Here the wisdom from above,
Beaming holiness and love,
Stirring hope, dispelling fear,
Shines to save ; for Christ is here :
Knowing, trusting Him, we come
From our wanderings gladly home.

4 Blessèd Saviour, Light Divine,
Thou hast bid us rise and shine ;
Grant Thy grace, and we shall be
Children of the day in Thee,
Showing all around the road
Back to life, and love, and God.

WILLIAM BRUCE, 1812–82.

Also the following :

196 Come, Holy Ghost, our hearts inspire | 295 Almighty God, Thy word is cast

THE CHURCH

THE COMMUNION OF SAINTS

205 AURELIA. (7 6. 7 6. D.)

Doh = E♭. *In moderate time.* SAMUEL SEBASTIAN WESLEY, 1810–76.

```
:m  |m  :m  |f  :m  |m  :—  |r  :d  |d  :l  |s  :f  |m  :—  |—  ||
:d  |d  :d  |d  :d  |d  :—  |t, :d  |l, :d  |d  :t, |d  :—  |—  ||
:s  |s  :s  |l  :s  |s  :—  |s  :s  |r  :r  |m  :s  |s  :—  |—  ||
:d  |d  :d  |d  :d  |s, :—  |f, :m, |f, :f, |s, :s, |d  :—  |—  ||
```

```
:f  |s  :d' |d' :t  |t  :—  |l  :s  |f  :s  |m  :d  |r  :—  |—  ||
:t, |d  :d  |d  :r  |r  :—  |d  :m  |m  :r  |d  :d  |t, :—  |—  ||
:s  |s  :s  |se :se |se :—  |l  :t  |d' :r' |s  :fe |s  :—  |—  ||
:r  |m  :m  |m  :m, |f, :—  |f, :s, |l, :t, |d  :l, |s, :—  |—  ||
```

```
:r  |m  :f  |s  :l  |l  :—  |s  :d' |d' :-.t  |l  :m  |f  :—  |—  ||
:t, |d  :t, |d  :d  |d  :—  |d  :m  |m  :-.m  |m  :m  |r  :—  |—  ||
:s  |s  :s  |s  :f  |f  :—  |s  :l  |l  :-.se |l  :l  |l  :—  |—  ||
:s, |d  :r  |m  :f  |f  :—  |m  :l, |m  :-.r  |d  :de |r  :—  |—  ||
```

```
:r  |m  :m  |f  :m  |m  :—  |r  :d  |d  :r  |d  :t, |d  :—  |—  || d  |d  ||
:r  |d  :d  |d  :d  |l, :—  |l, :l, |l, :l, |s, :s, |s, :—  |—  || l, |s, ||
:s  |s  :s  |l  :s  |s  :—  |f  :f  |f  :f  |r  :f  |m  :—  |—  || f  |m  ||
:t, |d  :d  |d  :d  |f, :—  |f, :f, |r, :r, |s, :s, |d  :—  |—  || f, |d  ||
```

A-men.

THE Church's one foundation
  Is Jesus Christ her Lord :
She is His new creation
  By water and the word ;
From heaven He came and sought her
  To be His holy bride ;
With His own blood He bought her,
  And for her life He died.

2 Elect from every nation,
  Yet one o'er all the earth,
Her charter of salvation
  One Lord, one faith, one birth :
One holy Name she blesses,
  Partakes one holy food,
And to one hope she presses,
  With every grace endued.

3 Though with a scornful wonder
  Men see her sore oppressed,
By schisms rent asunder,
  By heresies distressed,
Yet saints their watch are keeping,
  Their cry goes up, 'How long ?'
And soon the night of weeping
  Shall be the morn of song.

4 'Mid toil and tribulation,
  And tumult of her war,
She waits the consummation
  Of peace for evermore,
Till with the vision glorious
  Her longing eyes are blest,
And the great Church victorious
  Shall be the Church at rest.

5 Yet she on earth hath union
  With God the Three in One,
And mystic sweet communion
  With those whose rest is won.
O happy ones and holy !
  Lord, give us grace that we,
Like them, the meek and lowly,
  On high may dwell with Thee.

Samuel John Stone, 1839–1900.

206

AUSTRIAN HYMN. (8 7. 8 7. D.)

Doh = F. *Moderately slow.* FRANZ JOSEF HAYDN, 1732–1809.

```
| d  :-.r | m  :r  | f  :m  | r.t, :d  | l     :s  | f  :m  | r   :m.d  | s  :— ||
| d  :-.d | d  :t, | s, :s, | s,   :s, | l,.t, :d  | r  :d  | r   :d    | t, :— ||
| m  :-.f | s  :s  | r  :m  | f.r  :m  | f     :s  | s  :s  | l   :l    | r  :— ||
| d  :-.d | d  :s, | t, :d  | s,   :d  | f     :m  | t, :d  | f,  :fe,  | s, :— ||
```

```
| d  :-.r | m  :r  | f  :m  | r.t, :d  | l     :s  | f  :m  | r   :m.d  | s  :— ||
| d  :-.d | d  :t, | s, :s, | s,   :s, | l,.t, :d  | r  :d  | r   :d    | t, :— ||
| m  :-.f | s  :s  | r  :m  | f.r  :m  | f     :s  | s  :s  | l   :l    | r  :— ||
| d  :-.d | d  :s, | t, :d  | s,   :d  | f     :m  | t, :d  | f,  :fe,  | s, :— ||
```

```
| r  :m  | r.t, :s, | f  :m  | r.t, :s, | s  :f      | m  :-.m  | fe :-.fe | s  :— ||
| s, :s, | s,   :s, | s, :s, | s,   :s, | s, :l,.t,  | d  :-.d  | d  :-.d  | t, :— ||
| t, :d  | t,.r :t, | r  :d  | t,.r :t, | m  :r      | d  :-.d  | r  :-.l  | s  :— ||
| s, :s, | s,   :s, | t, :d  | s,   :s, | m, :f,.s,  | l, :-.l, | r  :-.r  | s, :— ||
```

```
| d' :-.t | l :s | l :-.s | s.f :m | r  :m.f | s.l :f.r  | d  :m.r | d :— || d  | d  ||
| d  :-.d | d :d | d :-.d | r   :d | t, :t,  | d   :d.l, | s, :t,  | d :— || l, | s, ||
| s  :-.s | f :m | f :-.s | s   :s | s  :s   | s.d :l.f  | m  :s.f | m :— || f  | m  ||
| m  :-.m | f :d | f :-.m | t,  :d | s, :f,  | m,  :f,   | s, :s,  | d :— || f, | d  ||
```

A-men.

GLORIOUS things of thee are spoken,
Zion, city of our God;
He whose word cannot be broken
Formed thee for His own abode.
On the Rock of Ages founded,
What can shake thy sure repose?
With salvation's walls surrounded,
Thou mayst smile at all thy foes.

2 See! the streams of living waters,
Springing from eternal love,
Well supply thy sons and daughters,
And all fear of want remove.
Who can faint while such a river
Ever flows their thirst to assuage,—
Grace, which, like the Lord the Giver,
Never fails from age to age?

3 Round each habitation hovering,
See! the cloud and fire appear,
For a glory and a covering,
Showing that the Lord is near.
Blest inhabitants of Zion,
Washed in the Redeemer's blood,
Jesus, whom their souls rely on,
Makes them kings and priests to God.

4 Saviour, if of Zion's city
I, through grace, a member am,
Let the world deride or pity,
I will glory in Thy Name.
Fading is the worldling's pleasure,
All his boasted pomp and show;
Solid joys and lasting treasure
None but Zion's children know.

John Newton, 1725-1807.

207 TANTUM ERGO SACRAMENTUM. (87. 87. 87.)

Doh = E♭. *Unison or in Harmony.* *Slow.* French Melody.

d :r |m :d |m.r :m.f |s :m |s :s |f :f
s, :t, |d :s, |d.r :d.d |t, :d |s, :m |d :r
m :s |s :m |s :-.f |r :m |d' :s |l :s
d :s, |d.r :m.r |d.t, :d.l, |s, :d |m :d |l, :t,

m.r :m.d |r :— |r :m |f :-.m |f.m :r.d |r :s,
d :-.d |t, :— |s, :d |d :-.d |l, :-.l, |t, :s,
s :-.s |s :— |r :s |f :-.s |l.s :f.m |s :r
d :-.m, |s, :— |t, :d |l, :-.d |f, :-.l, |s, :t,

d :d |r :r |m.r :m.f |s :— |s.l :s.f |m :m
l, :d |d :t, |d :-.d |d :t, |d :-.t, |d :d
m :l.s |f :s |s.f :s.l |r :— |s :-.s |s :s
l, :f.m |r :s, |d :-.l, |s, :— |m :-.r |d.r :d.t,

f.s :f.m |r :r |s.l :s.f |m.s :d'.f |m :r.,d |d :— ||d |d ||
d :-.d |d :t, |d :-.r |m.r :d.r |r.d :-.t, |d :— ||l, |s, ||
f :-.s |l :s |s :l.t |d'.s :m.l |s :f |m :— ||f |m ||
l, :-.s, |f, :s,.f, |m, :m.r |d.t, :l,.f, |s, :s, |d :— ||f, |d ||

A - men.

Angularis fundamentum lapis Christus missus est.

CHRIST is made the sure foundation,
Christ the head and corner-stone,
Chosen of the Lord, and precious,
Binding all the Church in one,
Holy Zion's help for ever,
And her confidence alone.

2 To this temple, where we call Thee,
Come, O Lord of hosts, to-day:
With Thy wonted loving-kindness,
Hear Thy servants as they pray,
And Thy fullest benediction
Shed within its walls alway.

3 Here vouchsafe to all Thy servants
What they ask of Thee to gain,
What they gain from Thee for ever
With the blessèd to retain,
And hereafter in Thy glory
Evermore with Thee to reign.

4 Laud and honour to the Father,
Laud and honour to the Son,
Laud and honour to the Spirit,
Ever Three and ever One,
One in might, and One in glory,
While unending ages run.

Latin, 7th or 8th century;
tr. by JOHN MASON NEALE, 1818-66.

208

HELFER MEINER ARMEN SEELE. (7 7. 7 6.)

Doh = F. *In moderate time.* *Heilige Seelenlust*, 1657.

```
| m  :— :r  | d  :— :d  | r  :— :r  | m :— :— || t, :— :d  |
| d  :— :t, | l, :— :d  | d  :— :t, | d :— :— || s, :— :s, |
| s  :— :s  | m  :— :s  | l  :— :s  | s :— :— || m  :— :m  |
| d  :— :s, | l, :— :m, | f, :— :s, | d :— :— || m  :— :d  |

| r  :— :t, | l, :— :l,  | s, :— :— || s :— :l | f :— :s  |
| s, :— :s, | s, :— :fe, | s, :— :— || d :— :m | r :— :r  |
| r  :— :s  | r  :— :r   | t, :— :— || m :— :m | l :— :s  |
| t, :— :d  | r  :— :r,  | s, :— :— || m :— :d | r :— :t, |
```

Slower.

```
| m  :— :f  | r  :— :— | f      :m  | s  :m      | r  :—    | d  :— || d  | d  ||
| r  :d :r  | t, :— :— | d      :d  | d  :d      | d  :t,   | d  :— || l, | s, ||
                         We     be-   seech Thee,  hear       us.
| s  :— :l  | s  :— :— | d      :s  | s  :l      | r  :—    | m  :— || f  | m  ||
| d  :— :f, | s, :— :— | l,.t,  :d  | m, :f,     | s, :—    | d, :— || f, | d, ||
                                                                        A-men.
```

JESUS, with Thy Church abide;
Be her Saviour, Lord, and Guide,
While on earth her faith is tried:
We beseech Thee, hear us.

2 Keep her life and doctrine pure;
Grant her patience to endure,
Trusting in Thy promise sure:
We beseech Thee, hear us.

3 All her fettered powers release;
Bid our strife and envy cease;
Grant the heavenly gift of peace:
We beseech Thee, hear us.

4 May she one in doctrine be,
One in truth and charity,
Winning all to faith in Thee:
We beseech Thee, hear us.

5 May she guide the poor and blind,
Seek the lost until she find,
And the broken-hearted bind:
We beseech Thee, hear us.

6 May her scattered children be
From reproach of evil free,
Blameless witnesses for Thee:
We beseech Thee, hear us.

7 May her lamp of truth be bright;
Bid her bear aloft its light
Through the realms of heathen night:
We beseech Thee, hear us.

8 May she thus all glorious be,
Spotless and from wrinkle free,
Pure and bright, and worthy Thee:
We beseech Thee, hear us.

THOMAS BENSON POLLOCK, 1836–96.

209 RICHMOND. (C.M.)

Adapted from Thomas Haweis, 1734–1820,
by Samuel Webbe, the younger, 1770–1843.

Doh = G. *Moderately slow.*

```
| s, :d :m  | s :— :f      | m :f :r    | d :— :m    | r :s :d    |
| m, :s, :d | r :t, :l,    | s, :l, :f, | m, :— :fe, | s, :— :l,  |
| d :m :s   | s :— :d.r    | m :d :t,   | d :— :d    | r :— :m    |
| d :d :d   | t, :s, :l,.t, | d :f, :s, | d, :— :l,  | t, :— :d   |

| t, :d :l,    | s, :— || r  | m :r :d    | f :m :r        | s :f :m       |
| s, :— :fe,   | s, :— || s, | s, :— :l,  | f, :— :s,.l,   | ta, :— :ta,   |
| r :— :d      | t, :— || t, | d :t, :l,  | r :d :t,       | d :r :m       |
| r :— :r,     | s, :— || f, | m, :— :l,  | r, :— :f,      | m, :r, :d,    |

| l :— :s    | l, :f :m     | m.r:d :t,  | d :— :—   || d  | d  ||
| l, :— :d   | l, :t, :d    | l, :s, :s, | s, :— :—  || l, | s, ||
| d :— :s    | f :— :s      | f :m :r    | m :— :—   || d  | m  ||
| f, :— :m,  | m, :r, :d,   | f, :s, :s, | d, :— :—  || f, | d, ||
                                                          A-men.
```

FAUX-BOURDON VERSION.

Doh = G. Martin Shaw, 1876–

```
| s :m :d    | s, :l, :t,  | d :— :r    | m :— :s    |
| s :m :d    | s, :— :s,   | s, :l, :t, | d :— :s,   |
| s, :d :m   | s :— :f     | m :f :r    | d :— :m    |
| s, :d :m   | s :— :r     | m :f :r    | d :— :d,   |

                                              C.t.
| r :— :m     | s, :— :l,     | t, :— || r  | s :— :m     | (l)m' :— :d' |
| s, :— :s,   | r, :m, :fe,   | s, :— || t, | s, :— :d    | (l)m :— :l   |
| r :s :d     | t, :d :l,     | s, :— || r  | m :r :d     | (f)d' :t :l  |
| t,, :— :d,  | r, :— :r,     | s, :— || s, | m, :— :l,   | (f)d :— :f   |

              f.G.
| f' :m' :r'  | (s')d' :— :d  | l :— :s     | s.f:m :r    | m :— :—   ||
| l :— :t     | (d')f :— :d   | f :t, :d    | l, :d :s,   | s, :— :—  ||
| r' :d' :t   | (m')l :— :s   | l, :f :m    | m.r:d :t,   | d :— :—   ||
| r :— :s     | (d)f :— :m,   | r, :— :m,   | f, :s, :s,  | d, :— :—  ||
```

CITY of God, how broad and far
Outspread thy walls sublime!
The true thy chartered freemen are,
Of every age and clime.

2 One holy Church, one army strong,
One steadfast, high intent;
One working band, one harvest-song,
One King omnipotent.

3 How purely hath thy speech come down
From man's primeval youth!
How grandly hath thine empire grown,
Of freedom, love and truth!

4 How gleam thy watch-fires through the night
With never-fainting ray!
How rise thy towers, serene and bright,
To meet the dawning day!

5 In vain the surge's angry shock,
In vain the drifting sands:
Unharmed upon the eternal Rock
The eternal City stands.

SAMUEL JOHNSON, 1822–82.

210 ST. AUDOËN. (S.M.)

Doh=F. *In moderate time.* ROBERT PRESCOTT STEWART, 1825–94.

:m |s :f |m :r |d :— |— :d |r :m |f :l |r :— |— ||
:d |d :d |d :t, |l, :— |— :d |d :d |d :d |t, :— |— ||
:s |s :l |s :f |m :— |— :s |l :s |f :fe |s :— |— ||
:d |m, :f, |s, :se, |l, :— |— :m, |f, :s, |l, :r, |s, :— |— ||

:m |f :m |l :s |s :f |f :m |r :l, |t, :r |d :— |— || d |d ||
:d |d :d |l, :d |r :r |r :d |l, :l, |s, :t, |d :— |— || l, |s, ||
:s |f :s |f :s |l :l |s :s |f :f |r :f |m :— |— || f |m ||
:ta, |l, :d |f :m |r :-.d |t, :d |f, :r, |s, :s, |d :— |— || f, |d ||

A-men.

From Psalm cxxxvii.

I LOVE Thy Kingdom, Lord,
The house of Thine abode,
The Church our blest Redeemer saved
With His own precious blood.

2 I love Thy Church, O God:
Her walls before Thee stand,
Dear as the apple of Thine eye,
And graven on Thy hand.

3 For her my tears shall fall,
For her my prayers ascend,
To her my cares and toils be given,
Till toils and cares shall end.

4 Beyond my highest joy
I prize her heavenly ways,
Her sweet communion, solemn vows,
Her hymns of love and praise.

5 Jesus, Thou Friend Divine,
Our Saviour and our King,
Thy hand from every snare and foe
Shall great deliverance bring.

6 Sure as Thy truth shall last,
To Zion shall be given
The brightest glories earth can yield,
And brighter bliss of heaven.

TIMOTHY DWIGHT, 1752–1817.

211 NUN FREUT EUCH. (87. 87. 887.)

Wittenberg Gesangbuch, 1535.

Doh = G. *Slow.* D.C.

:d |d :m |r :d |r :r |m || d |m :f |s :m |r :— |d ||

:s, |s, :d |t, :d |d :t, |d || s, |s, :d |t, :d |d :t, |d ||

:m |d :s |s :m |l :s |s || m |s :f |r :d |l :s.f |m ||

:d, |m, :d, |s, :l, |f, :s, |d, || d |d :l, |s, :l, |f, :s, |d, ||

:m |f :m |r :d |t, :d |r || m |d :t, |d :s,

:d |d :d |t, :l, |se, :l, |t, || s, |s, :f, |s, :s,

:s |l :s |s :m |m :m |s || s |m :f |m :m.r

:d |l, :d |s, :l, |m, :l, |s, || d |m :r |d :d.t,

d :r |m || d |m :f |s :m |r :— |d || d |d ||

m, :l, |se, || l, |s, :d |d :d |d :t, |d || l, |s, ||

d :l, |t, || l,.t, |d :d |s :-.l |r :s.f |m || f |m ||

l,.s, :f, |m, || f, |d, :l, |m, :-.f, |s, :— |d, || f, |d, ||

A-men.

LAUS SEMPITERNA. (87. 87. 887.)

Doh = E♭. *In moderate time.*

EBENEZER PROUT, 1835–1909.

:s |m :-.m |m :s |d' :-.d' |d' :s |m :f |s :l |m :— |r ||

:s |d :-.d |d :t, |d :-.d |d :r |d :d |d :d |d :— |t, ||

:s |s :-.s |s :f |s :l |s :s |s :l |s :f |m :fe |s ||

:s, |d :-.d |d :r |m :f |m :t, |d :l, |m, :f, |s, :— |s, ||

B♭.t. f.E♭.

:s |m :-.m |m :s |d' :-.d' |(d)f :m |d :m |r :l, |t, :— |(d)s ||

:r |d :-.d |d :r |d :-.d |(m)l, :se, |l, :m, |f, :f, |f, :— |(m)t, ||

:s |s :-.s |s :s |m :l |(l)r :t, |d :t, |l, :r |r :— |(d)s ||

:t, |d :s, |d :t, |l, :m, |(l)r, :m, |l, :s, |f, :r, |s, :— |(d)s, ||

:r | r :r | s :d | f :-.f | m :m | m :m | l :r | s :-.s | f
:t_1 | t_1 :t_1 | d :d | d :t_1 | d :r | de :de | r :r | r :de | r
:s | s :s | s :s | l :s | s :s | l :l | l :l | ta :l | l
:s_1 | s_1 :f_1 | m_1 :m | r :s_1 | d :ta_1 | l_1 :s_1 | f_1 :f | m :l_1 | r

:f | m :r | d :r | t_1 :— | d || d | d ||
:r | d :t_1 | d :l_1 | s_1 :— | s_1 || l_1 | s_1 ||
:s | s :-.f | m :f | r :— | m || f | m ||
:t_1 | d :s_1 | l_1 :f_1 | s_1 :— | d || f_1 | d ||

A-men.

[By permission of the Congregational Union of England and Wales.]

WE come unto our fathers' God ;
Their Rock is our Salvation ;
The eternal arms, their dear abode,
We make our habitation ;
We bring Thee, Lord, the praise they brought ;
We seek Thee as Thy saints have sought
In every generation.

2 The fire divine their steps that led
Still goeth bright before us ;
The heavenly shield around them spread
Is still high holden o'er us ;
The grace those sinners that subdued,
The strength those weaklings that renewed,
Doth vanquish, doth restore us.

3 Their joy unto their Lord we bring ;
Their song to us descendeth ;
The Spirit who in them did sing
To us His music lendeth ;
His song in them, in us, is one ;
We raise it high, we send it on,—
The song that never endeth.

4 Ye saints to come, take up the strain,
The same sweet theme endeavour ;
Unbroken be the golden chain ;
Keep on the song for ever ;
Safe in the same dear dwelling-place,
Rich with the same eternal grace,
Bless the same boundless Giver.

THOMAS HORNBLOWER GILL, 1819–1906.

212 CORMAC. (Anapaestic irr.)

Doh = C. *Unison. In moderate time.* Irish Traditional Melody.

{ :s.s | d' :m'.d' | r' :t | d' :-.t | s :m | f :s.m | d :d | d :— | — ||

{ :m.f | s :l.t | d' :m' | r' :— | t :s.s | l :d'.l | s :m | r :— | — ||

{ :m.f | s :l.t | d' :m' | r' :-.d' | t :s | l :d'.l | l.s :s.m | r :— | — ||

{ :s.s | d' :m'.d' | r' :t | d' :-.t | s :m | f :s.m | d :d | d :— | — ||

d	d	
l,	s,	
f	m	
f,	d	
A - men.

FOR the might of Thine arm we bless Thee, our God, our fathers' God;
Thou hast kept Thy pilgrim people by the strength of Thy staff and rod;
Thou hast called us to the journey which faithless feet ne'er trod;
For the might of Thine arm we bless Thee, our God, our fathers' God.

2 For the love of Christ constraining, that bound their hearts as one;
For the faith in truth and freedom in which their work was done;
For the peace of God's evangel wherewith their feet were shod;
For the might of Thine arm we bless Thee, our God, our fathers' God.

3 We are watchers of a beacon whose light must never die;
We are guardians of an altar that shows Thee ever nigh;
We are children of Thy freemen who sleep beneath the sod;
For the might of Thine arm we bless Thee, our God, our fathers' God.

4 May the shadow of Thy presence around our camp be spread;
Baptize us with the courage Thou gavest to our dead;
O keep us in the pathway their saintly feet have trod;
For the might of Thine arm we bless Thee, our God, our fathers' God.

CHARLES SILVESTER HORNE, 1865–1914.

213 OLDBRIDGE. (8 8. 8 4.)

Doh = G. *In moderate time.* ROBERT NEWTON QUAILE, 1867–

m :m :m |m :— :d |r :— :m |d :— :— |s :s :s
s, :s, :se, |l, :— :s, |l, :— :s, |s, :— :— |d :t, :l,
m :m :r |d :— :d |d :— :t, |m :— :— |m :m :m
d :d :t, |l, :— :m, |f, :— :s, |d :— :— |m :r :d

f :— :r |m :— :d |r :— :— ||t, :d :r |m :— :m
l, :— :s, |s, :— :d |t, :— :— ||s, :l, :t, |d :— :ta,
r :— :s |m :— :fe |s :— :— ||s :s :f |m :— :m
d :— :t, |d :— .t, :l, |s, :— :— ||f, :m, :r, |d, :— :d,

m :— :d |l, :— :s, |d :— :— |r :— :— |d :— :— ||d |d ||
l, :— :l, |r, :— :m, |m, :— :— |s, :— :f, |m, :— :— ||f, |m, ||
d :— :d |d :— :d |l, :— :— |t, :— :— |d :— :— ||l, |s, ||
f, :— :f, |fe, :— :s, |s, :— :— |s, :— :— |d, :— :— ||f, |d, ||

A-men.

FATHER of all, from land and sea
The nations sing, 'Thine, Lord, are we,
Countless in number, but in Thee
May we be one.'

2 O Son of God, whose love so free
For men did make Thee Man to be,
United to our God, in Thee
May we be one.

3 Join high with low, join young with old,
In love that never waxes cold;
Under one Shepherd, in one fold,
Make us all one.

4 O Spirit blest, who from above
Cam'st gently gliding like a dove,
Calm all our strife, give faith and love;
O make us one.

5 So, when the world shall pass away,
We shall awake with joy and say,
'Now in the bliss of endless day
We all are one.'

CHRISTOPHER WORDSWORTH, 1807–85.

214 ST. OSWALD. (8 7. 8 7.)

Doh = D. *With vigour.* JOHN BACCHUS DYKES, 1823–76.

```
s  :-.m | l   :d' | t  :l  | s  :m | d  :d   | r  :m | s  :l   | s  :— ||
m  :-.m | d   :d  | f  :m  | r  :d | d  :l,  | t, :d | r  :r.d | t, :— ||
d' :-.t | l   :s  | f  :l  | r  :s | l  :l.s | f  :s | s  :fe  | s  :— ||
d  :-.d | f   :m  | r  :d  | t, :d | l, :f.m | r  :d | t, :r   | s, :— ||
```

A.t. f.D.

```
s :-.m | [l]r   :f  | m   :r   | [d]s   :s | s  :d' | d' :m | s  :r   | d  :— || d  | d  ||
d :-.d | [m]l,  :l, | se, :m,  | [m]t,  :r | s  :m  | m  :d | d  :t,  | d  :— || l, | s, ||
m :-.s | [d']f  :r  | t,  :t,  | [d]s   :t | d' :s  | l  :s | s  :s.f | m  :— || f  | m  ||
d :-.d | [l]r,  :r, | m,  :se, | [l,]m  :f | m  :d  | l, :d | m, :s,  | d  :— || f, | d  ||
```

A-men.

MARCHING. (8 7. 8 7.)

Doh = A. *With vigour.* MARTIN SHAW, 1876–

```
m,  :f,  | s,  :-.s, | l,  :t,  | d   :t,  | d   :r   | m   :-.r | d   :l,  | s,  :— ||
d,  :d,  | r,  :m,   | f,  :f,  | s,  :s,  | l,  :t,  | d   :se, | l,  :fe, | s,  :— ||
s,  :l,  | t,  :s,   | d   :r   | m   :r   | f   :f   | m   :t,  | m   :r   | t,  :— ||
d,  :l,  | s,  :s,   | f,  :r,  | d,  :s,  | f,  :r,  | l,  :t,  | d   :r   | s,  :— ||
```

```
r   :f   | m   :-.r  | d   :r   | t,  :s,  | s   :-.m | d   :r   | m   :r   | d   :— || d  | d  ||
s,  :s,  | s,  :s,   | l,  :fe, | s,  :s,  | d   :t,  | l,  :d   | d   :t,  | d   :— || l, | s, ||
r   :t,  | d   :r    | m   :r   | r   :t,  | d   :m   | l   :fe  | s   :r   | m   :— || f  | m  ||
t,  :s,  | d   :t,   | l,  :r,  | s,  :s,  | m,  :s,  | l,  :r,  | s,  :s,  | d,  :— || f, | d, ||
```

A-men.

[*Copyright*, 1915, *by J. Curwen & Sons, Ltd.*]

Igjennem Nat og Trængsel.

THROUGH the night of doubt and sorrow
Onward goes the pilgrim band,
Singing songs of expectation,
Marching to the promised land.

2 Clear before us, through the darkness,
Gleams and burns the guiding light;
Brother clasps the hand of brother,
Stepping fearless through the night;

3 One the light of God's own presence,
O'er His ransomed people shed,
Chasing far the gloom and terror,
Brightening all the path we tread;

Unison.

4 One the object of our journey,
One the faith which never tires,
One the earnest looking forward,
One the hope our God inspires;

5 One the strain that lips of thousands
Lift as from the heart of one;
One the conflict, one the peril,
One the march in God begun;

Harmony.

6 One the gladness of rejoicing
On the far eternal shore,
Where the one Almighty Father
Reigns in love for evermore.

BERNHARDT SEVERIN INGEMANN, 1789–1862;
tr. by SABINE BARING-GOULD, 1834–1924.

[May be sung to YN Y GLYN, No. 529.]

215 THORNBURY. (7 6. 7 6. D.)

Doh = D. *Slow.*

vv. 1, 2, 4 in *Unison.* v. 3 in *Harmony.* BASIL HARWOOD, 1859–

:s |m :t, |d :l |d :— |t, :r |s :l |f.m :r |m :— |— ||s |m :t,
:d |d :t, |s, :d |s, :l, |t, :t, |d :d |d :r |r :t, |d ||d |d :t,
:m |s :f |s :l |s :fe |s :s |s :f |l :t |s :— |— ||m |s :se
:d |d :r |m :f |m :r |s :f |m :f |r :s |d :— |— ||d |d :m

A.t.

|d :l |d :— |t, :r |s :l |f.m :r |d :— |— ||[m]l, |l,.t, :d |t, :l,
|l, :d |s, :l, |t, :t, |d :d |d :t, |d :— |— ||[d]f, |m, :l, |f, :r,
|l :l |s :fe |s :s |s :f |l :f |f :r |m ||[s]d |d :m |r :l,.t,
|l :f |m :r |s :f |m :f |r :s, |d :— |— ||[d]f, |l, :d, |r, :f,

f.D.

|l, :se, |l, :t, |d.r :m |l, :se, |l, :— |— ||[d]s |s :l.t |d' :m |f :s
|m, :— |m, :m, |m, :l, |f, :m,.r, |d, :f, |m, ||[s,]r |s :f |m :d |d :m
|d :t, |d :t, |l, :m |m.r :d.t, |d :r |d ||[m]t |d' :s |s :d' |d' :—
|m, :— |l, :se, |l, :d, |r, :m, |l, :— |— ||[ta,]f |m :r |d :t |l :s

one Faith, one Lord.*

|l :s |d' :— |— :s |d :— |l :— |s :— |— :— |— : | ||f |m
|r :s |d' :— |— :s |d :— |l :— |s :d |f :m.r |m : | ||d |d
one Faith, one Lord, one Faith, one Lord. A- men.
|d' :t |d' :— |— :s |d :— |l :— |s :d' |l :t |d' : | ||l |s
|fe :s |d' :— |— :s |d :— |l :— |s :m |r :s |d : | ||f, |d
one Faith, one

THY hand, O God, has guided
Thy flock, from age to age;
The wondrous tale is written,
Full clear, on every page;
Our fathers owned Thy goodness,
And we their deeds record;
And both of this bear witness,
One Church, one Faith, one Lord.

2 Thy heralds brought glad tidings
To greatest, as to least;
They bade men rise, and hasten
To share the great King's feast;
And this was all their teaching,
In every deed and word,
To all alike proclaiming
One Church, one Faith, one Lord.

3 Through many a day of darkness,
Through many a scene of strife,
The faithful few fought bravely
To guard the nation's life.
Their Gospel of redemption,
Sin pardoned, man restored,
Was all in this enfolded,
One Church, one Faith, one Lord.

4 Thy mercy will not fail us,
Nor leave Thy work undone;
With Thy right hand to help us,
The victory shall be won;
And then, by men and angels,
Thy Name shall be adored,
And this shall be their anthem,
One Church, one Faith one Lord.

EDWARD HAYES PLUMPTRE, 1821–91.

*vv. 1, 2, & 4 end thus:— |s :— |— :— |— :— |— ||
Lord.

216 CLOISTERS. (11 11. 11 5.)

Doh = E♭. *In moderate time.* JOSEPH BARNBY, 1838–96.

```
| m  :m  :m  | m  :—  :m  | s .f  :m  :r  | r  :m  :—  || m  :m  :m  |
| d  :d  :d  | d  :—  :d  | d .d  :d  :t, | t, :d  :—  || r  :r  :r  |
| s  :s  :s  | l  :—  :l  | ta.l  :s  :f  | f  :m  :—  || se :se :se |
| d  :d  :d  | l, :—  :l, | m,.f, :s, :s, | d  :d  :—  || t, :t, :t, |

            Bb.t.                          f.Eb.
| m  :—  :^d'f | m   :-.r   :d .t,     | t,  :^ds :— || s  :s  :s  | l  :—  :l  |
| d  :—  :^ml, | se, :-.se, :se,.se,   | se, :^lm :— || m  :m  :m  | m  :r  :r  |
| l  :—  :^lr  | r   :t,    :m .r      | r   :^ds :— || ta :ta :ta | l  :—  :l  |
| l, :—  :^lr, | m,  :-.m,  :m, .m,    | l,  :^lm :— || d  :d  :d  | f, :—  :f  |

| t :-.t:l .t  | t  :d' :—  || d' :l  :f  | r  :—  :—  | d :— :— || d  | d  ||
| r :-.r:r .r  | r  :d  :—  || d  :d  :d  | d  :t, :—  | d :— :— || l, | s, ||
| l :se  :ba.se| se :l  :—  || l  :f  :l  | s  :—  :f  | m :— :— || f  | m  ||
| m :-.m:m .m  | l, :l, :—  || f, :f, :f, | s, :—  :—  | d :— :— || f, | d  ||
                                                                  A - men.
```

HERZLIEBSTER JESU. (11 11. 11 5.)

JOHANN CRÜGER, 1598–1662.
Arranged by JOHANN SEBASTIAN BACH, 1685–1750.

Lah = G. Doh = B♭. *Unison or in Harmony.* *Very slow and solemn.*

```
| :l, | l,     :l,    | se, :m,  | l,  :t,  | d      :d  | r   :d  | t,  || t,  |
| :m, | f,     :d,.r, | m,  :t,, | m,  :m,  | m,     :m, | m,  :—  | m,  || se, |
| :d  | r      :l,    | t,  :se, | l,  :se, | l,.t,  :d  | t,  :l, | se, || m   |
| :l, | r,.m,  :f,    | m,  :r,  | d,  :m,  | l,,    :l, | se, :l, | m,  || m,  |

                                                             F.t.                f.Bb.
| d  :r  | m.r :d   | f  :f  | m.r  :m     | r   :—     | d  || ^df  | m   :r   | d  :^lm,.f, |
| l, :t, | d   :s,  | f, :s, | s,   :d .t, | l,  :s,.f, | m, || ^ml, | t,  :se, | l, :^mt,,   |
| m  :f  | s.f :m.r | d  :r  | d    :d     | d   :t,    | s, || ^lr  | m   :m   | m  :^ds,    |
| l, :r  | d   :ta, | l, :t, | d.t, :l,.s, | f,  :s,    | d, || ^lr  | se, :m,  | l, :- .^sr, |
```

```
| s,     :s,     | l,  :s,   | f,     :—     | m,  || m,  | r      :d      | t,     :—    | l,  :— | — || l,  | l,  ||
| m,.f,  :s,.m,  | f,  :m,   | m,     :r,.d, | t,, || d,  | f,     :m,     | m,     :-.r, | d,  :— | — || r,  | de, ||
| d      :d      | d   :d.t, | l,     :—     | se, || l,  | l,.se, :l,     | l,     :se,  | l,  :— | — || f,  | m,  ||
| d,.r,  :m,.d,  | f,  :d,   | r,     :—     | m,  || l,, | t,,    :d,.r,  | m,     :—    | l,, :— | — || r,  | l,, ||
```

A-men.

ALTERNATIVE VERSION.

Harmonized by JOHANN SEBASTIAN BACH, 1685–1750, in *The Passion according to St. Matthew.*

Lah = G. Doh = B♭.

```
:l,  | l,  :l,  | se, :m,  | l,  :t,  | d    :d  | r   :d  | t,  || t,
:s,  | f,  :fe, | m,  :t,, | l,, :m,  | m,   :l, | t,  :l, | se, || m,
:m   | r   :d   | t,  :se, | r   :r   | d.r  :m  | f   :m  | m   || se,
:de, | r,  :re, | m,  :m,  | ba, :se, | l,   :l, | se, :l, | m,  || m,

d  :r  | m.r  :d      | f      :f      | m.r  :m      | r      :—  | d  || d  | t,      :l, | s,.f, :m,.f,
m, :s, | s,   :l,.s,  | f,.s,  :l,     | l,   :l,     | r,.m,  :f, | m, || l, | r,      :d, | r,    :d,.r,
l, :t, | d.t, :l,     | l,     :r      | d.t, :d      | d      :t, | s, || m, | ba,.se, :l, | r,    :s,
l, :s, | d,   :f,.m,  | r,.m,  :f,.s,  | l,   :s,.fe, | s,     :—  | d, || d, | r, .m,  :f, | t,,   :d,

| s,    :s,    | l,    :s,     | f,     :—  | m,  || m   | r      :d     | t,      :—    | l,  :— | — || l, | l,  ||
| m,    :m,    | f,    :m,     | m,.de, :r, | de, || l,  | l,.se, :l,    | l,.ba,  :se,  | m,  :— | — || f, | m,  ||
| d     :d     | d.r   :m      | l,     :—  | l,  || d   | t,     :m,    | m       :-.r  | de  :— | — || r  | de  ||
| d.ta, :l,.s, | f,.m, :r,.de, | r,     :—  | l,, || l,, | t,,    :d,.r, | m,      :—    | l,, :— | — || r, | l,, ||
```

A-men.

Christe, du Beistand deiner Kreuzgemeine.

LORD of our life, and God of our salvation,
Star of our night, and Hope of every nation,
Hear and receive Thy Church's supplication,
Lord God Almighty.

2 See round Thine ark the hungry billows curling;
See how Thy foes their banners are unfurling;
Lord, while their darts envenomed they are hurling,
Thou canst preserve us.

3 Lord, Thou canst help when earthly armour faileth;
Lord, Thou canst save when deadly sin assaileth;
Lord, o'er Thy rock nor death nor hell prevaileth;
Grant us Thy peace, Lord.

4 Grant us Thy help till foes are backward driven;
Grant them Thy truth that they may be forgiven;
Grant peace on earth, and, after we have striven,
Peace in Thy heaven.

PHILIP PUSEY, 1799–1855; based on MATTHÄUS APELLES VON LÖWENSTERN, 1594–1648.

217

PSALM 36 (68). (887. 887. D.)

Doh = E♭. *In moderate time, very dignified.*

v. 2 in *Unison*. MATTHÄUS GREITER, *c.* 1500–52.

```
|d  :—  |d  :r  |m  :d    |m  :f     |s  :—  |s  :—  |f  :m  |r  :d    |m  :f
|s, :—  |l, :t, |d  :s,   |d  :l,.t, |d  :—  |t, :—  |d  :d  |t, :d    |d  :r.d
|m  :—  |m  :s  |s  :m    |l  :f     |m  :—  |r  :—  |f  :s  |s  :m    |l  :l
|d  :—  |l, :s, |d  :d.t, |l, :r     |d  :—  |s, :—  |l, :d  |s, :d.t, |l, :r
```

D.C.

```
|s  :—  |l  :—  |s  :f     |m  :d  |r  :—  |d  :—  |—  :—  ||d' :—  |d'  :d'
|t, :—  |r  :—  |t, :r     |d  :d  |d  :t, |d  :—  |—  :—  ||m  :—  |m   :m
|s  :—  |f  :—  |m  :l     |l  :s  |s  :f  |m  :—  |—  :—  ||s  :—  |s   :s.l
|s, :—  |r, :—  |m, :f,.s, |l, :m, |s, :—  |d  :—  |—  :—  ||d  :—  |m.r :m.f
```

```
|t  :s  |l  :l  |s  :—  |d' :—   |d' :d' |t  :s   |l  :l  |s  :—  |m  :—
|r  :s  |s  :f  |m  :—  |m  :—   |r  :r  |r  :m   |m  :re |m  :—  |m  :—
|t  :d' |d' :d' |d' :—  |d' :-.t |l  :fe |s  :t   |l  :t  |t  :—  |d' :-.t
|s  :m  |f  :f  |d  :—  |l  :-.s |fe :r  |s  :m.r |d  :t, |m  :—  |d  :—
```

```
|f  :l  |s  :m  |f  :—  |m  :—  |—  :—  ||r  :—  |m  :f  |s  :f  |m  :m   |r  :—
|d  :f  |m  :d  |r  :d  |t, :—  |—  :—  ||t, :—  |d  :d  |r  :r  |r  :de  |r  :—
|l  :t  |d' :l  |l  :—  |se :—  |—  :—  ||s  :—  |s  :l  |ta :l  |l  :l.s |f  :—
|f  :r  |m  :l, |r  :—  |m  :—  |—  :—  ||s  :—  |d  :l, |s, :r  |l, :l,  |r  :—
```

```
|s  :—  |l  :t  |d' :t  |l  :l   |s  :—  |d  :—  |r  :m  |f  :m  |r  :—   |d  :—  ||d  |d  ||
|t, :—  |r  :r  |d  :r  |m  :r.d |t, :—  |d  :—  |t, :d  |d  :d  |d  :t,  |d  :—  ||l, |s, ||
|s  :—  |f  :s  |s  :s  |s  :fe  |s  :—  |m  :—  |s  :s  |l  :s  |s  :-.f |m  :—  ||f  |m  ||
|m  :—  |r  :s  |m  :r  |d  :r   |s, :—  |l, :—  |s, :d  |f, :d  |s, :—   |d  :—  ||f, |d  ||
                                                                                      A-men.
```

Verzage nicht, du Häuflein klein.

FEAR not, thou faithful Christian flock;
God is thy shelter and thy rock;
Fear not for thy salvation.
Though fierce the foe and dark the night,
The Lord of hosts shall be thy might,
Christ thine illumination.
Arise! Arise! thy foe defy!
Call on the Name of God most high,
With heavenly succour arm you!
'Gainst world and flesh and powers of hell,
Now for His honour quit you well.
Lo! there is nought can harm you.

2 From drear oblivion's shades ye came,
Through idol shrines of earthly shame,
From brutish terror savèd.
Ye, who the chains of tyrants broke,
Ye, who cast off the priestly yoke,
Ye shall not be enslavèd.

Arise! Arise! the foe defy!
Call on the Name of God most high,
That He with might endue you:
And Christ, your everlasting Priest,
In all your conflicts shall assist,
From strength to strength renew you.

Yattendon Hymnal, No. 72, 1899; based on JOHANN MICHAEL ALTENBURG, 1584–1640.

218 ST. KENTIGERN. (88. 84.)

Doh = F. *In moderate time.* EDWARD ARTHUR, 1874–

```
.s :d.r |m :-.s |l :m |s :— |-.t,:d.r |m :d |f :m |r :— |— ||
.s,:d.t,|d :-.r |d :d |t, :— |-.t,:l,.s,|s, :l, |d :d |t, :— |— ||
.m :s.f |m :-.r |m :l |s :— |-.f :m.r |d :m |l :s |s :— |— ||
.d :m.r |d :-.t,|l, :d |m :— |-.s,:l,.t,|d :l, |f, :d |s, :— |— ||

:r |m :f |s :-.m |f :s |l :r |m :— |r :— |d :— |-. ||d |d ||
:t, |d :l, |s, :-.t,|d :d |d :r |r :d |— :t, |d :— |-. ||l, |s, ||
:s |s :f.m |r :-.s |f :m |f :l |s :— |s :-.f |m/d :— |-. ||f |m ||
:s.f |m :r.d |t, :-.s,|l, :d |f :f, |s, :— |s, :— |d, :— |-. ||f, |d, ||
                                                        A-men.
```

[*Copyright*, 1927, *by Edward Arthur.*]

FOR those we love within the veil,
Who once were comrades of our way,
We thank Thee, Lord; for they have won
To cloudless day;

2 And life for them is life indeed,
The splendid goal of earth's strait race;
And where no shadows intervene
They see Thy face.

3 Not as we knew them any more,
Toilworn, and sad with burdened care,—
Erect, clear-eyed, upon their brows
Thy Name they bear.

4 Free from the fret of mortal years,
And knowing now Thy perfect will,
With quickened sense and heightened joy
They serve Thee still.

5 O fuller, sweeter is that life,
And larger, ampler is the air:
Eye cannot see nor heart conceive
The glory there;

6 Nor know to what high purpose Thou
Dost yet employ their ripened powers,
Nor how at Thy behest they touch
This life of ours.

7 There are no tears within their eyes;
With love they keep perpetual tryst;
And praise and work and rest are one,
With Thee, O Christ.

WILLIAM CHARTER PIGGOTT, 1872–

[May be sung to ES IST KEIN TAG, No. 19.]

219

PSALM 84 (JERVAULX ABBEY). (88. 88. 88.) *French Psalter*, 1562.

Adapted by ALEXANDER GALLOWAY, 1847–1926.

Doh = E♭. *Unison or in Harmony.* *In moderate time.*

|d :— |s :f |m :r |d :— |r :— |m :— ||m :— |l :l |s :m
|s, :— |m :d |d :t, |l, :— |t, :— |d :— ||d :— |d :d |r :d
|m :— |s :l |s :s |m :— |s :— |s :— ||s :— |f :m |r :s
|d :— |d :f, |d :s, |l, :— |s, :— |d :— ||d :— |f, :l, |t, :d

s :—	f :—	m :—		s :—	f :m	r :s	f :—	m :—	r :—	
t, :d	r :—	de :—		d :—	r :d	t, :d	d :—	d :—	d :t,	
s :—	l :—	l :—		s :—	l :s	s :s	l :—	s :—	s :—	
m :—	r :—	l, :—		m, :—	r, :m,.f,	s, :m,	f, :—	d :—	s, :—	

|d :— |m :f |s :— |l :— |s :fe |s :— ||d' :— |t :l |s :—
|s, :— |d :r |m :— |m :— |r :-.d |t, :— ||d :— |r :d |r :—
|m :— |l :l |d' :— |d' :— |t :l |s :— ||s :— |s :m |r :—
|d :— |l, :r |d :— |l, :— |t,.d :r |s, :— ||m, :— |s, :l, |t, :—

m :—	f :s	l :—		d :—	m :s	r :f	m :—	r :—	d :—		d	d	
d :ta,	l, :d	d :—		d :—	d :d	t, :r	r :d	— :t,	s, :—		l,	s,	
s :—	f :m	f :—		s :—	l :s	s :l	s :—	— :s	m :—		f	m	
d :—	r :d	f, :—		m, :—	l, :m,	s, :r,	m, :-.f,	s, :—	d :—		f,	d	

A-men.

REST. (88. 88. 88.)

JOHN STAINER, 1840–1901.

Doh = C. *In moderate time.*

G.t.

:m |m :-.r |d :s |s :f |m :s |d' :-.t |[1]r :d |s :f |m ||
:d |t, :-.t, |d :d |d :r |m :m |m :-.m |[m]l, :d |d :t, |t, ||
:s |s :-.s |s :s |l :t |d' :m |l :-.se |[1]r :re |m :r |m ||
:d |f :-.f |m :m |r :s, |d :d |l, :-.t, |[d]f, :fe, |s, :s, |se, ||

f.C.

:r |d :-.d |f :m |l :s |f :m |r :l, |d :-.t, |l, :s, |d s ||
:t, |l, :-.l, |d :t, |l, :l, |t, :de |r :f, |f, :-.f, |f, :f, |m t, ||
:m |m :-.m |l, :t, |d :de |r :s |f :d |r :-.r |d :t, |d s ||
:se, |l, :-.l, |l, :s, |f, :m, |r, :m, |f, :l, |s, :-.s, |s, :s, |d s, ||

:s |m :-.r |d :l |f :m |r :d' |t :l |s :d |m :— |r :— |d :— |— |f |m ||
:s |m :-.r |d :l |f :m |r :r |r :r |r :d |d :— |t, :— |d :— |— |d |d ||
:s |m :-.r |d :l |f :m |r :r |m :fe |s :m |s :— |f :— |m :— |— |l |s ||
:s |m :-.r |d :l |f :m |r :fe, |s, :l, |t, :d |s, :— |s, :— |d :— |— |f, |d ||

A-men.

[*By permission of Novello & Co., Ltd.*]

THE saints of God! their conflict past,
And life's long battle won at last,
No more they need the shield or sword;
They cast them down before their Lord:
O happy saints, for ever blest,
At Jesus' feet how safe your rest!

2 The saints of God! their wanderings done,
No more their weary course they run,
No more they faint, no more they fall,
No foes oppress, no fears appal:
O happy saints, for ever blest,
In that dear home how sweet your rest!

3 The saints of God! life's voyage o'er,
Safe landed on that blissful shore,
No stormy tempests now they dread,
No roaring billows lift their head:
O happy saints, for ever blest
In that calm haven of your rest!

4 O God of saints, to Thee we cry;
O Saviour, plead for us on high;
O Holy Ghost, our Guide and Friend,
Grant us Thy grace till life shall end,
That with all saints our rest may be,
In that bright Paradise with Thee.

WILLIAM DALRYMPLE MACLAGAN, 1826-1910.

220 SINE NOMINE. (10 10. 10 4.)

Doh = G. *In moderate time.*

Vv. 1, 2, 3, and 7, 8. *Unison.* RALPH VAUGHAN WILLIAMS, 1872–

| s :— | :s | m :r | d :— | — :s, | l, :d | r :s, | m :— | — :m |

1. For all the saints who from their la - bours rest, Who
2. Thou wast their Rock, their Fort - ress, and their Might;
3. O may Thy sol - diers, faith - ful, true, and bold,
7. But, lo! there breaks a yet more glo - rious day; The
8. From earth's wide bounds from o - cean's far - thest coast, Through

| r :— | r : | r :— | — :d | t, :— | t, :— | d :r | t, :l, | s, :— | — ||

Thee by faith be - fore the world con - fessed,
Thou, Lord, their Cap - tain in the well - fought fight;
Fight as the saints who no - bly fought of old,
saints tri - um - phant rise in bright ar - ray;
gates of pearl streams in the count - less host,

| : | d :— | d :d | :s, | d :— | d :— | s :— | — :s | f :s | f.m :r.d | r :— | s :— | l |

Thy Name, O Je - sus, be for ev - er blest.
Thou, in the dark - ness drear, their one true Light.
And win, with them, the vic - tor's crown of gold.
The King of Glo - ry pas - ses on His way.
Sing - ing to Fa - ther, Son, and Ho - ly Ghost.
Hal -

| :s.f | s :— | d :— | — :r.m | f :m | r :— | d :— | — :— ||

- le - lu - jah! Hal - le - lu - jah!

| d :— | d :— |
| l, :— | s, :— |

A - men.

| f :— | m :— |
| f, :— | d, :— ||

Vv. 4, 5, & 6. *Harmony.*

:s |m :r |d :— |— :s_1 |l_1 :d |r :s_1
:d |d :t_1 |l_1 :— |— :s_1 |f_1 :s_1 |f_1 :s_1
4. O blest com - mu - - nion, fel - low - ship di -
5. And when the strife is fierce, the war - fare
6. The gol - den even - - ing bright - ens in the
:s |l :f |m :— |— :d |d :d |d :t_1
d_1 :m_1 |f_1 :s_1 |l_1 :— |— :m_1 |f_1 :m_1 |r_1 :s_1

m :— |— :— |r :— |r :d |t_1 :— |t_1 :—
s_1 :— |— :— |s_1 :— |s_1 :l_1 |r_1 :— |s_1 :—
vine! We fee - bly strug - gle,
long, Steals on the ear the
west; Soon, soon to faith - ful
d :— |— :— |r :— |m :fe |s :— |r :—
d_1 :— |— :— |t_1 :— |t_1 :l_1 |s_1 :— |fe_1 :—

|d :-.d
d :r |t_1 :l_1 |s_1 :— |— ‖ s_1 |d :— |d :—
s_1 :s_1 |s_1 :fe_1 |s_1 :— |— ‖ r_1 |s_1 :— |s_1 :f_1
they in glo - ry shine; Yet all are
dis - tant tri- umph song, And hearts are
war - riors com - eth rest; Sweet is the
|d :d
m :r |m :d |t_1 :— |— ‖ t_1 |d :— |d :—
m_1 :t_2 |d_1 :r_1 |s_1 :— |— ‖ f_1 |m_1 :f_1 |m_1 :r_1

s :— |— :s |f :s |f.m :r.d |r :— |s :— |l
m_1 :— |d :— |d :r |d :s_1 |t_1 :— |d :ta_1 |l_1
one in Thee, for all are Thine. } Hal - - -
brave a - gain, and arms are strong. }
calm of Pa - ra - dise the blest. }
d :— |m :— |f :r |s :s |s :— |s :— |f
d_1 :— |d :t_1 |l_1 :t_1 |d :m_1 |s_1 :f_1 |m_1 :— |f_1

Hal - le - lu - jah!
:s.f |s :— |d :— |— :r.m |f :m |r :— |d :— |— :—
:d |d :t_1 |l_1 :— |d :ta_1 |l_1 :s_1 |f_1 :s_1 |m_1 :— |— :—
le - lu - - jah! Hal - - le lu - jah!
:l |s :— |s :f |m :r.d |f :d |d :t_1 |d :— |— :—
:r_1 |m_1 :— |l_1 :— |s_1 :— |f_1 :s_1 |l_1 :s_1 |d_1 :— |— :—

WILLIAM WALSHAM HOW, 1823–97.

221 GRESHAM. (7 6. 8 6. D.)

In moderate time. GEOFFREY TURTON SHAW, 1879-

Doh = F. Vv. 1 and 4 in *Unison*, v. 2 Tenors and Basses, v. 3 Trebles.

:m | r :d | r :m | r :d | — :m | f :s | f :m | r :—

| — :m | r :d | r :m | r :d | l_1 :s_1 | d :r | m :d

| s :— | — :l | s :f | s :l | s :f | — :s | f :m

| r :f | m :— | — :m | r :d | r :m | f :r | m :f

| s :— | — :l | f :m | r :-.d | d :— | — ‖ d d / l_1 s_1 / f m / f_1 d_1 ‖

A-men.

[*Copyright*, 1915, *by J. Curwen & Sons, Ltd.*]

TEN thousand times ten thousand,
In sparkling raiment bright,
The armies of the ransomed saints
Throng up the steeps of light;
'Tis finished, all is finished,
Their fight with death and sin;
Fling open wide the golden gates,
And let the victors in.

2 What rush of hallelujahs
Fills all the earth and sky!
What ringing of a thousand harps
Bespeaks the triumph nigh!
O day for which creation
And all its tribes were made!
O joy, for all its former woes
A thousandfold repaid!

ALFORD. (76. 86. D.)

Doh = A♭. *In moderate time.* JOHN BACCHUS DYKES, 1823–76.

```
:m  |f  :-.f  |d  :r  |m  :d  |— :m  |s  :m  |d  :r  |d  :— |— ||
:s, |f, :-.f, |f, :f, |m, :s, |— :d  |d  :d  |l, :t, |d  :— |— ||
:d  |l, :-.l, |l, :la,|s, :m  |— :d  |m  :s  |m  :f  |m  :— |— ||
:d, |d, :-.d, |d, :d, |d, :d  |— :l, |s, :s, |l, :s, |d  :— |— ||
```

E♭.t. f.A♭.

```
:^m l  |s :-.s  |d' :s |t  :l |s  :f |m  :-.d  |f  :t, |^d s,  :— |— ||
:^s, d |r :-.t, |d  :d |r  :d |m  :r |d  :-.s, |t, :s, |^s, r, :— |— ||
:^m l  |t :-.s  |s  :s |se :l |ta :l |s  :-.m  |r  :f  |^m t,  :— |— ||
:^d f  |f :-.f  |m  :m |f  :f |de :r |s, :-.s, |s, :s, |^d s,  :— |— ||
```

```
:s, |r  :-.r  |d  :r     |m  :m   |— :m  |f  :r  |m  :r.d |r   :—  |—  ||
:s, |f, :-.f, |m, :l,    |l, :se, |— :s, |f, :f, |m, :fe, |fe, :—  |s, ||
:s, |t, :-.t, |d  :l,.t, |d  :t,  |— :de |r  :t, |d  :d   |d   :l, |t, ||
:s, |s, :-.s, |l, :f,    |m, :m,  |— :l, |r, :s, |d, :l,  |r,  :—  |s, ||
```

```
:s, |l, :s, |d :d     |r  :-.m  |f  :r  |d  :-.s, |m  :r  |d      :— |— ||d  |d  ||
:s, |l, :s, |d :m,    |l, :-.s, |f, :l, |s, :-.s, |d  :t, |d      :— |— ||l, |s, ||
:s, |l, :s, |d :d     |l, :-.de |r  :l, |m  :-.f  |s  :f  |m      :— |— ||f  |m  ||
:s, |l, :s, |d :l,.s, |f, :-.m, |r, :f, |s, :-.s, |s, :s, |d d, } :— |— ||f, |d, ||
                                                                        A-men.
```

3 O then what raptured greetings
On Canaan's happy shore,
What knitting severed friendships up,
Where partings are no more!
Then eyes with joy shall sparkle
That brimmed with tears of late;
Orphans no longer fatherless,
Nor widows desolate.

4 Bring near Thy great salvation,
Thou Lamb for sinners slain;
Fill up the roll of Thine elect,
Then take Thy power and reign;
Appear, Desire of nations,—
Thine exiles long for home;
Show in the heaven Thy promised sign;
Thou Prince and Saviour, come.

HENRY ALFORD, 1810–71.

222

ALL SAINTS. (87. 87. 77.)

Doh = C. *Moderately slow, dignified.* *Darmstadt Gesangbuch*, 1698.

```
                                            G.t.
|d'  :s    |l   :l     |s   :- .f |m  :d  |s d   :r .m   |f   :m
|m   :s    |f   :f     |r   :t,   |d  :d  |r s,  :s,     |f,  :s,
|s   :d'   |d'  :r'    |s   :s    |s  :m  |s d   :t, .d  |d   :d
|d   :m    |f   :r .d  |t,  :s,   |d  :d  |t,m,  :s, .d  |l,  :s,

                      f.C.
|r   :r      |d   :— ||f d'  :s   |l   :l     |s   :- .f |m  :d
|l,  :s, .f, |m,  :— ||f,d   :m   |f   :f     |r   :t,   |d  :d
|d   :t,     |d   :— ||d s   :d'  |d'  :r'    |s   :s    |s  :m
|f,  :s,     |d,  :— ||l,m   :d   |f   :r .d  |t,  :s,   |d  :d

G.t.                                                f.C.
|s d   :r .m   |f   :m   |r   :r       |d   :—  ||s r'  :r'    |r'    :d' .r'
|r s,  :s,     |f,  :s,  |l,  :s, .f,  |m,  :—  ||d s   :l     |s     :s
|s d   :t, .d  |d   :d   |d   :t,      |d   :—  ||m t   :r'.d' |t     :d' .t
|t,m,  :s .d   |l,  :s,  |f,  :s,      |d,  :—  ||d s   :fe    |s .f  :m .r

                                                    (pause)
|m'  :r'.d' |r'  :—  |d'  :s   |l .t  :d'  |r'  :r'   |d'  :—  ||d' |d' ||
|s   :s     |s   :—  |m   :s   |f     :m   |l   :s.f  |m   :—  ||f  |m  ||
|d'  :t .d' |t   :—  |d'  :d'  |d'    :d'  |d'  :t    |d'  :—  ||l  |s  ||
|d   :s .m  |s   :—  |l   :m   |f     :l   |f   :s    |d   :—  ||f  |d  ||
                                                              A-men.
```

Wer sind die vor Gottes Throne?

WHO are these, like stars appearing,
These, before God's throne who stand?
Each a golden crown is wearing:
Who are all this glorious band?
Alleluia! hark, they sing,
Praising loud their heavenly King.

2 Who are these, of dazzling brightness,
These in God's own truth arrayed,
Clad in robes of purest whiteness,
Robes whose lustre ne'er shall fade,
Ne'er be touched by time's rude hand—
Whence comes all this glorious band?

3 These are they who have contended
For their Saviour's honour long,
Wrestling on till life was ended,
Following not the sinful throng;
These, who well the fight sustained,
Triumph through the Lamb have gained.

4 These are they whose hearts were riven,
Sore with woe and anguish tried,
Who in prayer full oft have striven
With the God they glorified:
Now, their painful conflict o'er,
God has bid them weep no more.

5 These like priests have watched and waited,
Offering up to Christ their will,
Soul and body consecrated,
Day and night to serve Him still:
Now in God's most holy place,
Blest they stand before His face.

Heinrich Theobald Schenck, 1656–1727; *tr.* by Frances Elizabeth Cox, 1812–97

223 ST. ASAPH. (D.C.M.)

Doh = G. *In moderate time.* GIOVANNI MARIE GIORNOVICHI, 1745-1804.

```
:s,    |d  :d  |r  :r  |m  :s.f   |m  :s  |f  :f  |m     :m   |r  :—  |—  ||
:s,    |l, :d  |d  :t, |d  :d.t,  |d  :d  |d  :r  |d     :d   |t, :—  |—  ||
:m     |m  :s  |l  :s  |s  :m.f   |s  :s  |l  :l  |s     :l   |r  :—  |—  ||
:d     |l, :m, |f, :s, |d  :m.r   |d  :m, |f, :r, |m,    :f,  |s, :—  |—  ||

:s,    |d  :d  |r  :r  |m  :m.f   |s  :s  |f  :f  |m     :r   |d  :—  |—  ||
:s,    |s, :m, |l, :s, |s, :d     |d  :t, |d  :r  |d     :t,  |d  :—  |—  ||
:t,    |d  :d  |d  :t, |d  :d.r   |m  :r  |f  :l  |s     :f   |m  :—  |—  ||
:s,.f, |m, :l, |f, :s, |d  :l,    |m, :s, |l, :r, |m,.f, :s,  |d, :—  |—  ||

:m     |f  :f  |r  :r  |s  :m.f   |s  :s  |l  :s  |f     :m   |r  :—  |—  ||
:d     |d  :d  |t, :t, |d  :d.t,  |d  :d  |d  :de |r     :d   |t, :—  |—  ||
:s     |f  :l  |s  :s  |s  :s.f   |m  :s  |f  :m  |f     :s.l |r  :—  |—  ||
:d     |l, :f, |s, :s, |m  :d.r   |m  :m, |f, :l, |r,    :m,.f, |s, :— |— ||

:s,    |d  :d  |r  :r  |m  :s.f   |m  :s  |f  :f  |m     :r   |d  :—  |—  || d  |d  ||
:s,    |s, :d  |d  :t, |d  :d.t,  |d  :d  |d  :r  |d     :t,  |d  :—  |—  || l, |s, ||
:t,    |d  :m  |l  :s  |s  :m.f   |s  :s  |l  :l  |s     :-.f |m  :—  |—  || f  |m  ||
:s,.f, |m, :l, |f, :s, |d  :m.r   |d  :m, |f, :r, |m,.f, :s,  |d, :—  |—  || f, |d, ||
```

A-men.

GLOUCESTER. (C.M.)

Doh = F. *Moderately slow.* *Ravenscroft's Psalter*, 1621.

```
|d  :— |s  :m |r  :d    |f  :s   |l  :— ||m :— |s  :m |f :s  |m :— ||
|s, :— |s, :d |t, :s,   |d  :-.ta, |l, :— ||d :— |t, :d |r :t, |d :— ||
|m  :— |r  :s |s  :m    |f  :m   |f  :— ||s :— |s  :s |l :s  |s :— ||
|d  :— |t, :d |s, :d.ta, |l, :s,  |f, :— ||d :— |s  :m |r :s, |d :— ||
```

|s :— |m :l |s :m |r :d |r :— ||f :— |m :s |r :r |d :— ||d |d ||

|r :— |s, :l,.t, |d :s, |s, :d |t, :— ||r :— |s, :d |d :t, |d :— ||l, |s, ||

|r :— |m :f |s :d |r :m.fe |s :— ||l :-.t |d' :s |l :s.f |m :— ||f |m ||

|t, :— |d :f, |m, :d |t, :l, |s, :— ||r :— |m :m, |f, :s, |d :— ||f, |d, ||

A-men.

From Rev. vii. 13–17.

HOW bright these glorious spirits shine !
  Whence all their white array ?
How came they to the blissful seats
  Of everlasting day ?
2 Lo ! these are they, from sufferings great
  Who came to realms of light,
And in the blood of Christ have washed
  Those robes which shine so bright.

3 Now, with triumphal palms, they stand
  Before the throne on high,
And serve the God they love, amidst
  The glories of the sky.
4 His presence fills each heart with joy,
  Tunes every mouth to sing :
By day, by night, the sacred courts
  With glad hosannas ring.

5 Hunger and thirst are felt no more,
  Nor suns with scorching ray ;
God is their sun, whose cheering beams
  Diffuse eternal day.
6 The Lamb which dwells amidst the throne
  Shall o'er them still preside,
Feed them with nourishment divine,
  And all their footsteps guide.

7 'Mong pastures green He'll lead his flock,
  Where living streams appear ;
And God the Lord from every eye
  Shall wipe off every tear.

ISAAC WATTS, 1674–1748, and WILLIAM CAMERON (?), 1751–1811,
as in *Scottish Paraphrases*, 1781.

224 O QUANTA QUALIA. (10. 10. 10. 10. Dactylic.)

Doh = G. *In moderate time.* *La Feillée's Mêthode du Plain-chant*, 1808.

d :—	d :r	m :—	d :d	f :—	m :r	r :—	d :—
s, :—	s, :t,	d :—	s, :s,	l, :—	s, :l,	t, :—	d :—
m :—	d :s	s :—	m :m	d :r	m :l	s :f	m :—
d, :—	m, :s,	d :—	m :d	l, :t,	d :f,	s, :—	d :—

s :—	m :d	f :—	m :m	m :r	m :s	fe :—	s :—	
t, :—	t, :d,	l, :t,	d :t,	d :s,	d :t,	r :d	t, :—	
m :—	m :m	r :—	s :m	d :r	s :m	l :—	s :—	
m, :—	s, :l,	r, :—	m, :s,	l, :t,	d :m	r :—	s, :—	

d :—	t, :d	l, :—	s, :s,	d :—	r :m	m :—	r :—
s, :—	s, :s,	f, :m,	r, :r,	s, :—	t, :d	d :—	t, :—
m :—	r :d	d :—	t, :t,	d :s	f :m	s :—	— :—
d :—	s, :m,	f, :—	s, :f,	m, :m	r :d	s, :—	— :—

s :—	d :d	m :r	r :r	m :—	d :r	r :—	d :—		d	d	
s, :—	d :t,	l, :—	t, :t,	d :t,	l, :l,	t, :—	d :—		l,	s,	
d :—	m :m	f :—	r :s	s :—	m :l	s :f	m :—		f	m	
m, :—	l, :s,	f, :—	s, :f,	m, :s,	l, :f,	s, :—	d d, :—		f,	d,	

A-men.

O quanta qualia sunt illa Sabbata.

O WHAT their joy and their glory must be,
Those endless Sabbaths the blessèd ones see!
Crown for the valiant; to weary ones rest;
God shall be all, and in all ever blest.

2 What are the Monarch, His court, and His throne?
What are the peace and the joy that they own?
Tell us, ye blest ones, that in it have share,
If what ye feel ye can fully declare.

3 Truly Jerusalem name we that shore,
'Vision of peace,' that brings joy evermore!
Wish and fulfilment can severed be ne'er,
Nor the thing prayed for come short of the prayer.

4 We, where no trouble distraction can bring,
Safely the anthems of Zion shall sing;
While for Thy grace, Lord, their voices of praise
Thy blessèd people shall evermore raise.

5 Low before Him with our praises we fall,
Of whom, and in whom, and through whom are all;
Of whom, the Father; and through whom, the Son;
In whom, the Spirit, with these ever One.

PIERRE ABELARD, 1079–1142; *tr.* by JOHN MASON NEALE, 1818–66.

225 KENT. (L.M.)

JOHANN FRIEDRICH LAMPE, 1703–51.

Doh = D. *In moderate time.*

:s |m :t, |d :l |s :f |m :m |r :s |fe :s.l |t :l |s
:d |s, :t, |l, :d |d :t, |d :d |r :r |r :t,.d |r :-.d |t,
:m |s :f |m :f |r :s |s :s |s :t |l :s |s :fe |s
:d |d :s, |l, :f, |s, :s, |d :d |t, :s, |r :m |t,.d :r |s,

:s |d' :s |l :s |f :m |r :s |l :r' |t :d' |f.m :r |d || d |d
:t, |d :m |f :d |l,.t, :d |t, :d |d :f |s.f :m |d :t, |d || l, |s,
:s |s :d' |d' :d' |f :s.l |t :s |f :l |r' :d' |l :f |m || f |m
:s |m :d |f :m |r :m.f |s :m |f :r |s, :l, |r :s, |d || f, |d

A-men.

HE wants not friends that hath Thy love,
And may converse and walk with Thee,
And with Thy saints here and above,
With whom for ever I must be.

2 In the communion of the saints
Is wisdom, safety and delight;
And, when my heart declines and faints,
It 's raisèd by their heat and light!

3 As for my friends, they are not lost;
The several vessels of Thy fleet,
Though parted now, by tempests tost,
Shall safely in the haven meet.

4 Still we are centred all in Thee,
Members, though distant, of one Head;
In the same family we be,
By the same faith and spirit led.

5 Before Thy throne we daily meet,
As joint-petitioners to Thee;
In spirit we each other greet,
And shall again each other see.

6 The heavenly hosts, world without end,
Shall be my company above;
And Thou, my best and surest Friend,
Who shall divide me from Thy love?

RICHARD BAXTER, 1615–91.

226

BRAINT. (2. 88. 88. 8.) Welsh Melody.
Lah = D. Doh = F. *Moderately slow.* Harmonized by DAVID EVANS, 1874–
vv. 1 & 3 in *Unison.* v. 2 in *Harmony.*

```
                                                          C.t.
| l, :—  | m  :—  | —  :m  | s  :fe | m  :r  | d  :l, | m  :—  |ᵐl  :—  | t  :r' |
| l, :—  | t, :—  | —  :m  | m  :re | m  :t, | l, :l, | se,:—  |ˡr  :d  | m  :f  |
| d  :—  | m  :—  | —  :s  | t  :l  | s  :s  | m  :d  | t, :—  |ᵐl  :—  | se :l  |
| l, :—  | s, :—  | —  :m, | m  :t, | d  :s, | l, :l, | m, :—  |ᵈf  :l  | m  :r  |

 f.F.
| l  :—  | —  :ˢr  | d  :—  | t, :—  | l, :—  | —  :—  || d  :—  | m  :m  |
| m  :—  | f  :ᵐt, | t, :l, | —  :se,| l, :—  | —  :—  || l, :—  | s, :d  |
| d' :—  | —  :ᵈ's | m  :—  | f  :m  | d  :—  | —  :—  || m  :—  | m  :l  |
| d  :l, | f  :ᵈs, | l, :d, | r, :m, | l, :—  | —  :—  || l, :—  | d  :l, |

| s  :s    | d  :m  | m  :—  | m  :—  | r  :r  | m  :m.r | d  :r.d | t, :—  |
| r  :m.r  | d  :l, | t, :—  | l, :d  | r  :t, | d  :t,  | l, :fe, | s, :—  |
| s  :m    | m  :l  | se :—  | m  :—  | s  :s  | s  :s.f | m  :r   | r  :—  |
| t, :d.t, | l, :d  | m  :—  | d  :l, | t, :s, | d  :s,  | l, :r,  | s, :—  |

| m  :—  | fe :l     | m   :—    | —  :r  | d  :—  | t, :—  | l, :—  || l, | l, ||
| t, :s, | l, :d     | s,  :d    | t, :t, | t, :l, | —  :se,| l, :—  || f, | m, ||
| s  :—  | fe :m.r   | d.r :m.fe | s  :s  | m  :—  | f  :m  | d  :—  || r  | de ||
| m, :m  | r  :l,.t, | d   :l,   | m  :s, | l, :d, | r, :m, | l, :—  || r, | l, ||
                                                                      A-men.
```

Braint, braint, Yw cael cymdeithas gyda'r saint.

O BLEST
Communion with the saints at rest!
O joy excelling this world's best!
All undistressed
In light they dwell!
Close is the bond that binds us here:
'Twill grow more dear
Than tongue can tell.

2 Our Lord,
From out His sacred wounds hath poured
Rich blessings from His bounteous hoard.
He doth afford
Us from above
Refreshing streams our souls to guide
To His full tide
Of boundless love.

3 Delight
Hath dawned on those gone from earth's night:
Death was to them but life and light:
In pastures bright
Serene they rest,
Around the Lamb who once was slain,
Untouched by pain,
For ever blest.

JOHN ROBERTS, 1731–1806; *tr.* by EVELINE MARTHA LEWIS, 1871–

227 FRENCH. (C.M.)

Doh = E♭. *Moderately slow.* *Scottish Psalter*, 1615.

```
| d  :—  | m  :f  | s  :d  | r  :m  | f  :—  || m  :—  | r  :d  | d  :t, | d  :—  ||
| s, :—  | d  :d  | d  :l, | t, :d  | d  :—  || d  :—  | t, :l, | l, :s, | s, :—  ||
| m  :—  | s  :l  | s  :m  | s  :s  | l  :—  || s  :—  | s  :m  | f  :r  | m  :—  ||
| d  :—  | d  :f, | m, :l, | s, :d  | f, :—  || d  :—  | s, :l, | f, :s, | d  :—  ||

| s  :—  | d' :t  | l  :s  | s  :fe | s  :—  || m  :—  | r  :d      | d  :t, | d  :—  || d  | d  ||
| d  :—  | m  :r  | d  :t, | l, :l, | t, :—  || s, :—  | l, :m,.f,  | s, :s, | s, :—  || l, | s, ||
| m  :—  | s  :s  | m  :r  | m  :r  | r  :—  || m  :—  | f  :d      | r  :r  | m  :—  || f  | m  ||
| d  :—  | d  :s, | l, :t, | d  :r  | s, :—  || d  :—  | f, :l,     | s, :s, | d  :—  || f, | d  ||
                                                                                        A-men.
```

FAUX-BOURDON SETTING.

THOMAS RAVENSCROFT, *c.* 1582–1635.

Doh. = E♭. f. A♭. E♭. t.

```
| m  :—  | s  :l  | r  :(m)t,  | d  :r  | m  :—  || (r)s :—  | s  :m  | f  :r  | m  :—  ||
| s, :—  | d  :d  | t, :(s)r,  | f, :f, | s, :—  ||      :(s)d | t, :l, | l, :s, | s, :—  ||
| d  :—  | m  :f  | s  :(d)s,  | l, :t, | d  :—  || (t)m :—  | r  :d  | d  :t, | d  :—  ||
|     :d | d  :l, | t, :(d)s,  | f, :r, | d, :—  || (s)d :—  | s, :l, | f, :s, | d  :—  ||

|     :m | m  :s  | f  :r  | m  :r  | r  :—  ||     :m  | f  :m.f | s  :r  | m  :—  ||
|     :s,| s, :r  | d  :t, | l, :l, | t, :—  ||     :s, | l, :l,  | r, :s, | s, :—  ||
| s  :—  | d' :t  | l  :s  | s  :fe | s  :—  || m  :—   | r  :d   | d  :t, | d  :—  ||
|     :d | d  :s, | l, :t, | d  :r  | s, :—  || d  :—   | f, :l,  | s, :s, | d  :—  ||
```

[*This version may be used in connexion with the other for one or more verses, the people singing the melody as usual.*]

LET saints on earth in concert sing
With those whose work is done;
For all the servants of our King
In earth and heaven are one.

2 One family, we dwell in Him,
One Church, above, beneath;
Though now divided by the stream,
The narrow stream of death.

3 One army of the living God,
To His command we bow;
Part of His host hath crossed the flood,
And part is crossing now.

4 Even now to their eternal home
There pass some spirits blest,
While others to the margin come,
Waiting their call to rest.

5 Jesus, be Thou our constant Guide;
Then, when the word is given,
Bid Jordan's narrow stream divide,
And bring us safe to heaven.

CHARLES WESLEY, 1707–88.

Also the following:

39 Ye holy angels bright | 590–600 *Hymns of the Life Everlasting*

WORSHIP—THE SANCTUARY

228 LASST UNS ERFREUEN. (88. 88. and Hallelujahs.)

Doh = E♭. *With vigour.* *Geistliche Kirchengesäng*, Cologne, 1623.

```
:d    |d .r :m .d :m .f |s  :—  :d  |d .r :m .d :m .f |s  :—  ||
:d    |d .r :m .d :m .f |s  :—  :d  |d .r :m .d :m .f |s  :—  ||
:d    |d .r :m .d :m .f |s  :—  :d  |d .r :m .d :m .f |s  :—  ||
:d    |d .r :m .d :m .f |s  :—  :d  |d .r :m .d :m .f |s  :—  ||

:d'.t  |l    :s   :d'.t   |l    :s   ||d' |d'.s :s .f :m .f
:s .s  |s .f :m   :d .r   |m .r :t,  ||d' |d'.s :s .f :m .f
:d'.d' |d'   :d'  :m .s   |s .fe :s  ||d' |d'.s :s .f :m .f
:m .m  |f    :d   :l,.t,  |d .r :s,  ||d' |d'.s :s .f :m .f

|s  :—  :d' |d'.s :s .f :m .f |s  :—  ||f .m   |r    :d   :f .m
|s  :—  :d' |d'.s :s .f :m .f |s  :—  ||d .d   |d .t, :d  :d .d
|s  :—  :d' |d'.s :s .f :m .f |s  :—  ||l .l   |l .s :s   :l .s
|s  :—  :d' |d'.s :s .f :m .f |s  :—  ||l,.s,  |f,   :m,  :r,.m,

|r    :d   :d'.t  |l    :s   :d'.t |l  :s  :f.m |r  :—  :—  |d  :—  ||d  |d  ||
|d .t, :l, :m .r  |m.r  :t,  :d'.t |l  :s  :f.m |r  :—  :—  |d  :—  ||l, |s, ||
|l .f :m   :m .s  |s.fe :s   :d'.t |l  :s  :f.m |r  :—  :—  |d  :—  ||f  |m  ||
|f,.s, :l, :l,.t, |d.r  :s,  :d'.t |l  :s  :f.m |r  :—  :—  |d  :—  ||f, |d  ||
                                                                      A-men.
```

From Psalm cxvii.

FROM all that dwell below the skies
Let the Creator's praise arise : *Hallelujah!*
Let the Redeemer's Name be sung
Through every land, in every tongue. *Hallelujah!*

2 Eternal are Thy mercies, Lord :
Eternal truth attends Thy word : *Hallelujah!*
Thy praise shall sound from shore to shore
Till suns shall rise and set no more. *Hallelujah!*

ISAAC WATTS, 1674–1748.

229 OLD 100TH. (L.M.)

Doh = G. *Slow and dignified.* *French Psalter*, 1551.

```
|d  :— |d  :t, |l, :s, |d  :— |r  :— |m  :— ||m  :— |m  :m |r  :d
|s, :— |s, :s, |m, :m, |m, :— |s, :— |s, :— ||s, :— |s, :d |t, :d
|m  :— |m  :r  |d  :t, |d  :— |t, :— |d  :— ||d  :— |m  :s |s  :m
|d  :— |d  :s, |l, :m, |l, :— |s, :— |d, :— ||d  :— |d  :d |s, :l,
```

|f :— |m :— |r :— ‖d :— |r :m |r :d |l, :— |t, :— |d :— ‖
|d :— |d :— |t, :— ‖d :— |s, :s, |s, :s, |l, :— |f, :— |s, :— ‖
|l :— |s :— |s :— ‖m :— |r :d |t, :d |d :— |r :— |m :— ‖
|f, :— |d, :— |s, :— ‖l, :— |t, :d |s, :m, |f, :— |r, :— |d, :— ‖

|s :— |m :d |r :f |m :— |r :— |d :— ‖d |d ‖
|s, :— |s, :d |t, :l,.t, |d :— |t, :— |s, :— ‖l, |s, ‖
|r :— |d :m.fe |s :l |s :— |s :f |m :— ‖f |m ‖
|t, :— |d :l, |s, :r, |m, :f, |s, :— |d, :— ‖f, |d, ‖

A - men.

FAUX-BOURDON SETTING.

John Dowland, 1562–1626.

Doh = G.

|m :— |m :r |f :m |m :— |s :— |s :— ‖s :— |s :s |s :m
|s, :— |s, :s, |l,.t, :d |d :— |t, :— |d :— ‖d :— |d :d |t, :l,
|d :— |d :t, |l, :s, |d :— |r :— |m :— ‖m :— |m :m |r :d
|d, :— |d, :s, |r, :m, |l, :— |s, :— |d, :— ‖d :— |d :d |s, :l,

|l :— |s :— |s :— ‖m :— |r :d |t, :s |f :— |r :— |m :— ‖
|d :— |d :— |t, :— ‖s, :— |t, :s, |s, :-.s, |l, :— |s, :— |s, :— ‖
|f :— |m :— |r :— ‖d :— |r :m |r :d |l, :— |t, :— |d :— ‖
|f, :— |d :— |s, :— ‖d, :— |s, :d, |s, :m, |f, :— |s, :— |d, :— ‖

|m :— |d :-.d |s :l |s :— |s :-.f |m :— ‖
|d :— |s, :d |t, :d |d :— |t, :— |d :— ‖
|s :— |m :d |r :f |m :— |r :— |d :— ‖
|d :— |d :l, |s, :f, |d :— |s, :— |d, :— ‖

[*This alternative version may be used for one or more verses, the people singing the melody.*]

From Psalm c.

ALL people that on earth do dwell,
Sing to the Lord with cheerful voice.
Him serve with mirth, His praise forth tell;
Come ye before Him and rejoice.

2 Know that the Lord is God indeed;
Without our aid He did us make;
We are His folk, He doth us feed,
And for His sheep He doth us take.

3 O enter then His gates with praise,
Approach with joy His courts unto;
Praise, laud, and bless His Name always,
For it is seemly so to do.

4 For why the Lord our God is good;
His mercy is for ever sure;
His truth at all times firmly stood,
And shall from age to age endure.

William Kethe, *c.* 1593, as in *Scottish Psalter*, 1650.

230 ANDERNACH. (L.M.)

Andernach Gesangbuch, 1608.

Doh = G. *In moderate time.*

```
|d  :—  |d  :d  |t, :s, |l, :—  |t, :—  |d  :—  ‖m  :—  |r  :—  |f  :—
|s, :—  |d  :s, |s, :s, |s, :f, |m, :r, |d, :—  ‖s, :—  |s, :t, |l, :s,
|m  :—  |s  :m  |r  :d  |d  :—  |s  :f  |m  :—  ‖d  :—  |r  :—  |d  :r
|d  :—  |m  :d  |s, :m, |f, :—  |s, :—  |l, :—  ‖d  :—  |t, :s, |l, :t,
```

```
|m  :r  |d  :r  |m  :—  |—  ‖d  |r  :d  |r  :m  |d  :r  |d  :—  ‖
|s, :t, |d  :s, |s, :—  |—  ‖d  |l, :l, |t, :d  |l, :l, |l, :—  ‖
|m  :s  |s  :t, |d  :—  |—  ‖m  |f  :m  |s  :s  |f  :f  |m  :—  ‖
|d  :s, |m, :s, |d  :—  |—  ‖l, |r, :l, |s, :m, |f, :r, |l, :—  ‖
```

```
|m  :—  |s  :—  |—  :f  |m  :d  |m  :—  |r  :—  |d  :—  ‖d  |d
|s, :—  |s, :t, |d  :r  |d  :l, |d  :—  |—  :t, |d  :—  ‖l, |s,
|d  :—  |r  :s  |m  :l  |s  :f  |m  :s  |—  :s.f|m  :—  ‖f  |m
|d  :—  |t, :s, |l, :r, |m, :f, |s, :—  |s, :—  |d  :—  ‖f, |d,
                                                          A-men.
```

From Psalm c.

BEFORE Jehovah's awful throne,
Ye nations, bow with sacred joy;
Know that the Lord is God alone;
He can create, and He destroy.

2 His sovereign power, without our aid,
Made us of clay, and formed us men;
And, when like wandering sheep we strayed,
He brought us to His fold again.

3 We are His people, we His care,—
Our souls and all our mortal frame:
What lasting honours shall we rear,
Almighty Maker, to Thy Name?

4 We'll crowd Thy gates with thankful songs,
High as the heavens our voices raise;
And earth, with her ten thousand tongues,
Shall fill Thy courts with sounding praise.

5 Wide as the world is Thy command,
Vast as eternity Thy love;
Firm as a rock Thy truth must stand,
When rolling years shall cease to move.

ISAAC WATTS, 1674–1748, and JOHN WESLEY, 1703–91.

231 GLORIA IN EXCELSIS. (87. 87. 66. 667.)

JAMES WILLIAM ELLIOTT, 1833–1915.

Doh = E. *Moderately fast.* vv. 1 & 4 in *Unison.* vv. 2 & 3 in *Harmony.*

10 measures Instrumental.

```
:d |m  :r  |d  :m  |s  :-.l  |s  :r  |m  :r  |d  :m  |s  :-.l |s  ‖
:d |d  :t, |d  :d  |t, :-.t, |t, :t, |d  :t, |d  :d  |r  :d   |r  ‖
:m |s  :f  |m  :d  |r  :-.r  |r  :s  |s  :s  |s  :s  |s  :—   |s  ‖
:d |d  :d  |d  :l, |s, :-.s, |s, :s, |d  :f  |m  :d  |t, :l,  |t, ‖
```

```
:r  |m  :m  |f  :s.l |s  :r  |m  :d  |m  :fe |s  :l .t  |l  :—  |s
:t, |d  :d  |r  :r   |r  :t, |d  :d  |d  :r  |r  :d .t, |d  :—  |t,
:s  |s  :l  |l  :f   |r  :s  |s  :m  |s  :l  |r  :fe.s  |s  :fe |s
:s, |d  :l, |r  :d   |t, :s, |d  :d  |d  :d  |t, :l,.s, |r  :—  |s,
```

```
f.A.                                d.f.G.
:(s)r  |f  :-.r  |l, :t, |d  :— |— :(d)r  |f  :-.r  |l, :t, |d  :— |—
:(s)r, |f, :-.r, |l, :f, |m, :— |— :(d)r, |f, :-.r, |l, :f, |m, :— |—
:(s)r  |f  :-.r  |l, :r  |d  :— |— :(d)r  |f  :-.r  |l, :r  |d  :— |—
:(s)r  |f  :-.r  |l, :s, |d, :— |— :(d)r  |f  :-.r  |l, :s, |d, :— |—
```

```
                                                         E.t.m.l.
:m  |r   :m   |l, ... 
```

```
:m  |r   :m   |d  :m  |t,  :—    |—   :m   |r   :m   |d  :l, |(m)s   :— |— :s
:s, |se, :se, |l, :l, |t,  :-.l, |se, :se, |t,  :se, |l, :l, |(se)t, :— |— :t,
                                                                       For
:m  |m   :m   |m  :m  |se  :-.ba |m   :m   |m   :m   |m  :m  |(m)s   :— |— :s
:d  |t,  :m,  |l, :d  |m   :—    |—   :m,  |se, :m,  |l, :d  |(m)s   :— |— :f
```

```
d' :-.t |l  :s  |s  :f  |s  :l  |r  :—  |—  :—  |d  :— |— ||f  |m
d  :—   |—  :d  |d  :f  |m  :r  |d  :t, |l, :t, |d  :— |— ||d  |d
ev  -    -   er  and     for     ev  -    -   -   er!        A- men.
s  :—   |f  :s  |l  :—  |s  :f  |r  :—  |f  :—  |m  :— |— ||l  |s
m  :—   |f  :m  |r  :—  |f, :f, |s, :—  |—  :—  |d  :— |— ||f, |d
```

[*By permission of Novello & Co., Ltd.*]

ALL lands and peoples, all the earth,
Put off the night of sadness;
Make cheer and music and high mirth,
And praise the Lord with gladness!
Serve Him with joyful heart,
All kingdoms do their part,
And let immortal song
Before His presence throng,
For ever and for ever!

2 O surely He is God alone,
The earth is mute before Him:
And He is ours, and we His own,
His people who adore Him.
We are His flock; our feet
Walk in His pastures sweet;
And, by cool brooks, the sleep
Is soft He gives His sheep,
For ever and for ever!

3 O enter then His temple courts
With trumpet-tongued thanksgiving:
Praise Him in dances and in sports,
Our Lord, the ever-living!
With incense to the skies
Our thankfulness arise;
His glory wide proclaim,
Speak good of His great Name,
For ever and for ever!

4 For gracious is the Lord our God:
He hears our dull complaining;
His mercy has a sure abode
And everlasting reigning;
And times and times roll by,
And nations fade and die;
But God's majestic truth
Leads on an eager youth,
For ever and for ever.

STOPFORD AUGUSTUS BROOKE, 1832–1916.

[May be sung to EIN' FESTE BURG, No. 526.]

232 MOREDUN. (12 10. 12 10.)

Doh = G. *In moderate time.* HENRY SMART, 1813–79.

```
| m  :s  :r  | m  :f  :s  | l   :s  :f  | m  :-.r :d  | s  :f  :m  |
| d  :d  :t, | d  :d  :d  | d   :t, :t, | d  :-.t,:d  | d  :t, :d  |
| s  :s  :s  | s  :l  :s  | f.m :r  :s  | s  :-.f :m  | m  :f  :s  |
| d  :m, :s, | d  :l, :m, | f,  :s, :s, | d  :-.s,:d  | m  :r  :d  |

| r  :t, :m  | d     :l, :r   | t, :— :— || r  :r  :s  | m :d  :m  | l  :s  :fe  |
| s, :s, :t, | l,.s, :s, :fe, | s, :— :— || t, :t, :r  | d :s, :s, | d  :t, :l,  |
| s  :r  :s  | m     :r  :r   | r  :— :— || s  :s  :s  | s :m  :m  | m  :r  :r   |
| t, :s, :m, | l,    :r  :r,  | s, :— :— || s, :s, :t, | d :m  :d  | l, :r  :-.d |

| s  :-.r :m  | f  :d  :r  | m   :t,  :d  | r  :t, :-.t, | d  :— :— || d  | d  ||
| r  :-.r :t, | d  :d  :l, | se, :se, :l, | l, :s, :-.f, | m, :— :— || f, | m, ||
| r  :-.s :s  | d  :f  :f  | t,  :m   :m  | f  :r  :-.r  | d  :— :— || l, | s, ||
| t, :-.t,:s, | l, :l, :f, | m,  :m,  :l, | r, :s, :-.s, | d, :— :— || f, | d, ||
                                                                          A-men.
```

WORSHIP the Lord in the beauty of holiness;
Bow down before Him, His glory proclaim;
Gold of obedience and incense of lowliness
Bring, and adore Him; the Lord is His Name!

2 Low at His feet lay thy burden of carefulness;
High on His heart He will bear it for thee,
Comfort thy sorrows, and answer thy prayerfulness,
Guiding thy steps as may best for thee be.

3 Fear not to enter His courts, in the slenderness
Of the poor wealth thou canst reckon as thine;
Truth in its beauty and love in its tenderness,
These are the offerings to lay on His shrine.

4 These, though we bring them in trembling and fearfulness,
He will accept for the Name that is dear,
Mornings of joy give for evenings of tearfulness,
Trust for our trembling, and hope for our fear.

5 Worship the Lord in the beauty of holiness;
Bow down before Him, His glory proclaim;
Gold of obedience and incense of lowliness
Bring, and adore Him; the Lord is His Name!

JOHN SAMUEL BEWLEY MONSELL, 1811–75.

233 KERRY. (S.M.)

Doh = E♭. *With vigour.* JOSEPH JOWETT, 1784–1856.

```
:d  | s  :—  :d  | r  :m  :f  | f  :m  :s  | d' :—  :m
:s, | s, :t, :d  | d  :—  :t, | d  :—  :d  | m  :—  :d
:m  | m  :f  :s  | l  :s  :s  | s  :—  :m  | s  :—  :s
:d  | d  :r  :m  | f  :s  :s, | d  :—  :d  | d  :—  :ta,

| f  :s  :l  | m  :r  || m | l  :—  :de | r  :m  :f   | s  :—  :t,
| d  :—  :d  | d  :t, || d | de :—  :l, | l, :de :r.d | t, :—  :s,
| f  :m  :r  | s  :—  || s | l  :—  :l  | l  :—  :l   | s  :—  :s
| l, :s, :f, | s, :—  || d | l, :l  :s  | f  :m  :r   | s, :s  :f

| d  :r  :m  | r .,m:f :m  | m .r :d :t, | d  :—  || d  | d  ||
| s, :t, :d  | s,  :t, :d  | l,  :s, :s, | s, :—  || l, | s, ||
| s  :—  :s  | s   :—  :s  | f   :m  :r  | m  :—  || f  | m  ||
| m  :r  :d  | t,  :s, :d  | f,  :s, :s, | d  :—  || f, | d  ||
                                                     A - men.
```

STAND up, and bless the Lord,
Ye people of His choice:
Stand up, and bless the Lord your God
With heart and soul and voice.

2 Though high above all praise,
Above all blessing high,
Who would not fear His holy Name,
And laud and magnify?

3 O for the living flame
From His own altar brought,
To touch our lips, our minds inspire,
And wing to heaven our thought!

4 God is our strength and song,
And His salvation ours;
Then be His love in Christ proclaimed
With all our ransomed powers.

5 Stand up, and bless the Lord;
The Lord your God adore;
Stand up, and bless His glorious Name
Henceforth for evermore.

JAMES MONTGOMERY, 1771–1854.

[May be sung to NARENZA, No. 546.]

234

GOTT IST GEGENWÄRTIG (ARNSBERG). (668. 668. 33. 66.)

Doh = G. *In moderate time.* JOACHIM NEANDER, 1650–80.

```
|m  :m  |m    :m    |r     :—    |r  :—   |d  :d  |d    :d    |t,  :—
|d  :d  |d    :d    |d     :t,.l,|t, :—   |l, :l, |l,   :l,   |l,  :se,.ba,
|s  :s  |s    :s    |s     :—    |s  :—   |m  :m  |m    :m    |m   :—
|d  :d  |d.r  :m.d  |s,    :—    |s, :—   |l, :l, |l,.t,:d.l, |m,  :—

|t,  :—  |l,    :l,    |s,     :d     |r  :m    |r  :—  |d  :—  |— :—  ||
|se, :—  |l,    :f,    |m,.f,  :s,.l, |t, :d    |d  :t, |d  :—  |— :—  ||
|m   :—  |d     :d     |d      :m     |s  :s    |s  :—  |m  :—  |— :—  ||
|m,  :—  |f,.s, :l,.f, |d      :-.l,  |s, :m,.f,|s, :—  |d, :—  |— :—  ||

|m  :m  |m    :m    |r     :—    |r  :—   |d  :d  |d    :d    |t,  :—
|d  :d  |d    :d    |d     :t,.l,|t, :—   |l, :l, |l,   :l,   |l,  :se,.ba,
|s  :s  |s    :s    |s     :—    |s  :—   |m  :m  |m    :m    |m   :—
|d  :d  |d.r  :m.d  |s,    :—    |s, :—   |l, :l, |l,.t,:d.l, |m,  :—

|t,  :—  |l,    :l,    |s,     :d     |r  :m    |r  :—  |d  :—  |— :—  ||
|se, :—  |l,    :f,    |m,.f,  :s,.l, |t, :d    |d  :t, |d  :—  |— :—  ||
|m   :—  |d     :d     |d      :m     |s  :s    |s  :—  |m  :—  |— :—  ||
|m,  :—  |f,.s, :l,.f, |d      :-.l,  |s, :m,.f,|s, :—  |d, :—  |— :—  ||

|m  :-.m |f  :—  |r  :-.r  |m  :—  |s  :s    |f  :m
|d  :-.d |d  :—  |t, :-.t, |d  :—  |d  :-.t, |l, :d
|s  :-.s |l  :—  |s  :-.s  |s  :—  |s  :m    |f  :s
|d  :-.d |f, :—  |s, :-.s, |d, :—  |m, :d,   |r, :m,

|r   :—  |m  :—  |s   :s    |f    :m   |r   :—    |d  :—  ||d  |d  ||
|d   :t, |d  :—  |s,  :m.r  |d.t, :d   |d   :t,   |d  :—  ||l, |s, ||
|l   :s  |s  :—  |r   :m    |f    :s   |l   :s.f  |m  :—  ||f  |m  ||
|f,  :s, |d  :—  |t,  :d.t, |l,   :s,  |f,  :s,   |d, :—  ||f, |d, ||
                                                              A-men.
```

Gott ist gegenwärtig.

GOD reveals His presence :
Let us now adore Him,
And with awe appear before Him.
God is in His temple :
All within keep silence,
Prostrate lie with deepest reverence.
Him alone
God we own,
Him our God and Saviour :
Praise His Name for ever.

2 God reveals His presence:
Hear the harps resounding,
See the crowds the throne surrounding ;
Holy, holy, holy !
Hear the hymn ascending,
Angels, saints, their voices blending.
Bow Thine ear
To us here ;
Hearken, O Lord Jesus,
To our meaner praises.

3 O Thou Fount of blessing
Purify my spirit,
Trusting only in Thy merit :
Like the holy angels
Who behold Thy glory,
May I ceaselessly adore Thee.
Let Thy will
Ever still
Rule Thy Church terrestrial,
As the hosts celestial.

GERHARD TERSTEEGEN, 1697–1769 ; *tr.* by FREDERICK WILLIAM FOSTER, 1760–1835 ; JOHN MILLER, 1756–90 ; WILLIAM MERCER, 1811–73.

235 MAIDSTONE. (77. 77. D.)

Doh = G. *Moderately fast.* WALTER BOND GILBERT, 1829-1910.

s, :l, :t, | d :r :m | f :m :r | m :— :— | s :f :m | r :m :f
m, :— :f, | m, :l, :s, | l, :s, :s, | s, :— :— | d :t, :d | l, :— :l,
d :— :r | d :— :d | d :— :t, | d :— :— | m :f :s | l :s :f
d :— :s, | l, :f, :m, | r, :s, :s, | d, :— :— | m :r :d | f, :m, :r,

D.C.

d :— :t, | d :— :— || r :— :m | f :— :m | r :— :d | t, :— :—
s, :— :s, | s, :— :— || s, :— :s, | f, :— :s, | l, :— :l, | s, :— :—
m :— :r | m :— :— || t, :— :de | r :— :de | r :— :r | r :— :—
s, :— :s, | d, :— :— || s, :— :m, | r, :— :m, | f, :— :fe, | s, :— :—

m :— :f | s :— :f | m :— :r | m :— :— || f :— :s | l :— :s
s, :— :l, | s, :— :l, | s, :— :s, | s, :— :— || d :— :d | d :— :d
d :— :d | d :— :d | d :— :t, | d :— :— || f :— :m | f :— :s
d :— :l, | m, :— :f, | d :— :s, | d :— :— || l, :— :d | f :— :m

f :— :m | r :— :— | s :f :m | r :m :f | d :— :t, | d :— :— || d | d ||
l, :t, :d | t, :— :— | d :t, :d | l, :— :l, | s, :— :s, | s, :— :— || l, | s, ||
r :— :m | s :— :— | m :f :s | l :s :f | m :— :r | m :— :— || f | m ||
r :— :d | s, :— :— | m :r :d | f :m :r | s, :— :s, | d, :— :— || f, | d, ||

A-men.

[*By permission of Novello & Co., Ltd.*]

From Psalm lxxxiv.

PLEASANT are Thy courts above,
In the land of light and love;
Pleasant are Thy courts below,
In this land of sin and woe.
O my spirit longs and faints
For the converse of Thy saints,
For the brightness of Thy face,
King of glory, God of grace!

2 Happy birds that sing and fly
Round Thy altars, O Most High!
Happier souls that find a rest
In a heavenly Father's breast!
Like the wandering dove that found
No repose on earth around,
They can to their ark repair,
And enjoy it ever there.

3 Happy souls! their praises flow
Even in this vale of woe;
Waters in the desert rise,
Manna feeds them from the skies;
On they go from strength to strength,
Till they reach Thy throne at length,
At Thy feet adoring fall,
Who hast led them safe through all.

4 Lord, be mine this prize to win:
Guide me through a world of sin;
Keep me by Thy saving grace;
Give me at Thy side a place.
Sun and shield alike Thou art;
Guide and guard my erring heart.
Grace and glory flow from Thee;
Shower, O shower them, Lord, on me.

HENRY FRANCIS LYTE, 1793–1847.

236 QUAM DILECTA. (66. 66.)

Doh = F. *In moderate time.* HENRY LASCELLES JENNER, 1820–98.

:m	f :m	m :r	d :—	— :s	l :m	r :d	r :—	—
:d	d :d	t_1 :t_1	d :—	— :d	d :s_1	l_1 :l_1	t_1 :—	—
:s	l :s	s :f	m :—	— :s	f :m	f :m	s :—	—
:d	d :d	s_1 :s_1	l_1 :—	— :m_1	f_1 :d	f_1 :l_1	s_1 :—	—

:r	m :s	s :l	s :—	— :r	m :f	m :-.r	d :—	—	d	d
:t_1	d :d	r :d	t_1 :—	— :r	d :d	d :t_1	d :—	—	l_1	s_1
:s	s :s	s :fe	s :—	— :s	s :f	s :-.f	m :—	—	f	m
:s_1	d :m	t_1 :r	s_1 :—	— :t_1	d :l_1	s_1 :s_1	d :—	—	f_1	d

A-men.

WE love the place, O God,
Wherein Thine honour dwells;
The joy of Thine abode
All earthly joy excels.

2 It is the house of prayer,
Wherein Thy servants meet;
And Thou, O Lord, art there,
Thy chosen flock to greet.

3 We love the word of life,
The word that tells of peace,
Of comfort in the strife,
And joys that never cease.

4 We love to sing below
For mercies freely given;
But O we long to know
The triumph song of heaven!

5 Lord Jesus, give us grace,
On earth to love Thee more,
In heaven to see Thy face,
And with Thy saints adore.

WILLIAM BULLOCK, 1798–1874, and HENRY WILLIAMS BAKER, 1821–77.

237

WIR PFLÜGEN (DRESDEN). (76. 76. D. and refrain.)

Doh = A. *In moderate time.* JOHANN ABRAHAM PETER SCHULZ, 1747–1800.

```
:s,  |d  :d  |s,  :s,  |m  :—  |d  :s,  |f,  :m,  |r,  :d,  |s,  :—  |—  ||
:s,  |d  :d  |s,  :s,  |m  :—  |d  :s,  |f,  :m,  |r,  :d,  |s,  :—  |—  ||
:s,  |d  :d  |s,  :s,  |m  :—  |d  :s,  |f,  :m,  |r,  :d,  |s,  :—  |—  ||
:s,  |d  :d  |s,  :s,  |m  :—  |d  :s,  |f,  :m,  |r,  :d,  |s,  :—  |—  ||
```

E.t.

```
:d f    |m   :r   |d   :l   |s   :f   |m   :d   |r   :l   |s   :t,  |d   :—  |—  ||
:s, d   |d   :t,  |d   :d   |d   :t,  |d   :d   |d   :d   |t,  :s,  |s,  :—  |—  ||
:d f    |s   :s   |s   :f   |m   :r   |d   :s   |l   :f   |r   :f   |m   :—  |—  ||
:m, l,  |s,  :f,  |m,  :f,  |s,  :—   |l,  :m,  |f,  :r,  |s,  :s,  |d   :—  |—  ||
```

f. A.

```
:d s,  |r   :r   |m   :m   |f   :—  |r   :r   |s   :s   |f   :m   |r   :—  |—  ||
:d s,  |s,  :s,  |s,  :s,  |l,  :—  |s,  :t,  |d   :s,  |t,  :d   |t,  :—  |—  ||
:d s,  |t,  :t,  |d   :d   |d   :—  |t,  :s   |s   :m   |f   :s   |s   :—  |—  ||
:d s,  |f,  :f,  |m,  :m,  |r,  :—  |s,  :f,  |m,  :m   |r   :d   |s,  :—  |—  ||
```

```
:s,  |d  :d  |s,  :s,  |l,  :—  |m,  :m,  |f,  :-.r,  |s,  :t,  |d   :—  |—  :—  ||
:s,  |d  :d  |s,  :s,  |l,  :—  |m,  :m,  |f,  :-.r,  |s,  :f,  |m,  :—  |—  :—  ||
:s,  |d  :d  |s,  :s,  |l,  :—  |m,  :m,  |f,  :-.r,  |s,  :r   |d   :—  |—  :—  ||
:s,  |d  :d  |s,  :s,  |l,  :—  |m,  :m,  |f,  :-.r,  |s,  :s,  |d,  :—  |—  :—  ||
```

REFRAIN.

```
|d   :d   |d   :d   |r   :—   |r   :r   |m  :-.s   |f   :m  |r   :—  |—  ||
|m,  :m,  |s,  :m,  |s,  :—   |s,  :t,  |d  :-.s,  |t,  :d  |t,  :—  |—  ||
|s,  :s,  |d   :d   |t,  :d   |r   :s   |s  :-.m   |f   :s  |s   :—  |—  ||
|d,  :s,  |m,  :d,  |s,  :l,  |t,  :s,  |d  :-.m   |r   :d  |s,  :—  |—  ||
```

:r	m :r	m :-.r	d :t,	d :-.s,	l, :r	d :t,	d :—	—	d	d
:s,	s, :t,	d :-.t,	l, :se,	l, :-.s,	f, :l,	s, :—	s, :—	—	f,	m,
:r	d :s	s :-.s	m :m	m :-.d	d :f	m :r	m :—	—	l,	s,
:t,	d :s,	d :-.s,	l, :m,	l, :-.m,	f, :r,	s, :—	d, :—	—	f,	d,

A - men.

Again the morn of gladness,
The morn of light, is here,
And earth itself looks fairer,
And heaven itself more near :
The bells, like angel voices,
Speak peace to every breast ;
And all the land lies quiet,
To keep the day of rest.
'Glory be to Jesus !'
Let all His children say ;
'He rose again, He rose again,
On this glad day !'

2 Again, O loving Saviour,
The children of Thy grace
Prepare themselves to seek Thee
Within Thy chosen place.
Our song shall rise to greet Thee,
If Thou our hearts wilt raise ;
If Thou our lips wilt open,
Our mouth shall show Thy praise.

3 The shining choir of angels
That rest not day or night,
The crowned and palm-decked martyrs,
The saints arrayed in white,
The happy lambs of Jesus
In pastures fair above,—
These all adore and praise Him
Whom we too praise and love.

4 The Church on earth rejoices
To join with these to-day ;
In every tongue and nation
She calls her sons to pray ;
Across the Northern snow-fields,
Beneath the Indian palms,
She makes the same pure offering,
And sings the same sweet psalms.

5 Tell out, sweet bells, His praises !
Sing, children, sing His Name !
Still louder and still farther
His mighty deeds proclaim,
Till all whom He redeemèd
Shall own Him Lord and King,
Till every knee shall worship,
And every tongue shall sing.
'Glory be to Jesus !'
Let all creation say ;
'He rose again, He rose again,
On this glad day !'

John Ellerton, 1826–93.

238 NEW CALABAR. (7 7. 7 7.)

Doh = G. *In moderate time.* JOHN DOWNING FARRER, 1829–1919.

m :-.r |d :t, |t, :l, |s, :— |d :r.m |f :m |r :d |r :— ||
d :-.t, |d :s, |s, :f, |m, :— |s, :s, |d :t, |l, :l, |t, :— ||
s :-.f |m :m.r |d :d.r |m :— |m :r |d.r :m |f :m |s :— ||
d :-.d |d :m, |f,.s, :l,.t, |d :— |d :t, |l, :s, |f, :l, |s, :— ||

s :-.f |m :d |r :m |f :— |r :m.f |s :m |r :r |d :— || d |d ||
s, :l,.t, |d :d |l,.r :-.de |r :— |t, :d.r |d :d |d :t, |d :— || l, |s, ||
m :-.f |s :d.m |l :s |f :— |s :s |d :m |l :s.f |m :— || f |m ||
m :-.r |d.t, :l,.s, |f, :m, |r, :— |s, :f, |m, :l,.s, |f, :s, |d, :— || f, |d, ||

A-men.

LORD, this day Thy children meet
In Thy courts with willing feet;
Unto Thee this day they raise
Grateful hearts in hymns of praise.

2 Not alone the day of rest
With Thy worship shall be blest;
In our pleasure and our glee,
Lord, we would remember Thee.

3 Help us unto Thee to pray,
Hallowing our happy day,
From Thy presence thus to win
Hearts all pure and free from sin.

4 All our pleasures here below,
Saviour, from Thy mercy flow:
Little children Thou dost love;
Draw our hearts to Thee above.

5 Make, O Lord, our childhood shine
With all lowly grace, like Thine;
Then through all eternity
We shall live in heaven with Thee.

WILLIAM WALSHAM HOW, 1823–97.

239 HIERAPOLIS. (L.M.)

SAMUEL WESLEY, 1766–1837.

Doh = G. *In moderate time.*

:d |m :r |d :d |r :r |m :m |r :d |f :m |r :d |t, ||
:s, |d :t, |l, :s, |l, :s, |s, :d |t, :l, |l, :d |l, :l, |t, ||
:m |s :f |m :d |d :t, |d :s |s :m |f :s |l :m |r ||
:d |d :s, |l, :m, |f, :s, |d, :d |s, :l, |r, :m, |f, :fe, |s, ||

:r |r :m |f :d |d :r |m :s |f :m |l :r |m :r |d || d |d ||
:ta, |l, :de |r :l, |s, :l,.t, |d :s, |t, :d |d :d |d :t, |d || l, |s, ||
:s |r :s |l :f |d :f |s :d |r :m |r :l |s :f |m || f |m ||
:s, |f, :m, |r, :f, |m, :r, |d, :m, |r, :d, |f, :f, |s, :s, |d, || f, |d, ||

A-men.

From Psalm cxxii.

SWEET is the solemn voice that calls
The Christian to the house of prayer ;
I love to stand within its walls,
For Thou, O Lord, art present there.

2 I love to tread the hallowed courts
Where two or three for worship meet,
For thither Christ Himself resorts,
And makes the little band complete.

3 'Tis sweet to raise the common song,
To join in holy praise and love,
And imitate the blessèd throng
That mingle hearts and songs above.

4 Within these walls may peace abound ;
May all our hearts in one agree;
Where brethren meet, where Christ is found,
May peace and concord ever be.

HENRY FRANCIS LYTE, 1793–1847.

[May be sung to MELCOMBE, No. 259.]

240 HUDDERSFIELD. (77. 75.)

Doh = D. *Moderately slow.* WALTER PARRATT, 1841–1924.

m :s	f :m	r :m	d :r	m :f	s :se	l :t	t :—	
d :r	d :t_1	l_1 :t_1	d :t_1	d :d	m :m	m :re	m :—	
s :s	l :m	f :f	m :s	s :l	t :t	l :fe	se :—	
d :t_1	l_1 :s_1	f_1 :s_1	l_1 :s_1	d :f	m :r	d :t_1	m :—	

d^1 :t	l :s	f :m	l :—	d :r	m :s	— :s	s :—		d	m	
d :r	m :l_1	r :de	r :—	d :d	d :s_1	l_1 :t_1	d :—		d	d	
m :se	l :l	l :s	f :—	l :f	m :—	f :r	m :—		l	s	
l_1 :t_1	d :de	r :m	f :—	f_1 :f_1	s_1 :—	— :s_1	d :—		f	d	

A-men.

GOD of pity, God of grace,
When we humbly seek Thy face,
Bend from heaven, Thy dwelling-place ;
Hear, forgive, and save.

2 When we in Thy temple meet,
Spread our wants before Thy feet,
Pleading at Thy mercy-seat,
Look from heaven and save.

3 When Thy love our hearts shall fill,
And we long to do Thy will,
Turning to Thy holy hill,
Lord, accept and save.

4 Should we wander from Thy fold,
And our love to Thee grow cold,
With a pitying eye behold ;
Lord, forgive and save.

5 Should the hand of sorrow press,
Earthly care and want distress,
May our souls Thy peace possess ;
Jesus, hear and save.

6 And, whate'er our cry may be,
When we lift our hearts to Thee,
From our burden set us free ;
Hear, forgive, and save.

ELIZA FANNY MORRIS, 1821–74.

[May be sung to CAPETOWN, No. 282.]

241 EISENACH. (L.M.)

JOHANN HERMANN SCHEIN, 1586–1630.
Arranged by JOHANN SEBASTIAN BACH, 1685–1750.

Doh = D. *Slow.*

```
                                                   At.
:d.r | m    :f    | s   :s    | f    :m    | r ‖ ˢd  | r    :m     | f    :m
:s,  | d    :d    | d   :d    | d.t, :d    | t,‖ ʳs, | l,   :t,    | d.s, :s,
:m.f | s    :l    | ta  :l.s  | l    :s    | s ‖ ᵗm  | r    :s     | d.r  :m
:d   | d    :l,   | m,  :l,   | r    :m.f  | s ‖ ˢd  | t,   :l,.s, | l,.t,:d

               t.D.
r    :r   | d  ‖ ᵈs   | d'   :t    | l    :s     | f    :m     | r  ‖ s
l,   :t,  | s, ‖ ˢr   | m    :r    | d.r  :m     | r    :s,.l, | t, ‖ m.r
f.m  :r   | m  ‖ ᵐt.l | s.m  :f.s  | l    :l     | l.t  :d'    | s  ‖ t
f,   :s,  | d, ‖ ᵈs.f | m.d  :r.m  | f.m  :r.de  | r    :m.f   | s  ‖ m

f     :m    | r.m  :f   | m     :r    | d  ‖ d  | d  ‖
d.r   :r.d  | d.t, :d   | d     :t,   | s, ‖ l, | s, ‖
l.s   :s    | s    :f   | s     :-.f  | m  ‖ f  | m  ‖
l,.t, :d    | s,   :l,  | s,.f, :s,   | d  ‖ f, | d  ‖
                                            A-men.
```

COMMAND Thy blessing from above,
O God, on all assembled here;
Behold us with a Father's love,
While we look up with filial fear.

2 Command Thy blessing, Jesus, Lord;
May we Thy true disciples be;
Speak to each heart the mighty word;
Say to the weakest, 'Follow Me.'

3 Command Thy blessing in this hour,
Spirit of truth, and fill this place
With humbling and exalting power,
With quickening and confirming grace.

4 O Thou, our Maker, Saviour, Guide,
One true eternal God confessed,
May nought in life or death divide
The saints in Thy communion blest.

5 With Thee and these for ever bound,
May all who here in prayer unite,
With harps and songs Thy throne surround,
Rest in Thy love, and reign in light.

JAMES MONTGOMERY, 1771–1854.

242 BEDFORD. (C.M.)

Doh = E♭. *Slow and dignified.* WILLIAM WEALE, ?-1727.

```
:s  |m  :— :d  |l  :— :s  |f  :m  :—  |r  :— :s  |d' :—  :t
:m  |d  :— :d  |d  :— :d  |t, :d  :—  |t, :— :r  |d  :—  :r
:s  |s  :— :s  |l  :— :d' |f  :s  :—  |s  :— :r  |m  :fe :s
:d  |d  :— :m  |f  :— :m  |r  :d  :—  |s, :— :t, |l, :—  :t,

l  :l  :—  |s  :—  ||m  |f  :— :s  |l  :— :s  |f  :m  :—
m  :r  :—  |t, :—  ||d  |d  :— :m  |f  :— :r  |d  :d  :—
s  :—  :fe |s  :—  ||s  |f  :— :d' |d' :— :ta |l  :s  :l
d  :r  :—  |s, :—  ||d  |l, :— :d  |f, :— :s, |l, :d  :—

r  :— :s  |d' :— :m  |f  :r  :—  |d  :—  ||d  |d  ||
r  :— :t, |d  :— :d  |d  :— :t,  |d  :—  ||l, |s, ||
t  :— :s  |s  :— :m  |l  :s  :—  |m  :—  ||f  |m  ||
s, :— :s, |m, :— :l, |f, :s, :—  |d  :—  ||f, |d  ||
                                  d,          A - men.
```

[*This tune is sometimes sung in duple time. To effect this, all the semibreves must be counted as minims.*]

BEHOLD us, Lord, a little space
From daily tasks set free,
And met within Thy holy place
To rest awhile with Thee.

2 Around us rolls the ceaseless tide
Of business, toil, and care,
And scarcely can we turn aside
For one brief hour of prayer.

3 Yet these are not the only walls
Wherein Thou mayst be sought;
On homeliest work Thy blessing falls,
In truth and patience wrought.

4 Thine is the loom, the forge, the mart,
The wealth of land and sea,
The worlds of science and of art,
Revealed and ruled by Thee.

5 Then let us prove our heavenly birth
In all we do and know,
And claim the kingdom of the earth
For Thee, and not Thy foe.

6 Work shall be prayer, if all be wrought
As Thou wouldst have it done,
And prayer, by Thee inspired and taught,
Itself with work be one.

JOHN ELLERTON, 1826–93.

243 BONT-NEWYDD. (10. 10. 10. 10.)

Doh = E♭. *In moderate time.* JOHN ROBERTS (IEUAN GWYLLT), 1822–77.

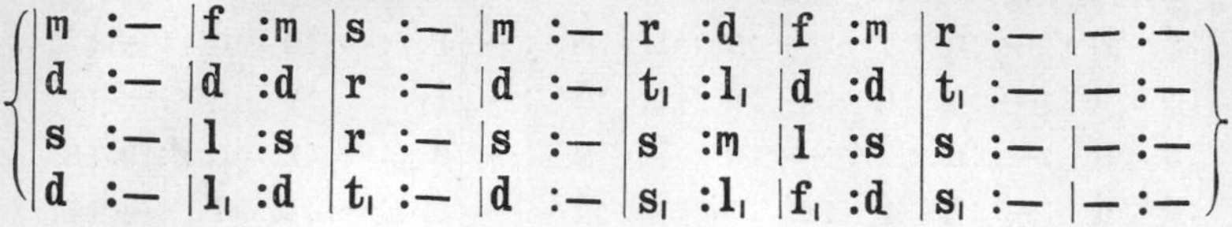

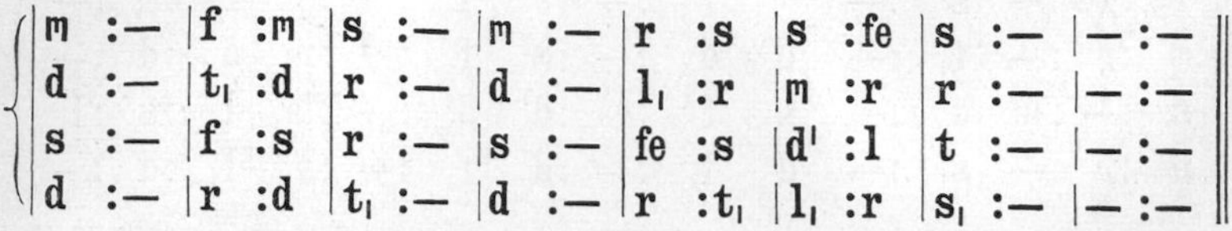

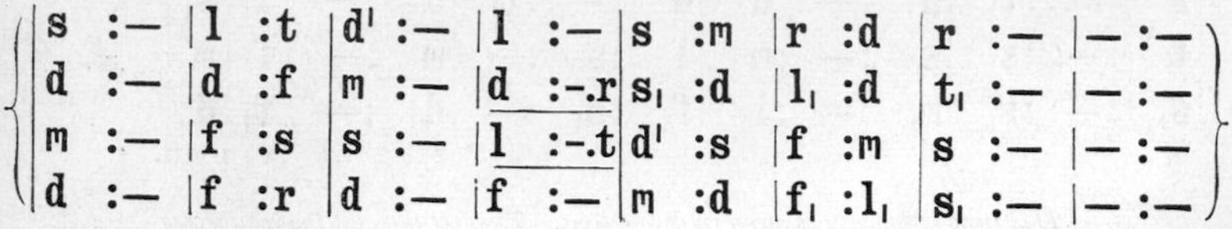

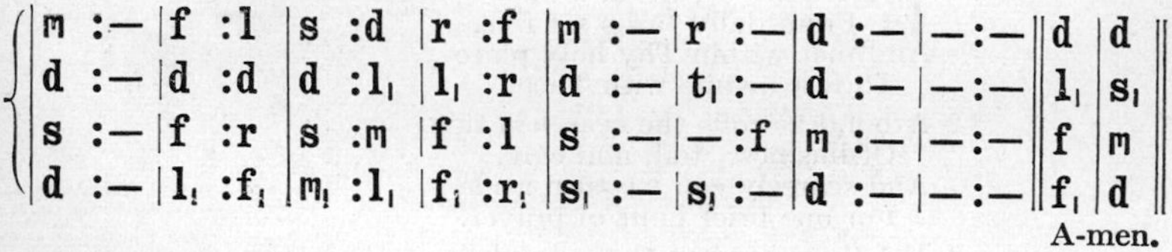

m :—	f :m	s :—	m :—	r :d	f :m	r :—	— :—
d :—	d :d	r :—	d :—	t_1 :l_1	d :d	t_1 :—	— :—
s :—	l :s	r :—	s :—	s :m	l :s	s :—	— :—
d :—	l_1 :d	t_1 :—	d :—	s_1 :l_1	f_1 :d	s_1 :—	— :—

m :—	f :m	s :—	m :—	r :s	s :fe	s :—	— :—	
d :—	t_1 :d	r :—	d :—	l_1 :r	m :r	r :—	— :—	
s :—	f :s	r :—	s :—	fe :s	d' :l	t :—	— :—	
d :—	r :d	t_1 :—	d :—	r :t_1	l_1 :r	s_1 :—	— :—	

s :—	l :t	d' :—	l :—	s :m	r :d	r :—	— :—
d :—	d :f	m :—	d :-.r	s_1 :d	l_1 :d	t_1 :—	— :—
m :—	f :s	s :—	l :-.t	d' :s	f :m	s :—	— :—
d :—	f :r	d :—	f :—	m :d	f_1 :l_1	s_1 :—	— :—

m :—	f :l	s :d	r :f	m :—	r :—	d :—	— :—		d	d	
d :—	d :d	d :l_1	l_1 :r	d :—	t_1 :—	d :—	— :—		l_1	s_1	
s :—	f :r	s :m	f :l	s :—	— :f	m :—	— :—		f	m	
d :—	l_1 :f_1	m_1 :l_1	f_1 :r_1	s_1 :—	s_1 :—	d :—	— :—		f_1	d	

A-men.

MAGDA. (10. 10. 10. 10.)

Doh = D. *In moderate time, not too slow.* RALPH VAUGHAN WILLIAMS, 1872–

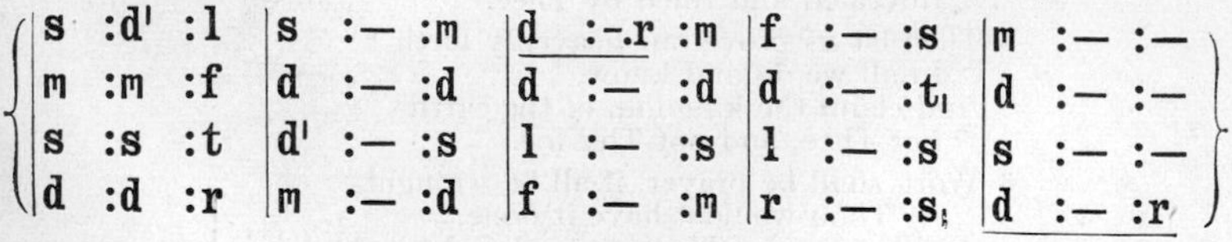

s :d' :l	s :— :m	d :-.r :m	f :— :s	m :— :—
m :m :f	d :— :d	d :— :d	d :— :t_1	d :— :—
s :s :t	d' :— :s	l :— :s	l :— :s	s :— :—
d :d :r	m :— :d	f :— :m	r :— :s_1	d :— :r

```
| s  :d'  :l  | r'  :—  :s  | m   :-.fe :s  | s   :—  :fe | s   :—  :—  ||
| d  :m   :r  | r   :—  :t, | d   :—    :r  | m   :r  :—  | r   :—  :—  ||
| s  :s   :fe | s   :—  :s  | s   :—    :s  | d'  :l  :—  | t   :—  :—  ||
| m  :d   :r  | t,  :—  :m  | d   :—    :t, | l,  :r  :—  | s,  :—  :—  ||

| l  :l   :l  | r'  :—  :t  | s   :-.l  :t  | d'  :—  :l  | f   :m  :r
| r  :r   :s  | f   :—  :f  | m   :—    :f  | m   :—  :m  | r   :d  :t,
| l  :l   :l  | l   :—  :t  | d'  :—    :r' | d'  :—  :d' | l   :—  :t
| f  :f   :m  | r   :—  :r  | m   :—    :r  | l,  :—  :d  | r   :—  :f

| s  :l   :s  | d'  :—  :l  | s   :—    :l  | f   :m  :r  | d   :—  :—  || f  | m  ||
| d  :—   :t, | d   :—  :t, | d   :—    :d  | r   :d  :t, | d   :—  :—  || d  | d  ||
| s  :—   :f  | m   :—  :f  | s   :—    :m  | f   :s  :s  | m   :—  :—  || l  | s  ||
| m  :—   :r  | d   :—  :r  | m   :—    :l, | r   :m  :s  | d   :—  :—  || f, | d  ||
                                                                        A-men.
```

[*Copyright*, 1925, *by R. Vaughan Williams.*]

FATHER, again in Jesus' Name we meet,
And bow in penitence before Thy feet;
Again to Thee our feeble voices raise,
To sue for mercy, and to sing Thy praise.

2 O we would bless Thee for Thy ceaseless care,
And all Thy work from day to day declare;
Is not our life with hourly mercies crowned?
Does not Thine arm encircle us around?

3 Alas! unworthy of Thy boundless love,
Too oft our feet from Thee, our Father, rove;
But now, encouraged by Thy voice, we come.
Returning sinners, to a Father's home.

4 O by that Name in whom all fulness dwells,
O by that love which every love excels,
O by that blood so freely shed for sin,
Open blest mercy's gate, and take us in!

Lucy Elizabeth Georgina Whitmore, 1792–1840.

244 DULCINA. (8 7. 8 7.)

Doh = C. *In moderate time.* Old English Melody.

m :-.f	s :s	f :m	r :d	l :-.t	d' :d'	t :l	s :—	
d :-.d	r :r	d .r :d	t, :d	f :-.f	s :s	s :f	r :—	
s :-.l	s :t	l :s	f :s	d' :-.r'	s :m'	m' :d'	t :—	
d :-.l,	t, :s,	l,.t, :d	r :m	f :-.r	m :d	m :f	s :—	

m :-.f	s :s	l :s	l :t	d' :-.r'	m' :m'	r' :-.d'	d' :—		d'	d'	
d :-.d	r :m	m :m	f :f	s :-.s	s :s	l :s	m :—		f	m	
l :-.d'	t :t	d' :d'	d' :r'	s :-.t	d' :d'	d' :t	d' :—		l	s	
l :-.l	s :m	l, :d	f :r	m :-.s	d' :d	f :s	d :—		f	d	
A - men.

O BE with us, gracious Father,
While before Thy feet we bow;
Let the angel of Thy presence
Hover o'er Thy temple now.

2 Here are hearts that Thou canst soften,
Earthly dross to purge away;
Darkened minds, on which Thy Spirit
Yet may pour celestial day.

3 From the world's entrancing vision,
From the spirit's sullen night,
From the tempter's dark dominion,
Free us, by Thy saving might.

4 Let Thy Spirit's glad communion
Waken thoughts of peace and love,
And prepare us for Thy presence
In the nobler courts above,

5 There to join in perfect worship,
There to swell the angels' song,
And in higher, sweeter measure,
Earth's imperfect praise prolong.

Alfred Rooker, 1814–75.

245 CAMPFIELDS. (86. 886.)

Doh = D. *In moderate time.* MARK JAMES MONK, 1858–

:m |r :m |f :m |r :m |f :r |s :-.s |s :f |m :— |— ||
:d |d :d |d :d |t$_1$:d |d :t$_1$ |d :d |d :d |d :— |— ||
:s |f :s |l :s |s :s |l :s |s :s |l :l |s :— |— ||
:d |d :d |d :d |f :m |r :f |m :m$_1$ |f$_1$:l$_1$ |d :— |— ||

A.t.

:[m]l$_1$ |t$_1$:d |r :d |t$_1$:l$_1$ |s$_1$:s$_1$ |d :-.d |r :r
:[d]f$_1$ |s$_1$:s$_1$ |f$_1$:m$_1$ |f$_1$:r$_1$ |s$_1$:s$_1$ |m$_1$:-.d |d :t$_1$
:[s]d |r :d |s$_1$:s$_1$ |s$_1$:t$_1$ |d :d |d :-.m |s :s
:[d]f$_1$ |f$_1$:m$_1$ |t$_2$:d$_1$ |r$_1$:f$_1$ |m$_1$:m$_1$ |l$_1$:-.l$_1$ |s$_1$:s$_1$

f.D.

[m]t :l	s :f	m :-.m	m :r	d :—	—		d	d	
[d]s :f	m :r	d :d	d :t$_1$	d :—	—		l$_1$	s$_1$	
[s]r^1 :t	d^1 :s	s :s	l :f	m :—	—		f	m	
[d]s :s$_1$	l$_1$:t$_1$	d :m$_1$	f$_1$:s$_1$	d :—	—		f$_1$	d	

A-men.

DEAR Lord and Father of mankind,
Forgive our foolish ways:
Reclothe us in our rightful mind;
In purer lives Thy service find,
In deeper reverence, praise.

2 In simple trust like theirs who heard,
Beside the Syrian sea,
The gracious calling of the Lord,
Let us, like them, without a word
Rise up and follow Thee.

3 O Sabbath rest by Galilee!
O calm of hills above,
Where Jesus knelt to share with Thee
The silence of eternity,
Interpreted by love!

4 With that deep hush subduing all
Our words and works that drown
The tender whisper of Thy call,
As noiseless let Thy blessing fall
As fell Thy manna down.

5 Drop Thy still dews of quietness,
Till all our strivings cease;
Take from our souls the strain and stress,
And let our ordered lives confess
The beauty of Thy peace.

6 Breathe through the heats of our desire
Thy coolness and Thy balm;
Let sense be dumb, let flesh retire;
Speak through the earthquake, wind, and fire,
O still small voice of calm!

JOHN GREENLEAF WHITTIER, 1807–92.

246 ELGIN. (C.M.)

Lah = G. Doh = B♭. *Slow.* *Scottish Psalter*, 1625.

d :—	t_1 :l_1	t_1 :—	m :—	r :d	t_1 :— ‖	l_1 :—	r :d
m_1 :—	m_1 :m_1	m_1 :—	m_1 :—	se_1 :l_1	se_1 :— ‖	l_1 :—	r_1 :m_1
l_1 :—	t_1 :d	se_1 :—	l_1 :—	t_1 :d.r	m :— ‖	d :—	l_1.t_1 :d
l_1 :—	se_1 :l_1	m_1 :—	d_1 :—	t_2 :l_2	m_1 :— ‖	l_1 :—	f_1 :m_1

t_1 :l_1	t_1 :— ‖	m :—	d :m	r :t_1	d :r	t_1 :— ‖
f_1 :m_1	m_1 :— ‖	m_1 :—	s_1 :s_1	l_1 :s_1	m_1 :f_1	m_1 :— ‖
r :d.l_1	se_1 :— ‖	s_1 :—	s_1 :d	l_1 :r	d :t_1.l_1	se_1 :— ‖
r_1 :l_2	m_1 :— ‖	d_1 :—	m_1 :d_1	f_1 :s_1	l_1 :r_1	m_1 :— ‖

l_1 :—	r :d	t_1 :t_1	l_1 :—	— :— ‖	l_1	l_1 ‖
m_1 :—	r_1 :m_1	m_1 :-.r_1	d_1 :—	— :— ‖	r_1	de_1 ‖
l_1 :—	se_1 :l_1	l_1 :se_1	l_1 :—	— :— ‖	f_1	m_1 ‖
d_1 :—	t_2 :l_2	m_1 :m_1	l_2 :—	— :— ‖	r_1	l_2 ‖

A-men.

DEAR Shepherd of Thy people, hear;
Thy presence now display;
As Thou hast given a place for prayer,
So give us hearts to pray.

2 Within these walls let holy peace
And love and concord dwell;
Here give the troubled conscience ease,
The wounded spirit heal.

3 May we in faith receive Thy word,
In faith present our prayers,
And in the presence of our Lord
Unbosom all our cares.

4 The hearing ear, the seeing eye,
The humbled mind bestow;
And shine upon us from on high,
To make our graces grow.

JOHN NEWTON, 1725–1807.

BAGINTON. (C.M.)

Doh = D. *In moderate time.* FREDERICK GOOCH, *c.* 1858.

```
:d  |m  :r   |d  :l     |s  :f   |m  :m  |r  :d  |r  :m
:d  |d  :t,  |d  :d     |d  :t,  |d  :d  |t, :d  |t, :d
:m  |s  :f   |m  :f     |s  :s   |s  :s  |s  :s  |s  :s
:d  |d  :s,  |d  :f     |m  :r   |d  :d  |f  :m  |r  :d

|r  :—  |—  ||d'  |t  :l      |s  :l   |s  :f   |m  :m
|t, :—  |—  ||d   |d  :d.t,   |d  :d   |d  :t,  |d  :d
|s  :—  |—  ||d'  |d' :d'.r'  |s  :d'  |s  :s   |s  :s
|s  :—  |—  ||l   |s  :f      |m  :f   |m  :r   |d  :d

|r  :d    |d   :t,  |d  :—  |—  ||d  |d  ||
|l, :d    |s,  :s,  |s, :—  |—  ||l, |s, ||
|f  :m.f  |r.m :f   |m  :—  |—  ||f  |m  ||
|f, :l,   |s,  :s,  |d  :—  |—  ||f, |d  ||
                                  A-men.
```

DEAR Shepherd of Thy people, hear;
Thy presence now display;
As Thou hast given a place for prayer,
So give us hearts to pray.

2 Within these walls let holy peace
And love and concord dwell;
Here give the troubled conscience ease,
The wounded spirit heal.

3 May we in faith receive Thy word,
In faith present our prayers,
And in the presence of our Lord
Unbosom all our cares.

4 The hearing ear, the seeing eye,
The humbled mind bestow;
And shine upon us from on high,
To make our graces grow.

JOHN NEWTON, 1725-1807.

247 LLANDAF. (L.M.)

DAVID EVANS, 1874–

Doh = E♭. *In moderate time.* B♭.t.

```
m  :s  :d  | f  :— :m  | m  :r  :l  | s  :— :ˢd  | f  :m  :r  | l, :t, :d
s, :r  :d  | d  :— :d  | d  :— :r  | m  :— :ᵈf, | l, :— :l, | s, :f, :m,
d  :r  :m  | f  :— :s  | l  :— :t  | d' :— :ˢd  | l, :s  :f  | m  :r  :d
d  :t, :d  | l, :— :s, | f, :— :f  | m  :— :ᵐl, | r, :m, :f, | s, :— :l,
```

f.E♭.

```
m  :— :r  | ᵈs  :— :— || s :f     :m   | l  :— :s   | l :t  :d' | d' :t  :t
s, :— :f, | ᵐt  :— :— || d :l,.t, :d   | m  :— :m.r | d :r  :d  | m  :r  :r
d  :l, :t, | ᵈs  :— :— || s :s     :s   | d' :— :t   | l :— :s  | s  :— :s
s, :— :s, | ᵈs, :— :— || m :r     :d   | l, :d  :m  | f :— :m  | s  :— :s,
```

```
d' :m  :l   | s  :m  :d  | m  :— :r  | d :— :— || f  | m ||
d  :—  :r   | s, :t, :d  | d  :l, :t, | d :— :— || d  | d ||
m  :s  :l.t | d' :s  :m  | s  :— :f  | m :— :— || l  | s ||
l, :s, :f,  | m, :s, :l, | s, :— :s, | d :— :— || f, | d ||
```

A-men.

JESUS, where'er Thy people meet,
There they behold Thy mercy-seat;
Where'er they seek Thee Thou art found,
And every place is hallowed ground.

2 For Thou, within no walls confined,
Inhabitest the humble mind;
Such ever bring Thee where they come,
And, going, take Thee to their home.

3 Dear Shepherd of Thy chosen few,
Thy former mercies here renew;
Here to our waiting hearts proclaim
The sweetness of Thy saving Name.

4 Here may we prove the power of prayer
To strengthen faith and sweeten care,
To teach our faint desires to rise,
And bring all heaven before our eyes.

5 Lord, we are few, but Thou art near,
Nor short Thine arm, nor deaf Thine ear;
O rend the heavens, come quickly down,
And make a thousand hearts Thine own.

WILLIAM COWPER, 1731–1800.

248 ADSIS, JESU. (6 5. 6 5.)

Doh = G. *In moderate time.* WILLIAM HENRY MONK, 1823–89.

m :m	s :m	r :—	d :—	r :d	t, :l,	s, :—	— :—	
s, :d	t, :d	d :t,	d :—	s, :-.l,	s, :fe,	r, :—	m, :—	
m :d	r :m.f	s :—	m :—	r :m	r :-.d	t, :—	— :—	
d :l,	s, :s,	s, :—	d :—	t, :d	r :r,	s, :—	— :—	

l, :l,	d :r	m :—	r :—	f :m	r :r	d :—	— :—		d	d	
f, :f,	s, :f,	m, :s,	s, :—	l, :s,	s, :-.f,	m, :—	— :—		f,	m,	
d :d	d :-.t,	d :—	t, :—	d :d	d :t,	d :—	— :—		l,	s,	
f, :f,	m, :r,	d, :m,	s, :—	f, :d,	s, :s,	d, :—	— :—		f,	d,	

A-men.

JESUS, stand among us
In Thy risen power;
Let this time of worship
Be a hallowed hour.

2 Breathe the Holy Spirit
Into every heart;
Bid the fears and sorrows
From each soul depart.

3 Thus with quickened footsteps
We pursue our way,
Watching for the dawning
Of eternal day.

WILLIAM PENNEFATHER, 1816–73.

249 SELMA. (S.M.)

Doh = E. *In moderate time.* ROBERT ARCHIBALD SMITH, 1780–1829.

:d | m :r | d :r.m | s :— | — :s | l :s | m :s.,l | l :— | — ||
:s, | d :t, | d :s, | t, :— | — :d | d :d | d :d | d :— | — ||
:m | s :s.f | m :r.d | r :— | — :m | f :s | s :m.,f | f :— | — ||
:d | d :s, | l, :t,.d | s, :— | — :d | f :m | d :d | f, :— | — ||

:l | s :l.d' | d' :s | l :m | r :d | r.m :s | r :r | d :— | — || d | d ||
:d | d :d | d :d | d :d | t, :d | s, :d | d :t, | d :— | — || l, | s, ||
:f | m :l | s :m | f :s | s :m | r.d :s | l :s.f | m :— | — || f | m ||
:f, | d :f | m :d | f, :d | s, :l, | t,.d :m, | f, :s, | d :— | — || f, | d ||

A-men.

Lux alma Jesu mentium.

LIGHT of the anxious heart,
Jesus, Thou dost appear,
To bid the gloom of guilt depart,
And shed Thy sweetness here.

2 Joyous is he with whom,
God's Word, Thou dost abide,
Sweet Light of our eternal home,
To fleshly sense denied.

3 Brightness of God above,
Unfathomable grace,
Thy presence be a fount of love
Within Thy chosen place.

Attributed to ST. BERNARD OF CLAIRVAUX, 1091–1153;
tr. by JOHN HENRY NEWMAN, 1801–90.

250 FIFTH MODE MELODY. (84. 86. D.)

Doh = F. *Moderately slow.* THOMAS TALLIS, *c.* 1500–85.

d :m :f	s :—:s	l :— :f	s :—:f	m :—:r	m :—:—
s_1 :d :d	r :—:d	d :— :r	s_1 :—:r	d :—:t_1	d :—:—
1. En - ter Thy	courts, Thou	Word of	life, My	joy and	peace;
3. In heaven and	earth Thy	law en-	dures, Thy	word a -	bides:
m :s :f	r :—:m	f :-.s:l.t	d^1 :—:l	s :—:s	s :—:—
d :d :l_1	t_1 :—:d	f_1 :— :f_1	m_1 :—:f_1	s_1 :—:s_1	d :—:—

d :m :f	s :— :s	l :— :t	d^1 :— :s	l :— :s
s_1 :d :d	r :— :d	d :f :r	m :— :r	d :-.r :m
Let the glad	sound there-	in be	heard, Bid	plain - tive
My trou - bled	flesh trem -	bleth in	awe, My	heart in
m :s :f	r :— :m	f :f :—	s :— :r	f :— :m
d :d :l_1	t_1 :— :d	f :r :—	d :— :t_1	l_1 :-.t_1 :d

f :m :—	r :— :—	r :m :f	s :— :r	s :— :fe
r :— :de	r :— :—	t_1 :s_1 :l_1	t_1 :-.d :r	d :l_1 :—
sad - ness	cease.	Com - fort my	heart, Thou	Truth most
ter - ror	hides.	Yet still on	Thee my	hope is
l :— :l	f :— :—	s :s :d	r :— :s	m :r :—
f_1 :l_1 :—	r_1 :— :—	s_1 :d :l_1	s_1 :-.l_1 :t_1	d :r :—

s :— :s	l :— :l	s :— :—	m :s :f	m :— :l
t_1 :— :d	l_1 :— :r	t_1 :— :—	d :d :d	d :— :d
fair; O	en - ter	in,	Chas-ing de -	spair and
set; On	Thee, O	Lord,	I will a -	wait and
r :— :s	fe :-.m :fe	s :— :—	s :m :l	s :— :d^1
s_1 :— :m_1	r_1 :— :r_1	s_1 :— :—	d :d :f_1	d :— :f_1

s :-.f :m	r :— :m	f :— :m	r :— :r	d :— :—	d	d
m :-.r :d	t_1 :— :d	d :— :d	l_1 :t_1 :—	d :— :—	l_1	s_1
earth - born	care, My	woe and	sloth-ful	sin.		
not for -	get The	pro - mise	of Thy	word.	A-	men.
d^1 :— :s	s :— :s	l :— :s	f :r :—	m :— :—	f	m
d :— :d	s_1 :— :d	f_1 :— :d	f_1 :s_1 :—	d_1 :— :—	f_1	d

FAUX-BOURDON SETTING FOR v. 2.

Doh = F. THOMAS TALLIS, *c.* 1500–85.

s, :d :r | m :— :d | f :— :r | m :—:r | d :— :t, | d :—:—
m, :l, :t, | d :— :d | f, :-.s, :l,.t, | d :—:l, | s, :— :s, | s, :—:—
2. Glad was the | time when | I would | sing Thy | heaven - ly | praise;
d :m :f | s :—:s | l :— :f | s :—:f | m :— :r | m :—:—
d :l, :r | d :— :m | r :— :r | d :—:f, | d :— :s, | d :—:—

s, :d :r | m :— :s | f :— :r | m :— :r | f :— :m
m, :l, :t, | d :— :d | d :f, :— | s, :— :t, | d :— :d
Hap - py my | heart when | Thou wert | nigh, Di - | rect - ing
d :m :f | s :— :s | l :— :t | d' :— :s | l :— :s
d :l, :r | d :— :m | f :r :— | d :— :t, | l, :-.t, :d

r :— :de | r :— :— | t, :s, :l, | t, :-.d :r | m :r :—
l, :— :l, | l, (f,) :— :— | s, :s, :d, | r, :— :s, | d :l, :—
all my | ways. | O let Thy | light, Thy | joy a -
f :m :— | r :— :— | r :m :f | s :— :r | s :— :fe
f, :l, :— | r, :— :— | s, :d :l, | s, :-.l, :t, | d :r :—

r :— :m | fe :-.m :fe | s :— :— || d :m :l | s :— :f
t, :— :d | r :— :r | t, :— :— || d :d :d | d :— :d
gain Re - | turn to | me; || Nor in dis - | dain from
s :— :s | l :— :l | s :— :— || m :s :f | m :— :l
s, :— :m, | r, :— :r, | s, :— :— || d :d :f, | d :— :f,

m :-.r :d | t, :— :d | r :— :m | f :r :— | m :— :—
d :— :s, | s, :— :s, | l, :— :s, | l, :t, :— | d :— :—
me re - | frain, Who | lift my | soul to | Thee.
s :-.f :m | r :— :m | f :— :m | r :— :r | d :— :—
d :— :d | s, :— :d | f, :— :d | f, :s, :— | d, :— :—

Yattendon Hymnal, No. 98, 1899.

251

SAMUEL. (66. 66. 88.)

Doh = D. *In moderate time.* ARTHUR SEYMOUR SULLIVAN, 1842–1900.

```
 :m |m :s |f :-.m |f :l |s :fe |s :d' |d' :— |t ||d' |l :s
 :d |d :d |t, :-.t, |t, :t, |d :-.d |d :d |r :— |— ||d |d :d
 :s |s :m |s :-.s |s :s |s :-.s |s :fe |s :— |— ||s |f :s
 :d |d :s, |r :-.r |s, f |m :-.m |m, :l, |s, :— |— ||m |f :m

          A.t.                              f.D.
|f :s |[m]l, :t, |d :r |m :— |— :r |[d]s :— |— ||s |r' :-.t |s :f
|d :t, |[d]f, :s, |s, :l, |s, :— |t, :— |[d]s :— |— ||s |f :-.f |m :r
|l :s |[s]d :r |d :d |d :— |f :— |[m]t :— |— ||s |t :-.t |d' :s
|r :s, |[d]f, :f, |m, :f, |s, :— |s, :— |[d]s, :— |— ||s |s :s, |l, :t,

|m :f |s :d |d :l |s :f |m :— |— :r |d :— |— :— ||d |d ||
|d :t, |d :d |d :d |de :r |d :— |t, :— |d :— |— :— ||l, |s, ||
|s :s |s :ta |l :l |l :l |s :— |f :— |m :— |— :— ||f |m ||
|d :r |m :m |f :f |m :r |s :— |s, :— |d :— |— :— ||f, |d ||
                                                      A-men.
```

[*By permission of Novello & Co., Ltd.*]

HUSHED was the evening hymn,
The temple courts were dark,
The lamp was burning dim
Before the sacred ark,
When suddenly a voice Divine
Rang through the silence of the shrine.

2 The old man, meek and mild,
The priest of Israel, slept;
His watch the temple child,
The little Levite, kept;
And what from Eli's sense was sealed
The Lord to Hannah's son revealed.

3 O give me Samuel's ear,
The open ear, O Lord,
Alive and quick to hear
Each whisper of Thy word,—
Like him to answer at Thy call,
And to obey Thee first of all.

4 O give me Samuel's heart,
A lowly heart, that waits
Where in Thy house Thou art,
Or watches at Thy gates
By day and night—a heart that still
Moves at the breathing of Thy will.

5 O give me Samuel's mind,
A sweet unmurmuring faith,
Obedient and resigned
To Thee in life and death,
That I may read, with childlike eyes,
Truths that are hidden from the wise.

JAMES DRUMMOND BURNS, 1823–64.

252 ANGEL VOICES. (8 5. 8 5. 8 4. 3.)

Doh = D. *In moderate time.* EDWIN GEORGE MONK, 1819–1900.

| m :s | l :s | d' :l | s :m | d :r | m :f | r :— | — :— || m :s
| d :m | f :f.m | f :f | r :t, | d :d | d :d | d :— | t, :— || d :d
| s :d' | t :d' | l :f | s :s | m :f | s :l | s :— | — :— || s :d'
| d :d | d :d | d :d | t, :s, | l, :l, | s, :f, | s, :— | — :— || d :m

A.t. f.D.

| d' :^{l}r | s :-.f | m :d | r :l, | d :t, | d :— | — :— || d :d | d :^{r}l
| d :^{m}l, | s, :t, | d :s, | l, :l, | l, :s, | s, :— | — :— || d :t, | l, :^{l}m
| d' :^{d}f | r :s | s :s | f :f | f :f | f :m.r | m :— || m :m | m :^{r}l
| l :-.^{s}d | t, :s, | d :m, | f, :f,.m, | r, :s, | d, :— | — :— || l, :s, | fe, :^{fe}de

f :f	f :s	m :s	l :d'	r' :—	— :t	d' :—	— :—		d'	d'	
f :m	r :r	m :d	f :m	s :—	— :f	m :—	— :—		f	m	
l :l	l :s	s :d'	d' :d'	d' :—	t :r'	d' s :—	— :—		l	s	
r :d	t, :t,	d :m	f :l	s :—	— :s,	d :—	— :—		f	d	

A-men.

ANGEL voices, ever singing
Round Thy throne of light,
Angel harps, for ever ringing,
Rest not day nor night;
Thousands only live to bless Thee,
And confess Thee
Lord of might.

2 Yea, we know that Thou rejoicest
O'er each work of Thine;
Thou didst ears and hands and voices
For Thy praise design;
Craftsman's art and music's measure
For Thy pleasure
All combine.

3 In Thy house, great God, we offer
Of Thine own to Thee,
And for Thine acceptance proffer,
All unworthily,
Hearts and minds and hands and voices,
In our choicest
Psalmody.

4 Honour, glory, might, and merit
Thine shall ever be,
Father, Son, and Holy Spirit,
Blessèd Trinity.
Of the best that Thou hast given,
Earth and heaven
Render Thee.

FRANCIS POTT, 1832–1909.

253 WAREHAM. (L.M.)

Doh = B♭. *In moderate time.* WILLIAM KNAPP, 1698–1768.

```
:d  |d  :t,  :l,  |s,  :—  :d  |r  :d  :t,  |d  :—  :r  |m  :r  :d
:m, |m, :—   :f,  |s,  :—  :m, |l, :s, :s,  |s, :—  :s, |s, :—  :s,.fe,
:s, |d  :—   :d   |d   :—  :d  |f  :m  :r   |m  :—  :t, |d  :r  :m.d
:d, |d, :—   :f,  |m,  :—  :l, |f, :s, :s,  |d, :—  :s, |d  :t, :l,

|t, :d  :r   |d  :t, :l,  |s, :— |s, |l, :s, :l,.t, |d  :— :t, |d  :— :r
|s, :—  :s,  |l, :s, :fe, |s, :— |s, |f, :s, :f,    |s, :— :s, |m, :— :l,
|r  :d  :t,  |m  :r  :d   |t, :— |d  |d  :— :f      |m  :d :r  |d  :t, :l,
|s, :m, :t,, |d, :r, :r,  |s, :— |m, |f, :m, :r,    |d, :m, :s,|l, :s, :f,

|m  :— :r.m    |f  :m  :r  |d  :t, :d  |r  :d  :t, |d  :— || d  |d
|se,:— :l,.s,  |f, :s, :l, |s, :f, :m, |l, :s, :s, |s, :— || f, |m,
|t, :— :l,     |t, :d  :f  |m  :r  :d  |f  :m  :r  |m  :— || l, |s,
|m, :— :f,.m,  |r, :m, :f, |s, :— :l,  |f, :s, :s, |d, :— || f, |d,
                                                           A-men.
```

Laying foundation-stone of a Church.

THIS stone to Thee in faith we lay;
We build the temple, Lord, to Thee:
Thine eye be open, night and day,
To guard this house and sanctuary.

2 Here, when Thy people seek Thy face,
And dying sinners pray to live,
Hear Thou, in heaven Thy dwelling-place,
And when Thou hearest, O forgive!

3 Here, when Thy messengers proclaim
The blessèd Gospel of Thy Son,
Still, by the power of His great Name,
Be mighty signs and wonders done.

4 'Hosanna!' to their heavenly King
When children's voices raise that song,
'Hosanna!' let their angels sing,
And heaven, with earth, the strain prolong.

5 But will indeed Jehovah deign
Here to abide, no transient guest?
Here will the world's Redeemer reign,
And here the Holy Spirit rest?

6 That glory never hence depart!
Yet choose not, Lord, this house alone;
Thy kingdom come to every heart:
In every bosom fix Thy throne.

JAMES MONTGOMERY, 1771–1854.

254

HERR JESU CHRIST. (L.M.) *Pensum Sacrum*, Görlitz, 1648.
Arranged by JOHANN SEBASTIAN BACH, 1685–1750.

Doh = F. *Slow and dignified.*

```
:d  |m :s |m :r |m :fe |s || l |s.f :m |r :d.r
:s, |d :r |r.d :d.t, |d :d |t, || r |r :-.d |t, :d
:m  |s :s |s :s |s :d |r || f |s :s |s :s.l
:d, |d :t, |d :s, |d.t, :l, |s, || r.d |t, :d |s,.f, :m,.f,

|m :r |d || r |m :m |r :s |s :fe |s || m
|d :t, |d || t, |d :d |d :t, |l,.d :r.d |t, || s,
|s :-.f |m || s |s :s |s :r |m :r |r || d
|s, :s, |d || s, |d :m, |s,.l, :t,.s, |d.l, :r |s, || d.t,

|f :m |r :d |d :t, |d || d |d
|l, :s,.l, |t, :-.l, |s, :s, |s, || l, |s,
|d.r :m |s.f :m |m :r |m || f |m
|l,.t, :d |s, :l, |m,.f, :s, |d, || f, |d,
```

A-men.

Dedication of a Church.

ALL things are Thine; no gift have we,
Lord of all gifts, to offer Thee:
And hence with grateful hearts to-day,
Thine own before Thy feet we lay.

2 Thy will was in the builders' thought;
Thy hand unseen amidst us wrought;
Through mortal motive, scheme and plan,
Thy wise eternal purpose ran.

3 In weakness and in want we call
On Thee for whom the heavens are small;
Thy glory is Thy children's good,
Thy joy Thy tender Fatherhood.

4 O Father, deign these walls to bless;
Fill with Thy love their emptiness;
And let their door a gateway be
To lead us from ourselves to Thee.

JOHN GREENLEAF WHITTIER, 1807–92.

[May be sung to EISENACH, No. 241.]

255

INTERCESSION. (75. 75. 75. 75. 88.) WILLIAM HUTCHINS CALLCOTT, 1807-82.

Doh = A♭. *In moderate time.* Last two lines from MENDELSSOHN, 1809-47.

```
s, :-.m  |m   :r   |d   :d     |d   :—  |t,  :d   |r   :m    |r    :—  |—   :—  ||
s, :-.d  |t,  :t,  |l,  :l,    |l,  :—  |s,  :s,  |s,  :s,   |s,   :—  |—   :f, ||
m  :-.s  |s   :f   |m   :m     |f   :m  |r   :d   |t,  :d    |t,   :—  |s,  :—  ||
d  :-.d  |s,  :s,  |l,  :s,    |f   :—  |f,  :m,  |r,  :d,   |s,   :—  |t,, :—  ||

s, :-.m  |m   :r   |d   :r.m   |f   :—  |l,  :l,  |t,  :t,   |d    :—  |—   :—  ||
m, :-.s, |se, :se, |l,  :l,    |l,  :—  |f,  :f,  |f,  :f,   |m,   :—  |—   :—  ||
s, :-.d  |t,  :m   |m   :l.s   |f   :—  |r   :r   |r   :r    |d    :—  |—   :—  ||
d, :-.d, |m,  :m,  |l,  :f,.m, |r,  :—  |f,  :r,  |s,  :s,   |d,   :—  |—   :—  ||

                                                   E♭.t.
m  :-.m   |r   :d   |d   :r    |m   :—  |m   :m   |(m)l :t    |d'   :—  |—   :—  ||
m, :-.ba, |se, :l,  |l,  :l,   |se, :—  |l,  :se, |(l)r :r    |d    :—  |—   :—  ||
d  :-.d   |r   :m   |m   :l,   |t,  :—  |d   :t,  |(d)f :s.f  |m    :—  |—   :—  ||
d  :-.d   |t,  :l,  |s,  :f,   |m,  :—  |d,  :m,  |(l)r :s,   |d    :—  |—   :—  ||

                                                              f.A♭.
d' :-.t  |l   :s   |s   :f     |m   :—  |s   :f.r |d   :t,  |(d)s, :—  |—   :—  ||
d  :-.d  |d   :d   |d   :r     |d   :—  |ta, :l,  |s,  :s,  |(s)r, :—  |—   :—  ||
m  :-.m  |f   :s   |d   :s     |s   :—  |d   :r.f |m   :r   |(m)t, :—  |—   :—  ||
l, :-.s, |f,  :m,  |l,  :t,    |d   :—  |m,  :f,  |s,  :s,  |(d)s, :—  |f,  :—  ||

s,  :—  |l,  :r   |d   :—  |t,  :t,  |d   :—  |f   :f   |f   :—  |—
s,  :—  |s,  :f,  |m,  :—  |r,  :r,  |d,  :d  |t,  :l,  |s,  :—  |—
d   :—  |d   :l   |s   :—  |f   :f   |m   :—  |f   :m   |r   :—  |—
m,  :—  |f,  :f,  |s,  :—  |—   :s,  |l,  :—  |r   :d   |t,  :—  |—

:f  |m  :—  |m   :—  |r   :l,  |t,  :d  |d   :—  |t,  :t,  |d   :—  |—  :—  ||d  |d  ||
:s, |s, :—  |ta, :—  |l,  :—   |l,  :—  |s,  :—  |—   :s,  |s,  :—  |—  :—  ||l, |s, ||
:r  |d  :—  |s   :—  |fe  :—   |f   :—  |r   :—  |—   :r   |m   :—  |—  :—  ||f  |m  ||
:t, |d  :—  |de  :—  |r   :—   |r,  :—  |s,  :—  |—   :s,  |d,  :—  |—  :—  ||f, |d, ||
                                                                        A-men.
```

WHEN the weary, seeking rest,
To Thy goodness flee;
When the heavy-laden cast
All their load on Thee;
When the troubled, seeking peace,
On Thy Name shall call;
When the sinner, seeking life,
At Thy feet shall fall;
Hear then in love, O Lord, the cry,
In heaven, Thy dwelling-place on high.

2 When the child, with grave fresh lip,
Youth, or maiden fair,
When the agèd, weak and grey,
Seek Thy face in prayer;
When the widow weeps to Thee,
Sad and lone and low;
When the orphan brings to Thee
All his orphan woe;
Hear then in love, O Lord, the cry,
In heaven, Thy dwelling-place on high.

3 When the stranger asks a home,
All his toils to end;
When the hungry craveth food,
And the poor a friend;
When the sailor on the wave
Bows the fervent knee;
When the soldier on the field
Lifts his heart to Thee;
Hear then in love, O Lord, the cry,
In heaven, Thy dwelling-place on high.

4 When the man of toil and care,
In the city crowd,
When the shepherd on the moor,
Names the Name of God;
When the learnèd and the high,
Tired of earthly fame,
Upon higher joys intent,
Name the blessèd Name;
Hear then in love, O Lord, the cry,
In heaven, Thy dwelling-place on high.

5 When the worldling, sick at heart,
Lifts his soul above;
When the prodigal looks back
To his Father's love;
When the proud man from his pride
Stoops to seek Thy face;
When the burdened brings his guilt
To Thy throne of grace;
Hear then in love, O Lord, the cry,
In heaven, Thy dwelling-place on high.

HORATIUS BONAR, 1808–89.

Also the following:

115–27 *Hymns of our Lord's Resurrection*
183 Spirit Divine, attend our prayers
207 Christ is made the sure foundation
449 My God, is any hour so sweet
450 Come, my soul, thy suit prepare
451 Approach, my soul, the mercy-seat
452 Present with the two or three
493 Father of men, in whom are one

MORNING.

256 MORNING HYMN. (L.M.)

FRANÇOIS HIPPOLYTE BARTHÉLÉMON, 1741–1808.
Arranged by SAMUEL SEBASTIAN WESLEY, 1810–76.

Doh = A♭. *Moderately quick.* E♭.t.

```
:d  |m  :m  |m  :f.m |r  :r     |r  :[s]d' |t  :d'   |t.l :s.f |m  :r  |d
:s, |d  :d  |d  :r.d |t, :t,.l, |s, :[s]d  |f  :m    |d   :r   |d  :t, |d
:m  |s  :s  |l  :l   |r  :fe, d |s  :[r]s  |s  :s.d' |d'  :l   |s  :s.f|m
:d  |d  :d  |l, :f,  |s, :l,    |t, :[t]m  |r  :d    |f   :f,  |s, :s, |d
```

f.A♭.

```
:[d]s,.l, |t,:d   |r  :t,.d   |r  :m  |f  :m  |l, :t, |d.m:s.f   |m  :r  |d  || d  |d
:[d]s,    |s,:fe, |s, :s,     |s, :s, |f, :s, |l, :f, |s, :d     |d  :t, |d  || l, |s,
:[m]t,.d  |r :r   |r  :s,.l,  |t, :de |r  :d  |d  :r  |d  :s.l   |s  :s.f|m  || f  |m
:[d]s,    |s,:l,  |t, :s,     |f, :m, |r, :m, |f, :r, |m, :m,.f, |s, :s, |d, || f, |d,
```

A-men.

AWAKE, my soul, and with the sun
Thy daily stage of duty run;
Shake off dull sloth, and joyful rise,
To pay thy morning sacrifice.

2 Thy precious time misspent redeem;
Each present day thy last esteem;
Improve thy talent with due care;
For the great day thyself prepare.

3 In conversation be sincere;
Keep conscience as the noontide clear;
Think how all-seeing God thy ways
And all thy secret thoughts surveys.

4 Wake, and lift up thyself, my heart,
And with the angels bear thy part,
Who all night long unwearied sing
High praise to the eternal King.

5 I wake, I wake, ye heavenly choir!
May your devotion me inspire,
That I, like you, my age may spend,
Like you, may on my God attend.

Unison. *Slow.* 6 Praise God, from whom all blessings flow;
Praise Him, all creatures here below;
Praise Him above, ye heavenly host;
Praise Father, Son, and Holy Ghost.

THOMAS KEN, 1637–1711.

257

ST. OLAVE. (L.M.)

Robert Hudson, 1732–1815.
Arranged by Samuel Sebastian Wesley, 1810–76.

Doh = E. *In moderate time.*

:d | m.,f:s :l | d :t, :d | f :m :r | m :— :d | m :— :l
:d | d :— :l, | s, :— :d | r :d :t, | d :— :d | d :— :m
:m | d.,r:m :f | m :r :d | l :s :s | s :— :m | s :— :d'
:d | d :— :f, | s, :— :l, | f, :s, :— | d :— :d | d :—.t,:l,

| s :fe :s | l :s :fe | s :— | m | f :l :d' | l :s :d | r.,m:f :m
| r :— :t, | m :r :— | r :— | d | d :— :d | d :— :d | t,.,d:r :d
| t :l :s | d' :t :l | t :— | s | f :— :l | f :m :s | s :— :s
| r :— :m | d :r :— | s :— || d | l, :— :f, | d :— :m | r.,d:t, :d

m :r :m.f	s :d'.t :l.s	s :f :m	f :m :r	d :—		d	d	
d :t, :d	d :— :d	r :t, :d	d :— :t,	d :—		l,	s,	
s :— :d.r	m :l.s :f.m	s :— :s	l :s :s.f	m :—		f	m	
s, :— :d	d :— :d	t, :s, :d	f, :s, :s,	d :—		f,	d	

A-men.

ALL praise to Thee who safe hast kept,
And hast refreshed me while I slept!
Grant, Lord, when I from death shall wake,
I may of endless light partake.

2 Lord, I my vows to Thee renew;
Disperse my sins as morning dew;
Guard my first springs of thought and will,
And with Thyself my spirit fill.

3 Direct, control, suggest, this day,
All I design, or do, or say,
That all my powers, with all their might,
In Thy sole glory may unite.

Unison. 4 Praise God, from whom all blessings flow;
Praise Him, all creatures here below;
Praise Him above, ye heavenly host;
Praise Father, Son, and Holy Ghost.

Thomas Ken, 1637–1711.

258 IAM LUCIS. (L.M.)

Doh = G. *In free rhythm.* Plainsong Melody.

Doh	:r	:-.d	:d	‖	Doh	:d	:t,	:r	:-.r	:m ‖
Soh,	:s,	:-.s,	:s,	‖	Soh,	:s,	:s,	:l,	:s,	:s, ‖
Me	:s	:-.m	:m	‖	Doh	:d	:r	:r	:t,	:d ‖
Doh	:t,	:-.d	:d	‖	Me,	:m,	:s,	:f,	:s,	:d, ‖

Me	:r	:-.d	:d	‖	Doh	:d	:d	:r	:-.d	:d	:— ‖	d :—	|	d :— ‖
Doh	:t,	:-.l,	:l,	‖	Me,	:s,	:m,	:s,	:s,	:m,	:— ‖	l, :—	|	s, :— ‖
Soh	:s	:-.m	:m	‖	Doh	:d	:d	:d	:t,	:d	:— ‖	d :r	|	m :— ‖
Doh	:s,	:-.l,	:l,	‖	Lah,	:m,	:l,	:s,	:s,	:d,	:— ‖	f, :—	|	d, :— ‖
												A	-	men.

Iam lucis orto sidere.

NOW that the daylight | fills the sky,
We lift our | hearts to God on high,
That He, in all we | do or say,
Would keep us | free from harm to-day:

2 Would guard our hearts and | tongues from strife,
From anger's | din would hide our life,
From all ill sights would | turn our eyes,
Would close our | ears from vanities:

3 Would keep our inmost | conscience pure,
Our souls from | folly would secure,
Would bid us check the | pride of sense
With due and | holy abstinence.

4 So we, when this new | day is gone
And night in | turn is drawing on,
With conscience by the | world unstained,
Shall praise His | Name for victory gained.

8th century: *tr.* by JOHN MASON NEALE, 1818–66.

259 MELCOMBE. (L.M.)

SAMUEL WEBBE, 1740–1816.

Doh = E♭. *Moderately slow.*

:s |s :f |m :r |d :l |s :s |d' :t |l :s |s :fe |s
:d |s, :l,.t, |d :t, |l, :d |d :r |d :r |r :t, |m :r.d |t,
:m |m :f |s :s.f |m :f |m :s |fe :s |fe :s |l :l |s
:d |m :r |d :s, |l, :f, |d :t, |l, :t,.d |r :m |d :r |s,

:m |m :f |s :m |r :-.m |f :f |m :r |s :f |m :r |d || f |m
:d |d :t,.l, |s, :d |t, :-.de |r :r |d :t, |d :d |d :t, |d || d |d
:s |s :f |m :s |s :-.s |l :s |s :s |s :l |s :s.f |m || l |s
:d |d :r |m :d |s :-.m |r :t, |d :s,.f, |m, :f, |s, :s, |d || f, |d

A-men.

O TIMELY happy, timely wise,
Hearts that with rising morn arise,
Eyes that the beam celestial view
Which evermore makes all things new !

2 New every morning is the love
Our wakening and uprising prove,
Through sleep and darkness safely brought,
Restored to life, and power, and thought.

3 New mercies, each returning day,
Hover around us while we pray,—
New perils past, new sins forgiven,
New thoughts of God, new hopes of heaven.

4 If, on our daily course, our mind
Be set to hallow all we find,
New treasures still, of countless price,
God will provide for sacrifice.

5 We need not bid, for cloistered cell,
Our neighbour and our work farewell,
Nor strive to wind ourselves too high
For sinful man beneath the sky ;

6 The trivial round, the common task,
Will furnish all we ought to ask,—
Room to deny ourselves, a road
To bring us daily nearer God.

7 Seek we no more ; content with these,
Let present rapture, comfort, ease,
As Heaven shall bid them, come and go :
The secret this of rest below.

8 Only, O Lord, in Thy dear love,
Fit us for perfect rest above ;
And help us, this and every day,
To live more nearly as we pray.

[May be sung to WINSCOTT, No. 338.]

JOHN KEBLE, 1792–1866.

260 BRISTOL. (C.M.)

Ravenscroft's Psalter, 1621.

Doh = G. *Moderately slow.* f.C.

|s :— |f :r |m :d |r :-.r |d :— ‖ f d' :— |t :l |l :se |l :— ‖
|s, :— |l, :s, |s, :s, |l, :t, |d :— ‖ l m :— |m :d.r |m :-.r |de :— ‖
|m :— |r :t, |d :s |f :r |m :— ‖ r l :— |se :l |t :t |l :— ‖
|d :— |f, :s, |d, :m, |f, :s, |d, :— ‖ r l, :— |m :f |m :m |l, :— ‖

G.t.

|l r :— |m :f |m :d |r :d |t, :— ‖ s :— |m :f |r :r |d :— ‖ d |d ‖
|r s, :— |s, :f, |s, :s, |f, :m,.f, |s, :— ‖ r :— |d :d |d :t, |d :— ‖ l, |s, ‖
|fe t, :— |d :d |d :d |l, :d |r :— ‖ s :— |s :l |r :s.f |m :— ‖ f |m ‖
|r s, :— |d :l, |d :m, |f, :l, |s, :— ‖ t, :— |d :f, |s, :s, |d, :— ‖ f, |d, ‖

A-men.

FAUX-BOURDON SETTING.

Thomas Ravenscroft, *c.* 1582–1635.

Doh = G. f.C.

|d :— |r :t, |d :s |f :r |m :— ‖ :r l |se :l |d' :t |l :— ‖
| :s, |l, :s, |s, :-.d |l, :t, |d :— ‖ l m :— |m :d.r |m :-.r |de :— ‖
|s :— |f :r |m :d |r :-.r |d :— ‖ f d' :— |t :l |l :se |l :— ‖
|d :— |f, :s, |d, :m, |f, :s, |d, :— ‖ r l, :— |m :f |m :m |l, :— ‖

G.t.

| :fe t, |d :d |d :s |f :m.f |s :— ‖ m :r |-.d :d |— :t, |d :— ‖
|r s, :— |s, :l, |s, :-.d |l, :l, |r, :— ‖ :ta, |s, :l, |s, :-.f, |m, :— ‖
|l r :— |m :f |m :d |r :d |t, :— ‖ s :— |m :f |r :r |d :— ‖
|r s, :— |d :l, |d :m, |f, :l, |s, :— ‖ s, :— |d :f, |s, :s, |d, :— ‖

Iam lucis orto sidere.

NOW that the daystar glimmers bright,
We suppliantly pray
That He, the uncreated Light,
May guide us on our way.

2 No sinful word, nor deed of wrong,
Nor thoughts that idly rove,
But simple truth be on our tongue,
And in our hearts be love.

3 And while the hours in order flow,
O Christ, securely fence
Our gates, beleaguered by the foe,—
The gate of every sense.

4 And grant that to Thine honour, Lord,
Our daily toil may tend:
That we begin it at Thy word,
And in Thy blessing end.

8th century; *tr.* by John Henry Newman, 1801–90.

261

PSALM 135 (MINISTRES DE L'ÉTERNEL). (7 7. 7 7. 7 7.)

Doh = D. *In moderate time.* *French Psalter*, 1562.

|d' :— |l :— |s :s |l :t |d' :— |— :— |s :— |l :— |s :f |m :r
|m :— |f :— |s :m |f :f |m :— |— :— |m :r |d :r |m :r |d :t,
|s :— |t :— |d' :d' |d' :r' |s :— |— :— |d' :t |l :t |d' :l |s :s
|d :— |r :— |m :d |f :r |d :— |— :— |m :— |f :— |m :f |s :s,

|d :— |— :— ||d :— |m :— |r :d |m :f |s :— |— :— |m :—
|l, :— |— :— ||l, :— |t, :— |l, :d |d :d |d :— |t, :— |d :—
|m :— |— :— ||d' :— |s :— |l :s |s :f |r :— |s :— |s :—
|l, :— |— :— ||l :— |s :— |f :m |d :l, |s, :— |— :— |d :r

|s :— |l :t |d' :l |s :— |— :— ||s :— |f :— |m :s |f :m
|d :t, |m :m |m :r |t, :— |r :— ||d :— |r :— |m :r |r :de
|s :— |s :s |s :fe |s :— |t :— ||d' :s |l :t |d' :ta |l :l
|m :r |d :t, |l, :r |s, :— |s :f ||m :— |r :— |d :s, |l, :l,

r :—	— :—	r :—	m :—	s :f	m :—	r :—	d :—	— :—	— :—		d	d	
r :—	— :—	r :—	de :—	m :r	d :—	t, :—	d :—	— :—	— :—		l,	s,	
f :—	— :—	f :—	l :—	l :l	s :—	s :f	m :—	— :—	— :—		f	m	
r :—	d :—	ta, :—	l, :—	r :r	m :f	s :s,	d :—	— :—	— :—		f,	d	

A-men.

CHRIST, whose glory fills the skies,
Christ, the true, the only Light,
Sun of Righteousness, arise,
Triumph o'er the shades of night.
Dayspring from on high, be near ;
Daystar, in my heart appear.

2 Dark and cheerless is the morn
Unaccompanied by Thee ;
Joyless is the day's return,
Till Thy mercy's beams I see,
Till they inward light impart,
Glad my eyes, and warm my heart.

3 Visit, then, this soul of mine ;
Pierce the gloom of sin and grief ;
Fill me, Radiancy Divine ;
Scatter all my unbelief ;
More and more Thyself display,
Shining to the perfect day.

[May be sung to JESU, MEINE ZUVERSICHT, No. 394.] CHARLES WESLEY, 1707–88.

262 MORGENGLANZ DER EWIGKEIT. (77. 77. 73.)

Freylinghausen's Gesangbuch, 1704.

Doh = Eb. *In moderate time.* *D.C.*

m :r.d	s :l	s :f	m :—	d' :t	l :t	d' :t	l :—	s :—	— :—	
s, :l,	d :d	t, :l,.t,	d :—	d :r	r :r	d :r	m :r.d	t, :—	— :—	
d :m	s :f	r :f	s :—	l :s	fe :s	s :—	— :fe	s :—	— :—	
d :l,	m, :f,	s, :r	d :—	l, :t,.d	r :t,	m :r	d :r	s, :—	— :—	

s :s	l :s	f :m	r :—	m :—	r :—	d :—	— :—		d	d	
d :d.t,	l, :t,	d :d	t, :—	d :—	— :t,	d :—	— :—		l,	s,	
m :s	f :m.r	d :s	s :—	s :l	r :s.f	m :—	— :—		f	m	
d :m,	f, :s,	l, :d	s, :—	m, :f,	s, :—	d :—	— :—		f,	d	

A-men.

Morgenglanz der Ewigkeit.

JESUS, Sun of Righteousness,
Brightest Beam of love divine,
With the early morning rays
Do Thou on our darkness shine,
And dispel with purest light
All our night.

2 As on drooping herb and flower
Falls the soft, refreshing dew,
Let Thy Spirit's grace and power
All our weary souls renew,
Showers of blessing over all
Softly fall.

3 Like the sun's reviving ray,
May Thy love, with tender glow,
All our coldness melt away,
Warm and cheer us forth to go,
Gladly serve Thee and obey,
All the day.

4 O, our only Hope and Guide,
Never leave us nor forsake;
Keep us ever at Thy side
Till the eternal morning break,
Moving on to Zion hill,
Homeward still.

5 Lead us all our days and years
In Thy straight and narrow way;
Lead us through the vale of tears
To the land of perfect day,
Where Thy people, fully blest,
Safely rest.

CHRISTIAN KNORR VON ROSENROTH, 1636–89; *tr.* by JANE LAURIE BORTHWICK, 1813–97.

263 CHRISTE SANCTORUM. (11 11. 11 5.)

Doh = Eb. *Unison. In moderate time.* *La Feillée's Méthode du Plain-Chant*, 1808.

|s :m.f |m.r :d |m.,f :s.s |l :s |s :l.t |d' :s |d'.,t :l.t |l :s ||

|d' :s.l |s.f :m |f.,m :f.s |f.m :r |s :d.f |m :r |d :— ||

	d :— :t,	d :—	
	l, :— :s,	s, :—	
	m :f :r	m :—	
	l, :f, :s,	d/d, :—	

A - men.

Nocte surgentes.

FATHER, we praise Thee, now the night is over ;
Active and watchful, stand we all before Thee ;
Singing, we offer prayer and meditation :
Thus we adore Thee.

2 Monarch of all things, fit us for Thy mansions ;
Banish our weakness, health and wholeness sending ;
Bring us to heaven, where Thy saints united
Joy without ending.

3 All-holy Father, Son and equal Spirit,
Trinity blessèd, send us Thy salvation ;
Thine is the glory, gleaming and resounding
Through all creation.

Attributed to St. Gregory the Great, 540-604 ; *tr.* by Percy Dearmer, 1867-

264 EPWORTH. (C.M.)

Doh = E♭. *In moderate time.* Charles Wesley, 1757-1834.

:d | m :s | d' :-.m | r.l :s.f | m :s | d' :t | l.s :fe | s :— | — ||
:d | d :r | d :d | d :t, | d :d | d :r | m :r | r :— | — ||
:m | s :s | m :m | f :r | m :m | m.fe :s | d' :l | t :— | — ||
:d | d :t, | l, :s, | f, :s, | d :d.t, | l, :t, | d :r | s, :— | — ||

:s | f :m | l :-.f | m :r | s :s | d' :d.r | m :r | d :— | — || d | d ||
:m | r :de | r :-.r | d :t, | d :d | d :d | d :t, | d :— | — || l, | s, ||
:t | l :l | l :-.l | s :s | s :m | m :l | s :-.f | m :— | — || f | m ||
:m | l :s | f :m.r | s :f | m :d | l, :f, | s, :s, | d :— | — || f, | d ||

A-men.

O LORD of life, Thy quickening voice
Awakes my morning song !
In gladsome words I would rejoice
That I to Thee belong.

2 I see Thy light, I feel Thy wind ;
The world, it is Thy word ;
Whatever wakes my heart and mind
Thy presence is, my Lord.

3 Therefore I choose my highest part,
And turn my face to Thee ;
Therefore I stir my inmost heart
To worship fervently.

4 Lord, let me live and will this day—
Keep rising from the dead ;
Lord, make my spirit good and gay—
Give me my daily bread.

5 Within my heart speak, Lord, speak on,
My heart alive to keep,
Till comes the night, and, labour done,
In Thee I fall asleep.

George MacDonald, 1824-1905.

265

BARMOUTH. (77. 77. 77.)

Doh = C. *In moderate time.* WALTER CECIL MACFARREN, 1826–1905.

```
|d  :r  |m  :-.m  |m  :f  |s  :—  |l  :t  |d' :t  |l  :t    |s  :—  ||
|d  :t, |d  :-.d  |d  :d  |r  :—  |m  :s  |s  :s  |s  :fe   |s  :—  ||
|s  :s  |d' :-.d' |d' :d' |t  :—  |d' :r' |d' :r' |m' :r'.d'|t  :—  ||
|m  :s  |d' :-.d' |t  :l  |s  :—  |s  :f  |m  :r  |d  :r    |s  :—  ||

|s  :s  |l  :-.t  |d' :r' |s  :—  |d' :l  |f  :-.f |s  :m  |r  :—  ||
|r  :r  |f  :-.s  |s  :f  |m  :—  |d  :m  |r  :-.r |r  :d  |r  :—  ||
|t  :t  |d' :-.r' |d' :s  |s  :—  |s  :l  |l  :-.l |s  :s  |t  :—  ||
|s  :s  |f  :-.f  |m  :t, |d  :—  |m  :d  |r  :-.d |t, :d  |s  :—  ||

|d :r   |m :-.m   |m :f   |s :—  |l :t |d' :— |s :— |m' :— |r' :— |d' :— ||d' |d' ||
|d :r   |m :-.m   |m :d   |d :—  |d :r |d  :— |m :— |s  :— |f  :— |m  :— ||f  |m  ||
|d':d'  |d' :-.d' |d':d'  |ta :— |l :s |s  :— |s :— |l  :— |t  :— |d' :— ||l  |s  ||
|d':d'  |d' :-.d' |ta :l  |m :—  |f :f |m  :— |d :— |s, :— |s, :— |d  :— ||f  |d  ||
                                                                      A-men.
```

AT Thy feet, O Christ, we lay
Thine own gift of this new day;
Doubt of what it holds in store
Makes us crave Thine aid the more;
Lest it prove a time of loss,
Mark it, Saviour, with Thy Cross.

2 If it flow on calm and bright,
Be Thyself our chief delight;
If it bring unknown distress,
Good is all that Thou canst bless;
Only, while its hours begin,
Pray we, keep them clear of sin.

3 We in part our weakness know,
And in part discern our foe;
Well for us, before Thine eyes
All our danger open lies;
Turn not from us, while we plead
Thy compassions and our need.

4 Fain would we Thy word embrace,
Live each moment on Thy grace,
All our selves to Thee consign,
Fold up all our wills in Thine,
Think, and speak, and do, and be
Simply that which pleases Thee.

5 Hear us, Lord, and that right soon;
Hear, and grant the choicest boon
That Thy love can e'er impart,
Loyal singleness of heart;
So shall this and all our days,
Christ our God, show forth Thy praise.

WILLIAM BRIGHT, 1824–1901.

266 MORNING. (77. 77. 77.)

Doh = D. *Brightly.* WILLIAM HENRY MONK, 1823–89.

s :-.s	d^1 :m	m :r	d :—	m :-.m	l :s	f :m	r :—
m :-.f	s :d	d :t_1	d :—	d :-.d	d :d	r :d	t_1 :—
d^1 :-.t	d^1 :s	s :-.f	m :—	s :-.s	f :m	s :s	s :—
d :-.r	m :-.f	s :s_1	d :—	d :-.d	f_1 :d	t_1 :d	s_1 :—

A.t. f.D.

m :-.m	d^1 :t	^{l}r :d	d :t_1	d :-.r	m :s	m :r	^{d}s :—
d :-.r	d :r	$^{m}l_1$:l_1	s_1 :—	m_1 :-.s_1	s_1 :s_1	s_1 :s_1.f_1	$^{m}t_1$:—
s :-.se	l :se	^{l}r :f	m :r	d :-.t_1	d :d	d :t_1	^{d}s :—
d :-.t_1	l_1 :t_1	$^{d}f_1$:f_1	s_1 :—	l_1 :-.s_1	d_1.r_1 :m_1.f_1	s_1 :s_1	$^{d}s_1$:—

s :-.s	l :f	r :s	m :—	f :s	l :s	l :t	d^1 :—		d^1	d^1	
d :-.d	d :d	d :t_1	d :—	d :d	d :d	f :r	m :—		f	m	
m :-.m	f :l	s :s	s :—	f :m	f :d^1	d^1 :s	s :—		l	s	
d :-.d	f :r	s :s_1	d :—	l_1 :d	f :m	f :s	d :—		f	d	

A-men.

HAIL, thou bright and sacred morn,
Risen with gladness in thy beams !
Light, which not of earth is born,
From thy dawn in glory streams ;
Airs of heaven are breathed around,
And each place is holy ground.

2 Great Creator, who this day
From Thy perfect work didst rest,
By the souls that own Thy sway
Hallowed be its hours and blest ;
Cares of earth aside be thrown,
This day given to heaven alone.

3 Saviour, who this day didst break
The dark prison of the tomb,
Bid my slumbering soul awake,
Shine through all its sin and gloom ;
Let me, from my bonds set free,
Rise from sin, and live to Thee.

4 Blessèd Spirit, Comforter,
Sent this day from Christ on high,
Lord, on me Thy gifts confer,
Cleanse, illumine, sanctify ;
All Thine influence shed abroad ;
Lead me to the truth of God.

JULIA ANNE ELLIOTT, ? –1841.

267 DOMINICA. (S.M.)

Doh = A. *Brightly.* HERBERT STANLEY OAKELEY, 1830–1903.

s, :s,.s, | d :r | m :— | — :m | r :m | f :r | t, :— | — ||
m, :f,.f, | m, :l, | se, :— | — :l, | l, :l,.s, | f, :l, | l, :s, | — ||
d :r.t, | d :l, | t, :— | — :d | r :de | r :r | r :— | — ||
d :t,.s, | l, :f, | m, :— | — :l, | f, :m, | r, :f, | s, :— | — ||

:s, | l, :t, | d :t, | d :r | m :s | f :m | r :t, | d :— | — :— || d | d ||
:r, | m, :s, | s, :s, | s, :f, | m, :l, | l,.t, :d | l, :s, | s, :— | — :— || l, | s, ||
:t, | d :r | m :r | d :t, | d :m | r :s | f :r | m :— | — :— || f | m ||
:s, | s, :f, | m, :f, | m, :r, | d, :de | r, :m, | f, :s, | d, :— | — :— || f, | d, ||

A-men.

FAREHAM. (S.M.)

Doh = G. *Brightly.* JOHN GOSS, 1800–80.

:s, | d :m | s :l | s :— | — :m | r :d | r :f | m :— | — ||
:s, | s, :s, | d :d | d :— | — :d | t, :d | d :t, | d :— | — ||
:m | m :m | m :f | m :— | — :s | s :m | l :s | s :— | — ||
:d | d :d | d :f, | d :— | — :d | s, :l, | f, :s, | d, :— | — ||

D.t. f.G.

:^{m}l | s :f | d' :l | s :f | m :^{d}s, | d :f | m :r | d :— | — || l, | d ||
:^{s}d | d :t, | d :d | r :t, | d :^{d}s, | s, :l, | s, :f, | m, :— | — || f, | m, ||
:^{d}f | m :f | s :l | r :s | s :^{m}t, | d :d | d :t, | d :— | — || d | d ||
:^{d}f | d :r | m :f | t, :s, | d :^{ta}f, | m, :r, | s, :s, | d, :— | — || f, | d, ||

A-men.

[*By permission of Novello & Co., Ltd.*]

THIS is the day of light:
Let there be light to-day;
O Dayspring, rise upon our night,
And chase its gloom away.

2 This is the day of rest:
Our failing strength renew;
On weary brain and troubled breast
Shed Thou Thy freshening dew.

3 This is the day of peace:
Thy peace our spirits fill;
Bid Thou the blasts of discord cease,
The waves of strife be still.

4 This is the day of prayer:
Let earth to heaven draw near;
Lift up our hearts to seek Thee there,
Come down to meet us here.

5 This is the first of days:
Send forth Thy quickening breath,
And wake dead souls to love and praise,
O Vanquisher of death!

JOHN ELLERTON, 1826–93.

268

BERNO. (76. 76. D.)

Doh = D. *In moderate time.* ARTHUR HENRY MANN, 1850-

:s |m :r |d :d' |t :l |s :f |m :f |s :l |r :— |—
:d |d :t, |d :d |d :r |s, :t, |d :t, |d :d |d :— |t,
:m |s :f |s :se |l :t |d' :s |s :f |m :l |s :— |—
:d |d :r |m :m |f :— |m :r |d :r |m :f |s :— |—

A.t. f.D.

:s |m :r |d :ᵈ'f |f :m |r :d |d :-.m |m :r |ᵈs :— |—
:t, |d :t, |d :ʳs, |d :— |l, :l, |s, :-.s, |f, :f, |ᵐt, :— |—
:s |s :f |s :ˡr |s :— |f :re |m :-.d |l, :t, |ᵈs :— |—
:s, |d :r |m :ᶠᵉt, |d :— |f, :fe, |s, :-.s, |s, :s, |ᵈ,s, :— |—

:f |m :-.m |f :m |l :— |m :m |r :-.r |m :r |s :— |—
:t, |d :-.s, |se, :se, |l, :— |l, :d |l, :-.l, |l, :l, |r :— |—
:s |s :-.m |r :m |m :— |m :s |fe :-.fe |s :fe |s :— |—
:s, |d :-.d |t, :r |d :— |d :l, |r :-.r |d :d |t, :— |—

:s |s :d' |t :l |s :f |m :l |s :-.d |m :r |d :— |— ||d |d
:f |m :d |f :l, |r :t, |d :d |d :-.d |t, :t, |s, :— |— ||l, |s,
:t |d' :s |f :m |s :— |s :r |m :-.m |s :f |m :— |— ||f |m
:s, |d :m |r :d |t, :s, |d :fe, |s, :-.s, |s, :s, |d :— |— ||f, |d

A-men.

O DAY of rest and gladness,
O day of joy and light,
O balm of care and sadness,
Most beautiful, most bright!
On thee the high and lowly,
Before the eternal throne,
Sing 'Holy, holy, holy,'
To the great Three in One.

2 On thee, at the creation,
The light first had its birth;
On thee, for our salvation,
Christ rose from depths of earth;
On thee our Lord victorious
The Spirit sent from heaven:
And thus on thee most glorious
A triple light was given.

3 To-day on weary nations
The heavenly manna falls;
To holy convocations
The silver trumpet calls,
Where gospel light is glowing
With pure and radiant beams,
And living water flowing
With soul-refreshing streams.

4 New graces ever gaining
From this our day of rest,
We reach the rest remaining
To spirits of the blest.
To Holy Ghost be praises,
To Father, and to Son;
The Church her voice upraises
To Thee, blest Three in One.

CHRISTOPHER WORDSWORTH, 1807-85.

269 HOLY CROSS. (8 6. 8 4.)

ARTHUR HENRY BROWN, 1830–1926.

Doh = E. *In moderate time.* B.t.

m :f :m | r :— :s | d :— :f | m :r :— | [s]d :m :r

d :d :d | d :t, :t, | d :— :r | d :t, :— | [r]s, :l, :l,

s :l :s | s :— :f | m :— :l | s :— :— | [s]d :d :r

d :d :d | s, :— :s, | l, :— :f, | s, :— :— | [t]m, :l, :f,

f.E.

f :— :t, | [d]s :— || s | s :f :m | l :— :r | f :m :r

l, :— :s,.f, | [m]t, :— || r | m :r :de | r :— :r | r .d:t, :t,

r :— :r | [d]s :— || t | t :l :l | l :— :l | l :s :s

r, :— :s, | [d,]s, :— || s | m :l :-.s | f :— :f .m | r :s :-.f

s :— :d | r :— :— | f :— :— | m :— :— || f | m

d :— :d | d :— :— | t, :— :— | d :— :— || d | d

s :— :m | l :— :— | s :— :— | s :— :— || l | s

m :— :l, | f, :— :— | s, :— :— | d :— :— || f, | d

A-men.

HAIL, sacred day of earthly rest,
From toil and trouble free!
Hail, quiet spirit, bringing peace
And joy to me!

2 A holy stillness, breathing calm
On all the world around,
Uplifts my soul, O God, to Thee,
Where rest is found.

3 No sound of jarring strife is heard,
As weekly labours cease,
No voice but those that sweetly sing
Sweet songs of peace.

4 On all I think or say or do
A ray of light divine
Is shed, O God, this day by Thee,
For it is Thine.

5 All earthly things appear to fade
As, rising high and higher,
The yearning voices strive to join
The heavenly choir.

6 Accept, O God, my hymn of praise
That Thou this day hast given,
Sweet foretaste of that endless day
Of rest in heaven.

GODFREY THRING, 1823–1903.

270 DEVONSHIRE. (76. 76.)

Doh = F. *In moderate time.* English Traditional Melody.

:d | m .m :m :- .m | m .r :d :- .r | m .s :s :f .m | r :— ||
:s, | d .d :d :- .d | d .t, :l, :- .s, | d .t, :l, :l, | t, :— ||
:m | s .s :m :- .f | s .f :m :- .s | s .s :d :f | s :— ||
:d | d .d :d :t,.l, | s, :l, :- .t, | d .m, :f, :r, | s, :— ||

:r | m .f :s :- .l | s .m :d :- .d | d .m :f :-.m.r | d :— || d | d ||
:s, | s,.d :d :- .d | t, :d :- .s, | l, .d :d :-.l,.t, | d :— || l, | s, ||
:f | m .d :d :- .d | m .s :s :f .m | f .s :l :f | m :— || f | m ||
:t, | d .l, :m, :- .f, | s, :l, :- .s, | f, .m, :r, :s, | d d, :— || f, | d, ||

A-men.

THE darkness now is over,
And all the world is bright;
Praise be to Christ, who keepeth
His children safe at night!

2 We cannot tell what gladness
May be our lot to-day,
What sorrow or temptation
May meet us on our way;

3 But this we know most surely,
That, through all good or ill,
God's grace can always help us
To do His holy will.

4 Then, Jesus, let the angels,
Who watched us through the night,
Be all day long beside us,
To guide our steps aright;

5 And help us to remember,
In thought and deed and word,
That we are heirs of heaven,
And children of the Lord.

6 Then, when the evening cometh,
We'll kneel again to pray,
And thank Thee for the blessings
Bestowed throughout the day.

The Children's Hymn Book, 1881.

Also the following:

1 Holy, holy, holy, Lord God Almighty
24 Lord of all being, throned afar
167 When morning gilds the skies
231 All lands and peoples, all the earth
237 Again the morn of gladness
651 Forth in Thy Name, O Lord, I go
115–27 *Hymns of our Lord's Resurrection*

EVENING.

271 SUNSET. (98. 98.)

Doh = E♭. *Unison.* *Moderately slow.* GEORGE GILBERT STOCKS, 1877-

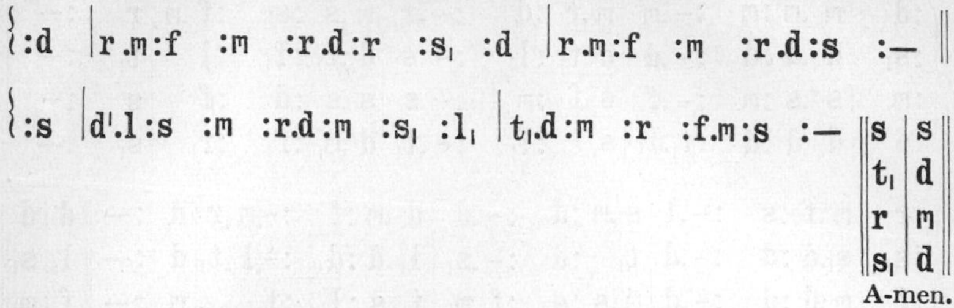

```
:d |r .m :f  :m  :r .d :r  :s,  :d |r .m :f  :m  :r .d :s  :—  ||
:s |d'.l :s  :m  :r.d :m  :s,  :l, |t,.d :m  :r  :f.m :s  :—  ||s |s
                                                              ||t,|d
                                                              ||r |m
                                                              ||s,|d
                                                               A-men.
```

GOTTLOB, ES GEHT. (98. 98.) Old German Melody.

Doh = G. *In moderate time.* Arranged by JOHANN SEBASTIAN BACH, 1685-1750.

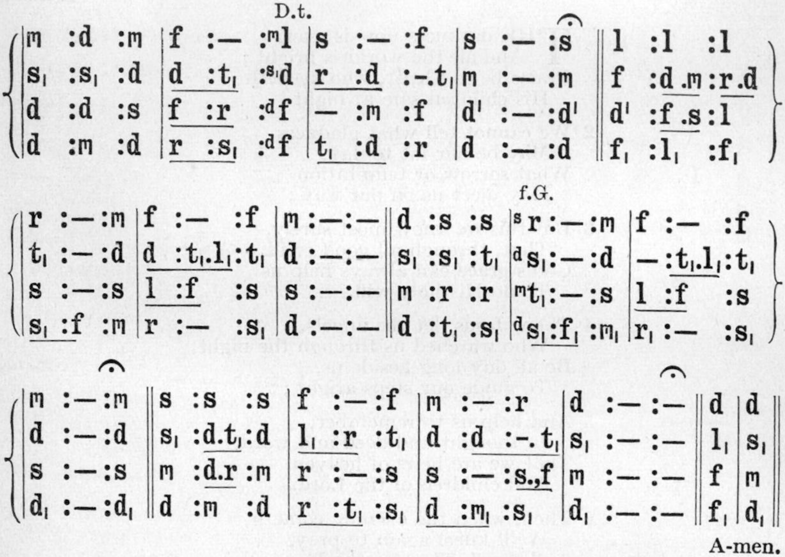

```
                 D.t.
m  :d  :m  |f  :—  :(m)l |s  :—  :f    |s  :— :s  ||l  :l    :l
s, :s, :d  |d  :t, :(s)d |r  :d  :-.t, |m  :— :m  ||f  :d.m  :r.d
d  :d  :s  |f  :r  :(d)f |—  :m  :f    |d' :— :d' ||d' :f.s  :l
d  :m  :d  |r  :s, :(d)f |t, :d  :r    |d  :— :d  ||f, :l,   :f,

                                          f.G.
r  :—:m |f  :—     :f  |m :—:— ||d  :s  :s  |(s)r  :—:m  |f  :—     :f
t, :—:d |d  :t,.l, :t, |d :—:— ||s, :s, :t, |(d)s, :—:d  |—  :t,.l, :t,
s  :—:s |l  :f     :s  |s :—:— ||m  :r  :r  |(m)t, :—:s  |l  :f     :s
s, :f :m|r  :—     :s, |d :—:— ||d  :t, :s, |(d)s, :f,:m,|r, :—     :s,

m  :—:m  ||s  :s    :s |f  :—:f  |m :—:r     |d  :—:— ||d  |d
d  :—:d  ||s, :d.t, :d |l, :r :t, |d :d :-.t, |s, :—:— ||l, |s,
s  :—:s  ||m  :d.r  :m |r  :—:s  |s :—:s.,f  |m  :—:— ||f  |m
d, :—:d, ||d  :m    :d |r  :t,:s, |d :m,:s,   |d, :—:— ||f, |d,
                                                         A-men.
```

BEFORE the day draws near its ending,
And evening steals o'er earth and sky,
Once more to Thee our hymns ascending
Shall speak Thy praises, Lord Most High.

2 Thy Name is blessed by countless numbers
In vaster worlds unseen, unknown,
Whose duteous service never slumbers,
In perfect love and faultless tone.

3 Yet Thou wilt not despise the weakest
Who here in spirit bend the knee ;
Thy Christ hath said, ' Thou, Father, seekest
For such as these to worship Thee.'

4 And through the swell of chanting voices,
The blended notes of age and youth,
Thine ear discerns, Thy love rejoices,
When hearts rise up to Thee in truth.

5 O Light all clear, O Truth most holy,
O boundless Mercy pardoning all,
Before Thy feet, abashed and lowly,
With one last prayer Thy children fall :—

6 When we no more on earth adore Thee,
And others worship here in turn,
O may we sing that song before Thee,
Which none but Thy redeemed can learn.

JOHN ELLERTON, 1826–93.

272 ST. COLUMBA. (64. 66.)

Doh = F. *In moderate time.* HERBERT STEPHEN IRONS, 1834–1905.

:s | f :m | r :r | d :— | — :m | s :— | l :— | r :— | — ||
:d | d :d | d :t_1 | d :— | — :d | r :— | d :— | t_1 :— | — ||
:m | f :s | l :s | m :— | — :s | s :— | fe :— | s :— | — ||
:d | l_1 :m_1 | f_1 :s_1 | d_1 :— | — :d | t_1 :— | l_1 :— | s_1 :— | — ||

:s | s :m | r :m | f :f | m :d | r :— | r :— | d :— | — || d | d ||
:t_1 | ta_1 :ta_1 | l_1 :de | r :t_1 | d :d | d :— | t_1 :— | s_1 :— | — || l_1 | s_1 ||
:r | r :s | f :l | l :f | s :m | s :— | s :— | m :— | — || f | m ||
:s_1 | s_1 :s_1 | l_1 :l_1 | r :r_1 | m_1 :l_1 | s_1 :— | s_1 :— | d_1 :— | — || f_1 | d_1 ||

A-men.

Sol praeceps rapitur.

THE sun is sinking fast,
The daylight dies ;
Let love awake, and pay
Her evening sacrifice.

2 As Christ upon the Cross
His head inclined,
And to His Father's hands
His parting soul resigned,

3 So now herself my soul
Would wholly give
Into His sacred charge
In whom all spirits live ;

4 So now beneath His eye
Would calmly rest—
Without a wish or thought
Abiding in the breast,

5 Save that His will be done,
Whate'er betide—
Dead to herself, and dead
In Him to all beside.

6 Thus would I live ; yet now
Not I, but He
In all His power and love
Henceforth alive in me :

Unison.
7 One sacred Trinity,
One Lord Divine ;
Myself for ever His,
And He for ever mine.

Tr. by EDWARD CASWALL, 1814–78.

273 GLOAMING. (8 4. 8 4. D.)

Doh = E♭. *In moderate time.* JOHN STAINER, 1840–1901.

```
:m  |f  :r   |m  :m    |f  :r   |m  :—  |d  :—  |t, :l,  |r  :—  |—  ‖
:d  |r  :r   |d  :ta,  |l, :t,  |d  :—  |s, :—  |fe,:fe, |s, :—  |—  ‖
:s  |l  :s   |s  :s    |f  :s   |s  :—  |d  :m  |r  :d   |d  :—  |t, ‖
:d  |d  :t,  |d  :de   |r  :s,  |d  :t, |l, :—  |l, :l,  |s, :—  |—  ‖
```

B♭.t. f.E♭.

```
:m  |f  :r   |m  :[s]d   |r  :t,  |d  :r   |m  :d  |r  :—  |[d]s :—  |—  ‖
:m  |r  :r   |d  :[m]l,  |l, :se, |l, :fe, |s, :—  |t, :—  |[d]s :—  |—  ‖
:s  |l  :s   |s  :[m]l,  |t, :r   |d  :d   |d  :m  |f  :—  |[m]t :—  |—  ‖
:d  |d  :t,  |d  :[d]f,  |m, :m,  |l, :l,  |s, :—  |s, :—  |[d]s :—  |—  ‖
```

```
:s  |l  :-.m   |m  :l  |se :l  |t  :—  |d' :—  |l  :f   |m  :—  |r  ‖
:r  |de :-.de  |de :r  |r  :d  |m  :r  |d  :—  |d  :d   |d  :—  |t, ‖
:t  |l  :-.l   |l  :l  |t  :l  |se :—  |l  :—  |l  :d'  |s  :—  |—  ‖
:s  |s  :-.s   |s  :f  |m  :m  |m  :—  |l, :—  |l  :l   |s  :—  |—  ‖
```

```
:r  |m  :f  |s  :se |l  :m   |f  :r   |d  :—  |m  :r  |d  :—  |—  ‖ d  |d  ‖
:t, |d  :r  |m  :m  |f  :ta, |l, :l,  |s, :l, |t, :—  |d  :—  |—  ‖ l, |s, ‖
:s  |d' :t  |ta :ta |l  :s   |f  :f   |m  :—  |f  :—  |m  :—  |—  ‖ f  |m  ‖
:f  |m  :r  |d  :d  |f  :de  |r  :f,  |s, :—  |s, :—  |d  :—  |—  ‖ f, |d  ‖
                                                                  A-men.
```

[*By permission of Novello & Co., Ltd.*]

THE sun declines ; o'er land and sea
Creeps on the night ;
The twinkling stars come one by one
To shed their light ;
With Thee there is no darkness, Lord ;
With us abide,
And 'neath Thy wings we rest secure,
This eventide.

2 Forgive the wrong this day we've done,
Or thought, or said ;
Each moment with its good or ill
To Thee has fled ;
O Father, in Thy mercy great
Will we confide ;
Thy benediction now bestow,
This eventide.

3 And when with morning light we rise,
Kept by Thy care,
We'll lift to Thee, with grateful hearts,
Our morning prayer.
Be Thou through life our Strength and Stay,
Our Guard and Guide
To that dear home where there will be
No eventide.

ROBERT WALMSLEY, 1831–1905.

274 DURHAM. (C.M.)

Doh = F. *Slow.* *Ravenscroft's Psalter*, 1621.

|d :— |s :m |l :s |m :d |r :— ‖ f :— |m :s |l :l |s :— ‖
|s$_1$:— |s$_1$:s$_1$ |l$_1$:t$_1$ |d :d |t$_1$:— ‖ d :— |d :t$_1$ |r :r.d |t$_1$:— ‖
|m :— |r :d |f :r |d :s |s :— ‖ l :— |s :s |s :fe |s :— ‖
|d :— |t$_1$:d |f$_1$:s$_1$ |l$_1$:m$_1$ |s$_1$:— ‖ f$_1$:— |d :m |r :r |s$_1$:— ‖

|s :— |f :m |s :d |t$_1$:d |r :— ‖ m :— |r :f |m :r |d :— ‖ d |d ‖
|s$_1$:— |l$_1$.t$_1$:d |r :s$_1$ |s$_1$:s$_1$ |s$_1$:— ‖ d :— |l$_1$:r |d :t$_1$ |d :— ‖ l$_1$ |s$_1$ ‖
|m :— |f :s |s :m |r :d |t$_1$:— ‖ s :— |f :l |s :s.f |m :— ‖ f |m ‖
|m :— |r :d |t$_1$:d |s$_1$.f$_1$:m$_1$ |s$_1$:— ‖ d$_1$:— |f$_1$:r$_1$ |m$_1$.f$_1$:s$_1$ |d$_1$:— ‖ f$_1$ |d$_1$ ‖

A-men.

BURFORD. (C.M.)

Lah = G. Doh = B♭. *Moderately slow.* *Chetham's Psalmody*, 1718.

:l$_1$ |l$_1$:— :t$_1$ |d :— :r |m :r :d |t$_1$:— :se$_1$ |l$_1$:— :t$_1$ |d :— :r |m :—
:m$_1$ |m$_1$:— :m$_1$ |m$_1$:— :se$_1$ |l$_1$:se$_1$:l$_1$ |se$_1$:— :m$_1$ |m$_1$:— :m$_1$ |m$_1$:— :l$_1$ |se$_1$:—
:d |l$_1$:— :se$_1$ |l$_1$:m :r |d :r :m |m :— :t$_1$ |l$_1$:— :se$_1$ |l$_1$:— :l$_1$ |t$_1$:—
:l$_2$ |d$_1$:— :m$_1$ |l$_1$:— :t$_1$ |d :t$_1$:l$_1$ |m$_1$:— :r$_1$ |d$_1$:— :m$_1$ |l$_1$:s$_1$:f$_1$ |m$_1$:—

:m |r :d :t$_1$ |d :— :r |m :r :d |t$_1$:— :se$_1$ |l$_1$:— :d |t$_1$:l$_1$:se$_1$ |l$_1$:— ‖ l$_1$ |l$_1$ ‖
:s$_1$ |l$_1$:— :s$_1$ |s$_1$:— :s$_1$ |s$_1$:— :m$_1$ |m$_1$:— :m$_1$ |d$_1$:— :l$_1$ |f$_1$:— :m$_1$ |m$_1$:— ‖ f$_1$ |m$_1$ ‖
:m |f :m :r |d :— :t$_1$ |d :t$_1$:l$_1$ |se$_1$:— :t$_1$ |l$_1$:— :m |r :d :t$_1$ |d :— ‖ r |de ‖
:d$_1$ |f$_1$:— :s$_1$ |m$_1$:— :s$_1$ |d :s$_1$:l$_1$ |m$_1$:— :m$_1$ |f$_1$:— :d$_1$ |r$_1$:— :m$_1$ |l$_2$:— ‖ r$_1$ |l$_2$ ‖

A-men.

Labente iam solis rota.

AS now the sun's declining rays
At eventide descend,
Even so our years are sinking down
To their appointed end.

2 Lord, on the Cross Thine arms were stretched
To draw the nations nigh;
O grant us then that Cross to love,
And in those arms to die.

3 To God the Father, God the Son,
And God the Holy Ghost,
All glory be from saints on earth,
And from the angel host.

CHARLES COFFIN, 1676–1749; *tr.* by JOHN CHANDLER, 1806-76.

275

UFFINGHAM. (L.M.)

Lah = F. Doh = A♭. *Slow.* JEREMIAH CLARK, 1670–1707.

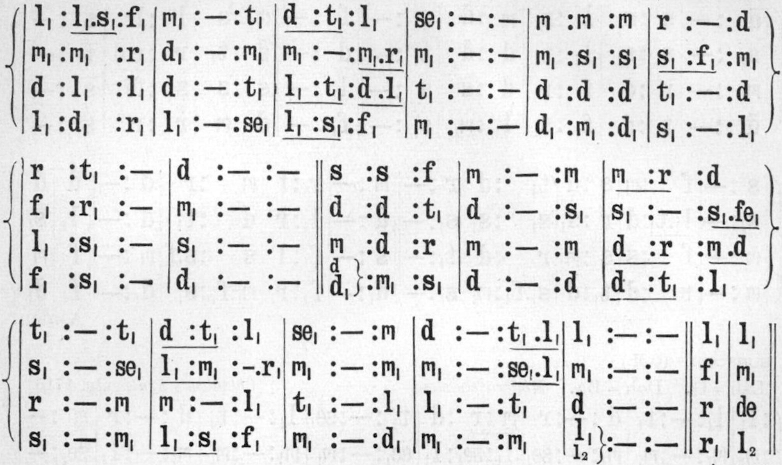

l, :l,.s, :f, | m, :— :t, | d :t, :l, | se, :— :— | m :m :m | r :— :d
m, :m, :r, | d, :— :m, | m, :— :m,.r, | m, :— :— | m, :s, :s, | s, :f, :m,
d :l, :l, | d :— :t, | l, :t, :d.l, | t, :— :— | d :d :d | t, :— :d
l, :d, :r, | l, :— :se, | l, :s, :f, | m, :— :— | d, :m, :d, | s, :— :l,

r :t, :— | d :— :— || s :s :f | m :— :m | m :r :d
f, :r, :— | m, :— :— || d :d :t, | d :— :s, | s, :— :s,.fe,
l, :s, :— | s, :— :— || m :d :r | m :— :m | d :r :m.d
f, :s, :— | d, :— :— || d d, :m, :s, | d :— :d | d :t, :l,

t, :— :t, | d :t, :l, | se, :— :m | d :— :t,.l, | l, :— :— || l, l, ||
s, :— :se, | l, :m, :-.r, | m, :— :m, | m, :— :se,.l, | m, :— :— || f, m, ||
r :— :m | m :— :l, | t, :— :l, | l, :— :t, | d :— :— || r de ||
s, :— :m, | l, :s, :f, | m, :— :d, | m, :— :m, | l, l₂ :— :— || r, l₂ ||

A-men.

WOOLMER'S. (L.M.)

Doh = F. *Moderately slow.* FREDERICK ARTHUR GORE OUSELEY, 1825–89.

:d | d :r | t, :t, | d :r | m :s | f :r | m :d | t, :l, | s, ||
:s, | l, :l, | s, :s, | s, :s, | s, :s, | d :s, | s, :s, | s, :fe, | s, ||
:m | m :f | r :r | d :t, | d :r | f :f | m :s | r :-.d | t, ||
:d | l, :f, | s, :f, | m, :s, | d :t, | l, :t, | d :m | r :r, | s, ||

:t, | d :r | m :d | f :s | l :l | s :f | m :s | d :r | d || d d ||
:se, | l, :t, | d :s, | d :ta, | l, :r | m :r | d :d | l, :t, | d || l, s, ||
:m | m :s | s :m | f :r.m | f :t | d' :s | s :s | m :f | m || f m ||
:m, | l, :s, | d :ta, | l, :s, | f, :f | m :t, | d :m, | l, :s, | d || f, d ||

A-men.

AGAIN, as evening's shadow falls,
We gather in these hallowed walls;
And vesper hymn and vesper prayer
Rise mingling on the holy air.

2 May struggling hearts that seek release
Here find the rest of God's own peace,
And, strengthened here by hymn and prayer,
Lay down the burdens and the care.

3 O God, our Light, to Thee we bow;
Within all shadows standest Thou:
Give deeper calm than night can bring;
Give sweeter songs than lips can sing.

4 Life's tumult we must meet again;
We cannot at the shrine remain;
But in the spirit's secret cell
May hymn and prayer for ever dwell.

SAMUEL LONGFELLOW, 1819-92.

276 ST. AMBROSE. (C.M.)

Doh = A♭. *In moderate time.* CHARLES STEGGALL, 1826-1905

:d |d :r |m :d |d :t, |d :m |r :t, |l, :l, |s, :— |—

:s, |l, :t, |d :d |l, :s, |s, :s, |s, :s, |s, :fe, |s, :— |—

:m |m :s |s :s |f :r |m :d |r :r |r :r |t, :— |—

:d |l, :s, |d :m, |f, :s, |d, :d |t, :t,.d |r :r, |s, :— |—

:r |f :m |r :m |d :l, |s, :s, |l, :d |d :t, |d :— |— || d |d ||

:s, |l, :s, |s, :s, |m, :f, |m, :s, |f, :m,.f, |s, :s, |s, :— |— || l, |s, ||

:t, |d :d |t, :t, |d :d |d :d |d :d |r :r |m :— |— || f |m ||

:s, |f, :d |s, :m, |l, :f, |d :m, |f, :l, |s, :s, |d, :— |— || f, |d, ||

A-men.

DUNDEE (WINDSOR). (C.M.)

Damon's Psalmes, 1591.

Lah = G. Doh = B♭. *Moderately slow.*

|l, :— |l, :t, |d :t, |l, :l, |se, :— || d :— |m :r |d :t, |d :— ||

|m, :— |m, :m, |m, :m, |m, :m, |m, :— || m, :— |s, :l, |s, :-.f, |m, :— ||

|d :— |d :t, |l, :se, |l, :d |t, :— || d :— |d :f |m :r |d :— ||

|l, :— |l, :se, |l, :m, |d, :l,, |m, :— || l, :— |m, :f, |s, :s, |d, :— ||

|d :— |m :r |d :t, |l, :l, |se, :— || d :— |t, :l, |l, :se, |l, :— || l, |l, ||

|s, :— |s, :s, |m, :s, |f, :f, |m, :— || s, :— |s, :m, |f, :m, |m, :— || f, |m, ||

|m :— |d :t, |d :m |d :r |t, :— || m :— |r :d |r :t, |d :— || r |de ||

|d, :— |d :s, |l, :m, |f, :r, |m, :— || d, :— |s, :l, |r, :m, |l, :— || r, |l,, ||

A-men.

As darker, darker fall around
The shadows of the night,
We gather here, with hymn and prayer,
To seek the eternal light.

2 Father in heaven, to Thee are known
Our many hopes and fears,
Our heavy weight of mortal toil,
Our bitterness of tears.

3 We pray Thee for all absent friends,
Who have been with us here;
And in our secret heart we name
The distant and the dear.

4 For weary eyes, and aching hearts,
And feet that from Thee rove,
The sick, the poor, the tried, the fallen,
We pray Thee, God of love.

5 We bring to Thee our hopes and fears,
And at Thy footstool lay;
And, Father, Thou who lovest all
Wilt hear us when we pray.

ANON.

277 ANGELUS. (L.M.)

Doh = E♭. *Moderately slow.* *Heilige Seelenlust*, 1657.

```
:d  |d  :— :r  |m  :fe :s  |s  :— :fe |s  :— :s  |l  :— :t
:s, |s, :— :s, |d  :r  :r  |m  :— :r  |r  :— :r  |r  :— :r
:m  |m  :— :s  |s  :l  :s  |d' :— :l  |t  :— :t  |l  :— :s
:d  |d  :— :t, |d  :— :t, |l, :— :r  |s, :— :s  |fe :— :f

|d' :— :t  |l  :— :l  |s  :— :— ||r  :r  :m  |f  :— :f  |d  :— :r
|d  :m  :r |m  :r  :d |t, :— :— ||t, :t, :de |r  :— :r  |d  :— :l,
|s  :— :s  |s  :fe :fe|s  :— :— ||s  :s  :s  |l  :— :l  |l  :— :l
|m  :l, :t,|d  :r  :r |s, :— :— ||s, :f  :m  |r  :— :r  |f  :— :f

|m  :— :— |t,  :d  :r  |m  :— :f  |r  :— :r  |d  :— ||d  |d  ||
|t, :— :— |se, :l, :t, |d  :— :d  |d  :— :t, |d  :— ||l, |s, ||
|se :— :— |m   :m  :s  |s  :— :l  |s  :— :f  |m  :— ||f  |m  ||
|m  :— :— |m   :l, :s, |d  :— :f, |s, :— :s, |d  :— ||f, |d  ||
                                                        A-men.
```

At even, when the sun was set,
The sick, O Lord, around Thee lay ;
O in what divers pains they met !
O with what joy they went away !

2 Once more 'tis eventide, and we,
Oppressed with various ills, draw near ;
What if Thy form we cannot see,
We know and feel that Thou art here.

3 O Saviour Christ, our woes dispel :
For some are sick, and some are sad,
And some have never loved Thee well,
And some have lost the love they had ;

4 And some are pressed with worldly care,
And some are tried with sinful doubt ;
And some such grievous passions tear,
That only Thou canst cast them out ;

5 And some have found the world is vain,
Yet from the world they break not free ;
And some have friends who give them pain,
Yet have not sought a friend in Thee ;

6 And none, O Lord, have perfect rest,
For none are wholly free from sin ;
And they who fain would serve Thee best
Are conscious most of wrong within.

7 O Saviour Christ, Thou too art Man ;
Thou hast been troubled, tempted, tried ;
Thy kind but searching glance can scan
The very wounds that shame would hide ;

8 Thy touch has still its ancient power ;
No word from Thee can fruitless fall :
Hear in this solemn evening hour,
And in Thy mercy heal us all.

HENRY TWELLS, 1823–1900.

278 ACH BLEIB BEI UNS. (L.M.)

Geistliche Lieder, Leipsic, 1589.
Arranged by JOHANN SEBASTIAN BACH, 1685–1750.

Doh = G. *Slow.*

```
                     f.C.                       G.t.
:m   |m.f :s    |m  :ᵈs       |l    :t     |d'  ||ᵗm  |r      :d      |d      :-.r    |m    :m
:d   |d   :r    |d  :ᵈs       |f.m  :r     |m   ||ʳs, |s,.f,  :m,     |l,     :—      |s,   :s,
:s   |s   :s    |s  :ˢr'.d'   |d'   :s     |s   ||ˢd  |t,     :d      |f      :—      |m.r  :d
:d,  |d   :t,   |d  :ˡm       |f    :s     |d   ||ˢd, |s,     :l,.s,  |f,.s,  :l,.t,  |d    :m,.f,
```

```
|r.d  :r      |d   :—  |—  ||m   |r    :m    |d     :l,    |t,  :d      |r   ||
|s,   :-.f,   |m,  :—  |—  ||d   |t,   :t,   |l,.s, :fe,   |s,  :-.fe,  |s,  ||
|d    :t,     |d   :—  |—  ||s   |s.f  :m    |m     :r     |r   :d      |t,  ||
|s,   :s,     |d,  :—  |—  ||d,  |s,   :se,  |l,    :r.d   |t,  :l,     |s,  ||
```

```
:m    |d      :d       |d    :-.r     |m   :m      |r.d  :r     |d   :—  |—  ||d   |d   ||
:se,  |m,     :l,      |s,   :l,.t,   |d   :s,     |s,   :-.f,  |m,  :—  |—  ||f,  |m,  ||
:t,   |d      :f       |m.f  :m.r     |d   :d      |d    :t,    |d   :—  |—  ||l,  |s,  ||
:m,   |l,.s,  :l,.t,   |d.r  :d.t,    |l,  :m,.f,  |s,   :s,    |d,  :—  |—  ||f,  |d,  ||
                                                                                A-men.
```

Ach bleib bei uns, Herr Jesu Christ.

NOW cheer our hearts this eventide,
Lord Jesus Christ, and with us bide ;
Thou that canst never set in night,
Our heavenly Sun, our glorious Light.

2 May we and all who bear Thy Name
By gentle love Thy Cross proclaim,
Thy gift of peace on earth secure,
And for Thy truth the world endure.

Yattendon Hymnal, No. 13, 1899 ; based on NICOLAUS SELNECKER, 1532–92.

279

ST. GABRIEL. (8 8. 8 4.)

FREDERICK ARTHUR GORE OUSELEY, 1825–89.

Doh = E♭. *In moderate time.*

```
:m  |s  :f  |m  :f  |m  :-.r |d  :d   |l      :s  |f  :s  |m     :fe |s  ||
:d  |d  :d  |d  :d  |d  :t,  |d  :ta, |l,.t,  :de |r  :r  |d     :d  |t, ||
:d' |t  :l  |s  :l  |s  :f   |m  :s   |f      :s  |l  :s  |s     :l  |r  ||
:d  |d  :d  |d  :f, |s, :s,  |l, :m   |f      :m  |r  :t, |d.t,  :l, |s, ||
```

```
:s   |s  :m  |f  :r  |m  :m  |f  :m  |d  :—  |r  :—  |d  :—  |—  ||d  |d  ||
:ta, |l, :l, |l, :r  |r  :de |r  :t, |d  :—  |—  :t, |d  :—  |—  ||l, |s  ||
:r   |de :m  |r  :l  |ta :l  |l  :se |l  :m  |f  :—  |m  :—  |—  ||f  |m  ||
:s,  |l, :de |r  :f, |s, :l, |r  :m  |l, :—  |s, :—  |d  :—  |—  ||f, |d  ||
```

A- men.

THE radiant morn hath passed away,
And spent too soon her golden store;
The shadows of departing day
Creep on once more.

2 Our life is but an autumn day,
Its glorious noon how quickly past!
Lead us, O Christ, Thou living Way,
Safe home at last.

3 O by Thy soul-inspiring grace
Uplift our hearts to realms on high:
Help us to look to that bright place,
Beyond the sky,

4 Where light, and life, and joy, and peace
In undivided empire reign,
And thronging angels never cease
Their deathless strain;

5 Where saints are clothed in spotless white,
And evening shadows never fall;
Where Thou, Eternal Light of light,
Art Lord of all.

GODFREY THRING, 1823–1903.

[May be sung to WIMBLEDON, No. 539.]

280 DIVA SERVATRIX. (11 11. 11 5.)

Doh = G. *Unison.* *Moderately slow.* Bayeux Church Melody.

| m :m.f | m :d | r .,d :r .m | r :d | m :m.s | f :m |

| r .,d :t_1 .d | l_1 :s_1 (pause) || m :r .d | f :m | d .,r :m .f |

| s :s | m :r .d | r :d (pause) || d :r | d :t_1 | d :— ||

l_1 :—	s_1 :—	s_1 :—
m :f	m :r	m :—
l_1 :r_1	m_1 .f_1 :s_1	d_1 :—	

A - - - men.

Die Nacht ist kommen, drin wir ruhen sollen.

NOW God be with us, for the night is closing;
The light and darkness are of His disposing,
And 'neath His shadow here to rest we yield us,
For He will shield us.

2 Let evil thoughts and spirits flee before us;
Till morning cometh, watch, Protector, o'er us;
In soul and body Thou from harm defend us;
Thine angels send us.

3 Let holy thoughts be ours when sleep o'ertakes us;
Our earliest thoughts be Thine when morning wakes us;
All day serve Thee, in all that we are doing
Thy praise pursuing.

4 We have no refuge, none on earth to aid us,
Save Thee, O Father, who Thine own hast made us;
But Thy dear Presence will not leave them lonely
Who seek Thee only.

5 Father, Thy Name be praised, Thy Kingdom given,
Thy will be done on earth as 'tis in heaven;
Keep us in life, forgive our sins, deliver
Us now and ever.

PETRUS HERBERT, ? –1571; *tr.* by CATHERINE WINKWORTH, 1829–78.

281 SEBASTE. (Irr.)

Φῶς ἱλαρὸν ἁγίας δόξης.

JOHN STAINER, 1840–1901.

Doh = E♭. *In free rhythm.*

Me	f:s	m:—	Lah	s :d	m :r	r :—
Doh	r:r	d:—	Doh	d :d	d :d	t, :—
Hail, gladdening Light, of Hís pure	glo-ry	pour'd	Who is the immórtal	Fa-ther,	heavenly,	blest,
Soh	l:s	s:—	Fah	s :s	s :fe	s :—
Doh	d:t,	d:—	Fah	m :m	l, :r	s, :—

d' :-.d'	t :l	s :d	s :f	m :d	r :—	d :—
d :-.d	d :d	d :d	m :r	d :s,	t, :—	d :—
Ho - li -	est of	Ho - lies,	Je - sus	Christ,	our	Lord !
m :-.m	m :f	s :m	l :l	s :m	f :—	m :—
l, :-.l,	s, :f,	m, :l,	f, :f,	s, :—	s, :—	d :—

Me	f :s	m :—	Lah	s :d	m :r	r :—
Doh	r :r	d :—	Doh	d :d	d :d	t, :—
Now we are come to the sún's	hour of	rest,	The líghts of	even-ing	round us	shine,
Soh	l :s	s :—	Fah	s :s	s :fe	s :—
Doh	d :t,	d :—	Fah	m :m	l, :r	s, :—

:d'	d' :-.d'	t :l	s :d	s :f	m :d	r :-.d	d :—
:d	d :-.d	d :d	d :d	m :r	d :s,	t, :-.d	d :—
We	hymn the	Fa - ther,	Son, and	Ho - ly	Spi -	rit Di-	vine.
:m	m :-.m	m :f	s :m	l :l	s :m	f :-.m	m :—
:l,	l, :-.l,	s, :f,	m, :l,	f, :f,	s, :—	s, :-.d	d :—

Me	f :s	m :—	l	s :d	m :r	r :—
Doh	r :r	d :—	d	d :d	d :d	t, :—
Worthiest art Thou at áll times to	be	sung	With	un - de	fil - ed	tongue,
Soh	l :s	s :—	f	s :s	s :fe	s :—
Doh	d :t,	d :—	f	m :m	l, :r	s, :—

d' :— | t :l | s :— | s.s :f | m :— | r :— | s :— | — :—
d :— | d :d | d :— | m.m :r | d :— | t, :— | d :— | f :—
Son of our God, Giv-er of life, a - lone:
m :— | m :f | s :— | l.l :l | s :— | s :— | s :— | t :—
l, :— | s, :f, | m, :— | f,.f, :f | s :— | f :— | m :— | r :—

d' :d'.d' | t :l | s :d | s :f | m :— | r :— | d :— | — :— || d | d
m :m.m | m :f | d :d | m :r | d :— | t, :— | d :— | — :— || l, | s,
There-fore in all the world Thy glor-ies, Lord, they own. A- men.
d' :d'.d' | d' :d' | d' :s | l :l | s :— | f :— | m :— | — :— || f | m
d :l.l | s :f | m :m | f :f | s :— | s, :— | d :— | — :— || f, | d

4th century; *tr.* by John Keble, 1792–1866.

282 CAPETOWN. (77. 75.)

Doh = D. *In moderate time.* Friedrich Filitz, 1804–76.

s :m | l :s | f :f | m :— | d' :t | d' :s | f :m | r :—
d :d | d :d | d :t, | d :— | m :r | d :d | l,.t, :d | t, :—
m :s | f :s | l :s | s :— | s :s | m :m | f :s | s :—
d :d | f :m | r :s, | d :— | d :s, | l, :m | r :d | s, :—

s :d' | t :l | s :fe | s :— | m :m | r :r | d :— | — :— || d | d
d :d | r :m | r :—.d | d :t, | d :d | d :t, | d :— | — :— || l, | s,
s :fe | s :d' | t :l | s :— | s :l | l :s.f | m :— | — :— || f | m
m :l, | t, :d | r :r | s, :— | d :l, | f, :s, | d :— | — :— || f, | d
A-men.

HOLY Father, cheer our way
With Thy love's perpetual ray;
Grant us, every closing day,
Light at evening time.

2 Holy Saviour, calm our fears
When earth's brightness disappears;
Grant us in our latter years
Light at evening time.

3 Holy Spirit, be Thou nigh
When in mortal pains we lie;
Grant us, as we come to die,
Light at evening time.

4 Holy, blessèd Trinity,
Darkness is not dark to Thee;
Those Thou keepest always see
Light at evening time.

Richard Hayes Robinson, 1842–92.

283 EVENING HYMN. (887. 887.)

Doh = E♭. *Moderately slow.* WILLIAM JACKSON, 1815–66.

m :—:m	f :—:m	m :r :d	t$_1$:d :—	f :—:m	r :—:m
d :—:d	r :—:d	l$_1$:—:l$_1$	s$_1$:s$_1$:—	d :r :d	t$_1$:—:d
s :—:s	s :—:s	l :—:f	r :m :—	l :—:s	s :—:s
d :—:d	t$_1$:—:d	f$_1$:—:f$_1$	s$_1$:d :—	l$_1$:t$_1$:d	s :f :m

s :f :m	m :r :—	d^1 :f :l	s :d :f	m :—:r	d :—:—	
m :r :d	d :t$_1$:—	d :— :d	d :—:r	d :—:t$_1$	d :—:—	
l :—:s.l	s :s :—	m :f :r	s :—:l	s :—:f	m :—:—	
r :—:m.f	s :s$_1$:—	l$_1$:—.s$_1$:f$_1$	m$_1$:m :r	s :—:s$_1$	d :—:—	

r :—:r	m :—:s	l :s :m	s :f :m	r :—:f	m :—:s
t$_1$:—:t$_1$	d :—:r	d :r :m	r :—:d	d :t$_1$:r	r :d :d
s :—:s	s :—:r	m :s :d^1.t	l :—:s	s :—:s	s :—:s
s$_1$:—:s$_1$	d :—:t$_1$	l$_1$:t$_1$:d	r :—:m.f	s :—:s$_1$	d :—:m

l :s :d^1	t :l :s	f :—:m	m :r :f	m :—:r	d :—:—		d	d	
d :—:m	r :— :m	l$_1$:t$_1$:d	l$_1$:—:r	d :—:t$_1$	d :—:—		l$_1$	s$_1$	
f :s :s	s :l.t :d^1	f :—:s	s :f :l	s :—:f	m :—:—		f	m	
f :m :d	s :f :m	r :—:d	f$_1$:—:r$_1$	s$_1$:—:s$_1$	d :—:—		f$_1$	d	

A-men.

FATHER, in high heaven dwelling,
May our evening song be telling
Of Thy mercy large and free;
Through the day Thy love has fed us,
Through the day Thy care has led us,
With divinest charity.

2 This day's sins O pardon, Saviour,
Evil thoughts, perverse behaviour,
Envy, pride, and vanity;
From the world, the flesh, deliver,
Save us now, and save us ever,
O Thou Lamb of Calvary.

3 From enticements of the devil,
From the might of spirits evil,
Be our shield and panoply;
Let Thy power this night defend us,
And a heavenly peace attend us,
And angelic company.

4 While the night-dews are distilling,
Holy Ghost, each heart be filling
With Thine own serenity.
Softly let our eyes be closing,
Loving souls on Thee reposing,
Ever-blessèd Trinity.

GEORGE RAWSON, 1807–89.

284

INNSBRUCK. (776. 778.)

HEINRICH ISAAK, *c.* 1450–*c.* 1527.
Arranged by JOHANN SEBASTIAN BACH, 1685–1750.

Doh = G. *Slow and solemn.*

```
:m  |d   :r   |m.f  :s     |f      :—     |m  ‖m.f |s       :s      |r      :m
:d  |l,  :t,  |d.r  :m     |m      :r     |d  ‖d   |d.t,    :d.l,   |t,.l,  :s,
:s  |f   :f   |s.f  :m.r   |d      :s     |s  ‖l   |s       :s      |s      :t,
:d  |f.m :r   |d    :-.t,  |l,     :t,    |d  ‖l,  |m,.r,   :m,.f,  |s,.f,  :m,

|d     :—    |t,  ‖s,    |d    :r      |m      :m      |r   :—  |—  ‖
|s,    :fe,  |s,  ‖r,    |s,   :f,     |m,.f,  :s,     |s,  :—  |—  ‖
|d.t,  :d    |r   ‖t,.l, |s,   :l,.t,  |d      :d      |t,  :—  |—  ‖
|l,    :—    |s,  ‖f,    |m,   :r,     |d,.r,  :m,.f,  |s,  :—  |—  ‖

:m   |d    :r    |m.f  :s    |f      :—      |m   ‖m.f |s    :s     |r     :m
:t,  |l,   :s,   |s,   :l,   |l,.s,  :l,.t,  |de  ‖d   |r    :d.t,  |l,    :t,
:m   |m.f  :m.r  |d.r  :m    |r.m    :f.s    |l   ‖l   |s.f  :m     |fe    :t,
:se, |l,   :t,   |d    :de   |r      :r,     |l,  ‖l,  |t,   :d     |d.t,  :l,.se,

|d      :—    |t,   ‖s,  |d      :r       |m      :f       |m   :r      |d   ‖d   |d   ‖
|t,     :l,   |se,  ‖s,  |s,.l,  :s,.f,   |m,.s,  :l,.t,   |d   :t,     |s,  ‖l,  |s,  ‖
|m      :—    |m    ‖m   |m.f    :m.r     |d      :d       |l   :r.m,f  |m   ‖f   |m   ‖
|l,.t,  :d.r  |m    ‖m,  |l,     :t,      |d.t,   :l,.s,   |f,  :s,     |d,  ‖f,  |d,  ‖
                                                                              A-men.
```

Nun ruhen alle Wälder.

THE duteous day now closeth,
Each flower and tree reposeth,
Shade creeps o'er wild and wood:
Let us, as night is falling,
On God our Maker calling,
Give thanks to Him, the Giver good.

2 Now all the heavenly splendour
Breaks forth in starlight tender,
From myriad worlds unknown;
And man, the marvel seeing,
Forgets his selfish being,
For joy of beauty not his own.

3 His care he drowneth yonder,
Lost in the abyss of wonder;
To heaven his soul doth steal:
This life he disesteemeth,
The day it is that dreameth,
That doth from truth his vision seal.

4 Awhile his mortal blindness
May miss God's loving-kindness,
And grope in faithless strife:
But, when life's day is over,
Shall death's fair night discover
The fields of everlasting life.

Yattendon Hymnal, No. 83, 1899; based on PAUL GERHARDT, 1607–76.

285 LUGANO. (8 7. 8 7. D.)

Doh = G. *Moderately slow.* *Catholic Hymn Tunes and Litanies*, 1849.

```
d  :-.d  |t,  :d    |l,   :l,  |t,  :t,    |d  :-.t,  |l,.t,:d .r  |d  :t,  |d  :—
s, :-.s, |s,  :s,   |f,   :f,  |s,  :s,.f, |m, :s,    |l,   :s,.l, |s, :s,  |s, :—
m  :-.m  |r   :d    |d    :r   |r   :r     |d  :d     |d .r :m .f  |m  :r   |m  :—
d  :-.d  |s,  :m,   |f,   :r,  |s,  :s,    |l, :m,    |f,   :m,.r, |s, :s,  |d, :—
```

```
m  :-.m  |r   :m    |d     :d   |r    :r     |m  :r.m  |f   :m .f  |m   :r   |d  :—
s, :-.s, |s,  :t,   |l,.s, :fe, |s,   :t,.l, |s, :s,   |f,  :s,.l, |s,  :t,  |d  :—
d  :-.d  |r   :s    |m     :d   |t,.r :s .f  |m  :t,   |d   :d     |d.m :s.f |m  :—
d  :-.d  |t,  :s,   |l,    :l,  |t,   :s,    |d  :s,   |l,  :s,.f, |s,  :s,  |d  :—
```

```
m  :-.m  |r   :s    |s   :fe  |s   :s   |s  :-.s  |f   :m     |r   :r   |m   :—
s, :-.s, |s,  :s,   |l,  :l,  |t,  :t,  |t, :-.t, |d   :d .t, |l,  :l,  |se, :—
d  :-.d  |t,  :r    |m   :r   |r   :r   |m  :-.m  |d.r :m     |f   :l,  |t,  :—
d, :-.m, |s,  :t,   |d   :r   |s,  :s,  |m, :-.m, |l,  :l,.s, |f,  :f,  |m,  :—
```

```
m  :-.m  |r    :s    |s  :fe  |s  :s   |s   :s   |f     :m   |r  :r    |d  :— || d  |d
l, :fe,  |s,.r :d.t, |l, :l,  |t, :t,  |t,  :l,  |l,.t, :d   |d  :t,   |s, :— || l, |s,
d  :d    |r    :m    |m  :r   |r  :r   |m.r :de  |r     :s   |l  :s.f  |m  :— || f  |m
l, :l,   |t,   :m.r  |d  :r   |s, :s,  |m,  :l,  |r,    :m,  |f, :s,   |d  :— || f, |d,
```

A-men.

ZUM FRIEDEN. (8 7. 8 7. D.)

May be sung in unison or as a solo. JOHANN SEBASTIAN BACH, 1685–1750.

Lah = D. Doh = F. *Slow and dignified.* *D.C.*

```
m  :d    |l,  :l   |f     :m     |f     :m   || r   :d   |f    :m     |r      :d   |t,  :—
d  :l,   |l,  :d   |d.t,  :t,.l, |l,.s, :s,  || t,  :d   |d.t, :t,.l, |l,.se, :l,  |se, :—
l  :l    |m   :m   |r     :m     |r     :d   || m   :m   |r    :m     |t,     :d.r |m   :—
l, :-.t, |d   :l,  |r     :d     |t,    :d   || se, :l,  |r    :d     |t,     :l,  |m   :—
```

C.t. f.F.

t_1 :t_1	t_1 :m	d :t_1	d :d		d :t_1	d :^{l} r'	se :-.l	^{l} m :—	
se_1 :ba_1	se_1 :t_1	l_1 :se_1	l_1 :l_1		l_1 :t_1	l_1 :^{d} f	m :r	$^{de}se_1$:—	
m :ba	m :m	m :m	m :m		m :m	m :^{m} l	t :t	^{l} m :—	
m :re	m :se_1	l_1 :m_1	l_1 :l_1		l_1 :se_1	l_1 :$^{fe}t_1$	m :m	$^{l_1}m_1$:—	

m :r.d	f :m	l.se :l.t	se :m		m :l.s	f.m :r.d	t_1 :- .l_1	l_1 :—		l_1	l_1	
t_1 :l_1	d.t_1 :m	m.r :d.t_1	t_1 :se_1		l_1.t_1 :d	l_1 :l_1	l_1 :se_1.l_1	l_1 :—		f_1	m_1	
m :m	f :l	f :f	m :m		m :m	r :m	m :r	d :—		r	de	
se_1 :l_1	r :d	f :r	m :m.r		d .t_1 :l_1	r :l_1	m :m_1	l_1 :—		r_1	l_1	

A-men.

SAVIOUR, breathe an evening blessing
  Ere repose our spirits seal;
Sin and want we come confessing:
  Thou canst save, and Thou canst heal.
Though destruction walk around us,
  Though the arrow past us fly,
Angel guards from Thee surround us;
  We are safe if Thou art nigh.

2 Though the night be dark and dreary,
  Darkness cannot hide from Thee;
Thou art He who, never weary,
  Watchest where Thy people be.
Should swift death this night o'ertake us,
  And our couch become our tomb,
May the morn in heaven awake us,
  Clad in light and deathless bloom.

JAMES EDMESTON, 1791–1867.

286

EVENTIDE. (10 10. 10 10.)

Doh = E♭. *In moderate time.* WILLIAM HENRY MONK, 1823–89.

m :—	m :r	d :—	s :—	l :s	s :f	m :—	— :—	
d :—	t, :t,	d :—	d :—	d :t,	d :r	d :—	— :—	
s :—	s :f	m :—	d :—	d :s	s :s	s :—	— :—	
d :—	s, :s,	l, :—	m, :—	f, :s,	l, :t,	d :—	— :—	

m :—	f :s	l :—	s :—	f :r	m :fe	s :—	— :—	
d :—	d :d	d :—	d :—	d :r	d :d	t, :—	— :—	
s :—	f :m	f :—	m :—	l :s	s :d	r :—	— :—	
d :t,	l, :s,	f, :—	d :—	r :t,	d :l,	s, :—	— :—	

m :—	m :r	d :—	s :—	s :f	f :m	r :—	— :—	
d :—	t, :t,	d :—	d :—	d :d	de :de	r :—	— :—	
m :f	s :f	m :—	d' :t	l :l	l :s	f :—	— :—	
d :—	s, :s,	l, :—	m, :—	f, :-.s,	l, :l,	r :—	— :—	

r :—	m :f	m :r	d :f	m :—	r :—	d :—	— :—		d	d	
t, :—	d :t,	d :t,	d :r	d :—	t, :—	d :—	— :—		l,	s,	
s :—	s :s	s :f	m :l	s :—	— :f	m :—	— :—		f	m	
f :—	m :r	d :s,	l, :f,	s, :—	s, :—	d :—	— :—		f,	d	

A - men.

ABIDE with me: fast falls the eventide;
The darkness deepens; Lord, with me abide:
When other helpers fail, and comforts flee,
Help of the helpless, O abide with me.

2 Swift to its close ebbs out life's little day;
Earth's joys grow dim, its glories pass away;
Change and decay in all around I see:
O Thou who changest not, abide with me.

3 I need Thy presence every passing hour;
What but Thy grace can foil the tempter's power?
Who like Thyself my guide and stay can be?
Through cloud and sunshine, O abide with me.

4 I fear no foe, with Thee at hand to bless;
Ills have no weight, and tears no bitterness:
Where is death's sting? where, grave, thy victory?
I triumph still if Thou abide with me.

5 Hold Thou Thy Cross before my closing eyes,
Shine through the gloom, and point me to the skies;
Heaven's morning breaks, and earth's vain shadows flee:
In life and death, O Lord, abide with me.

HENRY FRANCIS LYTE, 1793–1847.

[May be sung to CONGLETON, No. 98.]

287 ST. ANATOLIUS. (76. 76. 88.)

Doh = E♭. *In moderate time.* ARTHUR HENRY BROWN, 1830–1926.

```
:s  |l  :s  |d  :f  |m  :—  |r  :d  |r  :m  |f  :l  |s  :—  |—  ||
:d  |d  :s, |l, :r  |d  :—  |t, :d  |l, :de |r  :m  |r  :—  |—  ||
:m  |f  :m  |m  :l  |s  :—  |s  :m  |f  :s  |l  :m  |s  :—  |—  ||
:d  |d  :d  |l, :f, |s, :—  |s, :l, |f  :m  |r  :d  |t, :—  |—  ||

:s  |l  :s  |d  :f  |m  :—  |r  :d  |r  :f  |m     :r  |d  :—  |—  ||
:d  |d  :s, |l, :r  |d  :—  |t, :d  |l, :r  |d     :t, |d  :—  |—  ||
:m  |f  :m  |m  :l  |s  :—  |s  :m  |f  :l  |s     :f  |m  :—  |—  ||
:d  |d  :d  |l, :f, |s, :—  |s, :l, |f, :r, |m,.f, :s, |d  :—  |—  ||

B♭.t.                        f.E♭.
:ᵈf   |m   :r   |d  :r   |m  :r    |ᵈs   :s   |f  :m |r  :d    |d   :t, |d (fermata) ||d  |d  ||
:ᵐl,  |se, :se, |l, :l,  |s, :-.f, |ᵐt,  :ta, |l, :d |r  :l,   |s,  :s, |s,          ||l, |s, ||
:ˡr   |t,  :t,  |l, :l,  |d  :t,   |ᵈs   :m   |f  :s |l  :f.m  |r.m :f  |m           ||f  |m  ||
:ˡr,  |m,  :m,  |f, :fe, |s, :s,   |ᵈs,  :d   |r  :m |f  :f,   |s,  :s, |d           ||f, |d  ||
                                                                                    A-men.
```

Τὴν ἡμέραν διελθών.

THE day is past and over:
 All thanks, O Lord, to Thee;
I pray Thee now that sinless
 The hours of dark may be.
O Jesus, keep me in Thy sight,
And guard me through the coming night.

2 The joys of day are over:
 I lift my heart to Thee,
And pray Thee that offenceless
 The hours of dark may be.
O Jesus, keep me in Thy sight,
And guard me through the coming night.

3 The toils of day are over:
 I raise the hymn to Thee,
And pray that free from peril
 The hours of dark may be.
O Jesus, keep me in Thy sight,
And guard me through the coming night.

4 Be Thou my soul's Preserver,
 O God, for Thou dost know
How many are the perils
 Through which I have to go.
Lover of men, O hear my call,
And guard and save me from them all.

6th century; *tr.* by JOHN MASON NEALE, 1818–66.

288 LYNDHURST. (65. 65. D.)

Doh = A♭. *In moderate time.* F. W. Blunt, 1839–1921.

```
|s,  :l,  |t,  :d   |d   :—  |t,  :—  |s,  :s,  |l,  :s,  |s,  :—  |—  :—  ||
|m,  :m,  |m,  :m,  |f,  :—  |f,  :—  |f,  :f,  |f,  :f,  |m,  :—  |—  :—  ||
|s,  :s,  |s,  :s,  |s,  :—  |s,  :—  |r   :r   |t,  :t,  |d   :—  |—  :—  ||
|d,  :d,  |d,  :d,  |r,  :—  |r,  :—  |t,  :t,  |s,  :s,  |d,  :—  |—  :—  ||
```

E♭.t. f.A♭.

```
|l,r   :m   |f   :l   |l   :—  |s   :—  |s   :r   |m   :r   |ds,  :—  |—  :—  ||
|m,l,  :l,  |l,  :l,  |d   :—  |d   :—  |t,  :t,  |t,  :t,  |s,r, :—  |—  :—  ||
|df    :m   |r   :r   |m   :—  |m   :—  |r   :f   |s   :f   |mt,  :—  |—  :—  ||
|d,f,  :f,  |f,  :f,  |s,  :—  |s,  :—  |s,  :s,  |s,  :s,  |ds,  :—  |—  :—  ||
```

```
|s,  :m   |r   :d   |d   :—  |t,  :—  |s,  :f   |m   :r   |s   :—  |—  :—  ||
|m,  :m,  |m,  :m,  |f,  :—  |f,  :—  |s,  :s,  |s,  :s,  |s,  :—  |—  :—  ||
|d   :s,  |s,  :s,  |s,  :—  |s,  :—  |t,  :t,  |t,  :t,  |d   :—  |—  :—  ||
|d,  :d,  |d,  :d,  |r,  :—  |r,  :—  |r,  :r,  |f,  :f,  |m,  :—  |—  :—  ||
```

```
|s   :s   |f   :m   |r   :—  |l,  :—  |t,  :l,  |s,  :r   |d   :—  |—  :—  ||d   |d   ||
|ta, :ta, |ta, :ta, |l,  :—  |f,  :—  |f,  :f,  |f,  :f,  |m,  :—  |—  :—  ||f,  |m,  ||
|de  :de  |de  :de  |r   :—  |r   :—  |r   :d   |t,  :t,  |d   :—  |—  :—  ||l,  |s,  ||
|m,  :m,  |m,  :m,  |f,  :—  |r,  :—  |s,  :s,  |s,  :s,  |d,  :—  |—  :—  ||f,  |d,  ||
```

A-men.

[*By permission of Novello & Co., Ltd.*]

EUDOXIA. (65. 65.)

Doh = G. *Moderately slow.* Sabine Baring-Gould, 1834–1924.

```
|m   :m   |f   :f   |s   :—  |m   :—  |f   :f   |m   :m   |r   :—  |—  :—  ||
|s,  :s,  |l,  :d   |t,  :—  |s,  :—  |l,  :l,  |s,  :s,  |s,  :—  |—  :—  ||
|d   :d   |d   :d   |r   :—  |m   :—  |d   :d   |d   :d   |t,  :—  |—  :—  ||
|d   :d   |l,  :l,  |s,  :—  |d   :—  |f,  :f,  |d   :d,  |s,  :—  |—  :—  ||
```

m :m	r :d	f :—	m :—	m :m	r :r	d :—	— :—	d	d
s_1 :s_1	s_1 :m_1	l_1 :—	s_1 :—	l_1 :s_1	l_1 :s_1.f_1	m_1 :—	— :—	f_1	m_1
d :d	t_1 :d	d :—	d :—	d :d	d :t_1	d :—	— :—	l_1	s_1
m_1 :m_1	s_1 :l_1	f_1 :—	d :—	l_1 :m_1	f_1 :s_1	d_1 :—	— :—	f_1	d_1

A-men.

[*By permission of* A. W. *Ridley & Co.*]

NOW the day is over,
Night is drawing nigh,
Shadows of the evening
Steal across the sky.

2 Now the darkness gathers,
Stars begin to peep,
Birds, and beasts, and flowers
Soon will be asleep.

3 Jesus, give the weary
Calm and sweet repose ;
With Thy tender blessing
May mine eyelids close.

4 Grant to little children
Visions bright of Thee ;
Guard the sailors tossing
On the deep blue sea.

5 Comfort every sufferer
Watching late in pain ;
Those who plan some evil
From their sin restrain.

6 Through the long night-watches,
May Thine angels spread
Their white wings above me,
Watching round my bed.

7 When the morning wakens,
Then may I arise
Pure, and fresh, and sinless
In Thy holy eyes.

8 Glory to the Father,
Glory to the Son,
And to Thee, blest Spirit,
Whilst all ages run.

SABINE BARING-GOULD, 1834–1924.

289

LES COMMANDEMENS DE DIEU. (98. 98.) *French Psalter*, 1549.

Composed or arranged by LOUIS BOURGEOIS, 1510– ? .

Doh = G. *Moderately slow.*

```
d  :d.r :m  :m  :f.f :m :r  || m  :f.m :r.d :t,  :d  :r  ||
s, :l,.t, :d :d :d.d :d :t, || d  :d.d :l,.m, :s, :d :t, ||
m  :m.s :s  :s  :f.l :s :s  || s  :f.s :f.d :r   :s  :s  ||
d  :l,.s, :d :d, :l,.f, :d :s, || d :l,.d :f,.l, :s, :m, :s, ||
```

```
s  :f.m :r :t, :d.t, :l, :s, || m :f.m :r.d :m :r :d || d | d  ||
d  :r.d :l, :s, :m,.s, :s,.fe, :s, || s, :l,.s, :t,.d :s,.l, :t, :d || l, | s, ||
s  :l.s :f :r :d.r :m.r :t, || d :d.m :s.m :d :s.f :m || f | m ||
m, :r,.m, :f, :s, :l,.t, :d.r :s, || d :l,.d :s,.l, :m,.f, :s, :d, || f, | d, ||
```

A-men.

RADFORD. (98. 98.)

Doh = G. *In moderate time.* SAMUEL SEBASTIAN WESLEY, 1810–76.

```
:s, | d  :— :r  | m :— :d | f  :— :m  | m  :r  :r  | m  :— :f
:s, | s, :— :t, | d :— :d | r  :— :d  | d  :t, :s, | s, :— :t,
:m  | m  :— :f  | s :— :m | l  :— :l  | s  :s  :t, | d  :— :f
:d  | d  :— :d  | d :— :d | f, :— :f, | s, :s, :f, | m, :— :r,
```

```
s  :— :m  | m  :— :r  | d :— || d  | t, :— :l,  | s, :— :f  | m  :— :r
d  :— :d  | d  :— :t, | d :— || l, | s, :— :fe, | s, :— :d  | d  :— :t,
m  :— :s  | s  :— :f  | m :— || m  | r  :— :d   | t, :— :d  | s  :— :s
d, :— :m, | s, :— :s, | d :— || d, | r, :— :r,  | s, :— :l, | s, :— :f,
```

```
s  :f  :m | l  :— :s   | f  :m :r   | d  :r :t,  | d  :— || d  | d  ||
d  :t, :d | d  :— :ta, | l, :— :l,  | s, :— :s, | s, :— || l, | s, ||
s  :s  :s | f  :— :m   | f  :s :f   | m  :f :r   | m  :— || f  | m  ||
m, :s, :d | f, :— :f,  | f, :— :f,  | s, :— :s, | d, :— || f, | d, ||
```

A-men.

ST. CLEMENT. (98. 98.)

Doh = A. *In moderate time.* CLEMENT COTTERILL SCHOLEFIELD, 1839–1904.

```
:s, | m  :f  :m  | s  :m  :r  | d  :r  :l, | d  :t, :l, | s, :—  :s,
:s, | s, :—  :d  | t, :—  :t, | l, :—  :f, | f, :f, :f, | f, :m, :s,
:s, | d  :—  :d  | r  :s  :f  | m  :f  :r  | r  :r  :d  | r  :d  :r
:s, | d, :—  :d  | s, :—  :s, | l, :r, :f, | s, :s, :l, | t, :d  :t,

d  :r  :m  | r  :—  :d   | t, :—  || s, | m  :f  :m  | s  :m  :r  | d  :r  :l,
l, :—  :s, | fe, :— :fe, | s, :—  || s, | s, :—  :d  | t, :—  :t, | l, :—  :f,
m  :—  :d  | l, :—  :r   | r  :—  || r  | d  :—  :d  | r  :s  :f  | m  :f  :r
l, :—  :l, | r, :—  :r,  | s, :—  || t, | d  :—  :d  | s, :—  :s, | l, :r, :f,

d  :t, :l, | s, :l, :t, | d  :m  :r  | l, :d  :t, | d  :—  || d  | d
f, :f, :r, | s, :—  :f, | m, :s, :l, | l, :—  :s, | s, :—  || l, | s,
r  :r  :t, | d  :—  :r  | d  :—  :f  | f  :—  :f  | m  :—  || f  | m
s, :s, :f, | m, :—  :s, | l, :m, :f, | r, :—  :s, | d, :—  || f, | d,
                                                             A - men.
```

THE day Thou gavest, Lord, is ended;
The darkness falls at Thy behest;
To Thee our morning hymns ascended,
Thy praise shall sanctify our rest.

2 We thank Thee that Thy Church unsleeping,
While earth rolls onward into light,
Through all the world her watch is keeping,
And rests not now by day or night.

3 As o'er each continent and island
The dawn leads on another day,
The voice of prayer is never silent,
Nor dies the strain of praise away.

4 The sun that bids us rest is waking
Our brethren 'neath the western sky,
And hour by hour fresh lips are making
Thy wondrous doings heard on high.

5 So be it, Lord! Thy throne shall never,
Like earth's proud empires, pass away;
Thy Kingdom stands and grows for ever,
Till all Thy creatures own Thy sway.

JOHN ELLERTON, 1826–93.

290 DAY OF PRAISE. (S.M.)

Doh = F. *In moderate time.* CHARLES STEGGALL, 1826–1905.

:s |m :d |l, :r |t, :— |— :d |l,.t,:d |f :m.r |m :— |— ||
:t, |d :s, |f, :l, |s, :— |— :s, |f, :s, |l, :t, |d :— |— ||
:s |s :m |d :f |r :— |— :m |d :m |l :s |s :— |— ||
:s, |d :m, |f, :r, |s, :— |— :m, |f, :m, |r, :s, |d, :— |— ||

:m |m :- .r |d :m |l :f |r :s |d.r:m |r :r |d :— |— || f |m ||
:l, |se,:l, .t, |d :t, |l, :r |t, :d |l, :d |d :t, |d :— |— || d |d ||
:d |m :m |m :m |f :l |s :s |m :s |s :-.f |m :— |— || l |s ||
:l, |m, :ba,.se, |l, :s, |f, :r, |s, :m, |l, :m,.f, |s, :s, |d :— |— || f, |d ||

A-men.

OUR day of praise is done;
The evening shadows fall;
But pass not from us with the sun,
True Light, that lightenest all!

2 Around the throne on high,
Where night can never be,
The white-robed harpers of the sky
Bring ceaseless hymns to Thee.

3 Too faint our anthems here;
Too soon of praise we tire;
But O the strains, how full and clear,
Of that eternal choir!

4 Yet, Lord, to Thy dear will
If Thou attune the heart,
We in Thine angels' music still
May bear our lower part.

5 'Tis Thine each soul to calm,
Each wayward thought reclaim,
And make our life a daily psalm
Of glory to Thy Name.

6 A little while, and then
Shall come the glorious end,
And songs of angels and of men
In perfect praise shall blend.

JOHN ELLERTON, 1826–93.

291 TALLIS' CANON (Simple version). (L.M.)

Doh = G. *Slow and dignified.* THOMAS TALLIS, *c.* 1510–85.

```
|d  :—  |d  :t,  |d  :d  |r  :r  |m  :d  |f  :f  |m  :m  |r  :r  |d  ||
|s, :—  |s, :s,  |m, :s, |l, :s, |s, :d  |l, :t, |d  :s, |l, :s, |s, ||
|m  :—  |r  :r   |d  :d  |d  :t, |d  :d  |r  :r  |m  :d  |f  :f  |m  ||
|d, :—  |s, :s,  |l, :m, |f, :s, |d, :m, |r, :r, |d, :d  |d  :t, |d  ||

:s |f  :r  |m  :m  |r  :r  |d  :s, |l, :t, |d  :m  |r  :r  |d  :— ||d  |d  ||
:d |l, :s, |s, :s, |l, :t, |d  :d, |l, :s, |m, :s, |f, :r, |m, :— ||f, |m, ||
:m |r  :r  |d  :s  |f  :r  |m  :m  |r  :r  |d  :s, |l, :t, |d  :— ||l, |s, ||
:d |r  :t, |d  :d, |f, :s, |d, :m, |f, :s, |l, :m, |f, :s, |d, :— ||f, |d, ||
                                                                      A-men.
```

Unison. ALL praise to Thee, my God, this night,
For all the blessings of the light!
Keep me, O keep me, King of kings,
Beneath Thy own almighty wings.

Harmony. 2 Forgive me, Lord, for Thy dear Son,
The ill that I this day have done,
That with the world, myself, and Thee,
I, ere I sleep, at peace may be.

3 Teach me to live, that I may dread
The grave as little as my bed;
Teach me to die, that so I may
Rise glorious at the awful day.

4 O may my soul on Thee repose,
And may sweet sleep mine eyelids close,—
Sleep that may me more vigorous make
To serve my God when I awake.

5 When in the night I sleepless lie,
My soul with heavenly thoughts supply;
Let no ill dreams disturb my rest,
No powers of darkness me molest.

Unison. 6 Praise God, from whom all blessings flow;
Praise Him, all creatures here below;
Praise Him above, ye heavenly host;
Praise Father, Son, and Holy Ghost.

THOMAS KEN, 1637–1711.

291 TALLIS' CANON (Full version). (L.M.) *

Doh = G. *Slow and dignified.* THOMAS TALLIS, *c.* 1510–85.

All praise to Thee, All praise to Thee, my God, this
:s_1 |s_1 :s_1 |s_1 :d |d :t_1 |d :d |r :r
:d_1 |r_1 :r_1 |m_1 :d_1 |f_1 :r_1 |s_1 :s_1 |l_1 :s_1
All praise to Thee, my God, this night, All praise to
:d |d :t_1 |d :d |r :r |m :d |d :t_1
:d |s_1 :s_1 |d_1 :m_1 |r_1 :r_1 |d_1 :m_1 |f_1 :s_1

night, All praise to Thee, my God, this night, For all the
m :d |d :t_1 |d :d |r :r |m :d |f :f
s_1 :s_1 |f_1 :r_1 |s_1 :s_1 |ta_1 :-.l_1 |s_1 :s_1 |f_1 :r_1
Thee, my God, this night, For all the bless - ings of the
d :d |r :r |m :d |f :f |m :m |r :r
d_1 :m_1 |r_1 :r_1 |d_1 :d |ta_1 :ta_1 |d :d |d :t_1

bless - ings of the light! For all the bless - ings of the
m :m |r :r |d :d |f :f |m :m |r :r
s_1 :s_1 |ta_1 :-.l_1 |s_1 :s_1 |f_1 :r_1 |s_1 :d |l_1 :ta_1
light! For all the bless - ings of the light! Keep me, O
d :d |f :f |m :m |r :r |d :s |f :r
d :d_1 |r_1 :ta_2 |d_1 :d |d :t_1 |d :d |r :ta_1

light! Keep me, O keep me, King of kings, Keep me, O
d :s |f :r |m :m |r :r |d :s |f :r
s_1 :d |l_1 :t_1 |d :d |l_1 :ta_1 |s_1 :d |l_1 :t_1
keep me, King of kings, Keep me, O keep me, King of
m :m |r :r |d :s |f :r |m :m |r :r
d :d_1 |f_1 :s_1 |d_1 :d |r :ta_1 |d :d_1 |f_1 :s_1

keep me, King of kings, Be - neath Thy own al - migh - ty

| *m* :*m* | *r* :*r* | *d* :s$_1$ | l$_1$:t$_1$ | **d** :m | r :r |

| *d* :d | l$_1$:s$_1$ | m$_1$:s$_1$ | f$_1$:r$_1$ | m$_1$:*m*$_1$ | *l*$_1$:*s*$_1$ |

kings, Be - neath Thy own al - migh - ty wings. *Be - neath Thy*

| *d* :s$_1$ | l$_1$:t$_1$ | **d** :m | r :r | **d** :*s*$_1$ | *l*$_1$:*t*$_1$ |

| *d*$_1$:m$_1$ | f$_1$:s$_1$ | l$_1$:m$_1$ | f$_1$:s$_1$ | d$_1$:*d*$_1$ | *f*$_1$:*s*$_1$ |

wings. *Be - neath Thy own al - migh - ty wings.*

| **d** :*s*$_1$ | *l*$_1$:*t*$_1$ | *d* :(*m* | *r* :*r* | *d*) :— || **d** | **d** ||

| *m*$_1$:-.*s*$_1$ | *f*$_1$:*r*$_1$ | *m*$_1$:— | — :— | — :— || f$_1$ | m$_1$ ||

own al - migh - ty wings. . . . . A- men.

| *d* :*m* | *r* :*r* | *d* :— | — :— | — :— || l$_1$ | s$_1$ ||

| *l*$_1$:*m*$_1$ | *f*$_1$:*s*$_1$ | *d*$_1$:— | — :— | — :— || f$_1$ | d$_1$ ||

* The heavy-type notes to be sung by the main body of voices; the italic notes by an echo choir softly.

Note.—The alto and bass parts may have relatively fewer voices than the two melody parts.

2 Forgive me, Lord, for Thy dear Son,
The ill that I this day have done,
That with the world, myself, and Thee,
I, ere I sleep, at peace may be.

3 Teach me to live, that I may dread
The grave as little as my bed;
Teach me to die, that so I may
Rise glorious at the awful day.

4 O may my soul on Thee repose,
And may sweet sleep mine eyelids close,—
Sleep that may me more vigorous make
To serve my God when I awake.

5 When in the night I sleepless lie,
My soul with heavenly thoughts supply;
Let no ill dreams disturb my rest,
No powers of darkness me molest.

6 Praise God, from whom all blessings flow;
Praise Him, all creatures here below;
Praise Him above, ye heavenly host;
Praise Father, Son, and Holy Ghost.

THOMAS KEN, 1637-1711

292 ABENDS. (L.M.)

Doh = A♭. *In moderate time.* HERBERT STANLEY OAKELEY, 1830–1903.

s, :d :t,	l, :— :l,	f :— :m	r :— :—	r :m :f	s :— :d
m, :f, :s,	s, :f, :l,	l, :s, :s,	s, :— :—	s, :s, :t,	d :— :s,
d :d :d	d :— :de	r :t, :d	t, :— :—	t, :d :r	m :— :d
d, :r, :m,	f, :— :m,	r, :— :m,.f,	s, :— :—	f, :m, :r,	d, :— :m,

t, :— :l,	s, :— :—		t, :d :r	f :— :m	r :— :d	t, :— :—
s, :— :fe,	s, :— :—		s, :s, :s,	l, :— :d	l, :t, :d.fe,	s, :— :—
r :— :d	t, :— :—		f :m :r	d :— :s	f :— :m.r	r :— :—
r, :— :r,	s, :— :—		r :d :t,	d :— :d	f, :s, :l,	s, :— :f,

d :r :m	s :— :f	m :— :r	d :— :—		d	d	
s, :s, :s,	ta, :— :l,	s, :— :s,	s, :— :—		l,	s,	
d :f :m	d :— :d	d :— :t,.f	m :— :—		f	m	
m, :r, :d,	m, :— :f,	s, :— :s,	d :— :—		f,	d,	

A - men.

HERR GOT VATER. (L.M.)

Doh = E♭. *In moderate time.* SAMUEL BESLER, 1574–1625.

d :d :d	r :— :r	m :— :f	s :— :—		s :s :m	l :— :t
s, :f, :s,	l, :— :s,	d :— :d	d :— :t,		d :d :d	d :— :f
m :r :m	f :— :s	m :— :r	r :— :—		s :s :l	l :—.s :f
d :d :d	d :— :t,	l, :— :r	s, :— :f,		m, :m, :l,	f :—.m :r

d' :—.t :l	s :— :—		s :l :s	m :— :s	f :— :m	r :—	
m :—.r :d	d :— :t,		d :l, :t,	d :— :d	l, :r :d	t, :—	
s :— :fe	s :— :—		s :f :s	l :— :s	l :—.s :l	t :—	
d :— :r	s, :— :—		m :f :m	l, :— :m	r :—.m :f	s :—	

:m | s :m :f | m :r.d :r | d :— :t,.l, | t, :— :— | d :— :— || d | d ||
:d | r :d :r | d :s, :l, | s, :— :— | s, :— :— | s, :— :— || l, | s, ||
:s | s :— :l | s :— :f | m :— :r.d | r :— :f | m :— :— || f | m ||
:d | t, :d :r, | m, :— :f, | s, :— :— | s, :— :— | d :— :— || f, | d ||

A-men.

HURSLEY. (L.M.)

Doh = F. *In moderate time.* *Katholisches Gesangbuch*, Vienna, *c.* 1774.

```
d  :d  :d  | d  :t, :d  | r  :m  :r  | d  :— :— | m  :m  :m  | m  :r  :m
s, :s, :s, | s, :— :s, | t, :— :t, | d  :— :— | d  :d  :d  | d  :t, :d
m  :m  :m  | m  :r  :m  | f  :s  :f  | m  :— :— | s  :s  :s  | s  :— :s
d  :d  :d  | d  :— :d  | s, :— :s, | d  :— :— | d  :d  :d  | d  :— :d

s  :f  :m  | r  :— :— || r  :r  :m  | f  :— :r  | m  :— :f  | s  :— :—
d  :t, :d  | t, :— :— || t, :r  :de | r  :l, :t, | d  :— :d  | t, :— :—
s  :— :s  | s  :— :— || s  :l  :s  | f  :— :s  | s  :— :d  | r  :— :m
m  :r  :d  | s, :— :— || s  :f  :m  | r  :— :s, | d  :— :l, | s, :— :—

l  :l  :l  | s  :— :m  | f  :m  :r  | d  :— :— || d  | d  ||
l, :d  :d  | d  :t, :d  | d  :— :t, | d  :— :— || l, | s, ||
f  :f  :f  | r  :— :d  | l  :s  :f  | m  :— :— || f  | m  ||
f, :f, :f, | s, :— :l, | f, :s, :s, | d  :— :— || f, | d  ||
                                                  A-men.
```

SUN of my soul, Thou Saviour dear,
It is not night if Thou be near;
O may no earth-born cloud arise
To hide Thee from Thy servant's eyes.

2 When the soft dews of kindly sleep
My wearied eyelids gently steep,
Be my last thought, how sweet to rest
For ever on my Saviour's breast.

3 Abide with me from morn till eve,
For without Thee I cannot live;
Abide with me when night is nigh,
For without Thee I dare not die.

4 If some poor wandering child of Thine
Have spurned to-day the voice divine,
Now, Lord, the gracious work begin;
Let him no more lie down in sin.

5 Watch by the sick; enrich the poor
With blessings from Thy boundless store;
Be every mourner's sleep to-night,
Like infant's slumbers, pure and light.

6 Come near and bless us when we wake,
Ere through the world our way we take,
Till in the ocean of Thy love
We lose ourselves in heaven above.

JOHN KEBLE, 1792–1866.

293

TEMPLE. (84. 84. 8884.)

Doh = D. *In moderate time.* EDWARD JOHN HOPKINS, 1818–1901.

```
|m  :m  |f  :m  |m  :r  |r  :d  |l  :—  |s  :r  |m  :—  |—  :—  ||
|d  :d  |d  :d  |t, :t, |t, :d  |d  :—  |d  :t, |d  :—  |—  :—  ||
|s  :s  |l  :s  |s  :f  |f  :m  |f  :m  |r  :s  |s  :—  |—  :—  ||
|d  :d  |d  :d  |s, :s, |l, :l, |f, :—  |s, :s, |d  :—  |—  :—  ||

|m  :m  |f  :m  |m  :r  |d  :m  |l  :—  |s  :fe |s  :—  |—  :—  ||
|d  :d  |d  :d  |t, :t, |d  :d  |m  :—  |d  :d  |t, :—  |—  :—  ||
|s  :s  |l  :s  |se :se |l  :l  |l  :—  |l  :l  |s  :—  |—  :—  ||
|d  :d  |d  :d  |m  :m  |l, :l, |d  :—  |r  :r  |s, :—  |—  :—  ||

|s  :s  |d' :t  |t  :l  |s  :m  |m  :m  |l  :s  |s  :f  |f  :m   ||
|r  :r  |s  :s  |s  :f  |r  :d  |d  :d  |d  :d  |d  :d  |r  :r   ||
|t  :t  |d' :d' |d' :d' |s  :s  |d' :t  |l  :m  |m  :l  |t  :t   ||
|s  :f  |m  :m  |f  :l, |t, :d  |d  :d  |f  :m  |l, :l, |se, :se, ||

|m  :m  |f  :m  |r  :l  |t  :d' |s  :—  |f  :r  |d  :—  |—  :—  ||f  |m ||
|d  :d  |de :de |r  :r  |r  :d  |d  :—  |t, :t, |d  :—  |—  :—  ||d  |d ||
|l  :l  |l  :l  |l  :l  |f  :f  |m  :—  |r  :f  |m  :—  |—  :—  ||l  |s ||
|l, :l  |s  :s  |f  :f  |r  :r  |s, :—  |s, :s, |d  :—  |—  :—  ||f, |d ||
                                                                 A-men.
```

GOD, that madest earth and heaven,
Darkness and light,
Who the day for toil hast given,
For rest the night:
May Thine angel guards defend us,
Slumber sweet Thy mercy send us,
Holy dreams and hopes attend us,
This livelong night.

2 Guard us waking, guard us sleeping;
And, when we die,
May we, in Thy mighty keeping,
All peaceful lie.
When the last dread trump shall wake us,
Do not Thou, our Lord, forsake us,
But to reign in glory take us
With Thee on high.

1 v. REGINALD HEBER, 1783–1826.
2 v. RICHARD WHATELY, 1787–1863.

294

THANET. (8. 3 3. 6.)

Doh = G. *Moderately slow.* JOSEPH JOWETT, 1784–1856.

```
| m  :r  | d  :-.d | f  :m  | m  :r  || m  :fe | s  :—  |
| s, :t, | d  :-.d | t, :d  | d  :t, || d  :d  | t, :—  |
| m  :f  | s  :-.s | s  :s  | s  :s  || s  :l  | s  :—  |
| d  :r  | m  :-.m | r  :d  | s, :s, || d  :l, | m  :r  |

| m  :fe | s  :—  || f  :-.s | m  :r.d | d  :t, | d  :—  || d  | d  ||
| d  :d  | t, :—  || d  :r   | d  :l,  | s, :—  | s, :—  || l, | s, ||
| s  :l  | r  :—  || l  :s   | s  :f   | m  :r  | m  :—  || f  | m  ||
| d  :l, | s, :—  || l, :t,  | d  :f,  | s, :—  | d, :—  || f, | d, ||
```

A-men.

CWMDU. (8. 3 3. 6.)

Lah = C. Doh = E♭. *Moderately slow.* DAVID EMLYN EVANS, 1843–1913.

```
| m  :m  | m  :-.m  | l  :d' | d' :t  || t  :d' | l  :—  |
| d  :r  | m  :-.r  | d  :m  | m  :m  || r  :r  | d  :—  |
| l  :se | l  :-.se | l  :l  | l  :se || se :se | l  :—  |
| l, :t, | d  :-.t, | l, :l, | m  :m  || m  :m  | l, :—  |

| s  :l  | f  :—  || m  :l  | l  :-.se | t  :—  | l  :—  || f  | m  ||
| de :de | r  :—  || t, :m  | r  :-.r  | r  :—  | d  :—  || r  | de ||
| m  :l  | l  :—  || se :l  | t  :-.t  | se :—  | l  :—  || l  | l  ||
| l, :l, | r  :—  || m  :d  | f  :-.f  | m  :—  | l, :—  || r  | l, ||
```

A-men.

ERE I sleep, for every favour
This day showed
By my God,
I will bless my Saviour.

2 O my Lord, what shall I render
To Thy Name,
Still the same,
Gracious, good, and tender?

3 Thou hast ordered all my goings
In Thy way,
Heard me pray,
Sanctified my doings.

4 Leave me not, but ever love me;
Let Thy peace
Be my bliss,
Till Thou hence remove me.

5 Visit me with Thy salvation;
Let Thy care
Now be near,
Round my habitation.

6 Thou my Rock, my Guard, my Tower,
Safely keep,
While I sleep,
Me, with all Thy power.

7 So, whene'er in death I slumber,
Let me rise
With the wise,
Counted in their number.

JOHN CENNICK, 1718–55.

Also the following:

4 O Trinity, O blessèd Light | 127 Jesus, Lord, Redeemer

CLOSE OF WORSHIP

295 DUNFERMLINE. (C.M.)

Doh = F. *Moderately slow.* *Scottish Psalter*, 1615.

d :—	d :r	m :f	s :s	m :—		m :—
s, :—	s, :l,.t,	d :d	d :t,	d :—		d :—
m :—	m :f	s :d	r :s	s :—		s :—
d :—	m :r	d :l,	s, :s,	d :—		d :—

l :s	s :fe	s :—		s :—	m :s	l :s
l,.t, :d	r :r.d	t, :—		r :—	d :d.t,	l, :t,
f :s	l :l	s :—		s :—	s :d	f.m :r
f :m	r :r	s, :—		t, :—	d :m,	f, :s,

f :m	r :—		m :—	r :d	d :t,	d :—		d	d	
d.r :d	t, :—		d :—	t, :d	l, :s,	s, :—		l,	s,	
l :s	s :—		s :—	s.f :m	f.m :r	m d :—		f	m	
l,.t, :d	s, :—		d :—	s, :l,	f, :s,	d, :—		f,	d,	

A-men.

ALMIGHTY God, Thy word is cast
Like seed into the ground ;
Now let the dew of heaven descend,
And righteous fruits abound.

2 Let not the foe of Christ and man
This holy seed remove,
But give it root in every heart
To bring forth fruits of love.

3 Let not the world's deceitful cares
The rising plant destroy,
But let it yield a hundredfold
The fruits of peace and joy.

4 Oft as the precious seed is sown,
Thy quickening grace bestow,
That all whose souls the truth receive
Its saving power may know.

JOHN CAWOOD, 1775-1852.

296 SALISBURY. (C.M.)

Doh = G. *Moderately slow.* *Ravenscroft's Psalter*, 1621.

```
|d  :—  |r  :f  |m :s  |s :fe  |s  :— ||m  :— |l    :s |f :f  |m :— ||
|s, :—  |l, :s, |d :t, |m :r.d |t, :— ||s, :— |l,.t,:d |d :t, |d :— ||
|m  :—  |f  :r  |s :s  |l :l   |s  :— ||m  :— |f    :s |l :f  |s :— ||
|d  :—  |d  :t, |d :m  |d :r   |s, :— ||d  :— |f    :m |r :r  |d :— ||

|s  :— |m  :f  |r  :m  |d  :r  |t, :— ||f  :—   |m  :m  |r  :r  |d  :— |— :— ||d  |d  ||
|s, :— |s, :l, |s, :t, |d  :l, |s, :— ||l, :-.t,|d  :d  |d  :t, |d  :— |— :— ||l, |s, ||
|r  :— |m  :d  |r  :s  |m  :f  |r  :— ||r  :—   |s  :m  |l  :s.f|m  :— |— :— ||f  |m  ||
|t, :— |d  :l, |t, :s, |l, :f, |s, :— ||r, :—   |m, :l, |f, :s, |d, :— |— :— ||f, |d, ||
                                                                              A-men.
```

AND now the wants are told that brought
Thy children to Thy knee;
Here lingering still, we ask for nought,
But simply worship Thee.

2 For Thou art God, the One, the Same,
O'er all things high and bright;
And round us, when we speak Thy Name,
There spreads a heaven of light.

3 O wondrous peace, in thought to dwell
On excellence divine,
To know that nought in man can tell
How fair Thy beauties shine!

4 O Thou, above all blessing blest,
O'er thanks exalted far,
Thy very greatness is a rest
To weaklings as we are;

5 For when we feel the praise of Thee
A task beyond our powers,
We say, 'A perfect God is He,
And He is fully ours.'

6 All glory to the Father be,
All glory to the Son,
All glory, Holy Ghost, to Thee,
While endless ages run.

William Bright, 1824–1901.

297 WHITEHALL. (L.M.)

Doh = A. *In moderate time.* HENRY LAWES, 1596–1662.

d :— |t, :l, |d :m, |f, :l, |s, :— ||s, :— |l, :t,
s, :— |s, :f, |m, :d, |d, :f, |d, :— ||m, :— |f, :f,
m :— |m :d |d :t, |l, :t, |d :— ||d :— |d :r
d, :— |m, :f, |l, :s, |f, :r, |m, :— ||d, :— |f, :r,

d :t, |l, :m |r :— ||r :— |f :m |l, :t, |d :r
s, :s, |f, :s, |s, :— ||s, :— |l, :s, |s, :f, |m, :l,
d :d |d :d |t, :— ||ta, :— |l, :d |d :s |s :f
m, :m, |f, :d, |s, :— ||s, :— |r, :m, |f, :s, |l, :t,

m :— ||m :— |s :r |f :m |r :r |d :— ||d |d ||
s, :— ||l, :— |t, :ta, |l, :l,.s, |f, :s, |m, :— ||f, |m, ||
m :— ||d :— |r :r |d :d |d :t, |d :— ||l, |s, ||
d :— ||l, :— |s, :ta, |f, :l, |r, :s, |d, :— ||f, |d, ||

A - men.

COME, dearest Lord, descend and dwell
By faith and love in every breast;
Then shall we know, and taste, and feel
The joys that cannot be expressed.

2 Come, fill our hearts with inward strength,
Make our enlargèd souls possess
And learn the height and breadth and length
Of Thine unmeasurable grace.

3 Now to the God whose power can do
More than our thoughts or wishes know,
Be everlasting honours done
By all the Church, through Christ His Son.

ISAAC WATTS, 1674–1748.

298 HENLLAN. (8 7. 8 7. 7 7 8 7 7.)

Doh = A♭. *Moderately slow.* DAVID EVANS, 1874–

s_1 :s_1	l_1 :l_1	s_1 :d	d :t_1	d :r	m :d	t_1 :l_1	s_1 :—
m_1 :r_1	d_1 :r_1	m_1 :s_1	s_1 :s_1	m_1 :s_1	s_1 :l_1	s_1 :fe_1	s_1 :—
Of Thy	love some	gra-cious	to - ken	Grant us,	Lord, be -	fore we	go;
d :t_1	l_1 :t_1	d :m	m :r	d :t_1	d :m	r :d	t_1 :—
d_1 :d_1	f_1 :f_1	m_1 :d_1	s_1 :s_1	l_1 :s_1	d :d_1	r_1 :r_1	s_1 :—

s_1 :s_1	l_1 :l_1	s_1 :d	d :t_1	d :r	m :d	d :t_1	d :—
m_1 :r_1	d_1 :r_1	m_1 :s_1	s_1 :s_1	m_1 :s_1	s_1 :d	l_1 :s_1	s_1 :—
Bless Thy	word which	has been	spo-ken;	Life and	peace on	all be -	stow.
d :t_1	l_1 :t_1	d :m	m :r	d :t_1	d :s	f :r	m :—
d_1 :d_1	f_1 :f_1	m_1 :d_1	s_1 :s_1	l_1 :s_1	d :m_1	f_1 :s_1	d_1 :—

m :m	r :r	d :r	m :—	l_1 :t_1	d :r	d :t_1	l_1 :—
s_1 :d	d :t_1	l_1 :l_1	se_1 :—	l_1 :se_1	l_1 :t_1	l_1 :se_1	l_1 :—
When we	join the	world a -	gain,	Let our	hearts with	Thee re-	main;
d :m	s :f	m :r	t_1 :—	m :r	d :f	m :r	d :—
d :d	s_1 :s_1	l_1 :f_1	m_1 :—	d :t_1	l_1 :r_1	m_1 :m_1	l_1 :—

s_1 :d	d :t_1	d :m	m :r	d :d	r :m	f :m
r_1 :m_1	s_1 :s_1	s_1 :d	l_1 :t_1	s_1 :d	t_1 :d	r/s_1 } :s_1.l_1
O di -	rect us,	and pro -	tect us,	Till we	gain the	heaven-ly
r :d	m :r	d :s	fe :s	m :s	f :m	r :m.fe
t_1 :l_1	s_1 :-.f_1	m_1 :d_1	d :t_1	d :m	r :d	t_1 :d

r :—	d :r	m :d	d :t_1	d :—	d	d
t_1 :—	l_1 :t_1	d :s_1	l_1 :s_1	s_1 :—	l_1	s_1
shore,	Where Thy	peo - ple	want no	more.	A-	men.
s :—	m :s	s :d	f :r	m :—	f	m
s_1 :—	l_1 :s_1	d :m_1	f_1 :s_1	d_1 :—	f_1	d_1

THOMAS KELLY, 1769–1854.

[*Copyright*, 1927, *by David Evans.*]

299

HOLYWOOD (ST. THOMAS). (8 7. 8 7. 8 7.)

Doh = E♭. *Moderately slow.* 18th cent.

```
|d  :r  |m  :d  |r    :m  |f  :m  |l  :s      |f    :m    |r  :r     |d  :—  ||
|s, :t, |d  :s, |t,   :d  |r  :d  |d  :d      |l,.t, :d   |d  :t,    |d  :—  ||
|m  :s  |s  :m  |f    :s  |s  :s  |f  :s      |r    :m.f  |s  :-.f   |m  :—  ||
|d  :s, |d  :m  |r    :d  |t, :d  |f  :m      |r    :d    |s, :s,    |d  :—  ||

                                   B♭.t.
|d' :t  |d' :s  |l    :s  |f    :m  |[l]r  :m     |f  :m      |r  :r     |d  :—  ||
|m  :r  |d  :d  |l,.t,:d  |r    :s, |[m]l, :- .s, |f, :s,     |s, :- .f, |m, :—  ||
|s  :f  |m  :m  |f    :s  |l.t  :d' |[d']f :m     |r  :d      |d  :t,    |d  :—  ||
|d  :r  |m  :d  |f    :m  |r    :d  |[l]r, :de,   |r, :m,.f,  |s, :s,    |d, :—  ||

f.E♭.           ://:
|[d]s  :s  |m  :d  |r  :m  |f    :m  |s  :m  |l    :s.f   |m  :r   |d  :—  || d  | d  ||
|[f,]d :r  |s, :d  |d  :d  |d.t, :d  |d  :d  |d.r  :m.r   |d  :t,  |d  :—  || l, | s, ||
|[d]s  :r  |m  :s  |l  :s  |f    :s  |s  :s  |l.t  :d'.l  |s  :-.f |m  :—  || f  | m  ||
|[l]m  :t, |d  :m  |f  :m  |r    :d  |m  :d  |f    :m.f   |s  :s,  |d  :—  || f, | d  ||
                                                                         A-men.
```

LORD, dismiss us with Thy blessing;
Fill our hearts with joy and peace;
Let us each, Thy love possessing,
Triumph in redeeming grace;
O refresh us,
Travelling through this wilderness.

2 Thanks we give and adoration
For Thy Gospel's joyful sound;
May the fruits of Thy salvation
In our hearts and lives abound;
May Thy presence
With us evermore be found.

JOHN FAWCETT, 1740–1817.

300 KEINE SCHÖNHEIT HAT DIE WELT. (77. 77.)

Doh = C. *In moderate time.* GEORG JOSEPH, *c.* 1657.

m :f :s	f :— :m	r :— :r	d :— :—	m :— :r
d :— :d	d :r :d	d :— :t_1	d :— :—	d :— :t_1
s :— :s	l :— :s	l :— :s	m :— :—	s :— :s
d :r :m	l_1 :t_1 :d	f_1 :— :s_1	d :— :—	d :— :s_1

m :fe :s	s :— :fe	s :— :—	d^1 :— :d^1	t :— :s	l :— :l
d :— :r	m :— :r	r :— :—	d :m :l	s :— :r	m :— :r
s :l :t	d^1 :— :l	t :— :—	l :— :m^1	m^1 :— :s	s :— :fe
d :— :t_1	l_1 :— :r	s_1 :— :—	l_1 :d :l_1	m :— :t_1	d :— :r

s :— :—	m :f :s	l :t :d^1	r^1 :— :r^1	d^1 :— :—	d^1	d^1
t_1 :— :—	d :— :s	f :— :m	l :— :s	m :— :—	f	m
s :— :—	s :d^1 :t	l :r^1 :d^1	d^1 :— :t	d^1 :— :—	l	s
s_1 :— :—	d :r :m	f :s :l	f :— :s	d :— :—	f	d

A-men.

NOW may He who from the dead
Brought the Shepherd of the sheep,
Jesus Christ, our King and Head,
All our souls in safety keep.

2 May He teach us to fulfil
What is pleasing in His sight,
Perfect us in all His will,
And preserve us day and night.

3 To that dear Redeemer's praise,
Who the covenant sealed with blood,
Let our hearts and voices raise
Loud thanksgivings to our God.

JOHN NEWTON, 1725–1807.

301

ELLERS. (10 10. 10 10.)

Doh = A♭. *Moderately quick.*

EDWARD JOHN HOPKINS, 1818–1901.

s, :s, .l,	s, :d	d .t, :d .r	m :—	d :d .r
m, :m, .m,	s, :s,	f, .f, :f, .f,	m, :—	s, :s, .s,
d :d .d	d :d	s, .s, :l, .t,	d :—	m :m .m
d, :d, .d,	m, :m,	r, .r, :r, .r,	d, :—	d :d .d

d :[m]l (E♭.t.)	l .s :l .t	[d']s :— (f.A♭.)	s :d .d	f :f
l, :[d]f	f .f :f .f	[m]t, :—	s, :s, .s,	l, :l,
m :[m]l	t .t :l .s	[s]r :—	d :m .m	f :r
l, :[l,]r	s, .s, :s, .s,	[d]s, :—	m, :m .m	r :d

f .r :m .f	m :—	d :r .d	d :l,	s, .s, :l, .s,	s, :—
s, .s, :s, .s,	s, :—	m, :m, .m,	r, :r,	r, .r, :f, .f,	m, :—
r .r :t, .t,	d :—	d :d .d	l, :d	t, .t, :t, .t,	d :—
t, .t, :s, .s,	d, :—	l, :l, .l,	f, :f,	s, .s, :s, .s,	d, :—

l,	d
f,	s,
d	m
f,	d,

A-men.

SAVIOUR, again to Thy dear Name we raise
With one accord our parting hymn of praise;
We stand to bless Thee ere our worship cease,
Then, lowly kneeling, wait Thy word of peace.

2 Grant us Thy peace upon our homeward way;
With Thee began, with Thee shall end the day;
Guard Thou the lips from sin, the hearts from shame,
That in this house have called upon Thy Name.

PAX DEI. (10 10. 10 10.)

Doh = D. *Moderately quick.* John Bacchus Dykes, 1823–76.

```
d  :—   |m  :s   |s   :-.f |m   :d   |m   :—   |r  :d   |d  :—   |t,  :—  ||
s, :—   |d  :d   |d   :-.d |d   :d   |d   :t,  |l, :—   |s, :—   |—   :—  ||
m  :—   |s  :ta  |l   :-.l |s   :l   |s   :—   |f  :m   |m  :—   |r   :f  ||
d  :—   |d  :d   |d   :-.d |d   :l,  |m,  :—   |f, :—   |s, :—   |—   :—  ||

                  A.t.                                    f.D.
d  :—   |m  :s   |(d)f  :m   |d  :r   |m  :—   |—  :r   |(d)s  :—  |— :—  ||
s, :—   |d  :r   |(m)l, :se, |m, :l,  |s, :d   |t, :—   |(s)r  :—  |— :—  ||
m  :—   |s  :s   |(s)d  :t,  |d  :d   |d  :r.m |f  :—   |(m)t  :—  |— :—  ||
d  :—   |d  :t,  |(l)r, :m,  |l, :f,  |s, :—   |s, :—   |(d)s  :—  |f :—  ||

s  :—   |l  :m   |f  :—   |s  :r   |m  :s   |d' :d'  |t  :—   |— :—  ||
m  :r   |de :de  |r  :d   |t, :—   |d  :r   |m  :r.d |r  :—   |— :—  ||
d' :ta  |l  :s   |l  :—   |s  :f   |s  :s   |s  :fe  |s  :—   |— :—  ||
m  :—   |l, :m   |r  :—   |s, :r   |d  :t,  |l, :l,  |s, :—   |— :—  ||

t  :—   |d' :d  |d :r  |m :f.r  |d  :—  |—  :t,  |d  :—  |— :—  || d  |d  ||
r  :—   |d  :d  |d :d  |d :l,   |s, :l, |s, :s,  |s, :—  |— :—  || l, |s, ||
t  :-.l |s  :s  |l :l  |s :f    |m  :f  |m  :r.f |m  :—  |— :—  || f  |m  ||
s  :f   |m  :m  |f :f  |m :r.f, |s, :—  |—  :s,  |d  :—  |— :—  || f, |d  ||
                                                                  A-men.
```

3 Grant us Thy peace through this approaching night;
Turn Thou for us its darkness into light;
From harm and danger keep Thy children free,
For dark and light are both alike to Thee.

4 Grant us Thy peace throughout our earthly life,
Our balm in sorrow, and our stay in strife;
Then, when Thy voice shall bid our conflict cease,
Call us, O Lord, to Thine eternal peace.

John Ellerton, 1826–93.

[May be sung to Magda, No. 243.]

302

ST. MATTHIAS. (88. 88. and refrain.)

WILLIAM HENRY MONK, 1823-89.

Doh = F. *In moderate time.* C.t. f.F.

```
:m   |r  :d  |f  :m  |r  :-.m |d  :m l  |s  :f    |s  :d'    |l  :t  |d s   ||
:d   |t, :d  |d  :d  |d  :t,  |d  :d f  |d  :f    |m  :s     |s  :f  |m t,  ||
:s   |f  :m  |f  :s  |l  :s   |m  :s d' |d' :-.t  |d' :d'.m' |m' :r' |d s   ||
:d   |s, :d  |l, :s, |f, :s,  |d  :d f  |m  :r    |d  :m     |f  :s  |d s,  ||

:s     |s  :f  |m :m       |m  :r   |d  :r.m   |f  :l, |t, :d    |r  :-.r |d ||
:t,.d  |r  :t, |d :se,.l,  |t, :se, |l, :l,    |l, :l, |s, :s,.d |d  :t,  |d ||
:s     |s  :s  |s :m       |m  :m   |m  :r.de  |r  :r  |r  :d    |l  :f   |m ||
:s,.l, |t, :r  |d :m,.ba,  |se,:t,  |l, :f,.m, |r, :f, |s, :m,   |f, :s,  |d ||

:d |r :m |f :m     |f :s     |l :l  |s   :m.r |d :f  |m :- |- :r  |d :- |- ||f  |m ||
:d |t,:d |d :d     |d :-.ta, |l,:d  |d.l,:t,  |d :d  |d :- |- :t, |d :- |- ||d  |d ||
:m |s :s |f :s     |f :m     |f :f.m|r   :f   |m :l  |s :m |f :f  |m :- |- ||l  |s ||
:d |s,:d |l,:d.ta, |l,:s,    |f,:f, |s,  :s,  |l,:f, |s,:- |- :s, |d :- |- ||f, |d ||
```

A-men.

O SAVIOUR, bless us ere we go ;
Thy word into our minds instil ;
And make our lukewarm hearts to glow
With lowly love and fervent will.
Through life's long day and death's dark night,
O gentle Jesus, be our light !

2 The day is done, its hours have run,
And Thou hast taken count of all,—
The scanty triumphs grace hath won,
The broken vow, the frequent fall.

3 Grant us, dear Lord, from evil ways
True absolution and release ;
And bless us, more than in past days,
With purity and inward peace.

SURREY. (88. 88. and refrain.)

Doh = F. *Moderately slow.* HENRY CAREY, 1692–1743.

```
:s | f  :m  :l  | d  :t, :d  | f  :m  :r  | m  :— :m | r  :— :fe
:d | d  :—  :l, | s, :—  :m, | l, :s, :s, | s, :— :d | r  :— :d
:m | l  :s  :f  | m  :r  :d  | d  :—  :t, | d  :— :s | s  :— :d
:d | d  :—  :f, | s, :—  :l, | f, :s, :s, | d, :— :d | t, :— :l,

                        D.C.
s  :—   :s, | d :t, :l,  | s, :— || s | l :—:s.f | s :—:f.m | f:—:m.r
t, :—   :s, | l,:s, :fe, | s, :— || d | d :—:d   | d :—:r.d | r:l,:d.t,
r  :—   :r  | m :r  :r.d | t, :— || s | f :—:s.l | s :—:l   | l:f :s
s, :-.l,:t, | d :r  :r,  | s, :— || m | f :—:m.r | m :—:l,  | r:—:s,

m :— :m  | r  :—  :f  | m  :r   :d  | r  :d  :t, | d  :— || d  | d
d :— :d  | d  :t, :r  | d  :t,  :d  | l, :s, :s, | s, :— || l, | s,
s :— :s  | s  :—  :l  | s  :-.f :m  | f  :m  :r  | m  :— || f  | m
d :— :d, | s, :—  :r, | m, :s,  :l, | f, :s, :s, | d  :— || f, | d
                                                          A-men.
```

4 Do more than pardon : give us joy,
Sweet fear, and sober liberty,
And loving hearts without alloy,
That only long to be like Thee.

5 Labour is sweet, for Thou hast toiled,
And care is light, for Thou hast cared ;
Let not our works with self be soiled,
Nor in unsimple ways ensnared.

6 For all we love, the poor, the sad,
The sinful, unto Thee we call ;
O let Thy mercy make us glad ;
Thou art our Jesus and our All.

FREDERICK WILLIAM FABER, 1814–63.

303

PAX VOBISCUM. (7 7. 7 7.)

Doh = F. *In moderate time.* EDWARD ARTHUR, 1874–

```
|d  :—  |l, :—  |d  :—  |—  :—  |s  :—  |m  :d  |r  :—  |—  :—  |f  :m
|m, :—  |f, :—  |s, :—  |—  :—  |r  :—  |s, :d  |t, :—  |—  :—  |d  :d
|d  :—  |d  :r  |m  :—  |—  :—  |r  :—  |d  :s  |s  :—  |—  :—  |d  :s
|d, :—  |f, :—  |d, :—  |—  :—  |t, :—  |d  :m, |s, :—  |—  :—  |l, :d

                                 f.B♭.
|l  :s  |f  :—  |m  :fe |s  :—  |—  :—  ||(f)d  :—  |t, :—  |l, :t, |d  :r
|d  :d  |r  :—  |s, :d  |t, :—  |—  :—  ||(l)m, :l, |—  :se,|l, :m, |m, :s,
|f  :s  |l  :t  |d' :d  |r  :—  |—  :—  ||(f)d  :—  |m  :—  |m  :se,|l, :t,
|f  :m  |r  :—  |d  :l, |s, :—  |—  :—  ||(r)l, :—  |m, :—  |d, :m, |l, :s,

                 F.t.
|m  :—  |—  :—  |(m,)l, :t, |d  :r  |m  :—  |d  :r  |d  :—  |—  :—  ||d  |d
|s, :—  |—  :—  |(d,)f, :f, |s, :s, |s, :—  |l, :t, |d  :—  |—  :—  ||l, |s,
|d  :—  |—  :—  |(s,)d  :r  |d  :t, |d  :—  |m  :f  |m  :—  |—  :—  ||f  |m
|d  :—  |—  :—  |(d,)f, :r, |m, :s, |d  :t, |l, :s, |d, :—  |—  :—  ||f, |d,
                                                                    A-men.
```

[*Copyright*, 1927, *by Edward Arthur.*]

PART in peace: Christ's life was peace,
Let us live our life in Him;
Part in peace: Christ's death was peace,
Let us die our death in Him.

2 Part in peace: Christ promise gave
Of a life beyond the grave,
Where all mortal partings cease;
Brethren, sisters, part in peace.

SARAH FLOWER ADAMS, 1805–48.

Also the following:

35 Praise the Lord! ye heavens, adore Him | 228 From all that dwell below the skies

BAPTISM.

304 DAS NEUGEBORNE KINDELEIN. (8 8. 8 8. and refrain.)

MELCHIOR VULPIUS, *c.* 1560–1616.
Arranged by JOHANN SEBASTIAN BACH, 1685–1750.

Lah = F. Doh = A♭. *Moderately slow.* E♭.t.

l, :l, :l, | m :-.r :d | m :r :d | t, :— :— || [m]l :l :t | d' :— :t
m, :m, :l, | t, :— :l, | l, :se, :l, | se, :— :— || [l,]r.m :f :f | m :— :r
d :m :d | m :— :m.r | d :r :m | m :— :— || [m]l :r' :r' | d' :ba :se
l,.t, :d :t,.l, | se, :— :l, | d :t, :l, | m, :— :— || [d]f :m.r :se, | l, :— :t,

f.A♭. *D.C.*

l :— :se | [l]m :— :— || m :r :t, | d :-.r :m | r :d :t,
d :— :t, | [de]se, :— :— || l, :f, :m, | m, :l, :s, | l, :s, :s,
l :m :— | [m]t, :— :— || d :t, :t, | l, :f :m | f :m :r
d.r :m :m, | [l,]m, :— :— || l,, :l, :se, | l, :-.t, :d | f, :s, :s,

d :— :— || s :l :s | m :-.r :d | t, :l, :se, | l, :— :— || l, l,
s, :— :— || d :d :t, | t, :— :l, | f, :m, :m, | m, :— :— || f, m,
m :— :— || m :r :r | t, :m :m | r :d :t, | de :— :— || r de
d, :— :— || d :f, :s, | se, :— :l, | r, :m, :m, | l,, :— :— || r, l,,

A-men.

Ach lieber Herre, Jesu Christ.

LORD Jesus Christ, our Lord most dear,
As Thou wast once an infant here,
So give this child of Thine, we pray,
Thy grace and blessing day by day.
O holy Jesus, Lord Divine,
We pray Thee guard this child of Thine.

2 As in Thy heavenly Kingdom, Lord,
All things obey Thy sacred word,
Do Thou Thy mighty succour give,
And shield this child by morn and eve.

3 Their watch let angels round *him* keep
Where'er *he* be, awake, asleep ;
Thy holy Cross now let *him* bear,
That *he* Thy crown with saints may wear.

HEINRICH VON LAUFENBERG, 15th cent. ; *tr.* by CATHERINE WINKWORTH, 1829–78.

[May be sung to ST. CHRYSOSTOM, No. 430.]

305 COMMANDMENTS. (L.M.)

French Psalter, 1549.

Doh = G. *Moderately slow.*

:d |d :r |m :m |f :m |r ||m |f :m |r :d |t, :d |r ||

:s, |l, :t, |d :d |d :d |t, ||s, |d :d |t, :l, |se, :m, |s, ||

:m |m :s |s :d |l :s |s ||d |d.r :m.f |s :m |m :d |t, ||

:d |l, :s, |d :l, |f, :d, |s, ||d |l, :d |s, :l, |m, :l, |s, ||

:s |f :m |r :t, |d :l, |s, ||m |f :m |r :d |m :r |d ||d |d ||

:t, |r :d.t, |l, :s, |s, :fe, |s, ||s, |d :d |t, :l, |s, :-.f, |m, ||f, |m, ||

:r |l :s |f :r |m :r.d |t, ||d |d.r :m.f |s :m |d :t, |d ||l, |s, ||

:s, |r, :m, |f, :s, |d, :r, |s, ||d |l, :d |s, :l, |m,.f, :s, |d, ||f, |d, ||

A-men.

ST. ALKMUND (INTERCESSION). (L.M.)

Doh = G. *In moderate time.* *Easy Music for Church Choirs*, 1853.

:d |m :r :d |f :m :r |d :r :t, |d :— ||t, |d :— :r

:s, |s, :— :d |d.r :d :l, |s, :— :s, |s, :— ||s, |s, :— :l,.t,

:m |s :f :m |l :s :f |m :f :r |m :— ||f |s :— :f

:d |d :— :d |l,.t, :d :f, |s, :— :s, |d :— ||r |m :— :r

|m :f :m |m :r :d |r :— ||d |m :r :d |f :m :r |r :m :r

|d :s, :d.t, |l, :— :l, |t, :— ||s, |s, :l,.t, :d |f, :s, :l, |t, :— :t,

|m :r :m |f :— :m |s :— ||m |s :f :m.r |d :— :l |s :— :f

|d :t, :d |f, :— :l, |s, :— ||d |d :— :d.t, |l, :s, :f, |s, :— :s,

|d :— ||d |r :— :m |f :m :r |d :r :t, |d :— ||d |d ||

|d :— ||d |l, :— :l, |l, :— :l, |s, :— :s, |s, :— ||l, |s, ||

|m :— ||m |r :— :de |r :s :f |m :f :r |m :— ||f |m ||

|l, :— ||l, |f, :— :m, |r, :m, :f, |s, :— :s, |d, :— ||f, |d, ||

A-men.

A LITTLE child the Saviour came,
The Mighty God was still His Name,
And angels worshipped as He lay
The seeming infant of a day.

2 He who, a little child, began
The life divine to show to man,
Proclaims from heaven the message free,
'Let little children come to Me.'

3 We bring them, Lord, and with the sign
Of sprinkled water name them Thine:
Their souls with saving grace endow;
Baptize them with Thy Spirit now.

4 O give Thine angels charge, good Lord,
Them safely in Thy way to guard;
Thy blessing on their lives command,
And write their names upon Thy hand.

5 O Thou who by an infant's tongue
Dost hear Thy perfect glory sung,
May these, with all the heavenly host,
Praise Father, Son, and Holy Ghost.

William Robertson, 1820–64.

306 MORAVIA. (C.M.)

Doh = F. *In moderate time.* *Wolder's Gesangbuch*, 1598.

:d | d :s | m :d | d :m | r :m | s :f | m :r | d :— | —
:s_1 | l_1 :s_1 | s_1 :s_1 | l_1 :d | t_1 :d | d :d.r | d :t_1 | d :— | —
:m | m :r | d :d | f :s | s :s | s :l | s :s.f | m :— | —
:d | l_1 :t_1 | d :m_1 | f_1 :d | s_1 :d | m_1 :f_1 | s_1 :s_1 | d :— | —

:m | s :f | m :d | d :m | r :m | s :f | m :r | d :— | — || d | d
:d | t_1 :r | d :d.ta_1 | l_1 :s_1.l_1 | t_1 :d | d :d.r | d :t_1 | d :— | — || l_1 | s_1
:d | r :s | s :s | f :m.fe | s :s | s :l | s :s.f | m :— | — || f | m
:l_1 | s_1 :t_1 | d :m_1 | f_1 :d | s_1 :d | m_1 :f_1 | s_1 :s_1 | d :— | — || f_1 | d

A-men.

OUR children, Lord, in faith and prayer,
We now devote to Thee;
Let them Thy covenant mercies share,
And Thy salvation see.

2 Such helpless babes Thou didst embrace,
While dwelling here below;
To us and ours, O God of grace,
The same compassion show.

3 In early days their hearts secure
From worldly snares, we pray;
O let them to the end endure
In every righteous way.

Thomas Haweis, 1734–1820.

[May be sung to St. Peter, No. 419.]

307

LIEBSTER JESU. (78. 78. 88.) JOHANN RODOLPH AHLE, 1625–73.
Arranged by JOHANN SEBASTIAN BACH, 1685–1750.

Doh = G. *Slow.*

```
m    :r.d  | r   :s   | m    :d      | r   :—  ‖ l,  :d   | d   :d   | r     :m
s,   :s,   | s,  :t,  | s,   :s,.l,  | t,  :—  ‖ l,  :ta, | l,  :s,  | l,.t, :d
d.r  :m    | r   :r   | m.f  :s      | s   :—  ‖ m   :m   | f   :d   | f     :s
d,   :d    | t,  :s,  | d.r  :m.d    | s,  :—  ‖ l,  :s,  | f,  :m,  | r,    :d,.m,
```

D.C.

```
r   :—    | d   :—  | —  :—  ‖ s,  :s,  | l,      :t,  | d   :r.d  | t,.l, :s,
d   :t,   | d   :—  | —  :—  ‖ m,  :r,  | m,.fe,  :s,  | l,  :l,   | s,    :r,
l   :s.f  | m   :—  | —  :—  ‖ d   :r   | d       :r   | m   :r    | r.d   :t,
f,  :s,   | d,  :—  | —  :—  ‖ d   :t,  | l,      :s,  | s,  :fe,  | s,    :s,
```

```
d   :d    | d   :d   | r      :m   | r   :—    | d   :—  | —  :—  ‖ d   | d
l,  :ta,  | l,  :s,  | l,.t,  :d   | d   :t,   | d   :—  | —  :—  ‖ l,  | s,
m   :m    | f   :d   | f      :s   | s   :-.f  | m   :—  | —  :—  ‖ f   | m
l,  :s,   | f,  :m,  | r,     :d,  | s,  :—    | d,  :—  | —  :—  ‖ f,  | d,
```

A-men.

Liebster Jesu, wir sind hier.

BLESSED Jesus, here we stand,
  Met to do as Thou hast spoken;
And this child, at Thy command,
  Now we bring to Thee in token
  That to Christ it here is given,
  For of such shall be His heaven.

2 Therefore hasten we to Thee;
  Take the pledge we bring, O take it;
Let us here Thy glory see,
  And in tender pity make it
  Now Thy child, and leave it never—
  Thine on earth, and Thine for ever.

3 Make it, Head, Thy member now;
  Shepherd, take Thy lamb and feed it;
Prince of Peace, its peace be Thou;
  Way of life, to heaven O lead it;
Vine, this branch may nothing sever,
  Grafted firm in Thee for ever.

4 Now upon Thy heart it lies,
  What our hearts so dearly treasure;
Heavenward lead our burdened sighs;
  Pour Thy blessing without measure;
  Write the name we now have given,
  Write it in the book of heaven.

BENJAMIN SCHMOLK, 1672–1737; *tr.* by CATHERINE WINKWORTH, 1829–78.

308 ST. FRANCIS. (10 6. 10 6. 8 8 4.)

Doh = F. *In moderate time.* ARTHUR SEYMOUR SULLIVAN, 1842–1900.

Me | s :f | m :r | d :-.d | r :f | m :— | — :— || Me | s :-.s | f :m
Doh | d :t, | d :t, | d :-.d | d :t, | d :— | — :— || Doh | d :-.d | t, :d
Soh | s :s | s :f | m :s | l :s | s :— | — :— || Soh | s :-.s | s :s
Doh | m :r | d :s, | l, :m, | f, :s, | d :— | — :— || Doh | m :-.m | r :d

r :r | m :r | r :— | — || r | r :d.r | m :m | r :d.r | m :m
r :r | d :d | t, :— | — || t, | t, :l,.s, | s, :d | t, :l,.s, | s, :d
s :s | fe :fe | s :— | — || s | f :m.r | d :s | f :m.r | d :s
t, :t, | l, :l, | s, :— | — || s, | s, :l,.t, | d :d | s, :l,.t, | d :d

f :s.l | s :m | f :f | m :— || r :— | m :r | d :— | — :— || d | d
d :d | d :de | r :l, | se, :— || l, :— | s, :f, | m, :— | — :— || f, | m,
f :m.f | s :s | f :r | t, :— || l, :— | t, :t, | d :— | — :— || l, | s,
l, :s,.f, | m, :l, | r, :r, | m, :— || f, :— | s, :s, | d, :— | — :— || f, | d,

A-men.

[*By permission of Novello & Co., Ltd.*]

O Vaterherz, das Erd und Himmel schuf.

O FATHER, Thou who hast cre-|ated all
In wisest love, we pray,
Look on this babe, who at Thy | gracious call
Is entering on life's way;
Bend o'er *him* in Thy tenderness,
Thine image on *his* soul impress;
O Father, hear.

2 O Son of God, who diedst for | us, behold,
We bring our child to Thee;
Thou tender Shepherd, take *him* | to Thy fold,
Thine own for aye to be;
Defend *him* through this earthly strife,
And lead *him* on the path of life,
O Son of God.

3 O Holy Ghost, who broodedst | o'er the wave,
Descend upon this child;
Give *him* undying life, *his* | spirit lave
With waters undefiled;
Grant *him*, while yet a babe, to be
A child of God, a home for Thee,
O Holy Ghost.

4 O Triune God, what Thou com-| mand'st is done;
We speak, but Thine the might;
This child hath scarce yet seen our | earthly sun,
Yet pour on *him* Thy light,
In faith and hope, in joy and love,
Thou Sun of all below, above,
O Triune God.

ALBERT KNAPP, 1798–1864; *tr.* by CATHERINE WINKWORTH, 1829–78.

309 BELMONT. (C.M.)

Doh = A♭. *In moderate time.* *Gardiner's Sacred Melodies*, 1812.

```
:s, | m  :— :r  | d  :— :t, | t, :l, :d  | s, :— :s  | s  :f  :m
:m, | s, :— :f, | m, :— :s, | s, :f, :f, | m, :— :s, | s, :— :s,
:d  | d  :— :t, | d  :— :m  | d  :— :d  | d  :— :m  | r  :— :s
:d, | d  :— :s, | l, :— :m, | f, :— :l, | d  :— :d  | t, :— :d

m  :r  :d   | d  :t, ‖ s, | m  :— :r  | d  :— :t, | t, :l, :d
l, :—  :l,  | s, :—  ‖ s, | s, :— :f, | m, :— :s, | s, :f, :f,
s  :f  :m   | m  :r  ‖ r  | d  :— :t, | d  :— :m  | d  :— :d
f, :—  :fe, | s, :—  ‖ t, | d  :— :s, | l, :— :m, | f, :— :l,

s, :— :s  | s  :f  :r  | d  :m  :r  | d  :— ‖ d  | d  ‖
m, :— :s, | l, :— :l, | s, :— :f, | m, :— ‖ f, | m, ‖
d  :— :d  | d  :— :f  | m  :d  :t, | d  :— ‖ l, | s, ‖
d  :— :m, | f, :— :f, | s, :— :s, | d, :— ‖ f, | d, ‖
                                             A-men.
```

BY cool Siloam's shady rill
  How sweet the lily grows!
How sweet the breath, beneath the hill,
  Of Sharon's dewy rose!

2 Lo! such the child whose early feet
  The paths of peace have trod,
Whose secret heart with influence sweet
  Is upward drawn to God.

3 O Thou whose infant feet were found
  Within Thy Father's shrine,
Whose years, with changeless virtue crowned,
  Were all alike divine,

4 Dependent on Thy bounteous breath,
  We seek Thy grace alone,
In childhood, manhood, age, and death,
  To keep us still Thine own.

REGINALD HEBER, 1783–1826.

310 BRYNTIRION. (8 7. 8 7. 8 7.)

Doh = F. *Moderately slow.* ASCAN HENRI THÉODORE LUTTEROTH, 1802–89.

```
m  :— :f  | s  :— :s | l  :— :l   | s :m :— | m :— :r   | d  :— :d
d  :— :d  | r  :— :d | d  :— :d.r | m :d :— | d :— :t,  | l, :— :d
s  :— :f  | r  :— :m | f  :— :f   | m :s :— | s :— :s.f | m  :— :s
d  :— :l, | t, :— :d | f, :— :l,  | d :d :— | d :— :s,  | l, :— :m,
```

r :—:r |m :—:— ||m :—:f |s :— :s |l :— :l |s :m :—
d :—:t, |d :—:— ||d :—:d |t, :— :d.t, |l, :-.t, :d .r |m :d :—
l :—:s |s :—:— ||s :—:f |r :— :s |d :— :f |m :s :—
f, :—:s, |d :—:— ||d :—:l, |s, :-.f, :m, |f, :-.s, :l,.t, |d :d :—

C.t. f.F.

sd' :— :t |l :— :l |l :— :se |l :— :— ||taf :m :r |m :— :m
rs :— :f |m :— :d |f :m :m |m :— :— ||s r :d :t, |d :— :d
sd' :— :r' |m' :d' :l |r' :d' :t |d' :— :— ||taf :— :s |s :— :s
df :m :r |d :— :f |r :m :m |l :— :— ||s r :— :s, |d :— :d,

r :d :t, |d :—:d |r :m :f |m :—:m |r :—:r |d :—:— ||d |d
l, :—:se, |l, :—:d |d :—:t, |d :—:d |d :—:t, |d :—:— ||l, |s,
f :m :r |m :—:m |l :s :f |s :d :l |r :s :-.f |m :—:— ||f |m
r, :—:m, |l, :—:l, |f :m :r |d :l, :f, |s, :—:s, |d :—:— ||f, |d

A-men.

GRACIOUS Saviour, gentle Shepherd,
Little ones are dear to Thee;
Gathered with Thine arms and carried
In Thy bosom, may they be
Sweetly, fondly, safely tended,
From all want and danger free.

2 Tender Shepherd, never leave them
From Thy fold to go astray;
By Thy look of love directed,
May they walk the narrow way;
Thus direct them, and protect them,
Lest they fall an easy prey.

3 Let Thy holy word instruct them;
Fill their minds with heavenly light;
Let Thy love and grace constrain them
To approve whate'er is right,
Take Thine easy yoke and wear it,
And to prove Thy burden light.

4 Taught to lisp the holy praises
Which on earth Thy children sing,
Both with lips and hearts unfeignèd
Glad thank-offerings may they bring;
Then, with all the saints in glory,
Join to praise their Lord and King.

JANE ELIZA LEESON, 1807–82, and JOHN KEBLE, 1792–1866.

Also the following:

562 O God of Bethel! by whose hand | **650** Father, our children keep

THE LORD'S SUPPER

311 BROMLEY. (L.M.)

Doh = F. *Moderately slow.* JEREMIAH CLARK, 1670–1707.

```
:d  | m :— :f.r | d :m :s  | s :-.l :s.f | f :m :d    | f :— :m
:s, | d :— :l,  | s, :d :d | r :— :r    | r :d :s,   | f, :d :—
:m  | s :l :r   | s :— :m  | r :— :s     | s :— :m    | d :-.r :m
:d  | d :l, :f, | m, :d, :d | t, :— :t,  | d :— :d.t, | l, :— :s,
```

s.d.f.A♭.

```
| l :— :s  | s :f :m   | r :—  || [r]t,   | d :— :d   | f :— :m    | re :— :re
| d :— :d  | d :r :d   | t, :— || [t,]se, | l, :— :l, | l, :— :l,  | l,.,t, :d :t,.l,
| f :— :s  | l :— :s   | s :—  || [s]m    | m :— :m   | r :— :d    | d.,t, :l, :l,
| f, :f :m | l, :t, :d | s, :— || [s]m,   | l, :— :l, | r, :— :m,  | f, :— :f,
```

F.t.m.l.

```
| [m]s :— :l     | r :— :s     | d :f :m      | m.r :d :t,  | d :—   || d  | d
| [l]d :t, :d    | d :t, :ta,  | l, :t, :d    | l, :s, :s,  | s, :—  || l, | s,
| [t,]r :— :r    | r :s :d     | f :— :s      | f :m :r     | m :—   || f  | m
| [m]s, :— :fe,  | s, :— :m,   | f, :r, :d,   | f, :s, :s,  | d, :—  || f, | d,
```

A-men.

MY God, and is Thy table spread?
And does Thy cup with love o'erflow?
Thither be all Thy children led,
And let them all its sweetness know.

2 Hail, sacred feast, which Jesus makes,
Rich banquet of His flesh and blood!
Thrice happy he who here partakes
That sacred stream, that heavenly food!

3 Let crowds approach with hearts prepared;
With hearts inflamed let all attend,
Nor, when we leave our Father's board,
The pleasure or the profit end.

4 O let Thy table honoured be,
And furnished well with joyful guests;
And may each soul salvation see
That here its sacred pledges tastes.

PHILIP DODDRIDGE, 1702–51.

312

ROCKINGHAM (COMMUNION). (L.M.)

Doh = E♭. *Moderately slow.* Adapted by EDWARD MILLER, 1731–1807.

:d | m :f :r | d :—:m | s :—:l | s :—:s | d^1 :—:t | l :—:s
:d | d :—:t_1 | d :—:d | d :—:d | d :—:r | d :—:d | d :r :m
:m | s :l :s.f | m :—:s | s :—:f | m :—:s | m :f :s | l :t :d^1
:d | d :f_1 :s_1 | d :—:d | m :—:f | d :—:t_1 | l_1 :—:s_1 | f_1 :f :m

s :f :m | m :r ‖ r | s :— :l | t :— :s | d^1 :m :fe
m :r :d | d :t_1 ‖ t_1 | r :— :r | r :— :t_1 | d :m :r.d
d^1 :s :s | s :— ‖ s | s :— :fe | s :— :s.f | m :d^1 :l
l_1 :t_1 :d | s_1 :— ‖ s_1 | t_1 :— :r | s :— :s_1 | l_1 :— :r

s :— :d | f :— :m | r :— :d | d.r:m :r | d :— ‖ d | d
t_1 :— :d | d :r :d | l_1 :t_1 :d | d :— :t_1 | d :— ‖ l_1 | s_1
s :— :s | l :— :s | f :— :m | m.f:s :f | m :— ‖ f | m
s_1 :— :m | l_1 :t_1 :d | f_1 :s_1 :l_1 | s_1 :— :s_1 | d :— ‖ f_1 | d

A-men.

[The Faux-bourdon at No. 106 may be used.]

From St. Matthew xxvi. 26–29.

'TWAS on that night when doomed to know
The eager rage of every foe,
That night in which He was betrayed,
The Saviour of the world took bread;

2 And, after thanks and glory given
To Him that rules in earth and heaven,
That symbol of His flesh He broke,
And thus to all His followers spoke:

3 'My broken body thus I give
For you, for all; take, eat, and live:
And oft the sacred rite renew
That brings My wondrous love to view.'

4 Then in His hands the cup He raised,
And God anew He thanked and praised,
While kindness in His bosom glowed,
And from His lips salvation flowed.

5 'My blood I thus pour forth,' He cries,
'To cleanse the soul in sin that lies;
In this the covenant is sealed,
And Heaven's eternal grace revealed.

6 'With love to man this cup is fraught,
Let all partake the sacred draught;
Through latest ages let it pour
In memory of My dying hour.'

JOHN MORISON, 1750–98, as in *Scottish Paraphrases*, 1781.

313

BANGOR. (C.M.)

Lah = C. Doh = Eb. *Moderately slow.* *Tans'ur's Harmony of Zion*, 1735.

|m :— |d :t, |l, :m |l :s.f |m ‖m |m :s .fe |m :re |m :— ‖
|se, :— |l, :se, |l, :d |d :r |d ‖t, |l, :t,.d |t, :-.l, |se, :— ‖
|t, :— |d :r |m :m |f :l |l ‖r' |d' :t .l |s :fe |m :— ‖
|m, :— |l, :t, |d.t, :l,.s, |f, :r, |l, ‖se, |l, :s,.l, |t, :t, |m, :— ‖

|m :— |l :se |l :d'.t |l :s.f |m ‖m |l :m.r |d :t, |l, :— ‖r |de ‖
|t, :— |m :r |d :d |d :t, |d ‖m.r |d :l, |l, :se, |l, :— ‖l, |l, ‖
|se :— |l :t |m :s |f.m :r.s |s ‖m |m :m.f |m :-.r |d :— ‖f |m ‖
|m :-.r |d :t, |l, :m, |f, :s, |d ‖d.t, |l,.t, :d.r |m :m, |l, :— ‖r, |l, ‖

A-men.

BALLERMA. (C.M.)

Doh = Ab. *In moderate time.* Adapted by ROBERT SIMPSON, 1790–1832.

:d |m :— :r |d :— :l, |s, :— :l, |d :— :d |m :— :r |m :s :m |r :— ‖
:m, |s, :— :f, |m, :— :f, |d, :— :d, |m, :— :m, |s, :— :s, |s, :— :s, |s, :— ‖
:d |d :— :t, |d :— :d |d :— :l, |s, :— :s, |d :— :t, |d :m :d |t, :— ‖
:d, |d :— :s, |l, :s, :f, |m, :— :f, |d, :— :d, |d, :m, :s, |d :— :d, |s, :— ‖

:d |m :— :r |d :— :l, |s, :— :m, |s, :— :d |m :s :m |r :m :r |d :— ‖d |d ‖
:m, |s, :— :f, |m, :— :f, |d, :— :d, |r, :— :s, |s, :— :s, |l, :s, :f, |m, :— ‖f, |m, ‖
:d |d :— :t, |d :— :d |d :— :d |t, :— :d |d :m :d |d :— :t, |d :— ‖l, |s, ‖
:d, |d :— :s, |l, :s, :f, |m, :— :l, |s, :— :m, |d, :— :d, |f, :s, :s, |d, :— ‖f, |d, ‖

A-men.

ACCORDING to Thy gracious word,
In meek humility,
This will I do, my dying Lord,
I will remember Thee.

2 Thy body, broken for my sake,
My bread from heaven shall be;
Thy testamental cup I take,
And thus remember Thee.

3 Gethsemane can I forget?
Or there Thy conflict see,
Thine agony and bloody sweat,
And not remember Thee?

4 When to the Cross I turn mine eyes,
And rest on Calvary,
O Lamb of God, my sacrifice,
I must remember Thee,—

5 Remember Thee, and all Thy pains,
And all Thy love to me;
Yea, while a breath, a pulse remains,
Will I remember Thee.

6 And when these failing lips grow dumb,
And mind and memory flee,
When Thou shalt in Thy Kingdom come,
Jesus, remember me.

JAMES MONTGOMERY, 1771–1854.

314 ST. KERRIAN. (7 7 7.)

Doh = E♭. *Moderately slow.* MS. Dresden, 1761.

d :d	r :m	f :r	m :— ‖ r :r	d :s
s_1 :d	t_1 :de	r :t_1	d :— ‖ l_1 :t_1	d :d
m :s	s :s	l :s	s :— ‖ l :s	s :s.l
d :m	f :m	r :s	d :— ‖ f :f	m :m

| s :fe | s :— ‖ r :m | f :m | r :r | d :— ‖ d | d ‖
| r :-.d | t_1 :— ‖ ta_1 :ta_1 | l_1 :s_1.d | d :t_1 | d :— ‖ l_1 | s_1 ‖
| t :l | s :— ‖ s :d | d :m | s :-.f | m :— ‖ f | m ‖
| r :r | s_1 :— ‖ s_1 :s_1 | f_1 :d | s_1 :s_1 | d :— ‖ f_1 | d ‖

A-men.

LACRYMAE. (7 7 7.)

Doh = E♭. *Moderately slow.* ARTHUR SEYMOUR SULLIVAN, 1842–1900.

m :— :m	m :f :s	d :— :r	m :— :— ‖ s :— :s	d' :— :t
d :— :d	d :— :d	d :— :t_1	d :— :— ‖ r :— :r	d :— :r
s :— :s	s :— :s	m :— :f	m :— :— ‖ r :— :r	m :fe :s
d :— :d	d :r :m	s_1 :— :s_1	d :— :— ‖ t_1 :— :t_1	l_1 :— :t_1

| l :— :l | s :— :— ‖ l :— :s | f :m :r | s :— :t_1 | d :— :— ‖ d | d ‖
| m :r :d | t_1 :— :— ‖ r :— :l_1 | l_1 :— :l_1 | t_1 :— :s_1 | s_1 :— :— ‖ l_1 | s_1 ‖
| s :— :fe | s :— :— ‖ f :— :de | r :m :f | f :— :f | m :— :— ‖ f | m ‖
| d :r :r_1 | s_1 :— :— ‖ r_1 :— :m_1 | f_1 :— :f_1 | s_1 :— :s_1 | d :— :— ‖ f_1 | d ‖

A-men.

[*By permission of Novello & Co., Ltd.*]

JESUS, to Thy table led,
Now let every heart be fed
With the true and living Bread.

2 When we taste the mystic wine,
Of Thine outpoured blood the sign,
Fill our hearts with love divine.

3 While upon Thy Cross we gaze,
Mourning o'er our sinful ways,
Turn our sadness into praise.

4 Draw us to Thy wounded side,
Whence there flowed the healing tide;
There our sins and sorrows hide.

5 From the bonds of sin release;
Cold and wavering faith increase;
Lamb of God, grant us Thy peace.

6 Lead us by Thy piercèd hand,
Till around Thy throne we stand,
In the bright and better land.

ROBERT HALL BAYNES, 1831–95.

315 CARDEN PLACE. (76. 76.)

Lah = B. Doh = D. *In moderate time.* JOHN MACDONNELL NISBET, 1857-

d' :—	t :l	s :l	s :m	l :—	s :f	d :r	m :—	
m :—	m :d.r	m :m	r :d	m :—	m :d	d :t,	d :—	
l :—	s :l.t	d' :m.f	s :s	d' :—	t :l	m :s	s :—	
l, :—	m :f	d :d	t, :d	l, :—	m :f	l, :s,	d :—	

m :—	ba :se	l :l	t :d'	l :—	r' :l	d' :t	l :—		l	l	
d :—	r :m	m :m	r :d	d :—	f :r	m :m	d :—		r	de	
l :—	l :t	l :m	se :l	l :—	l :l	l :se	l :—		f	m	
l, :—	r :r	d :d	t, :l,	f :—	r :f	m :m	l, :—		r	l,	

A-men.

[*Copyright*, 1927, *by Oxford University Press.*]

THOU standest at the altar,
Thou offerest every prayer;
In faith's unclouded vision
We see Thee ever there.

2 Out of Thy hand the incense
Ascends before the throne,
Where Thou art interceding,
Lord Jesus, for Thine own.

3 And, through Thy blood accepted,
With Thee we keep the feast:
Thou art alone the Victim;
Thou only art the Priest.

4 We come, O only Saviour;
On Thee, the Lamb, we feed:
Thy flesh is bread from heaven;
Thy blood is drink indeed.

5 To Thee, Almighty Father;
Incarnate Son, to Thee;
To Thee, Anointing Spirit,—
All praise and glory be.

EDWARD WILTON EDDIS, 1825-1905.

316 LEICESTER. (C.M.)

Doh = E♭. *In moderate time.* WILLIAM HURST, 1849-

:s |s :m :r |d :— :d |r :m :f |m :— :s |d :r :m |s :f :m |r :— ||
:d |d :— :t, |d :— :d |d :— :t, |d :— :d |l, :— :d |r :— :d |t, :— ||
:m |s :— :f |m :— :s |l :— :s |s :— :s |l :— :s |s :— :s |s :— ||
:d |m :— :s, |l, :— :m, |f, :— :s, |d :— :m |f :— :m |t, :— :d |s, :— ||

:m |f :s :l |s :— :m |l :— :d |d :t, :d |f :— :m |r :l, :t, |d :— || d | d ||
:d |d :— :d |d :— :d |d :— :l, |s, :— :s, |t, :— :d |l, :— :s, |s, :— || l, | s, ||
:s |l :m :f |m :— :s |f :d :r |r :— :m |s :— :s |f :— :f |m :— || f | m ||
:d.ta, |l, :s, :f, |d :— :d |f, :— :fe, |s, :— :m |r :— :d |f, :— :s, |d :— || f, | d ||

A-men.

I AM not worthy, holy Lord,
That Thou shouldst come to me;
Speak but the word; one gracious word
Can set the sinner free.

2 I am not worthy; cold and bare
The lodging of my soul;
How canst Thou deign to enter there?
Lord, speak, and make me whole.

3 I am not worthy; yet, my God,
How can I say Thee nay,—
Thee, who didst give Thy flesh and blood
My ransom price to pay?

4 O come, in this sweet morning[1] hour,
Feed me with food divine;
And fill with all Thy love and power
This worthless heart of mine.

[1] *Or* evening.

HENRY WILLIAMS BAKER, 1821–77.

317 AUCTOR VITAE. (66. 66. 88.)

Doh = D. *Moderately slow.* HENRY WALFORD DAVIES, 1869–

d :m :s :s :-.l :l | m :r :m :f :-.m :m :—
d :m :s :s :-.l :l | m :r :d :t_1 :-.m :m :—
1. Au - thor of life di-vine, Who hast a ta - ble spread,
2. Our need - y souls sus-tain With fresh sup - plies of love,
d :m :s :s :-.l :l | d'.t :l :l :l :-.se :se :—
d :m :s :s :-.l :l | l .s :f :m :r :-.m :m :—

d :m :s :s :l :s | m :r :m :f .m :r .d :r
d :t_1 :d :m :d :r | d.t_1 :l_1 :d :r :l_1 :—
Fur - nished with mys - tic wine And ev - er - last - -
Till all Thy life we gain, And all Thy ful - - -
d' :t :s :m :m :s | s :l :s :f .s :l :—
l :s :m :d :l_1 :t_1 | d :f :m :r .m :f :—

:m :m :— || s :d' :t :l :s :l :s :m :s :—
:se_1 :l_1 :— || t_1 :d :r :m :d :d :— :m :r :—
ing bread, Pre - serve the life Thy - self hast given,
ness prove, And, strength-ened by Thy per - fect grace,
:t :d' :— || t .l :s :s :m :s :d' :— :t .l :t :—
:m :l :— || s .f :m :s :d :m :f :m :d :s_1 :—

m :d :r :m :f :m :r :-.d :d :— || d | d
t_1 :l_1 :t_1 :d :r .d :t_1.l_1 :t_1 :-.d :d :— || l_1 | s_1
And feed and train us up for heaven.
Be - hold with - out a veil Thy face. A- men.
s :m :s :s :l :s :f :-.m :m :— || f | m
s_1 :l_1 :s_1 :m :r :s_1 :— :-.d :d :— || f_1 | d

CHARLES WESLEY, 1707–88.

318

PSALM 118 (RENDEZ À DIEU). (98. 98. D.) *French Psalter*, 1543.

Composed or arranged by LOUIS BOURGEOIS, 1510– ? .

Doh = G. *Slow and dignified.*

```
|d :—  |l, :s, |d :d   |r :f   |m :—   |r :—  || s :—  |m :m   |d :f
|s, :— |m, :s, |l, :d  |l, :r  |d :—   |t, :— || s, :— |s, :t, |l, :r
 Bread   of     the world, in mer-cy bro  -  ken,  Wine   of   the soul, in
|m :—  |d :r   |m :s   |f :l   |s :—   |s :—  || t, :— |t, :s  |m :l
|d, :— |d :t,  |l, :m, |f, :r, |m, :f, |s, :— || m, :— |s, :m, |l, :r,
```

```
|m :—   |r :—   |d :—  || d :—  |l, :s, |d :d   |r :f   |m :—  |r :—
|d :l,  |t, :—  |d :—  || s, :— |f, :r, |s, :l, |t, :d  |d :—  |t, :—
 mer  -  cy      shed,    By     whom the words of life were spo - ken,
|s :—   |— :f   |m :—  || m :—  |d :t,  |d :m   |s :l   |s :—  |s :—
|m, :f, |s, :—  |d, :— || d, :— |f, :s, |m, :l, |s, :f, |d :m, |s, :—
```

```
|s :—  |f :m   |r :d   |d :t,  |d :—  || s :— |s :f   |m :—   |r :—  |d :t,
|d :—  |r :d   |l, :l, |s, :s, |s, :— || d :— |m, :f, |s, :l, |t, :— |l, :s,
 And    in whose death our sins are dead :  Look   on    the heart  by  sor-row
|d :—  |l :s   |f :m   |r :r   |m :—  || m :— |d :t,  |d :—   |s :f  |m :r
|m, :— |r, :m, |f, :f, |s, :s, |d, :— || d :— |d, :r, |m, :f, |s, :— |l, :t,
```

```
|l, :—   |s, :— || s, :— |d :d   |t, :l, |d :—  |r :—  |m :—   || d :—  |d :r
|s, :fe, |s, :— || m, :— |s, :l, |s, :m, |l, :— |l, :— |se, :— || m, :— |l, :t,
 bro  -   ken,     Look    on  the tears by sin  -  ners  shed ;    And    be Thy
|m :r    |t, :— || d :—  |d :f   |r :d   |d :—  |l, :— |t, :—  || d :—  |m :s
|d :r    |s, :— || d, :— |m, :f, |s, :l, |f, :— |f, :— |m, :—  || l, :— |l, :s,
```

```
|m :d   |f :f   |m :—    |r :—  || s :—  |f :m   |r :d      |d :t,  |d :—  || d  | d
|d :m,  |l, :l, |ta, :l, |f, :— || s, :— |d :d   |l, :s,.l, |s, :s, |s, :— || l, | s,
 feast to us  the to   -  ken      That  by Thy grace our souls are fed.     A - men.
|s :d   |d :r   |r :de   |r :—  || d :—  |l :s   |f :m      |r :r   |m :—  || f  | m
|d :l,  |f, :f, |s, :l,  |r, :— || m, :— |f, :d, |r, :m,.f, |s, :s, |d, :— || f, | d,
```

REGINALD HEBER, 1783–1826.

[*As this hymn consists of one verse only, it is suggested that it be sung twice over; once by the* CHOIR ALONE *and again by choir and people in unison. It may also be used as a short motet for unaccompanied singing by the choir.*]

319

ADORO TE. (10 10. 10 10.) Proper Melody (from the Solesmes Version).

Doh = D. *Unison.* *In free rhythm.* *D.C.*

| d :m :s :s :s :l :s :f :m :r :-.d :d :— ||

| s :l :t :d' :d' :t :s :l :s :f :m :r :— ||

| m :s :f :m :r :d :r :m :d :r :-.d :d :— ||

d :r :d :t_1	d :—	
l_1 :— :s_1 :—	s_1 :—
m :f :m :r	m :—
l_1 :r_1 :m_1 :s_1	d_1 :—

A - - men.

Adoro te devote, latens Deitas.

THEE we adore, O hidden Saviour, Thee,
Who in Thy sacrament dost deign to be:
Both flesh and spirit at Thy presence fail,
Yet here Thy presence we devoutly hail.

2 O blest memorial of our dying Lord!
Thou living Bread, who life dost here afford,
O may our souls for ever live by Thee,
And Thou to us for ever precious be.

3 Fountain of goodness, Jesus, Lord, and God,
Cleanse us, unclean, with Thy most cleansing blood;
Make us in Thee devoutly to believe,
In Thee to hope, to Thee in love to cleave.

4 O Christ, whom now beneath a veil we see,
May what we thirst for soon our portion be,
There in the glory of Thy dwelling-place
To gaze on Thee unveiled, and see Thy face.

ST. THOMAS AQUINAS, 1227–74; *tr.* by JAMES RUSSELL WOODFORD, 1820–85.

320 UNDE ET MEMORES. (10 10. 10 10. 10 10.)

Doh = D. *In moderate time.* WILLIAM HENRY MONK, 1823–89.

:m |m :-.d|d :r |m :-.m|m :f |s :— |—:m |r :m |f :-.f
:d |d :-.d|d :d |d :-.d|d :t, |d :— |—:d |t, :d |r :-.r
:s |s :-.m|m :f |s :-.s|s :s |s :— |—:s |s :s |l :-.l
:d |d :-.d|d :d |d :-.d|d :r |m :— |—:d |f :m |r :-.d

|f :m |s :m |r :— |— ||m |m :-.d|d :r |m :-.m |m :f |s :— |—:m
|r :d |d :d |t, :— |— ||d |d :-.d|d :d |d :-.d |d :d |d :— |—:d
|s :s |s :s |s :— |— ||s |s :-.m|m :f |s :-.d |d :r |m :— |—:s
|t, :d |m, :-.f, |s, :— |— ||d |d :-.d|d :d |d :-.l, |l, :l, |m, :— |—:d

|l :s |fe :-.fe|s :l |t :l |s :— |— ||s |d' :s |f :m |l :l
|d :d |d :-.d |t, :m |r :d |t, :— |— ||t, |d :d |t, :d |d :d
|f :s |l :-.l |s :s |s :fe |s :— |— ||s |s :s |s :s |f :f
|f :m |r :-.r |m :d |r :r |s, :— |— ||f |m :m |r :d |f, :f,

d' :l	s :—	—:s	f :m	r :d	l :-.f	m :r	d :—	—		f	m	
d :f	m :—	—:d	t, :d	t, :d	d :-.r	d :t,	d :—	—		d	d	
f :d'	d' :—	—:s	s :s	f :m	f :-.l	s :f	m :—	—		l	s	
l, :f,	d :—	—:m	r :d	s, :l,	f, :-.f,	s, :s,	d :—	—		f,	d	

A-men.

AND now, O Father, mindful of the love
That bought us, once for all, on Calvary's Tree,
And having with us Him that pleads above,
We here present, we here spread forth to Thee
That only offering perfect in Thine eyes,
The one true, pure, immortal sacrifice.

2 Look, Father, look on His anointed face,
And only look on us as found in Him;
Look not on our misusings of Thy grace,
Our prayer so languid, and our faith so dim:
For lo! between our sins and their reward
We set the passion of Thy Son our Lord.

3 And then for those, our dearest and our best,
By this prevailing presence we appeal;
O fold them closer to Thy mercy's breast,
O do Thine utmost for their souls' true weal;
From tainting mischief keep them white and clear,
And crown Thy gifts with strength to persevere.

4 And so we come: O draw us to Thy feet,
Most patient Saviour, who canst love us still;
And by this food, so awful and so sweet,
Deliver us from every touch of ill:
In Thine own service make us glad and free,
And grant us never more to part with Thee.

WILLIAM BRIGHT, 1824–1901.

[May be sung to SONG 1, No. 489.]

321 HINTON-MARTELL. (7 7. 77. 77.)

Doh = E♭. *Moderately slow.* DAVID EVANS, 1874–

s :l |r :s |s :f |m :— |d :r |m :d |r :r |d :— ||
d :d |r :t, |d :r |d :s, |l, :l, |t, :d |d :t, |d :— ||
m :m |s :r |d :s |s :— |d :l |se :m |l :s.f |m :— ||
d :l, |t, :s, |l, :t, |d :t, |l, :s,.f, |m, :l, |f, :s, |d :— ||

B♭.t.

(m)l, :t, |d :l, |t, :t, |l, :— |d :r |m :d |r :r |d :— ||
(s,)d, :f, |m, :d, |f, :m,.r, |d, :— |m, :l, |se, :m, |l, :s,.f, |m, :— ||
(m)l, :se, |l, :l, |l, :se, |l, :— |l, :l, |t, :d |d :t, |d :— ||
(d)f, :m,.r, |d, :f, |r, :m, |l₂ :— |l, :s,.f, |m, :l, |f, :s, |d, :— ||

f.E♭.

(d)s :l |r :s |s :f |m :— |m :f |s :d |r :r |d :— || d || d
(f,)d :d |t, :d |d :r.d |t, :r |d :d |d :d |d :t, |d :— || l, || s,
(l,)m :f |s :s |l :t.l |se :t |l :l |s :m |l :s.f |m :— || f || m
(f,)d :f, |f :m |r :r |m :se, |l, :s,.f, |m, :l, |f, :s, |d :— || f, || d

A-men.

'TILL He come!' O let the words
Linger on the trembling chords;
Let the little while between
In their golden light be seen;
Let us think how heaven and home
Lie beyond that 'Till He come'.

2 When the weary ones we love
Enter on their rest above,
Seems the earth so poor and vast,
All our life-joy overcast?
Hush, be every murmur dumb;
It is only till He come.

3 Clouds and conflicts round us press;
Would we have one sorrow less?
All the sharpness of the cross,
All that tells the world is loss,
Death, and darkness, and the tomb
Only whisper 'Till He come'.

4 See, the feast of love is spread;
Drink the wine, and break the bread—
Sweet memorials,—till the Lord
Call us round His heavenly board,
Some from earth, from glory some,
Severed only till He come.

EDWARD HENRY BICKERSTETH, 1825–1906.

[May be sung to PETRA, No. 413.]

322 MEMORIA. (88. 84.)

SAMUEL SEBASTIAN WESLEY, 1810–76.

Doh = E♭. *Moderately slow.* B♭.t.

```
:m |s  :— :m |m  :— :r  |d  :— :f  |m  :r  :[r]s,  |l, :— :t,
:d |r  :— :d |d  :— :t, |d  :— :r  |d  :t, :[t]m,  |f, :— :f,
:s |s  :— :s |s  :— :f  |m  :— :l  |s  :— :[s]d    |d  :— :r
:d |t, :— :d |s, :— :s, |l, :s, :f, |s, :— :[s]d,  |f, :— :r,
```

f.E♭.

```
|d   :—  :r   |m  :— :r   |[d]s   :— ||s |l :—   :t |d' :— :m
|m,  :—  :l,  |s, :— :f,  |[m]t,  :— ||d |d :—   :f |f  :m :d
|d   :—  :d   |d  :— :t,  |[d]s   :— ||s |f :—   :f |s  :— :s
|l,  :s, :fe, |s, :— :s,, |[d,]s, :— ||m |f :-.m :r |d  :— :d
```

```
|f  :— :s  |l  :— :l  |d  :— :— |r  :— :— |d :— ||d  |d  ||
|d  :— :d  |d  :— :d  |d  :— :— |t, :— :— |d :— ||l, |s, ||
|d' :— :ta |l  :— :r  |m  :— :— |f  :— :— |m :— ||f  |m  ||
|l, :— :m, |f, :— :f, |s, :— :— |s, :— :— |d :— ||f, |d  ||
```

A-men.

BY Christ redeemed, in Christ restored,
We keep the memory adored,
And show the death of our dear Lord
Until He come.

2 His body, broken in our stead,
Is here in this memorial bread,
And so our feeble love is fed
Until He come.

3 The drops of His dread agony,
His life-blood shed for us, we see;
The wine shall tell the mystery
Until He come.

4 And thus that dark betrayal night
With the last advent we unite,
By one blest chain of loving rite,
Until He come.

5 O blessèd hope! with this elate,
Let not our hearts be desolate,
But, strong in faith, in patience wait
Until He come.

GEORGE RAWSON, 1807–89.

323 ST. AGNES. (10 10. 10 10.)

JAMES LANGRAN, 1835–1909.

Doh = F. *In moderate time.* C.t.

```
|m :— |d :r |m :— |s  :— |f  :m |m  :r  |d :— |— :— |[m]l  :— |l :s |d' :—
|d :— |d :d |d :— |d  :— |d  :d |d  :t, |d :— |— :— |[d]f  :— |r :r |s  :—
|s :— |m :f |s :— |s  :— |l  :s |s  :f  |m :— |— :— |[s]d' :— |t :t |d' :—
|d :— |d :d |d :— |m, :— |f, :d |s, :s, |d :— |— :— |[d]f  :— |f :f |m  :—
```

f.F.

s :—	l :s	s :f	$^{m}t_1$:—	— :—	d :—	d :d	f :—	m :—	s :-.m	r :d'
d :—	d :d	d :r	$^{d}s_1$:—	— :—	d :—	d :d	t_1 :—	d :—	d :-.d	l_1 :l_1
d' :—	f :s	l :t	$^{d'}s$:—	— :—	s :—	l :s	s :—	s :—	m :-.s	f :m
m :—	f :m	r :s_1	$^{d}s_1$:—	— :—	m :—	f :m	r :—	d :—	d :-.d	f_1 :f_1

t_1 :—	— :—	d :—	r :d	d :r	m :f	m :—	r :—	d :—	— :—	d	d
s_1 :—	— :—	s_1 :—	s_1 :s_1	l_1 :t_1	d :d	d :—	t_1 :—	d :—	— :—	l_1	s_1
r :—	— :—	s :—	ta :ta	l :la	s :l	s :—	f :—	m :—	— :—	f	m
s_1 :—	— :—	m :—	m :m	f :f	m :r	s :—	s_1 :—	d :—	— :—	f_1	d

A-men.

[By permission of Novello & Co., Ltd.]

HERE, O my Lord, I see Thee face to face;
Here would I touch and handle things unseen,
Here grasp with firmer hand the eternal grace,
And all my weariness upon Thee lean.

2 Here would I feed upon the bread of God,
Here drink with Thee the royal wine of heaven;
Here would I lay aside each earthly load,
Here taste afresh the calm of sin forgiven.

3 This is the hour of banquet and of song;
This is the heavenly table spread for me;
Here let me feast, and, feasting, still prolong
The brief, bright hour of fellowship with Thee.

4 Too soon we rise; the symbols disappear;
The feast, though not the love, is past and gone;
The bread and wine remove, but Thou art here,
Nearer than ever, still my Shield and Sun.

5 I have no help but Thine; nor do I need
Another arm save Thine to lean upon;
It is enough, my Lord, enough indeed;
My strength is in Thy might, Thy might alone.

6 Mine is the sin, but Thine the righteousness;
Mine is the guilt, but Thine the cleansing blood;
Here is my robe, my refuge, and my peace—
Thy blood, Thy righteousness, O Lord my God.

7 Feast after feast thus comes and passes by,
Yet, passing, points to the glad feast above,
Giving sweet foretaste of the festal joy,
The Lamb's great bridal feast of bliss and love.

HORATIUS BONAR, 1808–89.

[May be sung to ELLERS, No. 301.]

324

SCHMÜCKE DICH. (88. 88. D. Trochaic.)

JOHANN CRÜGER, 1598–1662.

Doh = E♭. *Slow.*

|m :— |r :— |d :r |m :s |f :— |m :— |s :— |m :—
|d :— |t, :— |l, :s, |d :d |d :— |d :— |r :— |d :—
|s :— |— :f |m :r |s :s |l :— |s :— |s :— |s :—
|d :— |s, :— |l, :t, |d :m, |f, :— |d :— |t, :— |d :—

|f :m.r |d :m |r :— |d :— ‖ m :— |r :— |d :r |m :s
|d :t, |l, :d |d :t, |d :— ‖ d :— |t, :— |l, :s, |d :d
|l :s.f |m :s |s :— |m :— ‖ s :— |— :f |m :r |s :s
|f, :s, |l, :m, |s, :— |d :— ‖ d :— |s, :— |l, :t, |d :m,

|f :— |m :— |s :— |m :— |f :m.r |d :m |r :— |d :— ‖
|d :— |d :— |r :— |d :— |d :t, |l, :d |d :t, |d :— ‖
|l :— |s :— |s :— |s :— |l :s.f |m :s |s :— |m :— ‖
|f, :— |d :— |t, :— |d :— |f, :s, |l, :m, |s, :— |d :— ‖

|s :— :l |d' :— :d' |t :s |l :— |s :— |s :— :l
|d :— :m |s :— :m |f :s |s :f |m :— |d :— :d
|m :— :d' |s :— :s |f :d' |d' :— |d' :— |s :— :m
|d :— :l, |m :— :d |r :m |f :— |d :— |m :— :d

f.A♭.

|d' :— :d' |t :s |l :— |s :— ‖ r :— |m :— |fd :d
|m :— :d |r :t, |r :-.d |t, :— ‖ t, :— |d :— |rl, :s,
|l :— :m |s :s |s :fe |s :— ‖ s :— |s :— |lm :m
|l, :— :l, |t, :m |r :— |s, :— ‖ s :— |f :m |rl, :l,

E♭.t.

|t, :l, |l, :se, |l, :— |t,m :— |s :— |f :m |r :d |r :— |d :— ‖ f |m ‖
|f, :r, |m, :— |m, :— |s,d :— |s, :— |l, :s, |l, :d |d :t, |d :— ‖ d |d ‖
|r :l, |t, :— |de :— |rs :— |d :— |d :m |f :m |s :— |m :— ‖ l |s ‖
|r, :f, |m, :— |l, :— |s,d :— |m, :— |l, :d |f, :l, |s, :— |d :— ‖ f, |d ‖

A-men.

Schmücke dich, o liebe Seele.

DECK thyself, my soul, with gladness,
Leave the gloomy haunts of sadness,
Come into the daylight's splendour,
There with joy thy praises render
Unto Him whose grace unbounded
Hath this wondrous banquet founded;
High o'er all the heavens He reigneth,
Yet to dwell with thee He deigneth.

2 Hasten as a bride to meet Him,
And with loving reverence greet Him,
For with words of life immortal
Now He knocketh at thy portal;
Haste to ope the gates before Him,
Saying, while thou dost adore Him,
'Suffer, Lord, that I receive Thee,
And I never more will leave Thee.'

3 Sun, who all my life dost brighten;
Light, who dost my soul enlighten;
Joy, the sweetest man e'er knoweth;
Fount, whence all my being floweth:
At Thy feet I cry, my Maker,
Let me be a fit partaker
Of this blessèd food from heaven,
For our good, Thy glory, given.

4 Jesus, Bread of Life, I pray Thee,
Let me gladly here obey Thee;
Never to my hurt invited,
Be Thy love with love requited:
From this banquet let me measure,
Lord, how vast and deep its treasure;
Through the gifts Thou here dost give me,
As Thy guest in heaven receive me.

JOHANN FRANCK, 1618–77; *tr.* by CATHERINE WINKWORTH, 1829–78.

Also the following:

138 Alleluia! sing to Jesus
156 Ye servants of the Lord
157 Thou art coming, O my Saviour
420 Jesus, Thou Joy of loving hearts
438 The King of Love my Shepherd is
453 O King of mercy, from Thy throne on high
455 O help us, Lord; each hour of need
494–522 *Hymns of Consecration and Discipleship*
533 Much in sorrow, oft in woe

MARRIAGE

325

ERSKINE. (88. 86.)

WILLIAM HENRY GLADSTONE, 1840-91.

Doh = E♭. *In moderate time.*

```
:s  |f  :m  |r  :f  |m  :r  |d  :d  |r  :f  |m  :l  |s  :fe |m  ||
:d  |d  :d  |d  :d  |d  :t, |d  :s, |s, :t, |d  :d  |t, :t, |s, ||
:m  |f  :s  |l  :l  |s  :s  |m  :m  |r  :r  |d  :m  |m  :re |m  ||
:d  |l, :s, |f, :f, |s, :s, |d  :d  |t, :s, |d  :l, |t, :t, |m  ||

:s  |s  :s  |d' :s  |l  :s  |d  :f  |m  :r  |d  :t, |d  :— |— ||d  |d  ||
:t, |d  :r  |m  :d  |d  :t, |d  :r  |d  :l, |s, :s, |s, :— |— ||l, |s, ||
:f  |m  :r  |d  :d  |f  :f  |m  :s  |s  :f  |m  :r  |m  :— |— ||f  |m  ||
:r  |d  :t, |l, :m, |f, :s, |l, :t, |d  :f, |s, :s, |d/d, :— |— ||f, |d  ||
```

A-men.

O GOD of Love, to Thee we bow,
And pray for these before Thee now,
That, closely knit in holy vow,
They may in Thee be one.

2 When days are filled with pure delight,
When paths are plain and skies are bright,
Walking by faith and not by sight,
May they in Thee be one.

3 When stormy winds fulfil Thy will,
And all their good seems turned to ill,
Then, trusting Thee completely, still
May they in Thee be one.

4 Whate'er in life shall be their share
Of quickening joy or burdening care,
In power to do and grace to bear,
May they in Thee be one.

5 Eternal Love, with them abide;
In Thee for ever may they hide,
For even death cannot divide
Those whom Thou makest one.

WILLIAM VAUGHAN JENKINS, 1868–1920.

326 AURELIA. (76. 76. D.)

Doh = E♭. *In moderate time.* SAMUEL SEBASTIAN WESLEY, 1810–76.

:m |m :m |f :m |m :— |r :d |d :l |s :f |m :— |—
:d |d :d |d :d |d :— |t, :d |l, :d |d :t, |d :— |—
:s |s :s |l :s |s :— |s :s |r :r |m :s |s :— |—
:d |d :d |d :d |s, :— |f, :m, |f, :f, |s, :s, |d :— |—

:f |s :d' |d' :t |t :— |l :s |f :s |m :d |r :— |—
:t, |d :d |d :r |r :— |d :m |m :r |d :d |t, :— |—
:s |s :s |se :se |se :— |l :t |d' :r' |s :fe |s :— |—
:r |m :m |m :m, |f, :— |f, :s, |l, :t, |d :l, |s, :— |—

:r |m :f |s :l |l :— |s :d' |d' :-.t |l :m |f :— |—
:t, |d :t, |d :d |d :— |d :m |m :-.m |m :m |r :— |—
:s |s :s |s :f |f :— |s :l |l :-.se |l :l |l :— |—
:s, |d :r |m :f |f :— |m :l, |m :-.r |d :de |r :— |—

:r |m :m |f :m |m :— |r :d |d :r |d :t, |d :— |— ‖ d |d
:r |d :d |d :d |l, :— |l, :l, |l, :l, |s, :s, |s, :— |— ‖ l, |s,
:s |s :s |l :s |s :— |f :f |f :f |r :f |m :— |— ‖ f |m
:t, |d :d |d :d |f, :— |f, :f, |r, :r, |s, :s, |d :— |— ‖ f, |d

A-men.

O FATHER, all creating,
Whose wisdom, love, and power
First bound two lives together
In Eden's primal hour,
To-day to these Thy children
Thine earliest gifts renew,—
A home by Thee made happy,
A love by Thee kept true.

2 O Saviour, Guest most bounteous
Of old in Galilee,
Vouchsafe to-day Thy presence
With these who call on Thee;
Their store of earthly gladness
Transform to heavenly wine,
And teach them, in the tasting,
To know the gift is Thine.

3 O Spirit of the Father,
Breathe on them from above,
So mighty in Thy pureness,
So tender in Thy love;
That, guarded by Thy presence,
From sin and strife kept free,
Their lives may own Thy guidance,
Their hearts be ruled by Thee.

4 Except Thou build it, Father,
The house is built in vain;
Except Thou, Saviour, bless it,
The joy will turn to pain;
But nought can break the union
Of hearts in Thee made one;
And love Thy Spirit hallows
Is endless love begun.

JOHN ELLERTON, 1826–93.

327 O PERFECT LOVE. (11 10. 11 10.)

Doh = E♭. *In moderate time.* JOSEPH BARNBY, 1838–96.

```
d  :—  |m  :s  |s  :—  |s  :—  |s  :s  |d'  :t  |t  :—  |l  :—
s, :—  |d  :d  |t, :—  |t, :—  |d  :d  |d   :d  |d  :—  |d  :—
m  :—  |s  :s  |f  :—  |f  :—  |s  :m  |f   :s  |f  :—  |f  :—
d  :—  |d  :m  |r  :—  |r  :—  |m  :d  |r   :m  |f  :—  |f  :—

r  :—  |m  :f  |s  :—  |m  :—  |d  :d  |m   :r  |t, :—  |—  :—
l, :—  |t, :t, |d  :—  |t, :—  |l, :l, |l,  :l, |s, :—  |—  :—
l  :—  |s  :s  |s  :—  |se :—  |l  :m  |s   :f  |r  :—  |—  :—
                                        |r   :r
f  :—  |f  :f  |m  :—  |m  :—  |l, :l, |r,  :r, |s, :—  |—  :—

d  :—  |m  :s  |s  :—  |s  :—  |s  :s  |d'  :t  |t  :—  |l  :—
s, :—  |d  :d  |t, :—  |t, :—  |d  :d  |m   :r  |r  :—  |d  :—
m  :—  |s  :s  |f  :—  |f  :—  |s  :s  |se  :se |se :—  |l  :—
d  :—  |d  :m  |r  :—  |—  :f  |m  :m  |m   :m  |f  :—  |f  :—

l  :—  |s  :f  |m  :s  |f  :r  |l, :—  |t,  :—  |d  :—  |—  :—  ||d  |d
f  :—  |m  :r  |d  :de |r  :l, |l, :—  |s,  :—  |s, :—  |—  :—  ||l, |s,
l  :—  |t  :t  |d' :ta |l  :f  |f  :—  |f   :—  |m  :—  |—  :—  ||f  |m
f, :—  |s, :s, |l, :m, |f, :f, |s, :—  |s,  :—  |d  :—  |—  :—  ||f, |d
                                                                  A-men.
```

[*By permission of Novello & Co., Ltd.*]

O PERFECT Love, all human thought transcending,
Lowly we kneel in prayer before Thy throne,
That theirs may be the love which knows no ending
Whom Thou for evermore dost join in one.

2 O perfect Life, be Thou their full assurance
Of tender charity and steadfast faith,
Of patient hope, and quiet brave endurance,
With childlike trust that fears nor pain nor death.

3 Grant them the joy which brightens earthly sorrow ;
Grant them the peace which calms all earthly strife,
And to life's day the glorious unknown morrow
That dawns upon eternal love and life.

DOROTHY FRANCES GURNEY, 1858–

Also the following :

562 O God of Bethel, by whose hand

328 RAMOTH. (77. 77. D.)

Doh = D. *In moderate time.* JOHN BAPTISTE CALKIN, 1827–1905.

```
s :-.s |d' :d' |t :l |s :— |m :-.m |s :d |d :r |d :— ||
d :-.d |d :d |d :d |r :— |d :-.d |t, :l, |s, :t, |d :— ||
m :-.m |m :m |m :f |r :— |s :-.s |s :f |m :f |m :— ||
d :-.d |l, :l, |s, :f, |t, :— |d :-.d |m, :f, |s, :s, |d :— ||

s :-.s |d' :d' |t :l |s :— |m :-.m |s :d |d :r |d :— ||
t, :-.t, |d :m |re :fe |m :— |m :-.d |ta, :l, |s, :t, |d :— ||
s :-.s |s :s |fe :t |t :— |d' :-.d |d :-.r |m :f |m :— ||
m :-.m |l, :l, |t, :re |m :— |d :-.d |m, :f, |s, :s, |d :— ||

m :l |l :se |l :f |m :— |m :l |l :se |l :d' |t :— ||
d :m |m :m |m :r |t, :— |d :-.r |m :m |m :fe |s :f ||
l :l |t :t |l :l |se :— |l :-.t |d' :t |d' :d' |r' :— ||
l, :d |m :-.r |d :r |m :— |d :f |m :m |l :l |s :— ||

d' :-.d' |m :l |s :m |d :— |d :-.d |f :m |m :r |d :— || f |m ||
m :-.d |d :d.r |m :t, |d :— |d :-.d |d :d |t, :t, |d :— || d |d ||
d' :-.d' |t :l.t |d' :s |m :— |m :-.m |l :s |s :f |m :— || l |s ||
l :-.l |s :f |m :s, |l, :— |s, :-.s, |s, :s, |s, :s, |d :— || f, |d ||
                                                          A-men.
```

SAFELY, safely gathered in,
No more sorrow, no more sin,
No more childish griefs or fears,
No more sadness, no more tears;
For the life, so young and fair,
Now hath passed from earthly care;
God Himself the soul will keep,
Giving His belovèd sleep.

2 Safely, safely gathered in,
Free from sorrow, free from sin,
Passed beyond all grief and pain,
Death for thee is truest gain:
For our loss we must not weep,
Nor our loved one long to keep
From the home of rest and peace,
Where all sin and sorrow cease.

3 Safely, safely gathered in,
No more sorrow, no more sin
God has saved from weary strife,
In its dawn, this young fresh life,
Which awaits us now above,
Resting in the Saviour's love.
Jesus, grant that we may meet
There, adoring at Thy feet.

HENRIETTA OCTAVIA DE LISLE DOBREE, 1831–94.

329

ST. DUNSTAN. (77. 77.)

Doh = D. *In moderate time.* RICHARD REDHEAD, 1820–1901.

m :m	r :m	f :-.f	m :—	s :s	d' :l	fe :-.fe	s :—	
d :d	t, :d	d :-.d	d :—	d :m	m :m	r :-.r	r :—	
s :s	s :s	l :-.l	s :—	m :s	l :l	l :-.l	t :—	
d :d	s, :d	f, :-.f,	d :—	d :-.t,	l, :d	r :-.r	s :—	

s :s	s :f	r :-.r	m :—	m :m	r :m	f :-.f	m :—		r	m	
de :r	m :r	t, :-.t,	d :—	d :d	t, :d	d :-.d	d :—		t,	d	
ta :ta	ta :l	s :-.s	s :—	s :s	s :s	l :-.l	s :—		s	s	
m :r	de :r	s, :-.s,	d :—	d :d	s, :d	f, :-.f,	d :—		s,	d	

A-men.

WHEN our heads are bowed with woe,
When our bitter tears o'erflow,
When we mourn the lost, the dear,
Jesus, Son of Mary, hear!

2 Thou our throbbing flesh hast worn:
Thou our mortal griefs hast borne:
Thou hast shed the human tear:
Jesus, Son of Mary, hear!

3 When the sullen death-bell tolls
For our own departing souls,
When our final doom is near,
Jesus, Son of Mary, hear!

4 Thou hast bowed the dying head:
Thou the blood of life hast shed:
Thou hast filled a mortal bier:
Jesus, Son of Mary, hear!

5 When the heart is sad within
With the thought of all its sin,
When the spirit shrinks with fear,
Jesus, Son of Mary, hear!

6 Thou the shame, the grief, hast known,
Though the sins were not Thine own:
Thou hast deigned their load to bear:
Jesus, Son of Mary, hear!

HENRY HART MILMAN, 1791–1868.

330

FIRST TUNE.

REQUIESCAT. (77. 77. and refrain.)

JOHN BACCHUS DYKES, 1823–76.

Doh = C. *In moderate time.* G.t.

```
|m  :s  |d' :t  |t  :l  |s  :—  |d' :-.d'|t  :l  |s  :m  |m  :r  ||m  :s  |d' :(d')f |
|m  :r  |d  :d  |s  :f  |m  :—  |m  :-.m |m  :d  |d  :d  |d  :t, ||m  :r  |d  :(m)l, |
|d' :t  |l  :s  |f  :l  |d' :—  |d' :-.d'|d' :d' |s  :s  |s  :—  ||s  :t  |l  :(s)d  |
|d  :d  |d  :d  |d  :d  |d  :—  |l  :-.l |s  :f  |m  :d  |s, :—  ||d  :d  |d  :(d)f, |
```

f.C.

```
|m  :r  |s  :—  |s  :f  |m  :d  |f  :r.m |r  :d  ||(d)s  :— |s :—  |s  :s  |r' :d' |
|s, :s, |s, :—  |l, :l, |d  :s, |t, :t, |t, :d  ||(s,)r :— |r :—  |r  :m  |f  :f  |
|t, :t, |t, :d  |m  :r  |s  :m  |r  :f.s |f  :m  ||(m)t  :— |t :—  |r' :d' |t  :l  |
|s, :f, |m, :—  |f, :f, |s, :s, |s, :s, |s, :d, ||(d)s  :— |s :—  |s  :s  |s  :s  |
```

```
|t  :l  |s  :—  |s  :d' |m  :s  |s  :d   |d  :—  |—  :—          |d  :—  ||d  :r  |m  :— ||
|f  :—  |f  :—  |m  :f  |m  :r  |d  :ta, |l, :—  |—  :—          |s, :—  ||d  :t, |d  :— ||
|r' :d' |r' :—  |d' :d' |d' :t  |s  :s   |f  :—  |—  :—          |m  :—  ||m  :s  |s  :— ||
                                          f  :—  |d  :r
|s  :l  |t  :—  |d' :l  |s  :f  |m  :m   |f  :—  |f, :—          |d  :—  ||l, :s, |d  :— ||
                                                                            A  -  men.
```

NOW the labourer's task is o'er,
Now the battle-day is past;
Now upon the farther shore
Lands the voyager at last.
Father, in Thy gracious keeping
Leave we now Thy servant sleeping.

2 There the tears of earth are dried;
There its hidden things are clear;
There the work of life is tried
By a juster Judge than here.

3 There the penitents that turn
To the Cross their dying eyes
All the love of Jesus learn
At His feet in Paradise.

4 'Earth to earth, and dust to dust,'
Calmly now the words we say;
Leaving *him* to sleep, in trust,
Till the resurrection day.

JOHN ELLERTON, 1826–93.

Alternative last verse for USE AT SEA:—

5 'Till the sea gives up its dead,'—
Calmly now the words we say,—
Laid in ocean's quiet bed
Till the resurrection day,
Father, in Thy gracious keeping
Leave we now Thy servant sleeping.

SECOND TUNE.

330

HAZEL. (7 7. 7 7. and refrain.)

Lah = B♭. Doh = D♭. *Unison.* *Slow.* Basil Harwood, 1859–

| m .r :d .r | m :l | m .r :d .r | m :— | m .r :d .r | m :l |

1. Now the la - bourer's task is o'er, Now the bat - tle -
2. There the tears of earth are dried; There its hid - den
3. There the pen - i - tents that turn To the Cross their
4. 'Earth to earth, and dust to dust,' Calm - ly now the

| s :m | r :— || Ab.t. sd.t, :l,.t, | d :f | d.t, :l,.t, | d :r |

day is past; Now up - on the far - ther shore
things are clear; There the work of life is tried
dy - ing eyes All the love of Je - sus learn
words we say; Leav - ing *him* to sleep, in trust,

| m :f | s :d | r :f | s,.l, :t, | d :— | — :— ||

Lands the voy - a - ger at last.
By a just - er Judge than here.
At His feet in Pa - ra - dise.
Till the re - sur - rec - tion day.

f.D♭. *Very sustained.*

| lm :— | r :— | d :d | f :m | r :d | s :— | d' :t.l | s :m |
| fd :— | t, :l, | d :d | l,.t, :d | l, :d | d :t, | d :— | — :de |

Fa - ther, in Thy gra - cious keep - ing Leave . . . we

| ds :— | s :l | s :l.s | f :s | f :m | s :— | m :-.f | s :l |
| fd :m | s :f | m :f.m | r :d | f, :l, | s, :— | l, :s,.f, | m, :l, |

rall. e dim. *sleep - ing.* *Unison, if preferred.*

| f :s | f.m :r .d | : | s :— | m :— | — :— | d :— | r :t, | d :— | — :— |
| r :r | d.s, :l,.d | : | t, :— | d :— | — :— | d .t, :l,.s, | l, :-.s, | s, :f, | l, :s, |

now Thy ser - vant sleep - - ing. A - - - men.

| l :s | s :fe | r :— | — :s | s :— | — :— | l .m :f .s | r :m.f | f :— | r :m |
| r :t, | d :l, | : | s, :— | d :— | — :— | l,.s, :f,.m, | f, :s, | d :— | — :— |

sleep - ing.

John Ellerton, 1826–93.

Alternative last verse for Use at Sea :—

5 'Till the sea gives up its dead,'—
Calmly now the words we say,—
Laid in ocean's quiet bed
Till the resurrection day,
Father, in Thy gracious keeping
Leave we now Thy servant sleeping.

331

VULPIUS. (88. 84. and Hallelujahs.) MELCHIOR VULPIUS, 1560–1616.

Doh = C. *In moderate time.* Arranged by HENRY GEORGE LEY, 1887–

|d' :t :l |s :— :s |l :— :t |d' :— :— |d' :d' :r' |s :— :d' |

1. O Lord of life, wher - e'er they be, Safe in Thine own - e -

|t :l :— |s :— :— |s :m :l |s :— :f |m :r :— |d :— :— |

ter - ni - ty, Our dead are liv - ing un - to Thee.

|d' :— :t |d' :-.t :l |s :— :fe |s :-.f :m |

|s :— :s |m :— :f |d :m :r |r :t, :d |

Hal - le - lu - jah! Hal - le - lu - jah!

|m' :— :r' |d' :— :d' |d' :-.t :l |s :— :d |

|d' :— :s |l :-.s :f |m :d :r |t, :s, :l, |

|r :d :t, |d :— :— ||d' :— :— |f' :— :— |m' :— :— ||

|l, :s, :s, |s, :— :— ||f :— :— |l :— :— |s :— :— ||

Hal - le - lu - jah! A - - - - - men.

|f :m :r |m :— :— ||l :— :— |— :— :t |d' :— :— ||

|f, :s, :s, |d :— :— ||f :— :— |— :— :— |d :— :— ||

[*Copyright*, 1925, *by Oxford University Press.*]

O LORD of life, where'er they be,
Safe in Thine own eternity,
Our dead are living unto Thee.
Hallelujah!

2 All souls are Thine, and, here or there,
They rest within Thy sheltering care;
One providence alike they share.
Hallelujah!

3 Thy word is true, Thy ways are just;
Above the requiem, 'Dust to dust,'
Shall rise our psalm of grateful trust,
Hallelujah!

4 O happy they in God who rest,
No more by fear and doubt oppressed;
Living or dying, they are blest.
Hallelujah!

FREDERICK LUCIAN HOSMER, 1840–

[May be sung to VICTORY, No. 122.]

332 COLCHESTER. (88. 88. 88.)

Doh = E♭. *Moderately slow.* SAMUEL SEBASTIAN WESLEY, 1810–76.

:m |s :d |f :r |d :t, |d :s |d' :t |l :r |s :f.m |r
:d |t, :d |l, :l, |s, :s, |s, :r |d :s, |l, :t, |d :r.d |t,
:s |s :m |l :f |m :r |m :s |m :s |d :s |s :l |t
:d |s, :l, |r, :f, |s, :s, |d :t, |l, :m, |f, :f |m :f |s

:m |d :f |f :m |r :l |s :s |l :d' |t :l |s :fe |s
:t, |d :d |r :d |d :t, |d :d.t, |m :d |r :m |r :r.d |t,
:s |m :l |s :s |l :r |s :m |m :m.ba |se :l |t :l |s
:s, |l, :l, |t, :d |f :f, |m, :m.r |d :l, |t, :d |r :r |s,

:t, |d :r |m :m |f :s |l :l |t :d' |r :m.f |m :r |d || f |m
:s, |s, :t, |d :d |d :d |d :d |f :m |d :d |d :t, |d || d |d
:s |s :s |s :s |f :m |f :f |f :s |l :f |s :s.f |m || l |s
:f |m :r |d :ta, |l, :s, |f, :m |r :d |f :r |s, :s, |d || f, |d
f, :r,

A-men.

GOD of the living, in whose eyes
Unveiled Thy whole creation lies,
All souls are Thine; we must not say
That those are dead who pass away;
From this our world of flesh set free,
We know them living unto Thee.

2 Released from earthly toil and strife,
With Thee is hidden still their life;
Thine are their thoughts, their works, their powers,
All Thine, and yet most truly ours;
For well we know, where'er they be,
Our dead are living unto Thee.

3 Thy word is true, Thy will is just;
To Thee we leave them, Lord, in trust;
And bless Thee for the love which gave
Thy Son to fill a human grave,
That none might fear that world to see,
Where all are living unto Thee.

4 O Giver unto man of breath,
O Holder of the keys of death,
O Quickener of the life within,
Save us from death, the death of sin;
That body, soul, and spirit be
For ever living unto Thee.

JOHN ELLERTON, 1826–93.

Also the following:

140–48 *Hymns of our Lord's Sympathy and Intercession*
219 The saints of God! their conflict past
223 How bright these glorious spirits shine
226 O blest communion with the saints at rest
227 Let saints on earth in concert sing
583 For ever with the Lord
584 When the day of toil is done
585 Days and moments quickly flying
586 Sooner or later: yet at last
590 There is no night in heaven
592 There is a land of pure delight
597 Brief life is here our portion
601 O God, our help in ages past

Ordination (333–334).

333

MAINZER. (L.M.)

JOSEPH MAINZER, 1801–51.

Doh = C. *In moderate time.*

```
:s  |s  :s  |d' :t  |l  :l   |s  :l  |f  :s  |m  :d' |t  :l  |s  ||
:m  |d  :r  |m  :s  |f  :f   |m  :m  |r  :r  |m  :l  |s  :fe |s  ||
:d' |m' :r' |d' :d' |d' :l.t |d' :l  |l  :s  |s  :m' |r' :d' |t  ||
:d  |d' :t  |l  :m  |f  :f   |d  :de |r  :t, |d  :l, |r  :r  |s, ||

:s  |s  :s  |d' :t  |l  :l   |s  :s  |l   :t  |d' :m'.r' |d' :t  |d' ||d' |d' ||
:r  |m  :f  |m  :s  |s  :f   |m  :m  |f   :f  |m  :f     |m  :r  |m  ||f  |m  ||
:t  |d' :t  |d' :d' |d' :l.t |d' :d' |d'  :r' |d' :l     |s  :s  |s  ||l  |s  ||
:f  |m  :r  |d  :m  |f  :f   |d  :d  |f.m :r  |l  :f     |s  :s, |d  ||f  |d  ||
                                                                        A - men.
```

POUR out Thy Spirit from on high ;
  Lord, Thine ordainèd servants bless ;
Graces and gifts to each supply,
  And clothe Thy priests with righteousness.

2 Within Thy temple when they stand,
  To teach the truth, as taught by Thee,
Saviour, like stars in Thy right hand
  The angels of the churches be !

3 Wisdom and zeal and faith impart,
  Firmness with meekness, from above,
To bear Thy people on their heart,
  And love the souls whom Thou dost love ;

4 To watch and pray, and never faint ;
  By day and night strict guard to keep ;
To warn the sinner, cheer the saint,
  Nourish Thy lambs, and feed Thy sheep ;

5 Then, when their work is finished here,
  In humble hope their charge resign.
When the Chief Shepherd shall appear,
  O God, may they and we be Thine.

JAMES MONTGOMERY, 1771–1854.

334 ELY. (L.M.)

THOMAS TURTON, 1780–1864.

Doh = A. *In moderate time.*

```
:d   |d  :r  |m  :d  |l,  :t, |d  :r  |m  :d  |t, :d  |t, :l,   |s,  ||
:s,  |s, :s, |s, :s, |s,  :f, |m, :s, |s, :fe,|s, :s, |s, :fe,  |s,  ||
:m   |m  :r  |d  :d  |d   :r  |s, :t, |d  :d  |r  :d  |r  :-.d  |t,  ||
:d   |d  :t, |d  :m, |f,  :r, |d, :s, |d  :l, |s, :m, |r, :r,   |s,  ||

:s,    |s  :f  |m :d   |f     :m |r  :s,   |l, :d  |s, :m  |r  :r      |d  || l, |d  ||
:s,    |s, :t, |d :l,  |l,.t, :d |t, :s,   |s, :f, |m, :s, |l, :s,.f,  |m, || f, |s, ||
:t,    |d  :r  |m :l.s |f     :s |s  :s,.d |d  :d  |d  :d  |d  :t,     |d  || d  |m  ||
:s,.f, |m, :s, |d :f.m |r     :d |s, :m,   |f, :l, |d  :m, |f, :s,     |d, || f, |d, ||
                                                                              A-men.
```

O THOU who makest souls to shine
With light from brighter worlds above,
And droppest glistening dew divine
On all who seek a Saviour's love,

2 Do Thou Thy benediction give
On all who teach, on all who learn,
That all Thy Church may holier live,
And every lamp more brightly burn.

3 Give those that teach pure hearts and wise,
Faith, hope, and love, all warmed by prayer;
Themselves first training for the skies,
They best will raise their people there.

4 Give those that learn the willing ear,
The spirit meek, the guileless mind;
Such gifts will make the lowliest here
Far better than a kingdom find.

5 O bless the shepherd, bless the sheep,
That guide and guided both be one,
One in the faithful watch they keep,
Until this hurrying life be done.

6 If thus, good Lord, Thy grace be given,
Our glory meets us ere we die;
Before we upward pass to heaven
We taste our immortality.

JOHN ARMSTRONG, 1813–56.

Also the following:

182 Come, Holy Ghost, our souls inspire

Consecration of Church-workers (335–339).

335 COELI ENARRANT. (76. 76. D.)

Doh = F. *In moderate time.* ROBERT PRESCOTT STEWART, 1825–94.

:d |m :-.f |s :l |l :— |s :d |r :r |m :f |m :— |—
:d |d :-.d |d :d |d :— |d :d |d :d |t, :t, |d :— |—
:m |s :-.s |s :f |f :— |m :m |l :l |s :s |s :— |—
:d |d :-.r |m :f |d :— |d :l, |f, :f, |s, :s, |d :— |—

C.t. f.F.

:ᵐl |s :d' |f' :m' |m' :— |r' :l |d' :d' |t :d'.r' |ᵈ's :— |—
:ˡr |s :s |s :s |f :— |f :l |s :m |f :f |ᵐt, :— |—
:ᶠᵉt |d' :s |t :d' |l :— |l :f' |m' :d' |r' :t |ᵈ's :— |—
:ᵈf |m :m |r :d |f :— |f :f |s :s |s, :s, |ᵈs, :— |—

:s |m :m |l :s |s :— |f :m |r :l, |t, :d |t, :— |—
:t, |de :de |de :de |r :— |r :l, |l, :f, |fe, :fe, |s, :— |—
:s |s :s |m :l |l :— |l :de |r :r |r :r |r :— |—
:m, |l, :l, |l, :l, |r :— |r, :m, |f, :f, |r, :r, |s, :— |—

:r |s :-.f |m :r |d :— |f :m |r :l, |t, :r |d :— |— ‖ d |d
:t, |d :-.d |d :t, |l, :— |r :d |l, :l, |s, :t, |d :— |— ‖ l, |s,
:s |s :-.l |s :f |m :— |s :s |f :f |r :f |m :— |— ‖ f |m
:f, |m, :-.f, |s, :se, |l, :— |t, :d |f, :r, |s, :s, |d :— |— ‖ f, |d

A-men.

LORD of the living harvest
That whitens o'er the plain,
Where angels soon shall gather
Their sheaves of golden grain,
Accept fresh hands to labour,
Fresh hearts to trust and love,
And deign with them to hasten
Thy Kingdom from above.

2 As labourers in Thy vineyard,
Lord, send them out to be,
Content to bear the burden
Of weary days for Thee,
Content to ask no wages
When Thou shalt call them home,
But to have shared the travail
That makes Thy Kingdom come.

3 Be with them, God the Father,
Be with them, God the Son,
Be with them, God the Spirit,
Eternal Three in One!
Make them a royal priesthood,
Thee rightly to adore,
And fill them with Thy fulness
Now and for evermore.

JOHN SAMUEL BEWLEY MONSELL, 1811–75.

336 HAWARDEN. (66. 66. D.)

Samuel Sebastian Wesley, 1810–76.

Doh = D. *In moderate time.* D.C.

:s |d' :t |t :l |s :— |s :— |d :r |m :r |d :— |— ||
:m |m :s |s :f |m :— |r :— |d :d |d :t, |d :— |— ||
:s |s :m |f :l |d' :— |s :— |m :l |s :-.f |m :— |— ||
:d |d :d |d :d |d :— |t, :— |l, :f, |s, :s, |d :— |— ||

A.t. f.D.

:d |m :d |s :m |$^{d'}$f :— |m :— |m :r |d :t, |^{d}s :— |— ||
:d |d :d |d :d |^{m}l, :— |se, :— |l, :l, |s, :s, |^{s,}r :— |— ||
:m |s :m |m :s |^{fe}t, :— |t, :— |d :r |m :f |^{m}t :— |— ||
:d |d :d |t, :t, |^{l,}r, :— |m, :— |l, :f, |s, :s, |^{d}s, :— |— ||

:s |l :l |l :t.d' |t :— |d' :— |r :m.f |m :r |d :— |— || f |m ||
:r |m :m |r :r |r :— |d :— |d :d |d :t, |d :— |— || d |d ||
:t |d' :d' |l :l |s :— |s :— |l :d' |s :-.f |m :— |— || l |s ||
:s |s :d |f :f |f :— |m :— |f :s.l |s :s, |d :— |— || f, |d ||

A-men.

SHINE Thou upon us, Lord,
True Light of men, to-day,
And through the written word
Thy very self display;
That so, from hearts which burn
With gazing on Thy face,
Thy little ones may learn
The wonders of Thy grace.

2 Breathe Thou upon us, Lord,
Thy Spirit's living flame,
That so, with one accord,
Our lips may tell Thy Name;
Give Thou the hearing ear,
Fix Thou the wandering thought,
That those we teach may hear
The great things Thou hast wrought.

3 Speak Thou for us, O Lord,
In all we say of Thee;
According to Thy word
Let all our teaching be;
That so Thy lambs may know
Their own true Shepherd's voice,
Where'er He leads them go,
And in His love rejoice.

4 Live Thou within us, Lord;
Thy mind and will be ours;
Be Thou beloved, adored,
And served with all our powers;
That so our lives may teach
Thy children what Thou art,
And plead, by more than speech,
For Thee, with every heart.

John Ellerton, 1826–93.

337 LLANSANNAN. (87. 87. D.)

Welsh Melody.

Lah = C. Doh = E♭. *In moderate time, dignified.* D.C.

```
|m  :l     |s  :l    |s  :m  |d   :r  |m  :l  |s  :m.r |d  :t,  |l, :—  ||
|l, :d     |d  :d    |r  :d  |d   :t, |s, :d  |r  :d.t,|l, :se, |l, :—  ||
|d  :d.r   |m  :m.fe |s  :s  |s.fe:s  |m  :m  |r  :m.f |m  :m.r |d  :—  ||
|l, :l,.t, |d  :l,   |t, :d  |l,  :s, |d  :l, |t, :d.r |m  :m,  |l, :—  ||

|l, :t,  |l, :l,    |r  :d  |r  :m  |l    :t  |d' :l   |se :t   |l  :—  ||
|l, :se, |l, :l,    |l, :l, |t, :d  |m    :r  |d  :d.r |m  :m.r |d  :—  ||
|m  :r   |m  :m     |f  :m  |s  :s  |m.ba :se |l  :l   |t  :m   |m  :—  ||
|d  :t,  |l, :l,.s, |f, :l, |s, :d  |d    :t, |l, :f   |m  :se, |l, :—  ||

|d' :l   |s  :l  |s  :m |d  :r   |m  :l  |s  :m.r  |d  :t,  |l, :— ||r  |de ||
|f  :d.r |m  :d  |r  :d |l, :t,  |d  :d  |r  :d.t, |l, :se, |l, :— ||l, |l, ||
|l  :l.t |d' :m  |s  :s |l  :s.f |m  :m  |r  :m.f  |m  :m.r |d  :— ||f  |m  ||
|f, :f   |d  :l, |t, :d |f  :m.r |d  :l, |t, :d.r  |m  :m,  |l, :— ||r, |l, ||
                                                                     A-men.
```

LORD of light, whose Name outshineth
All the stars and suns of space,
Deign to make us Thy co-workers
In the Kingdom of Thy grace;
Use us to fulfil Thy purpose
In the gift of Christ Thy Son:
Father, as in highest heaven,
So on earth Thy will be done.

2 By the toil of lowly workers
In some far outlying field;
By the courage where the radiance
Of the Cross is still revealed;
By the victories of meekness,
Through reproach and suffering won,—
Father, as in highest heaven,
So on earth Thy will be done.

3 Grant that knowledge, still increasing,
At Thy feet may lowly kneel;
With Thy grace our triumphs hallow,
With Thy charity our zeal;
Lift the nations from the shadows
To the gladness of the sun:
Father, as in highest heaven,
So on earth Thy will be done.

4 By the prayers of faithful watchmen
Never silent day or night;
By the Cross of Jesus bringing
Peace to men, and healing light;
By the love that passeth knowledge,
Making all Thy children one:
Father, as in highest heaven,
So on earth Thy will be done.

HOWELL ELVET LEWIS, 1860–

338 WINSCOTT. (L.M.)

Doh = F. *In moderate time.* SAMUEL SEBASTIAN WESLEY, 1810–76.

m :m :r	d :— :l	s :— :f	m :— :—	m :f :m
d :d :t,	d :— :d	t, :— :r	d :— :—	d :r :d
s :s :f	m :— :r	r :— :s	s :— :—	s :s :s
d :d :s,	l, :— :f,	s, :— :t,	d :— :—	d :t, :d

r :— :d	t, :— :d	r :— :—		s :f :m	m :r :m	f :— :l
l, :— :d	s, :— :s,	t, :— :—		t, :l, :ta,	l, :— :l,	l, :— :l,
l :— :s	f :— :m	s :— :—		s :l :s	f :— :m	r :— :r
f :— :m	r :— :d	s, :— :—		m, :f, :s,	l, :— :de	r :— :d

s :— :—	f :m :r	d :— :r	d :— :t,	d :— :—		d	d	
r :— :—	t, :t, :t,	l, :— :l,	s, :— :s,	s, :— :—		l,	s,	
r :— :—	r :m :f	m :f :f	m :— :r	m :— :—		f	m	
t, :— :—	s, :s, :se,	l, :f, :r,	s, :— :s,	d :— :—		f,	d	

A - men.

LORD, speak to me, that I may speak
In living echoes of Thy tone;
As Thou hast sought, so let me seek
Thy erring children lost and lone.

2 O lead me, Lord, that I may lead
The wandering and the wavering feet;
O feed me, Lord, that I may feed
Thy hungering ones with manna sweet.

3 O strengthen me, that, while I stand
Firm on the rock, and strong in Thee,
I may stretch out a loving hand
To wrestlers with the troubled sea.

4 O teach me, Lord, that I may teach
The precious things Thou dost impart;
And wing my words, that they may reach
The hidden depths of many a heart.

5 O give Thine own sweet rest to me,
That I may speak with soothing power
A word in season, as from Thee,
To weary ones in needful hour.

6 O fill me with Thy fulness, Lord,
Until my very heart o'erflow
In kindling thought and glowing word,
Thy love to tell, Thy praise to show.

7 O use me, Lord, use even me,
Just as Thou wilt, and when, and where,
Until Thy blessèd face I see,
Thy rest, Thy joy, Thy glory share.

FRANCES RIDLEY HAVERGAL, 1836–79.

339

THANKSGIVING. (L.M.)

Doh = E. *In moderate time.* JOHN BACCHUS DYKES, 1823-76.

```
:d |m  :s  |d' :s  |f  :s  |m  :r  |m  :fe |s  :s
:d |d  :t, |d  :d  |d  :t, |d  :t, |d  :d  |t, :d
:m |s  :f  |s  :s  |l  :s  |s  :s  |s  :l  |s  :s
:d |d  :r  |m  :m  |r  :s, |d  :s, |d  :l, |m  :m
```

f.A. E.t.

```
|t  :l  |s   ||s r   |d  :t,  |d  :f  |m  :r  |m l  :t
|r  :r  |t,  ||ta, f,|m, :m,  |m, :l, |s, :s, |s d  :r
|s  :fe |s   ||r l,  |l, :se, |l, :d  |d  :t, |d f  :f
|r  :r  |s,  ||s, r, |m, :m,  |l, :f, |s, :s, |d f  :r
```

```
|d' :f  |m  :r  |m  :r  |d  ||d  |d  ||
|d  :r  |d  :d  |d  :t, |d  ||l, |s, ||
|s  :s  |s  :l  |s  :s  |m  ||f  |m  ||
|m  :t, |d  :f, |s, :s, |d  ||f, |d  ||
```

A-men.

O MASTER, let me walk with Thee
In lowly paths of service free;
Thy secret tell; help me to bear
The strain of toil, the fret of care.

2 Help me the slow of heart to move
By some clear winning word of love;
Teach me the wayward feet to stay,
And guide them in the homeward way.

3 Teach me Thy patience; still with Thee
In closer, dearer company,
In work that keeps faith sweet and strong,
In trust that triumphs over wrong,

4 In hope that sends a shining ray
Far down the future's broadening way,
In peace that only Thou canst give,
With Thee, O Master, let me live.

WASHINGTON GLADDEN, 1836-1918.

Home Missions (340–346).

340 LICHFIELD. (L.M.)

Doh = A. *In moderate time.* WILLIAM DALRYMPLE MACLAGAN, 1826–1910.

s, :d :m	m :— :r	d :— :t,	d :— :—	t, :d :r
m, :s, :s,	l, :— :l,	s, :— :s,	s, :— :—	s, :fe, :s,
d :d :d	d :— :r	m :— :f	m :— :—	r :r :r
d, :m, :d,	f, :— :f,	s, :— :s,	d, :— :—	s, :l, :t,

r :— :d	t, :— :l,	s, :— :—		d :d :t,	l, :— :t,	d :m :r
m, :t, :l,	s, :— :fe,	s, :— :—		s, :se, :se,	l, :— :se,	l, :m, :fe,
m :— :m	r :— :d	t, :— :—		m :m :r	d :— :m	m :d :r
d :— :d,	r, :— :r,	s, :— :—		d, :m, :m,	f, :— :m,	l, :— :l,

d :t, :—	d :r :m	f :— :l,	t, :— :r	d :— :—		d	d	
s, :— :—	s, :s, :d	d :— :f,	f, :— :f,	m, :— :—		f,	m,	
m :r :—	m :r :s	f :d :r	r :— :t,	d :— :—		l,	s,	
s, :— :—	d :t, :ta,	l, :— :r,	s, :— :s,	d, :— :—		f,	d,	

A - men.

LOOK from the sphere of endless day,
O God of mercy and of might,
In pity look on those who stray,
Benighted in this land of light.

2 In peopled vale, in lonely glen,
In crowded mart, by stream or sea,
How many of the sons of men
Hear not the message sent from Thee!

3 Send forth Thy heralds, Lord, to call
The thoughtless young, the hardened old,
A wandering flock, and bring them all
To the Good Shepherd's peaceful fold.

4 Send them Thy mighty word to speak,
Till faith shall dawn and doubt depart,
To awe the bold, to stay the weak,
And bind and heal the broken heart.

5 Then all these wastes, a dreary scene,
On which, with sorrowing eyes, we gaze,
Shall grow, with living waters, green,
And lift to heaven the voice of praise.

WILLIAM CULLEN BRYANT, 1794–1878.

341 ORIENTIS PARTIBUS. (77. 77.)

Doh = G. *Moderately fast.* Medieval French Melody.

```
d  :-.r |m  :d  |r  :t, |d  :—  |s  :s  |l  :m.f |s  :s  |m  :— ||
s, :-.t,|d  :s, |l, :s, |s, :—  |d  :d  |d  :d   |d  :t, |d  :— ||
m  :-.s |s  :d  |f  :r  |m  :—  |m  :m  |f  :d   |r  :s  |s  :— ||
d  :-.s,|d  :m, |f, :s, |d, :—  |d  :d  |f, :l,  |s, :s, |d  :— ||

m :r  |f  :m  |r  :d.r |m  :— |s :-.f  |m :d  |r  :t, |d  :— ||d  |d  ||
d :t, |l, :s, |f, :m,  |m, :— |d :-.t, |d :s, |l, :s, |s, :— ||l, |s, ||
s :s  |d  :m  |l  :l   |se :— |s :-.s  |s :d  |f  :r  |m  :— ||f  |m  ||
d :s, |l, :d  |f, :l,  |m, :— |m :-.r  |d :m, |f, :s, |d, :— ||f, |d, ||
                                                              A-men.
```

Unison. SOLDIERS of the Cross, arise!
Gird you with your armour bright;
Mighty are your enemies,
Hard the battle ye must fight.

Harmony. 2 O'er a faithless fallen world
Raise your banner in the sky;
Let it float there wide unfurled;
Bear it onward; lift it high.

3 'Mid the homes of want and woe,
Strangers to the living word,
Let the Saviour's herald go,
Let the voice of hope be heard.

4 Where the shadows deepest lie,
Carry truth's unsullied ray;
Where are crimes of blackest dye,
There the saving sign display.

5 To the weary and the worn
Tell of realms where sorrows cease;
To the outcast and forlorn
Speak of mercy and of peace.

6 Guard the helpless; seek the strayed;
Comfort troubles; banish grief;
In the might of God arrayed,
Scatter sin and unbelief.

Unison. 7 Be the banner still unfurled,
Still unsheathed the Spirit's sword,
Till the kingdoms of the world
Are the Kingdom of the Lord.

WILLIAM WALSHAM HOW, 1823–97.

342

ST. VICTOR. (76. 76.)

RICHARD REDHEAD, 1820–1901.

Doh = G. *In moderate time.*

:s, |d :m |d :t, |l, :— |s, :s, |d :r |m :s |r :— |— ||
:m, |s, :s, |s,.fe, :s, |fe, :— |s, :s, |s,.l, :t, |d :s, |s, :— |— ||
:d |m :d |d :r |r :d |t, :t, |d :f |m :d |t, :— |— ||
:d, |d :d |l, :s, |r, :— |s, :s,.f, |m, :r, |d, :m,.f, |s, :— |— ||

:m |f :m |r :l |s :— |s :s, |l, :d |d :t, |d :— |— || d |d ||
:s, |f, :s, |l, :t, |d :— |d :s, |s, :f, |s, :s, |s, :— |— || l, |s, ||
:d |d :d |d :r |s :— |s :d |d :d |r :r |m :— |— || f |m ||
:d |l, :s, |f, :f, |m, :— |m, :m, |f, :l, |s, :s, |d :— |— || f, |d ||

A-men.

PSALM 130. (76. 76. D.)

Lah = E. Doh = G. *In moderate time.*

French Psalter, 1539.

m :—	l, :t,	d :t,	l, :—	s, :—	d :—	l, :t,	d :—	r :—	m :—	
l, :—	l, :se,	l, :s,	s, :f,	m, :—	s, :—	s, :f,	m, :—	l, :—	se, :—	
d :—	m :r	d :m	d :—	d :—	d :—	d :r	m :—	r :—	t, :—	
l, :—	d :t,	l, :m,	f, :—	d, :—	m, :—	f, :r,	l, :—	f, :—	m, :—	

m :—	r :m	fe :s	fe :—	m :—	l :—	s :m	s :—	fe :—	m :—	
s, :—	s, :s,	t, :t,	t, :—	s, :—	l, :—	t, :d	t, :—	t, :—	s, :—	
d :—	s :m	r :m	m :re	m :—	d :f	m :d	r :m	— :re	m :—	
d :—	t, :d	t, :m,	t, :—	m, :—	f, :—	s, :l,	s, :—	t, :—	m, :—	

m :—	s :m	r :d	t, :—	l, :—	r :—	d :t,	l, :l,	s, :—	
l, :—	s, :s,	t, :l,	l, :s,	f, :—	l, :—	s, :s,	s, :fe,	s, :—	
d :—	r :m	s :m	m :—	d :—	f :—	m :r	m :r	t, :—	
l, :—	t, :d	s, :l,	m, :—	f, :—	r, :—	m, :s,	d, :r,	s, :—	

d :—	d :r	m :f	r :—	d :—	m :—	r :d	r :—	t, :—	l, :—		l,	l,	
s, :—	l, :t,	d :d	t, :—	d :—	l, :—	l, :l,	t, :l,	— :se,	l, :—		f,	m,	
d :—	d :f	m :l	s :f	m :—	m :—	f :m	f :—	m :—	d :—		r	de	
m, :—	f, :r,	d, :f,	s, :—	l, :—	d, :—	r, :l,	r, :—	m, :—	l, l₂ :—		r,	l,	

A-men.

BOWED low in supplication,
We come, O Lord, to Thee ;
Thy grace alone can save us ;
To Thee alone we flee.

2 We come for this our parish
Thy mercy to implore ;
On church, and homes, and people,
O Lord, Thy blessing pour.

3 Blot out our sins, O Father ;
Forgive the guilty past ;
Loose from their chains the captives
Whom Satan holdeth fast.

4 Wake up the slumbering conscience
To listen to Thy call ;
The weak and wavering strengthen,
And raise up them that fall.

5 Our crying sin drive from us
With Thy chastising rod,
That we may be a people
Fearing and loving God.

6 O be Thy house, Lord, hallowed
And hallowed be Thy day;
Let sin-stained souls find pardon,
And learn to love and pray.

7 With heavenly food supported,
O be they firm and strong
To follow all things holy,
To flee from all things wrong.

8 Lord, banish strife and variance ;
Knit sundered hearts in one ;
And bind us all together
In love to Thy dear Son.

WILLIAM WALSHAM HOW, 1823–97.

343 NORTH COATES. (65. 65.)

Doh = G. *In moderate time.* TIMOTHY RICHARD MATTHEWS, 1826–1910.

```
| s, :s,  | l, :l,   | d  :—  | d  :—  | t, :t, | d   :l,  | s, :— | — :— ||
| m, :m,  | f, :l,   | s, :—  | s, :—  | s, :s, | fe, :fe, | s, :— | — :— ||
| d  :d   | d  :f    | f  :—  | m  :—  | r  :r  | r   :d   | t, :— | — :— ||
| d, :d,  | f, :f,   | d, :—  | d, :—  | r, :r, | r,  :r,  | s, :— | — :— ||

| d  :d   | m  :m    | s  :—  | s  :—  | m  :m  | f   :r   | d  :— | — :— || d  | d  ||
| s, :s,  | d  :d    | t, :—  | d  :—  | d  :d  | l,  :t,  | d  :— | — :— || l, | s, ||
| m  :m   | s  :s    | f  :—  | m  :—  | s  :s  | f   :f   | m  :— | — :— || f  | m  ||
| d  :d   | d  :d    | r  :—  | m  :—  | d  :d  | f,  :s,  | d, :— | — :— || f, | d, ||
                                                                          A-men.
```

[*By permission of Novello & Co., Ltd.*]

CHRISTIAN, work for Jesus,
Who on earth for thee
Laboured, wearied, suffered,
Died upon the Tree.

2 Work, with lips so fervid
That thy words may prove
Thou hast brought a message
From the God of love.

3 Work, with heart that burneth
Humbly at His feet
Priceless gems to offer,
For His crown made meet.

4 Work, with prayer unceasing,
Borne on faith's strong wing
Earnestly beseeching
Trophies for the King.

Unison. 5 Work, while strength endureth,
Until death draw near ;
Then thy Lord's sweet welcome
Thou in heaven shalt hear.

MARY HASLOCH, 1816–92.

344 CARLISLE. (S.M.)

Doh = E♭. *Moderately slow, dignified.* CHARLES LOCKHART, 1745–1815.

```
:d  | s  :d  | m.r :d.t, | d  :—  | — :d    | f  :s .l   | s  :d .f   | m  :r  | — ||
:s, | s, :l, | l,  :s,   | s, :—  | — :s,   | d  :d      | d  :l,.r   | d  :t, | — ||
:m  | r  :m  | f   :m.r  | m  :—  | — :m    | f  :m.f    | s  :l      | s  :—  | — ||
:d  | t, :l, | f,  :s,   | d  :—  | — :d.t, | l, :s,.f,  | m, :f,     | s, :—  | — ||

:r  | m :r .d  | f :m.r  | s :f.m   | l :t | d' :d.f | m :r   | d :— | — || d  | d  ||
:t, | d :t,.d  | r :d.t, | d :d     | d :r | d  :d.r | d :t,  | d :— | — || l, | s, ||
:s  | s :s     | l :s    | s :d'.ta | l :f | s  :l   | s :-.f | m :— | — || f  | m  ||
:s, | d :f .m  | r :s.f  | m :l .s  | f :r | m  :f.r | s :s,  | d :— | — || f, | d  ||
```

A-men.

RISE up, O men of God !
Have done with lesser things ;
Give heart and soul and mind and strength
To serve the King of kings.

2 Rise up, O men of God !
His Kingdom tarries long ;
Bring in the day of brotherhood,
And end the night of wrong.

3 Rise up, O men of God !
The Church for you doth wait,
Her strength unequal to her task ;
Rise up and make her great.

4 Lift high the Cross of Christ !
Tread where His feet have trod ;
As brothers of the Son of Man
Rise up, O men of God !

WILLIAM PIERSON MERRILL, 1867–

345 ALBANO. (C.M.)

Doh = F. *Moderately slow.* VINCENT NOVELLO, 1781–1861.

```
:m | s :f  | m :r  | d  :r  | t, :t, | d  :d  | r  :r  | m  :— | — ||
:d | d :r  | d :t, | l, :l, | s, :s, | s, :d  | d  :t, | d  :— | — ||
:s | s :s  | s :f  | m  :f  | r  :r  | d  :m  | l  :s  | s  :— | — ||
:d | m :t, | d :s, | l, :f, | s, :f, | m, :l, | f, :s, | d, :— | — ||

:m   | l  :s | f  :m | r  :d      | t, :r  | s  :d  | d  :t, | d  :— | — || d  | d  ||
:ta, | l, :d | r  :d | l, :m,.f,  | s, :s, | s, :l, | l, :s, | s, :— | — || l, | s, ||
:s   | f  :s | s  :s | f  :d      | r  :t, | d  :m  | r  :f  | m  :— | — || f  | m  ||
:d   | f  :m | t, :d | f, :l,     | s, :f, | m, :l, | f, :s, | d, :— | — || f, | d, ||
```

A-men.

FOUNTAIN of good, to own Thy love
Our thankful hearts incline ;
What can we render, Lord, to Thee,
When all the worlds are Thine ?

2 But Thou hast needy brethren here,
Partakers of Thy grace,
Whose names Thou wilt Thyself confess
Before the Father's face.

3 And in their accents of distress
Thy pleading voice is heard ;
In them Thou mayst be clothed and fed,
And visited and cheered.

4 Thy face, with reverence and with love,
We in Thy poor would see ;
O may we minister to them,
And in them, Lord, to Thee.

PHILIP DODDRIDGE, 1702–51.

346 ST. GILES. (S.M.)

Doh = A♭. *In moderate time.* JOHN MONTGOMERIE BELL, 1837–1910.

```
:m   |r  :d   |d  :r   |m  :—  |—  :d   |t,  :l,    |l,  :t,   |s,  :—  |—  ||
:s,  |l, :s,  |l, :t,  |d  :—  |—  :m,  |r,  :l,.s, |fe, :fe,  |s,  :—  |—  ||
:d   |l, :d   |m  :s   |s  :—  |—  :l   |s   :m     |r   :r.d  |t,  :—  |—  ||
:d,  |f, :m,  |l, :s,  |d, :—  |—  :l,  |t,  :d     |r   :r,   |s,  :—  |—  ||

:s,    |s  :f.m |f  :f   |f  :m.r |m :m   |m     :r.l,   |d  :t,    |d  :— |— ||d  |d  ||
:s,    |s, :d   |l, :l,  |s, :t,  |d :s,  |l,.s, :f,.l,  |s, :s,.f, |m, :— |— ||f, |m, ||
:t,    |d  :d   |r  :f.m |r  :s   |s :d.t,|l,    :r.f    |m  :r     |d  :— |— ||l, |s, ||
:s,.f, |m, :l,  |r, :r.d |t, :s,  |d :m,  |f,    :f,.r,  |s, :s,    |d, :— |— ||f, |d, ||
                                                                                 A-men.
```

WE give Thee but Thine own,
Whate'er the gift may be ;
All that we have is Thine alone,
A trust, O Lord, from Thee.

2 May we Thy bounties thus
As stewards true receive,
And gladly, as Thou blessest us,
To Thee our first-fruits give.

3 O hearts are bruised and dead,
And homes are bare and cold,
And lambs for whom the Shepherd bled
Are straying from the fold.

4 To comfort and to bless,
To find a balm for woe,
To tend the lone and fatherless,
Is angels' work below.

5 The captive to release,
To God the lost to bring,
To teach the way of life and peace,
It is a Christ-like thing.

Unison.

6 And we believe Thy word,
Though dim our faith may be,—
Whate'er for Thine we do, O Lord,
We do it unto Thee.

WILLIAM WALSHAM HOW, 1823–97.

347 BLODYN. (11 10. 11 10.)

Doh = F. *In moderate time.* ARTHUR OWEN ROBERTS, 1889–

m :r :d | s :-.f :m | m :r :d | d :— :t, | r :m :r | d :s :l

d :t, :d | d :-.t, :d | l, :l, :d | s, :— :s, | t, :l, :t, | d :d :m

s :f :m | s :-.s :s | s :f :m | m :— :r | s :s :s | s :s :s

d :d :d | m :-.r :d | f, :f, :fe, | s, :— :s, | s :s :f | m :m :d

f.B♭. F.t.

t :t :l | s :— :— || [s]r :d :t, | m :t, :r | d :t, :l, | [s]d :— :t,

r :r :d | t, :— :— || [de]se, :l, :se, | l, :f, :m, | m, :m, :m, | [r,]s, :— :s,

s :m :fe | s :— :— || [m]t, :m :m | m :r :t, | l, :se, :l, | [t,]m :— :r

r :r :r | s, :— :— || [l,]m, :m, :r, | d, :r, :se,, | l,, :t,, :d, | [r,]s, :— :f,

d :r :m | f :s :l | s :m :r | d :— :— || d | d ||

s, :s, :s, | d :ta, :l, | d :d :t, | d :— :— || l, | s, ||

d :t, :d | d :r.m :f | m :s :f | m :— :— || f | m ||

m, :s, :d | l, :s, :f, | s, :s, :s, | d :— :— || f, | d ||

A-men.

Flower Service.

HERE, Lord, we offer Thee all that is fairest,
Bloom from the garden and flowers from the field,
Gifts for the stricken ones, knowing Thou carest
More for the love than the wealth that we yield.

2 Send, Lord, by these to the sick and the dying,
Speak to their hearts with a message of peace;
Comfort the sad who in weakness are lying,
Grant the departing a gentle release.

3 Raise, Lord, to health again those who have sickened;
Fair be their lives as the roses in bloom;
Give, of Thy grace, to the souls Thou hast quickened,
Gladness for sorrow and brightness for gloom.

[May be sung to SPRINGFIELD, No. 64.] ABEL GERALD WILSON BLUNT, 1827–1902.

Temperance Work (348–349).

348 ST. CATHERINE. (76. 76. D.)

Doh = C. *In moderate time.* REGINALD FRANCIS DALE, 1845–1919.

:d | m :m | s :s | d' :— | t :s | l :f | s :m | r :— | — ||

:d | d :d | r :r | m :r.d | r :d | d :r | r :d | t, :— | — ||

:m | s :s | s :s | s :fe | s :s | f :l | s :s | s :— | — ||

:d | d :d | t, :t, | l, :— | s, :m | f :r | t, :d | s, :— | — ||

:r |m :m |s :s |d' :— |t :d' |r' :s |l :-.s |s :— |—
:t, |d :d |r :r |d :— |r :r |r :t, |m :l, |t, :— |—
:s |s :s |s :r |m :fe |s :fe |s :s |s :fe |s :— |—
:s, |d :d |t, :t, |l, :— |s, :l, |t, :m |d :r |s, :— |—

:s |l :d' |t :l |se :— |l :t |d' :r' |m' :l |t :— |—
:d |f :s |f :r |m :— |m :s |l :f |l :l |se :— |—
:s |d' :s |r' :l |t :— |d' :m'.r' |d' :l |d' :r' |t :— |—
:m |f :m |r :f |m :— |d :t, |l, :r |d :f |m :— |—

:d' |l :t |s :l |f :— |m :f |s :d |r :-.d |d :— |— || d |d
:s |f :f |m :m |r :— |d :t, |d :d |d :t, |d :— |— || l, |s,
:s |d' :t |t :l |l :s |s :f |m :m |l :r |m :— |— || f |m
:m |m :r |r :d |d :t, |d :r |m :l, |f, :s, |d :— |— || f, |d

A-men.

O THOU, before whose presence
  Nought evil may come in,
Yet who dost look in mercy
  Down on this world of sin,
O give us noble purpose
  To set the sin-bound free,
And Christ-like tender pity
  To seek the lost for Thee.

2 Fierce is our subtle foeman:
  The forces at his hand,
With woes that none can number,
  Despoil the pleasant land;
All they who war against them,
  In strife so keen and long,
Must in their Saviour's armour
  Be stronger than the strong.

3 So hast Thou wrought among us
  The great things that we see!
For things that are, we thank Thee,
  And for the things to be:
For bright hope is uplifting
  Faint hands and feeble knees,
To strive, beneath Thy blessing,
  For greater things than these.

4 Lead on, O Love and Mercy,
  O Purity and Power,
Lead on till peace eternal
  Shall close this battle-hour;
Till all who prayed and struggled
  To set their brethren free,
In triumph meet to praise Thee,
  Most Holy Trinity.

SAMUEL JOHN STONE, 1839-1900.

349

QUEM PASTORES LAUDAVERE. (8 8. 8 7.)

Doh = F. *In moderate time.* German Melody, 14th cent.

d :— :m | s :— :m | f :s :l | s :— :r || m :f :s | f :m :r
s, :— :d | r :— :d | d :— :d | d :— :t, || d :— :d | l, :— :t,
m :— :l | s :— :s | f :m :f | r :— :s || s :f :m | f :— :s
d :t, :l, | t, :— :d | l, :s, :f, | s, :— :s, || d :— :m | r :— :s,

d :— :l, | t, :— :s, || m :— :f | s :— :l | s :— :r | m :— :d ||
d :m, :fe, | s, :— :s, || s, :— :d | t, :— :l, | d :— :t, | d :— :d ||
m :— :r | r :— :t, || d :— :d | r :m :f | s :— :s | s :— :m ||
l, :— :r, | s, :— :s, || d :t, :l, | s, :— :f, | m, :f, :s, | d :— :d ||

f :— :f | m :r :d | d :l, :t, | d :— :— || d | d ||
l, :— :t, | d :t, :l, | l, :— :s, | s, :— :— || l, | s, ||
r :m :f | s :— :m | f :— :r | m :— :— || f | m ||
r :— :r, | m, :— :l, | r, :— :s, | d (d,) :— :— || f, | d, ||

A-men.

FATHER, who on man dost shower
  Gifts of plenty from Thy dower,
To Thy people give the power
  All Thy gifts to use aright.

2 Give pure happiness in leisure,
Temperance in every pleasure,
Holy use of earthly treasure,
  Bodies clear and spirits bright.

3 Lift from this and every nation
All that brings us degradation;
Quell the forces of temptation;
  Put Thine enemies to flight.

4 Be with us, Thy strength supplying,
That with energy undying,
Every foe of man defying,
  We may rally to the fight.

5 Thou who art our Captain ever,
Lead us on to great endeavour;
May Thy Church the world deliver:
  Give us wisdom, courage, might.

6 Father, who hast sought and found us,
Son of God, whose love has bound us,
Holy Ghost, within us, round us—
  Hear us, Godhead infinite.

PERCY DEARMER, 1867–

350 COLCHESTER. (88. 88. 88.)

Doh = E♭. *Moderately slow.* SAMUEL SEBASTIAN WESLEY, 1810–76.

```
:m  |s  :d  |f  :r  |d  :t, |d  :s   |d' :t    |l  :r  |s  :f.m |r  ‖
:d  |t, :d  |l, :l, |s, :s, |s, :r   |d  :s,   |l, :t, |d  :r.d |t, ‖
:s  |s  :m  |l  :f  |m  :r  |m  :s   |m  :s    |d  :s  |s  :l   |t  ‖
:d  |s, :l, |r, :f, |s, :s, |d  :t,  |l, :m,   |f, :f  |m  :f   |s  ‖

:m  |d  :f  |f  :m  |r  :l  |s  :s   |l  :d'   |t  :l  |s  :fe  |s  ‖
:t, |d  :d  |r  :d  |d  :t, |d  :d.t,|m  :d    |r  :m  |r  :r.d |t, ‖
:s  |m  :l  |s  :s  |l  :r  |s  :m   |m  :m.ba |se :l  |t  :l   |s  ‖
:s, |l, :l, |t, :d  |f  :f, |m, :m.r |d  :l,   |t, :d  |r  :r   |s, ‖

:t, |d  :r  |m  :m   |f  :s  |l  :l  |t  :d' |r  :m.f |m  :r  |d  ‖ f  |m ‖
:s, |s, :t, |d  :d   |d  :d  |d  :d  |f  :m  |d  :d   |d  :t, |d  ‖ d  |d ‖
:s  |s  :s  |s  :s   |f  :m  |f  :f  |f  :s  |l  :f   |s  :s.f|m  ‖ l  |s ‖
:f  |m  :r  |d  :ta, |l, :s, |f, :m  |r  :d  |f  :r   |s, :s, |d  ‖ f, |d ‖
                                             f, :r,
                                                                 A-men.
```

Dumb creatures.

MAKER of earth and sea and sky,
  Creation's Sovereign, Lord and King,
Who hung the starry worlds on high
  With hands that shaped the sparrow's wing:
Bless the dumb creatures in our care,
And listen to their voiceless prayer.

2 For us they toil, for us they die,
  These humble creatures Thou hast made;
How shall we dare their rights deny
  On whom Thy seal of love is laid?
Teach Thou our hearts to heed their plea,
As Thou dost man's in prayer to Thee.

EMILY BRYANT LORD, 1839-86.

Medical Work (351–353).

351

NUN DANKET ALL (GRÄFENBERG). (C.M.)

Doh = F. *Moderately slow.* JOHANN CRÜGER, 1598–1662.

d :l,.s,	d :r	m.m :r	.m :s.f	m :r	d :—
m, :f,.s,	l, :t,	d.d :t,	.d :d.r	d :t,	d :—
d :t,.d	d :f	m.s :s	.s :s.l	s :s.f	m :—
d, :r,.m,	f, :r,	d,.m, :s,	.d :m,.f,	s, :s,	d, :—

s :m.s	l :s	f.m :r	.s :d.f	m :r	d :—	d	d
d :d.d	d :d	t,.d :t,	.t, :d.r	d :t,	d :—	l,	s,
m :m.d	d :d	f.s :s	.s :m.l	s :s.f	m :—	f	m
d :d.m,	f, :m,	r,.d, :s,	.m, :l,.r,	m,.,f, :s,	d, :—	f,	d,

A-men.

FROM Thee all skill and science flow,
All pity, care, and love,
All calm and courage, faith and hope ;
O pour them from above.

2 And part them, Lord, to each and all,
As each and all shall need,
To rise like incense, each to Thee,
In noble thought and deed.

3 And hasten, Lord, that perfect day
When pain and death shall cease,
And Thy just rule shall fill the earth
With health, and light, and peace ;

4 When ever blue the sky shall gleam,
And ever green the sod ;
And man's rude work deface no more
The Paradise of God.

CHARLES KINGSLEY, 1819–75.

352 HIMMEL. (87. 87. 77.)

Doh = E♭. *In moderate time.* FRIEDRICH HEINRICH HIMMEL, 1765–1814.

s :s | l :s | f :s | f :m | r :r | t :l | s :fe | s :— ||
d :d | l_1.t_1 :d | d :r | d :d | r :d | t_1 :m | r :r | t_1 :— ||
m :m | f :m | l :r | s :s | s :fe | s :m | t :l | s :— ||
d :d | f_1 :d | l_1 :t_1 | d :d | t_1 :l_1 | s_1 :d | r :r | s_1 :— ||

s :s | l :s | f :s | f :m | r :r | t :l | s :fe | s :— ||
d :r | m :r | d :t_1 | d :d | t_1 :l_1 | r :m | r :-.d | t_1 :— ||
m :s | d' :t | l :s | s :s | s :fe | s :d' | t :l | s :— ||
d :t_1 | l_1 :t_1.d | r :s_1 | d :d | r :d | t_1 :d | r :r | s_1 :— ||

m :s | d' :-.l | s :f | m :— | m :m | f :m | r :r | d :— || d | d ||
d :r | m :d | t_1 :d.r | d :— | d :t_1 | d :d | d :t_1 | d :— || l_1 | s_1 ||
d' :t.l | s :l | r :l | s :— | d :m | l :s | s :-.f | m :— || f | m ||
l_1 :s_1.f_1 | m_1 :f_1 | s_1 :l_1.t_1 | d :— | l_1 :s_1 | f_1 :d | s_1 :s_1 | d :— || f_1 | d ||

A-men.

THOU to whom the sick and dying
Ever came, nor came in vain,
Still with healing words replying
To the wearied cry of pain,
Hear us, Jesus, as we meet,
Suppliants at Thy mercy-seat.

2 Still the weary, sick, and dying
Need a brother's, sister's care;
On Thy higher help relying,
May we now their burden share,
Bringing all our offerings meet,
Suppliants at Thy mercy-seat.

3 May each child of Thine be willing,
Willing both in hand and heart,
All the law of love fulfilling,
Ever comfort to impart,
Ever bringing offerings meet,
Suppliant, to Thy mercy-seat.

4 So may sickness, sin, and sadness
To Thy healing virtue yield,
Till the sick and sad, in gladness,
Rescued, ransomed, cleansèd, healed,
One in Thee together meet,
Pardoned at Thy judgment-seat.

GODFREY THRING, 1823–1903.

353 CULROSS. (C.M.)

Scottish Psalter, 1634.

Lah = A. Doh = C. *Moderately slow.*

m :— |l :d' |t :l |se :l |t :— ‖ m :— |l :se |l :t |d' :— ‖
d :— |m :m |m :m |m.r :d |m :— ‖ t, :— |m :m |m :s |s :— ‖
l :— |l :l |se :l |m :l |se :— ‖ se :— |l :t |d' :r' |m' :— ‖
l, :— |d :l, |m :d |t, :l, |m :— ‖ m :— |d :m |l :s |d :— ‖

s :— |d' :m' |r' :d' |t :l |se :— ‖ m :— |l :d' |t :t |l :— ‖ l |l ‖
m :— |s :s |s :m |f :r |m :— ‖ m :— |m :m |f :m.r |d :— ‖ r |de ‖
d' :— |d' :d' |t :d' |r' :l |t :— ‖ se :— |l :l |l :se |l :— ‖ f |m ‖
d :— |m :d |s :l |r :f |m :— ‖ m :-.r |d :l, |r :m |l, :— ‖ r |l, ‖

A-men.

TALLIS. (C.M.)

Doh = E♭. *Moderately slow.* THOMAS TALLIS, *c.* 1510–85.

:d |m :f |s :s |l :l |s :s |d' :t |l :l |s :— |— ‖
:d |d :d |r :m |f :f |m :d |m :r |r :r |t, :— |— ‖
:m |s :l |t :s |d' :d' |d' :m |s :s |s :fe |s :— |— ‖
:d |d :l, |s, :d |f, :f, |d :d |d :s, |r :r |s, :— |— ‖

:d |m :f |s :s |l :l |s :d |f :m |r :r |d :— |— ‖ d |d ‖
:d |d :d |t, :d |d :d |d :d |d :d |d :t, |d :— |— ‖ l, |s, ‖
:m |s :f |r :m |f :f |m :m |l :s |s :s |m :— |— ‖ f |m ‖
:d |d :l, |s, :d |f :f, |d :d |l, :d |s, :s, |d :— |— ‖ f, |d ‖

A-men.

Medical Missions.

FATHER, whose will is life and good
For all of mortal breath,
Bind strong the bond of brotherhood
Of those who fight with death.

2 Empower the hands and hearts and wills
Of friends in lands afar,
Who battle with the body's ills,
And wage Thy holy war.

3 Where'er they heal the maimed and blind,
Let love of Christ attend :
Proclaim the good Physician's mind,
And prove the Saviour friend.

4 For still His love works wondrous charms,
And, as in days of old,
He takes the wounded to His arms,
And bears them to the fold.

5 O Father, look from heaven and bless,
Where'er Thy servants be,
Their works of pure unselfishness,
Made consecrate to Thee !

HARDWICKE DRUMMOND RAWNSLEY, 1851–1920.

354 FAIRFIELD. (86. 86. 86.)

Doh = D. *In moderate time.* JAMES TURLE, 1802–82.

```
:(m) |m :r.m   |d :d  |r  :m  |f :r  |m :s  |d' :t.l |t  :— |— ||
:(d) |d :t,.t, |d :d  |l, :de |r :r  |d :r  |m  :r   |r  :— |— ||
:(s) |s :f.s   |m :m  |f  :s  |l :s  |s :s  |s  :fe  |s  :— |— ||
:(d) |d :d.d   |d :l, |f  :m  |r :t, |d :t, |l, :r   |s, :— |— ||
```

(vv. 1 & 4.)

```
:s  |l  :f |l  :t  |s :l |f :m  |l  :l |d' :t      |l  :— |— ||
:d  |f  :d |f  :f  |m :m |r :t, |l, :r |m  :m.r    |d  :— |— ||
:d' |d' :l |d' :r' |t :l |l :se |l  :l |l  :se     |l  :— |— ||
:m  |f  :l |f  :r  |m :d |r :m  |f  :f |m  :m }    |l, :— |— ||
                                           :m, }
```

```
:d' |t :d' |l :l |s  :f.m |r :s  |s :f  |r  :r   |d :— |— :— || f  |m ||
:m  |m :m  |d :d |de :de  |r :r  |d :d  |d  :t,  |d :— |— :— || d  |d ||
:l  |t :s  |l :f |s  :l.s |f :f  |m :f  |l  :s.f |m :— |— :— || l  |s ||
:l  |s :m  |f :f |m  :l,  |r :t, |d :l, |f, :s,  |d :— |— :— || f, |d ||
                                                                 A-men.
```

DISMISS me not Thy service, Lord,
But train me for Thy will :
For even I, in fields so broad,
Some duties may fulfil ;
And I will ask for no reward,
Except to serve Thee still.

2 How many serve, how many more
May to the service come !
To tend the vines, the grapes to store,
Thou dost appoint for some ;
Thou hast Thy young men at the war,
Thy little ones at home.

3 All works are good, and each is best
As most it pleases Thee ;
Each worker pleases when the rest
He serves in charity ;
And neither man nor work unblest
Wilt Thou permit to be.

4 Our Master all the work hath done
He asks of us to-day ;
Sharing His service, every one
Share too His sonship may :
Lord, I would serve and be a son ;
Dismiss me not, I pray.

THOMAS TOKE LYNCH, 1818–71.

355 OLD 81ST. (D.C.M.)

Doh = D. *Boldly and in free time.* *English Psalter*, 1562.

d :m :f :s :—:s :l :—:l :s :— ‖ s :l :t :d' :—:l :t :—
d :d :d :t, :—:d :d :—:d :d :— ‖ d :d :m :m :—:r :r :—
m :s :l :r :—:m :f :—:f :m :— ‖ m :l :s :s :—:fe :s :—
d :d :l, :s, :—:d :l, :f, :—:d :— ‖ d :l, :m :d :—:r :s, :—

s :d' :—:t :l :—:s :f :m :s :— ‖ m :l :—:s :s :—:fe :s :—
d :m :—:m :d :—:d :l, :d :t, :— ‖ d :d :—:t, :d :—:l, :t, :—
m :l :—:s :f :—:m :r :s :s :— ‖ s :f :—:r :m :—:r :r :—
d :l, :—:m :f :—:d :r :d :s, :— ‖ d :f, :—:s, :d :—:r :s, :—

s :d' :t :l :—:s :f :—:m :r :— ‖ m :f :—:m :m :r :—:m :—
d :m :m :d :—:d :l, :d :—:t, :— ‖ d :d :—:d :d :t, :—:d :—
m :l :s :f :—:m :f :l :s :s :— ‖ s :l :—:s :s :s :—:s :—
d :l, :m, :f, :—:d :r :l, :d :s, :— ‖ d :f, :—:d :d :s, :—:d :—

m:l :s :f :—:m :r :—:d :t, :— ‖ m :r :—:d :d :—:t, :d :— ‖ d ‖ d
d:d :ta, :ta, :—:s, :t, :—:d :s, :— ‖ s, :t, :—:d :l, :—:s, :s, :— ‖ l, ‖ s,
s:f :r :r :—:m :s :—:m :s :— ‖ d :r :s :—:f :—:r :m :— ‖ f ‖ m
d:f, :s, :ta, :—:d :s, :—:l, :s, :— ‖ d :s, :—:m, :f, :—:s, :d { :d, } :— ‖ f, ‖ d

A-men.

ST. URSULA. (D.C.M.)

Doh = F. *Moderately fast.* FREDERICK WESTLAKE, 1840–98.

:m |s :-.f |m :d |m :r |d :s, |l, :d |d :-.r |t, :— |— ‖
:d |d :t, |d :l, |s, :s, |s, :m, |f, :m, |s, :l, |s, :— |— ‖
:s |m :f |s :f |f :f |m :d |d :d |d :f |r :— |— ‖
:d |d, :r, |m, :f, |s, :l,.t, |d :d { :d, } |f, :l, |m, :f, |s, :— |— ‖

C.t.

:r |s :-.f |m :l .s |f :-.m |r :m |^{d}f :l |d' :-.t |l :— |— ‖
:t, |d :-.t, |d :l, |l, :-.l, |l, :se, |^{l}r :f |m :r |d :— |— ‖
:s |s :-.s |s :d |r :-.de |r :t, |^{d}f :f .s |l :se |l :— |— ‖
:f, |m, :-.r, |d, :f,.m, |r, :-.m, |f, :m, |^{l}r :r |m :m |l, :— |— ‖

f.F.

```
:(d)s  | s :-.s | l :s | s :-.f | m :m | d :-.d | f :l | r :— | — ‖
:(m)t, | d :-.d | d :d | r :-.r | d :d | l, :-.l, | l, :l, | s, :— | — ‖
:(l)m  | m :-.m | f :m | r :-.s | s :s | f :-.f | f :f | s :f | m ‖
:(l)m.r | d :-.d | d :d | t, :-.t, | d :d | f :m | r :d | t, :l, | s, ‖

:r    | s :-.s | l :s | f :s | m :r | d :-.d | d :t, | d :— | — ‖ d | d ‖
:l,.t, | d :-.d | d :de | r :r | d :t, | d :-.l, | s, :s, | s, :— | — ‖ l, | s, ‖
:r    | d :-.d | f :m | r :r | s :f | m :-.f | m :r | m :— | — ‖ f | m ‖
:f,   | m, :-.m, | f, :l, | r :t, | d :s, | l, :-.f, | s, :s, | d } :— | — ‖ f, | d, ‖
                                                        :d, }          A-men.
```

Unison. O LORD of life, and love, and power,
How joyful life would be,
If in Thy service every hour
We lived and moved with Thee;
If youth in all its bloom and might
By Thee were sanctified,
And manhood found its chief delight
In working at Thy side!

Harmony. 2 'Tis ne'er too late, while life shall last,
A new life to begin;
'Tis ne'er too late to leave the past,
And break with self and sin:
And we this day, both old and young,
Would earnestly aspire
For hearts to nobler purpose strung,
And purified desire.

Unison. 3 Nor for ourselves alone we plead,
But for all faithful souls
Who serve Thy cause by word or deed,
Whose names Thy book enrols.
O speed Thy work, victorious King,
And give Thy workers might,
That through the world Thy truth may ring,
And all men see Thy light.

Ella Sophia Armitage, 1841-

356

DEUS TUORUM MILITUM. (L.M.)

Grenoble Church Melody.

Doh = C. *Unison.* *In moderate time.*

:d |m :— :s |d' :— :s |f :m :r |d :— :d' |m' :— :d'

|l :t :d' |s :— :fe |s :— ||s |l :— :t |d' :— :s |f :m :r

|m :— :s |l :t :d' |s :f :m |r :— :d |d :— || d :r |m
d :— |d
l :— |s
f :— |d
A - men.

GO, labour on: spend and be spent,
Thy joy to do the Father's will;
It is the way the Master went;
Should not the servant tread it still?

2 Go, labour on while it is day:
The world's dark night is hastening on;
Speed, speed thy work; cast sloth away;
It is not thus that souls are won.

3 Men die in darkness at thy side,
Without a hope to cheer the tomb;
Take up the torch and wave it wide,
The torch that lights time's thickest gloom.

4 Toil on, faint not, keep watch, and pray;
Be wise the erring soul to win;
Go forth into the world's highway,
Compel the wanderer to come in.

5 Toil on, and in thy toil rejoice;
For toil comes rest, for exile home;
Soon shalt thou hear the Bridegroom's voice,
The midnight peal, 'Behold, I come!'

HORATIUS BONAR, 1808-89.

357 DILIGENCE. (76. 75. D.)

Doh = E. *In moderate time.* LOWELL MASON, 1792–1872.

```
s  :m.,f |s  :s  |l  :—  |s  :—  |d  :d.,d   |d  :r  |m  :—  |— :—
m  :d.,r |m  :d  |l, :—  |d  :—  |d  :d.,d   |l, :t, |d  :—  |— :—
s  :s.,f |m  :m  |f  :—  |m  :—  |m  :m.,m   |m  :s  |s  :—  |— :—
d  :m.,r |d  :d  |f, :—  |d  :—  |l, :l,.,l, |l, :s, |d  :—  |— :—

s  :m.,f |s  :s  |l  :—  |s  :—  |d  :r  |m  :r  |d  :—  |— :—
m  :d.,r |m  :d  |l, :t, |d  :—  |d  :d  |d  :t, |d  :—  |— :—
s  :s.,f |m  :m  |d  :r  |m  :—  |s  :l  |s  :f  |m  :—  |— :—
d  :m.,r |d  :d  |f, :—  |d  :—  |m  :f  |s  :s, |d  :—  |— :—

r  :r.,r    |r  :m  |f  :—.m |r  :—  |m  :m.,m  |m  :fe |s  :—  |— :—
t, :r.,d    |t, :d  |r  :—.d |t, :—  |d  :m.,r  |d  :d  |t, :—  |— :—
s  :s.,fe   |s  :s  |s  :—   |s  :—  |s  :s.,s  |d' :l  |s  :—  |— :—
s, :t,.,l,  |s, :d  |t, :—.d |s, :—  |d  :d.,t, |l, :r  |s, :—  |— :—

s  :m.,f |s  :s  |l  :—  |s  :—  |d  :r  |m  :r  |d  :—  |— :— || d  d
m  :d.,r |m  :m  |d  :r  |m  :—  |d  :d  |d  :t, |d  :—  |— :— || l, s,
s  :s.,f |m  :d' |l  :t  |d' :—  |s  :l  |s  :f  |m  :—  |— :— || f  m
d  :m.,r |d  :d  |f  :—  |d  :—  |m  :f  |s  :s, |d  :—  |— :— || f, d
                                                                   A-men.
```

WORK, for the night is coming!
Work through the morning hours;
Work while the dew is sparkling;
Work 'mid springing flowers;
Work while the day grows brighter,
Under the glowing sun;
Work, for the night is coming,
When man's work is done.

2 Work, for the night is coming!
Work through the sunny noon;
Fill brightest hours with labour;
Rest comes sure and soon.
Give to each flying minute
Something to keep in store;
Work, for the night is coming,
When man works no more.

3 Work, for the night is coming!
Under the sunset skies,
While their bright tints are glowing,
Work, for daylight flies.
Work till the last beam fadeth,
Fadeth to shine no more;
Work while the night is darkening,
When man's work is o'er.

Adapted from ANNA LOUISA COGHILL, 1836–1907.

358 HELENSBURGH. (888.)

Doh = A♭. *Moderately slow.* KENNETH GEORGE FINLAY, 1882-

```
:d    |t, :l,     |t, :- .d  |r     :t, |s, ||s, |d  :t, |d .r :m     |f    :r
:s,   |f, :f,.m,  |r, :s,    |r,.m, :f, |m, ||s, |s, :s, |l,   :d     |r    :l,
:s,.l,|t, :d      |r  :- .m  |s     :r .d|t,||r  |d  :r  |f    :s     |l .s :f .m
:m,   |r, :r,     |s, :- .d, |t,.d, :r, |m, ||m, |l, :s, |f,   :f,.m, |r,   :f,

|t, ||s,    |s     :- .f |m .r :d      |r  :d     |t,   :— |d  :— |— ||d  |d
|s, ||s,    |s,.l, :t,   |d    :d .t,  |l, :—     |s,   :— |s, :— |— ||l, |s,
|r  ||t,    |d     :r    |m    :f .s   |f  :- .m  |r .d :r |m  :— |— ||f  |m
|s, ||s,.f, |m,    :- .r,|d,   :r,.m,  |f, :—     |s,   :— |d, :— |— ||f, |d,
```

A-men.

O YE who taste that love is sweet,
Set waymarks for all doubtful feet
That stumble on in search of it.

2 Sing notes of love: that some who hear
Far off, inert, may lend an ear,
Rise up and wonder and draw near.

3 Lead lives of love; that others who
Behold your life may kindle too
With love, and cast their lot with you.

CHRISTINA GEORGINA ROSSETTI, 1830-94.

359 PSALM 42. (87. 87. D.)

French Psalter, 1551.
Composed or arranged by LOUIS BOURGEOIS, 1510- ?.

Doh = G. *In moderate time, majestically.*

```
|d :— :r  |m :— :r  |d  :t, |l, :— |s, :— |d  :— :r
|d :— :t, |d :— :s, |l, :s, |s, :f,|m, :— |l, :— :s,
|m :— :s  |s :— :s  |m  :m  |d  :— |d  :— |m  :— :s
|d :— :s, |d :— :t, |l, :m, |f, :— |d, :— |l, :— :t,

|m :— :f  |m  :—  |r  :— |d  :— |— :— ||d  :— :r  |m :— :r
|d :— :l, |d  :—  |t, :— |d  :— |— :— ||l, :— :s, |s,:— :s,
|s :— :f  |s  :—  |—  :f |m  :— |— :— ||m  :— :r  |d :— :t,
|d :— :r, |m, :f, |s, :— |d, :— |— :— ||l, :— :t, |d :— :s,

|d  :t, |l, :—  |s, :— |d  :— :r  |m  :— :f  |m  :—  |r  :—  |d  :— |— :— ||
|m, :s, |s, :fe,|s, :— |l, :— :t, |d  :— :d  |d  :—  |—  :t, |d  :— |— :— ||
|d  :r  |m  :r  |t, :— |d  :— :f  |m  :— :l  |l  :—  |—  :s  |m  :— |— :— ||
|l, :t, |d  :r  |s, :— |f, :— :r, |d, :— :f, |l, :s, |f, :s, |d, :— |— :— ||
```

|m :— :m |s :— :f |m :r |m :— |m :— |s :— :s
|d :— :d |d :— :l_1 |d :t_1 |d :— |d :— |ta_1 :— :ta_1
|s :— :s |m :— :r |s :s |s :— |s :— |r :— :m
|d :— :d |d_1 :— :r_1 |m_1 :s_1 |d_1 :— |d_1 :— |s_1 :— :s_1

|l :— :s |f :m |r :— |— :— ||m :— :s |f :— :m
|l_1 :— :t_1 |d :d |d :— |t_1 :— ||d :— :t_1 |l_1 :— :s_1
|f :— :m |d :s |s :— |— :— ||s :— :s |d :r :m
|f_1 :— :s_1 |l_1 :d |s_1 :— |— :— ||d :— :m_1 |l_1 :t_1 :d

d :r	m :—	d :—	m :— :m	f :— :m	r :d	t_1 :—	d :—		d	d	
d :l_1	t_1 :—	d :—	de :— :de	r :— :d	l_1 :—	r_1 :—	m_1 :—		l_1	s_1	
m :l	l :se	l :—	l :— :l	l :— :s	f :m	s :—	s :—		f	m	
l_1 :f_1	m_1 :—	l_1 :—	l_1 :— :l_1	r_1 :— :m_1	f_1 :l_1	s_1 :—	d_1 :—		f_1	d_1	

A-men.

SON of God, eternal Saviour,
Source of life and truth and grace,
Son of Man, whose birth incarnate
Hallows all our human race;
Thou, our Head, who, throned in glory,
For Thine own dost ever plead,
Fill us with Thy love and pity,
Heal our wrongs, and help our need.

2 As Thou, Lord, hast lived for others,
So may we for others live;
Freely have Thy gifts been granted,
Freely may Thy servants give.
Thine the gold and Thine the silver,
Thine the wealth of land and sea,
We but stewards of Thy bounty,
Held in solemn trust for Thee.

3 Come, O Christ, and reign among us,
King of love, and Prince of peace;
Hush the storm of strife and passion,
Bid its cruel discords cease.
Ah, the past is dark behind us,
Strewn with wrecks and stained with blood;
But before us gleams the vision
Of the coming brotherhood.

4 See the Christlike host advancing,
High and lowly, great and small,
Linked in bonds of common service
For the common Lord of all.
Thou who prayedst, Thou who willest
That Thy people should be one,
Grant, O grant our hope's fruition:
Here on earth Thy will be done.

SOMERSET CORRY LOWRY, 1855- .

360

PSALM 12 (DONNE SECOURS). (11 10. 11 10.) *French Psalter*, 1551.
Composed or arranged by LOUIS BOURGEOIS, 1510– ?.

Lah = D. Doh = F. *Unison.* *Moderately slow.*

| m :d .r | m :s | m .d :r .d | t, :l, || m :m .r | m :l |

| m .l :s :fe | m :— || l, :d .d | t, :l, | m .m :r .t, | d :t, ||

| m :s .m | d :r | m .l, :d :t, | l, :— || l, | l, |
f, | m,
r | de
r, | l,
A-men.

O SON of God, our Captain of salvation,
Thyself by suffering schooled to human grief,
We bless Thee for Thy sons of consolation,
Who follow in the steps of Thee their Chief;

2 Those whom Thy Spirit's dread vocation severs
To lead the vanguard of Thy conquering host;
Whose toilsome years are spent in brave endeavours
To bear Thy saving Name from coast to coast;

3 Those whose bright faith makes feeble hearts grow stronger,
And sends fresh warriors to the great campaign,
Bids the lone convert feel estranged no longer,
And wins the sundered to be one again;

4 And all true helpers, patient, kind, and skilful,
Who shed Thy light across our darkened earth,
Counsel the doubting, and restrain the wilful,
Soothe the sick-bed, and share the children's mirth.

5 Thus, Lord, Thy blessèd saints in memory keeping,
Still be Thy Church's watchword, 'Comfort ye,'—
Till in our Father's house shall end our weeping,
And all our wants be satisfied in Thee.

JOHN ELLERTON, 1826–93.

361 ST. JOSEPH. (88. 84.)

JOHN BAPTISTE CALKIN, 1827–1905.

Doh = D. *In moderate time.*

:m | f :m | s :f | m :r | d :r | m :f | s :d' | t :l | s
:d | d :d | d :d | t, :t, | d :s, | d :t, | d :m | re :fe | m
:s | l :s | t :l | s :f | m :s | s :s | s :s | fe :t | t
:d | d :d | f, :f, | s, :s, | l, :t, | d :r | m :l, | t, :re | m

:s | d' :s | l :s | f :m | r :d | d :— | r :— | d :— | — || d | d
:r | s, :d | d :de | r :l, | l, :l, | s, :— | t, :— | d :— | — || l, | s,
:t | d' :ta | l :l | l :s | f :f | m :— | f :— | m :— | — || f | m
:f | m :m | f :l, | r :m | f :f, | s, :— | s, :— | d :— | — || f, | d

A-men.

DEAR Master, what can children do?
The angels came from heaven above
To comfort Thee; may children too
Give Thee their love?

2 No more, as on that night of shame,
Art Thou in dark Gethsemane,
Where worshipping, an angel came
To strengthen Thee.

3 But Thou hast taught us that Thou art
Still present in the crowded street,
In every lonely, suffering heart
That there we meet:

4 And not one simple, loving deed,
That lessens gloom, or lightens pain,
Or answers some unspoken need,
Is done in vain:

5 Since every passing joy we make
For men and women that we see,
If it is offered for Thy sake,
Is given to Thee.

6 O God, our Master, help us then
To bless the weary and the sad,
And, comforting our fellow-men,
To make Thee glad.

ANNIE MATHESON, 1853–1924.

362

INVERMAY. (56. 659.)

Doh = Eb. *In moderate time.* JAMES LAMB, 1835–1904.

:s |s :m :l |s :— :m.m |m :r :f |m :— ||s |d' :t :l |t :l :s
:d |r :s, :l,.t, |d :— :d.d |d :t, :r |d :— ||r |m :r :r |r :r :r
:m |r :m :f |m :— :s.s |s :f :r.s |s :— ||s |s :s :fe |s :fe :s
:d |t, :d :f, |d :— :d.m |s :s, :s, |d :— ||t, |l, :r :r |s, :l, :t,

|l :s :fe |s :— ||s |d' :s :m |l :f :r |s :— :— |d :— ||d |d
|m :r :d |t, :— ||t, |d :r :d |d :d :d |d :t, :— |d :— ||l, |s,
|d' :t :l |s :— ||s |s :s :s |f :f :l |r :— :f |m :— ||f |m
|d :r :r |s, :— ||f |m :t, :d |f, :l, :f, |s, :— :— |d :— ||f, |d

A-men.

THE fields are all white,
And the reapers are few;
We children are willing,
But what can we do
To work for our Lord in His harvest?

2 Our hands are so small,
And our words are so weak:
We cannot teach others;
How then shall we seek
To work for our Lord in His harvest?

3 We'll work by our prayers,
By the offerings we bring,
By small self-denials;
The least little thing
May work for our Lord in His harvest:

4 Until by and by,
As the years pass, at length
We too may be reapers,
And go forth in strength,
To work for our Lord in His harvest.

The Book of Praise for Children, 1881.

363

CHRISTMAS MORN. (76. 76. D.)

Doh = F. *In moderate time.* EDWARD JOHN HOPKINS, 1818–1901.

:d |m :— :m |m :r :m |s :— :— |m :— :d |r :— :r |r :d :r
:s, |d :— :d |d :t, :d |d :— :— |d :— :d |d :— :d |t, :l, :t,
:m |s :— :s |l :— :l |s :— :— |s :— :m |l :— :l |s :— :s
:d |d :— :d |l, :— :l, |m, :— :— |m, :— :l, |f, :— :f, |s, :— :s,

|m :— :— |— :— ||d |m :— :m |m :r :m |s :— :—
|d :— :— |— :— ||s, |d :— :d |d :t, :d |r :— :—
|s :— :— |— :— ||m |s :— :s |l :— :l |s :— :—
|d :— :— |— :— ||d |d :— :d |l, :— :l, |t, :— :—

```
C.t.                                    f.F.
|(t)m  :—  :f  |s   :—  :l   |t  :l  :t   |(d')s  :—  :—  |—  :—  ||
|(s)d  :—  :r  |m   :—  :m   |f  :—  :f   |(m)t,  :—  :—  |—  :—  ||
|(t)m' :—  :r' |d'  :—  :d'  |r' :—  :r'  |(d')s  :—  :—  |—  :—  ||
|(m)l  :—  :l  |s   :—  :s   |s  :—  :s   |(d)s,  :—  :—  |—  :—  ||

:s   |s  :—:s   |t  :l  :s   |s  :—:—  |m  :—:d  |l   :—:d   |r   :d  :r
:t,  |t, :—:t,  |r  :d  :t,  |d  :—:—  |d  :—:d  |d   :—:l,  |t,  :l, :t,
:s   |f  :—:f   |f  :—:f     |m  :—:—  |s  :—:m  |f   :—:f   |r   :—:r
:s   |r  :—:r   |s, :—:s,    |d  :—:—  |d  :—:d  |f,  :—:f,  |f,  :—:f,

m    :—  :—  |—  :—  ||r    |d   :—  :d   |d   :r  :d    |l   :—  :—  |d   :—
se,  :—  :—  |—  :—  ||t,   |l,  :—  :l,  |ta, :—  :ta,  |l,  :—  :—  |l,  :—
t,   :—  :—  |—  :—  ||m    |m   :—  :m   |m   :—  :m    |d   :—  :—  |f   :—
m,   :—  :—  |—  :—  ||se,  |l,  :—  :l,  |s,  :—  :s,   |f,  :—  :—  |f,  :—

:r   |m   :—  :m   |r   :d   :r   |d        :—  :—  |—  :—  ||d   |d   ||
:d   |d   :—  :d   |t,  :l,  :t,  |d        :—  :—  |—  :—  ||l,  |s,  ||
:l   |s   :—  :s   |f   :—   :f   |m        :—  :—  |—  :—  ||f   |m   ||
:f,  |s,  :—  :s,  |s,  :—   :s,  |{d / d,} :—  :—  |—  :—  ||f,  |d,  ||
                                                               A-men.
```

THE wise may bring their learning,
The rich may bring their wealth,
And some may bring their greatness,
And some bring strength and health;
We too would bring our treasures
To offer to the King;
We have no wealth or learning:
What shall we children bring?

2 We'll bring Him hearts that love Him;
We'll bring Him thankful praise,
And young souls meekly striving
To walk in holy ways:
And these shall be the treasures
We offer to the King,
And these are gifts that even
The poorest child may bring.

3 We'll bring the little duties
We have to do each day;
We'll try our best to please Him,
At home, at school, at play:
And better are these treasures
To offer to our King,
Than richest gifts without them;
Yet these a child may bring.

Congregational Church Hymnal, 1887.

Also the following:

156 Ye servants of the Lord
484–93 *Hymns of Brotherly Love*
495 Saviour, while my heart is tender
636 Judge Eternal, throned in splendour
640 And did those feet in ancient time
681 Rescue the perishing, care for the dying

MISSIONS

364

MOSCOW. (664. 6664.)

Doh = G. *In moderate time.* FELICE DE GIARDINI, 1716–96.

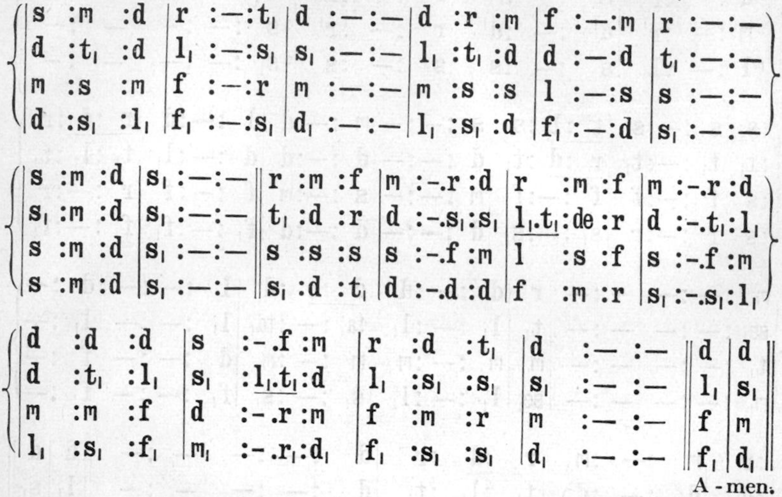

```
s  :m  :d  | r  :—:t,  | d  :—:— | d  :r  :m | f  :—:m | r  :—:—
d  :t, :d  | l, :—:s,  | s, :—:— | l, :t, :d | d  :—:d | t, :—:—
m  :s  :m  | f  :—:r   | m  :—:— | m  :s  :s | l  :—:s | s  :—:—
d  :s, :l, | f, :—:s,  | d, :—:— | l, :s, :d | f, :—:d | s, :—:—
```

```
s  :m :d | s, :—:— || r  :m :f  | m :-.r  :d  | r     :m  :f | m  :-.r  :d
s, :m :d | s, :—:— || t, :d :r  | d :-.s, :s, | l,.t, :de :r | d  :-.t, :l,
s  :m :d | s, :—:— || s  :s :s  | s :-.f  :m  | l     :s  :f | s  :-.f  :m
s  :m :d | s, :—:— || s, :d :t, | d :-.d  :d  | f     :m  :r | s, :-.s, :l,
```

```
d  :d  :d  | s  :-.f   :m  | r  :d  :t, | d  :— :— || d  | d
d  :t, :l, | s, :l,.t, :d  | l, :s, :s, | s, :— :— || l, | s,
m  :m  :f  | d  :-.r   :m  | f  :m  :r  | m  :— :— || f  | m
l, :s, :f, | m, :-.r,  :d, | f, :s, :s, | d, :— :— || f, | d,
                                                       A - men.
```

MALVERN. (664. 6664.) *The Hallelujah*, 1849.

Arranged by JOHN ROBERTS (IEUAN GWYLLT), 1822–77.

Doh = B♭. *With dignity.*

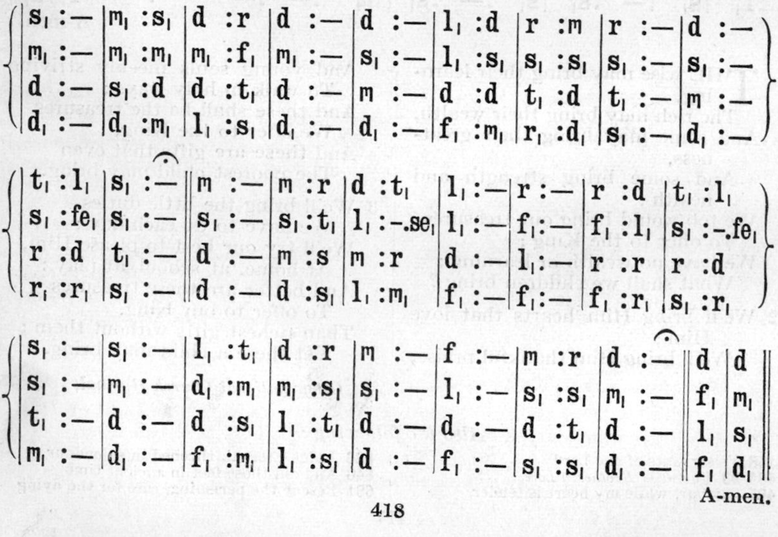

```
s, :— | m, :s, | d  :r  | d  :— | d  :— | l, :d  | r  :m  | r  :— | d  :—
m, :— | m, :m, | m, :f, | m, :— | s, :— | l, :s, | s, :s, | s, :— | s, :—
d  :— | s, :d  | d  :t, | d  :— | m  :— | d  :d  | t, :d  | t, :— | m  :—
d, :— | d, :m, | l, :s, | d, :— | d, :— | f, :m, | r, :d, | s, :— | d, :—
```

```
t, :l,  | s, :— || m :— | m  :r  | d  :t,     | l, :— | r  :— | r  :d  | t, :l,
s, :fe, | s, :— || s, :— | s, :t, | l, :-.se, | l, :— | f, :— | f, :l, | s, :-.fe,
r  :d   | t, :— || d :— | m  :s  | m  :r      | d  :— | l, :— | r  :r  | r  :d
r, :r,  | s, :— || d :— | d  :s, | l, :m,     | f, :— | f, :— | f, :r, | s, :r,
```

```
s, :— | s, :— | l, :t, | d  :r  | m  :— | f  :— | m  :r  | d  :— || d  | d
s, :— | m, :— | d, :m, | m, :s, | s, :— | l, :— | s, :s, | m, :— || f, | m,
t, :— | d  :— | d  :s, | l, :t, | d  :— | d  :— | d  :t, | d  :— || l, | s,
m, :— | d, :— | f, :m, | l, :s, | d  :— | f, :— | s, :s, | d, :— || f, | d,
                                                                    A-men.
```

THOU whose almighty word
Chaos and darkness heard
And took their flight,
Hear us, we humbly pray,
And, where the gospel day
Sheds not its glorious ray,
Let there be light.

2 Thou who didst come to bring,
On Thy redeeming wing,
Healing and sight,
Health to the sick in mind,
Sight to the inly blind,
O now to all mankind
Let there be light.

3 Spirit of truth and love,
Life-giving, holy Dove,
Speed forth Thy flight;
Move o'er the waters' face,
Bearing the lamp of grace,
And in earth's darkest place
Let there be light.

4 Blessèd and holy Three,
Glorious Trinity,
Wisdom, Love, Might,
Boundless as ocean's tide
Rolling in fullest pride,
Through the world far and wide
Let there be light.

JOHN MARRIOTT, 1780–1825.

365 GLASGOW. (C.M.)

Doh = G. *In moderate time.* *Moore's Psalm-Singer's Pocket Companion*, 1756.

```
:s, |d :— :r |m.,r :d :m |s.,l :s :f |m :— :m |r :— :f |m .,r :d :t, |d :— ||s |s :—
:m, |s, :— :t, |d.,t, :d :d |d :— :t, |d :— :d |l, :— :r |d .,l, :s, :s, |s, :— ||d |r :d
:d |s :— :s |s.,f :m :s |m.,f :m :r |d :— :s |f :— :l |s .,f :m :r |m :— ||m |s.,f :m
:d, |m, :— :s, |d.,r :m :d |s, :— :s, |d, :— :d |f, :— :r, |m,.,f, :s, :s, |d, :— ||d |t, :d

:m |f :— :l |s :f :m |r :— :s |d :r :m |f :m :r |d :— ||d |d ||
:d |d .,ta, :l, :d |s,.,l, :t, :d |t, :— :t, |d :s, :d |d :— :t, |d :— ||l, |s, ||
:s |f :— :d |d :r :m .fe |s :— :s .f |m :s :s |l :s :s .f |m :— ||f |m ||
:ta, |l,.,s, :f, :f, |m, :r, :d, |s, :— :s, |l, :t, :d |f, :s, :s, |d, :— ||f, |d, ||
```

A-men.

From Isaiah ii. 2–6.

BEHOLD! the mountain of the Lord
In latter days shall rise
On mountain tops above the hills,
And draw the wondering eyes.

2 To this the joyful nations round,
All tribes and tongues, shall flow;
Up to the hill of God, they'll say,
And to His house we'll go.

3 The beam that shines from Zion hill
Shall lighten every land;
The King who reigns in Salem's towers
Shall all the world command.

4 Among the nations He shall judge;
His judgments truth shall guide;
His sceptre shall protect the just,
And quell the sinner's pride.

5 No strife shall rage, nor hostile feuds
Disturb those peaceful years;
To ploughshares men shall beat their swords,
To pruning-hooks their spears.

6 No longer hosts encountering hosts
Shall crowds of slain deplore:
They hang the trumpet in the hall,
And study war no more.

7 Come then, O house of Jacob! come
To worship at His shrine;
And, walking in the light of God,
With holy beauties shine.

Scottish Paraphrases, 1781.

[May be sung to SOUTHWARK, No. 166.]

Jewish Missions (366–369).

366 BABYLON'S STREAMS. (L.M.)

Lah = E. Doh = G. *Moderately slow.* THOMAS CAMPION, *c.* 1575–1619.

:l, | d :r | m :— | — :m | r :d | t, :— | — | t, | d :r | m :-.m | r :r | d :— | — ||
:m, | l, :l, | se, :— | — :l, | l, :l, | se, :— | — | se, | l, :t, | d :-.d | d :t, | d :— | — ||
:d | m :l, | t, :— | — :d | f :m | m :— | — | m | m :s | s :-.s | l :s.f | m :— | — ||
:l, | l, :f, | m, :— | — :l, | r, :l, | m, :— | — | m, | l, :s, | d :-.m, | f, :s, | d :— | — ||

:m | s :m | r :t, | d :r | m :-. | .m | m :-.m | m :r.d | t, :t, | l, :— | — | l, | l, ||
:s, | s, :d | t, :t, | l, :l, | se, :-. | .se, | l, :t, | d :l, | l, :se, | l, :— | — | f, | m, ||
:m | r :d | r :m | m :l, | t, :-. | .t, | d :t, | m :f | t, :m.r | d :— | — | r | de ||
:d | t, :d | s, :s, | l, :f, | m, :-. | .m, | l, :se, | l, :r, | m, :m, | l, :— | — | r, | l, ||

A-men.

GREAT God of Abraham, hear our prayer:
Let Abraham's seed Thy mercy share;
O may they now at length return,
And look on Him they pierced, and mourn!

2 Remember Jacob's flock of old,
Bring home the wanderers to Thy fold;
Remember, too, Thy promised word,
'Israel at last shall seek the Lord.'

3 Lord, put Thy law within their hearts,
And write it in their inward parts;
The veil of darkness rend in two,
Which hides Messiah from their view.

4 O haste the day, foretold so long,
When Jew and Greek, a glorious throng,
One house shall seek, one prayer shall pour,
And one Redeemer shall adore.

THOMAS COTTERILL, 1779–1823.

[May be sung to WALTON, No. 109.]

367 MAINZER. (L.M.)

JOSEPH MAINZER, 1801–51.

Doh = C. *In moderate time.*

:s | s :s | d' :t | l :l | s :l | f :s | m :d' | t :l | s ||
:m | d :r | m :s | f :f | m :m | r :r | m :l | s :fe | s ||
:d' | m' :r' | d' :d' | d' :l.t | d' :l | l :s | s :m' | r' :d' | t ||
:d | d' :t | l :m | f :f | d :de | r :t, | d :l, | r :r | s, ||

:s | s :s | d' :t | l :l | s :s | l :t | d' :m'.r' | d' :t | d' | d' | d' ||
:r | m :f | m :s | s :f | m :m | f :f | m :f | m :r | m | f | m ||
:t | d' :t | d' :d' | d' :l.t | d' :d' | d' :r' | d' :l | s :s | s | l | s ||
:f | m :r | d :m | f :f | d :d | f.m :r | l :f | s :s, | d | f | d ||

A-men.

WHEN Israel, of the Lord beloved,
Out of the land of bondage came,
Her fathers' God before her moved,
An awful guide, in smoke and flame.

2 By day, along the astonished lands
The cloudy pillar glided slow;
By night, Arabia's crimsoned sands
Returned the fiery column's glow.

3 There rose the choral hymn of praise,
And trump and timbrel answered keen,
And Zion's daughters poured their lays,
With priest's and warrior's voice between.

4 No portents now their foes amaze;
Forsaken Israel wanders lone;
Their fathers would not know Thy ways,
And Thou hast left them to their own.

5 But, present still, though now unseen,
When brightly shines the prosperous day,
Be thoughts of Thee a cloudy screen
To temper the deceitful ray.

6 And O, when stoops on Judah's path,
In shade and storm, the frequent night,
Be Thou, long-suffering, slow to wrath,
A burning and a shining light!

WALTER SCOTT, 1771–1832.

368 CHRISTUS DER IST MEIN LEBEN (BREMEN). (76. 76.)

Doh = E♭. *Moderately slow.* MELCHIOR VULPIUS, 1560–1616.

:d	m :r	m :f	s :—	m :l	s :f	m :r	m :—	—	
:s,	d :t,	d :d	t, :—	d :d.r	m :l,.t,	d :t,	d :—	—	
:m	s :s	s :f	r :s	s :l.t	d' :f	s :s	s :—	—	
:d	d :s,	d :l,	s, :—	d :f	m :r	d.m :s	d :—	—	

:s	l :t	d' :t	l :—	s :m	f :m	r :r	d :—	—	d	d
:m	m :r	d :r	m :r.d	t, :d	l,.t, :d	d :t,	d :—	—	l,	s,
:m	fe :s	l :s	s :fe	s :s	f :s	l :s	m :—	—	f	m
:d	d :t,	l, :t,	d :r	s, :d	r :m	f :s	d :—	—	f,	d

A-men.

From Psalm xiv.

O THAT the Lord's salvation
Were out of Zion come,
To heal His ancient nation,
To lead His outcasts home!

2 Let fall Thy rod of terror;
Thy saving grace impart;
Roll back the veil of error;
Release the fettered heart.

3 Let Israel, home returning,
Her lost Messiah see;
Give oil of joy for mourning,
And bind Thy Church to Thee.

HENRY FRANCIS LYTE, 1793–1847.

369 TRURO. (L.M.)

Doh = D. *In moderate time.* Psalmodia Evangelica, 1789.

|d :m.,f |s :-.s |l :t |d' :-.s |d' :s |f .m :r .d
|d :d.,t, |d :-.m |f :f |m :-.t, |d :d |d :t, .d
|m :s.,s |s :-.d' |d' :f |s :-.s |s :s |d' :s
|d :d.,r |m :-.d |f :r |d :-.r |m :m |l .s :f .m

A.t. f.D.

|f :m |r :-. ||r s, |d :r |m :-.f |s .f :m .r |d s :-.s
|t, :d |t, :-. ||t m, |s, :s, |s, :-.l, |s,.l, :s,.f, |m t, :-.t,
|s :s |s :-. ||s d |d :t, |d :-.d |d :d.t, |d s :-.s
|r :d |s, :-. ||s d, |m, :s, |d :-.l, |m,.f, :s, |d s, :-.f

s :d'	r :f	m :r	d :—		f	m	
d :d	d :d	d :t,	d :—		d	d	
s :m	l :l	s :-.f	m :—		l	s	
m :d	f :r	s :s,	d :—		f,	d	

A-men.

ARM of the Lord, awake, awake!
Put on Thy strength, the nations shake,
And let the world, adoring, see
Triumphs of mercy wrought by Thee.

2 Say to the heathen from Thy throne,
'I am Jehovah, God alone';
Thy voice their idols shall confound,
And cast their altars to the ground.

3 Let Zion's time of favour come;
O bring the tribes of Israel home;
And let our wondering eyes behold
Gentiles and Jews in Jesus' fold.

4 Almighty God, Thy grace proclaim
In every clime of every name;
Let adverse powers before Thee fall,
And crown the Saviour Lord of all.

WILLIAM SHRUBSOLE, 1759-1829.

Also the following:

149 O come, O come, Immanuel
150 Come, Thou long-expected Jesus
162 Wake, awake! for night is flying
571 The God of Abraham praise

370 BISHOPGARTH. (87. 87. D.)

Doh = E. *In moderate time.* ARTHUR SEYMOUR SULLIVAN, 1842–1900.

:s, |m :m |m :m |f :-.m |r :r |s :l |m :r.d |r :— |d ||
:s, |d :d |d :d |t, :-.t, |t, :t, |d :d |d :r.d |t, :— |d ||
:s, |s :s |s :s.m |r :-.r |s :s |d :l |s :fe |f :— |m ||
:s, |d :m |s :m.d |s, :-.s, |s, :f, |m, :f, |s, :l, |s, :— |d ||

B.t. f.E.

:s, |m :m |m :^{m}l, |t, :-.l, |s, :s, |d :m |d :t,.l, |t, :— |^{d}s ||
:s, |d :d |d :^{d}f, |f, :-.f, |r, :s, |s, :se, |l, :f, |f, :— |^{m}t, ||
:s, |s :s |s :^{s}d |r :-.d |t, :t, |d :d |d :r |r :— |^{d}s ||
:s, |d :m |s :^{m}l,.f, |r, :-.r, |s, :f, |m, :m, |f, :r, |s, :— |^{d}s, ||

:s |d' :-.t |l :s |f :l |s :f |m :s |f :m.r |d :— |t, ||
:t, |d :-.d |d :d |d :d |t, :r |d :d |d :l, |s, :— |s, ||
:s |s :-.s |d' :s |l :f |r :s |s :ta |l :s.f |m :— |r ||
:s.f |m :-.m |m :m |r :r |s, :t, |d :m, |f, :f, |s, :— |s, ||

:s, |m :m |m :m |f :-.m |r :r |s :l |m :r.d |r :— |d || d |d ||
:s, |d :d |d :d |t, :-.t, |t, :t, |d :d |d :r.d |t, :— |d || l, |s, ||
:s, |s :s |s :s.m |r :-.r |s :s |d :l |s :fe |f :— |m || f |m ||
:s, |d :m |s :m.d |s, :-.s, |s, :f, |m, :f, |s, :l, |s, :— |d || f, |d d, ||

A - men.

[*By permission of Novello & Co., Ltd.*]

'FOR My sake and the Gospel's, go
And tell redemption's story';
His heralds answer, 'Be it so,
And Thine, Lord, all the glory!'
They preach His birth, His life, His Cross,
The love of His atonement
For whom they count the world but loss,
His Easter, His enthronement.

2 Hark! hark! the trump of jubilee
Proclaims to every nation,
From pole to pole, by land and sea,
Glad tidings of salvation;
As nearer draws the day of doom,
While still the battle rages,
The heavenly dayspring, through the gloom,
Breaks on the night of ages.

3 Still on and on the anthems spread
Of hallelujah voices;
In concert with the holy dead,
The warrior Church rejoices;
Their snow-white robes are washed in blood,
Their golden harps are ringing;
Earth and the Paradise of God
One triumph song are singing.

4 He comes whose advent-trumpet drowns
The last of time's evangels,
Immanuel, crowned with many crowns,
The Lord of saints and angels.
O Life, Light, Love, the great I AM
Triune, who changest never,
The throne of God and of the Lamb
Is Thine, and Thine for ever.

EDWARD HENRY BICKERSTETH, 1825–1906.

371 HEBER. (7 6. 7 6. D.)

Doh = E♭. *In moderate time.* LOWELL MASON, 1792–1872.

```
:d  |m  :s  |s  :l  |s  :—  |m  :d  |t, :d  |f    :m |r  :— |— ‖
:d  |d  :r  |d  :d  |d  :t, |d  :s, |s, :d  |l,.t,:d |t, :— |— ‖
:m  |s  :r  |m  :f  |r  :—  |m  :s  |s  :s  |f    :s |s  :— |— ‖
:d  |d  :t, |d  :f, |s, :—  |d  :m  |f  :m  |r    :d |s, :— |— ‖

:d  |m  :s  |s  :l  |s  :—  |m  :r  |m  :l  |s  :fe |s  :— |— ‖
:d  |d  :r  |d  :d  |d  :t, |d  :r  |d  :m  |r  :d  |t, :— |— ‖
:m  |s  :r  |m  :f  |r  :—  |m  :s  |s  :d' |t  :l  |s  :— |— ‖
:d  |d  :t, |d  :f, |s, :—  |d  :t, |d  :l, |r  :r  |s, :— |— ‖

:s  |d' :s  |f  :m  |l  :—  |s  :t  |d' :s  |f  :m  |r  :— |— ‖
:d  |m  :d  |t, :d  |d  :r  |m  :f  |m  :d  |t, :d  |t, :— |— ‖
:m  |s  :m  |f  :s  |l  :t  |d' :s  |s  :m  |f  :s  |s  :— |— ‖
:d  |d  :m  |r  :d  |f  :—  |m  :r  |d  :m  |r  :d  |s, :— |— ‖

:d  |m  :s  |s  :l  |s  :—  |m  :d  |r  :f  |m  :r  |d  :— |— ‖ f  |m ‖
:s, |d  :r  |d  :d  |d  :t, |d  :s, |l, :r  |d  :t, |d  :— |— ‖ d  |d ‖
:m  |s  :r  |m  :f  |r  :—  |m  :s  |f  :l  |s  :f  |m  :— |— ‖ l  |s ‖
:d  |d  :t, |d  :f, |s, :—  |d  :m  |f  :r  |s  :s, |d  :— |— ‖ f, |d ‖
```

A-men.

TALYLLYN. (7 6. 7 6. D.)

Welsh Traditional Melody.

Doh = A♭. *In moderate time.* *D.C.*

```
:s, |d  :t, |l, :d  |t, :l,  |s, :r  |m  :d  |r  :t, |d  :— |— ‖
:s, |s, :s, |f, :s, |s, :fe, |s, :s, |s, :l, |l, :s, |s, :— |— ‖
:s, |m  :m  |d  :d  |r  :d   |t, :t, |d  :m  |f  :r  |m  :— |— ‖
:s, |d, :m, |f, :m, |r, :—   |s, :s, |d  :l, |f, :s, |d, :— |— ‖
```

:d | m :t_1 | d :m | m :— | r :s_1 | t_1 :d | t_1 :l_1 | s_1 :— | — ||
:s_1 | s_1 :s_1 | s_1 :d | d :— | t_1 :s_1 | s_1 :l_1 | s_1 :fe_1 | s_1 :— | — ||
:m | d :r | m :s | s :— | s :t_1 | m :m | r :d | t_1 :— | — ||
:d_1 | d :s_1 | m_1 :d_1 | s_1 :— | s_1 :s_1 | m_1 :l_2 | t_2.d_1 :r_1 | s_1 :— | — ||

:r | m :f | s :d.r | m :— | r :r | m :d | r :t_1 | d :— | — || d | d ||
:s_1 | s_1 :l_1 | s_1 :m_1.f_1 | s_1 :— | s_1 :s_1 | s_1 :d.t_1 | l_1 :s_1 | s_1 :— | — || l_1 | s_1 ||
:s.f | m :d | r :d | d :— | t_1 :t_1 | d :m | f :r | m :— | — || f | m ||
:t_1 | d :d | t_1 :l_1 | s_1 :— | s_1 :s_1 | d :l_1 | f_1 :s_1 | d_1 :— | — || f_1 | d_1 ||

A-men.

FROM Greenland's icy mountains,
From India's coral strand,
Where Afric's sunny fountains
Roll down their golden sand,
From many an ancient river,
From many a palmy plain,
They call us to deliver
Their land from error's chain.

2 Can we, whose souls are lighted
With wisdom from on high,
Can we to men benighted
The lamp of life deny ?
Salvation ! O salvation !
The joyful sound proclaim,
Till each remotest nation
Has learnt Messiah's Name.

3 Waft, waft, ye winds, His story,
And you, ye waters, roll,
Till, like a sea of glory,
It spreads from pole to pole ;
Till o'er our ransomed nature
The Lamb for sinners slain,
Redeemer, King, Creator,
In bliss returns to reign.

Reginald Heber, 1783–1826.

372 LITTLE CORNARD. (66. 66. 88.)

Unison, vv. 1, 3, 5. *Harmony*, vv. 2 & 4. MARTIN SHAW, 1876–

Lah=C. Doh=E♭. *With vigour.*

```
| l, :d .r | m :m | l :— | s :m .d | r :m | l, :— ||
| l, :d .r | m :m | d :r | m :d .d | l, :se, | l, :— ||
| l, :d .r | m :m | l :t | d' :s .m | r :t, | d :— ||
| l, :d .r | m :m | f :— | d :d .d | f, :m, | l, :— ||
```

B♭.t. G minor. Lulled be your f. E♭.

```
| d f :m .r | d :t, | m :— | m :l,.t, | d :t, | l m :— | — || t, | d :r | m :s
| m l, :l,.l, | l, :se, | l, :d | l, :f, | m, :se, | l m :— | — || se, | l, :t, | d :t,
                     Lulled   be
                              Lulled be your
| l r :m .f | m :m | m :— | m :m .r | l, :t, | de se :— | — || m | m :s | s :s
| l r :d .r | m :r | d :l, | f, :r, | m, :m, | l m :— | — || m, | l, :s, | d :m
                       Lulled be
```

```
| l :-.s | m :r | m :s | d' :s | m :— | — :r | d :— | — :— || d | d ||
| l, :t, | d :s, | d :r | d :t, | l, :— | t, :— | d :— | — :— || l, | s, ||
| m :r | m :s | s :s | m :s | d' :— | s :— | m :— | — :— || f | m ||
| d :t, | l, :t, | d :t, | l, :m, | f, :— | s, :— | d/d, :— | — :— || f, | d ||
```

[*Copyright*, 1915, *by J. Curwen & Sons, Ltd.*] A-men.

HILLS of the North, rejoice:
River and mountain-spring,
Hark to the advent voice!
Valley and lowland, sing!
Though absent long, your Lord is nigh,
He judgment brings, and victory.

2 Isles of the Southern seas,
Deep in your coral caves
Pent be each warring breeze,
Lulled be your restless waves:
He comes to reign with boundless sway,
And make your wastes His great highway.

3 Lands of the East, awake!
Soon shall your sons be free,
The sleep of ages break,
And rise to liberty:
On your far hills, long cold and grey,
Has dawned the everlasting day.

4 Shores of the utmost West,
Ye that have waited long,
Unvisited, unblest,
Break forth to swelling song;
High raise the note, that Jesus died,
Yet lives and reigns—the Crucified!

5 Shout while ye journey home!
Songs be in every mouth!—
Lo, from the North we come,
From East, and West, and South:
City of God, the bond are free;
We come to live and reign in thee.

CHARLES EDWARD OAKLEY, 1832–65.

373 DUNBLANE CATHEDRAL. (10 10. 10 10.)

ARCHIE FAIRBAIRN BARNES, 1878–

Doh = C. *In moderate time.*

```
                                                    G.t.
d'  :t .l  |s  :- .s |s .d' :t .l |s  :—   ||m l,  :l, .l,  |l, .r  :d .t,  |
d'  :t .l  |s  :- .s |s .d' :t .l |s  :—   ||m l,  :l, .s,  |f, .l, :se,    |
d'  :t .l  |s  :- .s |s .d' :t .l |s  :—   ||s d   :de .de  |r .f   :m .r   |
d'  :t .l  |s  :- .s |s .d' :t .l |s  :—   ||d f, .s, :f, .m, |r,   :m,     |

                      f.C.
l, .f  :m .r    |d   :—  ||r l    :s .f  |m     :r .m    |f .s :l .d'    |d'  :t     ||
l, .d  :t, .t,  |s,  :—  ||s r    :de .r |m .de :l,      |r .r :r .l     |s   :- .f  ||
d .l   :s .f    |m   :—  ||r l    :l .l  |l     :l       |l .l :r' .r'   |m'  :r'    ||
f, .r, :s, .s,  |d   :—  ||d s .f :m .r  |de .l, :t, .de |r .m :f .fe    |s   :- .se ||

d'  :t .l    |s .m :s .l   |d'  :r'    |d'  :—  ||d' |d' ||
m   :m .f    |d .d :d .f   |m   :f     |m   :—  ||f  |m  ||
d'  :d' .d'  |s .s :s .d'  |d'  :d' .t |d'  :—  ||l  |s  ||
l   :s .f    |m .d :m .f   |s   :s,    |d   :—  ||f  |d  ||
                                                  A-men.
```

[*Copyright*, 1927, *by Oxford University Press.*]

FAR round the world Thy children sing their song:
From East and West their voices sweetly blend,
Praising the Lord in whom young lives are strong,
Jesus our Guide, our Hero, and our Friend.

2 Where Thy wide ocean, wave on rolling wave,
Beats through the ages, on each island shore,
They praise their Lord, whose hand alone can save,
Whose sea of love surrounds them evermore.

3 Thy sun-kissed children on earth's spreading plain,
Where Asia's rivers water all the land,
Sing, as they watch Thy fields of glowing grain,
Praise to the Lord who feeds them with His hand.

4 Still there are lands where none have seen Thy face,
Children whose hearts have never shared Thy joy;
Yet Thou wouldst pour on these Thy radiant grace,
Give Thy glad strength to every girl and boy.

5 All round the world let children sing Thy song:
From East and West their voices sweetly blend,
Praising the Lord in whom young lives are strong,
Jesus our Guide, our Hero, and our Friend.

BASIL JOSEPH MATHEWS, 1879–

374

MORNING. (77. 77.)

Doh = G. *In moderate time.* SAMUEL SEBASTIAN WESLEY, 1810–76.

m :r :d	d :t, :d	r :m :r	d :— :—	s :f :m	m :r :d
s, :— :s,	s, :— :d	d :— :t,	d :— :—	d :t, :d	d :t, :s,
s :f :m	m :r :s	l :s :f	m :— :—	s :— :s	s :— :s
d :— :d	s, :f, :m,	f, :s, :s,	d :— :—	m :r :d	s, :— :m,

t, :d :l,	s, :— :—		s, :d :t,	t, :— :l,	r :de :m	r :— :—
s, :l, :fe,	s, :— :—		s, :— :s,	s, :— :f,	f, :m, :s,	f, :— :—
r :m :d	t, :— :—		t, :d :d	d :— :d	l, :— :l,	l, :— :—
r, :d, :r,	s, :— :—		s, :m, :d,	f, :— :f,	l, :— :l,	r, :— :—

r :m :f	s :— :s	f :m :r	d :— :—		d	d	
s, :— :s,	s, :t, :d	d :— :t,	d :— :—		l,	s,	
t, :d :r	m :f :s	l :s :-.f	m :— :—		f	m	
f, :m, :r,	d, :r, :m,	f, :s, :s,	d, :— :—		f,	d,	

A-men.

ONCE again, dear Lord, we pray
For the children far away,
Who have never even heard
Name of Jesus, sweetest word.

2 Little lips that Thou hast made,
'Neath the far-off temple's shade
Give to gods of wood and stone
Praise that should be all Thine own.

3 Little hands, whose wondrous skill
Thou hast given to do Thy will,
Offerings bring, and serve with fear
Gods that cannot see or hear.

4 Teach them, O Thou heavenly King,
All their gifts and praise to bring
To Thy Son, who died to prove
Thy forgiving, saving love.

MARY JANE WILLCOX, 1835–1919.

375

SEFTON. (87. 87.)

Doh = E♭. *In moderate time.* HOWARD AUGUSTUS CROSBIE, 1844–1918.

s :m	d' :t	t :l	s :d	f :m	r :d	t, :d	r :—	
d :d	d :s	s :f	s :s,	d :d	l, :l,	s, :fe,	s, :—	
m :s	s :d'	d' :d'	d' :m	f :s	f :m	r :r	r :s	
d :d	m :m	f :f	m :d	l, :d	f, :f,	s, :l,	t, :—	

s :m	d' :t	t :l	s :f	m :s	d :r	m :r	d :—		f	m	
t, :d	d :r	m :t,	d :r	d :s,	l, :d	d :t,	d :—		d	d	
s :s	l :s	s :f	m :s	s :d	l :f	s :f	m :—		l	s	
m :d	l, :t,	d :r	m :t,	d :m,	f, :l,	s, :s,	d :—		f,	d	

A-men.

GOD of heaven, hear our singing;
Only little ones are we,
Yet, a great petition bringing,
Father, now we come to Thee.

2 Let Thy Kingdom come, we pray Thee;
Let the world in Thee find rest;
Let all know Thee, and obey Thee,
Loving, praising, blessing, blest.

3 Let the sweet and joyful story,
Of the Saviour's wondrous love,
Wake on earth a song of glory,
Like the angels' song above.

4 Father, send the glorious hour,
Every heart be Thine alone,
For the Kingdom, and the power,
And the glory are Thine own.

Frances Ridley Havergal, 1836–79.

376 HAMPTON. (S.M.)

Williams' Psalmody, 1770 (?).

Doh = D. *Moderately slow.*

:s | m .l :s :t | d' :— :d' | t .d' :t :l | s :— ||
:d | d .d :d :f | m :— :m | r .m :r :r .d | t, :— ||
:m | s .f :s :s | s :— :s | s .s :s :fe | s :— ||
:d | d .f :m :r | d :— :d | s .d :r :r | s, :— ||

:m | f .s :l :s | f .m :r :s | d'.f :m :r | d :— || f | m ||
:d | d .d :d :t, | d .d :t, :r | s,.d :d :t, | d :— || d | d ||
:s | f .m :f :r | l .s :s :t | d'.l :s :s .f | m :— || l | s ||
:d | l, .d :f, :s, | l, .d :s, :s .f | m .f :s :s, | d :— || f, | d ||

A-men.

O LORD our God, arise!
The cause of truth maintain,
And wide o'er all the peopled world
Extend her blessèd reign.

2 Thou Prince of Life, arise!
Nor let Thy glory cease;
Far spread the conquests of Thy grace,
And bless the earth with peace.

3 Thou Holy Ghost, arise!
Expand Thy quickening wing,
And o'er a dark and ruined world
Let light and order spring.

4 All on the earth, arise!
To God the Saviour sing;
From shore to shore, from earth to heaven,
Let echoing anthems ring.

Ralph Wardlaw, 1779–1853.

377 DIR, DIR JEHOVAH. (9 10. 9 10. 10 10.)

Doh = B♭. *Slow.* *Freylinghausen's Gesangbuch,* 1704.

:s, | d :s, | l, :l, | s, :f, | m, :d, || :r, | m, :fe, | s, :l,
:m, | s, :m, | d, :f, | r, :d,.r, | d, :d, || :t,, | d, :r, | r, :fe,
:d | s, :d.t, | l, :r | s, :l, | s, :m, || :s, | s, :l, | s, :r
:d, | m, :d, | f, :r, | t,, :l,, t,, | d, :d, || :s, | d, :d, | t,, :r,

D.C.

t, :d | t, :l, | s, || s, | d :r | m :d | f :f | m :m | r
s, :s, | s, :fe, | s, || r, | s, :f, | m, :s, | f, :l, | s, :s,.l, | t,
r :m | r :r.d | t, || t, | s, :t, | d :s, | d :d | d.r :m.fe | s
s, :d, | r, :r, | s, s,, || s,.f, | m, :r, | d, :m, | l, :f, | d :d, | s,

:m | r :d | t, :l, | s, :d | d :t, | d || d | d
:d | t, :l, | s, :f, | f, :m, | l, :s,.f, | m, || f, | m,
:s | s :m | m :d | t, :d | r :r | d || l, | s,
:d | s, :l, | m, :f, | s, :l, | f, :s, | d, || f, | d,

A-men.

Wach auf, du Geist der ersten Zeugen.

WAKE, Spirit, who in times now olden
Didst fire the watchmen of the Church's youth,
And 'gainst their every foe embolden,
To witness day and night the eternal truth;
Whose voices through the world are ringing still,
And bringing hosts to know and do Thy will.

2 Soon may that fire from heaven be lent us,
That swift from land to land its flame may leap!
Soon, Lord, that priceless boon be sent us,
Of faithful servants, fit for Thee to reap
The harvest of the soul; look down and view
How great the harvest, but the labourers few.

MISSIONS

Alternative setting for Choir (v. 3), the Congregation to sing the melody only.

Doh = B♭.

:s_1 | d :s_1 | l_1 :l_1 | s_1 :f_1 | m_1 :d_1 ‖ :r_1 | m_1 :fe_1
:m_1 | s_1.f_1 :m_1.r_1 | d_1 :r_1.m_1 | f_1.m_1 :-.r_1 | d_1 :d_1 ‖ :t_2 | d_1.m_1 :r_1.d_1
:d | s_1 :d.t_1 | l_1 :t_1.d | r.d :-.s_1 | s_1 :m_1 ‖ :s_1 | s_1 :l_1
:d_1 | m_1.r_1 :d_1 | f_1.m_1 :r_1.d_1 | t_2.d_1 :l_2.t_2 | d_1 :d_1 ‖ :s_2 | d_1 :t_2.l_2

D.C.

s_1 :l_1 | t_1 :d | t_1 :l_1 | s_1 (fermata) ‖ s_1 | d :r | m :d | f :f
r_1.s_1 :fe_1.m_1 | r_1 :s_1.l_1 | l_1.s_1 :-.fe_1 | s_1 ‖ r_1 | s_1 :-.f_1 | m_1 :d.t_1 | l_1.s_1 :f_1
r_1.r :- .d | t_1 :m | r :d | t_1 ‖ t_1 | m.r :d.t_1 | d :m | l_1 :-.t_1
t_2 :r_1 | s_1.fe_1 :m_1.l_2 | t_2.d_1 :r_1 | s_2 ‖ s_1.f_1 | m_1 :s_1 | d.t_1 :l_1.s_1 | f_1.m_1 :r_1

m :m | r (fermata) ‖ m | r :d | t_1 :l_1 | s_1 :d | d :t_1 | d (fermata) ‖
s_1.l_1 :s_1.fe_1 | s_1 ‖ s_1 | f_1 :m_1 | f_1.s_1 :l_1.f_1 | r_1 :s_1.m_1 | f_1.l_1 :s_1.f_1 | m_1
d :t_1.d | r ‖ d | l_1.t_1 :d.m | r :d | t_1 :d | l_1.f :r | d
m_1.fe_1 :s_1.l_1 | t_1 ‖ d.m_1 | f_1.s_1 :l_1.d_1 | r_1.m_1 :f_1.r_1 | s_1.f_1 :m_1.l_1 | f_1.r_1 :s_1.s_2 | d_1

3 Lord, to our earnest prayer now hearken,
The prayer we offer at Thy Son's command;
For, lo! while storms around us darken,
Thy children's hearts are stirred in every land,
To cry for help, with fervent soul, to Thee;
O hear us, Lord, and speak: 'Thus let it be!'

4 O speedily that help be granted!
Send forth evangelists, in spirit strong,
Armed with Thy word, a host undaunted,
Bold to attack the rule of ancient wrong;
And let them all the earth for Thee reclaim,
To be Thy Kingdom and to know Thy Name!

CARL HEINRICH BOGATZKY, 1690–1774; *tr.* by CATHERINE WINKWORTH, 1829–78.

378 DEERHURST. (8 7. 8 7. D.)

Doh = E♭. *In moderate time.* JAMES LANGRAN, 1835–1909.

m :s | m :d | t_1 :d | r :m | f :m | r :s | t :l | s :—
d :r | d :s_1 | s_1 :s_1 | s_1 :s_1 | d :d.t_1 | l_1 :r | r :d | t_1 :—
s :s | s :s | f :m | r :d | l :s | fe :s | s :fe | s :—
d :t_1 | d :m | r :d | t_1 :d | d :d | d :t_1 | r :r | s_1 :—

m :s | m :d | t_1 :d | r :m | f :m | l :s | m :r | d :—
d :r | d :s_1 | s_1 :s_1 | s_1 :s_1 | d :d | d :d | d :t_1 | d :—
s :s | s :s | f :m | r :d | d :m | f :s | s :f | m :—
d :t_1 | d :m | r :d | t_1 :d | l_1 :s_1 | f_1 :m_1 | s_1 :s_1 | d :—

m :s | d' :l | s :d | f :m | r :m | s :f | d :r | m :—
d :t_1 | d :d | d :d | t_1 :d | r :de | r :r | d :l_1 | t_1 :—
s :s | s :f | s :s | s :s | l :l | l :l | l :l | se :—
d :r | m :f | m :m | r :d | f :m | r :r | f :f | m :—

m :s | d' :l | s :d | f :m | r :m | s :f | l_1 :t_1 | d :— || d | d
d :r | d :d | d :d | t_1 :d | r :de | r :l_1 | l_1 :s_1 | s_1 :— || l_1 | s_1
l :s.f | m :f | s :s | s :s | l :l | l :r | r :f | m :— || f | m
l_1 :t_1 | d :f | m :m | r :d | f :m | r :r.m_1 | f_1 :s_1 | d d_1 :— || f_1 | d

A-men.

[*By permission of Novello & Co., Ltd.*]

LORD, her watch Thy Church is keeping;
When shall earth Thy rule obey?
When shall end the night of weeping,
When shall break the promised day?
See the whitening harvest languish,
Waiting still the labourers' toil;
Was it vain, Thy Son's deep anguish?
Shall the strong retain the spoil?

2 Tidings, sent to every creature,
Millions yet have never heard;
Can they hear without a preacher?
Lord Almighty, give the word.
Give the word; in every nation
Let the gospel trumpet sound,
Witnessing a world's salvation,
To the earth's remotest bound.

3 Then the end,—Thy Church completed,
All Thy chosen gathered in,
With their King in glory seated,
Satan bound, and banished sin,
Gone for ever parting, weeping,
Hunger, sorrow, death, and pain.
Lo! her watch Thy Church is keeping;
Come, Lord Jesus, come to reign.

HENRY DOWNTON, 1818–85.

379 ZURICH. (77. 77. 77.)

Doh = G. *Moderately slow.* *Weimar Gesangbuch*, 1681.

```
|d  :d  |t,  :s,  |l,  :t,  |d  :— ||m  :m  |f  :f  |m  :m  |r  :— ||
|s, :s, |s,  :s,  |f,  :f,  |s, :— ||s, :s, |l, :l, |s, :s, |s, :— ||
|m  :m  |r   :m   |d   :r   |m  :— ||d  :d  |d  :d  |d  :d  |t, :— ||
|d  :d  |s,  :m,  |f,  :r,  |d, :— ||d  :d  |f, :f, |d,.r, :m,.f, |s, :— ||

|m  :f  |s   :d    |t,  :d      |r  :—  ||m  :m  |r  :r      |d    :d    |t,  :— ||
|s, :d  |d .t, :l, |s,  :s,.fe, |s, :—  ||s, :s, |l, :s,.f,  |m,   :l,   |se, :— ||
|d  :d  |d   :f .m |r   :d      |d  :t, ||d  :d  |d  :t,     |d .t, :d .r |m  :— ||
|d  :l, |m,  :f,   |s,  :l,     |s, :—  ||d  :m, |f, :s,     |l,   :l,   |m,  :— ||

|d  :d  |r  :r  |m      :m     |f  :— ||m      :m      |r     :d  |d    :t,   |d  :— ||d  |d  ||
|l, :l, |t, :t, |d      :d .ta,|l, :— ||s,     :s,     |s,.f, :m, |l,   :s,   |s, :— ||l, |s, ||
|m  :m  |s  :s  |s      :d     |d  :— ||d      :d      |t,    :d  |f.m  :r.f  |m  :— ||f  |m  ||
|l, :l, |s, :s, |d.ta,  :l,.s, |f, :— ||d,.r,  :m,.f,  |s,    :l, |f,   :s,   |d, :— ||f, |d, ||
                                                                                    A-men.
```

From Psalm lxvii.

GOD of mercy, God of grace,
Show the brightness of Thy face;
Shine upon us, Saviour, shine,
Fill Thy Church with light divine,
And Thy saving health extend
Unto earth's remotest end.

2 Let the people praise Thee, Lord;
Be by all that live adored;
Let the nations shout and sing
Glory to their Saviour King,
At Thy feet their tribute pay,
And Thy holy will obey.

3 Let the people praise Thee, Lord;
Earth shall then her fruits afford,
God to man His blessing give,
Man to God devoted live—
All below and all above,
One in joy and light and love.

HENRY FRANCIS LYTE, 1793–1847.

[May be sung to HEATHLANDS, No. 509.]

380 ALVESTON. (Irr.)

Doh = G. *Unison.* *In moderate time.* BASIL HARWOOD, 1859-

| s, :d.t, | l, :t,.d | r :r | s, :s,.s, | s :m.m | f.m:f.s | m :— | — :— (: m.m) ||

| m :d.d | r :m.r | d :r.r | t, :m.m | t, :m.m | s.fe:m.re | m :— | — :— (: m) ||

| s :m.m | f :s | m.r:d.r | m :d | l, :d.d | f :m | r :— | — :s,.s,

| l, :t,.d | r :t,.s, | s :m.d | l :s.s, | l, :d | f.l, :d.t, | d :— | — :— || d f, l, f, | d m, s, d, ||

A-men.

GOD is working His purpose out, as year succeeds to year :
God is working His purpose out, and the time is drawing near—
Nearer and nearer draws the time—the time that shall surely be,
When the earth shall be filled with the glory of God, as the waters cover the sea.

2 From utmost east to utmost west, where'er man's foot hath trod,
By the mouth of many messengers goes forth the voice of God ;
Give ear to Me, ye continents—ye isles, give ear to Me,
That the earth may be filled with the glory of God, as the waters cover the sea.

3 What can we do to work God's work, to prosper and increase
The brotherhood of all mankind—the reign of the Prince of Peace ?
What can we do to hasten the time—the time that shall surely be,
When the earth shall be filled with the glory of God, as the waters cover the sea ?

4 March we forth in the strength of God, with the banner of Christ unfurled,
That the light of the glorious Gospel of truth may shine throughout the world :
Fight we the fight with sorrow and sin, to set their captives free,
That the earth may be filled with the glory of God, as the waters cover the sea.

5 All we can do is nothing worth, unless God blesses the deed ;
Vainly we hope for the harvest-tide, till God gives life to the seed ;
Yet nearer and nearer draws the time—the time that shall surely be,
When the earth shall be filled with the glory of God, as the waters cover the sea.

ARTHUR CAMPBELL AINGER, 1841–1919.

381 BROMSGROVE. (C.M.)

Psalmodia Evangelica, 1789.

Doh = B♭. *Moderately fast.*

```
                                                          v. 1. Star   of the
d  :— |d  :s, |l, :-.t,|d  :f  |m  :r |d  :t, |d  :— |— || d  | r  :— |m  :d
m, :— |m, :s, |f, :—   |s, :l, |s, :— |s, :— |s, :— |— || s, | s, :— |s, :l,
d  :— |d  :d  |d  :—   |—  :d  |d  :f |m  :r  |m  :— |— || m  | r  :— |d  :m
d, :— |d, :m, |f, :—   |m, :f, |s, :— |s, :— |d, :— |— || d, | t,, :— |d, :d,

                                         v. 3. To   the bright
t, :— |l,  :— |s, :— |— || r  | r  :— |— :r  |m  :— |d  :— |l, :— |r  :—
s, :— |fe, :— |s, :— |— || s, | s, :— |— :s, |s, :— |s, :— |f, :— |f, :—
r  :— |—   :d |t, :— |— || t, | r  :— |— :t, |d  :— |d  :— |d  :— |r  :—
r, :— |r,  :— |s, :— |— || s, | t, :— |— :s, |d  :— |m, :— |f, :— |r, :—

d  :—  |t, || r  | m  :d  |f  :r  |d  :— |t, :—  |d  :— |— :— || d  | d
m, :fe,|s, || s, | s, :—  |f, :l, |s, :— |s, :f, |m, :— |— :— || f  | m,
m  :—  |r  || t, | d  :—  |l, :r  |m  :— |r  :—  |d  :— |— :— || l, | s,
s, :—  |—  || s, | d, :m, |r, :f, |s, :— |s, :—  |d, :— |— :— || f, | d,
                                                                 A-men.
```

LIGHT of the lonely pilgrim's heart,
Star of the coming day,
Arise, and with Thy morning beams
Chase all our griefs away.

2 Come, blessèd Lord, bid every shore
And answering island sing
The praises of Thy royal Name,
And own Thee as their King.

3 Bid the whole earth, responsive now
To the bright world above,
Break forth in rapturous strains of joy,
In memory of Thy love.

4 Lord, Lord, Thy fair creation groans—
The air, the earth, the sea—
In unison with all our hearts,
And calls aloud for Thee.

5 Thine was the Cross, with all its fruits
Of grace and peace divine ;
Be Thine the crown of glory now,
The palm of victory Thine.

EDWARD DENNY, 1796–1889.

382 CONTEMPLATION. (87. 87. D.)

Doh = B♭. *In moderate time.* FELIX MENDELSSOHN-BARTHOLDY, 1809–47.

```
|s, :s,   |l,    :s,  |d   :m.r  |d  :t,  |l,     :t,    |d  :f   |m   :r    |d  :— ||
|m, :s,   |f,.m, :r,  |d,  :l,   |s, :s,  |s,.fe, :s,    |s, :f,  |s,  :s,   |s, :— ||
|d  :d    |d     :t,  |s   :s.f  |m  :r   |r      :r     |d  :d   |d   :t,.f |m  :— ||
|d, :m,   |f,    :f,  |m,  :f,   |s, :s,  |r,     :s,.f, |m, :l,  |s,  :s,   |d, :— ||

|s, :s,   |l, :s,  |d  :m.r  |d  :t,  |l, :t,  |d  :f     |m     :r     |d  :— ||
|s, :m,   |f, :f,  |m, :l,   |l, :se, |m, :se, |l, :l,    |s,    :-.f,  |m, :— ||
|m  :m.r  |d  :r   |d  :d.r  |m  :m   |m  :r   |d  :l,.t, |d     :t,    |d  :— ||
|d  :ta,  |l, :t,  |d  :f,   |m, :m,  |d  :t,  |l, :r,    |m,.f, :s,    |l, :— ||

F.t.
|(r)s     :f      |m :m    |f  :m    |r  :m   |d  :r  |m :m    |d  :t,   |l, :— ||
|(r,)s,   :l,     |s, :d   |d  :d.t, |l, :t,  |l, :t, |d :d    |l, :se,  |l, :— ||
|(l,)r    :d.r    |m :s    |f  :s    |l  :se  |m  :f  |m :m.f  |m  :-.r  |d  :— ||
|(fe,)t,  :l,.t,  |d :d.t, |l, :s,   |f, :m,  |l, :r  |d :d.r  |m  :m,   |l, :— ||

f.B♭.
|d  :r    |m :(d)s,     |d  :r      |m     :d   |d   :t,.l,  |s,  :d      |m  :r     |d  :— ||d  |d  ||
|l, :t,   |d :(s)r,     |s, :l,.t,  |d.ta, :l,  |f,  :s,.f,  |m,  :s,.l,  |s, :-.f,  |m, :— ||f, |m, ||
|m  :s.f  |m :(m)t,     |d  :f      |m     :f   |d   :r      |m   :d      |d  :t,    |d  :— ||l, |s, ||
|l, :s,   |d :(d)s,.f,  |m, :r,     |d,    :f,  |l,, :t,,    |d,  :m,.f,  |s, :s,    |d, :— ||f, |d, ||
                                                                                        A-men.
```

SAVIOUR, sprinkle many nations,
 Fruitful let Thy sorrows be;
By Thy pains and consolations
 Draw the Gentiles unto Thee.
Of Thy Cross the wondrous story,
 Be it to the nations told;
Let them see Thee in Thy glory
 And Thy mercy manifold.

2 Far and wide, though all unknowing,
 Pants for Thee each mortal breast;
Human tears for Thee are flowing,
 Human hearts in Thee would rest.
Thirsting, as for dews of even,
 As the new-mown grass for rain,
Thee they seek as God of heaven,
 Thee as Man for sinners slain.

3 Saviour, lo! the isles are waiting,
 Stretched the hand and strained the sight,
For Thy Spirit, new-creating,
 Love's pure flame and wisdom's light;
Give the word, and of the preacher
 Speed the foot and touch the tongue,
Till on earth by every creature
 Glory to the Lamb be sung.

ARTHUR CLEVELAND COXE, 1818–96.

383 CATHCART. (L.M.)

Doh = G. *In moderate time.* WILLIAM HENRY BELL, 1873-

s, :d .r	m .,m :m .m	l :—	s :m .r	d .,d :d .t,	l, :—	
s, :s,.s,	d .,d :t,.t,	l, :—	d :d .t,	l,.,l, :s,.s,	s, :f,	
m :m .m	m .,m :m .m	m :r	s :s .f	m .,m :m .r	d :—	
d :d .t,	l,.,l, :s,.s,	f, :—	m, :s,.s,	l,.,l, :m,.m,	f, :—	

.s, :d .r	m .,m :m .m	l .s :f .m :r .l,	r :-.d	d :—	d	d	
.s, :l,.t,	d .,d :r .r	d .d :d .d :l,.f,	l, :s,.s,	s, :—	l,	s,	
.d :m .s	s .,s :se.se	l .ta :l .s :f .r	d :t,.m	m :—	f	m	
.m, :l,.s,	d .,d :t,.t,	l,.d :f .d :r .r,	s, :-.d,	d, :—	f,	d,	

A - men.

FLING out the banner! let it float
Skyward and seaward, high and wide
The sun that lights its shining folds,
The Cross on which the Saviour died.

2 Fling out the banner! angels bend
In anxious silence o'er the sign,
And vainly seek to comprehend
The wonder of the love divine.

3 Fling out the banner! heathen lands
Shall see from far the glorious sight,
And nations, crowding to be born,
Baptize their spirits in its light.

4 Fling out the banner! let it float
Skyward and seaward, high and wide,
Our glory, only in the Cross,
Our only hope, the Crucified.

5 Fling out the banner! wide and high,
Seaward and skyward let it shine:
Nor skill, nor might, nor merit ours;
We conquer only in that sign.

GEORGE WASHINGTON DOANE, 1799-1859.

[May be sung to GONFALON ROYAL, No 23.]

384 GWALIA. (87. 87. D.)

Doh = F. *In moderate time.* Welsh Hymn Melody.

m :— :f	s,–,f :m :r	d :— :r	m,–,r :m :—	f :m :r
d :— :d	r :d :t,	l, :— :t,	d,–,t, :d :—	d :— :d
s :— :f	r :s :f	m :— :s	s :s :—	l :— :l
d :— :l,	t, :d :s,	l, :— :s,	d :d :—	f, :— :f,

D.C.

s,–,f :m :r	d :— :t,	d :— :—		s :— :s,–,m	s :— :s,l,ta
d :–.t, :l,	s, :— :s,	s, :— :—		d :— :d	r :— :d
s :d :f	m :r :s.f	m :— :—		s :— :m,–,s	s :–.f :m
m, :l, :f,	s, :— :s,	d :— :—		m :— :d	t, :— :d

l,–,s :f :m	m :r :—	s :— :s,–,m	s :— :s,l,ta	l,–,s :f :m
d :— :d	d :t, :—	t, :— :d	r :— :d	d :–.t, :d
f,–,s :l :l	s :s :—	s :— :m,–,s	s :–.f :m	f :— :s
f, :— :fe,	s, :s, :—	m :— :d	t, :— :d	f,–,m :r :d

r :— :—		m :— :f	s,–,f :m :r	d :— :r	m,–,r :m :—
t, :— :—		d :— :d	r :d :t,	l, :— :l,	l, :se, :—
s :— :—		s :— :f	r :s :f	m :— :l,	d :t, :—
s, :— :—		d :— :l,	t, :d :s,	l, :— :f,	m, :m, :—

f :m :r	s,–,f :m :r	d :— :t,	d :— :—		d	d	
l, :— :l,.t,	d :–.t, :l,	s, :— :s,	s, :— :—		l,	s,	
t, :d :r	m,–,f :s :f	m :r :s.f	m :— :—		f	m	
r, :m, :f,	m, :d, :f,	s, :— :s,	d, :— :—		f,	d d,	

A - men.

Marchog, Iesu, yn llwyddiannus.

ONWARD march, all-conquering Jesus,
Gird Thee on Thy mighty sword!
Sinful earth can ne'er oppose Thee;
Hell itself quails at Thy word.
Thy great Name is so exalted,
Every foe shrinks back in fear;
Terror creeps through all creation,
When it knows that Thou art near.

2 Free my soul from sin's foul bondage;
Hasten now the glorious dawn;
Break proud Babel's gates in sunder;
Let the massive bolts be drawn.
Forth, like ocean's heaving surges,
Bring in myriads ransomed slaves,
Host on host, with shouts of triumph,
Endless, countless as the waves.

3 Even to-day I hear sweet music,
Praises of a blood-freed throng:
Full deliverance, glorious freedom,
Are their themes for endless song;
Whiter than the snow their raiment,
Victor palms they wave on high,
As they pass, with fullest glory,
Into life's felicity.

4 How my raptured soul rejoices
That the jubilee is near;
Every word will be accomplished,
Spoken by our Saviour here.
North and South, in countless myriads,
From earth's darkest ends they come,
With the dance and gladsome music,
Into heaven's eternal home.

WILLIAM WILLIAMS, 1717–91; *tr.* by WILLIAM HOWELLS, 1855– .

[May be sung to MORIAH, No. 435.]

385 WARWICK. (C.M.)

Doh = D. *Moderately slow.* SAMUEL STANLEY, 1767–1822.

```
:d |m.s:d'.l |s :f.l |s.m:r |d :m.fe |s :l.d' |t.l :s.fe |s :— |— ||
:d |d :d |d :d.f |m.d:t, |d :d |r :m |r :r |t, :— |— ||
:m |s.m:s.l |d' :d' |d'.s:s.f |m :l |s :m |s.d':t.l |s :— |— ||
:d |d :m.f |m :l.f |s :s, |d :l, |t, :d.l, |r :r |s, :— |— ||

:s |l.f:d'.l |s :m |f.r:s.f |m :s |l.t:d'.r' |d' :t |d' :— |— || d' |d' ||
:d |d :f |s :d |r :r |d :d |d.f:m.r |m :r |m :— |— || f |m ||
:m |f.l:l.d' |d' :l |l.f:s |s :s |f :s.l |s :s |s :— |— || l |s ||
:d |f :l.f |m :l |r :t, |d :m |f.r:m.f |s :s, |d :— |— || f |d ||
```

A-men.

WINCHESTER. (C.M.)

Doh = F. *In moderate time.* *Este's Psalter*, 1592.

```
|d :— |m :-.m |r :d |f :f |m :— ||r :— |m :s |s :fe |s :— ||
|s, :— |d :-.d |t, :l, |l, :d |d :— ||t, :— |d :t, |r :r |t, :— ||
|m :— |s :-.s |s :m |f :l |s :— ||s :— |s :s |l :l |s :— ||
|d :— |d :-.d |s, :l, |f, :f, |d :— ||s, :— |d :m |r :r |s, :— ||

|m :— |l :-.s |f :m |r :d |t, :— ||m :— |r :d |d :t, |d :— ||d |d ||
|d :— |d :-.d |d :d |t, :l, |se, :— ||s, :— |t, :l, |l, :s, |s, :— ||l, |s, ||
|s :— |f :-.m |f :s |s :m |m :— ||m :— |s :m |f :r |m :— ||f |m ||
|d :— |f :-.d |l, :d |s, :l, |m, :— ||d :— |s, :l, |f, :s, |d :— ||f, |d, ||
```

A-men.

FAUX-BOURDON SETTING.

Doh = F. GEORGE KIRBYE, ? –1634.

```
|m :— |m :-.s |f :m |r :r |de :— ||f :— |m :r |r :-.r |r :— ||
|l, :— |d :-.s, |l, :l, |l, :l, |l, :— ||l, :— |l, :t, |l, :l, |t, :— ||
|d :— |m :-.m |r :d |f :f |m :— ||r :— |m :s |s :fe |s :— ||
|l, :— |l, :-.m, |f, :l, |r, :r, |l, :— ||r :— |d :t, |r :r |s, :— ||

|s :— |f :-.m |l :s |s :m |m :— ||s :— |s :m |f :r |m :— ||
|d :— |d :-.d |d :d |t, :l, |se, :— ||d :— |t, :l, |l, :s, |s, :— ||
|m :— |l :-.s |f :m |r :d |t, :— ||m :— |r :d |d :t, |d :— ||
|d :— |f, :-.d |f, :d, |s, :l, |m, :— ||d :— |s, :l, |f, :s, |d, :— ||
```

Unison.
LIFT up your heads, ye gates of brass,
Ye bars of iron, yield,
And let the King of Glory pass;
The Cross is in the field.

Harmony.
2 Ye armies of the living God,
His sacramental host,
Where hallowed footstep never trod,
Take your appointed post.

3 Follow the Cross; the ark of peace
Accompany your path,
To slaves and rebels bring release
From bondage and from wrath.

4 Though few and small and weak your bands,
Strong in your Captain's strength,
Go to the conquest of all lands;
All must be His at length.

5 O fear not, faint not, halt not now;
Quit you like men, be strong;
To Christ shall every nation bow,
And sing with you this song:

Unison.
6 'Uplifted are the gates of brass;
The bars of iron yield;
Behold the King of Glory pass!
The Cross hath won the field.'

JAMES MONTGOMERY, 1771–1854.

386 ST. ANSELM. (L.M.)

Arranged by LEIGHTON GEORGE HAYNE, 1836–83.

Doh = E. *In moderate time.*

:d |d :r |m :f |m :-.r |d ||m |s :l |s :d' |t :-.l |s ||
:s_1 |s_1 :s_1 |d :r |d :t_1 |d ||d |d :d |d :m |r :d |t_1 ||
:m |m :r |s :l |s :f |m ||s |s :f |s :s |s :fe |s ||
:d |d :t_1 |d :f_1 |s_1 :s_1 |d ||d |m :f |m :d |r :r |s_1 ||

:m |m :d |r :m |f :-.m |r ||r |s :s |m :d |r :r |d ||f |m ||
:d |d :d |l_1 :ta_1 |$l_1.t_1$:d |t_1 ||$l_1.t_1$ |d :r |s_1 :d |d :t_1 |d ||d |d ||
:s |s :s |f :s |f.r :m.f |s ||l |s :s |d' :m |l :s.f |m ||l |s ||
:d |d :m |r :de |r :d |s_1 ||f |m :t_1 |d.t_1 :$l_1.s_1$ |f_1 :s_1 |d ||f_1 |d ||

A-men.

O SPIRIT of the living God,
In all Thy plenitude of grace,
Where'er the foot of man hath trod,
Descend on our apostate race.

2 Give tongues of fire and hearts of love,
To preach the reconciling word;
Give power and unction from above,
Whene'er the joyful sound is heard.

3 Be darkness, at Thy coming, light;
Confusion order, in Thy path;
Souls without strength inspire with might;
Bid mercy triumph over wrath.

4 O Spirit of the Lord, prepare
All the round earth her God to meet;
Breathe Thou abroad like morning air,
Till hearts of stone begin to beat.

5 Baptize the nations; far and nigh
The triumphs of the Cross record;
The Name of Jesus glorify,
Till every kindred call Him Lord.

JAMES MONTGOMERY, 1771–1854

387 NEANDER. (87. 87. 87.)

Doh = C. *In moderate time.* JOACHIM NEANDER, 1650–80.

```
| d  :-.r | m  :d | m  :f  | s  :s | d'  :t.l | s  :m' | r' :r' | d' :— ||
| d  :-.d | d  :d | d  :d  | r  :r | d   :d   | d  :s  | l  :s  | m  :— ||
| m  :-.f | s  :s | s  :l  | t  :t | s   :f   | s  :d' | d' :t  | d' :— ||
| d  :-.d | d  :m | d  :l, | s, :s | m   :f   | m  :d  | f  :s  | d  :— ||

| d  :-.r | m  :d | m  :f  | s  :s | d'  :t.l | s  :m' | r' :r' | d' :— ||
| d  :-.d | d  :d | d  :d  | r  :r | d.r :m.f | s  :s  | l  :s  | m  :— ||
| m  :-.f | s  :s | s  :l  | t  :t | d'  :d'  | d' :d' | d' :t  | d' :— ||
| d  :-.d | d  :m | d  :l, | s, :s | l   :s.f | m  :d  | f  :s  | d  :— ||

                     //:
| m' :-.m' | r' :r' | d' :-.d' | t :t  | l   :-.l    | s  :d' | r' :t | d' :— || d' | d' ||
| s  :s    | s  :s  | m  :m    | m :m  | d   :f      | m  :m  | r  :r | m  :— || f  | m  ||
| d' :d'   | d' :t  | l  :l    | l :se | l.t :d'.r'  | m' :d' | l  :s | s  :— || l  | s  ||
| d  :m.f  | s  :s  | l  :d.r  | m :m  | f.s :l.t    | d' :l  | f  :s | d  :— || f  | d  ||
                                                                                  A-men.
```

BLAENCEFN. (87. 87. 87.)

Doh = A. *In moderate time.* JOHN THOMAS, 1839–1922.

```
| d    :m.r    | d  :s,  | l,.t, :d.r    | m  :r  | d  :m  | l,.t, :d.r    |
| m,   :s,.f,  | m, :s,  | f,    :s,.l,  | s, :s, | s, :s, | f,    :s,.l,  |
| s,   :s,     | s, :d   | d     :d      | d  :t, | d  :d  | d.r   :m.f    |
| d,   :d,     | d, :m,  | f,.r, :m,.f,  | s, :s, | m, :d, | f,    :m,.r,  |

| m  :r  | d  :— || d  :m.r   | d  :s,   | l,.t, :d.r | m  :r  |
| s, :f, | m, :— || m, :s,.f, | m, :s,   | s,    :fe, | s, :s, |
| d  :t, | d  :— || d  :t,    | d  :m.r  | d.r   :d   | d  :t, |
| s, :s, | d  :— || d, :d,    | d, :d.t, | l,    :l,  | s, :s, |
```

d :m | l_1.t_1 :d .r | d :t_1 | l_1 :— || t_1 :r .d | t_1.,l_1 :s_1

m_1 :se_1 | l_1.se_1 :l_1.t_1 | l_1 :se_1 | m_1 :— || s_1 :t_1.l_1 | s_1.,fe_1 :s_1

d :t_1 | m .r :m .f | m :r | d :— || r :r | r .,d :t_1

l_1 :m_1 | d .t_1 :l_1.r_1 | m_1 :m_1 | l_1 :— || s_1 :s_1 | s_1 :s_1

://:

m :s .f | m.,r :d | m :s | f :l_1.r | d :t_1 | d :— || d | d ||

s_1 :s_1 | s_1 :s_1.d | d :ta_1 | l_1 :l_1 | s_1 :s_1 | s_1 :— || l_1 | s_1 ||

d :m .r | d.,r :m | d :d | d :d .f | m :r | m :— || f | m ||

d :d | d :d .t_1 | l_1 :m_1 | f_1 :f_1.r_1 | s_1 :s_1 | d_1 :— || f_1 | d_1 ||

A-men.

Dros y bryniau tywyll niwlog.

O'ER those gloomy hills of darkness
Look, my soul; be still, and gaze;
All the promises do travail
With a glorious day of grace:
Blessèd jubilee!
Let thy glorious morning dawn.

2 Kingdoms wide that sit in darkness,
Let them have the glorious light;
And from eastern coast to western
May the morning chase the night,
And redemption,
Freely purchased, win the day.

3 Fly abroad, eternal Gospel!
Win and conquer, never cease;
May thy lasting wide dominions
Multiply and still increase;
May thy sceptre
Sway the enlightened world around.

William Williams, 1717-91.

388 WARRINGTON. (L.M.)

Doh = B♭. *In moderate time.* RALPH HARRISON, 1748–1810.

```
s,  :s,  :f,  |m,  :s,   :d     |d  :r  :t,  |d  :— :m   |r  :— :r   |m  :— :r .d
m,  :m,  :r,  |m,  :—    :m,.f, |s, :— :f,   |m, :— :s,  |s, :— :s,  |s, :— :s,
d   :d   :t,  |d   :—    :d .r  |m  :f  :r   |d  :— :d   |t, :— :t,  |d  :— :r .m
d,  :m,  :s,  |d   :-.t, :l,    |s, :— :s,   |d, :— :d,  |s, :— :s,  |d  :— :t,.d

t,  :— :l,    |s,  :— :—  ||d  :d  :s,  |l, :t, :d   |f  :- .m   :r .d   |d  :t,
s,  :— :fe,   |s,  :— :—  ||m, :s, :m,  |l, :— :s,   |f, :l,.s,  :f,.m,  |m, :r,
r   :— :d     |t,  :— :—  ||d  :d  :d   |d  :r  :s,  |l, :—      :l,     |s, :—
r   :— :r,    |s,  :— :—  ||d, :m, :d,  |f, :— :m,   |r, :- .m,  :f,     |s, :—

:l,     |s,  :—  :f,   |m,  :s,     :d      |d  :r  :t,  |d  :— :—  ||d   |d
:r,     |m,  :d, :t,,  |d,  :m,.f,  :s,.l,  |s, :— :s,   |s, :— :—  ||l,  |s,
:l,.t,  |d   :s, :s,   |s,  :d      :d      |m  :f  :r   |m  :— :—  ||f   |m
:f,     |m,  :—  :r,   |d,  :-.r,   :m,.f,  |s, :— :s,   |d, :— :—  ||f,  |d,
                                                                      A-men.
```

From Psalm lxxii.

JESUS shall reign where'er the sun
Does his successive journeys run;
His Kingdom stretch from shore to shore,
Till moons shall wax and wane no more.

2 For Him shall endless prayer be made,
And praises throng to crown His head;
His Name like sweet perfume shall rise
With every morning sacrifice.

3 People and realms of every tongue
Dwell on His love with sweetest song;
And infant voices shall proclaim
Their early blessings on His Name.

4 Blessings abound where'er He reigns:
The prisoner leaps to lose his chains,
The weary find eternal rest,
And all the sons of want are blest.

5 Let every creature rise and bring
Peculiar honours to our King,
Angels descend with songs again,
And earth repeat the long Amen.

ISAAC WATTS, 1674–1748.

389 THANKSGIVING. (77.77. D.)

Doh = C. *Moderately fast.* WALTER BOND GILBERT, 1829–1910.

d' :-.t |d' :s |l :s.f |m :— |m :fe |s :l |t :l |s :— ||d' :-.t
m :-.f |s :m |f :r |d :— |m :r |r :m |r :r.d |t, :— ||m :-.f
s :-.s |s :d' |d' :t |d' :— |s :l |s :s |s :fe |s :— ||s :-.r'
d :-.r |m :d |f :s |d :— |d :d |t, :d |r :r |s :— ||d :-.r

d' :s |l :s.f |m :— |m :fe |s :l |t :l |s :— ||s :s |m' :r'
s :m |f :r |r :— |d :r |r :s |s :fe |s :— ||m :m |s :s
d' :d' |d' :t |t :— |d' :l |t :de' |r' :r'.d' |t :— ||d' :d' |d' :t
m :d |f :s |se :— |l :d |t, :m |r :r |s :— ||d :d |d :r

d' :t.l |s :— |l :l |f' :m' |r' :d' |t :— ||d' :-.t |d' :s
s :f |m :— |l :s |f :l |l :l |s :— ||m :-.f |s :m
d' :d' |d' :— |d' :de' |r' :de' |r' :r' |r' :— ||d' :-.s |s :d'
m :f |d :— |f :m |r :m |f :fe |s :— ||d :-.r |m :d

l :s.f |m :— |s :s |l :d' |d' :— |t :— |d' :— |— :— ||d' |d'
f :r |d :— |s :m |f :m |s :— |r :— |m :— |— :— ||f |m
d' :t |d' :— |d' :d' |d' :d' |r' :— |s :— |s :— |— :— ||l |s
f :s |l :— |m :d |f :l |s :— |s, :— |d :— |— :— ||f, |d

A-men.

[*By permission of Novello & Co., Ltd.*]

HARK! the song of jubilee,
Loud as mighty thunders' roar,
Or the fulness of the sea
When it breaks upon the shore.
Hallelujah! for the Lord
God omnipotent shall reign;
Hallelujah! let the word
Echo round the earth and main.

2 Hallelujah! hark, the sound,
From the depths unto the skies,
Wakes above, beneath, around,
All creation's harmonies:
See Jehovah's banner furled,
Sheathed His sword; He speaks—'tis done,
And the kingdoms of this world
Are the kingdoms of His Son.

3 He shall reign from pole to pole
With illimitable sway;
He shall reign when, like a scroll,
Yonder heavens have passed away;
Then the end; beneath His rod
Man's last enemy shall fall;
Hallelujah! Christ in God,
God in Christ, is all in all.

JAMES MONTGOMERY, 1771–1854.

Also the following:

THE CHRISTIAN LIFE

THE GOSPEL CALL

390 COME UNTO ME. (76. 76 D.)

Doh = G. *In moderate time.* JOHN BACCHUS DYKES, 1823–76.

| : | : | : | : | : | : | : | : ||

| : | : | : | : | : | : | : | : ||

|d :— |d :d |l, :-.t, |d :d | :r |m :d |r :-.d |d :— ||

|d :— |d :d |l, :-.t, |d :d | :r |m :d |r :-.d |d :— ||

> > > > >> >

D.t. f.G.

|m :— |m :m |m :^l r' |r' :— |s :d' |m :l |f :-.r |^d s, :— |— ||

|s, :— |d :t, |l, :^d f |f :r |m :d |d :d |t, :-.t, |^d s, :— |— ||

|m :— |m :r |d :^m l |s :— |s :f |s :r |r :-.f |^m t, :— |— ||

|d :— |l, :l, |l, :^s, d |t, :— |d :l, |s, :f, |s, :-.s, |^d s, :— |— ||

:m |s :-.s |f :m |s :— |f :r |f :-.f |m :r |m :— |— ||

:t, |s, :-.t, |l, :l, |t, :de |r :l, |f, :-.l, |s, :s, |s, :— |— ||

:t, |m :-.r |de :de |r :m |f :l, |r :-.d |t, :f |m :— |— ||

:s, |m, :-.m, |l, :l, |l, :— |r, :f, |r, :-.r, |s, :s, |d :— |— ||

:m |d :-.d |d :d |s :— |m :d |s, :f |m :r |d :— ||d |d ||

:s, |l, :-.s, |fe, :d |d :— |s, :s, |s, :l, |s, :f, |m, :— ||f, |m, ||

:d |m :-.m |r :d |m :s |d :m |f :s, |l, :t, |d :— ||l, |d ||

:d |l, :-.l, |l, :l, |s, :— |s, :s, |s, :s, |s, :s, |d, :— ||f, |d, ||

A-men.

WHITFORD. (76. 76. D.)

Lah = G. Doh = B♭. *Moderately slow.* JOHN AMBROSE LLOYD, 1815–74.

|m :— |r :d |t, :l, |l, :se, | :m, |l, :t, |d :r |t, :— ||m :— |

|m, :— |m, :m, |m, :d, |m, :m, | :m, |m, :m, |m, :f, |m, :— ||m, :— |

|d :— |t, :l, |se, :l, |d :t, | :se, |l, :se, |l, :l, |se, :— ||l, :— |

|l, :— |se, :l, |m, :f, |m, :m, | :m, |d, :m, |l, :r, |m, :— ||d, :— |

```
r  :d  |t, :l, |l, :se, |    :m, |l, :t, |d  :t, |l, :— ||d  :—
f, :m, |m, :m, |m, :m,  |    :m, |d, :f, |m, :m, |d, :— ||m, :—
l, :l, |se,:d  |d  :t,  |    :l, |l, :l, |l, :se,|l, :— ||l, :—
r, :l2 |m, :l, |m, :m,  |    :d, |f, :r, |m, :m, |l2 :— ||l, :—

t, :d  |r  :t, |d  :l,  |    :d  |r  :m  |f  :r  |m  :— ||m  :—
m, :m, |se,:se,|l, :m,  |    :l, |l, :l, |l, :s, |s, :— ||s, :—
se,:l, |t, :m  |m  :d   |    :m  |r  :de |r  :t, |d  :— ||d  :—
m, :m, |m, :m, |l, :l,  |    :l, |f, :m, |r, :s, |d, :— ||d  :—

f  :m  |r  :d      |d  :t,  |    :d  |l, :t, |d  :t,  |l, :— ||l, |l,
s, :s, |s, :m,.l,  |l, :se, |    :l, |l, :l, |l, :se, |m, :— ||f, |m,
r  :d  |t, :l,.m   |m  :m   |    :m  |d  :f  |m  :m   |d  :— ||r  |de
t, :d  |s, :l,     |m, :m,  |    :d, |f, :r, |m, :m,  |l2 :— ||r, |l2
                                                                A-men.
```

'COME unto Me, ye weary,
And I will give you rest.'
O blessèd voice of Jesus,
Which comes to hearts oppressed!
It tells of benediction,
Of pardon, grace, and peace,
Of joy that hath no ending,
Of love which cannot cease.

2 'Come unto Me, ye wanderers,
And I will give you light.'
O loving voice of Jesus,
Which comes to cheer the night!
Our hearts were filled with sadness,
And we had lost our way;
But morning brings us gladness,
And songs the break of day.

3 'Come unto Me, ye fainting,
And I will give you life.'
O peaceful voice of Jesus,
Which comes to end our strife!
The foe is stern and eager,
The fight is fierce and long;
But Thou hast made us mighty,
And stronger than the strong.

4 'And whosoever cometh,
I will not cast him out.'
O patient voice of Jesus,
Which drives away our doubt,
Which calls us—very sinners,
Unworthy though we be
Of love so free and boundless—
To come, dear Lord, to Thee!

WILLIAM CHATTERTON DIX, 1837–98.

391

STEPHANOS. (85. 83.) HENRY WILLIAMS BAKER, 1821–77.

Doh = G. *In moderate time.* Harmonized by WILLIAM HENRY MONK, 1823–89.

```
|m   :m   |m   :r   |m   :s    |s   :f   |m   :m   |r   :d   |r   :— |— :
|s,  :s,  |s,  :s,  |s,  :s,   |d   :s,  |s,  :s,  |s,  :s,  |s,  :— |— :
|d   :d   |d   :t,  |d   :r    |m   :r   |d   :m   |f   :m   |t,  :— |— :
|d,  :m,  |s,  :s,  |d   :t,   |l,  :t,  |d   :d   |t,  :d   |s,  :— |— :

|s,  :l,.t, |d  :t,  |d   :r.m  |f   :m   |r   :— |r   :— |d   :— |— :— || d  | d
|s,  :s,    |s, :s,  |s,  :s,   |f,  :s,  |l,  :— |s,  :— |m,  :— |— :— || f, | m,
|s   :f     |m  :r   |m   :r    |d   :d   |d   :— |t,  :— |d   :— |— :— || l, | d
|m   :r     |d  :s,  |d   :t,   |l,  :s,  |f,  :— |s,  :— |d,  :— |— :— || f, | d,
```

A-men.

FRONDEG. (85. 83.)

Lah = G. Doh = B♭. *In moderate time.* DAVID EVANS, 1874–.

```
|m,  :l,   |l,  :se,    |l,  :t,   |d   :l,   |t,  :l,   |s,  :fe,    |m,  :— |— :—
|m,  :m,   |m,  :m,.r,  |d,  :m,   |m,  :fe,  |s,  :fe,  |m,  :re,    |m,  :— |— :—
|l,  :d    |d   :t,     |l,  :se,  |l,  :d    |t,  :d    |t,  :t,.l,  |s,  :— |— :—
|d,  :l,,  |m,  :m,     |f,  :m,   |l,  :l,   |s,  :l,   |t,  :t,,    |m,  :— |— :—

|l,  :t,   |d   :t,     |d   :r      |m   :l,  |t,  :—   |t,  :—   |l,   :— |— :— || l,  | l,
|m,  :m,   |m,  :s,     |s,  :s,.f,  |m,  :f,  |f,  :l,  |—   :se, |l,   :— |— :— || f,  | m,
|l,  :se,  |l,  :r      |d   :t,     |d   :d   |t,  :f   |m   :r   |d    :— |— :— || r   | de
|d,  :m,   |l,  :s,.f,  |m,  :r,     |d,  :f,  |r,  :—   |m,  :—   |l,,  :— |— :— || r,  | l,,
```

A-men.

ART thou weary, art thou languid,
Art thou sore distressed?
'Come to Me,' saith One, 'and, coming,
Be at rest.'

2 Hath He marks to lead me to Him,
If He be my Guide?
In His feet and hands are wound-prints,
And His side!

3 Is there diadem, as Monarch,
That His brow adorns?
Yea, a crown in very surety,
But of thorns!

4 If I find Him, if I follow,
What His guerdon here?
Many a sorrow, many a labour,
Many a tear!

5 If I still hold closely to Him,
What hath He at last?
Sorrow vanquished, labour ended,
Jordan passed!

6 If I ask Him to receive me,
Will He say me nay?
Not till earth and not till heaven
Pass away!

7 Finding, following, keeping, struggling,
Is He sure to bless?
Angels, martyrs, saints, and prophets
Answer, Yes!

JOHN MASON NEALE, 1818–66; based on ST. STEPHEN OF MAR SABA, 8th cent.

392 ASHBURTON. (8 7. 8 7. 4 7.)

Doh = F. *In moderate time.* SAMUEL SEBASTIAN WESLEY, 1810–76.

m :m	f :m	r :l	l :se	l :s.f	m :l,.t,	d :t,	l, :—	
s, :s,	t, :d	r :r	m :t,	d :r	d :l,	l, :se,	l, :—	
m :s	f :s	l :l	t :m	m :s	s :f	m :m.r	d :—	
d :d	r :m	f :f	m :m	l, :t,	d :r	m :m,	l, :—	

m :m	f :m	r :l	l :se	l :s.f	m :l,.t,	d :t,	l, :—	
s, :s,	t, :d	r :r	m :t,	d :r	d :l,	l, :se,	l, :—	
m :s	f :s	l :l	t :m	m :s	s :f	m :m.r	d :—	
d :d	r :m	f :f	m :m	l, :t,	d :r	m :m,	l, :—	

d :d.r	d :t,	d :d	d :-.r	d :t,	d :—		d	d	
s, :fe,	s, :s,	s, :se,	l, :-.l,	s, :s,	s, :—		l,	s,	
d :r	m :r	d :d	d :-.f	m :r	m :—		f	m	
l, :r,	s, :s,	m, :m,	f, :-.f,	s, :s,	d, :—		f,	d,	

A-men.

COME, ye souls by sin afflicted,
Bowed with fruitless sorrow down,
By the broken law convicted,
Through the Cross behold the crown;
Look to Jesus;
Mercy flows through Him alone.

2 Blessèd are the eyes that see Him,
Blest the ears that hear His voice;
Blessèd are the souls that trust Him
And in Him alone rejoice;
His commandments
Then become their happy choice.

3 Take His easy yoke and wear it;
Love will make obedience sweet;
Christ will give you strength to bear it,
While His wisdom guides your feet
Safe to glory,
Where His ransomed captives meet.

4 Sweet as home to pilgrims weary,
Light to newly opened eyes,
Or full springs in deserts dreary,
Is the rest the Cross supplies;
All who taste it
Shall to rest immortal rise.

JOSEPH SWAIN, 1761–96.

393 NEUADD WEN. (8 7. 8 7. 4 7.)

DAVID EVANS, 1874–

Lah = C. Doh = Eb. *In moderate time.*

```
                                                              Bb.t.
d  :—:l,  | m  :—   :l   | s  :—  :f     | m :l, :— | (t)m, :l, :d  | t, :—:m,
l, :—:l,  | l, :-.se,:l, | r  :—  :l,.t, | d :l, :— | (t)m, :— :m,  | m, :—:m,
m  :—:f   | m  :-.r  :d  | r  :-.m:f .s  | l :l, :— | (m)l, :— :l,  | r  :—:d
l, :d :r  | d  :-.t, :l, | t, :-.d:r     | l,:l, :— | (s)d, :— :l₂  | l, :se,:l,

           f.Eb.
f, :—:s,  | (m)t,  :—:— || d  :—:l, | m :—   :l   | s :-.f:m.r | m  :t,  :— ||
r, :—:r,  | (de)se,:—:— || l, :—:l, | l,:—   :m   | r :— :l,   | t, :se, :— ||
l, :—:t,  | (l,)m  :—:— || m  :—:f  | m :—   :d'.t| l :— :l    | se :m   :— ||
r, :—:r,  | (l₂)m, :—:— || l, :d :r | d :-.t,:l,  | r :— :f    | m  :m   :— ||

d  :m :fe | s  :— :m | l  :fe :—  | m  :— :— || m :—   | m  :—
l, :— :d  | t, :— :d | m  :— :re  | m  :— :— || m :—   | —  :r
m  :d :r  | m  :— :s | d' :— :t.l | s  :— :— || m :—   | ba :se
l, :— :l, | s, :m,:d | l, :— :t,  | m, :— :— || m :-.r | d  :t,

d' :— | t  :— | l  :s    | f :r     | m :— | m  :—  | l, :— | — :— || f  | m  ||
d  :m | m  :— | d  :m    | r :l,.t, | d :— | se,:t, | l, :— | — :— || r  | de ||
l  :— | se :— | l  :d'.t | l :l     | l :m | —  :r  | d  :— | — :— || l  | l  ||
l, :d | m  :— | f  :d    | r :f     | m :— | m, :—  | l, :— | — :— || r, | l, ||
                                                                     A-men.
```

[*Copyright*, 1927, *by David Evans.*]

COME, ye sinners, poor and wretched,
Weak and wounded, sick and sore;
Jesus ready stands to save you,
Full of pity joined with power:
He is able,
He is willing; doubt no more.

2 Ho! ye needy, come and welcome;
God's free bounty glorify;
True belief and true repentance,
Every grace that brings us nigh,
Without money
Come to Jesus Christ and buy.

3 Come, ye weary, heavy laden,
Bruised and broken by the fall;
If you tarry till you're better,
You will never come at all:
Not the righteous—
Sinners Jesus came to call.

4 Let not conscience make you linger,
Nor of fitness fondly dream;
All the fitness He requireth
Is to feel your need of Him:
This He gives you;
'Tis the Spirit's rising beam.

5 Lo! the Incarnate God, ascended
Pleads the merit of His blood;
Venture on Him, venture wholly;
Let no other trust intrude:
None but Jesus
Can do helpless sinners good.

JOSEPH HART, 1712–68.

[May be sung to CORINTH, No. 563.]

394

JESU, MEINE ZUVERSICHT. (77. 77. 77.) JOHANN CRÜGER, 1598–1662.

Doh = C. *Moderately slow.* *D.C.*

s :f .m	l :t	d' :d'	t :—	l .t :d'	s .f :m	f .m :r	d :—
d :t,.d	d :f	s :r	r :—	l :s	r :d	d :d .t,	d :—
m :f .s	l :r'	d'.t :l	s :—	d' :d'	r' :s	f .s :l .s	m :—
d :r .m	f :r	m :fe	s :—	f :m	t, :d.t,	l,.s, :f,.s,	d :—

m :ba	se :l.t	d' :t	l :—	t :d'	r' :m'	r' :r'	d' :—		f	m
d :r	r :m.f	m :m	m :—	f :s	s :s	l :s .f	m :—		d	d
s :l	t :l	l :se.r'	d' :—	r' :m'	r' :d'	d' :t	d' :—		l	s
d :d	t, :d.r	m :m	l, :—	r :d	d .t, :d	f :s	d :—		f	d

A-men.

Jesus nimmt die Sünder an.

SINNERS Jesus will receive :
Tell this word of grace to all
Who the heavenly pathway leave,
All who linger, all who fall ;
This can bring them back again :
'Christ receiveth sinful men.'

2 Shepherds seek their wandering sheep
O'er the mountains bleak and cold ;
Jesus such a watch doth keep
O'er the lost ones of His fold,
Seeking them o'er moor and fen :
Christ receiveth sinful men.

3 Sick and sorrowful and blind,
I with all my sins draw nigh ;
O my Saviour, Thou canst find
Help for sinners such as I ;
Speak that word of love again :
'Christ receiveth sinful men.'

4 Christ receiveth sinful men,
Even me with all my sin ;
Openeth to me heaven again ;
With Him I may enter in.
Death hath no more sting nor pain :
Christ receiveth sinful men.

ERDMANN NEUMEISTER, 1671–1756 ; *tr.* by EMMA FRANCES BEVAN, 1827–1909.

[May be sung to PSALM 135, No. 261.]

395 ST. MABYN. (87. 87.)

Doh = G. *Moderately slow.* ARTHUR HENRY BROWN, 1830–1926.

```
| m  :-.m  | r  :d   | s  :m   | m  :r   | f  :-.f  | m  :l,  | t, :d   | t, :—  ||
| d  :-.d  | t  :d   | d  :d   | d  :t,  | l, :t,   | d  :l,  | s, :fe, | s, :—  ||
| s  :-.s  | f  :m   | s  :s   | s  :s   | f  :-.f  | s  :m   | r  :r   | r  :—  ||
| d  :-.d  | s, :l,  | m, :d,  | s, :s,  | r  :-.r  | m  :d   | r  :r,  | s, :—  ||
```

```
| r  :-.r  | r  :m   | f  :r   | d  :t,   | d  :s   | s  :-.f  | m  :r   | d  :— || d  | d  ||
| t, :-.t, | l, :l,  | l, :l,  | s, :s,   | d  :d   | d  :-.r  | d  :t,  | d  :— || l, | s, ||
| s  :-.s  | l  :s   | f  :f   | m  :r    | s  :ta  | l  :-.l  | s  :-.f | m  :— || f  | m  ||
| s, :-.s, | f, :de, | r, :f,  | s, :-.f, | m, :m,  | f, :-.f, | s, :s,  | d, :— || f, | d, ||
```

A-men.

OMNI DIE. (87. 87.)

Doh = F. *Very slow and solemn.* *Corner's Gesangbuch*, 1631.

```
:d .d  | r  :d  :m .s  | f .   :m  || d .r  | m .s  :s    :fe  | s  :— ||
:s,.l, | t, :d  :d .d  | d .t, :d  || s,.t, | d .r  :d    :d   | t, :— ||
:m .m  | s  :m  :s .m  | f     :s  || m .s  | s .s  :m .r :d   | r  :— ||
:d .l, | s, :d  :d .d  | r     :d  || d .s, | d .t, :d .t,:l,  | s, :— ||
```

```
:s .s  | l  :s  :f .m  | r     :m   || d .r  | m .f  :r  :-.d | d  :— || d  | d  ||
:d .r  | d  :d  :d .d  | t,.l, :se, || l,.t, | d .d  :d  :t,  | d  :— || l, | s, ||
:m .r  | m  :m  :l .s  | s .l  :t   || m .s  | s .l  :s  :s   | m  :— || f  | m  ||
:d .t, | l, :d  :f,.d  | s,.f, :m,  || l,.s, | d .f, :s, :s,  | d, :— || f, | d, ||
```

A-men.

SOULS of men! why will ye scatter
Like a crowd of frightened sheep?
Foolish hearts! why will ye wander
From a love so true and deep?

2 Was there ever kindest shepherd
Half so gentle, half so sweet,
As the Saviour who would have us
Come and gather round His feet?

3 There 's a wideness in God's mercy,
Like the wideness of the sea;
There 's a kindness in His justice,
Which is more than liberty.

4 There is no place where earth's sorrows
Are more felt than up in heaven:
There is no place where earth's failings
Have such kindly judgment given.

5 For the love of God is broader
Than the measures of man's mind;
And the heart of the Eternal
Is most wonderfully kind.

6 There is plentiful redemption
In the blood that has been shed
There is joy for all the members
In the sorrows of the Head.

7 Pining souls! come nearer Jesus,
And O come, not doubting thus,
But with faith that trusts more bravely
His huge tenderness for us.

8 If our love were but more simple,
We should take Him at His word;
And our lives would be all sunshine,
In the sweetness of our Lord.

FREDERICK WILLIAM FABER, 1814-63.

[May be sung to HYFRYDOL, No. 479, or CHARTRES, No. 44.]

396 PEARSALL. (76. 76. D.)

Doh = D. *In moderate time.* *St. Gall Gesangbuch*, 1863.

```
:s  |d' :t  |d' :m  |l  :—  |s  :s  |f  :m  |r  :r    |m  :—  |—  ||
:d  |m  :r  |d  :d  |d  :r  |m  :d  |t, :d  |d  :t,   |d  :—  |—  ||
:m  |s  :f  |s  :s  |l  :t  |d' :m  |f  :s  |l  :s    |s  :—  |—  ||
:d  |d  :r  |m  :d  |f  :—  |d  :d  |r  :m  |f  :s    |d  :—  |—  ||

:d  |m  :f  |s  :s  |l  :—  |s  :s  |l  :t  |d' :r'.d' |t  :—  |—  ||
:s, |d  :d  |r  :d  |d  :r  |m  :m  |r  :r  |m  :r    |r  :—  |—  ||
:m  |s  :l  |s  :m  |l  :t  |d' :s  |fe :s  |s  :fe   |s  :—  |—  ||
:d  |d  :l, |t, :d  |f  :—  |d  :d  |d  :t, |l, :r    |s, :—  |—  ||

:d' |l  :s  |f  :m  |f  :—  |r  :l  |s  :f  |m  :r    |s  :—  |—  ||
:m  |f  :m  |r  :de |r  :—  |t, :t, |d  :t, |d  :d    |t, :—  |—  ||
:s  |l  :ta |l  :l  |l  :—  |t  :r' |s  :s  |s  :fe   |s  :—  |—  ||
:d  |f  :s  |l  :l, |r  :—  |s  :f  |m  :r  |d  :l,   |s, :—  |—  ||

:l.t |d' :t  |d' :m  |l  :—  |s  :s  |f  :m  |r  :r   |d  :—  |—  || f  |m  ||
:f   |m  :f  |m  :d  |d  :r  |m  :d  |d  :d  |d  :t,  |d  :—  |—  || d  |d  ||
:r'  |d' :r' |d' :d' |l  :t  |d' :s  |l  :s  |s  :s.f |m  :—  |—  || l  |s  ||
:s   |d  :s  |l  :s  |f  :—  |d  :m  |f  :d  |s, :s,  |d  :—  |—  || f, |d  ||
                                                                     A-men.
```

THE King of Glory standeth
  Beside that heart of sin;
His mighty voice commandeth
  The raging waves within;
The floods of deepest anguish
  Roll backward at His will,
As o'er the storm ariseth
  His mandate, 'Peace, be still.'

2 At times, with sudden glory,
  He speaks, and all is done;
Without one stroke of battle
  The victory is won,
While we, with joy beholding,
  Can scarce believe it true
That even our kingly Jesus
  Can form such hearts anew.

3 O Christ, Thy love is mighty;
  Long-suffering is Thy grace;
And glorious is the splendour
  That beameth from Thy face.
Our hearts up-leap in gladness
  When we behold that love,
As we go singing onward,
  To dwell with Thee above.

CHARITIE LEES DE CHENEZ, 1841–

397 LLANGLOFFAN. (76. 76. D.)

Lah = G. Doh = B♭. *In moderate time.* Welsh Hymn Melody.

:m, |l, :l, |t, :t, |d :-.t, |l, :l, |r :r |d :d |t, :— |— ||
:m, |m, :d, |f, :m, |d, :-.r, |m, :m, |r, :f, |m, :m, |m, :— |— ||
:m, |m, :l, |l, :se, |l, :-.t, |d :d |l, :t, |d :l, |se, :— |— ||
:m, |d, :l,, |r, :m, |l, :— |l, :s, |f, :r, |l,, :d, |m, :— |— ||

:m, |l, :l, |t, :t, |d :-.r |m :r |d :l, |t, :se, |l, :— |— ||
:m, |m, :l, |l, :se, |l, :-.t, |d :se, |l, :l, |f, :m, |m, :— |— ||
:se, |l, :d |f :m |m :-.r |d :r |m :d |r :t, |d :— |— ||
:m,.r, |d, :f,.m, |r, :m, |l, :— |l,, :t,, |d, :f, |r, :m, |l, :— |— ||

:m |m : d |t, :r |d :— |t, :l, |se, :l, |r :d |t, :— |— ||
:s, |s, : s, |f, :f, |m, :f, |s, :r, |m, :m,.ba, |se, :l, |se, :— |— ||
:d |d : m |r :l,.t, |d :— |r :l, |t, :d |r :m |m :— |— ||
:d, |d : d, |r,.m, :f,.s, |l, :— |s, :f, |m,.r, :d, |t,, :l,, |m, :— |— ||

:m, |l, :l, |t, :t, |d :-.r |m :r |d :l, |t, :se, |l, :— |— || l, |l, ||
:m, |m, :l, |l, :se, |l, :-.t, |d :se, |l, :l, |f, :m, |m, :— |— || f, |m, ||
:se, |l, :d |f :m |m :-.r |d :r |m :d |r :t, |d :— |— || r |de ||
:m,.r, |d, :f,.m, |r, :m, |l, :— |l,, :t,, |d, :f, |r, :m, |l,, :— |— || r, |l,, ||

A-men.

O JESUS, Thou art standing
Outside the fast-closed door,
In lowly patience waiting
To pass the threshold o'er.
Shame on us, Christian brothers,
His Name and sign who bear,
O shame, thrice shame upon us,
To keep Him standing there !

2 O Jesus, Thou art knocking ;
And, lo ! that hand is scarred,
And thorns Thy brow encircle,
And tears Thy face have marred.
O love that passeth knowledge
So patiently to wait !
O sin that hath no equal,
So fast to bar the gate !

3 O Jesus, Thou art pleading
In accents meek and low,
'I died for you, My children,
And will ye treat Me so ?'
O Lord, with shame and sorrow
We open now the door ;
Dear Saviour, enter, enter,
And leave us nevermore.

WILLIAM WALSHAM HOW, 1823–97.

398 PETERSHAM. (D.C.M.)

Doh = D. *In moderate time.* CLEMENT WILLIAM POOLE, 1328–1924.

```
:d  |m :s   |d' :l   |s  :-.f   |m :m   |r  :s   |l  :l   |s  :— |— ||
:d  |m :s   |d' :f   |r  :r     |m :d   |r  :t,  |r  :-.d |t, :— |— ||
:d  |m :s   |d' :d'  |d' :t     |d' :s  |s  :s   |s  :fe  |s  :— |— ||
:d  |m :s   |d' :f   |s  :s     |d :d   |t, :m   |r  :r   |s  :— |— ||

:s  |s :m   |d' :l   |s  :-.f   |m :m   |l  :l.t |d' :t   |l  :— |— ||
:s  |s :m   |m  :f.m |r  :t,    |d :m.r |d  :f   |m  :-.r |d  :— |— ||
:s  |s :m   |s  :f   |s  :s     |s :m   |l  :l   |l  :se  |l  :— |— ||
:s  |s :m   |d  :r.d |t, :s,    |d :m   |f  :r   |m  :m   |l, :— |— ||

:s  |m :-.r |d  :r   |m  :f     |s :s   |l  :-.s |l  :l   |t  :— |— ||
:r  |d :t,  |l, :r   |d  :d     |t, :d  |t, :-.d |f  :m   |s  :— |— ||
:r  |s :f   |m  :s   |s  :f     |r :s   |f  :-.s |d' :d'  |r' :— |— ||
:t, |d :s,  |l, :t,  |d  :l,    |s, :m  |r  :-.m |f  :l   |s  :— |— ||

:s  |d' :-.t |l  :s  |s  :-.f   |m :m   |f  :f   |r  :r   |d  :— |— || f  |m ||
:r  |s  :m   |f  :m  |r  :d.r   |d :d   |d  :d   |d  :t,  |d  :— |— || d  |d ||
:t  |d' :d'  |d' :d' |t  :s     |s :l   |l  :l   |s  :-.f |m  :— |— || l  |s ||
:f  |m  :d   |f  :d  |s, :l,.t, |d :l   |f  :r   |s  :s,  |d  :— |— || f, |d ||
```

A-men.

THE Lord is rich and merciful;
The Lord is very kind;
O come to Him, come now to Him,
With a believing mind.
His comforts, they shall strengthen thee,
Like flowing waters cool;
And He shall for thy spirit be
A fountain ever full.

Unison.

2 The Lord is glorious and strong;
Our God is very high;
O trust in Him, trust now in Him,
And have security.
He shall be to thee like the sea,
And thou shalt surely feel
His wind, that bloweth healthily
Thy sicknesses to heal.

Harmony.

3 The Lord is wonderful and wise,
As all the ages tell;
O learn of Him, learn now of Him,
Then with thee it is well.
And with His light thou shalt be blest,
Therein to work and live;
And He shall be to thee a rest
When evening hours arrive.

THOMAS TOKE LYNCH, 1818–71.

Also the following:

417 Hark, my soul! it is the Lord

679-707 *Hymns for Mission Services*

399 AGNES. (77. 76.)

Doh = E♭. *In moderate time.* EDWARD BUNNETT, 1834–1923.

m :s	f :m	m :-.r	d :—	f :m	l :s	s :fe	s :—
m :r	d :d	t, :t,	d :—	r :d	t, :d	r :d	t, :—
d' :t	l :s	s :-.f	m :—	s :s	f :s	t :l	s :—
d :d	d :d	s, :s,	l, :—	t, :d	r :m	r :r	s, :—

d' :-.t	l :r	s :f	m :—	s :d	f :m	r :—	d :—	d	d
d :d	d :t,	d :r	d :—	ta, :l,	t, :d	d :t,	d :—	l,	s,
s :s	l :s	s :s	s :—	s :l	s :s	s :-.f	m :—	f	m
m :m	f :f	m :t,	d :—	m :f	r :d	s, :—	d :—	f,	d
								A-	men.

JESUS, we are far away
From the light of heavenly day;
Lost in paths of sin we stray:
Lord, in mercy hear us.

2 Help us to bewail our sin,
And, in heavenly strength, begin
Daily victories to win:
Lord, in mercy hear us.

3 Keep us lowly, that we may,
Ever watchful, turn away
From the snares our tempters lay:
Lord, in mercy hear us.

4 On our darkness shed Thy light;
Lead our wills to what is right;
Wash our evil nature white:
Lord, in mercy hear us.

5 May Thy wisdom be our guide,
Comfort, rest, and peace provide
Near to Thy protecting side:
Lord, in mercy hear us.

6 Fix our hearts on things on high;
Let no evil thoughts come nigh;
Purge from sin our memory:
Lord, in mercy hear us.

7 May Thy grace within the soul
Nature's waywardness control,
Guiding towards the heavenly goal:
Lord, in mercy hear us.

THOMAS BENSON POLLOCK, 1836–96.

400 KILMARNOCK. (C.M.)

Doh = E♭. *In moderate time.* NEIL DOUGALL, 1776–1862.

```
:d  |m  :s  |l  :s.m |m  :r   |d :l  |s  :d'.l |s  :d.r |m  :r  |— ||
:s, |d  :d  |d  :d   |d  :t,  |d :d  |d  :d    |d  :d   |d  :t, |— ||
:m  |s  :s  |f  :s   |s  :s.f |m :f  |s  :f    |m  :fe  |s  :—  |— ||
:d  |d  :m  |f  :m.d |s  :s,  |d :f  |m  :r    |m  :l,  |s, :—  |— ||
```

```
:s |l :s    |d' :m.r |d  :r  |m :l  |s  :d.r |m  :r   |d :— |— || d  |d  ||
:d |d :d.t, |d  :se, |l, :t, |d :d  |d  :d   |d  :t,  |d :— |— || l, |s, ||
:s |f :s.f  |m  :m   |m  :s  |s :f  |s  :l   |s  :s.f |m :— |— || f  |m  ||
:m |f :m.r  |d  :t,  |l, :s, |d :f, |m, :f,  |s, :s,  |d :— |— || f, |d  ||
```

A-men.

FAUX-BOURDON SETTING.

Doh = E♭. vv. 3 and 5. PURCELL JAMES MANSFIELD, 1889-

```
:m    |d  :r  |f  :m   |d     :r      |m     :r      |s.l :s.f
:s,   |l, :t, |d  :t,  |t,.l, :s,.f,  |m,.s, :l,.t,  |d   :-.d
:d    |m  :s  |l  :s.m |m     :r      |d     :l      |s   :d'.l
:d.t, |l, :s, |f, :s,  |l,    :t,     |d     :f,     |m,  :m,.f,
```

```
|m    :r.d |d  :t, |— || r.m |f   :m   |l  :s
|d.s, :fe, |s, :—  |— || t,  |r.d :t,  |m  :-.m
|s    :d.r |m  :r  |— || s   |l   :s   |d' :m.r
|s,   :l,  |s, :—  |— || s   |r   :m.r |d  :d.t,
```

```
|d'  :t.l |s   :m.f |s.d' :t.l |s    :t,    |d       :— |— ||
|m.l :s.f |m.r :d   |d    :-.d |d.s, :s,.f, |m,      :— |— ||
|d   :r   |m   :l   |s    :d.r |m    :r     |d       :— |— ||
|l,  :t,  |d   :d.r |m.m, :f,  |s,   :s,    |d {d,}  :— |— ||
```

[*Copyright*, 1923, *by Bayley & Ferguson.*]

From Hosea vi. 1–4.

COME, let us to the Lord our God
With contrite hearts return;
Our God is gracious, nor will leave
The desolate to mourn.

2 His voice commands the tempest forth,
And stills the stormy wave;
And though His arm be strong to smite,
'Tis also strong to save.

3 Long hath the night of sorrow reigned,
The dawn shall bring us light:
God shall appear, and we shall rise
With gladness in His sight.

4 Our hearts, if God we seek to know,
Shall know Him, and rejoice;
His coming like the morn shall be,
Like morning songs His voice.

5 As dew upon the tender herb,
Diffusing fragrance round;
As showers that usher in the spring,
And cheer the thirsty ground:

6 So shall His presence bless our souls
And shed a joyful light;
That hallowed morn shall chase away
The sorrows of the night.

JOHN MORISON, 1750–98; as in *Scottish Paraphrases*, 1781.

401

ST. MARY. (C.M.)

Lah = D. Doh = F. *Slow.* *Prys's Psalms*, 1621.

l_1 :—	d :t_1	l_1 :l	s :f	m :—	m :—	s :d	m :r	d :—
l_1 :—	l_1 :s_1	f_1 :d	d :l_1	l_1 :—	s_1 :—	s_1 :l_1	d :t_1	d :—
d :—	m :m	d :f	m :r	de :—	d :—	r :m	s :-.f	m :—
l_1 :—	l_1 :m_1	f_1 :f_1	d :r	l_1 :—	d :—	t_1 :l_1	m_1.f_1 :s_1	d :—

m :—	s :l	t :m	r :d	s :—	r :—	m :l_1	d :t_1	l_1 :—	l_1	l_1
d :—	r :d	t_1 :d	s_1 :d	t_1 :—	s_1 :—	s_1 :l_1	l_1 :se_1	l_1 :—	f_1	m_1
s :—	s :-.fe	s :s	r :m.fe	s :—	t_1 :—	d :d.r	m :m.r	d :—	r	de
d :—	t_1 :l_1	s_1 :d	t_1 :l_1	s_1 :—	s_1 :—	d :f_1	m_1 :m_1	l_1 :—	r_1	l_1

A-men.

O LORD, turn not away Thy face
From him that lies prostrate,
Lamenting sore his sinful life,
Before Thy mercy-gate;

2 Which gate Thou openest wide to those
That do lament their sin:
Shut not that gate against me, Lord,
But let me enter in.

3 And call me not to mine account,
How I have livèd here;
For then I know right well, O Lord,
How vile I shall appear.

4 So come I to Thy mercy-gate,
Where mercy doth abound,
Requiring mercy for my sin,
To heal my deadly wound.

5 Mercy, good Lord, mercy I ask,
This is the total sum;
For mercy, Lord, is all my suit:
Lord, let Thy mercy come.

JOHN MARCKANT, 1562.

402 HELSINGFORS. (68. 86.)

HUGO NYBERG, 1873–

Lah = C. Doh = E♭. *In moderate time.*

:l,.t, | d :d | r :d.t, | l, :— | — :d.r | m :m | l :s.l | m :r | m ||
:l, | l, :l, | l, :se, | l, :— | — :l, | t, :d | d :t, | d :t, | d ||
:d.r | m :m | r :m.r | d :— | — :m.f | m :m | f :f | m :s | s ||
:l, | l, :l, | f, :m, | l, :— | — :l, | se, :l, | f, :s, | d :s, | d ||

:l.t | d' :d' | d' :t.se | l :s.f | m :d.r | m :m | r :d.t, | l, :— | — || l, | l, ||
:m | m :re.m | fe :m | m :r | d :d | t, :d | l, :se, | l, :— | — || f, | m, ||
:l.se | l :l | l :se.t | m :s | s :l | m :d | r :m.r | d :— | — || r | de ||
:d.m | l.s :fe.m | re :r | d :t, | d :l, | se, :l, | f, :m, | l, :— | — || r, | l, ||

A-men.

O THOU, my Judge and King—
My broken heart, my voiceless prayer,
My poverty, and blind despair,
To Thee, O Christ, I bring.

2 O Thou, my Judge and King—
My treason to Thy love most sweet,
My pride that pierced Thy weary feet,
To Thee, O Christ, I bring.

3 O Thou, my Judge and King—
My tearful hope, my faith's distress,
For Thee to pardon and to bless,
To Thee, O Christ, I bring.

4 O Thou, my Judge and King—
With no excuse, for Thou art just,
My sins, that set me in the dust,
To Thee, O Christ, I bring.

5 O Thou, my Judge and King—
My soul, from depths of my disgrace,
To seek for mercy at Thy face,
To Thee, O Christ, I bring.

LAUCHLAN MACLEAN WATT, 1867–

403 ST. BRIDE. (S.M.)

SAMUEL HOWARD, 1710–82.

Lah = G. Doh = B♭. *Moderately slow.*

l, :—	m, :l,	d :t,	l, :—		d :—	s, :d	m :r	d :—		m :—
m, :—	m, :d,.r,	m, :m,.r,	d, :—		m, :—	m, :—.f,	s, :s,.f,	m, :—		s, :—
d :—	l, :l,	l, :se,	l, :—		m :—	d :d	d :t,	d :—		d :—
l_2 :—	d, :f,	m, :m,	l_2 :—		l, :—	d.t, :l,	s, :s,	d, :—		d :—

r :d	t, :l,	s, :f,	m, :—		m :—	l, :r	d :t,	l, :—		l,	l,	
s, :m,	s, :f,	m, :r,.d,	t_2 :—		m, :—	d, :f,	l, :se,	l, :—		f,	m,	
t, :d	m :d	d.t, :l,	se, :—		se, :—	l, :l,.t,	d.r :m.r	d :—		r	de	
s, :l,	m, :f,	d, :r,	m, :—		m, :—	f, :r,	m, :m,	l_2 :—		r,	l_2	

A-men.

Μνώεο Χριστέ.

LORD Jesus, think on me,
And purge away my sin;
From earthborn passions set me free,
And make me pure within.

2 Lord Jesus, think on me,
With care and woe opprest;
Let me Thy loving servant be,
And taste Thy promised rest.

3 Lord Jesus, think on me,
Amid the battle's strife;
In all my pain and misery
Be Thou my health and life.

4 Lord Jesus, think on me,
Nor let me go astray;
Through darkness and perplexity
Point Thou the heavenly way.

5 Lord Jesus, think on me,
When flows the tempest high:
When on doth rush the enemy,
O Saviour, be Thou nigh.

6 Lord Jesus, think on me,
That, when the flood is past,
I may the eternal brightness see,
And share Thy joy at last.

SYNESIUS OF CYRENE, 375–430; *tr.* by ALLEN WILLIAM CHATFIELD, 1808–96.

404 ALICE. (87. 87.)

Lah = E. Doh = G. *Moderately slow.* ROBERT ROBERTS, 1863–

l_1 :m	r :d	t_1 :l_1.t_1	l_1 :se_1	r :d	f :m	m :r	m :—
m_1 :l_1	se_1 :l_1	f_1 :f_1	m_1 :m_1	m_1 :m_1	s_1 :s_1	l_1 :t_1.l_1	se_1 :—
d :d	r :m	r :d.r	d :t_1	t_1 :d	r :m	f :l_1	t_1 :—
l_1 :d	t_1 :l_1	r_1 :r_1	m_1 :m_1	se_1 :l_1	t_1 :d	f_1 :f_1	m_1 :—

l_1 :m	r :d	l :s.l	s :f	m :m	m :l_1.d	t_1 :t_1	l_1 :—	l_1	l_1
l_1 :s_1	s_1 :d.t_1	l_1 :m	m :r	t_1 :d	m_1 :l_1	l_1 :se_1	l_1 :—	f_1	m_1
d :d	f :m	m :m	l :l	se :l	d :m	f :m.r	d :—	r	de
l_1 :d	t_1 :d	de :de	r :r	m :d.t_1	l_1 :d_1	r_1 :m_1	l_1 :—	r_1	l_1

A-men.

LORD, Thy mercy now entreating,
Low before Thy throne we fall;
Our misdeeds to Thee confessing,
On Thy Name we humbly call.

2 Sinful thoughts and words unloving
Rise against us one by one:
Acts unworthy, deeds unthinking,
Good that we have left undone;

3 Hearts that far from Thee were straying,
While in prayer we bowed the knee;
Lips that, while Thy praises sounding,
Lifted not the soul to Thee;

4 Precious moments idly wasted,
Precious hours in folly spent;
Christian vow and fight unheeded;
Scarce a thought to wisdom lent.

5 Lord, Thy mercy still entreating,
We with shame our sins would own;
From henceforth, the time redeeming,
May we live to Thee alone.

6 Heavenly Father, bless Thy children;
Hearken from Thy throne on high;
Loving Saviour, Holy Spirit,
Hear and heed our humble cry.

MARY ANN SIDEBOTHAM, 1833–1913.

[May be sung to ST. NICOLAS, No. 150.]

405

HEILIGER GEIST. (7 7 7.)

Lah = E. Doh = G. *Very slow and solemn.* *Vollständige Psalmen*, Bremen, 1639.

```
l, :— :d  | t, :— :de | r :— :d  | t, :— :—  || d :— :r  | m :— :f
m, :— :l, | t, :— :l, | l, :— :l, | l, :— :se, || l, :— :l, | l, :s, :d
d :— :m   | m :— :m   | r :— :f  | t, :— :—  || l, :m :r | d :m :l
l, :— :l, | se, :— :s, | f, :— :r, | m, :— :— || l, :— :t, | d :— :r,

m :— :r      | d :— :— || m :— :d   | t, :— :l,      | l, :— :se,   | l, :— :—     || l, | l,
d :— :t,     | d :— :— || t, :— :l, | f, :— :r,      | m, :— :m,    | m, :— :—     || f, | m,
s :— :s      | m :— :— || m :— :m   | r :— :l,       | t, :-.d :r   | d :— :—      || r  | de
m, :-.f, :s, | d :— :— || se, :— :l, | r, :-.m, :f,  | m, :— :m,    | l, (l,2) :— :— || r, | l,
                                                                              A-men.
```

ST. PHILIP. (7 7 7.)

Doh = E♭. *Moderately slow.* William Henry Monk, 1823–89.

```
d :— :d   | r :— :m  | f :m :r    | d :— :— || m :— :f  | s :— :s
s, :— :l, | t, :— :d | d :— :t,   | d :— :— || s, :— :d | t, :— :d
m :— :m   | s :— :s  | l :s :f    | m :— :— || d :— :d  | r :— :s
d :— :l,  | s, :— :d | f, :s, :s, | d :— :— || d :— :l, | s, :— :m,

l :s :f     | m :— :— || m :— :r  | f :— :m   | r :— :r   | d :— :— || d  | d
d :— :t,    | d :— :— || d :— :s, | d :— :d   | d :— :t,  | d :— :— || l, | s,
f :d :r     | d :— :— || s :— :s  | f :— :s   | l :— :s   | m :— :— || f  | m
f, :m, :s,  | d :— :— || d :— :t, | l, :— :m, | f, :— :s, | d :— :— || f, | d
                                                                    A-men.
```

LORD, in this Thy mercy's day,
Ere it wholly pass away,
On our knees we fall and pray.

2 Holy Jesus, grant us tears,
Fill us with heart-searching fears,
Ere that awful doom appears.

3 Lord, on us Thy Spirit pour,
Kneeling lowly at Thy door,
Ere it close for evermore.

4 By Thy night of agony,
By Thy supplicating cry,
By Thy willingness to die,

5 By Thy tears of bitter woe
For Jerusalem below,
Let us not Thy love forgo.

6 Judge and Saviour of our race,
When we see Thee face to face,
Grant us 'neath Thy wings a place.

Isaac Williams, 1802–65.

406 WIGTOWN. (C.M.)

Doh = F. *Moderately slow.* *Scottish Psalter*, 1635.

```
| m  :—  | m  :m  | f  :-.m  | r.d   :r    | d  :—  || m  :—  | m  :r  | m   :f
| s, :—  | s, :l, | l, :-.d  | l,    :t,   | d  :—  || d  :—  | s, :s, | s,  :d
| s  :—  | m  :d  | r  :-.s  | f.m   :s.f  | m  :—  || s  :—  | d  :r  | d   :d
| d  :—  | d  :l, | r, :-.m, | f,.l, :s,   | d  :—  || d  :—  | d  :t, | d.t, :l,

| s  :—  || r   :—  | r   :m  | l  :s  | f     :m      | r  :—  || r  :—
| t, :—  || ta, :—  | ta, :d  | l, :t, | d.s,  :s,.l,  | t, :—  || s, :—
| r  :—  || s   :—  | s   :s  | f  :m  | m.r   :m.f    | s  :—  || s  :—
| s, :—  || s,  :—  | s,  :d  | f, :s, | l,.t, :d      | s, :—  || t, :—

| m  :f  | r  :r     | d  :—  | —  :—  || d  | d  ||
| s, :l, | s, :-.f,  | m, :—  | —  :—  || f, | m, ||
| m  :d  | d  :t,    | d  :—  | —  :—  || l, | s, ||
| d  :f, | s, :s,    | d, :—  | —  :—  || f, | d, ||
                                          A-men.
```

Śiṣyahī gaṇāyā nahī yogya j̊o tayālā.

ONE who is all unfit to count
As scholar in Thy school,
Thou of Thy love hast named a friend—
O kindness wonderful!

2 So weak am I, O gracious Lord,
So all unworthy Thee,
That even the dust upon Thy feet
Outweighs me utterly.

3 Thou dwellest in unshadowed light,
All sin and shame above—
That Thou shouldst bear our sin and shame,
How can I tell such love?

4 Ah, did not He the heavenly throne
A little thing esteem,
And not unworthy for my sake
A mortal body deem?

5 When in His flesh they drove the nails,
Did He not all endure?
What name is there to fit a life
So patient and so pure?

6 So, Love itself in human form,
For love of me He came;
I cannot look upon His face
For shame, for bitter shame.

7 If there is aught of worth in me,
It comes from Thee alone;
Then keep me safe, for so, O Lord,
Thou keepest but Thine own.

From the Marathi of NARAYAN VAMAN TILAK, 1862–1919;
tr. by NICOL MACNICOL, 1870–

407

ALLEIN GOTT IN DER HÖH SEI EHR (STETTIN). (8 7. 8 7. 8 8 7.)

Geistliche Lieder, Leipsic, 1539. Arranged by FELIX MENDELSSOHN-BARTHOLDY, 1809-47.

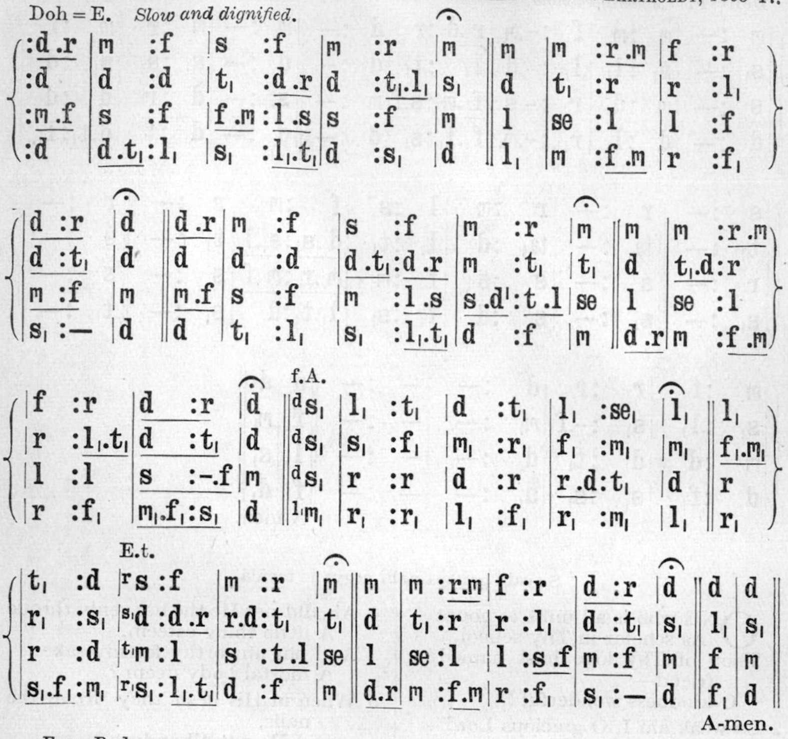

Doh = E. *Slow and dignified.*

:d .r |m :f |s :f |m :r |m ‖ m |m :r .m |f :r

:d |d :d |t, :d .r |d :t,.l, |s, ‖ d |t, :r |r :l,

:m .f |s :f |f .m :l .s |s :f |m ‖ l |se :l |l :f

:d |d .t, :l, |s, :l,.t, |d :s, |d ‖ l, |m :f .m |r :f,

|d :r |d ‖ d .r |m :f |s :f |m :r |m ‖ m |m :r .m

|d :t, |d ‖ d |d :d |d .t, :d .r |m :t, |t, ‖ d |t,.d :r

|m :f |m ‖ m .f |s :f |m :l .s |s .d' :t .l |se ‖ l |se :l

|s, :— |d ‖ d |t, :l, |s, :l,.t, |d :f |m ‖ d .r |m :f .m

f.A.

|f :r |d :r |d ‖ [d]s, |l, :t, |d :t, |l, :se, |l, ‖ l,

|r :l,.t, |d :t, |d ‖ [d]s, |s, :f, |m, :r, |f, :m, |m, ‖ f,.m,

|l :l |s :-.f |m ‖ [d]s, |r :r |d :r |r .d :t, |d ‖ r

|r :f, |m,.f, :s, |d ‖ [l]m, |r, :r, |l, :f, |r, :m, |l, ‖ r,

E.t.

|t, :d |[r]s :f |m :r |m ‖ m |m :r.m |f :r |d :r |d ‖ d |d ‖

|r, :s, |[s]d :d .r |r.d :t, |t, ‖ d |t, :r |r :l, |d :t, |s, ‖ l, |s, ‖

|r :d |[t]m :l |s :t .l |se ‖ l |se :l |l :s .f |m :f |m ‖ f |m ‖

|s,.f, :m, |[r]s, :l,.t, |d :f |m ‖ d.r |m :f.m |r :f, |s, :— |d ‖ f, |d ‖

A-men.

From Psalm cxxx.

Aus tiefer Noth schrei ich zu Dir.

FROM depths of woe I raise to Thee
  The voice of lamentation;
Lord, turn a gracious ear to me,
  And hear my supplication:
If Thou shouldst be extreme to mark
Each secret sin and misdeed dark,
  O who could stand before Thee?

2 To wash away the crimson stain,
  Grace, grace alone availeth;
Our works, alas! are all in vain;
  In much the best life faileth:
No man can glory in Thy sight,
All must alike confess Thy might,
  And live alone by mercy.

3 Therefore my trust is in the Lord,
And not in mine own merit;
On Him my soul shall rest, His word
Upholds my fainting spirit:
His promised mercy is my fort,
My comfort and my sweet support;
I wait for it with patience.

4 What though I wait the livelong night,
And till the dawn appeareth,
My heart still trusteth in His might;
It doubteth not, nor feareth:
So let the Israelite in heart,
Born of the Spirit, do his part,
And wait till God appeareth.

5 Although our sin is great indeed,
God's mercies far exceed it;
His hand can give the help we need,
However much we need it:
He is the Shepherd of the sheep
Who Israel doth guard and keep,
And shall from sin redeem him.

MARTIN LUTHER, 1483–1546; *tr.* by RICHARD MASSIE, 1800–87.

408 COLWINSTONE. (88. 84.)

Doh = E. *Moderately slow.* JOHN MORGAN LLOYD, 1880–

```
.m  :t,.d  |f   :-.m  :r .,r   |r  :—  :m    |f .l :m  :s   |r .,d :r  :-.s
.s, :s,.s, |s,  :-.s, :l,.,d   |t, :—  :d    |d .d :d  :d   |l,.,l,:t, :-.t,
.s  :f .m  |r   :-.m  :l .,r   |s  :—  :s    |f .f :s  :s   |m .,fe:s  :-.s
.d  :r .m  |t,  :-.d  :f,.,fe, |s, :—  :d.t, |l,.f,:d  :m,  |l,.,l,:s, :-.m,

|f .m  :f  :f   |m .r :d   |—  :r   |m  :—  :r   |d  :-.  ||d  |d  ||
|de.de :r  :d   |t,.t,:l,  |—  :d   |d  :—  :t,  |d  :-.  ||l, |s, ||
|l .s  :f  :l   |se.se:l   |m  :fe  |s  :—  :f   |m  :-.  ||f  |m  ||
|l,.l, :r, :r,  |m,.m,:l,  |—  :l,  |s, :—  :s,  |d  :-.  ||f, |d  ||
```

[*Copyright*, 1927, *by Oxford University Press.*] A-men.

THERE is a holy sacrifice
Which God in heaven will not despise,
Yea, which is precious in His eyes,
The contrite heart.

2 That lofty One, before whose throne
The countless hosts of heaven bow down,
Another dwelling-place will own,
The contrite heart.

3 The Holy One, the Son of God,
His pardoning love will shed abroad,
And consecrate as His abode
The contrite heart.

4 The Holy Spirit from on high
Will listen to its faintest cry,
And cheer and bless and purify
The contrite heart.

5 Saviour, I cast my hopes on Thee;
Such as Thou art, I fain would be;
In mercy, Lord, bestow on me
The contrite heart.

CHARLOTTE ELLIOTT, 1789–1871.

409 GIESSEN. (88. 88. 88.)

Doh = D. *In moderate time.* *Gauntlett's Comprehensive Tune Book*, 1851.

```
:m |m :d :s |s :m :d' |d' :t :l |s :— :f |m :r :d |l :— :s
:d |d :— :r |d :— :m |f :— :d |d :— :r |d :t, :d |d :r :m
:s |s :m :r |m :s :l |l :s :f |m :— :s |s :f :s |l :t :d'
:d |d :— :t, |d :— :l, |f, :— :l, |d :— :t, |d :r :m |f :— :m

                                 A.t.                           v. 1.
|s :f :m |r :— ||m |m :d :s |s :m :d' |d'f :m :r |m :— :(f)
|r :— :d |t, :— ||d |d :— :r |d :— :m |r s, :— :s, |s, :— :(f,)
|s :— :s |s :— ||s |s :m :r |m :s :l |fe t, :d :r |d :— :(d)
|t, :— :d |s, :— ||d |d :— :t, |d :— :l, |r s, :l, :t, |d :— :(l,)

                                 f.D.
|s :d :f |f :m :r |m :— :r |d :— ||d s |s :m :m |f :— :f
|d :ta, :l, |s, :— :l, |s, :— :f, |m, :— ||m t, |de :— :de |r :— :d
|d :s :f |t, :d :d |d :— :t, |d :— ||d s |m :— :l |l :— :f
|m, :m, :f, |r, :m, :f, |s, :— :s, |d, :— ||d s, |l, :— :l, |r :— :r
 Op - en  Thine arms

|f :r :r |m :— :m |m :r :d |l :t :d' |f :m :r |d :— ||d |d ||
|t, :— :t, |d :— :d |d :t, :d |d :r :d |d :— :t, |d :— ||l, |s, ||
|s :— :s |s :— :s |s :f :s |l :f :s |l :s :f |m :— ||f |m ||
|s, :— :s, |d :— :d |d :r :m |f :r :m |f :s :s, |d :— ||f, |d ||
                                                          A-men.
```

O JESUS, full of pardoning grace,
More full of grace than I of sin,
Yet once again I seek Thy face;
Open Thine arms and take me in,
And freely my backslidings heal,
And love the faithless sinner still.

2 Thou know'st the way to bring me back,
My fallen spirit to restore;
O, for Thy truth and mercy's sake,
Forgive, and bid me sin no more;
The ruins of my soul repair,
And make my heart a house of prayer.

3 Ah! give me, Lord, the tender heart
That trembles at the approach of sin;
A godly fear of sin impart,
Implant, and root it deep within,
That I may dread Thy gracious power,
And never dare offend Thee more.

CHARLES WESLEY, 1707–88.

410 VOX DILECTI. (D.C.M.)

Lah = G. Doh = B♭. *In moderate time.* JOHN BACCHUS DYKES, 1823–76.

```
:m, |m, :l, |l, :t, |d :-.d |t, :t, |l, :l, |l, :l, |se, :- |- ||
:m, |m, :l, |l, :t, |d :-.d |t, :f, |m, :m, |r, :f, |m, :- |- ||
:m, |m, :l, |l, :t, |d :-.d |t, :r |d :d |l, :r |t, :- |- ||
:m, |m, :l, |l, :t, |d :-.d |t, :s, |l, :l, |f, :r, |m, :- |- ||
```

G.t.m.l.

```
:m, |m, :l, |l, :t, |d :-.r |t, :m |r :d |t, :l, |s, :- |- ||
:m, |m, :m, |f, :f, |m, :-.m, |m, :t, |r, :m, |f, :fe, |s, :- |- ||
:t, |d :d |d :r |d :l, |t, :t, |l, :l, |t, :t,.l, |t, :- |- ||
:se, |l, :l, |f, :r, |l, :l, |s, :s, |f, :m, |r, :re, |s, :- |- ||
```

```
:s, |s, :m |r :d |d :l, |s, :s, |d :r.m |f :m.r |r :- |- ||
:s,.f, |m, :m, |f, :s, |l, :f, |m, :s, |m, :f,.s, |l,.t, :d |t, :- |- ||
:m.r |d :-.s, |l,.t, :d |d :d.r |m :r |d :d.t, |d.r :m.f |s :- |- ||
:s, |d :d, |d,.r, :m, |f, :l,.t, |d :t, |l, :l,.s, |f, :d |s, :- |- ||
```

v. 2. Of that
v. 3. In Him

```
:r |s :-.f |m :m |l :-.s |f :r |d :m |s :-.t, |d :- |- ||d |d ||
:s, |s, :-.s, |s, :l, |l, :-.l, |l, :l,.t, |d :d |t, :-.s, |s, :- |- ||l, |s, ||
:t,.d |r :-.r |d :de.r |m :-.m |r :f |m :s |f :-.f |m :- |- ||f |m ||
:s,.l, |t, :-.t, |d :l,.t, |de :-.de |r :f, |s, :s, |s, :-.s, |d, :- |- ||f, |d, ||
```

A-men.

I HEARD the voice of Jesus say,
 'Come unto Me and rest;
Lay down, thou weary one, lay down
 Thy head upon My breast':
I came to Jesus as I was,
 Weary, and worn, and sad;
I found in Him a resting-place,
 And He has made me glad.

2 I heard the voice of Jesus say,
 'Behold, I freely give
The living water; thirsty one,
 Stoop down and drink, and live':
I came to Jesus, and I drank
 Of that life-giving stream;
My thirst was quenched, my soul revived,
 And now I live in Him.

3 I heard the voice of Jesus say,
 'I am this dark world's Light;
Look unto Me, thy morn shall rise,
 And all thy day be bright':
I looked to Jesus, and I found
 In Him my Star, my Sun;
And in that light of life I'll walk,
 Till travelling days are done.

HORATIUS BONAR, 1808–89.

411 MISERICORDIA. (88. 86.)

Doh = E♭. *In moderate time.* HENRY SMART, 1813–79.

|m :r :d |f :— :m |l :— :l |s :— :— |s :t, :d
|d :s, :s, |d :— :d |d :— :r |s, :— :— |d :t, :l,
|s :f :m |f :— :s |l :— :t |d' :— :— |s :f :f
|d :d :d |l, :— :s, |f, :— :f |m :— :— |m :r :d

|r :— :m |d :— :f |m :r :— ||r :s :r |m :— :l
|s, :— :s, |l, :— :r |d :t, :— ||t, :r :t, |d :— :m
|f :— :m |f :— :l |s :— :— ||s :r :s |s :— :d'
|t, :— :d |f :m :r |s, :— :— ||s, :t, :s, |d :t, :l,

s :— :fe	s :l :t	d' :t :l	s :— :f	m :— :—		f	m	
r :— :r	r :— :r	d :— :d	d :— :t,	d :— :—		d	d	
t :— :l	s :fe :f	m :s :f	m :r :s	s :— :—		l	s	
r :— :d	t, :l, :se,	l, :m, :f,	s, :— :s,	d :— :—		f,	d	

A-men.

GWYNETH. (88. 86.)

Lah = G. Doh = B♭. *Moderately slow.* JOHN PRICE (BEULAH), 1857–

d :t,.l,	d :t,.l,	t, :l,	l, :se,.se,	l,.t, :d .r	m :-.m,	s, :fe,	m, :—	
m, :m,.m,	f, :- .m,	f, :m,.f,	m, :- .m,	m, :l,.se,	l, :-.m,	m, :re,	m, :—	
d :d .d	r :-.d	r :l,.t,	d :t, .t,	d .r :m	m :-.l,	t, :l,	s, :—	
l, :l,.l,	se, :- .l,	r, :d,.r,	m, :- .m,	l, :l,.t,	d :-.d,	t,, :t,,	m, :—	

s, :s,.s,	l, :-.l,	d :r	m :—	d :t,.l,	m, :t,	l, :—		l,	l,	
m, :m,.m,	m, :-.m,	l, :l,	s, :—	d :t,.l,	m, :se,	l, :—		f,	m,	
d :m .r	d :-.d	d :d	d :—	d :t,.l,	m :r	d :—		r	de	
d, :d .t,	l, :-.l,	f, :f,	d, :—	d :t,.l,	m, :m,	l, l,, :—		r,	l,,	

A-men.

[*Copyright*, 1927, *by Oxford University Press*.]

JUST as I am, without one plea
But that Thy blood was shed for me,
And that Thou bidd'st me come to Thee,
O Lamb of God, I come.

2 Just as I am, and waiting not
To rid my soul of one dark blot,
To Thee, whose blood can cleanse each spot,
O Lamb of God, I come.

3 Just as I am, though tossed about
With many a conflict, many a doubt,
Fightings and fears within, without,
O Lamb of God, I come.

4 Just as I am, poor, wretched, blind,—
Sight, riches, healing of the mind,
Yea, all I need, in Thee to find,
O Lamb of God, I come.

5 Just as I am, Thou wilt receive,
Wilt welcome, pardon, cleanse, relieve;
Because Thy promise I believe,
O Lamb of God, I come.

6 Just as I am—Thy love unknown
Has broken every barrier down—
Now to be Thine, yea, Thine alone,
O Lamb of God, I come.

7 Just as I am, of that free love
The breadth, length, depth, and height to prove,
Here for a season, then above,—
O Lamb of God, I come.

CHARLOTTE ELLIOTT, 1789–1871.

412 NONE OTHER LAMB. (8 10. 10 4.)

Lah = B. Doh = D. *In moderate time.* CHARLES JOSEPH RIDSDALE, 1840–

f.G.

```
:ʳl,  |t,  :t,  |d   :—  |—  :d   |r   :r   |m  :—  |—  :m   |f   :s
:ˡm,  |f,  :m,  |m,  :—  |—  :d   |d   :t,  |d  :—  |—  :l,  |l,  :s,
:ᶠd   |r   :r   |d   :—  |—  :m   |l   :s   |s  :—  |—  :m   |r   :r
:ʳl,  |l,  :se, |l,  :—  |—  :l,  |f,  :s,  |d  :—  |—  :d   |d   :t,

                          D.t.
|m  :r   |f   :m   |r   :r   |ᵈf   :—  |—  ||l  |se :l   |t   :se  |l  :t   |d' :d'
|s, :s,  |f,  :s,  |l,  :s,  |ᵐl,  :—  |—  ||d  |r  :m   |f   :m   |m  :m   |m  :re
|d  :r   |d   :d   |d   :t,  |ˢd   :—  |—  ||l  |t  :d'  |r'  :t   |l  :se  |l  :fe
|d  :t,  |l,  :s,  |f,  :s,  |ᵈf,  :—  |—  ||f  |f  :m   |r   :r   |d  :t,  |l, :l,

|t  :—  |— :—  |  :  |r' :—  |t :—  |t  :—  |l  :—  |— :—  |  :  ||l  |l
|m  :—  |— :—  |  :  |r  :—  |f :—  |m  :—  |d  :—  |— :—  |  :  ||r  |de
|se :—  |— :—  |  :  |l  :—  |l :—  |se :—  |l  :—  |— :—  |  :  ||f  |m
|m  :—  |— :—  |  :  |f  :—  |r :—  |m  :—  |l, :—  |— :—  |  :  ||r  |l,
                                                                   A-men.
```

NONE other Lamb, none other Name,
None other Hope in heaven or earth or sea,
None other Hiding-place from guilt and shame,
None beside Thee.

2 My faith burns low, my hope burns low;
Only my heart's desire cries out in me,
By the deep thunder of its want and woe,
Cries out to Thee.

3 Lord, Thou art Life, though I be dead;
Love's Fire Thou art, however cold I be:
Nor heaven have I, nor place to lay my head,
Nor home, but Thee.

CHRISTINA GEORGINA ROSSETTI, 1830–94.

413 PETRA. (77. 77. 77.)

Doh = D. *Moderately slow.* RICHARD REDHEAD, 1820–1901.

```
d  :d  |r  :m |f  :-.f |m  :— |d :d  |r  :m |r  :r  |d  :— ||
s, :s, |t, :d |d  :-.d |d  :— |s, :l, |t, :d |d  :t, |d  :— ||
m  :m  |s  :s |l  :-.l |s  :— |m :m  |s  :s |l  :s  |m  :— ||
d  :d  |s, :d |f, :-.f,|d  :— |d :l, |s, :d |f, :s, |d  :— ||
```

```
d :m  |s  :s  |l :l |s  :— |d :d |s  :s  |l :-.l |s  :— ||
d :d  |r  :m  |d :r |m  :— |d :d |r  :t, |m :r.d |t, :— ||
m :l  |t  :d' |l :t |d' :— |s :s |s  :s  |s :fe  |s  :— ||
d :l, |s, :d  |f :f |d  :— |m :d |t, :m  |d :r   |s  :— ||
```

```
d :d |r  :m |f  :-.f  |m :— |d :r  |m :r  |d  :t, |d  :— || d  |d  ||
d :d |t, :d |d  :-.d  |d :— |d :t, |d :l, |s, :s, |s, :— || l, |s, ||
s :s |f  :s |l  :-.l  |s :— |s :f  |s :f  |m  :r  |m  :— || f  |m  ||
m :m |r  :d |f, :-.f, |d :— |m :r  |d :f, |s, :s, |d  :— || f, |d  ||
```

A-men.

PASCAL. (77. 77. 77.)

Doh = F. *Moderately slow.* *Katholisches Gesangbuch*, Vienna, *c.* 1774.

```
d  :—:d  |d  :t, :d  |r  :m :r  |d :—:— |m :—:m |m :r  :m
s, :—:s, |s, :— :s,  |t, :— :t, |d :—:— |d :—:d |d :t, :d
m  :—:m  |m  :r  :m  |f  :s  :f |m :—:— |s :—:s |s :—  :s
d  :—:d  |d  :— :d   |s, :— :s, |d :—:— |d :—:d |d :—  :d
```

D.C.

```
s :f  :m |r  :— :— || r  :— :m  |f :—  :r  |m :— :f
d :t, :d |t, :— :— || t, :r  :de |r :l, :t, |d :— :d
s :—  :s |s  :— :— || s  :l  :s  |f :—  :s  |s :— :d
m :r  :d |s, :— :— || s  :f  :m  |r :—  :s, |d :— :l,
```

```
s  :— :—  |l  :— :l  |s  :— :m  |f  :m  :r  |d :— :— || d  |d  ||
t, :— :—  |l, :d  :d |d  :t, :d  |d  :—  :t, |d :— :— || l, |s, ||
r  :— :m  |f  :— :f  |r  :— :d  |l  :s  :f  |m :— :— || f  |m  ||
s, :— :—  |f, :— :f, |s, :— :l, |f, :s, :s, |d :— :— || f, |d, ||
```

A-men.

NICHT SO TRAURIG. (77. 77. 77.)

Ascribed to Johann Sebastian Bach, 1685–1750.

Lah = G. Doh = B♭. *Slow and dignified.*

```
| d  :t1.l1 | m     :r.d  | t1 :d  .r   | se1 :— || l1.t1 :d  | f1 :m1    | r1 :s1 | m1 :— ||
| m1 :r1    | d1.r1 :m1   | f1 :m1 .r1  | m1  :— || m1    :m1 | r1.t2 :d1 | d1 :t2 | d1 :— ||
| l1 :se1   | l1    :l1   | l1 :se1.l1  | t1  :— || l1    :l1 | l1 :s1    | s1 :s1 | s1 :— ||
| l2 :t2    | d1    :l2   | r1 :m1 .f1  | m1  :— || d1.t2 :l2 | r1 :m1.f1 | s1 :s2 | d1 :— ||

| d  :t1.l1 | m     :r.d  | t1 :d  .r   | se1 :— || l1.t1 :d  | f1 :m1    | r1 :s1 | m1 :— ||
| m1 :r1    | d1.r1 :m1   | f1 :m1 .r1  | m1  :— || m1    :m1 | r1.t2 :d1 | d1 :t2 | d1 :— ||
| l1 :se1   | l1    :l1   | l1 :se1.l1  | t1  :— || l1    :l1 | l1 :s1    | s1 :s1 | s1 :— ||
| l2 :t2    | d1    :l2   | r1 :m1 .f1  | m1  :— || d1.t2 :l2 | r1 :m1.f1 | s1 :s2 | d1 :— ||

| m  :s1 | fe1   :s1 | d  :t1.l1 | t1 :— || t1 :d.r | se1   :m     | d  :t1.l1 | l1 :— || l1 | l1  ||
| d1 :d1 | r1    :r1 | m1 :r1    | r1 :— || r1 :r1  | m1    :m1    | m1 :r1.d1 | d1 :— || r1 | de1 ||
| s1 :s1 | l1    :s1 | s1 :fe1   | s1 :— || s1 :l1  | t1    :l1    | l1 :se1   | l1 :— || f1 | m1  ||
| d1 :m1 | r1.d1 :t2 | l2 :r1    | s2 :— || s1 :f1  | m1.r1 :d1.r1 | m1 :m1    | l2 :— || r1 | l2  ||
```

A-men.

ROCK of Ages, cleft for me,
Let me hide myself in Thee ;
Let the water and the blood,
From Thy riven side which flowed,
Be of sin the double cure,
Cleanse me from its guilt and power.

2 Not the labours of my hands
Can fulfil Thy law's demands ;
Could my zeal no respite know,
Could my tears for ever flow,
All for sin could not atone :
Thou must save, and Thou alone.

3 Nothing in my hand I bring,
Simply to Thy Cross I cling ;
Naked, come to Thee for dress ;
Helpless, look to Thee for grace ;
Foul, I to the fountain fly ;
Wash me, Saviour, or I die.

4 While I draw this fleeting breath,
When mine eyelids close in death,
When I soar through tracts unknown,
See Thee on Thy judgment throne,
Rock of Ages, cleft for me,
Let me hide myself in Thee.

Augustus Montague Toplady, 1740–78.

414 HOLLINGSIDE. (77. 77. D.)

Doh = E♭. *In moderate time.* JOHN BACCHUS DYKES, 1823–76.

```
|m  :s  |l   :s  |s   :-.f |m  :—  |d'  :t   |l   :s   |m   :d   |r   :—  ||
|d  :d  |l,  :d  |d   :r   |s, :—  |d   :d   |d   :t,  |d   :d   |t,  :—  ||
|s  :s  |d'  :s  |l   :t   |d' :—  |s   :s   |f   :f   |s   :fe  |s   :—  ||
|d  :m  |f   :m  |r   :s,  |d  :—  |m   :m   |f   :r   |d   :l,  |s,  :—  ||
```

```
|m  :s  |l   :s  |s   :-.f |m  :—  |m   :f   |m   :r   |m   :-.r |d   :—  ||
|d  :d  |d.f :m  |r   :d   |t, :—  |d   :d   |d   :d   |d   :t,  |d   :—  ||
|s  :m  |f.l :d' |t   :l   |se :—  |l   :f   |s   :l   |s   :f   |m   :—  ||
|d  :d  |d   :d  |r   :r   |m  :—  |l,  :l,  |s,  :f,  |s,  :s,  |d   :—  ||
```

```
f.A♭.                               E♭.t.
|ds,   :d   |t,  :d   |f     :m  |r  :—  |ml  :l   |t   :d'  |f     :m  |r   :—  ||
|l,m,  :s,  |s,  :s,  |l,    :s, |t, :—  |s,d :d   |f   :m   |d.r   :d  |t,  :—  ||
|fd    :d   |r   :m   |d.r   :m  |s  :—  |ml  :s   |f   :s   |l     :s  |s   :—  ||
|f,d,  :m,  |s,  :d   |l,.t, :d  |s, :—  |df  :m   |r   :d   |l,.t, :d  |s,  :—  ||
```

```
|m  :s  |l   :s  |s   :-.f |m  :—  |m   :f   |m   :r   |m   :-.r |d   :—  ||d  |d  ||
|d  :d  |d.f :m  |r   :d   |t, :—  |d   :d   |d   :d   |d   :t,  |d   :—  ||l, |s, ||
|s  :m  |f.l :d' |t   :l   |se :—  |l   :f   |s   :l   |s   :f   |m   :—  ||f  |m  ||
|d  :d  |d   :d  |r   :r   |m  :—  |l,  :l,  |s,  :f,  |s,  :s,  |d   :—  ||f, |d  ||
                                                                             A-men.
```

ABERYSTWYTH. (77. 77. D.)

Lah = E. Doh = G. *Slow.* JOSEPH PARRY, 1841–1903.

```
|l,  :l,.t,   |d .r  :m      |d   :t,   |l,  :—  |d   :t,   |l,  :se,  |l,.t, :d   |t,   :—  ||
|m,  :l,.se,  |l,.t, :d      |l,  :se,  |m,  :—  |l,  :se,  |l,  :m,   |m,    :l,  |se,  :—  ||
|d   :m       |m     :m      |m   :m.r  |d   :—  |m   :m    |m   :m    |m     :m   |m    :—  ||
|l,  :m,      |l,    :d,.r,  |m,  :m,   |l,  :—  |l,  :t,   |d   :r    |d .t, :l,  |m,   :—  ||
```

l_1 :l_1.t_1	d.r :m	d :t_1	l_1 :—	t_1 :d .r	m :r	d :t_1	l_1 :—	
m_1 :m_1.se_1	l_1.t_1 :d	l_1 :se_1	m_1 :—	se_1 :l_1.t_1	d :t_1	l_1 :se_1	m_1 :—	
d.r :m	m :m	m :t_1 .r	d :—	m :m .s	s :f	m :m .r	d :—	
l_1.t_1 :d .t_1	l_1 :d_1.r_1	m_1 :m_1	l_1 :—	m_1 :l_1.s_1	d :r	m :m_1	l_1 :—	

l_1 :s_1	l_1 :t_1	d :m .r	d :—	d :t_1	d :r	m :s .fe	m :—	
f_1 :m_1	f_1 :f_1	s_1 :t_1	s_1 :—	l_1 :se_1	l_1 :t_1.s_1	s_1 :t_1.l_1	s_1 :—	
d :d	d :r	m :s .f	m :—	m :m	m :s .t_1	d .m :- .re	m :—	
f_1 :d_1	f_1.m_1 :r_1	d_1 :s_1	d_1 :—	l_1 :m_1	l_1 :s_1	d :t_1	m_1 :—	

l :l	s :m	d :r	m :—	l_1 :l_1.t_1	d .r :m	d :t_1	l_1 :—		l_1	l_1	
l_1 :d.t_1	d :s_1	l_1 :l_1	t_1 :—	l_1 :l_1.se_1	l_1.t_1 :d	l_1 :se_1	m_1 :—		f_1	m_1	
d :f	s :d	m :l	se :—	m .f :m .r	m :m	m :t_1,d.r	d :—		r	de	
f_1 :f	m :d	l_1 :f_1	m_1 :—	d .r :d .t_1	l_1 :d_1.r_1	m_1 :m_1	l_1 :—		r_1	l_1	

A-men.

[*By permission of Hughes & Son, Wrexham.*]

JESUS, Lover of my soul,
Let me to Thy bosom fly,
While the nearer waters roll,
While the tempest still is high;
Hide me, O my Saviour, hide,
Till the storm of life is past;
Safe into the haven guide;
O receive my soul at last!

2 Other refuge have I none;
Hangs my helpless soul on Thee;
Leave, ah! leave me not alone;
Still support and comfort me.
All my trust on Thee is stayed;
All my help from Thee I bring;
Cover my defenceless head
With the shadow of Thy wing.

3 Thou, O Christ, art all I want;
More than all in Thee I find;
Raise the fallen, cheer the faint,
Heal the sick, and lead the blind.
Just and holy is Thy Name,
I am all unrighteousness;
False and full of sin I am,
Thou art full of truth and grace.

4 Plenteous grace with Thee is found,
Grace to cover all my sin;
Let the healing streams abound;
Make and keep me pure within.
Thou of life the fountain art,
Freely let me take of Thee;
Spring Thou up within my heart,
Rise to all eternity.

CHARLES WESLEY, 1707–88.

415 OLIVET. (664. 6664.)

Doh = E♭. *In moderate time.* LOWELL MASON, 1792–1872.

d :—	m :s	s :-.f	m :—	r :—	r :f	f :-.m	r :—	m :—	r :fe
s, :—	d :d	r :-.r	d :—	t, :—	t, :r	r :-.d	t, :—	s, :—	t, :d
m :—	s :m	s :-.s	s :—	s :—	f :r	s :-.s	s :—	m :—	s :l
d :—	d :d	t, :-.t,	d :—	s, :—	s, :s,	t, :-.d	s, :—	d :—	r :r

s :—	— :—		s :—	m :f	s :-.l	s :—	s :—	m :f	s :-.l
t, :—	— :—		d :—	d :d	d :-.d	d :—	m :—	d :r	m :-.f
s :—	— :—		m :—	d :r	m :-.f	m :—	s :—	s :s	d' :-.d'
s, :—	— :—		d :—	d :d	d :-.d	d :—	d :—	d :d	d :-.d

s :—	d' :—	t :l	s :-.f	m :d	r :—	s :—	d :—	— :—		f	m	
m :r	d :—	r :r	m :-.r	d :d	d :—	t, :—	d :—	— :—		d	d	
d' :s	m :l	s :f	m :-.f	s :s	l :—	s :f	m :—	— :—		l	s	
d :t,	l, :—	t, :t,	d :-.r	m :m,	f, :—	s, :—	d :—	— :—		f,	d	

A-men.

DENBIGH. (664. 6664.)

Lah = G. Doh = B♭. *Moderately slow.* Welsh Melody.

l, :—	l, :t,	d :t,	l, :—	t, :—	d :r	m :r	m :—	m :r
m, :—	m, :f,	m, :r,	d, :—	m, :—	m, :s,	s, :l,	se, :—	m, :f,
d :—	d :t,	l, :se,	l, :—	se, :—	l, :t,	d :l,	t, :—	l, :—
l,, :—	d, :r,	m, :m,	l,, :—	m, :—	l, :s,	d, :f,	m, :—	d, :r,

d :t,	l, :—		m :—	m :r	d :r	t, :—	d :-.r	m :l,	s, :fe,
m, :r,	d, :—		s, :—	s, :s,	s, :s,.fe,	s, :—	m, :—	m, :m,	m, :re,
l, :se,	l, :—		d :—	d :f	m :r	r :—	d :-.t,	d :d	t, :l,
m, :m,	l,, :—		d :—	d :t,	d :l,	s, :—	l, :—	l, :l,,	t,, :t,,

m_1 :—	m_1 :—	l_1 :t_1	d :r	m :—	r :—	d :t_1	l_1 :—	l_1	l_1
m_1 :—	m_1 :—	m_1 :m_1	m_1 :s_1	s_1 :—	f_1 :—	m_1 :r_1	d_1 :—	r_1	de_1
s_1 :—	t_1 :—	d :se_1	l_1 :t_1	d :—	l_1 :—	l_1 :se_1	l_1 :—	f_1	m_1
m_1 :—	m_1 :–.r_1	d_1 :m_1	l_1 :s_1	d_1 :—	r_1 :—	m_1 :m_1	l_2 :—	r_1	l_2

A - men.

MY faith looks up to Thee,
Thou Lamb of Calvary,
Saviour Divine :
Now hear me while I pray ;
Take all my guilt away ;
O let me from this day
Be wholly Thine.

2 May Thy rich grace impart
Strength to my fainting heart,
My zeal inspire ;
As Thou hast died for me,
O may my love to Thee
Pure, warm, and changeless be,
A living fire.

3 While life's dark maze I tread,
And griefs around me spread,
Be Thou my Guide ;
Bid darkness turn to day,
Wipe sorrow's tears away
Nor let me ever stray
From Thee aside.

4 When ends life's transient dream,
When death's cold, sullen stream
Shall o'er me roll,
Blest Saviour, then, in love,
Fear and distrust remove ;
O bear me safe above,
A ransomed soul.

RAY PALMER, 1808-87.

Also the following :

5 Father of heaven, whose love profound
94-114 *Hymns of our Lord's Sufferings and Death*
416-37 *Hymns of Love and Gratitude*
449-83 *Hymns of Prayer, Aspiration, and Holiness*
690 Thou who didst on Calvary bleed

LOVE AND GRATITUDE

416

PENIEL. (88. 88. 88.)

Doh = G. *In moderate time.* SAMUEL SEBASTIAN WESLEY, 1810–76.

:d |m :s |r :m.r |d :r |m :m |m :r |d :f |f :m |r ||
:s, |s, :d |t, :t, |t,.l, :s, |s, :s, |s, :t, |d :d |s, :s, |s, ||
:m |s :s |s :m |m :s.f |m :d |d :s.f |m :d |r :d |t, ||
:d |d, :m, |s, :s, |l, :t, |d :d |s, :s, |l, :l, |t, :d |s, ||

D.t.

:m |d :l, |s, :d |r :m |f :r |m :^{s}d' |t :l |l :se |l ||
:s, |s, :d, |s, :m, |l, :t, |d :s, |s, :^{m}l, |t, :r |m :m |d ||
:d |d :d |d :m |r :t, |l, :r |d :^{t}m |f :l |d' :t |l ||
:d, |m, :f, |m, :l, |f, :s, |l, :t, |d :^{s}d |r :f |m :m |l, ||

f.G.

:^{l}m |s :s |d :d |m :m |l, :l, |s, :s, |d :r |m :r |d || d |d ||
:^{d}s,.d |d :t, |t, :m,.l, |l, :s, |s, :f, |f, :m,.r, |d, :d |d :t, |d || l, |s, ||
:^{l}m |r :s |m :d |t, :m |d :r |r :d.r |m :l |s :s.f |m || f |m ||
:^{f}d |s, :s, |l, :l, |m, :m, |f, :r |t, :d.t, |l,.s, :f, |s, :s, |d || f, |d, ||

A-men.

COME, O Thou Traveller unknown,
Whom still I hold but cannot see;
My company before is gone,
And I am left alone with Thee;
With Thee all night I mean to stay,
And wrestle till the break of day.

2 I need not tell Thee who I am,
My misery or sin declare;
Thyself hast called me by my name;
Look on Thy hands, and read it there.
But who, I ask Thee, who art Thou?
Tell me Thy Name, and tell me now.

3 Yield to me now, for I am weak,
But confident in self-despair;
Speak to my heart, in blessings speak;
Be conquered by my instant prayer.
Speak, or Thou never hence shalt move,
And tell me if Thy Name is Love.

4 'Tis Love! 'tis Love! Thou diedst for me!
I hear Thy whisper in my heart;
The morning breaks, the shadows flee;
Pure universal Love Thou art;
To me, to all, Thy mercies move;
Thy nature and Thy Name is Love.

5 I know Thee, Saviour, who Thou art,
Jesus, the feeble sinner's Friend;
Nor wilt Thou with the night depart,
But stay and love me to the end:
Thy mercies never shall remove;
Thy nature and Thy Name is Love.

CHARLES WESLEY, 1707–88.

[May be sung to ISRAEL, No. 110.]

417

ST. BEES. (77. 77.)

Doh = A♭. *In moderate time.* JOHN BACCHUS DYKES, 1823–76.

```
| d   :d   | d   :-.t, | l,  :t,  | d   :—  | r   :r   | m   :s,  | l,  :r   | t,  :—  ||
| s,  :s,  | f,  :-.f, | f,  :f,  | m,  :—  | s,  :s,  | s,  :s,  | s,  :f,  | r,  :—  ||
| m   :m   | r   :-.r  | d   :r   | m   :—  | r   :f   | m   :d   | d   :l,  | r   :—  ||
| d   :d   | s,  :-.s, | s,  :s,  | d   :—  | t,  :t,  | d   :m,  | f,  :f,  | s,  :—  ||

| r   :f   | m   :-.d  | t,  :r   | d   :—  | d   :r   | d   :d   | d   :-.t, | d   :—  || d  | d  ||
| s,  :s,  | s,  :-.s, | f,  :f,  | m,  :—  | l,  :l,  | s,  :s,  | s,  :-.s, | s,  :—  || l, | s, ||
| r   :r   | m   :-.m  | r   :t,  | d   :—  | f   :f   | m   :r.d | r   :-.r  | m   :—  || f  | m  ||
| t,  :t,  | d   :-.d  | s,  :s,  | l,  :—  | f,  :f,  | s,  :s,  | s,  :-.s, | d,  :—  || f, | d, ||
                                                                                         A-men.
```

NUN KOMM, DER HEIDEN HEILAND. (77. 77.) *Wittenberg Gesangbuch*, 1524.

Lah = G. Doh = B♭. *Slow.* Arranged by JOHANN SEBASTIAN BACH, 1685–1750.

```
| l,     :l,     | s,     :d         | t,.l,  :t,     | l,  :— || l,.t,   :d      | r      :d      | r,  :m      | d,  :— ||
| m,     :r,     | m,     :m,.f,,s,  | f,.m,  :r,     | d,  :— || m,      :-.fe,  | s,     :-.l,   | f,  :m,     | f,  :— ||
| d      :t,.l,  | t,     :l,        | l,     :-.se,  | m,  :— || d.t,    :l,     | t,     :d      | t,  :d.ta,  | l,  :— ||
| l,.s,  :f,     | m,.r,  :d,.l,,    | r,.d,  :r,.m,  | l,, :— || l,,     :l,     | s,.f,  :m,.f,  | r,  :d,     | f,  :— ||

| d      :r      | m.r    :d       | r.d    :t,     | l,  :— || l,        :l,       | s,     :d       | t,.l,  :t,     | l,  :— ||
| s,     :s,     | s,.se, :l,      | t,.l,  :se,    | m,  :— || re,.m,    :fe,      | m,     :m,      | f,.d,  :r,     | d,  :— ||
| s,     :r      | d.t,   :l,      | f      :t,     | d   :— || t,        :t,       | t,     :l,      | l,     :-.se,  | l,  :— ||
| m,.r,  :d,.t,, | d,     :f,.m,   | r,     :m,     | l,, :— || t,,.de,   :re,.t,,  | m,.r,  :d,.l,,  | r,.f,  :m,     | l,, :— ||
```

HARK, my soul! it is the Lord;
'Tis thy Saviour, hear His word;
Jesus speaks, and speaks to thee:
'Say, poor sinner, lov'st thou Me?

2 'I delivered thee when bound,
And, when bleeding, healed thy wound;
Sought thee wandering, set thee right;
Turned thy darkness into light.

3 'Can a woman's tender care
Cease towards the child she bare?
Yes, she may forgetful be,
Yet will I remember thee.

4 'Mine is an unchanging love,
Higher than the heights above,
Deeper than the depths beneath,
Free and faithful, strong as death.

5 'Thou shalt see My glory soon,
When the work of grace is done;
Partner of My throne shalt be;
Say, poor sinner, lov'st thou Me?'

6 Lord, it is my chief complaint
That my love is weak and faint;
Yet I love Thee, and adore;
O for grace to love Thee more!

WILLIAM COWPER, 1731–1800.

```
| l,  | l,  ||
| r,  | de, ||
| f,  | m,  ||
| r,  | l,, ||
  A - men.
```

418 SOUTHWELL. (C.M.)

Doh = E. *In moderate time.* HERBERT STEPHEN IRONS, 1834–1905.

```
:d   |m :m   |s  :d     |d  :l      |s :s    |d' :m     |r  :r  |r  :— |— ||
:s,  |d :d   |t, :d.t,  |l, :l,.t,  |d :m.r  |d  :d.t,  |l, :l, |t, :— |— ||
:m   |s :l   |r  :s     |f  :d.r    |m :s    |l  :l.s   |s  :fe |s  :— |— ||
:d   |d :l,  |s, :m,    |f, :f,     |d :d.t, |l, :d     |r  :r  |s, :— |— ||
```

```
:s   |s :l.s |f    :f   |f   :s.f |m :d     |d  :f  |m  :s  |d :— |— ||d  |d  ||
:r   |m :m   |m.de :r   |r.d :t,  |d :d.ta, |l, :r  |d  :t, |d :— |— ||l, |s, ||
:t   |t :l   |l    :l   |s   :s   |s :s     |l  :l  |s  :s.f|m :— |— ||f  |m  ||
:s.f |m :de  |r    :r.d |t,  :s,  |d :m,    |f, :r, |s, :s, |d :— |— ||f, |d  ||
```

A-men.

CLIFTON. (C.M.)

Doh = E♭. *Moderately slow.* JOHN CHARLES CLIFTON, 1781–1841.

```
                                                    B♭.t.
:d  |m  :—  :r  |d  :t,   :d  |r  :m   :—    |f  :— :^r s,    |d       :—  :l,.t, |
:s, |s, :d  :l, |s, :—    :s, |l, :ta, :l,.s,|f, :— :^l r,    |s,.,f,  :m, :f,    |
:m  |m  :—  :f  |m  :r    :m  |r  :—   :de   |r  :— :^fe t,   |d       :—  :d     |
:d  |d  :l, :f, |s, :—.f, :m, |f, :s,  :l,   |r, :— :^r s,.f, |m,.,r,  :d, :f,    |
```

```
                        f.E♭.
|d.,r   :m  :r       |d  :— |^d s.d' |d' :t  :d'.t |l    :—    :s.f    |m     :f.m   :r.d    |
|s,.,l, :s, :f,      |m, :— |^f d.m  |r  :—  :d    |d    :r.m  :s,.t,  |d     :—     :l,     |
|d      :—  :t,      |d  :— |^d s    |s  :—  :s    |l.s  :f.m  :r.s    |s     :f.s   :l      |
|m,.,f, :s, :s, (:s₂)|d, :— |^l m.d  |s  :—  :m    |f.m  :r.d  :t,.s,  |d.ta, :l,.s, :f,.fe, |
```

```
|m    :r  :s    |f     :—.s   :m     |m.r    :d  :t,  |d  :— ||d  |d  ||
|d    :t, :t,   |d.t,  :d.r   :d.ta, |l,     :s, :s,  |s, :— ||l, |s, ||
|m.fe :s  :r.m  |d.s   :f.r   :m.s   |f      :m  :r.f |m  :— ||f  |m  ||
|s,   :—  :s,   |l,.s, :l,.t, :d.m,  |f,.r,  :s, :s,  |d  :— ||f, |d  ||
```

A-men.

JESUS, these eyes have never seen
That radiant form of Thine;
The veil of sense hangs dark between
Thy blessèd face and mine.

2 I see Thee not, I hear Thee not,
Yet art Thou oft with me;
And earth hath ne'er so dear a spot
As where I meet with Thee.

3 Like some bright dream that comes unsought,
When slumbers o'er me roll,
Thine image ever fills my thought,
And charms my ravished soul.

4 Yet, though I have not seen, and still
Must rest in faith alone,
I love Thee, dearest Lord, and will,
Unseen but not unknown.

5 When death these mortal eyes shall seal,
And still this throbbing heart,
The rending veil shall Thee reveal
All glorious as Thou art.

RAY PALMER, 1808–87.

419 ST. PETER. (C.M.)

ALEXANDER ROBERT REINAGLE, 1799–1877.

Doh = E♭. *In moderate time.*

:s | d' :t | l :s | s :f | m :m | r :d | f :m | r :— | — ||
:d | m :m | d :d | r :t, | d :d | l, :s, | t, :d | t, :— | — ||
:m | s :s | f :s | s :s | s :s | f :s | s :s | s :— | — ||
:d | d :m | f :m | t, :s, | d :d | f :m | r :d | s, :— | — ||

:m | f :m | l :s | s :f | m :d | m :r | d :t, | d :— | — || d | d ||
:d | d :d.ta, | l,.t, :d | d :t, | d :l, | d :l, | s, :s, | s, :— | — || l, | s, ||
:s | f :s | d .r :m | l :s | d :m | s :f | m :r | m :— | — || f | m ||
:d.ta, | l, :s, | f, :m, | r, :s, | l, :l, | m, :f, | s, :s, | d :— | — || f, | d ||

A-men.

HOW sweet the Name of Jesus sounds
In a believer's ear!
It soothes his sorrows, heals his wounds,
And drives away his fear.

2 It makes the wounded spirit whole,
And calms the troubled breast;
'Tis manna to the hungry soul,
And to the weary rest.

Unison.

3 Dear Name! the rock on which I build,
My shield and hiding-place,
My never-failing treasury, filled
With boundless stores of grace.

4 Jesus, my Shepherd, Husband, Friend,
My Prophet, Priest, and King,
My Lord, my Life, my Way, my End,
Accept the praise I bring.

Harmony.

5 Weak is the effort of my heart,
And cold my warmest thought;
But, when I see Thee as Thou art,
I'll praise Thee as I ought.

6 Till then I would Thy love proclaim
With every fleeting breath;
And may the music of Thy Name
Refresh my soul in death.

JOHN NEWTON, 1725–1807.

420 MARYTON. (L.M.)

Doh = E. *In moderate time.* HENRY PERCY SMITH, 1825–98.

```
m :m :m | f :— :m | r :— :r | r :— :— | s :s :f | m :— :d'
d :d :d | d :— :d | l, :— :l, | t, :— :— | t, :d :r | d :— :m
s :s :s | l :— :s | l :— :r | s :— :— | s :s :s | s :— :s
d :d :d | d :— :d | f, :— :fe, | s, :— :— | s, :l, :t, | d :— :l,

d' :t :l | s :— :— || s :l :s | d' :— :t | t :l :s
m :r :d | t, :— :— || r :r :r | d :— :d | d :— :d
fe :— :fe | s :— :— || t :l :t | s :— :s | f :— :s
r :— :r | s, :— :— || f :f :f | m :— :m | f :— :m

f :— :m | r :— :d | f :— :m | r :l, :t, | d :— :— || d | d ||
d :t, :d | t, :— :l, | r :— :d | l, :— :s, | s, :— :— || l, | s, ||
s :— :s | f :— :m | s :— :s | f :— :r | m :— :— || f | m ||
r :— :d | s, :— :l, | t, :— :d | f, :r, :s, | d :— :— || f, | d ||
```

A-men.

JESU DULCIS MEMORIA. (L.M.)

Lah = G. Doh = B♭. *In moderate time.* *Andernach Gesangbuch*, 1608.

```
l, :s,.l, | t, :t, | d :t,.l, | t, :— | l, :s,.l, | t, :s,
m, :m,.m, | s, :s, | s, :s,.l, | se, :— | m, :m,.m, | m, :m,
d :t,.d | r :r | m :r.l, | m :— | d :t,.d | t, :t,
l, :m,.l, | s, :s, | d, :s,.f, | m, :— | l, :m,.l, | s, :m,

l, :s,.fe, | m, :— || l, :s,.l, | t, :t, | d :t,.l, | t, :—
m, :re, | m, :— || m, :m,.m, | s, :s, | s, :s,.l, | m, :—
d :t,.l, | se, :— || l, :t,.d | r :r | m :r.l, | se, :—
l,, :t,, | m, :— || d, :m,.l, | s, :s, | d, :s,.f, | m, :—

m :m.r | m :-.r | d :t, | l, :— || l, | l, ||
m, :s,.s, | s, :-.f, | m, :m, | d, :— || r, | de, ||
s, :d.t, | d :-.l, | l, :se, | l, :— || f, | m, ||
d, :d,.s, | d, :-.r, | m, :m, | l,, :— || r, | l,, ||
```

A-men.

Jesu, Dulcedo cordium.

JESUS, Thou Joy of loving hearts,
Thou Fount of life, Thou Light of men,
From the best bliss that earth imparts
We turn unfilled to Thee again.

2 Thy truth unchanged hath ever stood;
Thou savest those that on Thee call:
To them that seek Thee Thou art good,
To them that find Thee, all in all.

3 We taste Thee, O Thou living Bread,
And long to feast upon Thee still;
We drink of Thee, the Fountain-head,
And thirst our souls from Thee to fill.

4 Our restless spirits yearn for Thee,
Where'er our changeful lot is cast,—
Glad when Thy gracious smile we see,
Blest when our faith can hold Thee fast.

5 O Jesus, ever with us stay;
Make all our moments calm and bright;
Chase the dark night of sin away;
Shed o'er the world Thy holy light.

Attributed to St. Bernard of Clairvaux, 1091–1153;
tr. by Ray Palmer, 1808–87.

421 CHRISTE, REDEMPTOR OMNIUM. (L.M.)

Plainsong Melody, 13th cent. Mode i.

Ray = E. *Unison.* *In free rhythm.*

| d :r :m :s :s :f :m :r :f :m :r :d :r | d :m :s :s :l :l |

| :l :s :s :d' :t :l :s :l | l :d' :s :s :f :m :r :d :r :r :m :m |

| d :r :m :s :s :f :m :r :f :m :r :d :r :— || r :m :r :d :r ||

A - men.

Jesu dulcis memoria.

JESUS! the very thought is sweet,
In that dear Name all heart-joys meet;
But sweeter than the honey far
The glimpses of His presence are.

2 No word is sung more sweet than this,
No name is heard more full of bliss,
No thought brings sweeter comfort nigh
Than Jesus, Son of God most high.

3 Jesus, Thou sweetness pure and blest,
Truth's fountain, Light of souls distressed,
Surpassing all that heart requires,
Exceeding all that soul desires!

4 No tongue of mortal can express,
No pen can write the blessedness;
He only who hath proved it knows
What bliss from love for Jesus flows.

5 Jesus, the hope of souls forlorn,
How good to them for sin that mourn!
To them that seek Thee, O how kind!
But what art Thou to them that find!

6 We follow Jesus now, and raise
The voice of prayer, the hymn of praise,
That He at last may make us meet
With Him to gain the heavenly seat.

Attributed to St. Bernard of Clairvaux, 1091–1153;
tr. by John Mason Neale, 1818–66.

422 ROCHESTER. (C.M.)

Doh = F. *In moderate time.* CHARLES HYLTON STEWART, 1884–

C.t.

:(d) | d :r :m | f :m :r | d :— :r | m :— :fet | d' :— :s
:(s,) | m, :s, :d | l, :— :l, | s, :l, :s, | s, :— :df | s :f :m
:(m) | s :f :m | d :— :f | d :— :t, | d :— :d'f' | m' :r' :d'
:(d) | d :d :d, | r, :m, :f, | m, :f, :r, | d, :— :l,r | m :— :m

(Omit in vv. 1 & 5.)

f.F.

f :m :r | d :— || m(t,) | d :r :m | f :m :r | s :— :f
r :d :t, | d :— || d(s,) | d :t, :d | f, :s, :t, | d :l, :t,
l :s :f | m :— || s(r) | s :f :m | d :— :r | d :m :r
f :s :s, | d :— || d(s,) | m :r :d | l, :s, :f, | m, :f, :s,

(Omit in v. 5.)

m :f :s | l :— :s | f :m :r | d :— || d | d
d :— :t, | l, :t, :d | d :— :t, | d :— || l, | s,
d :— :m | f :— :s | l :— :r | m :— || f | m
l, :— :s, | f, :r, :m, | f, :— :s, | d d, :— || f, | d d, ||

[*Copyright, 1924, by J. Curwen & Sons, Ltd.*] A-men.

ST. AGNES, DURHAM. (C.M.)

Doh = G. *In moderate time.* JOHN BACCHUS DYKES, 1823–76.

m :m :m | r :— :m | f :— :t, | d :— :— | s, :s, :s,
s, :s, :s, | l, :— :s, | f, :l, :s, | s, :— :— | s, :s, :s,
m :m :d | f :— :d | r :— :r | m :— :— | f :m :r
d :d :m, | f, :— :m, | r, :— :s, | d :— :— | r :d :t,

m :— :r | r :— :— | f :f :m | r :— :d | t, :— :l,
s, :— :fe, | s, :— :— | l, :l, :s, | f, :— :fe, | s, :— :fe,
d :— :d | t, :— :— | l, :t, :de | r :— :r | r :— :d
d :— :l, | s, :— :— | r, :r, :r, | r, :— :r, | s, :— :s,

s, :— :— | s, :l, :d | m :— :r | d :— :— || d | d
s, :— :— | s, :s, :f, | m, :s, :f, | m, :— :— || f, | m,
t, :— :— | d :d :d | d :— :t, | d :— :— || l, | s,
s, :— :f, | m, :f, :l, | s, :— :s, | d, :— :— || f, | d, ||

A-men.

Jesu dulcis memoria.

JESUS, the very thought of Thee
 With sweetness fills my breast;
But sweeter far Thy face to see,
 And in Thy presence rest.

2 Nor voice can sing, nor heart can frame,
 Nor can the memory find
A sweeter sound than Thy blest Name,
 O Saviour of mankind!

3 O Hope of every contrite heart,
 O Joy of all the meek,
To those who fall how kind Thou art!
 How good to those who seek!

4 But what to those who find? Ah, this
 Nor tongue nor pen can show;
The love of Jesus, what it is
 None but His loved ones know.

5 Jesus, our only joy be Thou,
 As Thou our prize wilt be;
Jesus, be Thou our glory now,
 And through eternity.

Attributed to St. Bernard of Clairvaux, 1091–1153;
tr. by Edward Caswall, 1814–78.

423 METZLER. (C.M.)

Doh = D. *In moderate time.* Richard Redhead, 1820–1901.

```
:m |r  :d  |d' :s  |l  :l  |s  :s  |l  :t   |d' :t    |l  :— |— ||
:d |t, :d  |d  :d  |d  :r  |m  :m  |d  :f   |m  :-.r  |d  :— |— ||
:s |f  :m  |s  :d' |l  :t  |d' :d' |d' :t.l |l  :se   |l  :— |— ||
:d |s, :l, |m, :m  |f  :f  |d  :d  |f  :r   |m  :m,   |l, :— |— ||

:l |l :s |l :s.f |m :r    |s :d  |f     :m |r  :r    |d :— |— || d  |d  ||
:d |d :d |d :r   |d :t,   |d :l, |l,.t, :d |d  :t,   |d :— |— || l, |s, ||
:f |f :m |f :l   |s :s    |s :l  |f     :s |s  :-.f  |m :— |— || f  |m  ||
:f |f :d |f :r   |s :-.f  |m :f  |r     :d |s, :s,   |d :— |— || f, |d  ||
                                                                   A-men.
```

Jesu, Rex admirabilis.

O JESUS, King most wonderful,
 Thou Conqueror renowned,
Thou Sweetness most ineffable,
 In whom all joys are found!

2 When once Thou visitest the heart,
 Then truth begins to shine,
Then earthly vanities depart,
 Then kindles love divine.

3 O Jesus, Light of all below,
 Thou Fount of life and fire,
Surpassing all the joys we know,
 And all we can desire,—

4 May every heart confess Thy Name,
 And ever Thee adore,
And, seeking Thee, itself inflame
 To seek Thee more and more.

5 Thee may our tongues for ever bless;
 Thee may we love alone,
And ever in our lives express
 The image of Thine own.

Attributed to St. Bernard of Clairvaux, 1091–1153;
tr. by Edward Caswall, 1814–78.

424 INNELLAN. (88. 88. 6.)

Doh = A♭. *Moderately slow.* DAVID EVANS, 1874-

:s, |d :-.s, |l, :d |f :m.r |m :— |— :m, |l, :s, |d :m
:s, |d, :m, |f, :s, |l, :s, |s, :— |— :m, |l, :s, |d :s,
:s, |s :-.m |d :d |d :t, |d :— |— :m, |l, :s, |s :s,.l,
:s, |m, :d, |f, :m, |r, :s, |d, :— |— :m, |l, :s, |m, :d,

|r.t, :t,.l, |s, :— |— ‖ s |f :m |r :f |m :r |d :s,
|s, :fe, |s, :— |— ‖ ta, |l, :t,.de |r :f, |s, :l,.t, |d :s,
|t,.r :r.d |t, :— |— ‖ r |r :l, |l :-.l |s :f |m :s,
|r, :r, |s, :— |— ‖ s, |l, :s, |f, :r, |m, :f,.s, |l, :s,

|l, :d |f.m :r.d |t, :d |r :s, |s :-.m |d :r |d :— |— ‖
|l, :d |f.m :r.d |t, :d |r :s, |d :-.s, |l, :t, |d :— |— ‖
|l, :d |f.m :r.d |t, :d |r :s, |s :-.d |m :s.f |m :— |— ‖
|l, :d |f.m :r.d |t, :d |r :s, |m :m, |l, :s, |d, :— |— ‖

Last verse.

:s, |l, :d |f.m :r.d |t, :d |r :— |s :s.m |d :r
:s, |l, :d |f.m :r.d |t, :d |r :— |d :d.s, |l, :t,
And from the ground there blos - soms red Life that shall end - less
:s, |l, :d |f.m :r.d |t, :d |r :— |s :s.d |m :s.f
:s, |l, :d |f.m :r.d |t, :d |r :— |m :m,.m, |l, :s,

pp *rall.*

|d :— |— ‖ d :r.m |f :— |— :m :r |m :— :— ‖
|d :— |— ‖ d :t, |l, :— |-.t, :d :— |d :— :— ‖
be. A - - - - - - - men.
|m :— |— ‖ d :— |— :r.m |f :s :l |s :— :— ‖
|d, :— |— ‖ l, :s, |f, :m, |r, :m, :f, |d, :— :— ‖

[*Copyright*, 1927, *by David Evans.*]

ST. MARGARET. (88. 88. 6.)

Doh = A♭. *Slow.* ALBERT LISTER PEACE, 1844–1912.

```
:s,  |s,   :-.s,  |s,.l,  :t,.d      |d   :—  |t,  :t,  |t,  :-.t,  |t,.d  :r.m
:m,  |s,   :-.s,  |s,.s,  :fe,.fe,   |s,  :—  |—   :s,  |s,  :-.s,  |s,.s, :t,.d
:d   |m    :-.m   |m.m    :d.d       |m   :—  |r   :r   |f   :-.f   |f.s   :s.s
:d,  |d    :-.d   |d.d    :l,.l,     |s,  :—  |—   :s,  |f   :-.f   |f.m   :r.d

s  :—  |f  ||f   |m   :-.m   |m.r      :d.t,      |r   :—  |d   :d   |d    :-.d
r  :—  |—  ||s,  |s,  :-.s,  |se,.se,  :se,.se,   |l,  :—  |—   :m,  |fe,  :-.fe,
s  :—  |—  ||r   |m   :-.m   |m.m      :m.m       |m   :—  |—   :d   |d    :-.d
t, :—  |—  ||t,  |d   :-.d   |t,.t,    :m,.m,     |l,  :—  |—   :l,  |r,   :-.r,

|d.d      :t,.l,     |s,  :-.l,   |t,  :d   |m   :—  |—   :r  |d   :—  |—  ||d   |d
|fe,.fe,  :fe,.fe,   |s,  :-.s,   |s,  :s,  |d   :—  |t,  :—  |d   :—  |—  ||l,  |s,
|d.d      :r.d       |{m  :-.d    |r   :m   |s   :—  |f   :—  |m   :—  |—  ||f   |m
                      {d  :-.d}
|r,.r,    :r,.r,     |s,  :-.s,   |s,  :s,  |s,  :—  |s,  :—  |d,  :—  |—  ||f,  |d,
                                                                          A - men.
```

[*By permission of Novello & Co., Ltd.*]

O LOVE that wilt not let me go,
 I rest my weary soul in Thee :
I give Thee back the life I owe,
That in Thine ocean depths its flow
 May richer, fuller be.

2 O Light that followest all my way,
 I yield my flickering torch to Thee :
My heart restores its borrowed ray,
That in Thy sunshine's blaze its day
 May brighter, fairer be.

3 O Joy that seekest me through pain,
 I cannot close my heart to Thee :
I trace the rainbow through the rain,
And feel the promise is not vain,
 That morn shall tearless be.

4 O Cross that liftest up my head,
 I dare not ask to fly from Thee :
I lay in dust life's glory dead,
And from the ground there blossoms red
 Life that shall endless be.

GEORGE MATHESON, 1842–1906.

[*By permission of Novello & Co., Ltd.*]

425 AMOR DEI. (88. 86.)

Kirchen Gesänge, Bremen, 1707.

Doh = F. *In moderate time.*

```
:d |s  :f  |m :m  |r  :-.r |d  :r  |m :fe |s  :s   |s :fe  |s  ||
:d |d  :t, |d :d  |d  :t,  |l, :t, |d :r  |r  :de  |r :r.d |t, ||
:m |m  :f  |s :s  |l  :s.f |m  :s  |s :l  |s  :s.l |t :l   |s  ||
:d |m  :r  |d :m, |f, :s,  |l, :s, |d :d  |t, :m   |r :r   |s, ||

:s |l :s  |f :s  |m :r  |r  :s  |d  :r  |m  :r   |d :— |— || d  |d  ||
:d |d :de |r :r  |d :d  |t, :s, |s, :l, |d  :t,  |d :— |— || l, |s, ||
:m |f :s  |l :s  |s :fe |s  :t, |d  :l  |s  :-.f |m :— |— || f  |m  ||
:d |f :m  |r :t, |d :l, |s, :f, |m, :f, |s, :s,  |d :— |— || f, |d  ||
                                                         A - men.
```

O SAVIOUR, I have nought to plead,
In earth beneath or heaven above,
But just my own exceeding need,
And Thy exceeding love.

2 The need will soon be past and gone,
Exceeding great, but quickly o'er;
The love unbought is all Thine own,
And lasts for evermore.

JANE CREWDSON, 1809–63.

426 ST. MARY MAGDALENE. (76. 76.)

Lah = G. Doh = B♭. *Slow.*

HAROLD ARTHUR JEBOULT, 1871–1925.

```
:d     |t,.d :r     |d  :t,.l, |se,.l, :t,  |m, :m,      |l,    :s, |f,.m, :f,
:d,.r, |m,   :l,    |s, :f,    |m,     :—   |m, :m,.t,,  |d,.r, :m, |l,,   :l,,.t,,
:l,    |t,   :l,.t, |d  :r.d   |t,     :m.r |d  :t,      |l,.t, :d  |r     :f,
:l,    |s,   :f,    |m, :r,    |m,.ba, :se, |l, :s,      |f,    :m, |r,    :r,

|m, :— |— ||m  |r      :d      |t,  :d        |t,   :l,    |se, :m,
|d, :— |— ||s, |s,.f,  :m,.r,  |m,  :m,       |f,   :r,    |m,  :t,,
|s, :— |— ||d  |t,     :l,     |se, :m        |r.d  :t,.l, |t,  :se,
|d, :— |— ||d  |s,     :l,     |m,  :l,,.d,   |r,   :f,    |m,  :m,.r,

|l, :s,.f, |m,     :t,     |l,        :— |— || l, |l,  ||
|m, :m,.r, |d,     :m,.r,  |d,        :— |— || r, |de, ||
|l, :l,    |l,.ba, :se,    |l,        :— |— || f, |m,  ||
|d, :r,    |m,     :m,     |{m, / l,,} :— |— || r, |l,, ||
                                              A - men.
```

O THOU, whose mercy found me,
From bondage set me free,
And then for ever bound me
With three-fold cords to Thee!

2 Though all the world deceive me,
I know that I am Thine,
And Thou wilt never leave me,
O blessèd Saviour, mine!

3 O for a heart to love Thee
More truly as I ought,
And nothing place above Thee,
In deed, or word, or thought!

4 O for that choicest blessing
Of living in Thy love,
And thus on earth possessing
The peace of heaven above!

JOHN SAMUEL BEWLEY MONSELL, 1811–75.

427 BODLONDEB. (6 4. 6 4. 10 10.)

Doh = F. *In moderate time.* EDWARD ARTHUR, 1874–

```
:s, |m :d |r :m  |l :—   |s :—  |d :—  |r :-.d   |t, :— |—  ||
:s, |m :d |d :d  |d :—   |t, :— |l, :— |l, :-.l, |s, :— |—  ||
:s, |m :d |l :s  |f :—   |— :—  |m :—  |f :-.m   |r :—  |—  ||
:s, |m :d |f :m  |r :—   |s, :— |l, :— |f, :-.f, |s, :— |—  ||
```

C.t. f.F.

```
:(m)l |se :m |m' :t  |r' :d' |t :l  |s :d'  |— :t  |(d')s :— |— :— ||
:(s)d |m :m  |m :m   |f :m   |re :— |m :s   |f :—  |(m)t, :— |— :— ||
:(m)l |t :se |m :se  |l :—   |t :d' |d' :m' |r' :— |(d')s :— |— :— ||
:(d)f |m :r  |d :m   |l :—   |fe :— |s :—   |s :—  |(d)s, :— |— :— ||
```

```
|m :— |r :m  |f :-.f   |m :f    |ta :— |l :—  |s :— |— ||
|d :— |t, :d |d :-.d   |ta, :l, |d :—  |d :—  |d :— |— ||
|s :— |s :s  |f :-.f   |d :d    |s :—  |f :—  |m :— |— ||
|d :— |s, :d |l, :-.l, |s, :f,  |m, :— |f, :— |d :— |— ||
```

```
:s |l :-.r  |m :f   |s :—  |d :r   |m :—  |r :—  |d :— |— || d  |d  ||
:d |d :-.d  |d :r   |s, :— |d :d   |d :—  |t, :— |d :— |— || l, |s, ||
:m |f :-.l  |s :l.t |d' :— |m :f   |s :—  |— :f  |m :— |— || f  |m  ||
:d |f, :-.f |m :r   |m :—  |l, :l, |s, :— |s, :— |d :— |— || f, |d, ||
```

A-men.

[*Copyright*, 1927, *by Edward Arthur.*]

I LIFT my heart to Thee,
Saviour Divine;
For Thou art all to me,
And I am Thine.
Is there on earth a closer bond than this,
That my Belovèd's mine, and I am His?

2 Thine am I by all ties;
But chiefly Thine,
That through Thy sacrifice
Thou, Lord, art mine.
By Thine own cords of love, so sweetly wound
Around me, I to Thee am closely bound.

3 To Thee, Thou bleeding Lamb,
I all things owe;
All that I have and am,
And all I know.
All that I have is now no longer mine,
And I am not mine own; Lord, I am Thine.

4 I pray Thee, Saviour, keep
Me in Thy love,
Until death's holy sleep
Shall me remove
To that fair realm where, sin and sorrow o'er,
Thou and Thine own are one for evermore.

CHARLES EDWARD MUDIE, 1818–90.

428 ALLGÜTIGER, MEIN PREISGESANG. (886. 886.)

Doh = G. *In moderate time.* GEORG PETER WEIMAR, 1734–1800.

```
:s     |m      :r      |d      :d     |r.m   :f.s   |m   ||s   |l    :s       |f      :m  |r    :d       |t,  ||
:m,.f, |s,.l,  :t,     |l,     :s,    |d     :t,    |d   ||d   |d    :-.ta,   |l,.t,  :d  |l,   :m,.fe,  |s,  ||
:d.r   |m.f    :s      |m      :s     |f     :r     |s   ||s   |f    :m       |f      :s  |f    :d       |r   ||
:d     |d      :s,     |l,     :m,    |r,    :s,    |d,  ||m,  |f,   :d,      |r,     :m, |f,   :l,      |s,  ||
```

f.C.

```
:r      |m       :r.d    |t,     :l,   |s,  :—  |—  ||[r]l   |t    :t     |l  :t.r'  |d'    :t    |l  ||
:s,.f,  |m,.fe,  :s,     |s,     :fe,  |s,  :—  |—  ||[s,]r  |r    :m     |m  :f     |m     :-.r  |d  ||
:t,     |d       :s,.l,  |t,.d   :r    |t,  :—  |—  ||[t,]fe |s    :se    |l  :l     |l.ba  :se   |l  ||
:s,     |d,.r,   :m,     |r,     :r,   |s,  :—  |—  ||[s,]r  |s.f  :m.r   |d  :r     |m     :m    |l  ||
```

G.t.

```
:[l]r   |m  :m   |r      :m.s  |f      :m      |r   ||s   |l    :s.f    |m      :r   |d  :—  |—  ||d   |d   ||
:[r]s,  |s, :s,  |l,.s,  :s,   |l,.t,  :d      |t,  ||d   |d    :d      |d.l,   :t,  |d  :—  |—  ||l,  |s,  ||
:[l]r   |d  :d   |d.t,   :d.m  |f      :s      |s   ||s   |s.f  :m.f    |s      :s   |m  :—  |—  ||f   |m   ||
:[fe]t, |d  :m,  |f,.s,  :m,   |r,     :d,.m,  |s,  ||m,  |f,   :s,.l,  |s,     :s,  |d  :—  |—  ||f,  |d,  ||
```

A-men.

SONG 18. (886. 886.)

Lah = E. Doh = G. *Moderately slow.* ORLANDO GIBBONS, 1583–1625.

```
:m   |m   :—  :d   |r   :—  :m   |d   :t,  :—   |l,  :—  ||d   |d   :—  :r
:l,  |l,  :—  :l,  |t,  :—  :d   |l,  :—   :se, |l,  :—  ||l,  |l,  :—  :t,
:d   |d   :—  :m   |s   :—  :s   |f   :t,  :m   |d   :—  ||m   |m   :—  :s
:l,  |l,  :—  :l,  |s,  :—  :d,  |r,  :m,  :—   |l,  :—  ||l,  |l,  :—  :s,
```

```
|m  :—  :m   |m   :—   :re  |m   :—  ||m   |s   :—  :r   |m   :—  :d   |t,   :—  ||
|d  :—  :d   |s,  :t,  :—   |t,  :—  ||t,  |t,  :—  :s,  |s,  :—  :l,  |se,  :—  ||
|s  :—  :l   |m   :ba  :—   |se  :—  ||s   |m   :—  :r   |d   :—  :m   |m    :—  ||
|d  :—  :l,  |d   :t,  :—   |m,  :—  ||m   |m   :—  :t,  |d   :—  :l,  |m    :—  ||
```

```
:t,  |d   :— :l,  |r   :— :t,  |m  :r  :—   |d  :— ||d  |f   :— :m
:se, |l,  :— :l,  |t,  :— :t,  |d  :— :t,   |d  :— ||l, |l,  :— :l,
:m   |m   :— :fe  |fe  :— :s   |s  :— :-.f  |m  :— ||d  |r   :— :de
:m,  |l,  :— :r   |t,  :— :m   |d  :s, :—   |d, :— ||f, |r,  :— :l,

|r  :—  :d  |t, :— :l, |se, :— ||t, |r   :— :d  |l,  :t, :—   |l, :— ||l, |l, ||
|f, :—  :s, |s, :— :m, |m,  :— ||s, |s,  :— :s, |l,  :— :se,  |l, :— ||f, |m, ||
|r  :t, :d  |r  :— :d  |t,  :— ||m  |r   :— :m  |m   :— :m    |d  :— ||r  |de ||
|r, :—  :m, |s, :— :l, |m,  :— ||m, |t,, :— :d, |l,  :m, :—   |l, :— ||r, |l, ||
                                                                          A-men.
```

O LOVE Divine, how sweet thou art!
When shall I find my willing heart
All taken up by thee?
I thirst, I faint, I die to prove
The greatness of redeeming love,
The love of Christ to me.

2 Stronger His love than death or hell;
Its riches are unsearchable:
The first-born sons of light
Desire in vain its depth to see;
They cannot reach the mystery,
The length, and breadth, and height.

3 God only knows the love of God:
O that it now were shed abroad
In this poor stony heart!
For love I sigh, for love I pine;
This only portion, Lord, be mine,
Be mine this better part.

4 O that I could for ever sit
Like Mary at the Master's feet!
Be this my happy choice:
My only care, delight, and bliss,
My joy, my heaven on earth be this,
To hear the Bridegroom's voice.

Charles Wesley, 1707–88

429 DALKEITH. (10 10. 10 10.)

THOMAS HEWLETT, 1845–74.

Doh = D. *In moderate time.*

```
                                                                 A.t.
|s  :—  |m  :r   |d  :d  |r :m |s :-.f |m :— |m :— |m  :m  |^d f  :f
|d  :—  |t, :t,  |d  :d  |d :d |d :t,  |d :— |d :— |r  :d  |^m l, :l,
|m  :—  |s  :f   |m  :s  |l :s |l :s   |s :— |s :— |se :l  |^l r  :d
|d  :—  |s, :s,  |l, :m  |f :m |r :s,  |d :— |d :— |t, :l, |^l r, :r,

                           f.D.
|m   :d  |l,  :-.l, |se, :— ||^l m  :— |s :s  |s  :f |f  :m  |r  :l
|se, :m, |m,  :re,  |m,  :— ||^m t, :— |m :m  |m  :r |r  :d  |r  :r
|t,  :d  |d   :l,   |t,  :— ||^d s  :— |t :ta |l  :l |t  :d' |d' :t
|m,  :l, |f,  :f,   |m,  :— ||^l m  :— |m :r  |de :r |s, :s  |fe :f

|s  :— |d' :— |d' :-.d' |d' :l  |s  :fe |s  :r  |d :— ||d  |d  ||
|s  :— |s  :— |m  :m    |f  :d  |d  :d  |d  :t, |d :— ||l, |s, ||
|d' :— |d' :— |ta :ta   |l  :f  |m  :re |m  :f  |m :— ||f  |m  ||
|m  :— |m  :— |d  :d    |f  :f, |s, :l, |s, :s, |d :— ||f, |d  ||
                                                         A-men.
```

NOT what I am, O Lord, but what Thou art!
That, that alone can be my soul's true rest;
Thy love, not mine, bids fear and doubt depart,
And stills the tempest of my tossing breast.

2 It blesses now, and shall for ever bless,
It saves me now, and shall for ever save,
It holds me up in days of helplessness,
It bears me safely o'er each swelling wave.

3 'Tis what I know of Thee, my Lord and God,
That fills my soul with peace, my lips with song;
Thou art my health, my joy, my staff, my rod;
Leaning on Thee, in weakness I am strong.

4 I am all want and hunger; this faint heart
Pines for a fulness which it finds not here:
Dear ones are leaving, and, as they depart,
Make room within for something yet more dear.

5 More of Thyself, O shew me hour by hour,
More of Thy glory, O my God and Lord;
More of Thyself, in all Thy grace and power,
More of Thy love and truth, Incarnate Word!

HORATIUS BONAR, 1808–89.

430 ST. CHRYSOSTOM. (88. 88. 88.)

JOSEPH BARNBY, 1838–96.

Doh = Eb. *In moderate time.* Bb.t.

m :m :m	m :— :r	d :— :r	m :— :—	(s)d :d :d	d :— :t,
s, :d :t,	l, :— :l,	s, :— :t,	d :— :—	(t)m, :l, :s,	f, :— :f,
s :s :s	s :— :f	m :— :s	s :— :—	(s)d :m :m	m :l, :r
d :d :d	f, :— :f,	s, :— :s,	d :— :—	(m)l, :l, :l,	r, :— :r,

f.Eb.

l, :— :t,	(d)s :— :—		s :l :t	d' :— :s	m :f :s	l :— :l
m, :l, :se,	(l)m :— :—		t, :d :r	d :— :d	d :— :d	d :— :d
d :— :r	(d)s :— :—		f :f :f	m :— :s	d' :— :ta	l :— :f
m, :— :m,	(l)m :— :—		r :r :s,	d :— :d	d :r :m	f :— :f

f.Ab. *Slower.*

l :— :m	s :— :f	f :s :l	r :— :—		(d)s, :s, :s,	l, :— :l,
de :r :m	m :— :r	r :m :f	t, :— :—		(d)s, :s, :s,	f, :— :f,
m :— :l	l :— :l	l :s :f	f :— :—		(m)t, :t, :t,	r :— :r
l, :t, :de	r :— :r	f, :— :f,	s, :— :—		(l)m, :m, :m,	r, :— :r,

Eb.t.

t, :l, :s,	d :— :—		(d)f :m :r	d :— :d	d :— :d	d :— :—		d	d	
f, :— :f,	m, :— :—		(d)f :m :r	d :— :d	d :t, :l,	s, :— :—		l,	s,	
r :d :t,	d :— :—		(d)f :m :r	d :— :d	l :s :f	m :— :—		f	m	
s, :— :s,	d, :— :—		(d)f :m :r	d :— :d	f, :— :f,	d :— :—		f,	d	

A-men.

[*By permission of Novello & Co., Ltd.*]

JESUS, my Lord, my God, my All,
Hear me, blest Saviour, when I call;
Hear me, and from Thy dwelling-place
Pour down the riches of Thy grace.
Jesus, my Lord, I Thee adore;
O make me love Thee more and more.

2 Jesus, too late I Thee have sought;
How can I love Thee as I ought?
And how extol Thy matchless fame,
The glorious beauty of Thy Name?

3 Jesus, what didst Thou find in me
That Thou hast dealt so lovingly?
How great the joy that Thou hast brought,
So far exceeding hope or thought!

Unison.
4 Jesus, of Thee shall be my song;
To Thee my heart and soul belong;
All that I have or am is Thine,
And Thou, blest Saviour, Thou art mine.

HENRY COLLINS, 1827–1919.

431

NEW 113TH. (88. 88. 88.)

Doh = A. *Moderately slow.* WILLIAM HAYES, 1706–77.

```
:d  | t, :-.l,:s, | d  :r  :m  | m  :r  :d  | d  :t, :t, | d  :r  :m  | r.,m:f :m
:s, | f, :-  :r,  | s, :-  :s, | l, :-  :l, | s, :-  :s, | s, :f, :m, | s,  :-  :s,
:m  | r  :-  :t,  | d  :t, :d  | d  :f  :m  | r  :-  :r  | d  :t, :d  | r   :-  :d
:d, | r, :-  :f,  | m, :s, :d  | f, :-  :f, | s, :-  :f, | m, :r, :d, | t,, :-  :d,

| r  :d  :t,  | d  :-  || m  | r  :-  :m   | d  :-  :t,  | d  :t, :l,  | m   :-  :t,
| f, :m, :r,  | m, :-  || s, | s, :-  :m,  | m, :-  :se, | l, :m, :l,  | se, :-  :se,
| l, :-  :r   | d  :-  || d  | r  :-  :t,  | l, :-  :m   | m  :-  :m.r | t,  :-  :m
| f, :-  :s,  | d, :-  || d  | t, :-  :se, | l, :-  :m,  | l, :s, :f,  | m,  :-  :m,

| d  :-  :d  | d  :-  :d.,r    | m     :r  :d     | t, :- || t, | t, :d  :r  | s, :-  :l,
| l, :-  :l, | s, :-  :l,.,t,  | d     :s, :-.fe, | s, :- || s, | s, :-  :f, | s, :-  :f,
| m  :-  :f  | d  :-  :f       | s     :-  :d     | r  :- || r  | r  :d  :t, | d  :-  :f
| l, :-  :f, | m, :-  :r,      | d,.d:t, :l,      | s, :- || s, | f, :m, :r, | m, :-  :f,

| ta,:l, :s, | l, :-  :r  | t, :-  :d  | l, :f  :m  | r  :d  :t, | d  :- || d  | d  ||
| f, :-  :m, | f, :-  :l, | s, :-  :s, | l, :t, :d  | l, :s, :s, | s, :- || l, | s, ||
| r  :-  :m  | d  :-  :r  | r  :-  :s  | f  :-  :s  | f  :m  :r  | m  :- || f  | m  ||
| s, :-  :d, | f, :-  :f, | f, :-  :m, | m, :r, :d, | f, :s, :s, | d, :- || f, | d, ||
                                                                          A-men.
```

Ich will Dich lieben, meine Stärke.

THEE will I love, my Strength, my Tower;
Thee will I love, my Joy, my Crown;
Thee will I love with all my power,
In all Thy works, and Thee alone;
Thee will I love, till sacred fire
Fill my whole soul with pure desire.

2 I thank Thee, uncreated Sun,
That Thy bright beams on me have shined;
I thank Thee, who hast overthrown
My foes, and healed my wounded mind;
I thank Thee, whose enlivening voice
Bids my freed heart in Thee rejoice.

3 Uphold me in the doubtful race,
Nor suffer me again to stray;
Strengthen my feet with steady pace
Still to press forward in Thy way;
My soul and flesh, O Lord of might,
Fill, satiate, with Thy heavenly light.

4 Thee will I love, my Joy, my Crown;
Thee will I love, my Lord, my God;
Thee will I love, beneath Thy frown
Or smile, Thy sceptre or Thy rod;
What though my flesh and heart decay,
Thee shall I love in endless day.

JOHANN SCHEFFLER, 1624–77; *tr.* by JOHN WESLEY, 1703–91.

432 DAVID'S HARP. (88. 88. 88.)

Doh = D. *Moderately slow.* A.t. ROBERT KING, *c.* 1684–1711.

```
|m  :r.d   |t,  :d  |r  :m.f |m :-.[r]s, |l,    :t, |d     :d      |d  :-.t,
|s, :s,.l, |t,  :l, |d  :t,  |d :-.[r]s, |f,    :f, |m,    :f,.s,  |l, :s,
|d  :r.fe  |s.f :m  |l  :s   |s :-.[s]d  |d     :r  |d     :r.m    |f  :r
|d  :t,.l, |s,  :l, |f, :s,  |d :-.[t]m, |f,.m, :r, |l,.s, :f,.m,  |r, :s,
```

f.D.

```
|d  :— ||[f]d' :d'.t |l :l   |t  :-.d' |se :— |l :l.s  |f  :m
|s, :— ||[f]d  :d.d  |d :f   |f  :-.m  |m  :— |m :m.r  |d  :t,
|m  :— ||[d]s  :s.s  |l :d'  |r' :-.d' |t  :— |m :m.s  |l  :m
|d, :— ||[l]m  :m.m  |f :f.m |r  :l,   |m  :— |d :d.t, |l, :s,
```

A.t.

```
|r  :-.m |m  :— || :[l]r  |t, :s, |d     :m  |r  :m.f |m  :— |—
|l, :l,  |t, :— || :[d]f, |s, :r, |s,.f, :m, |l, :s,  |s, :— |—
|l  :l   |se :— || :[l]r  |r  :t, |d     :d  |d  :t,  |d  :— |—
|f, :f   |m  :— || :[l]r, |s, :f, |m,    :d, |f, :s,  |d, :— |—
```

f.D.

```
:[f]d' |l :f |r  :m.f  |r  :-.d   |d :— ||f  |m ||
:[f]d  |d :r |r  :d    |d  :t,.d  |d :— ||d  |d ||
:[d]s  |l :l |s  :s.l  |s  :f     |m :— ||l  |s ||
:[l]m  |f :r |t, :d.f, |s, :s,    |d :— ||f, |d ||
```

A-men.

O Jesu Christ, mein schönstes Licht.

JESUS, Thy boundless love to me
  No thought can reach, no tongue declare;
O knit my thankful heart to Thee,
  And reign without a rival there:
Thine wholly, Thine alone, I am:
Lord, with Thy love my heart inflame.

2 O grant that nothing in my soul
  May dwell, but Thy pure love alone;
O may Thy love possess me whole,
  My joy, my treasure, and my crown:
All coldness from my heart remove;
May every act, word, thought, be love.

3 O Love, how cheering is Thy ray!
  All pain before Thy presence flies;
Care, anguish, sorrow, melt away,
  Where'er Thy healing beams arise;
O Jesus, nothing may I see,
Nothing desire, or seek, but Thee.

4 In suffering, be Thy love my peace;
  In weakness, be Thy love my power;
And, when the storms of life shall cease,
  Jesus, in that tremendous hour,
In death, as life, be Thou my Guide,
And save me, who for me hast died.

PAUL GERHARDT, 1607–76;
tr. by JOHN WESLEY, 1703–91.

433

SONG 67 (ST. MATTHIAS). (C.M.)

Doh = D. *In moderate time.* ORLANDO GIBBONS, 1583–1625.

```
|d :— |s :m |f :s |l :l |s :s |d' :l |t :t |l :— |— ||
|d :— |r :d |d :m |m :r |m :d |d :m |m :-.r|d :— |— ||
|m :— |s :s |d' :t |l :t |d' :m |m :l |l :se |l :— |— ||
|d :— |t, :d |l, :s, |f, :f, |d :d |l, :d |m :m |l, :— |— ||

:d' |t :l |s :s |f :m |r :s |s :d |m :r |d :— ||d |d ||
:d.r |m :f |m :d |l,.t, :d |t, :t,.d |r :d |d :t, |d :— ||l, |s, ||
:m.f |s :l.t |d' :m |f :s |s :s |s.f :m |s :-.f |m :— ||f |m ||
:l, |s, :f, |d :m |r :d |s, :s,.l, |t, :d |s, :s, |d :— ||f, |d ||
                                                      A-men.
```

FIRST MODE MELODY. (D.C.M.)

Lah = F. Doh = A♭. *Moderately slow.* THOMAS TALLIS, *c.* 1510–85.

```
                                           E♭.t.
|l, :l, :l, |se, :— :l, |d :— :t, |t, :— :tm |m :— :l
|d, :m, :m, |m, :— :d, |l, :— :fe, |s, :— :sd |t, :-.d :r
|l, :d :d |t, :— :l, |m :— :r |m :— :tm |s :— :l
|l, :l, :l, |m, :— :l, |l, :— :t, |m, :— :ml, |m :— :f

|l :se :— |l :— :— ||l :l :l |s :— :s |f :-.m :r
|m :— :m |{m :— :—} {d :— :—} ||m :m :m |m :— :t, |d :l, :—
|t :— :t |l :— :— ||d' :d' :d' |t :— :s |l :f :—
|m :— :m |l, :— :— ||l, :l, :l, |m :— :m |l, :r :r

        f.A♭.
|de :— :rl, |t, :— :t, |l, :— :se, |l, :— :— ||
|l, :— :lm, |fe, :— :s, |m, :— :m, |{m, :— :—} {d, :— :—} ||
|m :— :fd |r :— :t, |d :t, :— |l, :— :— ||
|l, :— :rl, |r, :— :s, |l, :m, :— |l, :— :— ||

|d :d :d |d :— :d |d :— :t, |d :— :d |s :— :s
|l, :l, :l, |l, :— :l, |l, :s, :— |{s, :—} {m, :—} :m, |s, :-.l, :t,
|m :m :m |m :— :m |f :r :— |d :— :d |m :— :r
|l, :l, :l, |l, :— :l, |f, :s, :— |d, :— :d |d :— :s,
```

r :-.d :l,	r :— :— (pause) ‖ m :m :m	f :— :m	r :-.d :d
s, :l, :l,	t, :— :— ‖ d :d :d	d :— :d	l, :— :f,
s :— :fe	s :— :— ‖ s :s :s	l :— :s	f :— :d
t, :l, :—	s, :— :— ‖ d :d :d	f, :— :d	f, :l, :—

| t, :— :r | d :— :t, | l, :— :se, | l, :— ‖ l, | l, ‖
| s, :— :s, | s, :— :s, | m, :— :m, | {m, :— / d, :—} ‖ r, | de, ‖
| r :— :t, | m :— :r | d :t, :— | l, :— ‖ f, | m, ‖
| s, :— :s, | m, :-.fe, :s, | d, :m, :— | l, :— ‖ r, | l₂ ‖

A-men.

O Deus, ego amo te.

MY God, I love Thee ; not because
I hope for heaven thereby,
Nor yet because who love Thee not
Are lost eternally.

2 Thou, O my Jesus, Thou didst me
Upon the Cross embrace ;
For me didst bear the nails and spear,
And manifold disgrace,

3 And griefs and torments numberless,
And sweat of agony ;
Even death itself ; and all for one
Who was Thine enemy.

4 Then why, most loving Jesus Christ,
Should I not love Thee well,
Not for the sake of winning heaven,
Or of escaping hell ;

5 Not with the hope of gaining aught,
Not seeking a reward ;
But as Thyself hast lovèd me,
O ever-loving Lord ?

6 Even so I love Thee, and will love,
And in Thy praise will sing,
Solely because Thou art my God,
And my eternal King.

Attributed to St. Francis Xavier, 1506–52;
tr. by Edward Caswall, 1814–78.

434

TICHFIELD. (7 7. 7 7. D.)

Doh = E♭. *In moderate time.* JOHN RICHARDSON, 1816–79.

m :s.f |m :s |d' :t.l |s :— |s :d |f :m |m :-.r |r :—
d :r |d :t_1 |d :d |d :— |t_1 :d |l_1.t_1 :d |d :-.d |t_1 :—
s :s |s :f |m :f |m :— |s :m |f :s |l :m.fe |s :—
d :t_1 |d :s_1 |l_1 :f_1 |d :— |s_1 :l_1 |r :d |f_1 :l_1 |s_1 :—

m :s.f |m :s |d' :t.l |s :— |s :d |f :m |m :r |d :—
d :r |d :t_1 |d.m :r.d |t_1 :— |d :s_1 |l_1.t_1 :d |d :t_1 |d :—
s :s |s :f |m :fe |s :— |m :m |f :s |s :s.f |m :—
d :t_1 |d :s_1 |l_1 :r |s_1 :— |d :m |r :d |s_1 :s_1 |d :—

f :m |l :s |t :l.s |d' :— |t :l |s :m |s :f.m |r :—
d :d |d.r :m |r :d.t_1 |d :— |d :d.r |m :m |d :l_1 |t_1 :—
f :s |l.t :d' |s :s |m :— |f.s :l.t |d' :s |s :d |s :—
l_1 :d |f :m |s :s_1 |l_1 :— |f_1 :f |m :d |m_1 :f_1 |s_1 :—

m :s.f |m :s |d' :t.l |s :— |l :s |f :m |m :r |d :— ‖ f |m
d :r |d :t_1 |d :d |d :— |t_1 :d |d.r :d |d :t_1 |d :— ‖ d |d
s :s |s :f |m :f |s :— |f :s |l :s |s :s.f |m :— ‖ l |s
d :t_1 |d :s_1 |l_1 :f |m :— |r :m |l_1.t_1 :d |s_1 :s_1 |d :— ‖ f_1 |d

A-men.

LOVED with everlasting love,
Led by grace that love to know;
Spirit, breathing from above,
Thou hast taught me it is so.
O this full and perfect peace!
O this transport all divine!
In a love which cannot cease
I am His, and He is mine.

2 Heaven above is softer blue,
Earth around is sweeter green;
Something lives in every hue,
Christless eyes have never seen:
Birds with gladder songs o'erflow,
Flowers with deeper beauties shine,
Since I know, as now I know,
I am His, and He is mine.

3 His for ever, only His:
Who the Lord and me shall part?
Ah, with what a rest of bliss
Christ can fill the loving heart!
Heaven and earth may fade and flee,
First-born light in gloom decline;
But, while God and I shall be,
I am His, and He is mine.

GEORGE WADE ROBINSON, 1838–77.

435 SHARON. (87. 87.)

Doh = E♭. *In moderate time.* William Boyce, 1710–79.

```
| m  :d  | s  :d  | r.m:f  | f  :m  | l :s | t  :d' | f  :m | m  :r  ||
| s, :d  | t, :d  | d  :t, | t, :d  | d :d | s.f:m  | r  :d | d  :t, ||
| s  :m  | r  :d  | l  :s  | s  :s  | f :s | s  :s  | s  :s | s  :—  ||
| d  :d  | s, :l, | f, :s, | d  :d  | f :m | r  :d  | t, :d | s, :—  ||

| f.m:r.d | s  :t  | l.t:d' | d' :t   | d' :l | f   :m | f.m:r    | d  :— || d  | d  ||
| s, :s,  | s, :r  | m  :r  | r  :r   | d  :d | d.t,:d | d  :d.t, | s, :— || l, | s, ||
| s  :f.m | r  :s  | s  :fe | s  :s   | s  :f | s   :s | l.s:f    | f  :m || f  | m  ||
| d  :d   | t, :s, | d  :r  | s  :s.f | m  :f | r   :d | f, :s,   | d  :— || f, | d  ||
```

A-men.

MORIAH. (87. 87. D.)

Doh = F. *Moderately slow.* Welsh Melody.

```
| m :— :f.s,l | s :-.m :d  | s  :— :t,  | f     :m :— | l  :— :l  |
| d :— :d     | d :—   :d  | r  :— :t,  | d.r   :d :— | d  :— :t, |
| s :— :l.s,f | m :—   :m  | r  :— :s   | s     :s :— | f  :— :r  |
| d :— :f,    | d :—   :l, | t, :— :s,  | l,.t, :d :— | f, :— :f  |
```

Fine. *D.C.*

```
| s :-.m :d.r,m | f  :-.m :r     | d  :— :— || s :— :m | s  :— :s | l :— :s |
| d :—   :d     | d  :—   :t,    | s, :— :— || d :— :d | r  :— :d | d :— :d |
| s :—   :m     | l  :—   :r.m,f | m  :— :— || s :— :s | r  :— :m | f :— :s |
| m :—   :l,    | f, :—   :s,    | d, :— :— || m :— :d | t, :— :d | f :— :m |
```

D.C.

```
| f   :m  :— | s :— :d | s  :—   :s | l  :—   :s   | m :— :— || d  | d      ||
| r   :s, :— | d :— :d | r  :—   :d | d  :—   :t,  | d :— :— || l, | s,     ||
| l.t :d' :— | s :— :s | s  :-.f :m | f  :-.m :r.s | s :— :— || f  | m      ||
| r   :d  :— | m :— :d | t, :—   :d | f, :—   :s,  | d :— :— || f, | d (d,) ||
```

A-men.

COME, Thou Fount of every blessing,
Tune my heart to sing Thy grace;
Streams of mercy never ceasing
Call for songs of loudest praise.

2 Jesus sought me when a stranger,
Wandering from the fold of God;
He, to rescue me from danger,
Interposed His precious blood.

3 O to grace how great a debtor
Daily I'm constrained to be!
Let that grace now, like a fetter,
Bind my wandering heart to Thee.

4 Prone to wander—Lord, I feel it—
Prone to leave the God I love,
Take my heart, O take and seal it,
Seal it from Thy courts above.

Robert Robinson, 1735–90.

436

SARRATT. (L.M.)

Doh = F. *Moderately quick.* GEOFFREY CHARLES EDWARD RYLEY, 1866–

:m |m :— :d |f :-.m :r |s :— :l |s :— :— |s :l :m
:d |d :— :d |d :— :d |d :— :t$_1$ |d :— :— |d :de :de
:s |s :— :m |l :-.s :f |m :— :r |m :— :— |m :m :l
:d |d :— :d |d :— :d |d :— :d |d :— :— |d :l$_1$:l$_1$

|f :— :s |m :-.r :d |r :— :— ||r :m :t$_1$ |d :— :d |d :-.t$_1$:l$_1$
|r :-.d :t$_1$ |d :-.t$_1$:l$_1$ |t$_1$:— :— ||l$_1$:se$_1$:se$_1$ |l$_1$:— :s$_1$ |fe$_1$:— :fe$_1$
|l :— :s |s :-.f :m |r :— :— ||l$_1$:t$_1$:m |m :— :m |m :-.r :d
|r :— :s$_1$ |d :— :d |s$_1$:— :— ||f$_1$:m$_1$:m$_1$ |l$_1$:— :l$_1$ |r$_1$:— :l$_1$

r :— :s	d :— :r	m :-.f :s	m :— :r	d :—		d	d	
s$_1$:— :t$_1$	d :— :s$_1$	d :— :d	d :— :t$_1$	d :—		l$_1$	s$_1$	
t$_1$:— :f	m :— :s	s :— :s	s :— :f	m :—		f	m	
s$_1$:— :s$_1$	l$_1$:— :t$_1$	d :— :m$_1$	s$_1$:— :s$_1$	d :—		f$_1$	d	

A-men.

SOLOTHURN. (L.M.)

Doh = E♭. *In moderate time.* Swiss Traditional Melody.

.d |d .r :m .d |s :r |d :- . ||s |s .l :t .s |d' :l |s :- . ||

.s |d' .t :l .s |d'.l :s . ||s |d .r :m .f |s :r |d :- . ||d |d ||

A - men.

IT is a thing most wonderful,
Almost too wonderful to be,
That God's own Son should come from heaven,
And die to save a child like me.

2 And yet I know that it is true:
He chose a poor and humble lot,
And wept, and toiled, and mourned, and died,
For love of those who loved Him not.

3 It is most wonderful to know
His love for me so free and sure;
But 'tis more wonderful to see
My love for Him so faint and poor.

4 And yet I want to love Thee, Lord;
O light the flame within my heart,
And I will love Thee more and more,
Until I see Thee as Thou art.

WILLIAM WALSHAM HOW, 1823–97.

437 ST. BENEDICT. (77. 77.)

Doh = E♭. *In moderate time.* JOHN STAINER, 1840–1901.

```
| s  :s.f | m  :f  | m  :r  | d  :— | l  :s  | f  :r  | m  :f  | r  :— ||
| m  :r   | d  :r  | d  :t, | d  :— | d  :de | r  :r  | d  :r  | t, :— ||
| s  :s   | s  :l  | s  :f  | m  :— | f  :s  | l  :s  | s  :l  | s  :— ||
| d  :t,  | d  :f, | s, :s, | l, :— | f  :m  | r  :t, | d  :f  | s  :f ||

| s  :m   | d' :t  | l  :s  | f  :— | f  :m  | r.m:f  | m  :r   | d  :— || d  | d  ||
| d  :d   | m  :r  | d  :de | r  :— | r  :d  | d  :d  | d  :t,  | d  :— || l, | s, ||
| s  :s   | s  :se | l  :l  | l  :— | s  :s  | l  :l  | s  :s.f | m  :— || f  | m  ||
| m  :m   | m  :m  | f  :m  | r  :d | t, :d  | f  :r  | s  :s,  | d  :— || f, | d  ||
                                                                        A-men.
```

[*By permission of Novello & Co., Ltd.*]

SAVIOUR, teach me, day by day,
Love's sweet lesson to obey;
Sweeter lesson cannot be,
Loving Him who first loved me.

2 With a child's glad heart of love
At Thy bidding may I move,
Prompt to serve and follow Thee,
Loving Him who first loved me.

3 Teach me thus Thy steps to trace,
Strong to follow in Thy grace,
Learning how to love from Thee,
Loving Him who first loved me.

4 Love in loving finds employ,
In obedience all her joy;
Ever new that joy will be,
Loving Him who first loved me.

5 Thus may I rejoice to show
That I feel the love I owe;
Singing, till Thy face I see,
Of His love who first loved me.

JANE ELIZA LEESON, 1807–82.

Also the following:

399–415 *Hymns of Penitence and Faith*
438–48 *Hymns of Peace and Joy*

PEACE AND JOY

438 DOMINUS REGIT ME. (87. 87. Iambic.)

Doh = G. *In moderate time.* JOHN BACCHUS DYKES, 1823–76.

:m |s :f |m :m |r :r |d :s_1 |s_1 :-.l_1 |t_1 :d |m :— |r ||
:s_1 |t_1 :l_1 |s_1 :d |d :t_1 |l_1 :s_1 |s_1 :-.s_1 |fe_1 :fe_1 |s_1 :d |t_1 ||
:d |r :d.r |m :s |f.m:f |m :r.f |f :m |r :d |d :-.m |s ||
:d |s_1 :l_1.t_1 |d :m_1.f_1 |s_1 :s_1 |l_1 :t_1 |d :d |l_1 :l_1 |s_1 :— |s_1 ||

:s |f :m.r |m :m |r :d.t_1 |d :l_1 |s_1 :-.l_1 |t_1 :d |m :r |d || d | d ||
:d |d :t_1 |d :l_1 |l_1 :se_1 |l_1 :m_1.f_1 |f_1 :-.f_1 |f_1 :s_1 |t_1 :— |d || l_1 | s_1 ||
:s |l :s |s :m |f :m |m :d |t_1 :-.d |r :m |f :— |m || f | m ||
:m |r :s_1 |d :d |t_1 :m_1 |l_1 :l_1.f_1 |s_1 :-.s_1 |s_1 :s_1 |s_1 :— |d_1 || f_1 | d_1 ||

A-men.

DUNAHA. (87. 87. Iambic.)

Irish Folk-Song Melody. Arranged by ROBERT ALEXANDER STEWART MACALISTER, 1870–

Doh = E♭. *Unison.* *Moderately slow.*

{:m |m :m |s :-.s |r.m:f.r |m :-.r |d :-.d |d :d |t_1.d:r |— ||

vv. 1, 3, 5.

{:s |s.l:t.d' |t :-.l |s.l:t.s |l :-.r |m :-.r |d :d |t_1.r:d |— || d | d ||

vv. 2, 4, 6.

{:s |s.l:d'.l |t :-.l

2. And where the ver - dant
4. Thy rod and staff my
6. Good Shep-herd may I

	l_1	s_1	
	f	m	
	f_1	d	

A-men.

[*Copyright*, 1927, *by Oxford University Press.*]

From Psalm xxiii.

THE King of Love my Shepherd is,
Whose goodness faileth never;
I nothing lack if I am His
And He is mine for ever.

2 Where streams of living water flow
My ransomed soul He leadeth,
And where the verdant pastures grow
With food celestial feedeth.

3 Perverse and foolish oft I strayed;
But yet in love He sought me,
And on His shoulder gently laid,
And home rejoicing brought me.

4 In death's dark vale I fear no ill,
With Thee, dear Lord, beside me;
Thy rod and staff my comfort still,
Thy Cross before to guide me.

5 Thou spread'st a table in my sight;
Thy unction grace bestoweth;
And O what transport of delight
From Thy pure chalice floweth!

6 And so through all the length of days
Thy goodness faileth never;
Good Shepherd, may I sing Thy praise
Within Thy house for ever!

HENRY WILLIAMS BAKER, 1821–77.

439 BENTLEY. (76. 76. D.)

Doh = C. *In moderate time.* JOHN HULLAH, 1812–84.

```
:m |r  :m |f  :l |l  :— |s  :d' |t  :s |f  :l  |s  :— |— ||
:d |d  :d |d  :f |f  :— |m  :m  |m  :m |f  :f  |d  :— |— ||
:s |f  :s |l  :t |d' :— |d' :l  |t  :t |d' :t  |d' :— |— ||
:d |d  :d |d  :d |d  :— |d  :l  |s  :m |r  :f  |m  :— |— ||

:m |m  :r  |d  :s |s  :— |f  :m  |m  :f |d  :r  |m  :— |— ||
:d |t, :t, |d  :d |d  :— |d  :d  |d  :d |d  :l, |t, :— |— ||
:s |s  :s  |s  :s |l  :— |l  :ta |l  :l |l  :l  |se :— |— ||
:m |f  :f  |m  :m |r  :— |r  :d  |f  :f |f  :f  |m  :— |— ||

:m |r  :m |f  :l |l  :— |s  :d' |t  :s |l  :-.t |s  :— |— ||
:d |d  :d |d  :f |f  :— |m  :m  |m  :s |s  :fe  |s  :— |— ||
:s |f  :s |l  :t |d' :— |d' :l  |t  :t |d' :d'  |t  :— |— ||
:d |d  :d |d  :d |d  :— |d  :l  |s  :m |r  :r   |s  :— |— ||

:s |m' :d' |t :s |d' :— |d :s  |s :f |m :r  |d :— |— ||f  |m ||
:f |m  :m  |f :r |s  :— |d :t, |d :r |d :t, |d :— |— ||d  |d ||
:t |d' :s  |s :t |d' :— |s :f  |s :l |s :f  |m :— |— ||l  |s ||
:s |d  :d  |r :f |m  :— |m :r  |m :f |s :s, |d :— |— ||f, |d ||
                                                          A-men.
```

SOMETIMES a light surprises
The Christian while he sings;
It is the Lord who rises
With healing in His wings:
When comforts are declining,
He grants the soul again
A season of clear shining,
To cheer it after rain.

2 In holy contemplation,
We sweetly then pursue
The theme of God's salvation,
And find it ever new.
Set free from present sorrow,
We cheerfully can say,
'Even let the unknown to-morrow
Bring with it what it may:

3 'It can bring with it nothing
But He will bear us through;
Who gives the lilies clothing
Will clothe His people too.
Beneath the spreading heavens,
No creature but is fed;
And He who feeds the ravens
Will give His children bread.'

4 Though vine nor fig-tree neither
Their wonted fruit should bear,
Though all the fields should wither,
Nor flocks nor herds be there,
Yet, God the same abiding,
His praise shall tune my voice
For, while in Him confiding,
I cannot but rejoice.

WILLIAM COWPER, 1731–1800.

440 BINCHESTER. (C.M.)

Doh = G. *In moderate time.* William Croft, 1678–1727.

| m :r :d | t_1 :— :— | s :f :m | r :— :r | m :— :s | s :— :fe | s :— || r
| d :s_1 :s_1 | s_1 :— :— | d :t_1 :d | t_1 :— :s_1 | d :— :d.t_1 | r :— :d | t_1 :— || ta_1
| s :f :m | r :— :— | m :f :s | s :— :r | s :— :s | l :l :— | s :— || s
| d :t_1 :d | s_1 :— :— | m :r :d | s_1 :— :t_1 | d :— :m | r :— :r_1 | s_1 :— || s_1

r :-.f :m	f :— :m	m :— :r	m :— :s	d :r :m	m :— :r.d	d :—		d	d	
l_1 :— :l_1	l_1 :t_1 :d	d :-.t_1 :l_1	t_1 :— :d	l_1 :t_1 :d	d :— :t_1.d	d :—		l_1	s_1	
r :— :de	r :— :s	l :— :l	se :— :s	f :— :s	s :— :f	m :—		f	m	
f_1 :— :l_1	r_1 :— :m_1	f_1 :— :f_1	m_1 :— :m_1	f_1 :— :d_1	s_1 :— :s_1	d_1 :—		f_1	d_1	

A-men.

O quam iuvat fratres.

HAPPY are they, they that love God,
Whose hearts have Christ confest,
Who by His Cross have found their life,
And 'neath His yoke their rest.

2 Glad is the praise, sweet are the songs,
When they together sing;
And strong the prayers that bow the ear
Of heaven's eternal King.

3 Christ to their homes giveth His peace,
And makes their loves His own;
But ah, what tares the evil one
Hath in His garden sown!

4 Sad were our lot, evil this earth,
Did not its sorrows prove
The path whereby the sheep may find
The fold of Jesus' love.

5 Then shall they know, they that love Him,
How all their pain is good;
And death itself cannot unbind
Their happy brotherhood.

Yattendon Hymnal, No. 34, 1899;
based on Charles Coffin, 1676–1749.

441 OLDOWN. (84. 84. 84.)

Doh = E♭. *Unison.* Basil Harwood, 1859–

:d | t_1 :d | f :f | f :m | s :d | m :— | r :r | m :— | — ||

1. My God, I thank Thee, who hast made The earth so bright,
2. I thank Thee, too, that Thou hast made Joy to a-bound,
3. I thank Thee more that all our joy Is touched with pain,
4. For Thou, who know-est, Lord, how soon Our weak heart clings,
5. I thank Thee, Lord, that here our souls, Though am-ply blest,

:m | m : r | r :l | l.l :s | s :d^1 | t :— | l :l | s :— | — ||

So full of splen-dour and of joy, Beau-ty and light;
So ma-ny gen-tle thoughts and deeds Circ-ling us round,
That sha-dows fall on bright-est hours, That thorns re-main,
Hast given us joys, ten-der and true, Yet all with wings,
Can nev-er find, al-though they seek, A per-fect rest,

:s | s :f | f :f | f.f :m | s :d | m :— | r :r | d :— | — || d | d ||

So ma - ny glor - ious things are here, No - ble and right.
That in the dark - est spot of earth Some love is found.
So that earth's bliss may be our guide, And not our chain.
So that we see, gleaming on high, Di - vi ner things.
Nor ev - er shall, un - til they lean On Je - sus' breast. A - men.

Adelaide Anne Procter, 1825–64.

WENTWORTH. (84. 84. 84.)

Doh = C. *In moderate time.* v. 2. Frederick Charles Maker, 1844-1927.

:s | d' :d' | t :l | s :m | d :r | m :— | l :l | r :— | — ||
:s | d' :d' | t :l | s :m | d :t, | d :— | d :d | t, :— | — ||
:s | d' :d' | t :l | s :m | d :s | s :— | l :l | s :— | — ||
:s | d' :d' | t :l | s :m | d :s, | d :— | f :f | s :— | — ||

G.t. vv. 1 & 2.

:m | m :m | d' :t | l :s | fe t, :l, | s, :— | r :r | d :— | — ||
:d | d :r | m :m | m :m | r s, :f, | f, :— | f, :f, | m, :— | — ||
:s | s :se | l :r' | d' :ta | l r :d | r :— | t, :t, | d :— | — ||
:d | d :t, | l, :t, | d :de | r s, :l, | t, :— | s, :s, | d, :— | — ||

f.C. v. 1.

:d s | l :l | s :d | f :f | m :d | r :— | f :f | m :— | — || f | m ||
:s r | r :r | m :d | d :t, | d :d | d :— | t, :t, | d :— | — || d | d ||
:m t | t :t | d' :s | l :s | s :s | l :— | s :s | s :— | — || l | s ||
:d s | f :f | m :m | r :r | d :m | f :— | s :s | d :— | — || f | d ||

A-men.

[*By permission of the Psalms and Hymns Trust.*]

MY God, I thank Thee, who hast made
The earth so bright,
So full of splendour and of joy,
Beauty and light;
So many glorious things are here,
Noble and right.

2 I thank Thee, too, that Thou hast made
Joy to abound,
So many gentle thoughts and deeds
Circling us round
That in the darkest spot of earth
Some love is found.

3 I thank Thee more that all our joy
Is touched with pain,
That shadows fall on brightest hours,
That thorns remain,
So that earth's bliss may be our guide,
And not our chain.

4 For Thou, who knowest, Lord, how soon
Our weak heart clings,
Hast given us joys, tender and true,
Yet all with wings,
So that we see, gleaming on high,
Diviner things.

5 I thank Thee, Lord, that here our souls,
Though amply blest,
Can never find, although they seek,
A perfect rest,
Nor ever shall, until they lean
On Jesus' breast.

Adelaide Anne Proctor, 1825–64.

442 NYLAND. (76. 76. D.)

Doh = E. *Moderately slow.* Finnish Hymn Melody.

```
:s |m :r     |d :r.d  |l, :—  |s, :s   |s :l       |s :f      |m :— |—
:d |d :t,.l, |s, :l,  |l, :—  |s, :t,  |d :d       |d :r      |d :— |—
:m |s :f     |m :m    |f :m   |r :f    |m :f       |s :l      |l :— |—
:d |d :r     |m :l,   |r :d   |t, :r   |d :f       |m :r      |l, :— |—

:s |m :r     |d :r.d  |l, :—  |s, :s,  |d :r.m     |f.m :r    |d :— |—
:r |d :t,    |d :l,   |l, :—  |s, :s,  |l, :d      |d :—.t,   |d :— |—
:s |s :s     |s :m    |f :m   |r :m    |m :l.s     |f :s      |m :— |—
:t, |d :s.f  |m :l,   |r :d   |t, :m,  |l,.s, :f,.m, |r, :s,  |d :— |—

:s |d' :t    |l :s    |s :fe  |s :s    |l :s       |f :m      |r :— |—
:d |d :r     |d.r :m  |r :—   |r :s,   |d.r :m     |l,.t, :d  |d :— |t,
:m |s :f.s   |l.t :d'.t |l :— |t :d'.t |l.t :d'    |f :s      |s :— |—
:d |m :r.m   |f :d    |r :—   |s, :m   |f :m       |r :d      |s, :— |—

:s |m :r     |d :r.d  |l, :—  |s, :s   |d :r.m     |f.m :r    |d :— |— || d  |d
:r |d :t,.l, |s, :l,  |l, :—  |s, :t,  |d :d       |d :—.t,   |d :— |— || l, |s,
:r |s :f     |m :m    |f :m   |r :f    |m :l.s     |f :s      |m :— |— || f  |m
:t, |d :r    |m :l,   |r :d   |t, :s,  |l,.s, :f,.m, |r, :s,  |d :— |— || f, |d
```

A-men.

IN heavenly love abiding,
  No change my heart shall fear;
And safe is such confiding,
  For nothing changes here:
The storm may roar without me,
  My heart may low be laid;
But God is round about me,
  And can I be dismayed?

2 Wherever He may guide me,
  No want shall turn me back;
My Shepherd is beside me,
  And nothing can I lack.
His wisdom ever waketh,
  His sight is never dim:
He knows the way He taketh,
  And I will walk with Him.

3 Green pastures are before me,
  Which yet I have not seen;
Bright skies will soon be o'er me,
  Where the dark clouds have been.
My hope I cannot measure:
  My path to life is free:
My Saviour has my treasure,
  And He will walk with me.

Anna Laetitia Waring, 1820-1910.

443 LIKE A RIVER. (6 5. 6 5. D. and refrain.)

Doh = F. *Moderately fast.* JAMES MOUNTAIN, 1844– .

d :d |r :r |m :— |s :— |f :f |r :r |m :— |— :—
s, :d |d :t, |d :— |s, :— |l, :d |d :t, |d :— |— :—
m :s |f :f |m :— |d :— |d :l |s :s |s :— |— :—
d :m |r :r |d :— |m, :— |f, :f, |s, :s, |d :— |— :—

d :d |r :r |m :— |d :— |t, :t, |l, :l, |s, :— |— :—
s, :d |d :t, |s, :— |l, :— |s, :s, |s, :fe, |s, :— |— :—
m :s |f :f |m :— |m :— |r :r |m :r |t, :— |— :—
d :m |r :r |d :— |l, :— |t, :t, |d :r |s, :— |— :—

𝄋
s :s |s :s |l :— |s :— |f :f |m :m |r :— |— :—
r :d |t, :d |d :— |d :— |d :t, |d :d |t, :— |— :—
s :m |f :s |f :— |s :— |l :s |s :s |s :— |— :—
t, :d |r :m |f :— |m :— |r :s, |d :m, |s, :— |— :—

Dal 𝄋 *for Refrain.* FINE.

m :m |r :r |d :— |r :— |m :m |r :r |d :— |— :— || d |d
d :s, |l, :t, |d :— |d :— |d :s, |d :t, |d :— |— :— || l, |s,
s :s |f :f |m :— |l :— |s :m |s :f |m :— |— :— || f |m
d :m, |f, :s, |l, :— |fe, :— |s, :s, |s, :s, |d :— |— :— || f, |d

A-men.

LIKE a river glorious
  Is God's perfect peace,
Over all victorious
  In its bright increase;
Perfect, yet it floweth
  Fuller every day,—
Perfect, yet it groweth
  Deeper all the way.
    Stayed upon Jehovah,
      Hearts are fully blest,
    Finding, as He promised,
      Perfect peace and rest.

2 Hidden in the hollow
  Of His blessèd hand,
Never foe can follow,
  Never traitor stand;
Not a surge of worry,
  Not a shade of care,
Not a blast of hurry,
  Touch the spirit there.

3 Every joy or trial
  Falleth from above,
Traced upon our dial
  By the Sun of Love.
We may trust Him fully
  All for us to do;
They who trust Him wholly
  Find Him wholly true.

FRANCES RIDLEY HAVERGAL, 1836–79.

444

PAX TECUM. (10 10.)

GEORGE THOMAS CALDBECK, 1852– ?
Arranged by CHARLES JOHN VINCENT, 1852–

Doh = C. *Slow.*

```
|s   :—  |s    :s  |s   :—  |—   :s  |l   :l   |l   :s  |s   :—  |—  ||
|m   :—  |f    :f  |m   :—  |—   :m  |f   :f   |f   :f  |m   :—  |—  ||
|d'  :—  |t.d' :r' |d'  :—  |—   :d' |d'  :r'  |r'  :r' |d'  :—  |—  ||
|d   :—  |s    :s  |d   :—  |—   :d  |f   :r.d |t,  :t, |d   :—  |—  ||

:s  |d' :— |r' :— |m' :r' |d' :l  |s  :— |s  :f |m :— |— :— || f  |m ||
:m  |f  :— |fe :— |s  :s  |s  :f  |m  :— |r  :— |d :— |— :— || d  |d ||
:d' |d' :— |d' :— |d' :t  |d' :d' |d' :— |t  :— |s :— |— :— || l  |s ||
:ta |l  :— |la :— |s  :f  |m  :f  |s  :— |s, :— |d :— |— :— || f  |d ||
```

A-men.

SONG 46. (10 10.)

Doh = F. *Slow.*

ORLANDO GIBBONS, 1583–1625.

```
|d   :—  |m  :d   |s   :—  |—  :d  |f   :-.f  |f   :m  |r   :—  |—  ||
|s,  :—  |d  :s,  |s,  :—  |—  :d  |d   :-.d  |r   :d  |t,  :—  |—  ||
|m   :—  |s  :m   |r   :—  |—  :m  |f   :-.f  |ta  :s  |s   :—  |—  ||
|d   :—  |d  :d   |d   :t, |—  :d  |l,  :-.l, |ta, :d  |s,  :—  |—  ||

:r  |t,  :d  |l,  :s, |d   :m  |r   :r   |d  :— || d  |d  ||
:l, |s,  :s, |f,  :m, |l,  :d  |d   :t,  |d  :— || l, |s, ||
:f  |r   :d  |d   :d  |m   :s  |s   :-.f |m  :— || f  |m  ||
:r, |s,  :m, |f,  :d  |l,  :m, |s,  :s,  |d  :— || f, |d  ||
```

A-men.

PEACE, perfect peace, in this dark world of sin?
The blood of Jesus whispers peace within.

2 Peace, perfect peace, by thronging duties pressed?
To do the will of Jesus, this is rest.

3 Peace, perfect peace, with sorrows surging round?
On Jesus' bosom nought but calm is found.

4 Peace, perfect peace, with loved ones far away?
In Jesus' keeping we are safe, and they.

5 Peace, perfect peace, our future all unknown?
Jesus we know, and He is on the throne.

6 Peace, perfect peace, death shadowing us and ours?
Jesus has vanquished death and all its powers.

7 It is enough: earth's struggles soon shall cease,
And Jesus call us to heaven's perfect peace.

EDWARD HENRY BICKERSTETH, 1825–1906.

445 LLANGAN. (8 7. 8 7. D.)

Doh = G. *In moderate time.* Welsh Melody.

m :— :r | d :— :m | f :— :s | m :— :d | m :— :f | s :— :s
d :— :t, | d :— :s, | d :— :r | d :— :s, | d :— :d | d :t, :d
s :— :s | s :-.f :m | d :— :s | s :— :m | s :— :f | r :— :s
d :— :s, | m :-.r :d | l, :— :t, | d :— :d, | d :— :l, | s, :-.f, :m,

D.C.

f :m :r | m :— :— || d :— :m | d :-.t, :l, | r :— :r | t, :-.l, :s,
d :— :t, | d :— :— || l, :— :t, | l, :-.se, :l, | s, :— :fe, | s, :-.fe, :s,
l :s :s | s :— :— || m :— :m | m :— :m | r :— :r | r :-.d :t,
r, :s, :s, | d, :— :— || l, :— :se, | l, :-.t, :d | t, :— :l, | s, :— :s,

m :— :fe | s :— :d | t, :— :l, | s, :— :— || r :— :f | m :-.r :d
s, :— :l, | s, :— :s,.l, | s, :— :fe, | s, :— :— || l, :— :t, | d :-.t, :l,
d :— :d | r :s :m | r :— :r.d | t, :— :— || r :— :r | d :-.r :m
d :— :l, | t, :— :d | r :— :r, | s, :— :— || f, :— :r, | l, :— :l,

m :— :l | s :-.m :d | s :— :m | f :l :s.f | m :— :r | d :— :— || d | d
s, :d :d | t, :— :d | s, :r :d.t, | l, :d :d | d :— :t, | d :— :— || l, | s,
d :m :f | r :-.s :m | r :— :s | f :— :l | s :— :s.f | m :— :— || f | m
d :— :f, | s, :— :l, | t, :— :d | f, :— :r, | s, :— :s, | d, :— :— || f, | d,

A-men.

O llefara! addfwyn Iesu.

SPEAK, I pray Thee, gentle Jesus!
O, how passing sweet Thy words,
Breathing o'er my troubled spirit
Peace which never earth affords.
All the world's distracting voices,
All the enticing tones of ill,
At Thy accents mild, melodious,
Are subdued, and all is still.

2 Tell me Thou art mine, O Saviour,
Grant me an assurance clear;
Banish all my dark misgivings,
Still my doubting, calm my fear.
O, my soul within me yearneth
Now to hear Thy voice divine;
So shall grief be gone for ever,
And despair no more be mine.

WILLIAM WILLIAMS, 1717–91; *tr.* by RICHARD MORRIS LEWIS, 1849–1918.

446 PENTATONE. (D.C.M.)

Doh = E. *In moderate time.* HENRY WALFORD DAVIES, 1869–

```
:d.r |m  :s   |d' :l  |s  :-.m  |m  :l    |s  :m  |m  :r.m   |d  :—  |—  :l
:s,  |d  :m.r |d  :m  |m  :-.t, |t, :m    |m  :d  |d  :l,.t, |s, :—  |—  :d
:m.f |s  :s   |l  :m  |t  :-.s  |s  :d'   |d' :s  |s  :f.s   |m  :—  |—  :m
:d   |d  :d.t,|l, :d  |m  :-.m  |m  :l,   |d  :m  |s  :s,    |d  :—  |—  :l,.d

|s  :m   |m  :r.m |d  :-.l,  |l,  :t,.d |r  :m  |s  :m  |r  :—  |—   :m.f
|t, :t,  |t, :t,  |d  :-.m,  |m,  :l,   |l, :d  |r  :d  |l, :—  |ta, :—
|s  :s   |s  :f.s |m  :-.d   |d   :r.m  |f  :m  |t  :d' |f  :—  |s   :—
|m  :s   |s  :s,  |l, :-.d   |d   :l,   |r  :l, |s, :l, |r  :—  |s,  :—

|r  :l     |s  :m  |r  :-.l,  |l,  :l,.t, |d  :m     |l  :m  |s  :—  |—  :d.r
|l, :l,.t, |d  :d  |l, :-.fe, |fe, :l,    |l, :d.r   |m  :d  |t, :—  |—  :l,.t,
|f  :r     |s  :s  |fe :-.fe  |fe  :f     |m  :d'.t  |l  :d' |s  :—  |f  :s.f
|r  :f     |m  :d  |r  :-.r   |r   :r     |l, :l,.t, |d  :l, |m  :—  |r  :m.r

|m  :s    |d' :l  |s  :-.m |m  :l  |s  :m  |m  :r.m   |d  :—  |—  ||d  |d  ||
|d  :d    |d  :m  |t, :-.d |d  :m  |m  :d  |t, :l,.t, |s, :—  |—  ||l, |s, ||
|m  :m    |m  :m  |s  :-.s |s  :d' |d' :l  |s  :f.s   |m  :—  |—  ||f  |m  ||
|d  :d.t, |l, :d  |m  :-.d |d  :l, |d  :m  |s  :s,    |d  :—  |—  ||f, |d  ||
                                                                   A-men.
```

MY heart is resting, O my God,
I will give thanks and sing ;
My heart is at the secret source
Of every precious thing.
I thirst for springs of heavenly life,
And here all day they rise ;
I seek the treasure of Thy love,
And close at hand it lies.

2 I have a heritage of joy,
That yet I must not see ;
But the hand that bled to make it mine
Is keeping it for me.
And a new song is in my mouth,
To long-loved music set :
'Glory to Thee for all the grace
I have not tasted yet.'

3 My heart is resting, O my God,
My heart is in Thy care ;
I hear the voice of joy and health
Resounding everywhere.
'Thou art my portion, saith my soul,'
Ten thousand voices say,
And the music of their glad Amen
Will never die away.

ANNA LAETITIA WARING, 1820–1910.

447 MOUNT EPHRAIM. (S.M.)

BENJAMIN MILGROVE, *c.* 1731–1810.

Doh = D. *Moderately slow.*

```
                                               A.t.
:d  |m    :r   :d  |s.,f:m   :r   |d   :—  :d'f   |m    :r   :d
:d  |d    :t,  :d  |d   :—   :t,  |d   :—  :m l,  |d    :t,  :d
:m  |s    :f   :m  |s.,l:s   :f   |m   :—  :s d   |s    :f   :m
:d  |d    :—   :d  |m.,f:s   :s,  |d   :—  :d f,  |s,   :—   :l,

                        f.D.
|s.,f   :m   :r   |d   :—  ||ta f  |m.,r:d  :l  |s.,f:m   :s   |l.,s:l   :t
|s,.,l, :s,  :f,  |m,  :—  ||s, r  |d   :—  :d  |d   :—   :d   |d   :—   :f
|d      :—   :t,  |d   :—  ||d s   |s.,f:m  :f  |m.,r:d   :d'  |d'  :—   :r'
|m,.,f, :s,  :s,  |d,  :—  ||m, t, |d   :—  :d  |d   :—   :m   |f.,m:f   :r

|d'  :—  :l    |s.,f :m.r  :d.f    |m   :—  :r    |d  :—  ||d  |d  ||
|m   :—  :f    |d.,r :d.t, :l,.r   |d   :—  :t,   |d  :—  ||l, |s, ||
|d'  :—  :d'   |s    :-.f  :m.l    |s   :—  :f    |m  :—  ||f  |m  ||
|l,  :—  :f,   |m,   :s,   :l,.f,  |s,  :—  :s,   |d  :—  ||f, |d  ||
                                                          A-men.
```

COME, we that love the Lord,
And let our joys be known:
Join in a song with sweet accord,
And thus surround the throne.

2 Let those refuse to sing
That never knew our God;
But children of the heavenly King
Must speak their joys abroad.

3 The men of grace have found
Glory begun below;
Celestial fruits on earthly ground
From faith and hope may grow.

4 The hill of Zion yields
A thousand sacred sweets,
Before we reach the heavenly fields
Or walk the golden streets.

5 There shall we see His face,
And never, never sin;
There from the rivers of His grace
Drink endless pleasures in.

6 Then let our songs abound,
And every tear be dry;
We're marching through Immanuel's ground
To fairer worlds on high.

ISAAC WATTS, 1674–1748.

448

MEINE HOFFNUNG. (87. 87. 337.)

JOACHIM NEANDER, 1650–80.

Lah = C. Doh = E♭. *Moderately slow.* *D.C.*

l :se	l :t	d' :d'	t :m (fermata)	l :s	f :m	r :r	d :—
m :m	m :m.r	d.r :m	m :m	d.r :m	t, :d	d :t,	d :—
d' :t	l :m	m :l	l :se	l.t :d'	f :s	l :s.f	m :—
l, :m	d :se,	l,.t, :d.r	m :m	f :d	r :m.m,	f, :s,	d :—

d' :d'	t :—	l :l	se :—	m :ba	se :l	l :se	l :—		l	l
m :m	m :—	d :f	m :—	m :d	r :d	t, :t,	d :—		r	de
s :l	se :—	l :t	t :—	l :l	r :m	f :m	m :—		f	m
d :l,	m :—	f :r	m :—	d :l,	t, :d	r :m	l, :—		r	l,

A-men.

GROESWEN. (87. 87. 337.)

Doh = A. *In moderate time.*

JOHN AMBROSE LLOYD, 1815–74.

d :s,	l, :t,	d :r	m :d	f :l,	r :d	t, :l,	s, :—
m, :s,	f, :f,	m, :s,	s, :m,	l, :l,	s, :s,.l,	s, :fe,	s, :—
d :d	d :r	d :t,	d :m	r :m	f :m	r :d	t, :—
d, :m,	f, :r,	l, :s,	d :d,	r, :d,	t,, :d,	r, :r,	s, :—

d :s,	l, :t,	d :r	m :d	f :r	s :f	m :r	d :—
m, :s,	f, :f,	m, :s,	s, :m,	l, :s,	s, :l,	s, :f,	m, :—
d :d	d :r	d :t,	d :m	r :t,	d :d	d :t,	d :—
d, :m,	f, :r,	l, :s,	d :d,	r, :s,.f,	m, :f,	s, :s,	d, :—

d :m	r :—	r :f	m :—	m :s	f :r	d :t,	d :—	d	d
s, :s,	s, :—	s, :s,	s, :—	s, :s,	l, :l,	s, :f,	m, :—	f,	m,
d :d	t, :—	r :t,	d :—	d :d	d :f	m :r	d :—	l,	s,
m, :d,	s, :—	t, :s,	d :—	d :m,	f, :f,	s, :s,	d, :—	f,	d,

A-men.

Meine Hoffnung stehet feste.

ALL my hope on God is founded;
He doth still my trust renew.
Me through change and chance He guideth,
Only good and only true.
God unknown,
He alone
Calls my heart to be His own.

2 Pride of man and earthly glory,
Sword and crown betray his trust;
What with care and toil he buildeth,
Tower and temple, fall to dust.
But God's power,
Hour by hour
Is my temple and my tower.

3 God's great goodness aye endureth,
Deep His wisdom passing thought:
Splendour, light, and life attend Him,
Beauty springeth out of nought.
Evermore,
From His store
New-born worlds rise and adore.

4 Daily doth the Almighty Giver
Bounteous gifts on us bestow;
His desire our soul delighteth,
Pleasure leads us where we go.
Love doth stand
At His hand;
Joy doth wait on His command.

5 Still from man to God eternal
Sacrifice of praise be done,
High above all praises praising
For the gift of Christ His Son.
Christ doth call
One and all:
Ye who follow shall not fall.

Yattendon Hymnal, No. 69, 1899; based on JOACHIM NEANDER, 1650–80.

Also the following:

416–37 *Hymns of Love and Gratitude*

PRAYER, ASPIRATION, AND HOLINESS

449

AMBERG. (88. 84.)

Church of Scotland Hymn Tune Book, 1862.

Doh = C. *In moderate time.* G.t.

```
:m .f |s  :l  |s  :d' |r' :t  |d'  ||(d)f  |m  :r    |s  :f  |m  :r     |d  ||
:d .r |m  :f  |s  :m  |f  :r  |m   ||(d)f, |s, :s,   |s, :l, |s, :s,.f, |m, ||
:s    |d' :d' |d' :d' |l  :s  |s   ||(s)d  |d  :t,   |d  :d  |d  :t,    |d  ||
:d    |d  :f  |m  :l  |f  :s  |d   ||(m)l, |s, :s,.f,|m, :f, |s, :s,    |d, ||
```

f.C.

```
:(l)m.f |s  :l  |s  :m'   |r' :d'   |t  ||d' |l  :— |t  :—   |d' :— |— ||d' |d' ||
:(f)d.r |m  :f  |s  :s    |s  :m.fe |s  ||s  |f  :— |r  :m.f |m  :— |— ||f  |m  ||
:(d)s   |d' :d' |d' :d'   |t  :d'   |r' ||d' |d' :— |s  :—   |s  :— |— ||l  |s  ||
:(f)d   |d  :f  |m  :d    |s  :l    |s  ||m  |f  :— |s  :—   |d  :— |— ||f  |d  ||
```

A-men.

MY God, is any hour so sweet,
From blush of morn to evening star,
As that which calls me to Thy feet,
The hour of prayer?

2 Blest is that tranquil hour of morn,
And blest that hour of solemn eve,
When, on the wings of prayer upborne,
The world I leave;

3 For then a dayspring shines on me,
Brighter than morn's ethereal glow,
And richer dews descend from Thee
Than earth can know.

4 Then is my strength by Thee renewed;
Then are my sins by Thee forgiven;
Then dost Thou cheer my solitude
With hope of heaven.

5 No words can tell what sweet relief
There for my every want I find,
What strength for warfare, balm for grief,
What peace of mind.

6 Hushed is each doubt, gone every fear;
My spirit seems in heaven to stay;
And even the penitential tear
Is wiped away.

7 Lord, till I reach yon blissful shore,
No privilege so dear shall be
As thus my inmost soul to pour
In prayer to Thee.

CHARLOTTE ELLIOTT, 1789–1871.

450

RAVENNA. (77. 77.)

Doh = G. *In moderate time.* JUSTIN HEINRICH KNECHT, 1752–1817.

m :r | d :m | s :f | m :— | l, :t, | d :r | t, :l, | s, :— ||
d :t, | d :d | d :s, | s, :— | f, :s, | s, :l, | s, :fe, | s, :— ||
m :f | s :m | m :r | d :— | d :r | d :l, | r :r.d | t, :— ||
d :r | m :d | l, :t, | d :— | f, :f, | m, :fe, | s, :r, | s, :— ||

d :t, | l, :d | f :m | r :— | s :f | m :r | d :t, | d :— || d | d ||
m, :s, | f, :s, | l,.t, :d | t, :— | t, :r | d :l, | s, :s, | s, :— || l, | s, ||
d :m.r | d :s | f :s | s :— | r :s | s :f | m :r | m :— || f | m ||
l, :m, | f, :m, | r, :m,.f, | s, :— | s, :t, | d :f, | s, :s, | d, :— || f, | d ||

A-men.

COME, my soul, thy suit prepare;
Jesus loves to answer prayer;
He Himself has bid thee pray,
Therefore will not say thee nay.

Unison. 2 Thou art coming to a King;
Large petitions with thee bring;
For His grace and power are such,
None can ever ask too much.

Harmony. 3 With my burden I begin:
Lord, remove this load of sin;
Let Thy blood, for sinners spilt,
Set my conscience free from guilt.

4 Lord, I come to Thee for rest;
Take possession of my breast;
There Thy blood-bought right maintain.
And without a rival reign.

5 While I am a pilgrim here,
Let Thy love my spirit cheer;
As my Guide, my Guard, my Friend,
Lead me to my journey's end.

JOHN NEWTON, 1725–1807.

451 SPOHR. (C.M.)

Doh = G. *In moderate time.* Adapted from LUDWIG SPOHR, 1784–1859.

```
:s, |m :— :m |s :— :d |m :— :r |d :— :d |l :s :m |f :— :s |m :— ||m
:s, |d :— :d |s, :— :l, |d :— :t, |d :— :d |d :— :d |r :-.d :t, |d :— ||d
:s |s :— :d |d :— :m |s :— :f |m :— :m |f :s :l |l :— :s |s :— ||s
:s, |d :— :l, |m, :— :l, |s, :— :s, |d :— :d |f, :m, :l, |r, :— :s, |d :— ||d

|r :— :de |r :— :m |f :— :l |s :— :f |m :— :f |r :— :r |d :— ||d |d ||
|t, :— :le, |t, :— :de |r :— :ma |r :— :r |d :— :d |d :— :t, |d :— ||l, |s, ||
|s :f :m |r :— :s |l :— :fe |s :— :s |s :— :l |r :s :f |m :— ||f |m ||
|s, :— :s, |s, :f, :m, |r, :r :d |t, :— :t, |d :— :f, |s, :— :s, |d, :— ||f, |d, ||
```

A-men.

STRACATHRO. (C.M.)

Doh = D. *In moderate time.* CHARLES HUTCHESON, 1792–1860.

```
:d |m :— :r |d :— :r |m :d' :t |l :— :d' |s :m :d |m :— :r |d :— ||m
:d |d :— :t, |l, :— :s, |s, :m :r |d :— :m |r :d :d |d :— :t, |d :— ||d
:m |s :— :s.f |m :— :s |m :-.ba :se |l :— :l |r :s :l |s :— :f |m :— ||s
:d |d :— :s, |l, :— :t, |d :-.r :m |f :— :l, |t, :d :l, |m, :-.f, :s, |d :— ||d

|m :— :r |d :m :s |l :r' :d' |t :— :t |d' :s :l |m :— :r |d :— ||f |m ||
|d :— :t, |d :s, :s |d :f :m |r :— :r |d :— :d |d :— :t, |d :— ||d |d ||
|s :— :s |s :d' :t |l :— :s.l |t :— :s |s :d'.t :l |s :— :s.f |m :— ||l |s ||
|d :s :f |m :d :m |f :r :m.f |s :— :s.f |m :— :f |s :— :s, |d :— ||f, |d ||
```

A-men.

APPROACH, my soul, the mercy-seat,
Where Jesus answers prayer;
There humbly fall before His feet,
For none can perish there.

2 Thy promise is my only plea;
With this I venture nigh:
Thou callest burdened souls to Thee,
And such, O Lord, am I.

3 Bowed down beneath a load of sin,
By Satan sorely pressed,
By war without and fears within,
I come to Thee for rest.

4 Be Thou my Shield and Hiding-place,
That, sheltered near Thy side,
I may my fierce accuser face,
And tell him Thou hast died.

5 O wondrous love! to bleed and die,
To bear the Cross and shame,
That guilty sinners, such as I,
Might plead Thy gracious Name!

JOHN NEWTON, 1725–1807.

452 TYHOLLAND. (777.)

German Carol Melody, adapted by David Frederick Ruddell Wilson, 1871–

Doh = E♭. *In moderate time.*

d :— :m | s :— :l | s :m :f | s :— :— | d' :l :t | d' :— :s
s_1 :— :d | d :t_1 :l_1 | t_1 :d :d | d :— :t_1 | d :— :f | m :— :d
m :— :d | s :— :f.m | r :m :d | r :— :s | s :f :f | l :— :s
d :— :l_1 | m_1 :— :f_1 | s_1 :d :l_1 | s_1 :— :— | m :f :r | l_1 :— :m

s :— :f | m :— :— ‖ r :— :f | m :r :m | d :l_1 :t_1 | d :— :— ‖ d | d
d :t_1 :l_1 | s_1 :— :— ‖ ta_1 :— :d | d :t_1 :t_1 | l_1 :— :s_1 | s_1 :— :— ‖ l_1 | s_1
l :— :d | m :— :— ‖ f :— :l | s :— :s | s :f.m :r | m :— :— ‖ f | m
f :— :f_1 | d :— :— ‖ ta_1 :— :f_1 | d :s_1 :m_1 | f_1 :— :s_1 | d :— :— ‖ f_1 | d

A-men.

WESTON. (777.)

Samuel Sebastian Wesley, 1810–76.

Lah = E. Doh = G. *Moderately slow.*

l_1 :t_1 | d :$t_1.l_1$ | t_1 :se_1 | l_1 :— ‖ d :r | m :l
m_1 :se_1 | m_1 :f_1 | f_1 :m_1 | m_1 :— ‖ l_1 :t_1 | d :d
d :m | l_1 :d | t_1 :t_1 | d :— ‖ m :s | s :f.m
l_1 :m_1 | l_1 :f_1 | r_1 :m_1 | l_1 :— ‖ l_1 :s_1 | d :f_1

s :f | m :— ‖ t_1 :de | r :$l_1.t_1$ | d :t_1 | l_1 :— ‖ r | de
d :t_1 | d :— ‖ s_1 :s_1 | l_1 :l_1 | l_1 :se_1 | l_1 :— ‖ l_1 | l_1
r :s | s :— ‖ r :m | f :d.r | m :m | d :— ‖ f | m
s_1 :s_1 | d_1 :— ‖ s_1 :m_1 | r_1 :f_1 | m_1 :m_1 | l_1 :— ‖ r_1 | l_1

A-men.

PRESENT with the two or three
Deign, most gracious God, to be,
While we lift our souls to Thee.

2 Jesus, by Thy blood alone
Who didst for our sins atone,
Dare we come before Thy throne.

3 Thou who knowest all our need,
Grant the prayer of faith to plead,
Teach us how to intercede.

4 Holy Spirit, from on high
Helping our infirmity,
Aid us in our feeble cry.

5 Flesh and heart would faint and fail,
But there stands within the veil
One who ever doth prevail.

6 Glory to the Father, Son,
Holy Spirit, Three in One,
While the endless ages run.

Fanny Freer, 1801–91.

[May be sung to Lacrymae, No. 314.]

453

COENA DOMINI. (10 10.)

Doh = E♭. *Moderately slow.* ARTHUR SEYMOUR SULLIVAN, 1842–1900.

m :—	r :d	f :—	m :—	r :m	d :r	t_1 :—	— :—	
d :—	t_1 :d	t_1 :—	d :—	r :d	d :l_1	s_1 :—	— :—	
s :—	s :s	s :—	s :—	s :s	s :fe	r :—	— :—	
d :—	f :m	r :—	d :—	t_1 :d	l_1 :r	s_1 :—	— :—	

d :—	f :m	r :l	s :d	m :—	— :r	d :—	— :—		f	m	
s_1 :—	f_1 :s_1	l_1 :t_1	d :d	d :—	t_1 :—	d :—	— :—		d	d	
d :—	d :d	d :r	m :f	s :—	f :—	m :—	— :—		l	s	
m_1 :—	l_1 :s_1	f_1 :f_1	m_1 :l_1	s_1 :—	s_1 :—	d :—	— :—		f_1	d	

[*By permission of Novello & Co., Ltd.*] A-men.

O KING of mercy, from Thy throne on high
Look down in love, and hear our humble cry.

2 Thou tender Shepherd of the blood-bought sheep,
Thy feeble wandering flock in safety keep.

3 O gentle Saviour, by Thy death we live;
To contrite sinners life eternal give.

4 Thou art the Bread of heaven, on Thee we feed;
Be near to help our souls in time of need.

5 Thou art the mourner's Stay, the sinner's Friend,
Sweet Fount of joy and blessings without end.

6 O come and cheer us with Thy heavenly grace;
Reveal the brightness of Thy glorious face.

7 In cooling cloud by day, in fire by night,
Be near our steps, and make our darkness light.

8 Go where we go, abide where we abide,
In life, in death, our Comfort, Strength, and Guide.

9 O lead us daily with Thine eye of love,
And bring us safely to our home above.

THOMAS RAWSON BIRKS, 1810–83.

454

DURROW. (7 6. 7 6. D.)

Lah = C. Doh = E♭. *Unison.* *In moderate time.* Irish Traditional Melody.

:m | l :-.t | d' :t | l :-.s | m :r.t_1 | l_1 :-.t_1 | d :r | m :— | — ||

:m | l :-.t | d' :t | l :-.s | m :r.t_1 | m :r.t_1 | l_1 :l_1 | l_1 :— | — ||

vv. 2, 4, and 6.

:m.r | d :d | d :t_1.l_1 | t_1 :— | t_1 :l_1.s_1 | l_1 :-.t_1 | d :r | m :— | — ||

:m | l :-.t | d' :t | l :-.s | m :r.t_1 | m :r.t_1 | l_1 :l_1 | l_1 :— | — || l_1 | l_1 ||

A-men.

Deus Pater credentium.

O GOD, Thou art the Father
  Of all that have believed :
From whom all hosts of angels
  Have life and power received.

2 O God, Thou art the Maker
  Of all created things,
The righteous Judge of judges,
  The Almighty King of kings ;

3 High in the heavenly Zion
  Thou reignest God adored ;
And in the coming glory
  Thou shalt be Sovereign Lord.

4 Beyond our ken Thou shinest,
  The everlasting Light ;
Ineffable in loving,
  Unthinkable in might.

5 Thou to the meek and lowly
  Thy secrets dost unfold ;
O God, Thou doest all things,
  All things both new and old.

6 I walk secure and blessèd
  In every clime or coast,
In Name of God the Father,
  And Son, and Holy Ghost.

St. Columba, 521–97 ; *tr.* by Duncan Macgregor, 1854–1923.

455 ABBEY. (C.M.)

Doh = G. *Slow.* f.C. *Scottish Psalter*, 1615.

```
|d :—  |d :m  |r :d  |d :t,  |d :—  ||f d' :— |t :l    |l :se |l :—  ||
|s, :— |s, :d |t, :l, |l, :s, |s, :— ||d s :—  |f :d.r  |m :m  |m :—  ||
|m :—  |s :s  |s :m  |f :r   |m :—  ||f d' :— |r' :l   |t :t  |d' :— ||
|d :—  |m :d  |s, :l, |f, :s, |d :—  ||l m :—  |r :f    |m :m  |l :—  ||
```

G.t.

```
|r' s :— |m :d    |f :m    |r :d     |t, :— ||s, :— |l, :d  |d :t,   |d :—  ||d  d  ||
|r s, :— |s, :s,  |d :-.t, |l, :m,.f, |s, :— ||s, :— |f, :s, |l, :s,  |s, :— ||l, s, ||
|l r :—  |m :m    |f :s    |l :d     |r :—  ||d :—  |d :d   |f.m :r  |m :—  ||f  m  ||
|fe t, :— |d :d.t, |l, :s,  |f, :l,   |s, :— ||m, :— |f, :m, |r, :s,  |d, :— ||f, d, ||
                                                                          A-men.
```

O HELP us, Lord ; each hour of need
  Thy heavenly succour give ;
Help us in thought, and word, and deed,
  Each hour on earth we live.

2 O help us when our spirits bleed
  With contrite anguish sore ;
And, when our hearts are cold and dead,
  O help us, Lord, the more.

3 O help us, through the prayer of faith,
  More firmly to believe ;
For still the more the servant hath,
  The more shall he receive.

4 If, strangers to Thy fold, we call,
  Imploring at Thy feet
The crumbs that from Thy table fall,
  'Tis all we dare entreat.

5 But be it, Lord of mercy, all,
  So Thou wilt grant but this ;
The crumbs that from Thy table fall
  Are light and life and bliss.

6 O help us, Saviour, from on high ;
  We know no help but Thee :
O help us so to live and die
  As Thine in heaven to be.

Henry Hart Milman, 1791–1868.

456

LAWES (PSALM 32). (6 6. 6 6.)

Doh = G. *In moderate time.* HENRY LAWES, 1596–1662.

d :—	r :d	f :f	m :—		m :—	s :r	f :m	r :—	
s$_1$:—	l$_1$:d	d :t$_1$	d :—		s$_1$:—	s$_1$:s$_1$	l$_1$:s$_1$.l$_1$	t$_1$:—	
m :—	f :s	l :f	s :—		m :—	r :r	d :m.f	s :—	
d :—	f :m	r :r	d :—		d :—	t$_1$:ta$_1$	l$_1$:d	s$_1$:—	

r :—	r :m	d :r	t$_1$:—		s :—	f :s	m :r	d :—		d	d	
s$_1$:—	s$_1$:s$_1$	l$_1$:l$_1$	s$_1$:—		s$_1$:—	l$_1$:s$_1$	s$_1$.l$_1$:t$_1$	d :—		l$_1$	s$_1$	
t$_1$:—.d	r :d	m :f	r :—		d :—	d :d	d :r	m :—		f	m	
s$_1$:—.l$_1$	t$_1$:d	l$_1$:f$_1$	s$_1$:—		m$_1$:—	f$_1$:m$_1$.f$_1$	s$_1$:s$_1$	d/d$_1$:—		f$_1$	d$_1$	

A-men.

FINGAL. (6 6. 6 6. D.)

Irish Traditional Melody.

Lah = D. Doh = F. *Unison.* *Slow.* Arranged by LEOPOLD L. DIX, 1861– .

| m :m :m | m :d :r | m :— :r | d :l$_1$:l$_1$ | d :— :r | m :— :r ||

| m :l :l | s :m :r | m :— :r | d :l$_1$:t$_1$ | l$_1$:— :l$_1$ | l$_1$:— :— ||

| d :d :d | d :m :s | l :— :l | l :s :m | m :— :r | d :— :r ||

| m :l :l | s :m :r | m :— :r | d :l$_1$:t$_1$ | l$_1$:— :l$_1$ | l$_1$:— :— || d :— :r | m :— :— ||

A - men.

MY spirit longs for Thee
Within my troubled breast,
Though I unworthy be
Of so Divine a Guest.

2 Of so Divine a Guest
Unworthy though I be,
Yet has my heart no rest,
Unless it come from Thee.

3 Unless it come from Thee,
In vain I look around ;
In all that I can see
No rest is to be found.

4 No rest is to be found
But in Thy blessèd love :
O let my wish be crowned,
And send it from above !

JOHN BYROM, 1691–1763.

457 CHESHIRE. (C.M.)

Lah = E. Doh = G. *Slow.* *Este's Psalter*, 1592.

```
|l, :— |l, :t, |d :d |t, :-.t, |l, :— |— ‖ l, |d :-.d |r :s |m :— |— ‖
|m, :— |m, :m, |m, :l, |l, :se, |l, :— |— ‖ f, |m, :m, |s, :s, |s, :— |— ‖
|d :— |d :t, |l, :m |m :-.r |d :— |— ‖ l, |l,.t, :d |d :t, |d :— |— ‖
|l, :— |l, :se, |l, :d, |m, :m, |l, :— |— ‖ r, |l, :-.l, |s, :s, |d, :— |— ‖
```

```
:m |m :-.m |r :t, |d :r |m :— |— ‖ m |r :d |r :t, |l, :— |— :— ‖ l, |l, ‖
:d |d :-.d |t, :s, |d :l, |se, :— |— ‖ s, |t, :l, |l, :se, |l, :— |— :— ‖ f, |m, ‖
:s |s :-.s |s :s |m :r |t, :— |— ‖ s |s :m |f :m.r |d :— |— :— ‖ r |de ‖
:d, |d :-.d |s, :s, |l, :f, |m, :— |— ‖ d, |s, :l, |r, :m, |l, l₂ :— |— :— ‖ r, |l, ‖
```

A-men.

MARTYRDOM. (C.M.)

Doh = G. *Moderately slow and dignified.* HUGH WILSON, 1766–1824.

```
:s, |d :l, |s, :d.r |m :r |d :m |s :m.r |d :m |r :— |— ‖
:m, |s, :f, |m, :d |d :t, |d :s, |s, :t, |d :s, |s, :— |— ‖
:d |s, :l,.t, |d :m.f |s :s.f |m :d |r :s |m :d |t, :— |— ‖
:d, |m, :f, |d, :l, |s, :s, |d, :d |t, :s, |l, :m, |s, :— |— ‖
```

```
:s |m :r |d :m |f :m |r :m |s,.l, :d.r |m :r |d :— |— ‖ d |d ‖
:r |d :t, |l, :ta, |l,.t, :d |t, :d |s,.f, :m,.l, |s, :s,.f, |m, :— |— ‖ f, |m, ‖
:s |s :s |m :s |d.r :m.f |s :s |d :d |d :t, |d :— |— ‖ l, |s, ‖
:t, |d :s, |l, :s, |f, :d, |s, :d, |m,.f, :l,.f, |s, :s, |d, :— |— ‖ f, |d, ‖
```

A-men.

O FOR a closer walk with God,
A calm and heavenly frame,
A light to shine upon the road
That leads me to the Lamb!

2 Where is the blessedness I knew
When first I saw the Lord?
Where is the soul-refreshing view
Of Jesus and His word?

3 What peaceful hours I once enjoyed!
How sweet their memory still!
But they have left an aching void
The world can never fill.

4 Return, O Holy Dove! return,
Sweet messenger of rest!
I hate the sins that made Thee mourn,
And drove Thee from my breast.

5 The dearest idol I have known,
Whate'er that idol be,
Help me to tear it from Thy throne,
And worship only Thee.

6 So shall my walk be close with God,
Calm and serene my frame;
So purer light shall mark the road
That leads me to the Lamb.

WILLIAM COWPER, 1731–1800.

[May be sung to STRACATHRO, No, 451.]

458 HAREWOOD. (66. 66. 88.)

Doh = A. *Slow and stately.* SAMUEL SEBASTIAN WESLEY, 1810–76.

```
:s, |l, :t, |d  :r  |d  :t, |— :s  |f.m :r.d    |m  :r     |d  :— |— ||
:s, |s, :s, |m, :l, |s, :—  |— :s, |l,.s, :f,.m, |s, :s,.f, |m, :— |— ||
:m  |m  :r  |m  :f  |m  :r  |— :d  |d   :d      |d  :t,    |d  :— |— ||
:d  |d  :t, |l, :r, |s, :—  |— :m, |f,  :l,     |s, :s,    |d, :— |— ||

:r  |m  :s  |m  :r  |d  :—  |— :m   |r  :d  |t, :l,  |s, :— |— ||
:s, |s, :s, |s, :s, |m, :—  |— :fe, |s, :l, |s, :fe, |s, :— |— ||
:t, |d  :r  |d  :t, |d  :—  |— :d   |r  :m  |r  :d   |t, :— |— ||
:s, |d  :t, |d  :s, |l, :—  |— :l,  |t, :d  |r  :r,  |s, :— |— ||

:s, |l, :t, |d  :r  |m  :f  |r  :s  |s  :f     |m  :r.l, |d  :t,    |d  || d  |d  ||
:s, |s, :f, |m, :s, |s, :l, |s, :t, |l, :t,.l, |se, :l,  |s, :s,.f, |m, || f, |m, ||
:d  |d  :t, |l, :r  |d  :d  |t, :t, |m  :f     |t, :r    |m  :r     |d  || l, |s, ||
:m, |f, :r, |l, :t, |d  :f, |s, :m, |d, :r,    |m, :f,   |s, :s,    |d, || f, |d, ||
                                                                          A-men.
```

Ἄτερ ἀρχῆς ἀπέραντον.

O LIGHT that knew no dawn,
That shines to endless day,
All things in earth and heaven
Are lustred by Thy ray;
No eye can to Thy throne ascend,
Nor mind Thy brightness comprehend.

2 Thy grace, O Father, give,
That I may serve in fear;
Above all boons, I pray,
Grant me Thy voice to hear;
From sin Thy child in mercy free,
And let me dwell in light with Thee:

3 That, cleansed from stain of sin,
I may meet homage give,
And, pure in heart, behold
Thy beauty while I live;
Clean hands in holy worship raise,
And Thee, O Christ my Saviour, praise.

4 In supplication meek
To Thee I bend the knee;
O Christ, when Thou shalt come,
In love remember me,
And in Thy Kingdom, by Thy grace,
Grant me a humble servant's place.

5 Thy grace, O Father, give,
I humbly Thee implore;
And let Thy mercy bless
Thy servant more and more.
All grace and glory be to Thee,
From age to age eternally.

ST. GREGORY NAZIANZEN, 325–390; *tr.* by JOHN BROWNLIE, 1859–1925.

FIRST TUNE.

459

VATER UNSER. (88. 88. 88.) *Geistliche Lieder*, Leipsic, 1539.

Arranged by JOHANN SEBASTIAN BACH, 1685–1750.

Lah = C. Doh = Eb. *Slow.*

:m |m :d |r :m |d :t, |l, ‖m |m :r |s :m |d :r |m ‖
:d |t, :l, |se, :l,.t, |d :se, |l, ‖d |t, :l, |t, :d |d :t, |t, ‖
:l |m :m |r :l |l :m |d ‖l |m :f |s :s |l :l |se ‖
:l, |se, :l, |t, :d .r |m :m, |l, ‖l, |s, :f, |m,.s, :d |f :f |m ‖

Bb.t.

:m |s :l .t |d' :t |l :se |l ‖ ^{l}r |m :r |d :t, |l, :se, |l, ‖
:t, |m :r |d :r |d :t, |d ‖ ^{d}f, |m, :t, |m, :m,.r, |d,.r, :m, |m, ‖
:s |s.m :ba.se |l .s :f |fe :m |m ‖ ^{fe}t, |t,.l, :l,.se, |l, :se, |l, :t, |d ‖
:m.r |d :-.t, |l, :r |re :m |l, ‖ ^{r}s, |d, :t,, |l,, :m, |f, :m, |l,, ‖

f.Eb.

:^{r}l |s :fe |s :m |m :r |d ‖m |f :m.r |d :r |d :t, |l, ‖r |de ‖
:^{s}r |r :d |r :d |d :t, |s, ‖l, |r :d.t, |l, :t, |l, :se, |l, ‖l, |l, ‖
:^{t}fe |s :l |t :l |l.s :f |m ‖l |l :se |l .s :f |m :m.r |d ‖f |m ‖
:^{s}r.d |t, :l, |s, :l,.s, |f, :s, |d ‖de |r :m |f .m :r |m :m, |l, ‖r, |l, ‖

A-men.

Verborgne Gottesliebe du.

THOU hidden Love of God, whose height,
Whose depth unfathomed, no man knows,
I see from far Thy beauteous light,
Inly I sigh for Thy repose;
My heart is pained, nor can it be
At rest till it finds rest in Thee.

2 Thy secret voice invites me still
The sweetness of Thy yoke to prove;
And fain I would; but, though my will
Seem fixed, yet wide my passions rove;
Yet hindrances strew all the way;
I aim at Thee, yet from Thee stray.

3 'Tis mercy all, that Thou hast brought
My mind to seek her peace in Thee;
Yet, while I seek but find Thee not,
No peace my wandering soul shall see.
O when shall all my wanderings end,
And all my steps to Thee-ward tend?

4 Is there a thing beneath the sun
That strives with Thee my heart to share?
Ah! tear it thence, and reign alone,
The Lord of every motion there;
Then shall my heart from earth be free,
When it has found repose in Thee.

GERHARD TERSTEEGEN, 1697–1769; *tr.* by JOHN WESLEY, 1703–91.

SECOND TUNE.

459

ST. PETERSBURG. (88. 88. 88.)

Doh = C. *In moderate time.* DMITRI STEPANOVITCH BORTNIANSKI, 1752–1825.

```
:s  |s  :m  :f  |s  :—  :d' |r' :d' :t  |d' :—  :s  |l  :d' :l
:m  |m  :d  :r  |m  :—  :s  |f  :m  :r  |m  :—  :m  |f  :—  :f
:s  |s  :—  :s  |d' :—  :s  |l  :s  :s  |s  :—  :d' |d' :l  :d'
:d  |d  :—  :d  |d  :—  :m  |f  :s  :s, |d  :—  :d  |f  :—  :f

s  :—  :m  |s  :f  :m  |r  :—  ||s  |s  :m  :f  |s  :—  :d' |r' :d' :t
m  :—  :d  |r  :—  :d  |t, :—  ||r  |m  :d  :t, |d  :—  :m  |l  :s  :s
d' :—  :s  |s  :—  :s  |s  :—  ||s  |s  :m' :r' |d' :—  :d' |f' :m' :r'
d  :—  :d  |t, :—  :d  |s  :—  ||t, |d  :—  :r  |m  :—  :l  |f  :s  :f

d' :—  :s  |l  :d' :l  |s  :—  :m  |l  :m  :fe |s  :—  ||s  |r' :—  :t
s  :—  :m  |f  :—  :f  |m  :—  :d  |m  :—  :r  |r  :—  ||r  |s  :—  :s
s  :—  :d' |d' :l  :d' |d' :—  :s  |d' :—  :l  |t  :—  ||t  |t  :—  :r'
m  :—  :d  |f  :—  :f  |d  :—  :d  |l, :—  :r, |s, :—  ||s  |f  :—  :f

d' :—  :s  |m' :r'  :d'  |d' :t  :t  |d' :t  :l  |s  :—  :m  |f  :m  :r  |d  :—  ||f  |m
s  :—  :f  |m  :f   :m   |m  :r  :s  |s  :—  :f  |r  :—  :d  |d  :—  :t, |d  :—  ||d  |d
d' :—  :t  |d' :t.l :s   |s  :—  :r' |d' :—  :d' |r' :s  :s  |l  :s  :f  |m  :—  ||l  |s
m  :—  :r  |d  :r   :m.f |s  :—  :f  |m  :—  :f  |t, :—  :d  |f, :—  :s, |d  :—  ||f, |d
```

A-men.

Verborgne Gottesliebe du.

THOU hidden Love of God, whose height,
Whose depths unfathomed, no man knows,
I see from far Thy beauteous light,
Inly I sigh for Thy repose;
My heart is pained, nor can it be
At rest till it finds rest in Thee.

2 Thy secret voice invites me still
The sweetness of Thy yoke to prove;
And fain I would; but, though my will
Seem fixed, yet wide my passions rove;
Yet hindrances strew all the way;
I aim at Thee, yet from Thee stray.

3 'Tis mercy all, that Thou hast brought
My mind to seek her peace in Thee;
Yet, while I seek but find Thee not,
No peace my wandering soul shall see.
O when shall all my wanderings end,
And all my steps to Thee-ward tend?

4 Is there a thing beneath the sun
That strives with Thee my heart to share?
Ah! tear it thence, and reign alone,
The Lord of every motion there;
Then shall my heart from earth be free,
When it has found repose in Thee.

GERHARD TERSTEEGEN, 1697–1769; *tr.* by JOHN WESLEY, 1703–91.

French Psalter, 1543.
Composed or arranged by Louis Bourgeois, 1510– (?).
Adapted from the *Scottish Psalter*, 1564,
by James Smith Anderson, 1853– .

460

PSALM 86. (D.L.M.)

Lah = G. Doh = B♭. *Moderately slow.*

|l, :— |l, :se, |l, :t, |d :— |l, :— |t, :— ‖m, :— |l, :s, |d :t,

|m, :— |m, :m, |m, :se, |l, :— |l, :— |se, :— ‖m, :— |m, :m, |m, :m,

|d :— |d :t, |d :m |m :— |m :— |m :— ‖s, :— |d :t, |l, :se,

|l, :— |l, :m, |l, :m, |l, :— |d, :— |m, :— ‖m, :— |d, :m, |l, :m,

|l, :— |— :se, |l, :— ‖d :— |t, :s, |l, :— |d :— |t, :l, |se, :— ‖

|d, :— |m, :— |m, :— ‖l, :— |m, :m, |f, :— |s, :— |f, :f, |m, :— ‖

|l, :— |t, :— |d :— ‖m :— |t, :t, |d :— |d :— |r :r |t, :— ‖

|f, :— |m, :— |l, :— ‖l, :— |s, :s, |f, :— |m, :— |r, :r, |m, :— ‖

|s, :— |fe, :fe, |m, :l, |l, :se, |l, :— ‖d :— |r :m |m :r |d :— |r :—

|m, :— |fe, :r, |m, :m, |m, :m, |d, :— ‖m, :— |s, :s, |s, :s, |m, :— |s, :—

|t, :— |r :r |l, :d |t, :t, |l, :— ‖l, :— |t, :d |d :t, |d :— |t, :—

|m, :— |r, :r, |d, :l,, |m, :m, |l,, :— ‖l, :— |s, :d |d :s, |l, :— |s, :—

|d :— ‖d :— |r :m |m :r |d :— |r :— |d :— ‖d :— |t, :s, |l, :—

|m, :— ‖m, :— |s, :s, |s, :s, |m, :— |s, :— |m, :— ‖l, :— |m, :m, |f, :—

|d :— ‖d :— |t, :d |d :t, |d :— |t, :— |d :— ‖m :— |t, :t, |d :—

|d, :— ‖l, :— |s, :d |d :s, |l, :— |s, :— |d, :— ‖l, :— |s, :s, |f, :—

|d :— |t, :l, |se, :— ‖s, :— |fe, :fe, |m, :l, |l, :se, |l, :— ‖l, |l, ‖

|s, :— |f, :f, |m, :— ‖m, :— |fe, :r, |m, :m, |m, :m, |m, :— ‖f, |m, ‖

|d :— |r :r |t, :— ‖t, :— |r :r |l, :d |t, :t, |d :— ‖r |de ‖

|m, :— |r, :r, |m, :— ‖m, :— |r, :r, |d, :l,, |m, :m, |l, / l,, :— ‖r, |l,, ‖

A-men.

DEAR Master, in whose life I see
All that I would but fail to be,
Let Thy clear light for ever shine,
To shame and guide this life of mine.

2 Though what I dream and what I do
In my weak days are always two,
Help me, oppressed by things undone,
O Thou, whose deeds and dreams were one!

John Hunter, 1848–1917.

[May be sung to Winscott, No. 338.]

461 KILDROSTAN. (88. 84.)

DAVID EVANS, 1874–

Lah = G. Doh = B♭. *Unison or Harmony. Moderately slow.*

```
:l,  |l,  :m,  |l,     :t,.d   |r   :d.t,  |d   :l,     |m   :r .d      |t,   :l,
:m,  |m,  :m,  |m,     :l,     |l,  :se,   |l,  :l,     |se, :l, .l,    |t,   :m,
:d   |m   :r   |d      :r .m   |f   :m     |m   :l,     |t,  :l, .l,    |m .r :d
:l,  |d   :t,  |l,.s,  :f,.m,  |r,  :m,    |l,  :s,.f,  |m,  :ba,.ba,   |se,  :l,
                        v. 2. im - part,         Grate-ful and glad

|s,  :fe,    |m,  ||m,     |l,  :t,.d     |r      :t,     |d     :r     |m   :m,
|m,  :re,    |m,  ||m,.r,  |d,  :f,.m,    |r,.l,  :-.se,  |l,.d  :-.t,  |d   :m,
|t,  :t,.l,  |s,  ||d.t,   |l,  :se,.l,   |t,.f   :m.r    |d.m   :s     |s   :m.r
|t,  :t,,    |m,  ||d,     |f,.m, :r,.d,  |t,,    :m,     |l,    :s,    |d,  :d.t,

                                                   rall.
|d      :-      |t,  :-    |l,         :-  |-  ||f    :m.r  |de  :r   |l,  :-      |l,   :-  ||
|m,     :l,     |-   :se,  |l,         :-  |-  ||l,   :-    |-   :-   |-   :s,.f,  |m,   :-  ||
|d      :r .m   |f   :m.r  |d          :-  |-  ||r    :m.f  |m   :r   |-   :de.r   |de   :-  ||
|l,.s,  :f,.m,  |r,  :m,   |l, / l,,   :-  |-  ||l,,  :l,   |s,  :f,  |-   :m,.r,  |l,,  :-  ||
                                                 A     -     -    -    -    -      men.
```

[*Copyright*, 1927, *by David Evans.*]

ONE thing I of the Lord desire,—
 For all my way hath miry been—
Be it by water or by fire,
 O make me clean!

2 If clearer vision Thou impart,
 Grateful and glad my soul shall be;
But yet to have a purer heart
 Is more to me.

3 Yea, only as the heart is clean
 May larger vision yet be mine,
For mirrored in its depths are seen
 The things divine.

4 I watch to shun the miry way,
 And stanch the spring of guilty thought;
But, watch and wrestle as I may,
 Pure I am not.

5 So wash Thou me without, within,
 Or purge with fire, if that must be,—
No matter how, if only sin
 Die out in me.

WALTER CHALMERS SMITH, 1824–1908.

462

ST. CONSTANTINE. (65. 65.)

Doh = D. *In moderate time.* WILLIAM HENRY MONK, 1823–89.

m :r	f :m	r :—	d :—	r :s	fe :l	s :—	— :—
d :t_1	d :d	t_1 :—	d :—	s_1 :r	r :d	t_1 :—	— :—
s :s	f :s	f :—	m :—	s :t	l :fe	s :—	— :—
d :s_1	l_1 :d	s_1 :—	d :—	t_1 :s_1	r :r	s_1 :—	— :—

f :m	l :s	f :—	m :—	m :r	f :f	m :—	— :—
r :d	d :d	t_1 :—	d :—	d :r	d :r	t_1 :—	— :—
s :s	f :s	s :—	s :—	s :s	l :l	se :—	— :—
t_1 :d	f :m	r :—	d :—	d :t_1	l_1 :r	m :—	— :—

JESUS, meek and gentle,
Son of God most high,
Pitying, loving Saviour,
Hear Thy children's cry.

2 Pardon our offences,
Loose our captive chains,
Break down every idol
Which our soul detains.

3 Give us holy freedom,
Fill our hearts with love,
Draw us, holy Jesus,
To the realms above.

4 Lead us on our journey,
Be Thyself the Way
Through terrestrial darkness
To celestial day.

5 Jesus, meek and gentle,
Son of God most high,
Pitying, loving Saviour,
Hear Thy children's cry.

Last verse only.

m :r	f :f	m :—	— :—	f	m
d :r	d :d	d :—	— :—	d	d
Hear Thy	chil-dren's	cry.		A -	men.
s :s	l :l	s :—	— :—	l	s
d :t_1	l_1 :f_1	d :—	— :—	f_1	d

GEORGE RUNDLE PRYNNE, 1818–1903.

463

CHERRY TREE CAROL. (7 6. 7 6. Irr.)

Doh = A♭. *In moderate time.*

English Traditional Melody.
Arranged by MARTIN SHAW, 1876–

```
:s, |d  :t, |l, :s, |d  :—  |r  :m.f |s .f:m .r |d  :t, |l, :—  |—
:s, |s, :s, |m, :m, |m, :—  |s, :s,  |s,  :s,    |s, :s, |m, :—  |—
:s, |m  :r  |d  :t, |l, :—  |t, :t,  |d   :s     |m  :r  |d  :—  |—
:s, |d  :s, |l, :m, |l, :—  |s, :s,  |m,  :d,    |m, :s, |l, :—  |—
                 v. 3 friend,  And
```

```
:l, |s  :m  |d  :d  |r  :—   |s, :d.t, |l, :f, |s, :t, |d  :—  |— ||d  |d  ||
:l, |s, :s, |d  :l, |t, :-.l,|s, :s,   |d, :f, |m, :r, |m, :—  |— ||f, |m, ||
:l, |m  :m  |s  :m  |r  :-.d |t, :s,   |l, :r  |d  :s, |s, :—  |— ||l, |s, ||
:l, |d  :d  |m  :d  |s, :—   |s, :m,   |f, :r, |m, :s, |d, :—  |— ||f, |d, ||
                                                                  A-men.
```

MY soul, there is a country
Afar beyond the stars,
Where stands a wingèd Sentry
All skilful in the wars.

2 There, above noise, and danger,
Sweet peace sits, crowned with smiles,
And One born in a manger
Commands the beauteous files.

3 He is thy gracious friend,
And—O my soul, awake!—
Did in pure love descend,
To die here for thy sake.

4 If thou canst get but thither,
There grows the flower of peace,
The rose that cannot wither,
Thy fortress, and thy ease.

5 Leave then thy foolish ranges;
For none can thee secure,
But One, who never changes,
Thy God, thy Life, thy Cure.

HENRY VAUGHAN, 1621–95.

FIRST TUNE.

464

LEOMINSTER. (D.S.M.)

GEORGE WILLIAM MARTIN, 1828–81.

Doh = D. *In moderate time.* Arranged by ARTHUR SEYMOUR SULLIVAN, 1842–1900.

```
:m |m :m |m :m |f  :— |— :f  |r  :r  |r   :m   |r  :— |—
:d |d :d |d :d |d  :— |— :d  |d  :d  |d   :d   |t, :— |—
:s |s :s |s :s |l  :— |— :l  |l  :l  |l   :l   |r  :— |—
:d |d :d |d :d |f, :— |— :f, |f, :f, |fe, :fe, |s, :— |—
```

```
:r  | m :m    | s :s    | d' :d'  | d' :d    | d :m      | m :r    | d :— | — ||
:t, | d :d    | r :r    | d :ta,  | l, :l,   | s, :d     | t, :t,  | d :— | — ||
:s  | s :s    | s :s    | m :m    | f :r     | m :s      | s :f    | m :— | — ||
:s, | d :d    | t, :t,  | l, :s,  | f, :fe,  | s, :s,    | s, :s,  | d :— | — ||

:d  | f :-.f   | f :d    | m :— | — :m | l :-.l     | l :m    | s :— | — ||
:d  | d :-.d   | d :d    | d :— | — :d | m :-.m     | m :m    | m :— | — ||
:m  | l :-.l   | l :f    | s :— | — :s | d' :-.d'   | d' :l   | t :— | — ||
:d  | f, :-.f, | f, :l,  | d :— | — :d | l, :-.l,   | l, :d   | m :— | — ||

:s  | d' :-.d' | d' :t   | t :l    | s :f   | m :-.d    | m :r    | d :— | — || d  | d  ||
:f  | m :-.m   | r :r    | r :d    | de :r  | d :-.d    | t, :t,  | d :— | — || l, | s, ||
:t  | d' :s    | se :se  | se :l   | l :l   | s :-.m    | s :f    | m :— | — || f  | m  ||
:r  | d :-.d   | m :m,   | f, :f,  | l, :r  | s, :-.s,  | s, :s,  | d :— | — || f, | d  ||
                                                                    A-men.
```

[*By permission of Novello & Co., Ltd.*]

MAKE me a captive, Lord,
And then I shall be free;
Force me to render up my sword,
And I shall conqueror be.
I sink in life's alarms
When by myself I stand;
Imprison me within Thine arms,
And strong shall be my hand.

2 My heart is weak and poor
Until it master find;
It has no spring of action sure—
It varies with the wind.
It cannot freely move,
Till Thou hast wrought its chain;
Enslave it with Thy matchless love,
And deathless it shall reign.

3 My power is faint and low
Till I have learned to serve;
It wants the needed fire to glow
It wants the breeze to nerve;
It cannot drive the world,
Until itself be driven;
Its flag can only be unfurled
When Thou shalt breathe from heaven.

4 My will is not my own
Till Thou hast made it Thine;
If it would reach a monarch's throne
It must its crown resign;
It only stands unbent,
Amid the clashing strife,
When on Thy bosom it has leant
And found in Thee its life.

GEORGE MATHESON, 1842–1906.

SECOND TUNE.

464 LLANLLYFNI. (D.S.M.)

JOHN JONES (TALYSARN), 1797–1857.
Arranged by DAVID JENKINS, 1849–1915.

Lah = E. Doh = G. *Moderately slow.*

```
:l, |m .m :r :d |t, :— :d |t,.l, :l, :se, |l, :— ||
:l, |l,.l, :l, :l, |se, :— :l, |f,.f, :m, :m, |m, :— ||
:d |d .de :r :m .f |t, :— :m |r .r :d :t, .r |d :— ||
:l, |l,.s, :f, :m,.r, |m, :r, :d, |r,.r, :m, :m, |l, :— ||

:t, |d .t, :l, :t, |d .r :m :d |m .m :l, :t, |d :— ||
:se, |l,.se, :l, :se, |l,.l, :se, :l, |l,.l, :l,.s, :f, |m, :— ||
:m |m .r :d :m |m .l, :t, :d |d .d :d :r |m :— ||
:m, |l,.m, :f, :m, |l,.f, :m, :l, |l,.s, :f,.m, :r,.s, |d, :— ||

:m |s .m :r :d |t, :— :m |l .fe :m :re |m :— ||
:d |r .d :t, :l, |se, :— :se, |l,.l, :s,.t, :- .l, |s, :— ||
:m |r .m :s :m |m :— :m |m .d :t,.s :- .fe |m :— ||
:d |t,.d :s, :l, |m, :— :m .r |d .l, :t, :t, |m, :— ||

:d.,t, |l,.t, :m :m |r .d :t, :d .r |m .f :m .r :d .t, |l, :— ||l, |l, ||
:d.,t, |l,.s, :s, :s, |se,.l, :se, :l, |l, l, :l, :l,.se, |l, :— ||f, |m, ||
:d.,t, |l,.r :d :d |r .m :m :m .r |d .r :m .f :m .r |d :— ||r |de ||
:d.,t, |l,.s, :d, :d |t, .l, :m, :l,.f, |m,.r, :d,.r, :m, |l, :— ||r, |l, ||
                                                        A-men.
```

MAKE me a captive, Lord,
And then I shall be free;
Force me to render up my sword,
And I shall conqueror be.
I sink in life's alarms
When by myself I stand;
Imprison me within Thine arms,
And strong shall be my hand.

2 My heart is weak and poor
Until it master find;
It has no spring of action sure—
It varies with the wind.
It cannot freely move,
Till Thou hast wrought its chain;
Enslave it with Thy matchless love,
And deathless it shall reign.

3 My power is faint and low
Till I have learned to serve;
It wants the needed fire to glow,
It wants the breeze to nerve;
It cannot drive the world,
Until itself be driven;
Its flag can only be unfurled
When Thou shalt breathe from heaven.

4 My will is not my own
Till Thou hast made it Thine;
If it would reach a monarch's throne
It must its crown resign;
It only stands unbent,
Amid the clashing strife,
When on Thy bosom it has lent
And found in Thee its life.

GEORGE MATHESON, 1842–1906.

465 BUGAIL ISRAEL. (87. 87.)

Doh = E♭. *In moderate time.* TOM PRICE, 1857–1925.

:m .f | s :- .s :l .s | s :f :m .r | s :- .r :m .r | r :— ||
:d .t_1 | d :- .m :f .m | m :r :d .r | d :- .r :d .d | t_1 :— ||
:s .s | s :- .s :r .m | l :t :d^1 .t | d^1 :s :s .fe | s :— ||
:d .r | m :- .d :t_1 .d | r :s_1 :s .f | m :- .t_1 :d .r | s_1 :— ||

:s .s | l :- .l :t .d^1 | d^1 :r :t .l | s :- .m :r .m | d :— || d d ||
:r .r | m :- .m :f .m | r :r :re .re | m :- .d :t_1 .t_1 | d :— || l_1 s_1 ||
:s .s | s :- .s :s .s | l :l :t .d^1 | d^1 :- .s :f .s | m :— || f m ||
:t_1 .t_1 | d :- .d :r .m | f :f :fe .fe | s :- .s_1 :s_1 .s_1 | d :— || f_1 d ||

A-men.

BLESSÈD Jesus, high in glory,
Seen of saints and angels fair,
Children's voices now adore Thee ;
Listen to Thy children's prayer.

2 Gentle Jesus, Thou dost love us,
Thou hast died upon the Tree,
And Thou reignest now above us,
That we too might reign with Thee.

3 Give us grace to trust Thee wholly ;
Give us each a childlike heart ;
Make us meek and pure and holy,
Meet to see Thee as Thou art.

4 Father, Son, and Holy Spirit,
Bless us all our life below,
Till we each that heaven inherit
Which the childlike only know.

JOHN MACLEOD, 1840–98.

[May be sung to STUTTGART, No. 113.]

466 O GRANT US LIGHT. (L.M.)

Lah = D. Doh = F. *Moderately slow.* JOHN HENRY ROBERTS, 1848–1924.

```
|m   :—  |s   :f  |m   :—  |—   :m  |r   :d  |t,  :r   |d   :t,  |l,  :d
|d   :—  |r   :r  |d   :—  |t,  :l, |l,  :l, |se, :t,  |l,  :se, |m,  :l,
|l   :—  |l   :l  |l   :—  |se  :m  |f   :m  |r   :f   |m   :r   |m   :m
|l,  :—  |r   :r  |m   :—  |—   :d  |r   :l, |t,  :se, |l,  :t,  |d   :l,

|t,  :—  |t,  :—  |t,  :—  |—   :—  ||m   :—  |s   :f  |m   :—  |—   :l
|se, :—  |ba, :—  |se, :—  |—   :—  ||l,  :—  |r   :r  |d   :—  |t,  :d
|m   :—  |re  :—  |m   :—  |—   :—  ||m   :—  |l   :l  |l   :—  |se  :m
|t,  :—  |t,  :—  |m,  :—  |—   :—  ||d   :—  |r   :r  |m   :—  |—   :l,

|s   :m  |r   :f  |m   :d  |t,  :l, |t,  :—  |d   :—  |l,  :—  |—   :—  ||r   |de  ||
|r   :t, |l,  :r  |d   :l, |se, :l, |l,  :—  |se, :—  |l,  :—  |—   :—  ||l,  |l,  ||
|r   :m  |f   :l  |l   :m  |r   :m  |f   :—  |m   :—  |d   :—  |—   :—  ||f   |m   ||
|t,  :s, |f,  :r, |m,  :l, |t,  :d  |r   :—  |m   :—  |l,  :—  |—   :—  ||r,  |l,  ||
```

A-men.

O GRANT us light, that we may know
The wisdom Thou alone canst give;
That truth may guide where'er we go,
And virtue bless where'er we live!

2 O grant us light, that we may see
Where error lurks in human lore,
And turn our doubting minds to Thee,
And love Thy simple word the more.

3 O grant us light, that we may learn
How dead is life from Thee apart;
How sure is joy for all who turn
To Thee an undivided heart.

4 O grant us light, in grief and pain,
To lift our burdened hearts above,
And count the very cross a gain,
And bless our Father's hidden love.

5 O grant us light, when, soon or late,
All earthly scenes shall pass away,
In Thee to find the open gate
To deathless home and endless day.

LAWRENCE TUTTIETT, 1825–97.

467 ST. ETHELDREDA. (C.M.)

Doh = F. *In moderate time.* THOMAS TURTON, 1780–1864.

```
:d  |d  :r  |m  :r  |d  :t,  |d  :r  |m  :s |f    :m |r  :— |— ||
:s, |d  :t, |d  :l, |s, :s,  |s, :t, |d  :d |l,.t,:d |t, :— |— ||
:m  |m  :s  |s  :f  |m  :r   |m  :s  |s  :m |f    :s |s  :— |— ||
:d  |l, :s, |d  :f, |s, :s,  |d  :s, |d  :m |r    :d |s, :— |— ||
```

```
:m |f  :l  |s  :t,    |d  :f  |m  :s  |l  :f  |m  :r  |d :— |— ||f  |m ||
:d |d  :d  |d  :s,.f, |m, :s, |s, :ta,|l, :d  |d  :t, |d :— |— ||d  |d ||
:s |f  :f  |s  :m.r   |d  :r  |d  :d  |d  :f  |s  :-.f|m :— |— ||l  |s ||
:d |l, :f, |m, :s,    |l, :t, |d  :m, |f, :l, |s, :s, |d :— |— ||f, |d ||
                                                                  A-men.
```

O FOR a heart to praise my God!
A heart from sin set free;
A heart that always feels Thy blood,
So freely shed for me;

2 A heart resigned, submissive, meek,
My great Redeemer's throne,
Where only Christ is heard to speak,
Where Jesus reigns alone;

3 A humble, lowly, contrite heart,
Believing, true, and clean,
Which neither life nor death can part
From Him that dwells within;

4 A heart in every thought renewed,
And full of love divine,
Perfect and right and pure and good,
A copy, Lord, of Thine!

5 Thy nature, gracious Lord, impart;
Come quickly from above;
Write Thy new Name upon my heart,
Thy new, best Name of Love.

CHARLES WESLEY, 1707–88

468

TRES MAGI DE GENTIBUS. (77. 76.)

Doh = E♭. *Moderately quick.* *Andernach Gesangbuch*, 1608.

s :— :s | m :— :f | s :— :s | m :— :— || s :— :s | m :— :f
d :— :r | d :— :d | d :— :t, | d :— :— || t, :— :t, | d :— :d
m :— :s | s :— :f | r :— :s | s :— :— || s :— :s | l :— :l
d :— :t, | d :— :l, | s, :— :s, | d :— :— || m :— :m, | l, :— :f,

s :— :s | m :— :— || m :— :m | m :— :r | m :— :s
d :— :t, | d :— :— || d :— :d | t, :— :t, | d :— :d
s :— :s | s :— :— || s :— :l | s :— :s | s :— :m
m, :f, :s, | d :— :— || d :— :l, | m, :— :s, | d :— :d

f :— :— || m :— :m | r :— :d | r :— :— | d :— :— || d | d ||
d :— :— || d :— :d | l, :— :l, | t, :— :— | d :— :— || l, | s, ||
l :— :— || l :— :l | f :— :m | s :— :f | m :— :— || f | m ||
f, :— :— || l, :— :l, | r :— :l, | s, :— :— | d :— :— || f, | d ||

A-men.

Children's Litany.

JESUS, Saviour ever mild,
Born for us a little Child
Of the Virgin undefiled :
Hear us, Holy Jesus.

2 Jesus, at whose infant feet
Shepherds, coming Thee to greet,
Knelt to pay their worship meet :
Hear us, Holy Jesus.

3 Jesus, unto whom of yore
Wise men, hastening to adore,
Gold and myrrh and incense bore :
Hear us, Holy Jesus.

4 From all pride and vain conceit,
From all spite and angry heat,
From all lying and deceit,
Save us, Holy Jesus.

5 From all sloth and idleness,
From not caring for distress,
From all lust and greediness,
Save us, Holy Jesus.

6 From refusing to obey,
From the love of our own way,
From forgetfulness to pray,
Save us, Holy Jesus.

7 By Thy pattern bright and pure,
By the pains Thou didst endure
Our salvation to procure,
Save us, Holy Jesus.

8 By the Name we bow before,
Human Name, which evermore
All the hosts of heaven adore,
Save us, Holy Jesus.

9 By Thine own unconquered might,
By Thy glory in the height,
By Thy mercies infinite,
Save us, Holy Jesus.

RICHARD FREDERICK LITTLEDALE, 1833–90, and others.

469

LEBBAEUS. (77. 76.)

Doh = G. *Moderately slow.* Arranged by ARTHUR SEYMOUR SULLIVAN, 1842–1900.

m :-.m | m :r | d :d | s, :— | d :-.d | r :r | m :m | r :— ||
s, :-.s, | s, :f, | m, :m, | s, :— | m, :-.m, | s, :s, | s, :s, | s, :— ||
d :-.d | d :t, | d :d | r :— | d :-.d | t, :t, | d :d | t, :— ||
d, :-.d, | m, :s, | d :d | t, :— | l, :-.l, | s, :f, | m, :d, | s, :— ||

f :-.f | f :m | r :r | l, :— | s, :d | m :r | r :— | d :— || d | d ||
l, :-.l, | l, :l, | l, :r, | r, :— | m, :s, | d :t, | t, :— | d :— || l, | s, ||
r :-.r | r :de | r :l, | d :— | d :m | s :f | f :— | m :— || f | m ||
r, :-.r, | r, :m, | f, :f, | fe, :— | s, :s, | s, :s, | s, :— | d, :— || f, | d, ||

A-men.

[*By permission of Novello & Co., Ltd.*]

JESUS, from Thy throne on high,
Far above the bright blue sky,
Look on us with loving eye:
Hear us, Holy Jesus.

2 Be Thou with us every day,
In our work and in our play,
When we learn and when we pray:
Hear us, Holy Jesus.

3 May our thoughts be undefiled;
May our words be true and mild;
Make us each a holy child:
Hear us, Holy Jesus.

4 Jesus, Son of God most high,
Who didst in the manger lie,
Who upon the Cross didst die,
Hear us, Holy Jesus.

5 Jesus, from Thy heavenly throne
Watching o'er each little one,
Till our life on earth is done,
Hear us, Holy Jesus.

THOMAS BENSON POLLOCK, 1836–96.

470

CHENIES. (76. 76. D.)

Doh = G. *In moderate time.* Timothy Richard Matthews, 1826–1910.

:s, |s, :m |m :r |d :— |s, :s, |l, :d |d :t, |d :— |— ||
:m, |s, :s, |s, :f, |m, :— |s, :s, |f, :s, |l, :s, |s, :— |— ||
:d |d :d |d :t, |d :— |d :d |d :d |f :r |m :— |— ||
:d, |m, :d, |s, :s, |l, :— |m, :m, |f, :m, |r, :s, |d, :— |— ||

:s, |s, :m |m :r |r :— |d :d |r :-.r |m :fe |s :— |— ||
:s, |s, :d |d :t, |t, :— |d :d |t, :-.t, |d :l, |t, :— |— ||
:m |m :s |s :f |f :— |m :s |s :-.r |r :r |r :— |— ||
:d |m :d |s, :s, |s, :— |d :m |r :-.r |r, :r, |s, :— |— ||

:s, |r :r |r :r |m :-.r |d :d |l :l |l :l |s :— |— ||
:s, |s, :fe, |s, :t, |d :-.t, |d :d |l, :t, |d :r |s, :— |— ||
:t, |t, :d |r :s |s :-.f |m :d |f :f |f :f |m :— |— ||
:s, |s, :l, |t, :s, |d :— |d, :m, |f, :s, |l, :t, |d :— |— ||

:m |f :m |m :r |r :— |d :s, |l, :f |m :r |d :— |— ||d |d ||
:s, |s, :s, |se, :t, |t, :— |l, :s, |f, :r |d :t, |d :— |— ||l, |s, ||
:d |r :m |m :m |m :— |m :d |d :l |s :-.f |m :— |— ||f |m ||
:d |t, :d |m, :se, |se, :— |l, :m, |f, :f, |s, :s, |d, :— |— ||f, |d, ||

A-men.

[*By permission of Novello & Co., Ltd.*]

KILMOREY. (76. 76. D.)

Lah = G. Doh = B♭. *In moderate time.* John Ambrose Lloyd, 1840–1914.

:l, |l, :-.t, |d :r |m :— |t, :t, |d :-.t, |l, :d |t, :— |— ||
:m, |m, :-.m, |m, :l, |l, :— |se, :se, |l, :-.se, |l, :l, |se, :— |— ||
:d |d :-.r |d :l, |t, :— |m :r |d :-.r |m :m |m :— |— ||
:l, |l, :-.se, |l, :f, |m, :— |m, :m, |l, :-.t, |d :l, |m, :— |— ||

:se$_1$ |l$_1$:-.t$_1$ |d :r |m :— |d :m |m :r |d :t$_1$ |d :— |—
:m$_1$ |m$_1$:-.se$_1$ |l$_1$:s$_1$ |s$_1$:— |l$_1$:s$_1$ |l$_1$:l$_1$ |s$_1$:s$_1$ |s$_1$:— |—
:t$_1$ |m :-.m |m :r |d :— |m :d |d :r |m :f |m :— |—
:m$_1$ |d$_1$:-.m$_1$ |l$_1$:t$_1$ |d :— |l$_1$:m$_1$ |f$_1$:f$_1$ |s$_1$:s$_1$ |d$_1$:— |—

:m |m :-.r |d :m |r :— |t$_1$:t$_1$ |d :-.t$_1$ |l$_1$:d |t$_1$:— |—
:s$_1$ |s$_1$:-.s$_1$ |s$_1$:s$_1$ |s$_1$:— |s$_1$:f$_1$ |m$_1$:-.se$_1$ |l$_1$:l$_1$ |se$_1$:— |—
:d |d :-.t$_1$ |d :d |t$_1$:— |r :r |d :-.m |m :m |m :— |—
:d$_1$ |d :-.s$_1$ |m$_1$:d$_1$ |s$_1$:— |s$_1$:se$_1$ |l$_1$:-.m$_1$ |d$_1$:l$_2$ |m$_1$:— |—

:se$_1$ |l$_1$:-.t$_1$ |d :r |m :— |f :m |m :r |d :t$_1$ |l$_1$:— |— || l$_1$ |l$_1$
:m$_1$ |m$_1$:-.se$_1$ |l$_1$:l$_1$ |l$_1$:— |se$_1$:l$_1$ |l$_1$:l$_1$ |l$_1$:se$_1$ |l$_1$:— |— || f$_1$ |m$_1$
:t$_1$ |m :-.m |m :r |d :— |t$_1$:d |m :f |m :r |d :— |— || r |de
:r$_1$ |d$_1$:-.m$_1$ |l$_1$:f$_1$ |m$_1$:— |r$_1$:d$_1$ |d$_1$:r$_1$ |m$_1$:m$_1$ |l$_1$:— |— || r$_1$ |l$_2$

A-men.

O LAMB of God, still keep me
  Close to Thy piercèd side;
'Tis only there in safety
  And peace I can abide.
What foes and snares surround me,
  What lusts and fears within!
The grace that sought and found me
  Alone can keep me clean.

2 'Tis only in Thee hiding
  I feel myself secure;
Only in Thee abiding,
  The conflict can endure.
Thine arm the victory gaineth
  O'er every hateful foe;
Thy love my heart sustaineth
  In all its cares and woe.

3 Soon shall my eyes behold Thee
  With rapture face to face;
One half hath not been told me
  Of all Thy power and grace.
Thy beauty, Lord, and glory,
  The wonders of Thy love,
Shall be the endless story
  Of all Thy saints above.

JAMES GEORGE DECK, 1802–84.

471 AFFECTION. (L.M.)

Greenwood's Psalmody, Halifax, 1838.

Doh = C. *In moderate time.* G.t.

:s | d' :t | d' :-.f | m :r | d :-.ʳs, | l, :d | f .r :m.f
:m | s :f | m.,f:s .r | d :t, | d :-.ᵗm, | f, :s, | t,.s, :-.l,
:d' | d' :r' | d' :-.l | s :s.,f | m :-.ˢd | d :m | f :m.d
:d | m :s | d.,r:m.f | s :s, | d :-.ˢd, | f, :m, | r,.t, :d.f,

f.C.

m :r | d || ˢr' | t .s :l .t | d' :- .s | l :r' | d' :t .s
s, :s,.,f, | m, || ˢr | s :s | s :m | f :l | s :- .s
d :t, | d || ᵐt | r'.t :d'.r' | d' :d' | d' :f' | m' :r' .t
s, :s, | d, || ᵈs | s :f | m :d | f :r | s :- .f

d' :t | d' :-.f | m :r | d || f | m ||
s :f | m .,f:s .r | d :t, | d || d | d ||
d' :r' | s :-.l | s :s.,f | m || l | s ||
m :r | d .,r:m .f | s :s, | d || f, | d ||

A-men.

HYMNUS EUCHARISTICUS. (L.M.)

Lah = G. Doh = B♭. *Slow.* BENJAMIN ROGERS, 1614–98.

l, :l, :t, | d :-.r:m | r .d :t, :-.l, | l, :se, :— || se, :se, :l,
m, :m, :m, | m, :— :m, | f, :— :f, | m, :— :— || m, :m, :m,
d :d :se, | l, :— :t, | l, :r :-.d | t, :— :— || t, :t, :d
l, :l, :m, | l, :— :s, | f, :r, :— | m, :— :— || m, :m, :l,

t, :—:d | r :r :- .d | d :—:— || d :d :d | t, :—:d.t, | l, :l, :-.t,
s, :—:s, | f,.m, :r, :- .m, | m, :—:— || m, :m, :m, | r, :—:m, | m, :—:-.r,
r :—:m | r .d :d :t,.d | d :—:— || s, :s, :s, | s, :—:s, | l, :—:l,
s, :—:m, | f, :s, :— | d, :—:— || d, :d, :d, | s, :—:m, | f, :—:f,

l, :se, :— || l, :t, :d | r :— :r .d | d :t, :- .t, | l, :— :— || l, | l, ||
m, :— :— || d, :r, :m, | r, :-.m, :f, | m, :—:r,.m, | d, :— :— || r, | de, ||
t, :— :— || d :t, :s, | l, :— :t,.l, | l, :—:l,.se, | l, :— :— || f, | m, ||
m, :— :— || l, :s, :m, | f, :-.m, :r, | m, :— :m, | l₂ :— :— || r, | l₂ ||

A-men.

O THOU who camest from above,
The pure celestial fire to impart,
Kindle a flame of sacred love
On the mean altar of my heart.

2 There let it for Thy glory burn
With inextinguishable blaze,
And trembling to its source return,
In humble prayer and fervent praise.

3 Jesus, confirm my heart's desire
To work, and speak, and think for Thee;
Still let me guard the holy fire,
And still stir up Thy gift in me:

4 Ready for all Thy perfect will,
My acts of faith and love repeat,
Till death Thy endless mercies seal,
And make the sacrifice complete.

CHARLES WESLEY, 1707–88.

472 BRISTOL. (L.M.)

SAMUEL WESLEY, 1766–1837.

Doh = E♭. *In moderate time.*

B♭.t.

:m |m :— :f |m :r :d |f :m :r |m :— :^{s}d |f :— :m
:d |d :— :r |d :t$_1$:d |r :d :t$_1$ |d :— :^{m}l$_1$ |l$_1$:— :se$_1$
:s |s :— :l |s :f :m |l :s :s |s :— :^{s}d |t$_1$:— :d
:d |d :— :f$_1$ |s$_1$:— :l$_1$ |f$_1$:s$_1$:— |d :— :^{d}f$_1$ |r$_1$:— :m$_1$

f.E♭.

r :— :d |t$_1$:l$_1$:se$_1$ |l$_1$:— ||^{d}s s :— :f |f :m :— |r :d :-.r
l$_1$:m$_1$:m$_1$ |f$_1$:m$_1$:m$_1$.r$_1$ |d$_1$:— ||^{l}m m :— :r |r :d :— |l$_1$:fe$_1$:—
d :t$_1$:l$_1$ |r :d :t$_1$ |l$_1$:— ||^{m}t l :— :l |s :s :— |f :r :—
ba$_1$:se$_1$:l$_1$ |r$_1$:m$_1$:— |l$_1$:— ||^{s}r de :— :r |t$_1$:d :— |f$_1$:l$_1$:—

d :t$_1$:s |d' :— :l |f :— :m |m.r :d :t$_1$ |d :— ||d |d ||
s$_1$:— :t$_1$ |m :— :m |m :r :d |l$_1$:s$_1$:s$_1$ |s$_1$:— ||l$_1$ |s$_1$ ||
r :— :s |l :— :l |l :-.t :s |s.f :m :r |m :— ||f |m ||
s$_1$:— :m |l$_1$:— :d |r :r$_1$:m$_1$ |f$_1$:s$_1$:— |d :— ||f$_1$ |d ||

A-men.

FOR Thee, my God, for Thee alone,
My spirit longs with ardent love;
On earth beside Thee there is none,
And none but Thee in heaven above.

2 Fulfil, O God, my heart's desires;
While I look up, look down to bless;
Each holy wish Thy grace inspires
May I in Thy deep love possess.

3 My soul cleaves heavy to the dust,
But Thou canst raise and set it free;
And then, in calm and joyful trust,
It soars from earth to heaven and Thee.

4 Now in this stillness, as the breath
Of prayer steals upward to the skies,
O give my soul the wings of faith,
That it to Thee may gladly rise;

5 That, breaking through each fleshly link
Which binds its being to the clod,
At life's clear wellspring it may drink,
Rejoicing in the smile of God.

JAMES DRUMMOND BURNS, 1823–64

[May be sung to MARYTON, No. 420.]

473

WAINWRIGHT. (L.M.)

Doh = D. *In moderate time.* RICHARD WAINWRIGHT, 1758–1825.

d :d.m	r :l	s :f	m :—	s :s.s	d' :l
d :d.d	d :d	d :t,	d :—	m :r.t,	d :d
m :s.s	l :f	r :s	s :—	s :s.s	m :m
d :m.d	f :f,	s, :s,	d :—	d :t,.m	l, :l,

f :m	m :r		r :r.m	f :-.s	l :r'	d' :t
r :d	d :t,		t, :t,.de	r :-.m	f :f	m :r
s :s	s :—		s :s.s	l :-.d'	d' :l	s :-.f
t, :d	s, :—		s :f.m	r :-.d	f :f,	s, :—

d' :t.l	s :l	m :r	d :—		f	m	
d :r.r	m :d	d :t,	d :—		d	d	
m.l :s.f	m :f.l	s :f	m :—		l	s	
l, :t,.t,	d :f,	s, :s,	d :—		f,	d	

A - men.

From Psalm lxiii.

O GOD, Thou art my God alone,
Early to Thee my soul shall cry,
A pilgrim in a land unknown,
A thirsty land whose springs are dry.

2 O that it were as it hath been,
When, praying in the holy place,
Thy power and glory I have seen,
And marked the footsteps of Thy grace!

3 Yet through this rough and thorny maze
I follow hard on Thee, my God;
Thine hand unseen upholds my ways;
I safely tread where Thou hast trod.

4 Thee, in the watches of the night,
When I remember on my bed,
Thy presence makes the darkness light;
Thy guardian wings are round my head.

5 Better than life itself Thy love,
Dearer than all beside to me;
For whom have I in heaven above,
Or what on earth, compared with Thee?

6 Praise, with my heart, my mind, my voice,
For all Thy mercy I will give;
My soul shall still in God rejoice;
My tongue shall bless Thee while I live.

JAMES MONTGOMERY, 1771–1854.

474

ST. LEONARD. (C.M.)

Doh = C. *In moderate time.* HENRY SMART, 1813–79.

```
:s  |s  :m  |l  :s  |l  :t  |d' :r' |m' :d' |t  :l  |s  :—  |—  ||
:m  |m  :d  |d  :d  |f  :f  |m  :s  |s  :l  |s  :fe |s  :—  |—  ||
:d' |d' :s  |f  :s  |f  :f  |s  :t  |d' :m' |r' :d' |t  :—  |—  ||
:d  |d  :d  |f  :m  |r  :r  |d  :s  |d  :d  |r  :r  |s  :—  |—  ||

:r' |t  :s  |d' :r' |m' :d' |l  :r'  |s  :d' |d' :t  |d' :—  |—  || d' |d' ||
:s  |s  :r  |s  :s  |s  :s  |d  :f   |m  :m  |r  :r  |m  :—  |—  || f  |m  ||
:t  |r' :t  |d' :t  |d' :s  |l  :l.t |d' :d' |l  :s  |s  :—  |—  || l  |s  ||
:s  |s  :s.f|m  :r  |d  :m  |f  :r   |m  :l  |f  :s  |d  :—  |—  || f  |d  ||
                                                                    A-men.
```

O FOR a faith that will not shrink,
Though pressed by many a foe,
That will not tremble on the brink
Of poverty or woe,

2 That will not murmur nor complain
Beneath the chastening rod,
But, in the hour of grief or pain,
Can lean upon its God;

3 A faith that shines more bright and clear
When tempests rage without,
That when in danger knows no fear,
In darkness feels no doubt;

4 A faith that keeps the narrow way
Till life's last spark is fled,
And with a pure and heavenly ray
Lights up a dying bed!

5 Lord, give me such a faith as this,
And then, whate'er may come,
I taste even now the hallowed bliss
Of an eternal home.

WILLIAM HILEY BATHURST, 1796–1877.

475

LIVERPOOL. (64. 64. 664.)

Lah = A. Doh = C. *Moderately slow.* JOHN ROBERTS (IEUAN GWYLLT), 1822–77.

```
| l :— | m :s | l :l | s :— | l :— | d' :t | l :— | — :— || d' :— | d' :s | l :t
| m :— | d :r | f :f | m :— | m :— | m :r | d :— | — :— || d :— | d :m | f :f
| d' :— | l :t | d' :d' | d' :— | l :— | l :se | l :— | — :— || l :— | s :d' | d' :r'
| l :— | l :s | f :f | d :— | d :— | l, :m | l, :— | — :— || f :— | m :d | f :r
```

```
| d' :— | r' :— | t :l | s :— | — :— || m' :— | d' :m' | r' :d' | t :— | r' :— | d' :l
| m :— | r :— | r :d | t, :— | — :— || s :— | s :s | s :s | s :— | s :— | m :m
| s :— | s :— | s :fe | s :— | — :— || d' :— | m♯ :d' | f' :m' | r' :— | t :— | d' :d'
| d :— | t, :— | r :r | s, :— | — :— || d' :— | d' :d' | t :d' | s :— | s :— | l :l,
```

```
                 ://:
| s :fe | m :— || t :— | l :d' | d' :l | t :— | l :— | l :se | l :— | — :— || l | l ||
| m :re | m :— || m :— | m :m | m :-.re | m :— | m :— | f :m | d :— | — :— || r | de ||
| t :l | s :— || se :— | l :l | l :l | se :— | d' :— | t :t | l :— | — :— || f | m ||
| t, :t, | m :— || m :— | d :l, | l :f | m :— | d :— | r :m | l, :— | — :— || r | l, ||
```

A-men.

NENTHORN. (64. 64. 664.)

THOMAS LEGERWOOD HATELY, 1815–67.

Doh = E♭. *In moderate time.* B♭.t.

```
| m :s :l | s :-.f :m | m.r :d :t, | d :— :— || ^r s, :l, :t,
| d :d :d | d :-.r :d | l, :s, :s, | s, :— :— || ^t m, :f, :f,
| s :m :f | s :-.s :s | f :m :r | m :— :— || ^s d :d :r
| d :d :f | m :-.t, :d | f, :s, :s, | d :— :— || ^s d, :f, :r,
```

f.E♭.

```
| d :-.r :m | m.r :d :t, | ^d s :— :— || s :d' :d' | t :-.l :s
| m, :-.s, :s, | l, :s, :f, | ^m t, :— :— || d :d :d | d :-.d :d
| d :-.t, :d | f :m :r | ^d s :— :— || m :m :s | f :-.f :s
| l, :-.s, :d | f, :s, :s, | ^d s, :— :— || d :l, :m | f :-.f :m
```

```
| f :l :l | s :-.f :m | m.r :d :t, | d :— :— || d | d ||
| r :d :d | t, :-.t, :d | l, :s, :s, | s, :— :— || l, | s, ||
| l :f :f | r :-.r :d | f :m :r | m :— :— || f | m ||
| r :f :f, | s, :-.s, :l, | f, :s, :s, | d :— :— || f, | d ||
```

A-men.

PROPIOR DEO. (64. 64. 664.)

Doh = G. *In moderate time.* ARTHUR SEYMOUR SULLIVAN, 1842–1900.

```
|m    :r .m  |d .s, :l,  |s,   :t, .r  |m   :—  |m    :r .m   |d .s, :l, .d  |
|s,   :s, .s,|s, .m,:f,  |f,   :f, .f, |m,  :—  |s,   :s, .s, |s, .m,:f, .l, |
|s    :f .s  |m .d  :d   |t,   :r .t,  |d   :—  |s    :f .s   |m .d  :d .d   |
|d    :d .d  |d .d  :f,  |s,   :s, .s, |d,  :—  |d    :d .d   |d .d  :f, .f, |

|s,   :t, .r |d   :—  ||f    :f .s  |l .s   :f .m |r    :m .l,  |
|s,   :s,    |s,  :—  ||d    :d .d  |d .ta, :l,   |l,   :l, .l, |
|t,   :f     |m   :—  ||l    :f .m  |f .,f  :f    |f    :de .de |
|s,   :s,    |d   :—  ||f,   :l, .d |f .,f, :f,   |l,   :l, .l, |

                                  :||:
|f .m :r     |m   :r .m  |d   :l,  |s,   :t, .r  |d   :—  ||d  |d  ||
|l, .l,:t,   |d   :d .d  |s,  :f,  |f,   :s, .t, |d   :—  ||l, |s, ||
|r .m :f     |m   :f .s  |m   :d   |t,   :f .f   |m   :—  ||f  |m  ||
|r, .r,:s,   |d   :d .d  |d   :f,  |s,   :s, .s, |d,  :—  ||f, |d, ||
                                                            A-men.
```

[*By permission of Novello & Co., Ltd.*]

NEARER, my God, to Thee,
Nearer to Thee!
Even though it be a cross
That raiseth me,
Still all my song would be,
'Nearer, my God, to Thee,
Nearer to Thee!'

2 Though, like the wanderer,
The sun gone down,
Darkness be over me,
My rest a stone,
Yet in my dreams I'd be
Nearer, my God, to Thee,
Nearer to Thee!

3 There let the way appear
Steps unto heaven,
All that Thou send'st to me
In mercy given,
Angels to beckon me
Nearer, my God, to Thee,
Nearer to Thee!

4 Then, with my waking thoughts
Bright with Thy praise,
Out of my stony griefs
Bethel I'll raise,
So by my woes to be
Nearer, my God, to Thee,
Nearer to Thee!

5 Or if on joyful wing
Cleaving the sky,
Sun, moon, and stars forgot,
Upwards I fly,
Still all my song shall be,
'Nearer, my God, to Thee,
Nearer to Thee!'

SARAH FLOWER ADAMS, 1805–48.

476 WARUM SIND DER THRÄNEN. (65. 65. D.)

Doh = A♭. *In moderate time.* JOHANN ABRAHAM PETER SCHULZ, 1747–1800.

d :d |t, :t, |l, :— |s, :— |s :d |t, :d |r :— |— :— ||
s, :l, |l, :s, |f, :— |r, :— |s, :s, |s, :-.l, |t, :— |— :— ||
m :d.r |m :-.r |d :r.d |t, :— |d :s |f :m.fe |s :— |— :— ||
d :l, |m, :m, |f, :— |s, :f, |m, :m |r :d |s, :— |— :— ||

m :m |fe :fe |s :— |r :— |s, :s,.l, |t, :l, |s, :— |— :— ||
s, :d |t, :l, |s, :l, |t, :l, |s, :s, |s,.m, :fe, |s, :— |— :— ||
d :m |r :d |t, :d |r :f |m :d |r :r |t, :— |— :— ||
d :l, |r :r, |m, :— |t,, :— |d, :m, |r, :r, |s, :— |— :— ||

D♭.t.
r l :l |t :t |d' :— |l :— |r' :r' |d' :t |l :— |— :— ||
s, r :m |f :m.r |d :r |m :— |r :f |m :m.r |d :— |r :d ||
ta, f :l |l :se |l :t |d' :— |l :l |l.ba :se |l :— |fe :— ||
s, r :d |r :m |l, :— |l :s |f :r |m :m |l, :— |r :— ||

f.A♭.
s d :d |t, :t, |l, :— |s, :— |s :d.r |m :r |d :— |— :— || d |d ||
t m, :l, |s, :s, |s, :fe, |s, :— |s, :m,.f, |s, :-.f, |m, :— |— :— || f, |m, ||
s d :r |r :m |m :r.d |t, :— |d :-.d |d.l, :t, |d :— |— :— || l, |s, ||
m l, :fe, |s, :m, |d, :r, |s, :f, |m, :l, |s, :s, |d, :— |— :— || f, |d, ||

A-men.

SAVIOUR, blessèd Saviour,
Listen while we sing,
Hearts and voices raising
Praises to our King;
All we have to offer,
All we hope to be,
Body, soul, and spirit,
All we yield to Thee.

2 Nearer, ever nearer,
Christ, we draw to Thee,
Deep in adoration
Bending low the knee.
Thou for our redemption
Cam'st on earth to die;
Thou, that we might follow,
Hast gone up on high.

3 Clearer still and clearer
  Dawns the light from heaven,
In our sadness bringing
  News of sins forgiven;
Life has lost its shadows,
  Pure the light within;
Thou hast shed Thy radiance
  On a world of sin.

4 Onward, ever onward,
  Journeying o'er the road
Worn by saints before us,
  Journeying on to God,
Leaving all behind us,
  May we hasten on,
Backward never looking
  Till the prize is won.

5 Higher then and higher
  Bear the ransomed soul,
Earthly toils forgotten,
  Saviour, to its goal,
Where, in joys unthought of,
  Saints with angels sing,
Never weary raising
  Praises to their King.

GODFREY THRING, 1823–1903.

[May be sung to EVELYNS, No. 178.]

477 SLANE. (10 10. 10 10.) Rob tu mo bhoile, a Comdi cride.

Doh = E♭. *Unison.* *Moderately slow.* Irish Traditional Melody.

d	:d	:r .d	l,.,l,	:s,	:s,.l,	d	:d	:r	m	:—	:—
1. Be	Thou	my	Vi -	sion,	O	Lord	of	my	heart;		
2. Be	Thou	my	Wis -	dom,	. .	Thou	my	true	Word;		
3. Be	Thou	my	bat-tle-	shield,	. .	sword	for	the	fight;		
4. Rich -	es	I	heed	not,	nor	man's	emp -	ty	praise,		
5. High	King	of	hea -	ven,	af-ter	vic -	to -	ry	won,		

r	:r	:r	r	:m	:s	l	:s	:m	s	:—	:—
Naught	be	all	else	to	me,	save	that	Thou	art,—		
I	ev -	er	with	. .	Thee,	Thou	with	me,	Lord;		
Be	Thou	my	dig -	ni -	ty,	Thou	my	de -	light,		
Thou	mine	in -	her -	it -	ance,	now	and	al -	ways:		
May	I	reach	hea -	ven's	joys,	O	bright	heav'n's	Sun!		

l	:l .t	:d'.t	l	:s	:m	s	:d	:t,	l,	:—	:s,
Thou	my	best	thought,		by	day	or	by	night,		. . .
Thou	my	great	Fa -	-	ther,	I	Thy	true	son;		. . .
Thou	my	soul's	shel -	-	ter,	Thou	my	high	tower:		. . .
Thou	and	Thou	on -		ly,	first	in	my	heart,		. . .
Heart	of	my	own	heart,	what-	ev -	er	be -	fall,		. . .

d	:m	:s	l .s	:m	:d .m	r	:d	:d	d	:—	:—	d	d
Wak -	ing	or	sleep -	ing,	Thy	pres -	ence	my	light.				
Thou	in	me	dwell -	ing,	and	I	with	Thee	one.				
Raise	Thou	me	heaven -	ward,	O	Power	of	my	power.				
High	King	of	hea -	ven,	my	trea -	sure	Thou	art.				
Still	be	my	Vi -	sion,	O	Ru -	ler	of	all.			A-	men.

Ancient Irish, *tr.* by MARY BYRNE;
versified by ELEANOR HULL.

478 SWABIA. (S.M.)

Doh = D. *In moderate time.* *Spiess's Gesangbuch*, Heidelberg, 1745.

:s |m :f |r :r |d :— |— :r |m.fe:s |s :fe |s :— |— ‖
:m |d :d |d :t, |d :— |— :t, |d :r.m|r :r |r :— |— ‖
:d' |s :l |s :s |m :— |— :s |s :t |l :l |t :— |— ‖
:d |d :f, |s, :s, |l, :— |— :s, |d :t,.d|r :r |s, :— |— ‖

:s |l :s |l :t |d' :d' |d' :s |f :m |r :r |d :— |— ‖d |d ‖
:m |f :m |f :f |m :f |m :m |r :d |d :t, |d :— |— ‖l, |s, ‖
:d' |d' :d' |d' :r' |d' :l |s :d' |l.t:d' |s :s |m :— |— ‖f |m ‖
:d |f :d |f :r |l :f |d :d |r :m.f|s :s, |d :— |— ‖f, |d ‖

A - men.

BLEST are the pure in heart,
For they shall see their God:
The secret of the Lord is theirs;
Their soul is Christ's abode.

2 The Lord, who left the sky
Our life and peace to bring,
And dwelt in lowliness with men,
Their Pattern and their King,—

3 Still to the lowly soul
He doth Himself impart,
And for His dwelling and His throne
Chooseth the pure in heart.

4 Lord, we Thy presence seek;
Ours may this blessing be;
O give the pure and lowly heart,
A temple meet for Thee.

JOHN KEBLE, 1792–1866, and others.

[May be sung to FRANCONIA, No. 190.]

479 HYFRYDOL. (8 7. 8 7. D.)

Doh = F. *Moderately slow.* ROWLAND HUGH PRICHARD, 1811–87.

d :— :r	d :r :m	f :— :m	r :d :r	s :— :f	m :— :m
s, :— :t,	d :t, :d	d :r :d	t, :l, :t,	d :s, :l,.t,	d :— :d
m :— :s	s :f :m	l :— :s	s :— :s	d :m :f	s :— :s
d :— :s,	m :r :d	l, :t, :d	s, :— :f,	m, :m :r	d :— :m,

D.C.

r :d :r	d :— :— ‖s :— :s	s :f :m	f :— :f	f :m :r
l, :— :t,	d :— :— ‖t, :— :d	d :— :d	d :t, :l,	t, :d :s,
f :m :s	m :— :— ‖s :— :m	d :r :m	r :— :r	r :s :f
f, :l, :s,	d :— :— ‖m :— :d	l, :— :l,	r :— :r	s, :l, :t,

m :— :m	m :f :s	s :f :m	r :— :— ‖ s :m :s	f :r :f
s_1 :— :d	t_1 :l_1 :d	d :r :d	t_1 :— :— ‖ d :— :d	d :r :t_1
m :r :d	d :—.r :m	m :r :m.fe	s :— :— ‖ s :— :s	l :s :r
d :t_1 :l_1	s_1 :f_1 :m_1	l_1 :t_1 :d	s_1 :— :— ‖ m :d :m	r :t_1 :s_1

| m :d :m | r.m :f.m :r | s :— :s | l :s :f | m :— :r | d :— :— ‖ d | d ‖
| d :s_1 :d | t_1.d :r.d :t_1 | d :t_1 :d | l_1.t_1 :d :r | d :— :t_1 | d :— :— ‖ l_1 | s_1 ‖
| m :— :s | s :— :s | d :r :m | f :s :l | s :— :f | m :— :— ‖ f | m ‖
| d :m :d | s_1 :— :f_1 | m_1 :s_1 :d | f :m :r | s :— :s_1 | d :— :— ‖ f_1 | d ‖

A-men.

LOVE Divine, all loves excelling,
  Joy of heaven, to earth come down,
Fix in us Thy humble dwelling,
  All Thy faithful mercies crown.
Jesus, Thou art all compassion,
  Pure, unbounded love Thou art;
Visit us with Thy salvation,
  Enter every trembling heart.

2 Come, almighty to deliver;
  Let us all Thy life receive;
Suddenly return, and never,
  Never more Thy temples leave.
Thee we would be always blessing,
  Serve Thee as Thy hosts above,
Pray, and praise Thee, without ceasing,
  Glory in Thy perfect love.

3 Finish then Thy new creation:
  Pure and spotless let us be;
Let us see Thy great salvation,
  Perfectly restored in Thee,
Changed from glory into glory,
  Till in heaven we take our place,
Till we cast our crowns before Thee,
  Lost in wonder, love, and praise.

CHARLES WESLEY, 1707–88.

480 CITY BRIGHT. (66. 55. 6.)

Doh = G. *In moderate time.* James Sherman Tyler, 1842–1917.

```
|m  :—  |s  :f  |m  :—  |r  :—  |d  :—  |—  :—  |r  :—  |m  :s
|s, :—  |s, :l, |s, :—  |f, :—  |m, :—  |—  :—  |s, :—  |s, :d
|d  :—  |d  :d  |d  :—  |t, :—  |d  :—  |—  :—  |t, :—  |d  :s
|d  :—  |m, :f, |s, :—  |s, :—  |l, :—  |—  :—  |s, :—  |d  :m,

|f  :—  |m  :—  |r  :—  |—  :—  ||m  :—  |m  :f  |s  :—  |m  :—  |r  :—  |r  :m
|d  :—  |d  :—  |t, :—  |—  :—  ||d  :—  |d  :l, |s, :—  |d  :—  |l, :—  |t, :de
|l  :—  |s  :—  |s  :—  |—  :—  ||s  :—  |d  :d  |r  :—  |s  :—  |f  :—  |l  :s
|f, :—  |d  :—  |s, :—  |—  :—  ||d  :—  |l, :l, |t, :—  |d  :—  |r  :—  |l, :l,

|f  :—  |r  :—  |d  :—  |t, :d  |m  :—  |r  :—  |d  :—  |—  :—  ||d  |d  ||
|r  :—  |l, :—  |s, :—  |s, :s, |d  :—  |t, :—  |d  :—  |—  :—  ||l, |s, ||
|f  :—  |f  :—  |m  :—  |r  :m  |s  :—  |—  :f  |m  :—  |—  :—  ||f  |m  ||
|r, :—  |f, :—  |s, :—  |s, :s, |s, :—  |s, :—  |d, :—  |—  :—  ||f, |d, ||
                                                                 A-men.
```

THERE is a city bright;
Closed are its gates to sin;
Nought that defileth,
Nought that defileth
Can ever enter in.

2 Saviour, I come to Thee;
O Lamb of God, I pray,
Cleanse me and save me,
Cleanse me and save me,
Wash all my sins away.

3 Lord, make me, from this hour,
Thy loving child to be,
Kept by Thy power,
Kept by Thy power
From all that grieveth Thee,—

4 Till in the snow-white dress
Of Thy redeemed I stand,
Faultless and stainless,
Faultless and stainless,
Safe in that happy land.

Mary Ann Sanderson Deck, 1813–1902.

481 CAITHNESS. (C.M.)

Doh = E♭. *Moderately slow.* *Scottish Psalter*, 1635.

|d :— |m :f |s :d |t, :d |r :— ‖ m :— |f :s |l :l |s :— ‖
|s, :— |d :d |t, :s, |f, :s,.l, |t, :— ‖ d :— |d :ta, |l, :l,.t, |d :— ‖
|m :— |s :f |r :m |f :m |s :— ‖ s :— |f :m |f :d.r |m :— ‖
|d :— |d :l, |s, :m |r :d |s, :— ‖ d :— |l, :s, |f, :f, |d :— ‖

|s :— |l :t |d' :m |f :s |l :— ‖ s :— |f :m |r :r |d :— ‖ f |m ‖
|m :— |m :r |d :t, |d :d |d :— ‖ t, :— |d :d |d :t, |d :— ‖ d |d ‖
|m :— |m :s |l :m |l :s |f :— ‖ r :— |f :s |l :s.f |m :— ‖ l |s ‖
|d :— |d :t, |l, :s, |f, :m, |f, :— ‖ s, :— |l, :d |f, :s, |d :— ‖ f, |d ‖

A-men.

ST. PAUL. (C.M.)

Doh = G. *In moderate time.* *Chalmers's Collection*, Aberdeen, 1749.

|d :— |r :m |s, :d |r :t, |d :— ‖ m :— |r :s |f :m |r :— ‖
|s, :— |s, :s, |s, :m, |l, :s, |s, :— ‖ d :— |t, :d |l,.t, :d |t, :— ‖
|m :— |t, :d |r :m |f :r |m :— ‖ s :— |s.f :m |f :s |s :— ‖
|d :— |s, :d |t, :l, |f, :s, |d, :— ‖ d :— |s, :m |r :d |s, :— ‖

|d :— |r :m |f :m |r :d |t, :— ‖ s, :— |l, :f |m :r |d :— ‖ d |d ‖
|d :— |s, :s, |f, :s, |l, :m,.fe, |s, :— ‖ s, :— |f, :l, |d :t, |d :— ‖ l, |s, ‖
|m :— |r :d |d :s |f :d |r :— ‖ d :— |d :r |s :-.f |m :— ‖ f |m ‖
|d :— |t, :d |l, :d |f, :l, |s, :— ‖ m, :— |f, :r |m,.f, :s, |d, :— ‖ f, |d, ‖

A-men.

From Hebrews xiii. 20–21.

FATHER of peace, and God of love !
We own Thy power to save,
That power by which our Shepherd rose
Victorious o'er the grave.

2 Him from the dead Thou brought'st again,
When, by His sacred blood,
Confirmed and sealed for evermore
The eternal covenant stood.

3 O may Thy Spirit seal our souls,
And mould them to Thy will,
That our weak hearts no more may stray,
But keep Thy precepts still ;

4 That to perfection's sacred height
We nearer still may rise,
And all we think, and all we do,
Be pleasing in Thine eyes.

PHILIP DODDRIDGE, 1702–51 ; as in *Scottish Paraphrases*, 1781.

482 NOX PRAECESSIT. (C.M.)

Doh = G. *In moderate time.* JOHN BAPTISTE CALKIN, 1827–1905.

m :m .m |d :r |m :m |f :r |d :m |s :-.f |m :— |—
s, :se,.se, |l, :l, |se, :l, |l, :l, |s, :d |l, :t, |d :— |—
d :t,.t, |d :l, |t, :de |r :r |m :d |r :s |s :— |—
d, :m,.m, |l, :f, |m, :l, |r, :f, |s, :s, |s, :s, |d :— |—

:d |l :l .s |f :m |r :m |f :l, |t, :d |m :-.r |d :— |— :— ‖ d |d
:d |l, :l,.m |r :de |r :l, |l, :l, |l, :s, |t, :-.t, |d :— |— :— ‖ l, |s,
:m |f :f .ta |l :s |f :m |r :r |f :m |s :-.f |m :— |— :— ‖ f |m
:d |f, :f,.s, |l, :l, |r :de |r :f, |s, :s, |s, :-.s, |d, :— |— :— ‖ f, |d,

v. 5. Glo-ry shall A-men.

WALK in the light: so shalt thou know
That fellowship of love
His Spirit only can bestow
Who reigns in light above.

2 Walk in the light: and sin, abhorred,
Shall ne'er defile again;
The blood of Jesus Christ thy Lord
Shall cleanse from every stain.

3 Walk in the light: and thou shalt find
Thy heart made truly His
Who dwells in cloudless light enshrined,
In whom no darkness is.

4 Walk in the light: and thou shalt own
Thy darkness passed away,
Because that light hath on thee shone
In which is perfect day.

5 Walk in the light: and even the tomb
No fearful shade shall wear;
Glory shall chase away its gloom,
For Christ hath conquered there.

6 Walk in the light: and thine shall be
A path, though thorny, bright;
For God, by grace, shall dwell in thee,
And God Himself is Light.

BERNARD BARTON, 1784–1849.

483 NEWINGTON. (C.M.)

Doh = A♭. *Moderately slow.* WILLIAM JONES, 1726–1800.

:d |s :m |d :r .d |t, :d |r :m .f |s :d .r |m :r |d :— |—
:s, |s, :s, |l, :l, |s, :s,.fe, |s, :s, |s, :m,.f, |s, :s,.f, |m, :— |—
:m |r :d |m :f .m |r :d |t, :d |d :d |d :t, |d :— |—
:d |t, :d |l, :f, |s, :l, |s, :d |m, :l, |s, :s, |d :— |—

:m |f :r |m :f |s :r.d |t, :l, |s, :d.r |m :r |d :— |— || d |d

:s, |l, :s, |s, :s, |s, :l, |s, :r, |s, :m,.f, |s, :s,.f, |m, :— |— || f, |m,

:d |d :t, |d :d.t, |d :f.m |r :t, |d :d |d :t, |d :— |— || l, |s,

:d |f, :s, |d, :r, |m, :f, |s, :f, |m, :l, |s, :s, |d, :— |— || f, |d,

A-men.

ST. STEPHEN (ABRIDGE). (C.M.)

Doh = E♭. *In moderate time.* ISAAC SMITH, *c.* 1740–*c.* 1800.

:d |s :— :d' |d' :t :l |s :f :m |m :r :m |l :— :s

:s, |d :— :m |r :— :r |s, :t, :d |d :t, :d |m :— :r

:m |s :— :s |s :— :l.t |d' :s :s |s :— :s |d' :— :t

:d |m :— :d |s :— :f |m :r :d |s, :— :d |l, :— :t,

s :— :fe |s :— || s |m :f :l |s :— :s |l :t :d'

m :r :d |t, :— || r |d :— :d |d :t, :d |d :f :m

l :t :l |s :— || s |s :f :f |m :f :s |f :s :s

d :r :r |s, :— || t, |d :l, :f, |d :r :m |f.,m :r :d

d' :t :s |d' :m :s |f :m :r |d :— || d |d

m :r :t, |d :— :d |d :— :t, |d :— || l, |s,

s :— :s |s :— :ta |l :s :f |m :— || f |m

s, :— :s.f |m :d :m |f :s :s, |d :— || f, |d

A-men.

From 1 St. John iii. 1–4.

BEHOLD the amazing gift of love
The Father hath bestowed
On us, the sinful sons of men,
To call us sons of God!

2 Concealed as yet this honour lies,
By this dark world unknown,—
A world that knew not when He came,
Even God's eternal Son.

Unison.

3 High is the rank we now possess;
But higher we shall rise,
Though what we shall hereafter be
Is hid from mortal eyes.

Harmony.

4 Our souls, we know when He appears,
Shall bear His image bright;
For all His glory, full disclosed,
Shall open to our sight.

5 A hope so great, and so divine,
May trials well endure;
And purge the soul from sense and sin,
As Christ Himself is pure.

Scottish Paraphrases, 1781.

Also the following:

180–96 *Hymns of the Holy Spirit*
399–415 *Hymns of Penitence and Faith*

BROTHERLY LOVE

484 CHARITY. (77. 75.)

Doh = A♭. *Moderately slow.* JOHN STAINER, 1840–1901.

```
d  :f  |m  :r  |d  :r   |s, :—  |l, :t, |d  :l, |r  :d  |d  :t, ||
s, :s, |s, :se,|l, :l,  |s, :—  |m, :s, |s, :s, |fe,:l, |s, :—  ||
m  :r  |d  :r  |m  :r.d |d  :t, |d  :r  |d  :m  |l, :r  |r  :—  ||
d  :t, |d  :t, |l, :f,  |s, :—  |s, :f, |m, :d, |r, :fe,|s, :f, ||
```

Melody in Unison.

```
d  :s  |f  :m  |r  :d  |d  :t, |d  :s, |l, :f, |d  :—  |—  :—  ||t, |d  ||
s, :m, |f, :s, |l, :l, |s, :—  |                              ||s, |s, ||
d  :d  |d  :d  |f  :m  |m  :r  |                              ||r  |m  ||
m, :ta,|l, :s, |f, :fe,|s, :—  |                              ||s, |d, ||
Org.
d  :—  |d  :—  |l, :—  |s, :—
s, :—  |f, :—  |f, :—  |m, :—
d  :—  |l, :—  |d  :—  |—  :—
m, :—  |f, :—  |d, :—  |—  :—
```

A-men.

ST. AMBROSE. (77. 75.)

Doh = B♭. *Moderately slow.* HENRY JOHN GAUNTLETT, 1805–76. (Based on 8th Gregorian Tone.)

```
s, :l, |d  :d  |d  :r  |d  :—  |d  :d  |t, :d  |l, :l, |s, :—  ||
m, :f, |s, :f, |m, :f, |m, :—  |m, :fe,|s, :s, |s, :fe,|s, :—  ||
d  :d  |d  :d  |d  :t, |d  :—  |d  :d  |r  :d  |m  :r  |t, :—  ||
d, :f, |m, :l, |s, :s, |d, :—  |l, :l, |s, :m, |d, :r, |s, :—  ||
```

```
s, :l, |d  :d  |d  :r  |d  :—  |d  :d  |d  :l, |d  :—  |—  :—  ||r  |d  ||
m, :f, |s, :m, |f, :f, |m, :—  |s, :s, |f, :f, |m, :—  |—  :—  ||s, |m, ||
d  :d  |d  :d  |d  :t, |d  :—  |d  :d  |l, :l, |s, :—  |—  :—  ||t, |d  ||
d, :f, |m, :l, |l, :s, |d  :—  |m, :m, |f, :f, |d, :—  |—  :—  ||s, |d, ||
```

A-men.

From 1 Corinthians xiii.

GRACIOUS Spirit, Holy Ghost,
Taught by Thee, we covet most,
Of Thy gifts at Pentecost,
Holy, heavenly love.

2 Faith that mountains could remove,
Tongues of earth or heaven above,
Knowledge, all things, empty prove
Without heavenly love.

3 Though I as a martyr bleed,
Give my goods the poor to feed,
All is vain if love I need;
Therefore give me love.

4 Love is kind, and suffers long;
Love is meek, and thinks no wrong,
Love than death itself more strong;
Therefore give us love.

5 Prophecy will fade away,
Melting in the light of day;
Love will ever with us stay;
Therefore give us love.

6 Faith and hope and love we see,
Joining hand in hand, agree;
But the greatest of the three,
And the best, is love.

CHRISTOPHER WORDSWORTH, 1807–85.

485 INTERCESSOR. (11 10. 11 10.)

Lah = A. Doh = C. *Slow.* CHARLES HUBERT HASTINGS PARRY, 1848–1918.

```
:l   |s  :f    |m  :m    |f  :l   |d'  :d'     |t   :—    |l  ||
:m   |r  :d    |t, :m    |m  :r   |d   :m      |m   :- .r |d  ||
:d'  |t  :l    |se :l    |l  :l   |l   :l      |l   :se   |l  ||
:l,  |t, :d. r |m  :d    |r  :f   |l   :d      |m   :—    |l, ||

:l   |s  :f    |m  :- .m |f  :m   |d   :r      |m   :—    |—  ||
:m   |r  :r    |r  :d    |d  :d   |l,  :l,     |t,  :—    |—  ||
:d'  |r' :t    |s  :- .s |f  :s   |l   :l      |se  :—    |—  ||
:l,  |t, :s,   |d  :- .d |l, :d   |f   :f      |m   :—    |—  ||

:m'  |r' :d'   |t  :s    |l  :d'  |s   :s      |f   :—    |m  ||
:m   |s  :m .f |s  :m    |m  :r   |r   :d      |d   :t,   |d  ||
:d'  |t  :d'.r'|m' :t    |l  :l   |t   :d'     |r'  :—    |s  ||
:d   |s  :l    |m  :m    |f  :f   |m   :m      |r   :—    |d  ||

:m   |f  :s    |l  :- .l |d' :d'  |t   :t      |l   :—    |—  || l  |l   ||
:d   |d  :m    |f  :f    |m  :l   |l   :se     |l   :—    |—  || f  |m   ||
:s   |d' :ta   |l  :r'   |m' :m'  |m'  :- .r'  |de' :—    |—  || r' |de' ||
:d   |l, :d    |f  :r    |d  :l,  |m   :m      |l,  :—    |—  || r  |l,  ||
                                                                 A-men.
```

[*Copyright*, 1904, *by the Proprietors of 'Hymns Ancient and Modern'*.]

O BROTHER man, fold to thy heart thy brother!
Where pity dwells, the peace of God is there;
To worship rightly is to love each other,
Each smile a hymn, each kindly deed a prayer.

2 For he whom Jesus loved hath truly spoken:
The holier worship which He deigns to bless
Restores the lost, and binds the spirit broken,
And feeds the widow and the fatherless.

3 Follow with reverent steps the great example
Of Him whose holy work was doing good;
So shall the wide earth seem our Father's temple,
Each loving life a psalm of gratitude.

4 Then shall all shackles fall; the stormy clangour
Of wild war-music o'er the earth shall cease;
Love shall tread out the baleful fire of anger,
And in its ashes plant the tree of peace.

JOHN GREENLEAF WHITTIER, 1807–92.

486

OLD 22ND. (D.C.M.)

Anglo-Genevan Psalter, 1556.

Doh = E♭. *In moderate time, very dignified.*

d :— |d :r |m :— |s :— |f :f |m :— |— ‖
s, :— |l, :t, |d :— |d :— |d :t, |d :— |— ‖
m :— |m :s |s :— |s :— |l :f |s :— |— ‖
d :— |l, :s, |d :— |m :— |r :r |d :— |— ‖

:d |f :m |r :r |d :— (pause) ‖s :— |l :t |d' :— |t :—
:d |l, :d |d :t, |d :— ‖d :— |m :r |d :— |r :—
:l |l :s |s :s |m :— ‖m :— |m :s |l :— |s :—
:l, |f, :d |s, :s, |d :— ‖d :— |d :t, |l, :— |t, :—

l :l |s :— ‖m :— |f :m |r :— |r :— |d :— (pause) ‖
m :r |t, :— ‖d :— |l, :d |d :— |t, :— |d :— ‖
m :fe |s :— ‖d :— |r :s |l :— |s :f |m :— ‖
d :r |s, :— ‖l, :— |r, :m, |f, :— |s, :— |d :— ‖

d' :— |t :l |s :l |t :— |l :— |s :— ‖
m :— |m :d |d :d |t, :r |r :d |t, :— ‖
l :— |s :f |m :fe |s :— |fe :— |s :— ‖
l :— |m :f |d :l, |s, :t, |r :— |s, :— ‖

f.A♭. . . . . E♭.t.

(l)m :— |t, :d |r :m |r :— (pause) |(t)m :— |m :r |m :d
(l)m, :— |m, :m, |f, :s, |s, :— |(s)d :— |d :t, |d :s,
(f)d :— |t, :l, |l, :d |t, :— |(r)s :— |s :s |s :m
(r)l, :— |se, :l, |f, :d, |s, :— |(s)d :— |m, :s, |d :m.r

m :fe	s :—		m :—	r :m	f :—	r :—	d :—		d	d	
s_1 :d	t_1 :—		s_1 :—	r :d	d :—	t_1 :—	d :—		l_1	s_1	
m :d	r :—		m :—	s :s	l :—	s :f	m :—		f	m	
d :l_1	s_1 :—		d :—	t_1 :d	f_1 :—	s_1 :—	d :—		f_1	d	

A-men.

OUR Father, Thy dear Name doth show
The greatness of Thy love ;
All are Thy children here below,
As in Thy heaven above.
One family on earth are we,
Throughout its widest span :
O help us everywhere to see
The brotherhood of man.

2 Alike we share Thy tender care ;
We trust one heavenly Friend ;
Before one mercy-seat, in prayer,
With confidence we bend ;
Alike we hear Thy loving call,
One heavenly vision scan,—
One Lord, one faith, one hope for all,
The brotherhood of man.

3 Bring in, we pray, the glorious day
When warfare shall be stilled,
And bitter strife be swept away,
And hearts with love be filled.
Help us to banish pride and wrong,
Which, since the world began,
Have marred its peace ; and so make strong
The brotherhood of man.

Charles Herbert Richards, 1839–1925.

487

HOYLAKE. (88. 86.)

Doh = A. *In moderate time.* ARTHUR OWEN ROBERTS, 1869–

```
:d |d  :r  :m |f  :— :m |r  :l, :m   |r  :— :r  |s  :m  :r
:d |d  :—  :d |d  :— :d |l, :— :l,   |r, :s, :t, |d  :—  :t,
:m |m  :f  :s |l  :— :s |f  :r  :d   |t, :— :s  |s  :—  :s.f
:d |d  :—  :d |d  :— :d |f, :— :fe,  |s, :— :f, |m, :d, :s,
```

```
|d  :— :t,  |l,.d:t, :l,  |s, :— ||s, |r  :d  :t,  |d  :— :d
|d  :— :s,  |s,  :—  :fe, |s, :— ||s, |s, :—  :s,  |m, :— :l,
|m  :— :r   |m   :r  :d   |t, :— ||t, |f  :m  :r   |l, :— :l,
|l, :— :t,  |d   :r  :r,  |s, :— ||s, |s, :—  :s,  |l, :— :l,
```

```
|f  :m   :r  |m  :— :d  |s  :f  :m  |m.r:d  :t, |d  :— ||d  |d  ||
|l, :s,  :s, |s, :— :s, |s, :— :s,  |l, :s, :s, |s, :— ||l, |s, ||
|r  :m.d :t, |d  :— :m  |m  :t, :d  |d.r:m  :f  |m  :— ||f  |m  ||
|r, :s,  :s, |d  :— :d  |d, :r, :m, |f, :s, :s  |d, :— ||f, |d, ||
```

A-men.

ELMHURST. (88. 86.)

Doh = E♭. *In moderate time.* EDWIN DREWETT, 1850–1924.

```
:m |m  :-.m  |f :m |s  :r  |m :d  |l  :-.s |f  :m |m  :r  |r  ||
:d |s, :-.s, |d :d |t, :t, |d :s, |l, :-.d |t, :d |d  :d  |t, ||
:s |d' :-.t  |l :s |s  :f  |m :s  |f  :-.s |s  :s |s  :fe |s  ||
:d |d  :-.d  |d :d |s, :s, |d :m  |f  :-.m |r  :d |l, :l, |s, ||
```

```
:r  |m :-.f  |s :d' |t  :-.l |s :s  |f :r  |l, :t,  |d  :— |— ||d  |d  ||
:t, |d :-.t, |d :m  |re :re  |m :m  |r :l, |l, :s,  |s, :— |— ||l, |s, ||
:s  |s :-.s  |s :l  |fe :t   |t :ta |l :f  |f  :s.f |m  :— |— ||f  |m  ||
:s, |d :-.r  |m :l, |t, :t,  |m :de |r :f, |s, :s,  |d  :— |— ||f, |d  ||
```

A-men.

O GOD of mercy, God of might,
In love and pity infinite,
Teach us, as ever in Thy sight,
To live our life to Thee.

2 And Thou, who cam'st on earth to die
That fallen man might live thereby,
O hear us, for to Thee we cry,—
In hope, O Lord, to Thee.

3 Teach us the lesson Thou hast taught,
To feel for those Thy blood hath bought,
That every word and deed and thought
May work a work for Thee.

4 For all are brethren, far and wide,
Since Thou, O Lord, for all hast died;
Then teach us, whatsoe'er betide,
To love them all in Thee.

5 In sickness, sorrow, want, or care,
Whate'er it be, 'tis ours to share;
May we, where help is needed, there
Give help as unto Thee.

6 And may Thy Holy Spirit move
All those who live, to live in love,
Till Thou shalt greet in heaven above
All those who give to Thee.

GODFREY THRING, 1823–1903.

488 GRANDPONT. (10 10.)

Doh = E. *In moderate time.* JOHN STAINER, 1840–1901.

:m |m :r |d :l_1 |d :— |d :— |t_1 :f |— :m |m :— |r ||
:m |m :r |d :l_1 |d :— |s_1 :— |t_1 :— |d :— |d :— |t_1 ||
:m |m :r |d :l_1 |d :— |s :— |f :— |s :— |s :— |— ||
:m |m :r |d :l_1 |d :— |m :— |r :— |d :— |s_1 :— |— ||

:s |s :f |m :de |r :— |f :— |m :— |r :— |d :— |— || f |m ||
:r |de :r |ta_1 :l_1 |l_1 :— |l_1 :t_1 |d :— |d :t_1 |d :— |— || d |d ||
:t |ta :l |s :m |f :— |f :— |s :l |f :— |m :— |— || l |s ||
:s_1 |m_1 :f_1 |s_1 :l_1 |f_1 :— |r_1 :— |m_1 :f_1 |s_1 :— |d :— |— || f_1 |d ||

A - men.

[*By permission of Novello & Co., Ltd.*]

BELOVÈD, let us love: love is of God;
In God alone hath love its true abode.

2 Belovèd, let us love: for they who love,
They only, are His sons, born from above.

3 Belovèd, let us love: for love is rest,
And he who loveth not abides unblest.

4 Belovèd, let us love: for love is light,
And he who loveth not dwelleth in night.

5 Belovèd, let us love: for only thus
Shall we behold that God who loveth us.

HORATIUS BONAR, 1808–89.

489

SONG 1. (10 10. 10 10. 10 10.)

Doh = G. *Moderately slow.* ORLANDO GIBBONS, 1583–1625.

```
|s, :— |s, :s, |d :r |m :m |r :r |d :— || :m |m :f |s :s, |d :t,
|s, :— |s, :s, |l, :t, |d :d |d :t, |d :— || :d |d :d.r |t, :s, |s, :s,
|m :— |m :r |m :s |s :l |r :s.f |m :— || :s |s :f |r :t, |m :r
|d :— |d :t, |l, :s,.f, |m, :f, |s, :s, |d :— || :d |d :l, |s, :s, |d, :s,

                     C.t.                               f.G.
|l, :l, |s, :— || :r l |l :t |d' :— |— :s |s d :d |f :m |r :— |— ||
|s, :fe, |s, :— || :ta, f |f :s |s :f |m :d.r |m l, :s, |f, :s, |s, :— |— ||
|r :r.d |t, :— || :s r' |r' :r' |m' :r' |d' :m.f |s d :d |d.t, :d |t, :— |— ||
|r, :r, |s, :— || :s, r |r :s |d :— |— :d |d f, :m, |r, :d, |s, :— |— ||

|:r |t, :s, |d :r |m :s |r :r |d :— || :d |f :s
|:l, |s, :s, |s, :l,.t, |d :d |d :t, |d :— || :d |d :ta,
|:f.m |r :t, |d :f |s :s |s :-.f |m :— || :d |d :r.m
|:r, |s, :-.f, |m, :r, |d,.r, :m,.f, |s, :s, |d, :— || :d |l, :s,

|l :l |r :s |s :fe |s :— || :s, |d :r |m :r |f :m |r :r |d :— ||
|l, :d |t, :d |l, :l, |t, :— || :s, |s, :l,.t, |d :t, |l,.s, :d |d :t, |d :— ||
|f :f.m |r :d |r :r |r :— || :t, |d :f |s :s |d.r :m.f |s :s.f |m :— ||
|f, :f, |s, :m, |r, :r, |s, :— || :s,.f, |m, :r, |d, :s, |l,.t, :d |s, :s, |d, :— ||
```

ETERNAL Ruler of the ceaseless round
  Of circling planets singing on their way,
Guide of the nations from the night profound
  Into the glory of the perfect day:
Rule in our hearts, that we may ever be
Guided and strengthened and upheld by Thee.

2 We are of Thee, the children of Thy love,
  The brothers of Thy well-belovèd Son;
Descend, O Holy Spirit, like a dove,
  Into our hearts, that we may be as one;
As one with Thee, to whom we ever tend;
As one with Him, our Brother and our Friend.

3 We would be one in hatred of all wrong,
One in our love of all things sweet and fair,
One with the joy that breaketh into song,
One with the grief that trembleth into prayer,
One in the power that makes the children free
To follow truth, and thus to follow Thee.

4 O clothe us with Thy heavenly armour, Lord,
Thy trusty shield, Thy sword of love divine;
Our inspiration be Thy constant word;
We ask no victories that are not Thine:
Give or withhold, let pain or pleasure be;
Enough to know that we are serving Thee.

	d	d	
	l,	s,	
	f	m	
	f,	d,	
A-men.

JOHN WHITE CHADWICK, 1840–1904.

490 DONCASTER. (S.M.)

Doh = D. *In moderate time.* SAMUEL WESLEY, 1766–1837.

:s |d' :m |f :l |s :— |— :s |l :s |t :d' |r :— |— ||
:m |d :d |d :d |d :— |— :d |d :d |f :m |t, :— |— ||
:s |s :s |f :f |m :— |— :s |f :s |s :s |s :— |— ||
:d |m :d |l, :f, |d :— |— :m |f :m |r :d |s :— |— ||

:s |s :d' |t :m |m :l |s :l |f :m |r :r |d :— |— ||f |m ||
:r |d :m |r :r |d :d |d :d |r :d |d :t, |d :— |— ||d |d ||
:t |d' :s |s :t |d' :d' |d' :l |s :s |l :s.f |m :— |— ||l |s ||
:s |m :d |s :se |l :f |m :f |t, :d |f, :s, |d :— |— ||f, |d ||
A-men.

BLEST be the tie that binds
Our hearts in Jesus' love;
The fellowship of Christian minds
Is like to that above.

2 Before our Father's throne
We pour our ardent prayers;
Our fears, our hopes, our aims are one,
Our comforts, and our cares.

3 When for awhile we part,
This thought will soothe our pain,
That we shall still be joined in heart
And one day meet again.

4 This glorious hope revives
Our courage by the way;
While each in expectation lives,
And longs to see the day,

5 When from all toil and pain
And sin we shall be free,
And perfect love and friendship reign
Through all eternity.

JOHN FAWCETT, 1740–1817, and others.

491

FINNART. (L.M.)

Doh = D. *In moderate time.* KENNETH GEORGE FINLAY, 1882-

:d |m :r :d |s :— :l |d :— :r |m :— :m
:s, |t, :— :d |d :— :d |l, :— :t, |d :— :d
:m |s :f :m |d' :t :l |s :— :f |s :— :l
:d |s, :— :l, |m :— :f / m, :— :f, |f :m :r |d :— :d

|s :l :s |d' :— :r' |l :— :s |l :—
|r :— :s |f :m :r |m :— :m.r |d :—
|r' :— :r' |d' :— :s |d' :t :t |l :—
|t, :— :t, |l, :— :t, |d.r :m :m |f :—

:l |d' :— :d' |l :s :l |d' :— :l |m :r :d
:r |d :r :m |f :r :m.f |s :— :r.d |t, :— :d
:f |l :— :l |l :t :d' |s :— :l |s :— :s
:r |l, :t, :d |f :s :f / f, :s, :f, |f :m :f / f, :m, :f, |s :— / s, :— :m

|r :m :s |l :s :m |r :— :d |d :— ||d |d
|t, :d :s, |r :— :t, |d :t, :d |s, :— ||l, |s,
|f :s :d'.t |l :t :s |f :— :f |m :— ||f |m
|r :d :m |f :s :s, |l, :s, :— |d :— ||f, |d

A-men.

PLAISTOW. (L.M.)

Lah = D. Doh = F. *Slow.* *Magdalen Chapel Hymns*, 1760 (?).

:l, |m :t, |d :l, |r.m :f |m :t, |d :r |m.s :f.m
:m, |m, :se, |l, :l, |l, :l, |l, :t, |l, :t, |d.m :r.d
:d |t, :m |m :d |r :r |d :m |m :s |s :l
:l, |se, :m, |l, :l,.s, |f, :r, |l, :se, |l, :s, |d :f,

m :r |d ||m |s :m.r |d :r.m |f :f |m :se
d :t, |d ||d |r :t, |d :d |d :t,.l, |se, :t,
s :s.f |m ||s |r :s |m :l.s |f :t, |m :m
s, :s, |d, ||d |t, :s, |l,.s, :f,.m, |r, :r, |m, :r

l :m |f :m.r |d :t, |l, ||r |de ||
l, :d |r :l,.t, |l, :se, |l, ||l, |l, ||
m :l |l :l.f |m :r |d ||f |m ||
d :l, |r :d.r |m :m, |l, ||r, |l, ||
A-men.

ALMIGHTY Father, who dost give
The gift of life to all who live,
Look down on all earth's sin and strife,
And lift us to a nobler life.

2 Lift up our hearts, O King of kings,
To brighter hopes and kindlier things,
To visions of a larger good,
And holier dreams of brotherhood.

3 Thy world is weary of its pain,
Of selfish greed and fruitless gain,
Of tarnished honour, falsely strong,
And all its ancient deeds of wrong.

4 Hear Thou the prayer Thy servants pray,
Uprising from all lands to-day,
And o'er the vanquished powers of sin
O bring Thy great salvation in.

JOHN HOWARD BERTRAM MASTERMAN, 1867-

492

ERMUNTRE DICH. (87. 87. D. Iambic.)

JOHANN SCHOP, ? -1664.
Arranged by
JOHANN SEBASTIAN BACH, 1685-1750.

Doh = E♭. vv. 1 & 3 in *Unison.* *Moderately slow.*

```
:d     |d     :r     |m.fe  :s     |s     :fe    |s  || m   |f     :m     |r   :m
:s,    |l,    :t,    |s,.l, :t,    |l,.t, :d     |t, || t,  |l,    :s,.l, |t,  :d
:m     |m.f   :-.s   |m.r   :r     |r     :r     |r  || m.r |d.r   :m.f   |s   :s
:d.t,  |l,    :s,    |d     :t,.d  |r     :r,    |s, || se, |l,.t, :d.f,  |f.m :r.d
```

D.C.

```
|r      :—     |d  || r     |r     :m     |f     :f    |m.r :m    |r  ||
|d      :t,    |d  || t,.d  |r     :-.de  |r.de  :r    |r   :de   |l, ||
|s      :-.f   |m  || s.l   |t.l   :s     |l     :t    |m   :l.s  |f  ||
|s      :s,    |d  || s,    |s.f   :m     |r     :se,  |l,  :l,   |r, ||
```

```
:m      |m     :m     |f.s    :l     |l     :se   |l  || t   |d'    :m     |f     :m
:l,.se, |l,    :l,    |l,.t,  :d.t,  |t,.d  :r    |d  || r   |d.r   :m     |m.r   :r.d
:d.r    |m.f   :s.l   |f      :fe    |m     :—    |m  || s   |s     :d'    |d.r   :m
:l,.t,  |d     :de    |r      :re    |m     :m,   |l, || s.f |m.r   :d.t,  |l,.t, :d.l,
```

```
|r       :r        |r  || s    |l    :s    |f     :m.f |r        :—   |d  || d  |d  ||
|d       :d        |t, || d.t, |l,   :t,   |d.r   :s,  |l,       :s,  |s, || l, |s, ||
|l.s     :l.fe     |s  || s    |s.f  :f.m  |m.r   :d   |d.t,.l,  :t,  |m  || f  |m  ||
|fe,.m,  :fe,.r,   |s, || m,   |f,   :s,   |l,.t, :d   |f,       :s,  |d, || f, |d d, ||
```

A - men.

ALTERNATIVE SETTING FOR v. 2.

Doh = E♭. *Moderately slow.*
Harmony.

```
:d  |d   :r   |m.fe :s   |s   :fe  |s  || m |f     :m    |r   :m
:s, |l,  :t,  |d    :r   |m   :r   |t, || d |l,.t, :d    |t,  :d
:m  |m   :s   |s    :s   |d'  :l   |s  || s |f     :s.l  |t.l :s
:d  |l,  :s,  |d    :t,  |l,  :r   |s, || d |r     :m.f  |s.f :m.d
```

BROTHERLY LOVE

D.C. f.Ab.

r :—	d || r	$^{r}l_1$:t_1	d :d	$t_1.l_1$:t_1	l_1	
d :t_1	d	t_1	$^{r}l_1$:—.se_1	l_1 :l_1	l_1 :se_1	l_1
l :s	m	s	^{l}m :r	d :l_1	f :m.r	d
f_1 :s_1	d	s_1	^{f}d :t_1	$l_1.s_1$:$f_1.m_1$	r_1 :m_1	l_2

Eb.t.

:^{t_1}m	m :m	f.s :l	l :se	l	t	d' :m	f :m
:$^{m_1}l_1.se_1$	$l_1.t_1$:d	r :m	r :t_1	d	r	d :s_1	$l_1.t_1$:d
:^{s_1}d.r	m :l	l :m	f :m	m	s	s :d'	f :s
:$^{m_1}l_1.t_1$	d :l_1	r :d	t_1 :m	l_1	$s_1.f_1$	m_1 :$d.t_1$	l_1 :s_1

r :r	r	s	l :s	f :m.f	r :—	d
d :l_1	t_1	d	d :t_1	d.r :d	d :t_1	d
l :fe	s	s	f :r	l :s	s :—.f	m
fe_1 :r_1	s_1	m_1	f_1 :s_1	$l_1.t_1$:d	s_1 :—	d

O GOD our Father, throned on high,
Enrobed in ageless splendour,
To Thee, in awe and love and joy,
Ourselves we would surrender—
To live obedient to Thy will
As servants to each other,
And show our faithfulness to Thee,
By love to one another.

2 To serve by love! O teach us how;
Be this our great vocation—
To comfort grief, to seek the lost
With message of salvation;
In loving may our full hearts beat,
Our words be wise and winning;
In helping others may our joy
Have ever new beginning.

3 Thee, Lord, for Thy dear Son we bless;
His heart for us was broken;
O Love! upon the bitter Cross
Thy deepest word was spoken;
The echo of that word is heard
In love for every brother;
So test we, Lord, our love for Thee,
By loving one another.

George Thomas Coster, 1835–1912.

493 DELHI. (888.)

Doh = A. *In moderate time.* EDWARD FRANCIS RIMBAULT, 1816–76.

:s, |m :d |l, :f |m :r |d :m |r :t, |l, :d

:m, |s, :s, |s, :f,.l, |s, :-.f, |m, :s, |s, :s, |s, :s,

:d |d :d |d :d |d :t, |d :d |t, :r |m :m

:d, |d :m, |f, :r, |s, :s, |d, :d, |s, :t, |d :l,

t, :l, |s, :s, |l, :t, |d :r |m :r |d || d |d

s, :fe, |s, :s, |s, :f, |m, :l, |s, :s,.f, |m, || f, |m,

r :r.d |t, :d |d :r |d :d |d :t, |d || l, |s,

r :r, |s, :m, |f, :r, |l, :f, |s, :s, |d, || f, |d,

A - men.

LLANGOEDMOR. (888. D.)

Doh = C. *In moderate time.* Welsh Hymn Melody.

d' :— |s :m |d :— |f :-.m |f :s |d' :— |d' :—

m :— |r :d |d :— |d :— |d :t, |d :— |m :—

s :— |s :s |l :— |d' :— |l :f |s :— |s :—

d :— |t, :d |l, :— |l :-.s |f :r |m :— |d :—

|m' :d' |l :— |r' :-.d' |t :l |s :— |d' :— |m' :m'

|s :s |l :— |s :— |s :fe |s :— |s :— |l :t

|d' :d' |d' :— |r' :-.m' |r' :d' |t :— |d' :— |d' :t

|d' :m |f :— |t, :-.d |r :r |s :— |m :— |ba :se

|m' :— |d' :— |r' :r' |d' :— || s :— |l :r' |d' :—

|l :— |l :— |l :s.f |m :— || m :— |f :f |s :—

|d' :— |m' :— |r' :t |d' :— || d' :— |d' :t |d' :—

|l :— |l :s |f :s |d :— || d :— |f :r |m :—

BROTHERLY LOVE

|s :— |l :r' |d' :— |s :— |d' :m' |r' :— |d' :— |t :l
|s :— |f :f |m :— |s :— |m :s |s :— |s :— |s :fe
|m' :— |d' :t |d' :— |d' :— |d' :d' |t :— |d' :m' |r' :d'
|d :— |f :r |l :— |m :— |d :d' |s :— |m :d |r :r

s :—	m' :—	l :r'	s :—	d' :—	r' :r'	d' :—		d'	d'	
s :—	s :—	l :f	s :—	m :—	l :s.f	m :—		f	m	
t :—	d' :—	d' :t	d' :—	d' :—	d' :t	d' :—		l	s	
s :—	d :—	f :r	m :—	l :—	f :s	d :—		f	d	

Amen.

FATHER of men, in whom are one
All humankind beneath Thy sun,
Stablish our work in Thee begun.

2 Except the house be built of Thee,
In vain the builder's toil must be :
O strengthen our infirmity !

3 Man lives not for himself alone,
In others' good he finds his own ;
Life's worth in fellowship is known.

4 We, friends and comrades on life's way,
Gather within these walls to pray :
Bless Thou our fellowship to-day.

5 O Christ, our Elder Brother, who
By serving man God's will didst do,
Help us to serve our brethren too.

6 Guide us to seek the things above,
The base to shun, the pure approve,
To live by Thy free law of love.

7 In all our work, in all our play,
Be with us, Lord, our Friend, our Stay ;
Lead onward to the perfect day :

8 Then may we know, earth's lesson o'er,
With comrades missed or gone before,
Heaven's fellowship for evermore.

HENRY CARY SHUTTLEWORTH, 1850–1900.

Also the following :

87 What grace, O Lord, and beauty shone
90 Lord, as to Thy dear Cross we flee
213 Father of all, from land and sea
214 Through the night of doubt and sorrow
345 Fountain of good, to own Thy love
361 Dear Master, what can children do?
548 Father, I know that all my life

CONSECRATION AND DISCIPLESHIP

494 HOLYROOD. (S.M.)

Doh = E. *In moderate time.* JAMES WATSON, 1816–80.

:d |m :s |s :l |s :— |— :s |l :d' |t :l |s :— |—
:s_1 |d :d |r :r |s_1 :— |— :r |m :d |r :r.d |t_1 :— |—
:m |s :d' |t :l.t |d' :— |— :s |m :l |s :fe |s :— |—
:d |d :m |s :f |m :— |— :t_1 |d :l_1 |t_1.d :r |s_1 :— |—

:s |s :l |d' :m |f :l |s :m |r :f |t_1 :t_1 |d :— |— ‖ d |d
:d |s_1 :d |m :s_1 |d :d |t_1 :d.t_1 |l_1 :l_1 |s_1 :s_1 |s_1 :— |— ‖ l_1 |s_1
:m |d' :l |s :d' |f :f.m |r :d |r :r |r :s.f |m :— |— ‖ f |m
:d |m :f |m.r :d.ta_1 |l_1 :f_1 |s_1 :d |f_1 :r_1 |s_1 :s_1 |d :— |— ‖ f_1 |d

A-men.

FAIR waved the golden corn
In Canaan's pleasant land,
When full of joy, some shining morn,
Went forth the reaper band.

2 To God, so good and great,
Their cheerful thanks they pour,
Then carry to His temple gate
The choicest of their store.

3 For thus the holy word,
Spoken by Moses, ran:
'The first ripe ears are for the Lord,
The rest He gives to man.'

4 Like Israel, Lord, we give
Our earliest fruits to Thee,
And pray that, long as we shall live,
We may Thy children be.

5 Thine is our youthful prime,
And life and all its powers;
Be with us in our morning time,
And bless our evening hours.

6 In wisdom let us grow,
As years and strength are given,
That we may serve Thy Church below,
And join Thy saints in heaven.

JOHN HAMPDEN GURNEY, 1802–62.

495 ARUNDEL. (87. 87.)

Doh = A♭. *In moderate time.* JOHN BACCHUS DYKES, 1823–76.

```
s, :d  |t, :d  |r  :m     |m  :r  |m  :l,  |t, :d  |l, :l,  |s, :—
s, :s, |s, :s, |s, :m,.f, |s, :s, |s, :s,  |s, :s, |s, :fe, |s, :—
m  :m  |r  :d  |t, :d     |d  :t, |d  :m   |r  :d  |r  :d   |t, :—
d  :s, |f, :m, |r, :d,    |s, :s, |d, :d   |t, :l, |r, :r,  |s, :—

m  :m     |r  :r  |f  :f     |m  :m  |s  :d  |r     :m  |r  :r  |d  :— || d  |d
m, :s,    |s, :s, |f, :l,    |l, :l, |ta,:l, |s,.f, :m, |s, :f, |m, :— || f, |m,
d  :d     |t, :t, |r  :r     |d  :d  |d  :d  |t,    :d  |d  :t, |d  :— || l, |s,
d, :m,.f, |s, :s, |r, :f,.s, |l, :l, |m, :f, |r,    :d, |s, :s, |d, :— || f, |d,
                                                                          A-men.
```

SHIPSTON. (87. 87.)

Doh = E♭. *In moderate time.* English Traditional Melody.

```
d  :m |s :-.l  |s.f :m.r |m :d |d :m  |s  :-.l  |s.m :r.d |r  :—
s, :d |d :-.d  |t,  :t,  |d :d |d :d  |d  :-.d  |d   :l,  |t, :—
m  :s |s :-.d' |s   :s   |s :m |m :l  |s  :-.f  |m   :fe  |s  :—
d  :d |m :-.f  |s   :s,  |d :d |d :l, |m, :-.f, |s,  :l,  |s, :—

d  :m.f |s  :d' |s  :-.f |f :m |d  :-.r  |m :f.r |d  :t, |d  :— || d  |d
l, :d   |t, :d  |d  :r   |d :d |l, :-.t, |d :l,  |s, :s, |s, :— || l, |s,
m  :d   |r  :d  |d  :s   |s :s |l  :s.f  |m :l.f |m  :r  |m  :— || f  |m
l, :s,  |f, :m, |l, :t,  |d :m |f  :m.r  |d :f,  |s, :s, |d  :— || f, |d
                                                                    A-men.
```

SAVIOUR, while my heart is tender,
I would yield that heart to Thee,
All my powers to Thee surrender,
Thine, and only Thine, to be.

2 Take me now, Lord Jesus, take me;
Let my youthful heart be Thine;
Thy devoted servant make me;
Fill my soul with love divine.

3 Send me, Lord, where Thou wilt send me,
Only do Thou guide my way;
May Thy grace through life attend me,
Gladly then shall I obey.

4 Let me do Thy will or bear it;
I would know no will but Thine;
Shouldst Thou take my life or spare it,
I that life to Thee resign.

5 Thine I am, O Lord, for ever,
To Thy service set apart;
Suffer me to leave Thee never;
Seal Thine image on my heart.

JOHN BURTON, 1803–77.

496 SOUTH CERNEY. (88. 88. 88.)

Doh = E♭. *Moderately slow.* WILLIAM HENRY HADOW, 1859-

```
:m.f |s    :s    |f     :m   |r  :r  |m  :m  |r   :s     |s    :- .l
:m.r |d.t, :d    |l,.t, :d   |d  :t, |d  :d  |r   :-.t,  |m.r  :m
:s.f |m.f  :s.m  |f     :s   |l  :s  |s  :s  |s   :s     |s    :s
:d   |d.r  :m.d  |r     :m   |f  :s  |d  :d  |t,  :-.s,  |d.t, :d.de

                                                        B♭.t.
|t  :l    |s  ||s    |s    :s    |f   :m   |r   :r   |m  :[s]d
|r  :-.d  |t, ||t,   |d    :r    |d   :d   |d   :t,  |d  :[m]l,.s,
|s  :fe   |s  ||s.f  |m.f  :r.m  |f   :s   |l   :s   |s  :[s]d
|r  :r    |s, ||s,   |d    :t,   |l,  :s,  |f,  :s,  |d  :[d]f,.m,

                                     f.E♭.
|f      :m       |m      :-.r  |d   :t,   |l,  ||[l]m   |f   :m.r  |d    :d'.t
|f,.l,  :se,.t,  |l,.m,  :f,   |m,  :-.r, |d,  ||[f]d   |r   :t,   |d    :d.r
|r.d    :t,.r    |d      :-.t, |l,  :se,  |l,  ||[l]m   |l   :s.f  |m.f  :s
|r,     :m,      |l,     :r,   |m,  :m,   |l₂  ||[r]l,  |r,  :s,   |d.r  :m.r

|l  :l    |s   :t    |d'   :t.l  |s    :l    |r    :r   |d  ||d  |d
|m  :r.d  |t,  :r    |d    :r    |m.r  :d    |d    :t,  |d  ||l, |s,
|s  :fe   |s   :m    |m.l  :s.f  |m    :f.m  |r.m  :f   |m  ||f  |m
|d  :r    |s,  :se,  |l,   :t,   |d    :f,   |s,   :s,  |d  ||f, |d
                                                            A-men.
```

Liebe die du mich zum Bilde.

O LOVE, who formedst me to wear
The image of Thy Godhead here;
Who soughtest me with tender care
Through all my wanderings wild and drear:
O Love, I give myself to Thee,
Thine ever, only Thine to be.

2 O Love, who ere life's earliest morn
On me Thy choice hast gently laid;
O Love, who here as Man wast born,
And wholly like to us wast made:

3 O Love, who once in time wast slain,
Pierced through and through with bitter woe;
O Love, who wrestling thus didst gain
That we eternal joy might know:

4 O Love, who lovest me for aye,
Who for my soul dost ever plead;
O Love, who didst my ransom pay,
Whose power sufficeth in my stead:

5 O Love, whose voice shall bid me rise
From out this dying life of ours;
O Love, whose hand o'er yonder skies
Shall set me in the fadeless bowers:
O Love, I give myself to Thee,
Thine ever, only Thine to be.

JOHANN SCHEFFLER, 1624–77; *tr.* by CATHERINE WINKWORTH, 1829–78.

497 SAFFRON WALDEN. (88. 86.)

Doh = D. *Moderately slow.* ARTHUR HENRY BROWN, 1830–1926.

```
|m  :r  :d  |s  :—  :d' |d' :t  :l  |s  :—  :—  |s   :f  :m   |
|d  :t, :d  |d  :—  :s  |f  :—  :f  |f  :—  :—  |m.r :d  :-.t,|
|s  :f  :m  |s  :—  :s  |l  :t  :d' |r' :—  :—  |d'.t:l  :s   |
|d  :s, :l, |m, :—  :m  |r  :—  :d  |t, :—  :—  |d   :d  :d   |

|r  :t, :d  |f  :-.s:m |r  :—  ||r  |s  :—  :s  |s  :—  :d' |
|l, :s, :s, |l, :t, :d |t, :—  ||t, |t, :d  :r  |d  :—  :d  |
|f  :—  :s  |f  :—  :s |s  :—  ||s  |s  :l  :t  |d' :—  :ta |
|f  :—  :m  |r  :—  :d |s, :—  ||s  |s  :—  :f  |m  :—  :m  |

|d' :l  :f  |r  :—  :—  |s  :d  :r  |m  :—  :r  |d  :—  :—  ||d  |d  ||
|d  :—  :d  |t, :—  :—  |t, :d  :d  |d  :—  :t, |d  :—  :—  ||l, |s, ||
|l  :—  :l  |s  :—  :—  |s  :m  :l  |s  :—  :f  |m  :—  :—  ||f  |m  ||
|f  :—  :r  |s, :—  :—  |m, :l, :f, |s, :—  :s, |d  :—  :—  ||f, |d  ||
                                                              A-men.
```

JUST as I am, Thine own to be,
Friend of the young, who lovest me,
To consecrate myself to Thee,
O Jesus Christ, I come.

2 In the glad morning of my day,
My life to give, my vows to pay,
With no reserve and no delay,
With all my heart I come.

3 I would live ever in the light,
I would work ever for the right,
I would serve Thee with all my might,
Therefore to Thee I come.

4 Just as I am, young, strong and free,
To be the best that I can be
For truth, and righteousness, and Thee,
Lord of my life, I come.

MARIANNE FARNINGHAM, 1834–1909.

[May be sung to MISERICORDIA, No. 411.]

498 UNIVERSITY. (C.M.)

Doh = C. *Not too fast.* JOHN RANDALL, 1715–99.

```
:s |f .m  :r .d  |d'   :r' .m' |s  :f  |m :- .s |m .d :l .s
:d |d     :t, .d |d .s :f .m   |r  :t, |d :- .r |d    :d
:m |l .s  :f .m  |s    :t .d'  |r' :s  |s :- .s |s    :f .s
:d |d     :d     |m    :r .d   |t, :s, |d :- .t,|d .m :f .m

|f    :m |r  :— |— ||s    |d'   :d' .t |l    :s  |d  :r .m
|d .t,:d |t, :— |— ||r    |s    :m     |d .r :m  |d  :d
|l .f :s |s  :— |— ||t    |d'   :s     |l .t :d' |d' :- .t
|r    :d |s, :— |— ||s .f |m    :d     |f    :m  |l  :s

|f :- .s |l .d' :s .l  |m :r    |d :— |— ||f  |m ||
|d :- .d |d     :d     |d :t,   |d :— |— ||d  |d ||
|l :- .s |f .l  :d' .l |s :- .f |m :— |— ||l  |s ||
|f :- .m |f     :m .f  |s :s,   |d :— |— ||f, |d ||
                                           A - men.
```

LORD, in the fulness of my might,
  I would for Thee be strong :
While runneth o'er each dear delight,
  To Thee should soar my song.

2 I would not give the world my heart,
  And then profess Thy love ;
I would not feel my strength depart,
  And then Thy service prove.

3 I would not with swift-wingèd zeal
  On the world's errands go,
And labour up the heavenly hill
  With weary feet and slow.

4 O not for Thee my weak desires,
  My poorer, baser part !
O not for Thee my fading fires,
  The ashes of my heart !

5 O choose me in my golden time :
  In my dear joys have part !
For Thee the glory of my prime,
  The fulness of my heart !

THOMAS HORNBLOWER GILL, 1819–1906.

499 HEATON NORRIS. (L.M.)

Doh = C. *Moderately slow.* JOHN GRIMSHAW, ? –1819.

:s |d' :m.f |s :l.s |f :m.r |m :m |s :d' |t.d' :r'
:s |m :d |r :d |d :t, |d :m |r :d |r :s
:s |s :l |t :s |l :s |s :s |s.r :m.fe |s :s.t
:s |d :l |s :m |r :s |d :d |t, :l, |s,.l, :t,.s,

|r'.d' :t.l |s (pause) ||s |m' :r'.d' |d' :-.t |l.s :f.m |r :-.r
|s :s.fe |s ||s |s :f |m :s |f.m :r.d |t, :-.t,
|m' :r'.d' |t ||s |d' :t |d' :s |l :l |t :-.s
|d :r |s, ||s |d :s |l :m |f :f |s :-.s

|m.f :s.d' |s :l.f |m :r |d (pause) ||f |m
|d :d.l |s.m :d.r |r.d :d.t, |d ||d |d
|s :s.m' |r'.d' :l |s :s |m ||l |s
|d.r :m.l, |t,.d :f.r |s, :s, |d ||f, |d

A - men.

O HAPPY day, that fixed my choice
On Thee, my Saviour and my God!
Well may this glowing heart rejoice,
And tell its raptures all abroad.

2 O happy bond, that seals my vows
To Him who merits all my love!
Let cheerful anthems fill His house,
While to that sacred shrine I move.

3 'Tis done! the great transaction 's done!
I am my Lord's and He is mine;
He drew me, and I followed on,
Charmed to confess the voice divine.

4 Now rest, my long-divided heart;
Fixed on this blissful centre, rest!
O who with earth would grudge to part,
When called with angels to be blest?

5 High heaven, that heard the solemn vow,
That vow renewed shall daily hear
Till in life's latest hour I bow,
And bless in death a bond so dear.

PHILIP DODDRIDGE, 1702–51.

500 ST. ANDREW. (87. 87.)

EDWARD HENRY THORNE, 1834–1916.

Doh = C. *In moderate time.* G.t.

m :-.m	r :m	f :m	l :s	d' :-.d'	t :l	[s]d :r	d :—	
d :-.d	r :d	t, :d	r :s	m :-.m	m :f	[s]d :t,	s, :—	
s :-.s	s :s	s :s	t :d'	d' :-.d'	d' :d'	[d]f :f	m :—	
d :-.d	t, :d	r :d	f :m	l :-.l	s :f	[m]l, :s,	d :—	

f.C.

d :-.d	t, :d	r :d	f :m	[l]m' :-.d'	d' :-.l	d' :t	d' :—		d'	d'	
l, :-.l,	t, :l,	se, :l,	t, :d	[d]s :-.m	fe :-.fe	s :f	m :—		f	m	
m :-.m	m :m	m :m	se :l	[f]d' :-.d'	m' :-.d'	m' :r'	d' :—		l	s	
l, :-.l,	se, :l,	t, :l,	r :d	[f]d' :-.d'	l :-.l	s :s	d :—		f	d	

A-men.

JESUS calls us ! O'er the tumult
Of our life's wild restless sea,
Day by day His sweet voice soundeth,
Saying, ' Christian, follow Me ' :

2 As, of old, Saint Andrew heard it
By the Galilean lake,
Turned from home and toil and kindred,
Leaving all for His dear sake.

3 Jesus calls us from the worship
Of the vain world's golden store,
From each idol that would keep us,
Saying, 'Christian, love Me more.'

4 In our joys and in our sorrows,
Days of toil and hours of ease,
Still He calls, in cares and pleasures,
' Christian, love Me more than these.'

5 Jesus calls us ! By Thy mercies,
Saviour, make us hear Thy call,
Give our hearts to Thy obedience,
Serve and love Thee best of all.

CECIL FRANCES ALEXANDER, 1823–95.

501 HESPERUS. (L.M.)

Doh = F. *Moderately slow.*

HENRY BAKER, 1835–1910.

|m :m :m |s :— :d |r :— :r |m :— :— |s :s :s |f :— :s
|d :d :d |d :— :d |d :— :t, |d :— :— |d :d :d |d :— :t,
|s :s :s |s :— :m |l :— :s |s :— :— |s :s :d' |l :— :s
|d :d :d |m, :— :l, |f, :— :s, |d :— :— |m :m :m |r :— :s,

C.t. f.F.

|m :— :f |r :— :— |[r]s :s :s |s :— :s |t :— :t |[d']s :— :—
|d :— :r |t, :— :— |[t,]m :m :m |r :— :m |f :— :f |[m]t, :— :—
|s :l :l |s :— :— |[s]d' :d' :d' |t :— :d' |r' :— :r' |[d']s :— :—
|d :l, :f, |s, :— :— |[s]d :d :d |s :— :s |s :— :s |[d]s, :— :—

```
|m  :m  :m   |m  :r  :d    |d  :—  :t,  |d  :—  :—  ||d  |d  ||
|d  :d  :ta, |l, :—  :l,   |s, :—  :s,  |s, :—  :—  ||l, |s, ||
|s  :s  :s   |s  :f  :—.m  |r  :m  :f   |m  :—  :—  ||f  |m  ||
|d  :d  :d   |f, :—  :f,   |s, :—  :s,  |d  :—  :—  ||f, |d, ||
```

A-men.

BRESLAU. (L.M.)

As Hymnodus Sacer, Leipsic, 1625.
Arranged by FELIX MENDELSSOHN-BARTHOLDY, 1809–47.

Doh = G. *Slow.*

```
:d      |d     :d       |l, :d   |r     :t,      |l, ||l,  |t, :d   |r  :s,.l,  |t, :l,   |s, ||
:m,.f,  |s,.l, :ta,.s,  |f, :s,  |f,    :r,.m,   |d, ||f,  |s, :s,  |s, :s,     |s, :fe,  |s, ||
:d      |d     :m       |f  :d   |d.t,  :l,.se,  |l, ||d   |r  :m   |f  :m      |r  :—.d  |t, ||
:l,     |m,    :d,      |f, :m,  |r,    :m,      |l, ||f,  |f, :m,  |t,, :d,    |r, :r,   |s, ||

:s,     |d  :r   |m  :d   |f    :m      |r  ||r     |m  :s   |f     :m     |r  :r   |d  ||d  |d  ||
:s,     |s, :f,  |m, :l,  |l,   :s,     |s, ||l,    |s, :s,  |l,    :s,.d  |d  :t,  |d  ||l, |s, ||
:s,     |l, :t,  |d  :d   |d.t, :d      |t, ||l,.t, |d  :m   |d.r   :m     |f  :r   |m  ||f  |m  ||
:s,.f,  |m, :r,  |d, :f,  |r,   :m,.f,  |s, ||f,    |m, :d,  |l,.t, :d     |s, :s,  |d, ||f, |d, ||
```

A-men.

Unison. 'TAKE up thy cross,' the Saviour said,
'If thou wouldst My disciple be;
Take up thy cross, with willing heart,
And humbly follow after Me.'

Harmony. 2 Take up thy cross; let not its weight
Fill thy weak soul with vain alarm;
His strength shall bear thy spirit up,
And brace thy heart, and nerve thine arm.

3 Take up thy cross, nor heed the shame,
And let thy foolish pride be still:
Thy Lord refused not e'en to die
Upon a Cross, on Calvary's hill.

4 Take up thy cross, then, in His strength,
And calmly every danger brave;
'Twill guide thee to a better home,
And lead to victory o'er the grave.

Unison. 5 Take up thy cross, and follow Christ,
Nor think till death to lay it down;
For only he who bears the cross
May hope to wear the glorious crown.

CHARLES WILLIAM EVEREST, 1814–77.

502

BETHANY (CRUCIFER). (87. 87. D.)

Doh = F. *In moderate time.* HENRY SMART, 1813–79.

```
|m  :l  |s  :m  |d  :-.r |d  :t,  |l,  :s,  |d  :m  |s  :f.m |r  :—  ||
|d  :d  |d  :t, |d  :l,  |s, :s,  |r,  :r,  |s, :d  |d  :r.d |t, :—  ||
|s  :f  |s  :s  |m  :f   |m  :r   |t,  :t,  |d  :s  |s  :l   |r  :s  ||
|d  :f, |m, :s, |l, :f,  |s, :s,  |f,  :f,  |m, :d, |m, :f,  |s, :—  ||

|m  :l  |s  :m  |d  :-.r |d  :t,  |l,  :s,  |d  :f  |m  :r   |d  :—  ||
|s, :d  |r  :t, |l, :fe, |s, :s,  |r,  :r,  |s, :d  |d  :t,  |d  :—  ||
|m  :m  |r  :s  |m  :r   |r  :r   |t,  :t,  |d  :d  |s  :s.f |m  :—  ||
|d  :l, |t, :s, |l, :r,  |s, :s,  |f,  :f,  |m, :l, |s, :s,  |d  :—  ||

C.t.                                                     f.F.
|(r)s   :d' |d'  :t  |l   :l  |l  :s  |s  :m' |r' :l  |d' :t  |(d')s  :— ||
|(t,)m  :s  |s   :s  |f   :f  |f  :m  |s  :s  |f  :r  |m  :f  |(m)t,  :— ||
|(s)d'  :d' |r'  :r' |d'  :r' |d' :d' |d' :ta |l  :l  |s  :r' |(d')s  :— ||
|(s,)d  :m  |s   :s, |l,  :t, |d  :d  |m  :d  |f  :f  |s  :s  |(d)s,  :— ||

|t  :s  |d' :s  |f  :-.s |f  :m  |l  :s   |f  :m  |r  :r   |d  :— || f  |m ||
|r  :t, |d  :d  |d  :r   |d  :d  |d  :de  |r  :d  |d  :t,  |d  :— || d  |d ||
|s  :s  |s  :m  |l  :s   |s  :s  |f  :m   |f  :s  |l  :s.f |m  :— || l  |s ||
|s  :f  |m  :d  |l, :t,  |d  :d  |f, :l,  |r, :m, |f, :s,  |d  :— || f, |d ||
                                                              A-men.
```

TANYCASTELL. (87. 87. D.)

Doh = F. *In moderate time.* JOHN JONES (TALYSARN), 1797–1857.

```
|d  :— :d  |d  :t, :t, |r  :— :r  |m  :d  :— |f  :— :f  |f  :m :m  |
|s, :d :l, |s, :— :s, |l, :— :t, |d  :s, :— |d  :l, :d |d  :— :d  |
|m  :s :f  |m  :r :r  |f  :l :s  |s  :m  :— |d  :— :f  |l  :s :s  |
|d  :m, :f,|s, :— :s, |r, :f, :s,|d  :d  :— |l, :f, :l,|d  :— :d  |

                          D.C.
|f  :— :m      |r  :— :— || s  :— :s |s  :f  :m |s  :— :s  |s  :f    :m  |
|d  :r :s,.l,  |t, :— :— || d  :— :d |d  :t, :d |m  :r  :d  |d  :-.t, :d  |
|f  :r :m.fe   |s  :— :— || s  :f  :m |m  :r  :d |s  :— :s  |l  :—    :s  |
|l, :t, :d     |s, :— :— || m  :r  :d |s, :— :l,|s, :f, :m, |r, :—    :m, |
```

r :—:d	d :— :r	d :— :t,	l, :— :— ‖ r :— :f	f :m :r
l, :t, :d .t,	l, :— :l,	l, :— :se,	l, :— :— ‖ l, :— :r	d :—:s,
f :—:m	l :s :f	m :— :r	d :— :— ‖ f :— :l	l :s :f
f, :s, :l, .s,	f, :m, :r,	m, :— :m,	l, :— :— ‖ f, :-.m, :r,	l, :—:t,

m :— :s	s :f :m	l :—:l	s :—:m	r.d,r:m :r	d :—:— ‖ d	d
s, :d :d	l, :-.t, :d	d :—:d	d :—:d	d :—:t,	d :—:— ‖ l,	s,
m :— :m	r :l :s	f :—:f	m :—:s	l :s :s.f	m :—:— ‖ f	m
d :-.t, :l,	r :— :m	f :—:f,	d :—:d	f, :s, :s,	d :—:— ‖ f,	d,

A-men.

JESUS, I my cross have taken,
All to leave, and follow Thee ;
Destitute, despised, forsaken,
Thou from hence my all shalt be.
Perish every fond ambition,
All I've sought, and hoped, and known ;
Yet how rich is my condition !
God and heaven are still my own.

2 Man may trouble and distress me,
'Twill but drive me to Thy breast :
Life with trials hard may press me,
Heaven will bring me sweeter rest.
O 'tis not in grief to harm me,
While Thy love is left to me !
O 'twere not in joy to charm me,
Were that joy unmixed with Thee !

3 Take, my soul, thy full salvation ;
Rise o'er sin and fear and care :
Joy, to find in every station
Something still to do or bear.
Think what Spirit dwells within thee,
What a Father's smile is thine,
What thy Saviour died to win thee :
Child of heaven, shouldst thou repine ?

4 Haste then on from grace to glory,
Armed by faith, and winged by prayer :
Heaven's eternal day 's before thee ;
God's own hand shall guide thee there.
Soon shall close thy earthly mission ;
Swift shall pass thy pilgrim days,
Hope soon change to glad fruition,
Faith to sight, and prayer to praise.

HENRY FRANCIS LYTE, 1793–1847.

503

CHILTON FOLIAT. (10 10. 10 10.)

Doh = A. *Moderately slow.* George Clement Martin, 1844–1916.

```
:s, |d :s, |m, :-.f, |s, :s, |l, :t, |d :— |— :r |m :r |t, :s,
:s, |d :s, |m, :-.f, |s, :s, |s, :s, |s, :— |— :s, |s, :s, |s, :s,
:s, |d :s, |m, :-.f, |s, :t, |d :f |m :— |— :r |d :r |r :de
:s, |d :s, |m, :-.f, |s, :f, |m, :r, |d, :— |— :t, |d :t, |s, :m,

t, :-.d |t, :l, |s, :— |— ||s, |d :s, |m, :f, |s, :t, |d :r
s, :s, |fe, :fe, |r, :— |— ||r, |d, :r, |d, :d, |r, :s, |s, :s,
r :m |r :d |t, :— |— ||t, |s, :s, |s, :l, |t, :r |d :t,
r, :-.r, |r, :r, |s, :— |— ||f, |m, :t,, |d, :l, |s, :f, |m, :s,

m :— |— :d |r :m |f :d |m :-.f |m :r |d :— |— ||d |d ||
s, :— |— :m, |f, :ta, |l, :f, |s, :-.d |d :t, |s, :— |— ||l, |s, ||
d :— |— :d |d :d |d :d |d :-.l |s :f |m :— |— ||f |m ||
d, :— |— :ta, |l, :s, |f, :l, |s, :-.s, |s, :s, |d (d,) :— |— ||f, |d, ||
```

A-men.

[*Copyright*, 1897, *by Novello, Ewer & Co.*]

ALMIGHTY Father of all things that be,
Our life, our work, we consecrate to Thee,
Whose heavens declare Thy glory from above,
Whose earth below is witness to Thy love.

2 For well we know this weary, soilèd earth
Is yet Thine own by right of its new birth,
Since that great Cross upreared on Calvary
Redeemed it from its fault and shame to Thee.

3 Thine still the changeful beauty of the hills,
The purple valleys flecked with silver rills,
The ocean glistening 'neath the golden rays;
They all are Thine, and voiceless speak Thy praise.

4 Thou dost the strength to workman's arm impart;
From Thee the skilled musician's mystic art,
The grace of poet's pen or painter's hand
To teach the loveliness of sea and land.

5 Then grant us, Lord, in all things Thee to own,
To dwell within the shadow of Thy throne,
To speak and work, to think, and live, and move,
Reflecting Thine own nature, which is love;

6 That so, by Christ redeemed from sin and shame,
And hallowed by Thy Spirit's cleansing flame,
Ourselves, our work, and all our powers may be
A sacrifice acceptable to Thee.

Ernest Edward Dugmore, 1843–1925.

504 SAVANNAH. (77. 77.)

Doh = E♭. *In moderate time.* *John Wesley's Foundery Collection*, 1742.

```
|s  :s.f |m  :r  |d.r:m  |r  :—  |s  :s.f |m  :r  |d.r:m   |r  :—  ||
|d  :r   |d  :t, |d  :d  |t, :—  |d  :t,  |d  :t, |l,  :d   |t, :—  ||
|m  :s   |s  :s  |s  :s  |s  :—  |s  :s   |s  :f  |m   :l   |r  :—  ||
|d  :t,  |d  :f  |m  :d  |s, :—  |m  :r   |d  :s, |l,  :fe, |s, :f, ||

|s  :s    |l  :s.f |m   :fe |s  :—  |l  :t  |d' :m.r |m  :r  |d  :—  ||d  |d  ||
|d  :d    |d  :r   |d   :d  |t, :—  |d  :r  |d  :d   |d  :t, |d  :—  ||l, |s, ||
|d  :d'.ta|l  :r   |s   :l  |r  :—  |l  :se |l  :l   |s  :f  |m  :—  ||f  |m  ||
|m, :m    |f  :t,  |d.t,:l, |s, :—  |f, :m, |l, :f,  |s, :s, |d  :—  ||f, |d  ||
```

A-men.

THINE for ever! God of Love,
Hear us from Thy throne above;
Thine for ever may we be,
Here and in eternity.

2 Thine for ever! O how blest
They who find in Thee their rest!
Saviour, Guardian, Heavenly Friend,
O defend us to the end.

3 Thine for ever! Lord of Life,
Shield us through our earthly strife;
Thou the Life, the Truth, the Way,
Guide us to the realms of day.

4 Thine for ever! Shepherd, keep
These, Thy frail and trembling sheep;
Safe alone beneath Thy care,
Let us all Thy goodness share.

5 Thine for ever! Thou our Guide,
All our wants by Thee supplied,
All our sins by Thee forgiven,
Lead us, Lord, from earth to heaven.

MARY FAWLER MAUDE, 1819–1913.

505 LORICA PATRICII. (Irr.)

Traditional Irish Melodies.
Arranged by ROBERT ALEXANDER STEWART MACALISTER, 1870– .

Atomriug indiu niurt tren.

Doh = D♭. *Unison.* *Slow and dignified.* vv. 1, 2, 3, 4, & 5.

:   .m | f   .m   :r   :s   .,f | m   .r   :d   :   .m

1. To - day I a - rise, . . In -
2. To - day I a - rise, . . By
3. To - day I a - rise, . . By
4. To - day I a - rise, . . By
5. To - day I a - rise, . . With

| f, f.m :r   :s   .,d' | t   .l   :s   :   .d ,d | m ,m .s   :d'   :t   .,r

-vok-ing the Bless - ed Tri ni - ty, Con - fess-ing the Bless - ed
strength of Christ and His mys-tic Birth, By His Pas-sion, and Tri - umph's
ser - aphs serv - ing the Lord a - bove, By truths His an - cient
splen-dour of sun and fla - ming brand, By rush - ing wind, by
God my steers - man, stay and guide, To guard, to coun - sel, to

| f   .l   :s   :   .s ,s | l   .ta   :l   .f   :r   .t$_1$ | d   .d   :d ||

U - ni - ty, Cre - a - tor of all the things that be.
sa - ving worth, By his Com - ing a - gain to judge the earth.
her - alds prove, By saints in pu - ri - ty, la - bour, love.
light-ning grand, By depth of sea, by strength of land.
hear, to bide, His way be - fore, His hosts be - side—

A♭.t. vv. 6, 7, & 8.

:m l$_1$ | d :— | t$_1$:— | l$_1$:l$_1$ | t$_1$:t$_1$ | d :d
:t m$_1$ | m$_1$:l$_1$ | — :s$_1$ | s$_1$:f$_1$ | f$_1$:m$_1$ | m$_1$:l$_1$

6. Pro - tect - - - ing me now From craf - ty
7. Lord Je - - - sus the Christ, To - day sur -
8. Di - rect . . . . and con - trol The minds of

:m l$_1$ | m :— | — :— | d :d | t$_1$ .l$_1$:s$_1$ | l$_1$ .d :m
:s d$_1$ | l$_2$:d$_1$ | m$_1$:— | f$_1$:-.m$_1$ | r$_1$:m$_1$ | l$_1$:-.s$_1$

| r :d .t$_1$ | l$_1$:s$_1$ | l$_1$:l$_1$ | m :m | r :d
| l$_1$:f$_1$ | m$_1$:m$_1$ | m$_1$:l$_1$ | m$_1$:s$_1$ | s$_1$:m$_1$

wiles of de - mon crew, From foe - men, be they
- round me with Thy might; Be - fore, be - hind, on
all who think on me, The lips of all who

| r :r | d :t$_1$ | d :l$_1$ | m :m | t$_1$:d
| f$_1$:r$_1$ | m$_1$:m$_1$ | l$_1$:l$_1$ | m$_1$:d$_1$ | s$_1$:l$_1$

t, :l, |t,.d :d |l, :m, |m, :f, |l, :s, |l,
s, :f, |s, :s, |f,.d,:m,.r, |d, :l₂.t₂ |d,.r, :m, |m,

many or few, From lusts that I can scarce sub - due.
left and right, Be Thou in breadth, in length, in height.
speak to me, The eyes of all who look on me.

m :d |r :m |d .l,:l,.se, |l, :l, |l,.t,:d .r |d
m, :l, |s, :d, |f, :t₂ |d, :r, |m, :m, |l,

Doh = f.D♭. v. 9.

f

9. To - day I a - rise, In-vo-king the Bless - ed Tri-ni - ty,

dim.

Con-fess-ing the Bless - ed U - ni - ty:

Harmony. *Softly and solemnly.*

us sal - va - tion be!

Sa - viour, on us sal - - va - tion be!

A - men.

St. Patrick, 372–466; *tr.* by Robert Alexander Stewart Macalister, 1870–

506

ST. PATRICK. (D.L.M. and refrain.)

Lah = G. Doh = B♭. Atomriug indiu niurt tren.

Unison. *Rather quickly, and with strong rhythm.*

Traditional Irish Hymn Melody. Arranged by CHARLES VILLIERS STANFORD, 1852–1924.

f
:m, | l, :— :l, | s, :m, :s, | d :m :r.d | d :t, :t, | r :t, :s,

1. I bind un - to my - self to - day The strong Name

| s, :t, :r | d :— :d | t, :— :m | l, :-.t, :d.l, | s, :m, :d,

of the Trin - i - ty, By in - vo - ca - tion

| d :— :s, | l, :t, :d.r | m :— :r.m | d :l, :t, | l, :— :l, | l, :— ||

of the same, The Three in One, and One in Three.

Men, v. 2 ; *Trebles*, v. 3.

mf
:m, | l, :— :l, | s, :m, :s, | d :m :r.d | d :t, :t, | r :t, :s,

2. I bind this day to me for ev - er, By power of
3. I bind un - to my - self to - day The vir - tues

| s, :t, :r | d :— :d | t, :t, :m (*mp*) | l, :-.t, :d.l,

faith, Christ's In - car - na - tion; His bap - tism
of the star - lit heaven, The glo - rious

| s, :m, :d, | d :— :s, | l, :t, :d.r | m :— :r.m | d :l, :t,

in the Jor - dan riv - er; His death on Cross for
sun's life - giv - ing ray, The white - ness of the

All voices in Unison.

| l, :— :l, | l, :l, :— | — : *f* :s, | d :— :d | d :— :r.m

my sal - va - tion; His burst - ing from the
moon at e - ven, The flash - ing of the

| r :— :de | r :— :m | l, :— :l, | s, :t, :r | d :— :d

spi - ced tomb; His ri - ding up the heaven - ly
light - ning free, The whirl - ing wind's tem - pes - tuous

[*Copyright*, 1913, *by Stainer & Bell, Ltd.*]

| t, :— :m, | l, :-.t, :d .l, | s, :m, :d, | d :— :s, |

way; His com - - ing at the day of
shocks, The sta - - ble earth, the deep salt

| l, :t, :d .r | m :— :r .m | d :l, :t, | l, :— :l, | l, :— ||

doom: I bind un - to my - self to - day.
sea A - round the old e - ter - nal rocks.

mf Voices in Harmony with Organ.

:m, | l, :— :l, | s, :m, :s, | d :m :r .d | d :t, :t, |
:m, | m, :— :m, | r, :d, :r, | m, :— :l, | s, :— :s, |
4. I bind un - to my - self to - day The
:m | d :— :d | r :m :r | d :— :l, | m :r :r |
:m, | l, :— :d | t, :d :t, | l, :— :f, | s, :— :s, |

| r :t, :s, | s, :t, :r | d :— :d | t, :— :m | l, :-.t, :d .l, |
| s, :— :s, | s, :— :s, | s, :m, :fe, | s, :— :s, | f, :— :r, |
power of God to hold and lead, His eye to
| r :— :r | m :r :t, | d :— :d | r :— :d | d :-.t, :l, .d |
| t, :s, :t, | d :t, :s, .f, | m, :l, :l, | s, :— :d, | f, :— :f, |

f.Eb. Bb.t.

| s, :m, :d, | ^{d}s :— :r | ^{m}l, :t, :d .r | m :— :r .m | d :l, :t, |
| r, :m, :d, | ^{d}s, :l, :t, | ^{d}f, :— :d | d :t, :l, .t, | m, :f, :s, |
watch, His might to stay, His ear to heark - en
| t, :— :d | ^{f}d' :— :f | ^{s}d :r :m .f | s :— :f .s | d :r :r |
| s, :— :l, | ^{l}m :f :r | ^{d}f, :r, :l, | s, :— :s, | l, :r, :s, |

506 *(continued)*

```
                                              mp
l,  :—  :l,  | l,  :—  :    |     :    :s,  | d   :—  :d    | d   :—  :r .m
m,  :r, :f,  | f,  :m, :    |     :    :s,  | s,  :l, :f,   | s,  :—  :l,.s,
to      my   | need,        |          The  | wis  -   dom   | of      my
l,  :—  :r   | r   :d  :    |     :    :s,  | s,  :—  :s,   | s,  :d  :l,.ta,
s,  :f, :r,  | l,  :—  :    |     :    :s,  | m,  :f, :r,   | m,  :—  :f,.s,

r   :—  :de  | r   :—  :m   | l,  :—  :l,   | s,  :t, :r    | d   :—  :d
f,  :l, :l,  | l,  :—  :s,  | f,  :—  :f,   | f,  :—  :f,   | m,  :l, :ba,
God     to   | teach,   His | hand     to   | guide,   His  | shield   to
l,  :f  :m   | r   :d  :t,  | d   :r  :r    | r   :—  :t,   | d   :—  :d
l,  :—  :s,  | f,  :—  :s,  | l,  :r  :d    | t,  :s, :se,  | l,  :—  :l,

t,  :—  :m   | l,  :— .t, :d .l, | s,  :m,  :d,  | d   :—  :s,
se, :—  :m,  | m,  :—     :m,    | r,  :d,  :d,  | m,  :—  :d,
ward,   The  | word        of    | God       to  | give     me
m   :—  :r   | d   :— .r  :m .d  | r   :m   :s,  | d   :—  :d
m,  :—  :se, | l,  :—     :l,    | t,  :d   :m,  | l,  :—  :m,

                                   >
l,  :t, :d .r | m  :—  :r .m  | d   :l,  :t,  | l,  :—  :l,  | l,  :—
f,  :—  :d    | d  :t, :l,.t, | m,  :f,  :r,  | f,  :m, :r,  | m,  :—
speech,  His  | heaven - ly   | host      to  | be      my   | guard.
d   :r  :m .f | s  :—  :f .s  | d   :r   :t,  | r   :d  :t,  | d   :—
f,  :r, :l,   | s, :—  :s,    | l,  :f,  :s,  | l,  :—  :f,  | l,  :—
```

CLONMACNOISE. (88. 88. D. Trochaic.) Mode I, transposed. Ancient Irish Melody.
Lah = E. *Unison.* Arranged by RICHARD RUNCIMAN TERRY, 1865–

:^{de}m_1.s_1 | l_1 :l_1 :s_1 .l_1 | d :r :s .fe | m :d :t_1 .t_1

5. Christ be with me, Christ with-in me, Christ be - hind me, Christ be -

| l_1 :s_1 :m_1 .s_1 | l_1 :l_1 :s_1 .l_1 | d :r :s .fe

- fore me, Christ be - side me, Christ to win me, Christ to

| m :d :t_1 .t_1 | l_1 :l_1 :m .m | s :m :r .m

com - fort and re - store me, Christ be - neath me, Christ a -

| s :l :l .l | s :d :r .d | l_1 :s_1 :m_1 .s_1

- bove me, Christ in qui - et, Christ in dan - ger, Christ in

| l_1 :l_1 :s_1 .l_1 | d :r :s .fe | m :d :t_1 .t_1 | l_1 :l_1 ‖

hearts of all that love me, Christ in mouth of friend and stran - ger.

A little slower.
s.d.f.B♭.

f
:^{s}m_1 | l_1 :— :l_1 | s_1 :m_1 :s_1 | d :m :r .d

6. I bind un - to my - self the

| d :t_1 :t_1 | r :t_1 :s_1 | s_1 :t_1 :r | d :— :d

Name, The strong Name of the Tri - ni -

506 *(continued)*

| t_1 :— :m | l_1 :-.t_1 :d.l_1 | s_1 :m_1 :d_1 | d :— :s_1 |
-ty; By in - vo - ca - tion of the

| l_1 :t_1 :d.r *ff* | m :— :r.m | d :l_1 :t_1 | l_1 :— :l_1 |
same, The Three in One, and One in

| l_1 :— :— | — : :s_1 | d :— :d | d :— :r.m |
Three, Of whom all na - ture

| r :— :de | r :r :m | l_1 :— :l_1 | s_1 :t_1 :r |
hath cre - a - tion, E - ter - nal Fa - ther,

| d :— :d | t_1 :— :m_1 | l_1 :-.t_1 :d.l_1 | s_1 :m_1 :d_1 |
Spi - rit, Word. Praise to the Lord of

| d :— :s_1 | l_1 :t_1 :d.r | m :— :r.m | d :l_1 :t_1 |
my sal - va - tion: Sal - va - tion is of

| l_1 :— :l_1 | l_1 :— :— | — :— : | : : |
Christ the Lord.

rall
| l_1 :— :— | — :— :— | l_1 :— :— ||
A - - - - - - - - men.

St. Patrick, 372–466; version by Cecil Frances Alexander, 1823–95.

507

LANCASTER. (C.M.)

Doh = A. *In moderate time.* SAMUEL HOWARD, 1710–82.

:s_1 |d :r |m :d |f :m |r :r |m :d |t_1 :l_1 |s_1 :— |—
:m_1 |s_1 :s_1 |s_1 :l_1 |l_1 :s_1 |s_1 :s_1 |s_1 :s_1 |s_1 :fe_1 |s_1 :— |—
:d |d :t_1 |d :d |l_1.t_1 :d |t_1 :r |d :s_1 |r :r.d |t_1 :— |—
:d_1 |m_1 :s_1 |d :l_1 |r_1 :m_1.f_1 |s_1 :t_2 |d_1 :m_1 |r_1 :r_1 |s_1 :— |—

:s_1 |l_1 :t_1 |d :t_1 |d :r |m :m |s :f |m :r |d :— |— ‖ d |d
:s_1 |s_1 :f_1 |m_1 :s_1 |d :t_1 |d :d |s_1 :l_1 |s_1 :s_1.f_1 |m_1 :— |— ‖ f_1 |m_1
:d |d :r |d :r |s :f |m :d |d :d |d :t_1 |d :— |— ‖ l_1 |s_1
:m_1 |f_1 :r_1 |l_1 :s_1.f_1 |m_1 :r_1 |d_1 :l_1 |m_1 :f_1 |s_1 :s_1 |d_1 :— |— ‖ f_1 |d_1

A-men.

JACKSON. (C.M.)

Doh = D. *In moderate time.* THOMAS JACKSON, 1715–81.

:s |s :d^1.t |l :s |f :s.f |m :m |s :d^1 |t :l |s :— |—
:d |d :d |d :d |d :t_1 |d :d |r :m |r :-.d |t_1 :— |—
:m |s :m |f :s |l :s |s :d^1 |t :l.s |s :fe |s :— |—
:d |m :d |f :m |r :s_1 |d :l_1 |t_1 :d |r :r |s_1 :— |—

:s |m :m |f :s |l :r^1.d^1 |t :d^1 |s :l.f |m :r |d :— |— ‖ d |d
:r |d :d |d :d |d :f.m |r :m |d :d |d :t_1 |d :— |— ‖ l_1 |s_1
:s |s :s |f :m |f :l |t :s |d^1 :l |s :s.f |m :— |— ‖ f |m
:t_1 |d :ta_1 |l_1 :d |f :r |s :d |m :f |s :s_1 |d :— |— ‖ f_1 |d

A-men.

From 2 Tim. i. 12.

I'M not ashamed to own my Lord,
Or to defend His cause,
Maintain the glory of His Cross,
And honour all His laws.

2 Jesus, my Lord! I know His Name,
His Name is all my boast;
Nor will He put my soul to shame,
Nor let my hope be lost.

3 I know that safe with Him remains,
Protected by His power,
What I've committed to His trust,
Till the decisive hour.

4 Then will He own His servant's name
Before His Father's face,
And in the New Jerusalem
Appoint my soul a place.

ISAAC WATTS, 1674–1748, as in *Scottish Paraphrases*, 1781.

508

WOLVERCOTE. (76. 76. D.)

Doh = A. *Unison.* *In moderate time.* William Harold Ferguson, 1874–

{ :s, | d :f | m :r.m | d :l, | s, :m,.f, | s, :m | r.d:r | d :— | — ‖

{ :s, | d :f | m :r.m | d :l, | s, :m,.fe, | s, :l, | t,.d:l, | s, :— | — ‖

s.d.f.C.
{ :ˢm | d' :t | l :m.f | s :-.l | s :m.r | d :d' | t :t }

A.t.m.l.
{ | ᵗr :— | — ‖ s, | d :f | m :r.m | d :l, | s, :m,.f, }

{ | s, :m | r.d:r | d :— | — :— ‖ f :— | d :r | m :— | — :— ‖

A - - - men.

DAY OF REST. (76. 76. D.)

Doh = F. *In moderate time.* James William Elliott, 1833–1915.

:d | m :s | l :s.fe | s :— | m :r | d :r.m | f :l | r :— | — ‖
:d | d :m | re :re | m :— | d :t, | d :d | d :d | t, :— | — ‖
:m | s :s | fe :s.l | s :— | s :f | m :r.d | l :f | r :— | — ‖
:d | d :d | d :d | d :— | d :s, | l, :l, | r, :r, | s, :— | — ‖

C.t. f.F.

:r | m :ᵐl | t :l.s | d' :— | m :f | s :d' | r' :-.m' | ᵈ's :— | — ‖
:t, | d :ᵈf | s :r | d :— | d :d | d :m | f :-.s | ᵐt, :— | — ‖
:s | s :ˢd' | r' :d'.t | d' :s | s :f | m :s | l :t | ᵈs :— | — ‖
:s, | d :ᵈf | f :f | m :— | l, :l, | s, :s, | s, :s | ᵈs, :— | — ‖

:s |f :m |r :f |m :r |d :s |f :m |r :de |r :— |— ||
:s, |s, :s, |s, :s, |s, :t, |d :de |r :ta, |l, :l, |l, :— |— ||
:m |r :d |t, :d.r |m :f |s :s |l :s |f :m |f :— |— ||
:s, |s, :s, |s, :l,.t, |d :r |m :m, |f, :s, |l, :l, |r, :— |— ||

:r.m |f :d |t, :d |r :-.m |r :m |f :s.l |m :r |d :— |— ||d |d ||
:r.m |f :d |t, :d |r :-.m |r :d |d :d |d :t, |d :— |— ||l, |s, ||
:r.m |f :d |t, :d |r :-.m |r :s |f :m.r |s :f |m :— |— ||f |m ||
:r.m |f :d |t, :d |r :-.m |r :d |l, :s,.f, |s, :s, |d :— |— ||f, |d, ||

A-men.

[*By permission of Novello & Co., Ltd.*]

O JESUS, I have promised
To serve Thee to the end;
Be Thou for ever near me,
My Master and my Friend:
I shall not fear the battle
If Thou art by my side,
Nor wander from the pathway
If Thou wilt be my Guide.

2 O let me feel Thee near me:
The world is ever near;
I see the sights that dazzle,
The tempting sounds I hear;
My foes are ever near me,
Around me and within;
But, Jesus, draw Thou nearer,
And shield my soul from sin.

3 O let me hear Thee speaking
In accents clear and still,
Above the storms of passion,
The murmurs of self-will;
O speak to reassure me,
To hasten or control;
O speak, and make me listen,
Thou Guardian of my soul.

4 O Jesus, Thou hast promised,
To all who follow Thee,
That where Thou art in glory
There shall Thy servant be;
And, Jesus, I have promised
To serve Thee to the end;
O give me grace to follow,
My Master and my Friend.

John Ernest Bode, 1816–74.

509

HEATHLANDS. (77. 77. 77.)

Doh = E♭. *In moderate time.* HENRY SMART, 1813–79.

s :d' |t :s |l :l |s :— |f :r |m :f |s :f.m |r :—
d :m |r :m.r |d :d |d :— |d :r |d :d |d :r.d |t, :—
s :s |s :d'.t |l :f |m :— |l :s |s :f |m :l |r :—
m :d |s :m |f :l, |d :— |l, :t, |d :l, |m, :f, |s, :—

B♭.t. f.E♭.

s :s |m :ˢd |f :m |r :— |s :r |m :r.d |r :t, |ᵈs :—
r :t, |m :ʳs, |f, :s, |s, :— |s, :s, |s, :l, |l, :s, |ˢr :—
r :s |s :ʳs, |l,.t, :d |t, :— |r :t, |d :f.m |f :r |ᵐt :—
t, :s, |d :ᵗm, |r, :m,.f, |s, :— |t, :s, |d :l, |f, :s, |ᵈs, :—

s :s |l :l |t :t |d' :— |l :s |f :m |r :r |d :— || d |d
m :t, |d :d |f :m.r |d :— |d :d |d :d |d :t, |d :— || l, |s,
t :s |m :l.s |f :s.f |m :— |f :s |d :d.m |l :s.f |m :— || f |m
m :m |d :f.m |r :s, |l, :— |f, :m, |l, :s, |f, :s, |d :— || f, |d

A-men.

JESUS, Master, whose I am,
Purchased, Thine alone to be,
By Thy blood, O spotless Lamb,
Shed so willingly for me,
Let my heart be all Thine own,
Let me live to Thee alone.

2 Jesus, Master, I am Thine:
Keep me faithful, keep me near;
Let Thy presence in me shine,
All my homeward way to cheer.
Jesus, at Thy feet I fall,
O be Thou my All in All.

3 Jesus, Master, whom I serve,
Though so feebly and so ill,
Strengthen hand and heart and nerve
All Thy bidding to fulfil;
Open Thou mine eyes to see
All the work Thou hast for me.

4 Jesus, Master, wilt Thou use
One who owes Thee more than all?
As Thou wilt! I would not choose;
Only let me hear Thy call.
Jesus, let me always be
In Thy service glad and free.

FRANCES RIDLEY HAVERGAL, 1836–79.

510 FARLEY CASTLE. (10 10. 10 10.)

Doh = D. *In moderate time.* HENRY LAWES, 1596–1662.

d :— |m :f |s :m |f :s |l :t |d' :— || d' :— |t :l
s, :— |d :d |r :d |d :d |f :f |m :— || m :— |m :d
m :— |s :l |t :s |l :s |f :f |s :— || d' :— |s :l
d :— |d :l, |s, :d |f :m |r :r |d :— || l :— |m :f

d' :s |l :m |s :fe |s :— || s :— |m :l |s :f |m :f
m :d |d :d |r :r.d |t, :— || r :— |d :d |d :r |s, :d
s :d' |f :s |t :l |s :— || s :— |s :f |s :l.t |d' :d'
d :m |f :d |t, :r |s, :— || t, :— |d :f |m :r |d :l,

s :d |r :— || r :— |s :m |f :l |s :d' |d' :t |d' :— || d' |d' ||
d :d |t, :— || t, :— |r :d |d :t, |d :m |s :s |m :— || f |m ||
s :fe |s :— || s :— |s :s |l :f |s :l |r' :r' |d' :— || l |s ||
m, :l, |s, :— || s, :— |t, :d |f :r |m :l |s :s |d :— || f |d ||

A-men.

TEACH me, O Lord, to follow Him who trod
With loving zeal the pathway to His God;
Help me to rest my faith on Him alone
Who died for my transgression to atone.

2 Wean my rebellious heart from earthly things,
Show me the Fount whence living water springs;
Teach me to feel that, when afflictions come,
They're sent in love, to turn my thoughts to home.

3 So may I live, that in my daily race
The things of God may hold the highest place;
So may I die, that death to me may be
The opening dawn of immortality.

N. LAMBERT.

[May be sung to ST. AGNES, No. 323.]

511 SANDYS. (S.M.)

Doh = D. *In moderate time.* English Traditional Carol Melody.

```
:s |s  :d' |t   :s.l |t  :— |— :r' |d' :t  |d'.t:l |s  :— |—
:m |m  :d  |r   :m   |r  :— |— :r  |fe :s  |m   :fe |s  :— |—
:s |s  :s  |s   :s   |s  :— |— :s  |d' :r' |l   :l  |t  :— |—
:d |d  :m  |s   :d   |s, :— |— :t, |l, :s, |l,  :r  |s, :— |—
```

```
:s |s  :d  |l.t:d' |s  :-.l |s  :f  |m :d'  |m :r   |d :— |— ||d  |d
:r |d  :d  |d  :d  |r  :d   |r  :t, |d :d   |d :t,  |d :— |— ||l, |s,
:t |d' :s  |l  :s  |s  :d'  |s  :s  |s :s   |s :-.f |m :— |— ||f  |m
:f |m  :m  |f  :m  |t, :l,  |t, :s, |d :m.f |s :s,  |d :— |— ||f, |d
```

A-men.

TEACH me, my God and King,
In all things Thee to see;
And what I do in anything,
To do it as for Thee!

2 A man that looks on glass,
On it may stay his eye;
Or if he pleaseth, through it pass,
And then the heaven espy.

3 All may of Thee partake;
Nothing can be so mean,
Which with this tincture, 'for Thy sake',
Will not grow bright and clean.

4 A servant with this clause
Makes drudgery divine:
Who sweeps a room, as for Thy laws,
Makes that and the action fine.

5 This is the famous stone
That turneth all to gold;
For that which God doth touch and own
Cannot for less be told.

GEORGE HERBERT, 1593–1632.

512 CULFORD. (77.77. D.)

Doh = C. *In moderate time.* EDWARD JOHN HOPKINS, 1818–1901.

```
m :m |s  :s  |d' :d' |s  :— |l :l |s  :l  |f :-.m |m :—
d :d |t, :t, |d  :d  |d  :— |d :r |m  :d  |d :t,   |d :—
s :s |f  :f  |m  :m  |d' :— |l :t |d' :l  |l :s    |s :—
d :d |s, :s, |l, :l, |m  :— |f :f |m  :l, |r :s,   |d :—
```

```
                        G.t.                                f.C.
m :m |s  :s  |d' :d' |^l r  :— |t, :r  |s  :m  |r  :-.d |^d s   :—
d :d |t, :t, |d  :d  |^m l, :— |s, :s, |s, :s, |s, :f,  |^m t,  :—
s :s |f  :f  |m  :m  |^l r  :— |r  :t, |d  :d  |d  :t,  |^d s   :—
d :d |s, :s, |l, :l, |^d f, :— |s, :f, |m, :d, |s, :s,  |^d, s, :—
```

```
s  :l   |t  :r'  |d' :s   |l  :—  |l  :t   |d' :m'  |r' :l    |t  :—  ||
r  :r   |s  :s   |s  :m   |f  :—  |m  :m   |m  :l   |l  :f    |s  :—  ||
t  :d'  |r' :t   |d' :d'  |d' :—  |d' :r'  |d' :de' |r' :r'   |r' :—  ||
s  :s   |s  :f   |m  :d   |f  :—  |l  :l   |l  :s   |f  :r    |s  :—  ||
```

```
d' :-.d' |t  :m  |l  :l  |s   :—  |l  :t  |d' :m' |r' :-.d' |d' :— || d' | d' ||
s  :s    |m  :m  |m  :m  |m   :—  |f  :f  |m  :m  |l  :f    |m  :— || f  | m  ||
d' :s    |se :se |l  :l  |d'  :—  |d' :r' |d' :d' |d' :t    |d' :— || l  | s  ||
m  :m    |r  :r  |d  :d  |ta, :—  |l, :l, |l  :s  |f  :s    |d  :— || f  | d  ||
```

A-men.

PATMOS. (77. 77.)

Doh = D. *In moderate time.* WILLIAM HENRY HAVERGAL, 1793–1870.

```
d  :r   |m  :l  |s  :f   |m  :—  |m  :f  |s  :d'  |t  :l    |s  :—  ||
d  :t,  |d  :d  |d  :t,  |d  :—  |d  :r  |r  :m   |r  :-.d  |t, :—  ||
m  :s   |s  :l  |m  :f   |s  :—  |l  :l  |s  :s   |s  :fe   |s  :—  ||
d  :s,  |d  :f  |m  :r   |d  :—  |l, :r  |t, :d   |r  :r    |s, :—  ||
```

```
s  :t  |d' :m  |m  :r   |m  :—  |f  :s   |l.t :d'  |m  :r    |d  :— || f  | m ||
m  :r  |d  :d  |s, :l,  |t, :—  |r  :m   |f   :d   |d  :t,   |d  :— || d  | d ||
s  :f  |s  :l  |t  :l   |se :—  |l  :d'  |d'  :s.l |s  :-.f  |m  :— || l  | s ||
d  :r  |m  :l  |s  :f   |m  :—  |r  :d   |f   :m.f |s  :s,   |d  :— || f, | d ||
```

A-men.

TAKE my life, and let it be
Consecrated, Lord, to Thee.
Take my moments and my days;
Let them flow in ceaseless praise.

2 Take my hands, and let them move
At the impulse of Thy love.
Take my feet, and let them be
Swift and beautiful for Thee.

3 Take my voice, and let me sing
Always, only, for my King.
Take my lips, and let them be
Filled with messages from Thee.

4 Take my silver and my gold;
Not a mite would I withhold.
Take my intellect, and use
Every power as Thou shalt choose.

5 Take my will, and make it Thine;
It shall be no longer mine.
Take my heart—it is Thine own;
It shall be Thy royal throne.

6 Take my love; my Lord, I pour
At Thy feet its treasure-store.
Take myself, and I will be
Ever, only, all for Thee.

FRANCES RIDLEY HAVERGAL, 1836–79.

513

WETHERBY. (C.M.)

Doh = D. *In moderate time.* SAMUEL SEBASTIAN WESLEY, 1810–76.

```
:m | s  :—  :m.r | d  :—  :s  | l  :—  :l   | s  :—  :s
:d | m  :—  :t,  | d  :—  :d  | d  :—  :d   | d  :—  :r
:s | s  :—  :s.f | m  :—  :d  | d  :f  :d.r | m  :—  :s
:d | d  :—  :s,  | l, :—  :m, | f, :l, :f,  | d  :—  :t,

| d' :—  :t  | t.l :s :fe | s  :— || s  | t :— :r' | d' :— :s
| d  :—  :r  | m   :r :r  | t, :— || r  | r :— :t, | d  :— :m
| m  :fe :s  | d'  :t :l  | s  :— || t  | t :— :s  | s  :— :t
| l, :—  :t, | d   :r :r  | s, :— || s, | s :— :f  | m  :— :m

| s  :f :m  | f :— :l  | s :— :d | r :m :r    | d :— || d  | d
| m  :r :de | r :— :f  | m :— :d | d :— :t,   | d :— || l, | s,
| l  :— :l  | l :— :r  | m :— :s | l :s :s.f  | m :— || f  | m
| l, :— :l, | r :— :t, | d :— :m | f :s :s,   | d :— || f, | d
                                                        A-men.
```

O LORD and Master of us all,
Whate'er our name or sign,
We own Thy sway, we hear Thy call,
We test our lives by Thine.

2 Thou judgest us: Thy purity
Doth all our lusts condemn;
The love that draws us nearer Thee
Is hot with wrath to them.

3 Our thoughts lie open to Thy sight;
And naked to Thy glance
Our secret sins are, in the light
Of Thy pure countenance.

4 Yet, weak and blinded though we be,
Thou dost our service own;
We bring our varying gifts to Thee,
And Thou rejectest none.

5 Apart from Thee all gain is loss,
All labour vainly done;
The solemn shadow of Thy Cross
Is better than the sun.

6 Our Friend, our Brother, and our Lord,
What may Thy service be?
Nor name, nor form, nor ritual word,
But simply following Thee.

7 We faintly hear; we dimly see;
In differing phrase we pray;
But, dim or clear, we own in Thee
The Light, the Truth, the Way.

JOHN GREENLEAF WHITTIER, 1807–92.

514

ST. LEONARD. (88. 84.)

HERBERT STEPHEN IRONS, 1834–1905.

Doh = E♭. *In moderate time.*

:s |m :r |d :l |f :m |r :s |l :d' |t :l |s :fe |s ||
:d |d :t_1 |l_1 :d |t_1 :d |t_1 :r |m :r |r :d |t_1 :d |t_1 ||
:m |s :f |m :f |f :s |s :s |s :fe |s :m |r :l |s ||
:d |d :s_1 |l_1 :f_1 |r :d |s_1 :t_1 |d :r |s_1 :d |r :r |s ||

:s |d' :t |l :m |l :s |f :m |r :— |m :— |d :— |— || f |m ||
:t_1 |d :r |d :d |d :de |r :d |d :— |t_1 :— |d :— |— || d |d ||
:s |s :se |l :l |l :l |l :s |l :— |s :f |m :— |— || l |s ||
:f |m :m |l_1 :l_1 |f_1 :m_1 |r_1 :m_1 |f_1 :— |s_1 :— |d :— |— || f_1 |d ||

A-men.

THROUGH good report and evil, Lord,
Still guided by Thy faithful word—
Our staff, our buckler, and our sword,—
We follow Thee.

2 In silence of the lonely night,
In fullest glow of day's clear light,
Through life's strange windings, dark or bright,
We follow Thee.

3 Strengthened by Thee we forward go,
'Mid smile or scoff of friend or foe;
Through pain or ease, through joy or woe,
We follow Thee.

4 Great Master, point Thou out the way,
Nor suffer Thou our steps to stray;
Then, in the path that leads to day,
We follow Thee.

5 Thou hast passed on before our face;
Thy footsteps on the way we trace;
O keep us, aid us by Thy grace;
We follow Thee.

HORATIUS BONAR, 1808–89.

515

BUDE. (C.M.)

Doh = G. *In moderate time.* SAMUEL SEBASTIAN WESLEY, 1810–76.

```
:d  | m  :—  :r  | d  :—  :d  | f  :—  :m  | m  :r  :s,
:d  | d  :—  :t, | d  :—  :d  | d  :r  :d  | d  :t, :s,
:m  | s  :—  :f  | m  :—  :m  | l  :s  :s  | s  :—  :t,
:d  | d  :—  :s, | l, :—  :l, | l, :t, :d  | s, :—  :f,

| d  :r  :f  | m  :—  :r  | d  :—  || l  | s  :—  :f  | m  :—  :d
| s, :l, :f, | s, :—  :f, | m, :—  || l, | r  :—  :t, | d  :—  :l,
| d  :—  :d  | d  :—  :t, | d  :—  || m  | s  :—  :s  | s  :—  :m
| m, :f, :l, | s, :—  :s, | d, :—  || d  | t, :—  :s, | d  :—  :d,

| d  :t, :l,  | s, :—  :s, | d  :—  :d  | f  :m  :r  | d  :—  || d  | d
| l, :s, :fe, | s, :—  :r, | s, :—  :m, | l, :s, :s, | s, :—  || l, | s,
| r  :—  :d   | t, :—  :t, | d  :—  :d  | d  :—  :f  | m  :—  || f  | m
| r, :—  :r,  | s, :—  :f, | m, :—  :l, | f, :s, {:t, / :s,} | {d / d,} :— || f, | d,
                                                                     A-men.
```

THOUGH lowly here our lot may be,
High work have we to do—
In faith and trust to follow Him
Whose lot was lowly too.

2 Our days of darkness we may bear,
Strong in our Father's love;
We lean on His almighty arm,
And fix our hopes above.

3 Our lives enriched with gentle thoughts
And loving deeds may be,
As streams that still the nobler grow,
The nearer to the sea.

4 To duty firm, to conscience true,
However tried and pressed,
In God's clear sight high work we do,
If we but do our best.

5 Thus may we make the lowliest lot
With rays of glory bright;
Thus may we turn a crown of thorns
Into a crown of light.

WILLIAM GASKELL, 1805–84.

516 ALSTONE. (L.M.)

Doh = C. *Unison.* *In moderate time.* CHRISTOPHER EDWIN WILLING, 1830–1904.

{ :s | s :- .l | s :d' | m :r | d :r | m :- .f | s :l }

{ | s :m | r (fermata) || s | s :- .l | s :d' | m' :r' | d' :l }

{ | s :- .l | t :d' | m :r | d (fermata) || f d l f, | m d s d || A-men.

WE are but little children weak,
Nor born in any high estate ;
What can we do for Jesus' sake,
Who is so high and good and great ?

2 O, day by day, each Christian child
Has much to do, without, within,—
A life to live for Jesus' sake,
A constant war to wage with sin.

3 When deep within our swelling hearts
The thoughts of pride and anger rise,
When bitter words are on our tongues
And tears of passion in our eyes,

4 Then we may stay the angry blow,
Then we may check the hasty word.
Give gentle answers back again,
And fight a battle for our Lord.

5 With smiles of peace and looks of love
Light in our dwellings we may make,
Bid kind good-humour brighten there,
And still do all for Jesus' sake.

6 There 's not a child so small and weak
But has his little cross to take,
His little work of love and praise
That he may do for Jesus' sake.

CECIL FRANCES ALEXANDER, 1823–95.

517

PENTECOST. (L.M.)

Doh = G. *In moderate time.* WILLIAM BOYD, 1847–

```
m  :m  :m  | m  :—  :m  | r  :—  :d  | f  :—  :—  | m  :m  :m
s, :s, :s, | s, :—  :d  | t, :—  :d  | t, :—  :—  | s, :s, :d
d  :d  :d  | d  :m  :s  | s  :—  :s  | s  :—  :—  | d  :m  :s
d  :d  :d  | d  :—  :d  | f  :—  :m  | r  :—  :—  | d  :d  :d

m  :— :r  | r  :— :d   | r  :— :— || m  :m  :m   | m  :— :m  | r  :— :m
l, :— :l, | l, :— :fe, | s, :— :— || s, :s, :se, | l, :— :l, | l, :— :l,
s  :— :f  | r  :— :r   | t, :— :— || m  :m  :r   | d  :— :de | r  :— :de
f, :— :f, | fe,:— :l,  | s, :— :— || d  :d  :t,  | l, :— :s, | f, :— :m,

f  :— :— | r  :r  :r  | m  :— :d  | d  :— :t, | d  :— :— || d  | d
l, :— :— | s, :s, :s, | s, :— :l, | s, :— :f, | m, :— :— || f, | m,
r  :— :— | t, :t, :t, | d  :s  :f | f  :m  :r | d  :— :— || l, | s,
r, :— :— | s, :s, :s, | m, :— :f, | s, :— :s, | d, :— :— || f, | d,
                                                            A - men.
```

DUKE STREET. (L.M.)

Doh = E♭. *In moderate time.* JOHN HATTON, ? –1793.

```
d  :m .f  | s  :l .t  | d' :t .l  | s  :— | s  :s .s  | l  :s
s, :d .t, | d  :d .r  | m  :r .d  | t, :— | d  :t,.d  | d  :d .s,
m  :s .s  | s  :f     | s  :s .fe | s  :— | m  :f .s  | f  :s
d  :d .r  | m  :f .r  | d  :r     | s, :— | d  :r .m  | f  :m

f     :m    | r  :— || m  :m .r  | d .m :s .d' | l .s :f .m | r  :—
l, .t,:d    | t, :— || d  :d .t, | d    :m .d  | d    :t,.d | t, :—
r     :m .f | s  :— || s  :s .f  | m .s :d' .s | l .m :f .s | s  :—
r     :d    | s, :— || d  :d .r  | m    :d .m  | f .m :r .d | s, :—

s  :l .t  | d'     :–.f  | m  :r    | d  :— || f  | m
d  :d .f  | m      :–.r  | d  :t,   | d  :— || d  | d
s  :f .f  | s      :–.l  | s  :s .f | m  :— || l  | s
m  :f .r  | d .,r  :m .f | s  :s,   | d  :— || f, | d
                                              A-men.
```

FIGHT the good fight
With all thy might;
Christ is thy strength, and Christ thy right;
Lay hold on life, and it shall be
Thy joy and crown eternally.

2 Run the straight race
Through God's good grace,
Lift up thine eyes, and seek His face;
Life with its path before us lies;
Christ is the way, and Christ the prize.

3 Cast care aside;
And on thy Guide
Lean, and His mercy will provide,—
Lean, and the trusting soul shall prove
Christ is its life, and Christ its love.

4 Faint not, nor fear;
His arm is near;
He changeth not, and thou art dear;
Only believe, and thou shalt see
That Christ is all in all to thee.

JOHN SAMUEL BEWLEY MONSELL, 1811–75.

518 BOWDEN. (S.M.)

Doh = E♭. *Moderately slow.* Arranged by SAMUEL SEBASTIAN WESLEY, 1810–76.

```
:s |m  :f  |m  :r   |d :— |— :m |s  :d'  |t :l   |s  :— |— ||
:d |d  :d  |d  :t,  |d :— |— :d |r  :d   |r :r.d |t, :— |— ||
:m |s  :l  |s  :s.f |m :— |— :s |r  :m.l |s :fe  |s  :— |— ||
:d |d  :f, |s, :s,  |d :— |— :d |t, :l,  |r :r   |s  :— |— ||

:s |l     :s |f   :m    |l.t :d'    |t  :s    |l  :d'.f |m  :r   |d :— |— || f  |m ||
:d |l,.t, :d |r   :s,   |m   :m     |r  :m.r  |d  :d    |d  :t,  |d :— |— || d  |d ||
:m |f     :s |l.t :d'   |d'  :s.l   |t  :d'.t |l  :m.f  |s  :—.f |m :— |— || l  |s ||
:d |f     :m |r   :d.t, |l,  :m,.f, |s, :d    |f, :l,   |s, :s,  |d :— |— || f, |d ||
```

A-men.

A CHARGE to keep I have,
A God to glorify,
A never-dying soul to save,
And fit it for the sky:

2 To serve the present age,
My calling to fulfil:
O may it all my powers engage
To do my Master's will!

3 Arm me with jealous care,
As in Thy sight to live;
And O, Thy servant, Lord, prepare
A strict account to give.

4 Help me to watch and pray,
And on Thyself rely,
And let me ne'er my trust betray,
But press to realms on high.

CHARLES WESLEY, 1707–88.

519

ARMAGEDDON. (6 5. 6 5. 6 5. D.)

Doh = C. *In moderate time.*

Adapted by JOHN GOSS, 1800–80.

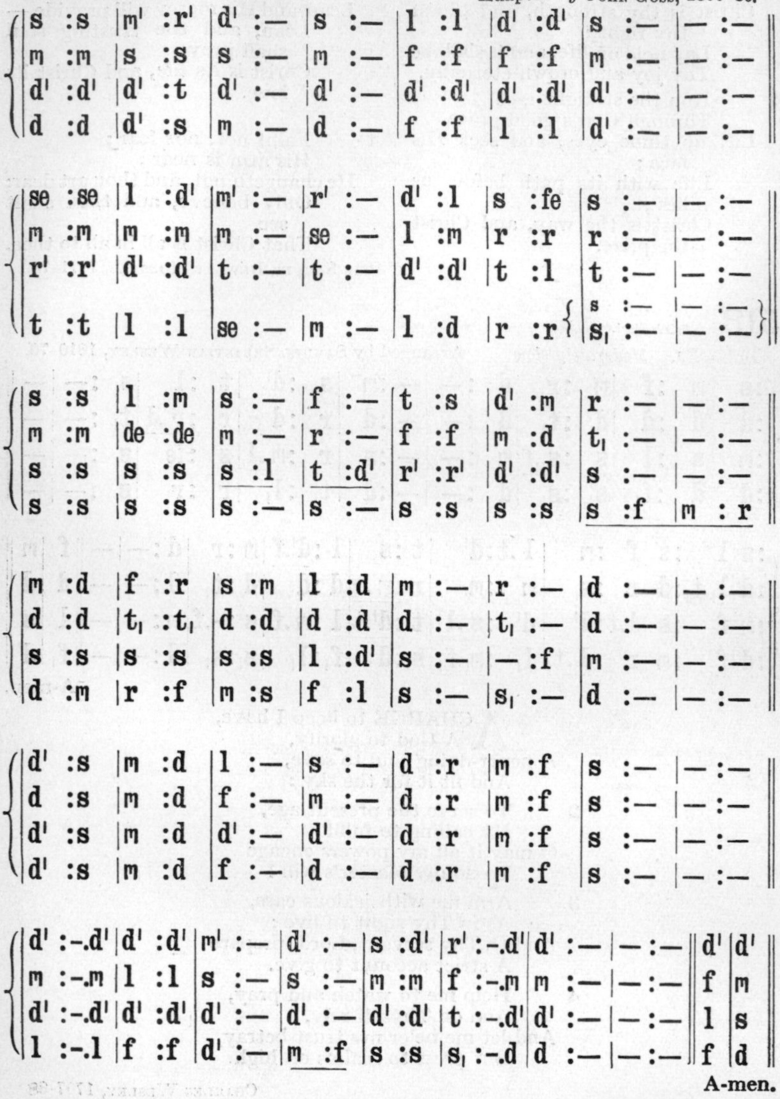

s :s |m' :r' |d' :— |s :— |l :l |d' :d' |s :— |— :— ||
m :m |s :s |s :— |m :— |f :f |f :f |m :— |— :— ||
d' :d' |d' :t |d' :— |d' :— |d' :d' |d' :d' |d' :— |— :— ||
d :d |d' :s |m :— |d :— |f :f |l :l |d' :— |— :— ||

se :se |l :d' |m' :— |r' :— |d' :l |s :fe |s :— |— :— ||
m :m |m :m |m :— |se :— |l :m |r :r |r :— |— :— ||
r' :r' |d' :d' |t :— |t :— |d' :d' |t :l |t :— |— :— ||
t :t |l :l |se :— |m :— |l :d |r :r |{ s :— |— :— / s, :— |— :— } ||

s :s |l :m |s :— |f :— |t :s |d' :m |r :— |— :— ||
m :m |de :de |m :— |r :— |f :f |m :d |t, :— |— :— ||
s :s |s :s |s :l |t :d' |r' :r' |d' :d' |s :— |— :— ||
s :s |s :s |s :— |s :— |s :s |s :s |s :f |m :r ||

m :d |f :r |s :m |l :d |m :— |r :— |d :— |— :— ||
d :d |t, :t, |d :d |d :d |d :— |t, :— |d :— |— :— ||
s :s |s :s |s :s |l :d' |s :— |— :f |m :— |— :— ||
d :m |r :f |m :s |f :l |s :— |s, :— |d :— |— :— ||

d' :s |m :d |l :— |s :— |d :r |m :f |s :— |— :— ||
d :s |m :d |f :— |m :— |d :r |m :f |s :— |— :— ||
d' :s |m :d |d' :— |d' :— |d :r |m :f |s :— |— :— ||
d' :s |m :d |f :— |d :— |d :r |m :f |s :— |— :— ||

d' :-.d' |d' :d' |m' :— |d' :— |s :d' |r' :-.d' |d' :— |— :— || d' |d' ||
m :-.m |l :l |s :— |s :— |m :m |f :-.m |m :— |— :— || f |m ||
d' :-.d' |d' :d' |d' :— |d' :— |d' :d' |t :-.d' |d' :— |— :— || l |s ||
l :-.l |f :f |d' :— |m :f |s :s |s, :-.d |d :— |— :— || f |d ||

A-men.

WHO is on the Lord's side ?
  Who will serve the King ?
Who will be His helpers
  Other lives to bring ?
Who will leave the world's side ?
  Who will face the foe ?
Who is on the Lord's side ?
  Who for Him will go ?
    By Thy call of mercy,
      By Thy grace divine,
    We are on the Lord's side ;
      Saviour, we are Thine.

2 Jesus, Thou hast bought us,
  Not with gold or gem,
But with Thine own life-blood,
  For Thy diadem.
With Thy blessing filling
  Each who comes to Thee,
Thou hast made us willing,
  Thou hast made us free.
    By Thy grand redemption,
      By Thy grace divine,
    We are on the Lord's side ;
      Saviour, we are Thine.

3 Fierce may be the conflict,
  Strong may be the foe,
But the King's own army
  None can overthrow.
Round his standard ranging,
  Victory is secure,
For His truth unchanging
  Makes the triumph sure.
    Joyfully enlisting,
      By Thy grace divine,
    We are on the Lord's side ;
      Saviour, we are Thine.

4 Chosen to be soldiers
  In an alien land,
Chosen, called, and faithful,
  For our Captain's band,
In the service royal
  Let us not grow cold ;
Let us be right loyal,
  Noble, true, and bold.
    Master, Thou wilt keep us,
      By Thy grace divine,
    Always on the Lord's side,
      Saviour, always Thine.

FRANCES RIDLEY HAVERGAL, 1836–79.

520 MARTYRS. (C.M.)

Ray = D. *Slow.* ***Unison or in Harmony.***

Scottish Psalter, 1615.

```
r  :—  |f  :r  |l  :—  |f   :—  |m  :r  |l   :— ||l   :—  |d' :l
l, :—  |r  :r  |m  :—  |l,  :t, |d  :r  |m   :— ||f   :—  |s  :f
f  :—  |l  :f  |m  :—  |f   :—  |s  :s  |d'  :— ||d'  :—  |d' :d'
r  :—  |r  :r  |d  :—  |r   :—  |d  :t, |l,  :— ||f   :—  |m  :f

t.d' :r'  |l   :— ||l  :— |d' :s  |l :f  |m :r  |l  :— ||
r.m  :f   |m   :— ||f  :— |s  :m  |d :t, |d :r  |m  :— ||
s    :l.t |de' :— ||d' :— |s  :d' |f :f  |s :s  |d' :— ||
s    :r   |l   :— ||f  :— |m  :d  |f :r  |d :t, |l, :— ||

d' :— |t  :s.l |t  :— |l  :— |r  :— |— :— ||d  |r  ||
d  :— |r  :m   |r  :— |r  :d |l, :— |— :— ||l, |l, ||
m  :— |s  :s   |s  :— |m  :— |f  :— |— :— ||m  |f  ||
l, :— |t, :d   |s, :— |l, :— |r  :— |— :— ||l, |r  ||
                                              A - men.
```

When sung in Unison ||r |r|| A-men.

WORKMAN of God ! O lose not heart,
But learn what God is like,
And, in the darkest battle-field,
Thou shalt know where to strike.

2 Thrice blest is he to whom is given
The instinct that can tell
That God is on the field when He
Is most invisible.

3 He hides Himself so wondrously,
As though there were no God ;
He is least seen when all the powers
Of ill are most abroad.

4 Ah ! God is other than we think ;
His ways are far above,
Far beyond reason's height, and reached
Only by childlike love.

LONDON NEW. (C.M.)

Scottish Psalter, 1635.

Doh = D. *Slow and dignified.*

d :—	s :m	d' :s	l :d'	t :—		s :—	d' :m	s :r	d :—	
d :—	r :d	d :d	d :m	r :—		r :—	d :d	d :t,	d :—	
m :—	s :s	l :m	f :s.l	t :—		t :—	l :l	s :—.f	m :—	
d :—	t, :d	l, :d	f :m.f	s :—		s, :—	l, :l,	m,.f, :s,	d :—	

s :—	d' :l	t :s	l :l	s :—		m :—	s :d'	m :r	d :—		f	m	
d :—	d :r	r :t,	m :r.d	t, :—		d :—	r :d	d :t,	d :—		d	d	
m :—	m :fe	fe :s	s :fe	s :—		s :—	s :m.f	s :—.f	m :—		l	s	
d :—	l, :r.d	t, :m	d :r	s, :—		d :—	t, :l,	s, :s,	d :—		f,	d	

A-men.

FAUX-BOURDON SETTING.

Martin Shaw, 1876–

Doh = D.

d' :—	t :s	l :m	f :l	s :—		:r'	s :—.l	m :r	m :—	
m :—	r :d	m :d	d :f	r :—		r :—	m :d	d :t,	s, :—	
d :—	s :m	d' :s	l :d'	t :—		s :—	d' :m	s :r	d :—	
d :—	s, :d	l, :d	f :f,	s, :—		t, :—	d :d	m,.f, :s,	d :—	

:m	m :fe	s :t	l :l	t :—		:d'	s :l	s :—.f	m :—	
d :—	d :—.r	m :s	s :fe	s :—		d :—	d :d	d :t,	d :—	
s :—	d' :l	t :s	l :l	s :—		m :—	s :d'	m :r	d :—	
d :—	l, :l	m :—.r	d :r	s, :—		l, :—	m, :f,	s, :s,	d :—	

5 Then learn to scorn the praise of men,
And learn to lose with God;
For Jesus won the world through shame,
And beckons thee His road.

6 For right is right, since God is God,
And right the day must win;
To doubt would be disloyalty,
To falter would be sin.

Frederick William Faber, 1814–63.

521

GUILD. (86. 86. D. 88.)

Doh = D. *In moderate time.* ALBERT LISTER PEACE, 1844–1912.

:s |s :d' |d' :t |t :-.l |l :l |s :s |l :s |s :— |— ||
:d |d :m |m :s |s :-.f |f :f |f :f |f :f |m :— |— ||
:m |m :s |s :d' |d' :-.d' |d' :d' |t :t |d' :t |d' :— |— ||
:d |d :d |d :d |f :-.f |f :f |s :s |s, :s, |d :— |— ||

A.t. f.D.

:s |s :^d'f |f :m |m :-.r |r :m |f :f |m :r |^d s :— |— ||
:d |d :^m l, |s, :s, |s, :-.s, |s, :s, |f, :f, |s, :f, |^m t, :— |— ||
:m |m :^s d |t, :d |d :-.t, |t, :d |l, :l, |t, :t, |^d s :— |— ||
:d |d :^d f, |r, :m,.f, |s, :-.s, |s, :m, |r, :r, |s, :s, |^d, s, :— |— ||

:s |t :t |l :s |s :-.d' |d' :s |t :t |l :s |s :— |— ||
:r |f :f |f :f |m :-.m |m :m |f :f |f :f |m :— |— ||
:t |r' :r' |d' :t |d' :-.d' |d' :d' |r' :r' |d' :t |d' :— |— ||
:s |s :s |s :s |d :-.d |d :d |s :s |s :s |d :— |— ||

:s |l :d' |t :l.l |l :s |s :d' |d' :t |l :t |d' :— |— ||
:m |f :l |s :f.f |f :m |m :m |f :f |f :f |m :— |— ||
:d' |d' :l |t :d'.d' |d' :d' |d' :s |s :s |s :s |s :— |— ||
:d |f :f |f :f.f |s :s |s :s |s :s |s, :s, |d :— |— ||

:s |s :-.m |m :s |l :-.f |f :l |s :f |m :f |m :— |r :— |d :— |— || f |m ||
:d |d :-.d |d :m |f :-.f |f :f |m :r |d :r |d :— |t, :— |d :— |— || d |d ||
:m |m :-.s |s :d' |d' :-.l |l :d' |d' :t |d' :l |s :— |— :f |m :— |— || l |s ||
:d |d :-.d |d :d |f :-.f |f :f |s :s |l :f |s :— |s, :— |d :— |— || f, |d ||

A-men.

Guild Hymn.

BELIEVING fathers oft have told
What things by God were done,
When faithful men in days of old
Their lifelong battle won ;
And now when God calls us to life,
And Satan tempts each man,
We choose our side in the mortal strife
To fight as best we can,—
Like brothers true, of one accord,
To hold one faith and serve one Lord.

2 Our King has come to claim His own,
Has paid the debt we owe,
Himself has fought the fight alone,
In straits we cannot know.
Amid the world's confusèd noise,
Where we but darkly see,
The Christ appeals, with sweet, clear voice,
'My brothers, follow Me,'—
Like brothers true, of one accord,
To hold one faith, to serve one Lord.

3 His Church our shelter, He our Guide,
Our strength His healing Cross,
We range ourselves upon His side,
Where none can suffer loss.
We're safe behind our Saviour's shield ;
He makes us heirs of heaven ;
We claim upon the embattled field
The victory Christ has given,—
Like brothers true, of one accord,
To hold one faith and serve one Lord.

4 And yet, O Christ, our Saviour King,
Unless Thou keep us Thine,
Our faith will soon dry at the spring,
Our love will shrink and pine.
So by Thy Spirit mould us, Lord ;
Inspire our hearts to pray ;
Our hungry souls feed with Thy word,
Teach all our Guild to say,
'True brothers we, of one accord,
We hold one faith, we serve one Lord.'

5 We fain would do our Master's part,
And help our fellow-men,
Would cheer some lonely brother's heart,
Some lost one bring again,
Would serve the Church abroad, at home,
With hearts from self set free,
Striving to make Thy Kingdom come.
O God, so may it be,
That, brothers true, with one accord
We hold the faith and serve the Lord !

ARCHIBALD HAMILTON CHARTERIS, 1835–1908.

522 HOPE. (L.M.)

Doh = E. *In moderate time.* HERBERT STEPHEN IRONS, 1834–1905.

```
m  :m  :m  |s  :—  :t, |d  :—  :r  |m  :—  :— |s  :l  :s  |d' :—  :m
d  :d  :d  |d  :t, :t, |t, :l, :s, |s, :—  :— |r  :r  :r  |d  :—  :d.m
s  :s  :s  |f  :—  :f  |m  :—  :s.f|m  :—  :— |r  :r  :s  |s  :f  :m.s
d  :d  :d  |s, :—  :s, |l, :—  :t, |d  :—  :— |t, :t, :t, |l, :—  :d

l  :—  :l  |r  :—  :— ||r  :m  :r  |s  :—  :m  |m  :f  :m  |l  :—
m  :r  :d  |d  :t, :— ||t, :t, :r  |r  :d  :d  |de :—  :m  |m  :r
s  :f  :m  |r  :—  :— ||s  :s  :s  |s  :—  :s  |l  :—  :l  |l  :—
f, :—  :f, |s, :—  :— ||f  :f  :f  |m  :—  :m  |s  :—  :s  |f  :—

:l |t  :d' :l  |s  :—  :m  |m  :f  :r  |d  :—  :— ||f  |m
:r |r  :d  :d  |r  :d  :d  |d  :r  :t, |d  :—  :— ||d  |d
:f |f  :m  :f  |f  :m  :s  |l  :—  :s.f|m  :—  :— ||l  |s
:r |s, :l, :l, |t, :d  :d  |l, :f, :s, |d  :—  :— ||f, |d
                                                      A-men.
```

HE liveth long who liveth well:
All other life is short and vain;
He liveth longest who can tell
Of living most for heavenly gain.

2 He liveth long who liveth well:
All else is being flung away;
He liveth longest who can tell
Of true things truly done each day.

3 Be what thou seemest; live thy creed;
Hold up to earth the torch divine:
Be what thou prayest to be made;
Let the great Master's steps be thine.

4 Fill up each hour with what will last;
Buy up the moments as they go;
The life above, when this is past,
Is the ripe fruit of life below.

5 Sow love, and taste its fruitage pure;
Sow peace, and reap its harvest bright;
Sow sunbeams on the rock and moor,
And find a harvest-home of light.

HORATIUS BONAR, 1808–89.

Also the following:

63 As with gladness men of old
87 What grace, O Lord, and beauty shone
90 Lord, as to Thy dear Cross we flee
106 When I survey the wondrous Cross
156 Ye servants of the Lord
242 Behold us, Lord, a little space
245 Dear Lord and Father of mankind
333–63 *Hymns on the Service of the Kingdom*
647 Land of our Birth, we pledge to thee
673 God, who created me

523 VIGILATE. (77. 73.)

Doh = E♭. *Moderately slow.* WILLIAM HENRY MONK, 1823–89.

```
|m  :m   |f  :m   |l  :-.l  |s  :—  |m  :-.m  |m  :m   |m  :f   |r  :—  ||
|d  :d   |d  :d   |d  :-.d  |d  :—  |d  :-.r  |d  :r   |d  :r   |t, :—  ||
|s  :s   |l  :s   |f  :-.f  |m  :—  |s  :se   |l  :t   |l  :l   |s  :—  ||
|d  :d   |d  :d   |d  :-.d  |d  :—  |d  :t,   |l, :se, |l, :f,  |s, :—  ||

|m  :-.m |f  :s   |l  :s    |d  :—  |f  :—     |—  :r   |d  :—  |—  :—  || d  | d  ||
|d  :-.d |d  :d   |d  :t,   |d  :—  |d  :t,.l, |t, :t,  |d  :—  |—  :—  || l, | s, ||
|s  :-.s |l  :m   |f  :f    |m  :—  |f  :—     |—  :f   |m  :—  |—  :—  || f  | m  ||
|d  :-.d |l, :s,  |f, :s,   |l, :—  |r  :—     |s, :s,  |d  :—  |—  :—  || f, | d  ||
                                    (r, :—)
                                                                           A-men.
```

ST. APOLLOS. (77. 73.)

Doh = A. *Brightly.* ALFRED PHILLIPS MORGAN, 1857–

```
|d  :s,   |l,    :d   |t,   :l,    |s, :—  |l, :t,  |d  :m    |r  :d   |r  :—  ||
|s, :s,   |s,.f, :m,  |s,   :f,    |m, :—  |f, :f,  |s, :s,   |l, :m,  |s, :—  ||
|m  :d    |d     :d   |d.s, :l,.t, |d  :—  |d  :r   |s, :d.t, |l, :d   |t, :—  ||
|d, :m,   |f,    :l,  |m,   :f,    |d, :—  |f, :r,  |m, :d,   |f, :l,  |s, :—  ||

|m  :r   |d  :t,  |r  :d   |l, :—     |s, :—    |l, :t,  |d  :—  |—  :—  || d  | d  ||
|s, :s,  |s, :s,  |l, :s,  |s, :f,.m, |r, :-.m, |f, :—   |m, :—  |—  :—  || f, | m, ||
|d  :t,  |d  :r.m |f  :s   |d  :—     |d  :t,   |d  :r   |s, :—  |—  :—  || l, | s, ||
|d  :s,  |m, :s,  |r, :m,  |f, :—     |s, :—    |f, :r,  |d, :—  |—  :—  || f, | d, ||
                                                                           A-men.
```

CHRISTIAN, seek not yet repose;
Hear thy guardian angel say,
'Thou art in the midst of foes:
Watch and pray.'

2 Principalities and powers,
Mustering their unseen array,
Wait for thy unguarded hours:
Watch and pray.

3 Gird thy heavenly armour on;
Wear it ever, night and day;
Ambushed lies the evil one:
Watch and pray.

4 Hear the victors who o'ercame;
Still they mark each warrior's way;
All with one sweet voice exclaim,
'Watch and pray.'

5 Hear, above all, hear thy Lord,
Him thou lovest to obey;
Hide within **thy heart** His word,
'Watch and pray.'

6 Watch, as if on that alone
Hung the issue of the day:
Pray, that help may be sent down:
Watch and pray.

CHARLOTTE ELLIOTT, 1789–1871.

524 ST. RAPHAEL. (87. 87. 47.)

Doh = A♭. *In moderate time.* EDWARD JOHN HOPKINS, 1818–1901.

```
|d   :d   |t,  :d   |l,  :-.t,|d   :s,  |l,  :t,  |d   :f   |r   :-.d  |d   :—  ||
|m,  :m,  |f,  :s,  |f,  :f,  |m,  :m,  |f,  :f,  |m,  :l,  |s,  :f,   |m,  :—  ||
|s,  :s,  |s,  :d   |d   :r   |s,  :d   |d   :r   |d   :d   |d   :t,   |d   :—  ||
|d,  :d,  |r,  :m,  |f,  :r,  |d,  :d,  |f,  :r,  |l,  :f,  |s,  :-.s, |d,  :—  ||
```

```
                                        E♭.t.                               f.A♭.
|d   :d   |t,  :d   |d   :r   |m   :t,  |(m)l     :-.l   |s   :d'  |t   :-.d' |(d)s  :—  ||
|m,  :f,  |s,  :s,  |l,  :l,  |se, :se, |(l,)r    :d     |d   :m   |r   :-.d  |(d)s, :—  ||
|d   :d   |r   :d   |d   :l,  |t,  :m   |(l,)r    :re    |m   :s   |f   :-.m  |(m)t, :—  ||
|l,  :l,  |s,  :m,  |f,  :f,  |m,  :m,  |(de,)fe, :-.fe, |s,  :s,  |s,  :-.d  |(d)s, :—  ||
```

```
|r   :d   |t,  :s,  |l,  :t,  |d   :m   |r   :—   |r   :—   |d   :—   |—  :—  ||d   |d   ||
|f,  :m,  |r,  :s,  |s,  :f,  |m,  :s,  |f,  :—   |f,  :—   |m,  :—   |—  :—  ||f,  |m,  ||
|t,  :d   |r   :m   |m   :r   |d   :de  |r   :l,  |t,  :—   |d   :—   |—  :—  ||l,  |s,  ||
|s,  :s,  |s,  :m,  |f,  :s,  |l,  :l,  |r,  :—   |s,  :—   |d,  :—   |—  :—  ||f,  |d,  ||
                                                                           A-men.
```

AD PERENNIS VITAE FONTEM. (87. 87. 47.)

Lah = D. Doh = F. **Unison.** *In free rhythm.* *Tours Breviary* (?).

```
|l,  :l,  :d   :r   :m   :l,  :r   :—   :t,  :—  ||d   :d   :r   :m
:f   :f   :m   :—   :—   :—  ||m   :f   :s   :s   :l   :s   :m   :—   :m   :—  ||
:m   :fe  :s   :d   :d   :r   :m   :—   :—   :—  ||r   :m   :m   :l,
 ://:
:r   :d   :t,  :—   :t,  :—  ||l,  :d   :r   :t,  :m   :f   :m   :—   :—   :—
```

```
|l   :—   :f   :—   :m   :—  ||
|m   :—   :—   :r.d :t,  :—  ||
|l   :—   :—   :—   :l   :se ||
|d   :—   :r   :—   :m   :—  ||
 A    -    -    -    men.
```

JESUS, Lord of Life and Glory,
  Bend from heaven Thy gracious ear;
While our waiting souls adore Thee,
  Friend of helpless sinners, hear:
    By Thy mercy,
  O deliver us, good Lord.

2 From the depth of nature's blindness,
  From the hardening power of sin,
From all malice and unkindness,
  From the pride that lurks within,
    By Thy mercy,
  O deliver us, good Lord.

3 When temptation sorely presses,
  In the day of Satan's power,
In our times of deep distresses,
  In each dark and trying hour,
    By Thy mercy,
  O deliver us, good Lord.

4 When the world around is smiling,
  In the time of wealth and ease,
Earthly joys our hearts beguiling,
  In the day of health and peace,
    By Thy mercy,
  O deliver us, good Lord.

5 In the weary hours of sickness,
  In the times of grief and pain,
When we feel our mortal weakness,
  When the creature's help is vain,
    By Thy mercy,
  O deliver us, good Lord.

6 In the solemn hour of dying,
  In the awful judgment day,
May our souls, on Thee relying,
  Find Thee still our Rock and Stay:
    By Thy mercy,
  O deliver us, good Lord.

JOHN JAMES CUMMINS, 1795–1867.

525 DUN ALUINN. (65. 65. D.)

Lah = G. Doh = B♭. *Moderately slow.* Irish Traditional Melody.

```
|m,  :l,   |l,  :t,  |d   :—    |l,  :—   |t,   :t,    |l,  :-.s, |l,  :— |— :— ||
|d,  :m,   |f,  :f,  |m,  :—    |l,  :m,  |m,   :s,    |f,  :f,   |m,  :— |— :— ||
|l,  :d    |d   :r   |d   :-.r  |m   :d   |t,   :m     |d   :t,   |d   :— |— :— ||
|l,  :-.s, |f,  :r,  |l,  :-.t, |d   :l,  |s,   :m,    |f,  :r,   |l,  :— |— :— ||

|m,  :m    |m   :d   |s,  :—    |r   :—   |d    :l,    |l,  :-.s, |l,  :— |— :— ||
|m,  :s,   |s,  :s,  |s,  :—    |l,  :—   |s,   :l,.s, |f,  :f,   |m,  :— |— :— ||
|t,  :t,   |d   :d   |t,  :r    |f   :—   |m.r  :d     |r.d :t,   |d   :— |— :— ||
|s,  :m,   |d,  :m,  |s,  :—    |r,  :—   |m,   :f,.m, |r,  :r,   |l,, :— |— :— ||

|d   :d    |t,  :l,  |t,  :-.s, |m,  :—   |l,   :t,    |d   :m    |t,  :— |— :— ||
|m,  :s,.l,|s,  :m,  |s,  :-.m, |t,, :d,  |d,   :f,    |s,  :s,   |s,  :— |— :— ||
|d   :m    |r   :d   |m   :-.t, |s,  :—   |l,   :r     |d   :d    |r   :— |— :— ||
|l,  :m,.f,|s,  :l,  |m,  :—    |—   :d,  |f,   :r,    |m,  :d,   |s,  :— |— :— ||

|d   :m    |m   :d   |r   :—    |r   :—   |d    :l,    |l,  :-.s, |l,  :— |— :— ||l,  :—   |l,  :— ||
|s,  :m,   |s,  :l,  |f,  :—    |s,  :—   |s,   :l,.s, |f,  :f,   |m,  :— |— :— ||d,  :f,   |m,  :— ||
|d   :s,   |d   :m   |r   :—    |t,  :—   |m.r  :d     |r.d :t,   |d   :— |— :— ||l,  :-.t, |de  :— ||
|m,  :d,   |d   :l,  |r,  :—    |s,  :—   |m,   :f,.m, |r,  :r,   |l,, :— |— :— ||f,  :r,   |l,, :— ||
                                                                               A      -    men.
```

ST. MARY MAGDALENE. (65. 65. D.)

Doh = F. *Moderately slow.* JOHN BACCHUS DYKES, 1823–76.

```
|d   :d   |r   :m   |f   :—   |m   :—   |m   :m   |r   :d   |t,  :—  |— :— ||
|s,  :d   |d   :d   |d   :—   |d   :—   |d   :t,  |l,  :s,  |s,  :—  |— :— ||
|m   :m   |f   :s   |l   :—   |s   :—   |s   :s   |f   :m   |r   :—  |— :— ||
|d   :d   |d   :d   |d   :—   |d   :—   |m,  :m,  |f,  :d   |s,  :—  |— :— ||
```

d :d |r :m |f :— |m :— |m :m |re :re |m :— |— :— ||
s_1 :d |d :d |d :l_1 |d :— |d :d |t_1 :t_1 |t_1 :— |— :— ||
m :m |f :s |l :f |s :— |fe :fe |fe :l |s :— |— :— ||
d :d |d :d |d :— |d :— |l_1 :l_1 |t_1 :t_1 |m :— |— :— ||

s :s |s :m |f :— |r :— |m :m |r :d |t_1 :— |— :— ||
m :r |de :de |r :d |t_1 :— |d :t_1 |l_1 :l_1 |s_1 :— |— :— ||
t :t |l :l |l :— |s :f |m :s |f :m |r :— |— :— ||
m :m |l_1 :l_1 |r :— |s_1 :— |d :d |f_1 :f_1 |s_1 :— |— :— ||

d :d |r :m |f :— |m :— |m :d |r :-.d |d :— |— :— || d |d ||
s_1 :d |t_1 :d |d :— |d :— |d :d |d :t_1 |d :— |— :— || l_1 |s_1 ||
m :s |f :m |l :— |s :— |s :m |r :f |m :— |— :— || f |m ||
d :m |r :d.t_1 |l_1 :f_1 |d :— |s_1 :s_1 |s_1 :s_1 |d :— |— :— || f_1 |d_1 ||

A-men.

IN the hour of trial,
Jesus, pray for me,
Lest by base denial
I depart from Thee;
When Thou seest me waver,
With a look recall,
Nor for fear or favour
Suffer me to fall.

2 With its witching pleasures
Would this vain world charm,
Or its sordid treasures
Spread to work me harm,—
Bring to my remembrance
Sad Gethsemane,
Or, in darker semblance,
Cross-crowned Calvary.

3 If with sore affliction
Thou in love chastise,
Pour Thy benediction
On the sacrifice;
Then, upon Thine altar
Freely offered up,
Though the flesh may falter,
Faith shall drink the cup.

4 When in dust and ashes
To the grave I sink,
While heaven's glory flashes
O'er the shelving brink,
On Thy truth relying
Through that mortal strife,
Lord, receive me, dying,
To eternal life.

JAMES MONTGOMERY, 1771–1854.

526

EIN' FESTE BURG. (8 7. 8 7. 6 6. 6 6 7.)

MARTIN LUTHER, 1483-1546.

Doh = D. *Very slow and solemn.*

:d' | d' :d' | s .l :t | d' .t :l | s

:s | s .f :m .f | s .m :f .s | m .r :d .r | t,

:m' .r' | d' :ta .l | d' :r' | s :s .fe | s

:d' .t | l :s .f | m :r | d :r | s,

D.C.

:d' | t :l | s :l .s | f .m :r | d || d | s :l | s :fe

:m | r .m :f | m .r :d | d :t, | s, || d | t,.m :r | r .m :r .d

:m .fe | s :r'.d' | t :l .t | d' :s .f | m || m .f | s .d' :t .l | t :l

:l, | t,.d :r | m :f .s | l .f :s .s, | d || d .r | m :fe | s .d :r

s :— | — :d | s :s | l :t | d' :— | — || t

t, :— | — :d | d :m | f .m :r | m :— | — || m

s :— | — :m .f | s :d' | d' :s | s :— | — || s

s, :— | — :l, | m :r .d | f :s | d :— | — || m

d' :t | l :l | s :— | — :l | l :s | l .s :f

m .fe :s | s :fe | s :— | — :r | d .r :m | m :m .r

l :r' | m' :r'.d' | t :— | — :f .s | l .t :d'.ta | l :l

l, :t, | d :r | s, :— | — :r .m | f :d | de :r

m :— | — :d' | t :l | s :l .s | f .m :r | d || d | d

de :— | — :m | r :d .f | f.m,r :m | f .l, :t, | s, || l, | s,

l :— | — :l .s | f .s :l | r'.t :d' | d' :s .f | m || f | m

l, :— | — :l, | r .m :f .r | t,.s, :d .t, | l,.f, :s, | d || f, | d

A - men.

From Psalm xlvi.

Ein' feste Burg ist unser Gott.

A SAFE stronghold our God is still,
A trusty shield and weapon;
He'll help us clear from all the ill
That hath us now o'ertaken.
The ancient prince of hell
Hath risen with purpose fell;
Strong mail of craft and power
He weareth in this hour;
On earth is not his fellow.

2 With force of arms we nothing can,
Full soon were we down-ridden;
But for us fights the proper Man,
Whom God Himself hath bidden.
Ask ye who is this same?
Christ Jesus is His Name,
The Lord Sabaoth's Son;
He, and no other one,
Shall conquer in the battle.

3 And were this world all devils o'er
And watching to devour us,
We lay it not to heart so sore;
Not they can overpower us.
And let the prince of ill
Look grim as e'er he will,
He harms us not a whit;
For why his doom is writ;
A word shall quickly slay him.

4 God's word, for all their craft and force,
One moment will not linger,
But, spite of hell, shall have its course;
'Tis written by His finger.
And, though they take our life,
Goods, honour, children, wife,
Yet is their profit small;
These things shall vanish all:
The city of God remaineth.

MARTIN LUTHER, 1483–1546; *tr.* by THOMAS CARLYLE, 1795–1881.

527 CHRISTUS DER IST MEIN LEBEN (BREMEN). (76. 76.)

Doh = E♭. *Moderately slow.* MELCHIOR VULPIUS, 1560–1616.

```
:d  |m :r  |m :f |s  :—  |m :l   |s  :f     |m   :r  |m :— |—
:s, |d :t, |d :d |t, :—  |d :d.r |m  :l,.t, |d   :t, |d :— |—
:m  |s :s  |s :f |r  :s  |s :l.t |d' :f     |s   :s  |s :— |—
:d  |d :s, |d :l,|s, :—  |d :f   |m  :r     |d.m :s  |d :— |—

:s |l  :t  |d' :t  |l :—   |s  :m |f      :m |r :r  |d :— |— || d  |d
:m |m  :r  |d  :r  |m :r.d |t, :d |l,.t,  :d |d :t, |d :— |— || l, |s,
:m |fe :s  |l  :s  |s :fe  |s  :s |f      :s |l :s  |m :— |— || f  |m
:d |d  :t, |l, :t, |d :r   |s, :d |r      :m |f :s  |d :— |— || f, |d
                                                          A-men.
```

From Psalm xxvii.

GOD is my strong salvation;
What foe have I to fear?
In darkness and temptation
My light, my help is near.

2 Though hosts encamp around me,
Firm to the fight I stand;
What terror can confound me,
With God at my right hand?

3 Place on the Lord reliance;
My soul, with courage wait;
His truth be thine affiance,
When faint and desolate.

4 His might thine heart shall strengthen,
His love thy joy increase;
Mercy thy days shall lengthen;
The Lord will give thee peace.

JAMES MONTGOMERY, 1771–1854.

528 PETERSHAM. (D.C.M.)

Doh = D. *In moderate time.* CLEMENT WILLIAM POOLE, 1828–1924.

:d |m :s |d' :l |s :-.f |m :m |r :s |l :l |s :— |— ||
:d |m :s |d' :f |r :r |m :d |r :t, |r :-.d |t, :— |— ||
:d |m :s |d' :d' |d' :t |d' :s |s :s |s :fe |s :— |— ||
:d |m :s |d' :f |s :s |d :d |t, :m |r :r |s :— |— ||

:s |s :m |d' :l |s :-.f |m :m |l :l.t |d' :t |l :— |— ||
:s |s :m |m :f.m |r :t, |d :m.r |d :f |m :-.r |d :— |— ||
:s |s :m |s :f |s :s |s :m |l :l |l :se |l :— |— ||
:s |s :m |d :r.d |t, :s, |d :m |f :r |m :m |l, :— |— ||

:s |m :-.r |d :r |m :f |s :s |l :-.s |l :l |t :— |— ||
:r |d :t, |l, :r |d :d |t, :d |t, :-.d |f :m |s :— |— ||
:r |s :f |m :s |s :f |r :s |f :-.s |d' :d' |r' :— |— ||
:t, |d :s, |l, :t, |d :l, |s, :m |r :-.m |f :l |s :— |— ||

:s |d' :-.t |l :s |s :-.f |m :m |f :f |r :r |d :— |— || f |m ||
:r |s :m |f :m |r :d.r |d :d |d :d |d :t, |d :— |— || d |d ||
:t |d' :d' |d' :d' |t :s |s :l |l :l |s :-.f |m :— |— || l |s ||
:f |m :d |f :d |s, :l,.t, |d :l |f :r |s :s, |d :— |— || f, |d ||

A-men.

YATTENDON. (D.C.M.)

CHRISTOPHER TYE, *c.* 1508–72.
Last four-bar section by HARRY ELLIS WOOLDRIDGE, 1845–1917.

Doh = F. *Moderately fast.*

:s, |d :-.r |m.f :s |s :fe |s :r |f :m |d :d |t, :— |— ||
:m, |s, :s, |d :t, |r :-.d |t,.l, :t, |l, :s, |s, :fe, |s, :— |— ||
:d |m :-.r |l :s |t :l |s :s |d :-.d |d :d |r :— |— ||
:d |d :-.t, |l, :m |r :r |s, :s, |l, :d |l, :l, |s, :— |— ||

```
:r  |m   :-.r |d    :t,.d |r.m  :f.r   |m  :m    |r.d   :d     |d  :t,
:t, |d   :-.l,|s,   :s,   |l,   :-.t,  |d  :-.t, |l,.s, :f,.m, |s, :-.f,
:s  |s   :-.f |m    :r.m  |f    :f     |s  :s    |f.m   :r.d   |r  :r
:s, |d,  :-.r,|m,.f,:s,   |f,.m,:r,    |d, :m,   |f,    :l,    |s, :s,

d  :— |— ||m |r.d :r.m |f     :f      |m.r :m.f |s.l :t
m, :— |— ||d |t,  :t,  |l,.s, :l,.t,  |d   :d   |t,  :r
d  :— |— ||s |s   :s   |f     :r      |d   :-.d |r   :-.m
d, :— |— ||d |s,  :s,  |r,.m, :f,.s,  |l,  :l,  |s,  :s,

l  :s  |s  :fe |s  :— |— ||s   |s :-.s  |f     :m
r  :r  |d  :r  |t, :— |— ||t,  |d :-.t, |l,.t, :d
fe :s  |l  :l  |s  :— |— ||s.f |m :-.m  |f     :s
r  :t, |l, :r  |s, :— |— ||s,  |d :d,   |r,    :m,

l   :-.s |f.m :r.d |t, :d  |d  :t,    |d  :— |— ||d  |d
d   :t,  |d   :l,  |s  :s, |s, :-.f,  |m, :— |— ||f, |m,
f.m :r   |d   :f.m |r  :m  |r  :r     |d  :— |— ||l, |s,
f,  :s,  |l,  :f,  |s, :d  |s, :s,    |d, :— |— ||f, |d,
                                                 A-men.
```

I FEEL the winds of God to-day;
To-day my sail I lift,
Though heavy oft with drenching spray,
And torn with many a rift;
If hope but light the water's crest,
And Christ my bark will use,
I'll seek the seas at His behest,
And brave another cruise.

2 It is the wind of God that dries
My vain regretful tears,
Until with braver thoughts shall rise
The purer, brighter years;
If cast on shores of selfish ease
Or pleasure I should be,
Lord, let me feel Thy freshening breeze,
And I'll put back to sea.

3 If ever I forget Thy love
And how that love was shown,
Lift high the blood-red flag above:
It bears Thy Name alone.
Great Pilot of my onward way,
Thou wilt not let me drift;
I feel the winds of God to-day,
To-day my sail I lift.

JESSIE ADAMS, 1863–

529 YN Y GLYN. (87. 87. D.)

Lah = C. Doh = E♭. *Moderately slow.* DAVID EVANS, 1874-

vv. 1 & 3 in *Harmony*, v. 2 in *Unison.*

|l, :l, |m :m |l :s,l,t |l :l |m :fe |s :m
|l, :l, |l, :se, |l, :r |d :d |t, :r |r :t,
|d :f |m :r |d :r |m :l |s :l |r :s
|l, :r |d :t, |l, :t, |d :l, |m :r .d |t, :s,

|d :r,d,r |m :— ||l, :l, |m :m |l :s,l,t |l :l
|d :l, |t, :— ||l, :l, |t, :t, |m :m |m :d
|m :l |se :— ||l :s .f |m .ba :se |l :t |d' :l
|l, :f, |m, :— ||l, :l, |se, :m .r |d :m |l :l,

|m :fe |s :d |m :r .t, |l, :— ||m :d .m |s :s |m :s
|d :r |r :d |l, :t,.se, |l, :— ||s, :s,.l, |t, :r |t, :m .r
|s :d' |t :l |m :f .m |d :— ||d :m .d |r :s |s :m
|d :l, |s, :l, |d :r .m |l, :— ||d :d .l, |s, :t, |m .r :d .t,

B♭.t.

|l :l |ᵐl, :f |m :d |r :t, |l, :— ||d :l, |f :m
|d :d |ᵐl, :l,.se, |l, :l, |l,.t, :se, |l, :— ||s, :f, |l, :l,.s,
|m :l |ᵈ'f :r |m :m |f :m .r |d :— ||d :d |r :de
|l, :l, |ˡr :t, |d :l, |r, :m, |l, :— ||m, :f, |r, :m,

f.E♭.

r :d .r	m :t,	ᵈs :m	l :d	m :r .t,	l, :—		r	de	
f, :f,	m, :m,	ᵐt, :d	m :l,	l, :t,.se,	l, :—		l,	l,	
r :l,	t, :se,	ˡm :s	d' :m	m :f .m	d :—		f	m	
f, :l,	se, :m,	ˡm .r :d .t,	l, :l,	d :r .m	l, :—		r,	l,	

A-men.

[*Copyright*, 1927, *by David Evans.*]

NORMAN. (87. 87.)

Doh = B♭. *In moderate time.* *Doles' Choralbuch*, Leipsic, 1785.

s, :d	t, :d	r :d.t,	d :d	m :m	r.d :t,	l, :l,	s, :—	
m, :s,	s, :s,	l, :s,	s, :s,	s, :l,	l, :s,	s, :fe,	s, :—	
d :d	r :d	f :r	m :m	d :d	r :r	r :r.d	t, :—	
d, :m,	s,.f, :m,	r, :s,	d, :d,	d :l,	fe, :s,	r, :r,	s, :—	

d :ta,	l, :l,	r :d	d :t,	d :r	m :f	m :r	d :—		d	d	
m, :s,	f, :f,	l, :s,	s, :s,	s, :s,	s, :l,	s, :-.f,	m, :—		f,	m,	
d :d	d :d	f :m	r :r	d :t,	d :d	d :t,	d :—		l,	s,	
d, :m,	f, :f,	r, :m,.f,	s, :-.f,	m, :s,	d :f,	s, :s,	d, :—		f,	d,	

A-men.

COURAGE, brother ! do not stumble,
Though thy path be dark as night ;
There's a star to guide the humble :
'Trust in God, and do the right.'

2 Let the road be rough and dreary,
And its end far out of sight,
Foot it bravely ; strong or weary,
Trust in God, and do the right.

3 Perish policy and cunning,
Perish all that fears the light !
Whether losing, whether winning,
Trust in God, and do the right.

4 Some will hate thee, some will love thee,
Some will flatter, some will slight ;
Cease from man, and look above thee :
Trust in God, and do the right.

5 Simple rule, and safest guiding,
Inward peace, and inward might,
Star upon our path abiding,—
Trust in God, and do the right.

6 Courage, brother ! do not stumble,
Though thy path be dark as night ;
There's a star to guide the humble :
'Trust in God, and do the right.'

NORMAN MACLEOD, 1812–72.

530 ST. ANNE. (C.M.) FIRST TUNE. WILLIAM CROFT, 1678–1727.

Doh = C. *Moderately slow.* Arranged by ARTHUR SEYMOUR SULLIVAN, 1842–1900.

Unison.

:	*f* :s	m :l	s :d'	d' :t	d'	s
	1. The	Son of	God goes	forth to	war,	A

d' :s	l :fe	s :—	— .	t	d' :l	r' :t
king - ly	crown to	gain;		His	blood - red	ban - ner

d' :l	t	s	l :d'	r' :t	d' :—
streams a -	far:	Who	fol - lows	in His	train?

* *Harmony.* vv. 2, 4, and 7.

mf :s	m :l	s :d'	d' :t	d'	s
:d	d :d .r	m :m	r :r	m	m
2. Who	best can	drink His	cup of	woe,	Tri -
4. Like	Him, with	par - don	on his	tongue	In
7. A	no - ble	ar - my,	men and	boys,	The
:m	s :l .t	d' :d'	l :s	s	d'
:d	d :f	m :l	f :s	d	d

d' :s	l :fe	s :—	:t	d' :l
m :m	m :r	r :—	:r	m :d
-um - phant	o - ver	pain,	Who	pa - tient
midst of	mor - tal	pain,	He	prayed for
ma - tron	and the	maid,	A -	round the
d' :t	l :l	t :—	:s	s :l
l_1 :m	d :r	s :—	:s	d :f

r' :t	d' :l	t	s	l :d'	r' :t	d' :—
f :r	m :-.r	t_1	d	f :m	r :r	m :—
bears his	cross be -	low,	He	fol - lows	in His	train.
them that	did the	wrong:	Who	fol - lows	in his	train?
Sa - viour's	throne re -	joice,	In	robes of	light ar -	rayed;
l :s	s :l	se	s	f :s	l :s	s :—
r :s	d :f	m	m	r :d	f :s	d :—

* If so desired, the music of verse 2 may be used for the Hymn throughout.

vv. 3 and 6 Men's Voices, v. 5 Trebles only.

| :s | m :l | s :d' | d' :t | d' | s |

mf 3. The martyr first, whose eagle eye Could
p 5. A glorious band, the chosen few On
f 6. They met the tyrant's brandished steel, The

| d' :s | l :fe | s :— | | :t | d' :l |

pierce beyond the grave, Who saw his
whom the Spirit came, Twelve valiant
lion's gory mane, *ff* They bowed their

| r' :t | d' :l | t | s | l :d' | r' :t | d' :— |

Master in the sky, And called on Him to save;
saints, their hope they knew, And mocked the cross and flame;
necks the death to feel: Who follows in their train?

v. 8. *Slower.* *ff*

| :s | m :l | s :d' | d' :t | d' | s | d' :s |
| :s | m :l | s :d' | d' :t | d' | s | d' :s |

8. They climbed the steep ascent of heaven, Through peril,

| :s | m :l | s :d' | d' :t | d' | s | d' :s |
| :s | m :l | s :d' | d' :t | d' | s | d' :s |

rall. . . 𝄐 *p*

| l :fe | s :— | —. | t | d' :l | r' :t | d' :l | t |
| l :fe | s :— | —. | f | m :f | f :f | m :fe | s |

toil, and pain; O God, to us may grace be given

| l :fe | s :— | —. | r' | d' :d' | t :r' | d' :d' | t |
| l :fe | s :— | —. | s | s :s | s :s | l :r | s |

pp 𝄐

| :s | l :d' | r' :t | d' :— | d' :d' | d' :— | d' :— |
| :m | f :f | t, :r | d :— | : | f :— | m :— |

To follow in their train! Amen, Amen.

| :ta | l :la | s :f | m :— | : | l :— | s :— |
| :d | f :r | s, :s, | d :— | : | f :— | d :— |

REGINALD HEBER, 1783–1826.

530 *(continued)*

SECOND TUNE.

OLD 44TH. (D.C.M.)

Doh = A♭. *Moderately slow.* *Anglo-Genevan Psalter*, 1556.

```
:d  |d  :t,  |d  :l,  |s,  :s,  |d  :s   |f    :m   |r  :r
:s, |l, :s,  |m, :f,  |r,  :r,  |s, :m,  |f,   :s,  |l, :s,
:m  |f  :r   |d  :d   |t,  :t,  |d  :d   |l,.t,:d   |d  :t,
:d, |f, :s,  |l, :f,  |s,  :f,  |m, :d,  |r,   :m,  |f, :s,

|d  :— |— ||d  |d  :t, |d  :l, |s, :s, |d  :m  |f  :m
|m, :— |— ||s, |l, :s, |m, :f, |r, :r, |s, :s, |l, :s,
|d  :— |— ||m  |f  :r  |d  :d  |t, :t, |d  :d  |d  :d
|d, :— |— ||d, |f, :s, |l, :f, |s, :f, |m, :d, |f, :d,

|r  :r      |d  :— |— ||d  |d  :r  |m  :f  |s  :f  |m  :r
|s, :s,.f,  |m, :— |— ||m, |m, :s, |s, :l, |t, :t, |d  :l,
|d  :t,     |d  :— |— ||d  |d  :t, |d  :d  |r  :r  |d  :f
|s, :s,     |d, :— |— ||d  |l, :s, |d  :l, |s, :s, |l, :r,

|d  :l, |t, :d  |r  :— |— ||d  |s, :l, |t, :d
|s, :f, |f, :m, |s, :— |— ||s, |s, :f, |r, :m,
|m  :d  |r  :d  |t, :— |— ||m  |d  :d  |s, :s,
|m, :f, |r, :l, |s, :— |— ||d, |m, :f, |s, :m,

|r  :m  |r  :d  |t, :d  |r  :r     |d  :— |— ||d  |d  ||
|f, :s, |s, :m, |s, :s, |l, :s,.f, |m, :— |— ||f, |m, ||
|l, :d  |t, :d  |r  :d  |d  :t,    |d  :— |— ||l, |s, ||
|r, :d, |s, :l, |s, :m, |f, :s,    |d, :— |— ||f, |d, ||
```

A-men.

THE Son of God goes forth to war,
A kingly crown to gain ;
His blood-red banner streams afar :
Who follows in His train ?
Who best can drink his cup of woe,
Triumphant over pain,
Who patient bears his cross below,
He follows in His train.

2 The martyr first, whose eagle eye
Could pierce beyond the grave,
Who saw his Master in the sky,
And called on Him to save ;
Like Him, with pardon on his tongue
In midst of mortal pain,
He prayed for them that did the wrong :
Who follows in his train ?

3 A glorious band, the chosen few
On whom the Spirit came,
Twelve valiant saints, their hope they knew,
And mocked the cross and flame ;
They met the tyrant's brandished steel,
The lion's gory mane,
They bowed their necks the death to feel :
Who follows in their train ?

4 A noble army, men and boys,
The matron and the maid,
Around the Saviour's throne rejoice,
In robes of light arrayed ;
They climbed the steep ascent of heaven,
Through peril, toil, and pain :
O God, to us may grace be given
To follow in their train.

REGINALD HEBER, 1783–1826.

531 BLACKBOURN. (C.M.)

Lah = C. Doh = E♭. *Moderately slow.* *Harrison's Sacred Harmony*, 1784.

:l |m .r :d :r |d .t, :l, :l, |l,.t, :d :r |m :— ||
:d |l,.se, :l, :l, |l,.se, :l, :m, |f,.f, :m, :s, |s, :— ||
:m |m .m :m :f |m .r :d :d |d .r :d :t, |d :— ||
:l, |d .t, :l, :r, |m,.m, :l, :l, |f,.r, :l, :s, |d :— ||

:s |d .r :m :l |se.l :t :t |d'.l :m :se |l :— || l | l ||
:s, |d .t, :d :d .r |m .m :re :m |m .m :d :t, |d :— || r | de ||
:r |m .s :s :l |t .m :ba :se |l .l :l :m |m :— || f | m ||
:t, |l,.s, :d :f |m .d :t, :m |l,.d :m :m, |l, :— || r | l, ||

A-men.

NORTHUMBERLAND. (D.C.M.)

Doh = D. *With dignity.* HENRY SMART, 1813–79.

:s |s :l |s :m .f |s :d' |t :l |s :d |f :r |m :— |— ||
:d |d :d |d :d |d :m |r :r |s, :l, |d :t, |d :— |— ||
:m |m :f |m :s |s :s |s :l .t |d' :m |l :s |s :— |— ||
:d |d :f (:f,) |d :d .r |m :d |s, :f |m :l, |f, :s, |d :— |— ||

A.t.

:m |s :m |[r]s, :m |r :d |t, :r |m :f |r :r |d :— |— ||
:d |d :d |[r]s, :s, |l, :f, |s, :s, |s, :l, |r, :s,.f, |m, :— |— ||
:s |s :s |[s]d :d |l, :d |r :t, |d :d |d :t, |d :— |— ||
:d |m :d |[t,]m, :d, |f, :l, |s, :s, |d :f, |s, :s, |d, :— |— ||

f.D.

:[d]s |t :d' |r' :l .t |d' :t |l :l |m :f |s :f .m |r :— |— ||
:[s,]r |s :s |f :r |m :m .r |d :d |d :d |d :r .d |t, :— |— ||
:[m]t |r' :s |l :l |l :se |l :m |l :l |s :l |r :— |— ||
:[d]s |s .f :m |r :f |m :m |l, :l,.t, |d :l, |m, :f, |s, :— |— ||

:s | s :l | s :m.f | s :d' | t :l | s :d | f :r | d :— | — || f | m ||
:r | d :d.r | m :d | d :r | r :r | s, :l, | d :t, | d :— | — || d | d ||
:t | d' :l.t | d' :s.f | m :fe | s :l.t | d' :m | l :s.f | m :— | — || l | s ||
:s.f | m :f | d :m.r | d.t, :l, | s, :f, | m, :l, | f, :s, | d :— | — || f, | d ||

A-men.

O GOD of truth, whose living word
Upholds whate'er hath breath,
Look down on Thy creation, Lord,
Enslaved by sin and death.

2 Set up Thy standard, Lord, that we,
Who claim a heavenly birth,
May march with Thee to smite the lies
That vex Thy groaning earth.

3 Fain would we join that blest array,
And follow in the might
Of Him, the Faithful and the True,
In raiment clean and white.

4 Yet who can fight for truth and God,
Enthralled by lies and sin?
He who would wage such war on earth
Must first be true within.

5 O God of truth, for whom we long,
O Thou that hearest prayer,
Do Thine own battle in our hearts,
And slay the falsehood there.

6 So, tried in Thy refining fire,
From every lie set free,
In us Thy perfect truth shall dwell,
And we may fight for Thee.

THOMAS HUGHES, 1823–96.

532 MORNING LIGHT. (76. 76. D.)

Doh = B♭. *In moderate time.* GEORGE JAMES WEBB, 1803–87.

```
:s,  |d   :-.d  |m   :d   |d   :—  |l,  :d   |s,  :d   |r   :m   |r   :—  |—  ||
:m,  |m,  :-.m, |s,  :s,  |l,  :—  |f,  :f,  |s,  :s,  |s,  :s,  |s,  :—  |—  ||
:d   |s,  :-.s, |d   :d   |d   :—  |d   :l,  |d   :d   |t,  :d   |t,  :—  |—  ||
:d,  |d,  :-.d, |d,  :m,  |f,  :—  |f,  :f,  |m,  :m,  |r,  :d,  |s,  :—  |—  ||

:s,  |d   :-.d  |m   :d   |d   :—  |l,  :d   |s,  :d   |m   :r   |d   :—  |—  ||
:s,  |m,  :-.m, |m,  :s,  |l,  :—  |f,  :f,  |s,  :m,  |s,  :f,  |m,  :—  |—  ||
:t,  |d   :-.d  |s,  :d   |d   :—  |d   :l,  |d   :d   |d   :t,  |d   :—  |—  ||
:s,  |d,  :-.d, |d,  :m,  |f,  :—  |f,  :f,  |m,  :d,  |s,  :s,  |d,  :—  |—  ||

:s,  |r   :-.r  |d   :r   |m   :—  |m   :m   |f   :m   |l,  :r   |d   :—  |t,  ||
:s,  |s,  :-.s, |s,  :s,  |s,  :—  |s,  :s,  |f,  :s,  |l,  :l,  |s,  :—  |—   ||
:s,  |t,  :-.t, |l,  :t,  |d   :—  |d   :d   |d   :d   |d   :f   |m   :—  |r   ||
:s,  |s,  :-.s, |s,  :s,  |d   :—  |d   :d.t,|l,  :s,  |f,  :f,  |s,  :—  |—   ||

:s,  |d   :-.d  |m   :d   |d   :—  |l,  :d   |s,  :d   |m   :r   |d   :—  |—  ||d   |d   ||
:f,  |m,  :-.m, |m,  :s,  |l,  :—  |f,  :f,  |s,  :m,  |s,  :f,  |m,  :—  |—  ||f,  |m,  ||
:t,  |d   :-.d  |s,  :d   |d   :—  |d   :l,  |d   :d   |d   :t,  |d   :—  |—  ||l,  |s,  ||
:s,  |d,  :-.d, |d,  :m,  |f,  :—  |f,  :f,  |m,  :d,  |s,  :s,  |d,  :—  |—  ||f,  |d,  ||
```

A-men.

STAND up! stand up for Jesus,
 Ye soldiers of the Cross!
Lift high His royal banner;
 It must not suffer loss.
From victory to victory
 His army He shall lead,
Till every foe is vanquished,
 And Christ is Lord indeed.

2 Stand up! stand up for Jesus!
 The trumpet-call obey;
Forth to the mighty conflict
 In this His glorious day!
Ye that are men, now serve Him
 Against unnumbered foes;
Your courage rise with danger,
 And strength to strength oppose.

3 Stand up! stand up for Jesus!
 Stand in His strength alone;
The arm of flesh will fail you;
 Ye dare not trust your own.
Put on the gospel armour,
 Each piece put on with prayer;
Where duty calls, or danger,
 Be never wanting there.

4 Stand up ! stand up for Jesus !
The strife will not be long ;
This day the noise of battle,
The next the victor's song.
To him that overcometh
A crown of life shall be ;
He with the King of Glory
Shall reign eternally.

GEORGE DUFFIELD, 1818–88.

533 UNIVERSITY COLLEGE. (77. 77.)

Doh = F. *In moderate time.* HENRY JOHN GAUNTLETT, 1805–76.

m :d	l :s	f :m	r :—	m :d	s :s	s :fe	s :—
d :d	d :d	r :d	t_1 :—	d :d	r :m	d :d	t_1 :—
s :m	f :s	s :s	s :—	s :s	s :m	l :l	r :—
d :d	f :m	t_1 :d	s_1 :—	d :m	t_1 :d	l_1 :l_1	s_1 :—

m :r	d :l	s :f	m :—	m :m	s :m	m :r	d :—	d	d
d :t_1	d :d	d :d.t_1	d :—	t_1 :d	t_1 :d	d :t_1	d :—	l_1	s_1
m :s.f	m :f.m	r :s	s :—	m :d	r :m.f	s :s.f	m :—	f	m
d :s_1	l_1 :f_1	s_1 :s_1	d :—	se_1 :l_1	s_1 :d	s_1 :s_1	d :—	f_1	d

A-men.

MUCH in sorrow, oft in woe,
Onward, Christians, onward go !
Fight the fight, maintain the strife,
Strengthened with the bread of life.

2 Onward, Christians, onward go !
Join the war, and face the foe ;
Faint not ! much doth yet remain,
Dreary is the long campaign.

3 Shrink not, Christians ! will ye yield ?
Will ye quit the painful field ?
Will ye flee in danger's hour ?
Know ye not your Captain's power?

4 Let your drooping hearts be glad ;
March, in heavenly armour clad ;
Fight, nor think the battle long ;
Victory soon shall tune your song.

5 Let not sorrow dim your eye,
Soon shall every tear be dry ;
Let not fears your course impede,
Great your strength, if great your need.

6 Onward then to battle move ;
More than conquerors ye shall prove ;
Though opposed by many a foe,
Christian soldiers, onward go !

HENRY KIRKE WHITE, 1785–1806; and FRANCES SARA COLQUHOUN, 1809–77.

534

ST. ETHELWALD. (S.M.)

Doh = G. *In moderate time.* WILLIAM HENRY MONK, 1823–89.

:s | f :m | r :m.f | m :— | — :m | r :s_1 | l_1 :l_1 | s_1 :— | — ‖
:d | l_1.t_1 :d | d :t_1 | d :— | — :s_1 | s_1 :s_1 | s_1 :fe_1 | s_1 :— | — ‖
:m | f :s | l :s | s :— | — :d | r :m.r | m :r | t_1 :— | — ‖
:d | r :m | f :s | d :— | — :d | t_1 :d.t_1 | d :r | s_1 :— | — ‖

:s_1 | l_1 :t_1 | d :m | r :r | m :m | f :m | r :r | d :— | — ‖ d | d ‖
:s_1 | s_1 :f_1 | m_1 :d.t_1 | l_1 :l_1 | se_1 :l_1 | l_1.t_1 :d | d :t_1 | d :— | — ‖ l_1 | s_1 ‖
:t_1 | d :r | d :d | r.d :t_1.l_1 | t_1 :de | r :d | d.r :m.f | m :— | — ‖ f | m ‖
:s_1 | f_1 :r_1 | l_1 :l_1.s_1 | f_1 :f_1 | m_1 :l_1 | r_1 :m_1.f_1 | s_1 :s_1 | d_1 :— | — ‖ f_1 | d_1 ‖

A-men.

SOLDIERS of Christ ! arise,
And put your armour on,
Strong in the strength which God supplies
Through His eternal Son ;

2 Strong in the Lord of hosts,
And in His mighty power ;
Who in the strength of Jesus trusts
Is more than conqueror.

3 Stand, then, in His great might,
With all His strength endued ;
And take, to arm you for the fight,
The panoply of God.

4 To keep your armour bright
Attend with constant care,
Still walking in your Captain's sight,
And watching unto prayer.

5 From strength to strength go on ;
Wrestle, and fight, and pray ;
Tread all the powers of darkness down,
And win the well-fought day,—

6 That, having all things done,
And all your conflicts passed,
Ye may o'ercome through Christ alone,
And stand complete at last.

CHARLES WESLEY, 1707–88.

CONFLICT AND VICTORY

FROM STRENGTH TO STRENGTH. (D.S.M.)

Doh = G. *Unison. Alla marcia.* EDWARD WOODALL NAYLOR, 1867–

| d :s_1 .,s_1 | $\dot{d}$:r | m :$\dot{d}$ | d :f | m :— | r :— |

1. Sol - diers of Christ! a - rise, And put your ar - mour
2. Stand, then, in His great might, With all His strength en -
3. From strength to strength go on; Wres - tle, and fight, and

| d :— ‖ m :r .d | t_1 :l_1 | t_1 :d | r :t_1 |

on, Strong in the strength which God sup - plies Through
- dued; And take, to arm you for the fight, The
pray; Tread all the powers of dark - ness down, And

| s_1 :d | t_1 :— | l_1 :— | s_1 :— ‖ s_1 :l_1 .t_1 |

His e - ter - nal Son; Strong in the
pan - o - ply of God. To keep your
win the well - fought day,— That, hav - ing

| d :— | d :— | d :l_1 | t_1 :d | r :— |

Lord of hosts, And in His migh -
ar - - mour bright At - tend with con -
all things done, And all your con -

| r :— | r :— ‖ d :r .m | f :- .f | m :r | s :m |

- ty power; Who in the strength of Je - sus trusts Is
- stant care, Still walk-ing in your Cap - tain's sight, And
- flicts passed, Ye may o'er-come through Christ a - lone, And

| d :r | m :— | r :- .d | d :— | — :— ‖ d | d ‖

more than con - - quer - or.
watch - ing un - - to prayer.
stand com - plete at last.

A - men.

CHARLES WESLEY, 1707–88.

535

ST. GERTRUDE. (6 5. 6 5. D. and refrain.)

Doh = F. *Brightly.* ARTHUR SEYMOUR SULLIVAN, 1842–1900.

s :s	s :s	s :-.l	s :—	r :r	d :r	m :—	— :—
m :m	m :m	f :—	f :—	t, :t,	l, :t,	d :—	— :—
d :m	s :d'	d' :—	t :—	s :s	s :s	s :—	— :—
d :d	d :d	r :—	s, :—	f :f	m :r	d :—	— :—

d :m	s :d'	d' :—	t :—	l :l	m :fe	s :—	— :—
d :d	d :d	r :—	r :—	d :d	d :d	t, :—	— :—
s :s	s :s	s :-.l	s :—	fe :fe	s :l	s :—	— :—
m :m	m :m	r :—	r :—	r :r	r :r	s, :—	— :—

r :r	s :r	m :-.f	m :—	s :s	d' :s	l :—	— :—
t, :t,	r :t,	d :-.r	d :—	d :d	d :d	d :—	— :—
s :s	s :s	s :—	s :—	m :m	s :m	f :—	— :—
s, :s,	t, :s,	d :—	d :—	d :d	m :d	f :—	— :—

l :s	f :s	l :s	f :s	l :s	f :m	r :—	— :—
d :d	d :d	d :—	d :—	d :d	r :d	t, :—	— :—
f :m	f :m	f :m	f :m	f :m	r :r	s :—	— :—
f :d	l, :d	f :d	l, :d	f, :f,	f, :f,	s, :—	— :—

d :d	d :d	d :t,.l,	t, :d	r :r	r :d.r	m :—	— :—
s, :s,	s, :s,	s, :—	s, :—	s, :s,	s, :s,	s, :—	— :—
m :m	m :m	f :—	f :—	f :f	f :f	m :—	— :—
d :s,	d :s,	r :s,	r :s,	t, :s,	t, :s,	d :—	— :—

s :s	d' :t	d' :—	s :—	f :m	r :-.d	d :—	— :—	d	d
m :m	f :f	m :—	d :—	d :d	t, :-.d	d :—	— :—	l,	s,
d' :d'	s :s	s :—	s :—	l :-.s	f :-.m	m :—	— :—	f	m
d :d	r :r	m :—	m, :—	f, :f,	s, :-.s,	d, :—	— :—	f,	d,

A-men.

[*By permission of Novello & Co., Ltd.*]

CONFLICT AND VICTORY

ONWARD! Christian soldiers,
Marching as to war,
With the Cross of Jesus
Going on before.
Christ, the Royal Master,
Leads against the foe;
Forward into battle,
See! His banners go.
Onward! Christian soldiers,
Marching as to war,
With the Cross of Jesus
Going on before.

2 At the sign of triumph
Satan's legions flee;
On then, Christian soldiers,
On to victory!
Hell's foundations quiver
At the shout of praise;
Brothers, lift your voices,
Loud your anthems raise.

3 Like a mighty army
Moves the Church of God;
Brothers, we are treading
Where the saints have trod.
We are not divided,
All one body we,
One in hope, in doctrine,
One in charity.

4 Crowns and thrones may perish,
Kingdoms rise and wane,
But the Church of Jesus
Constant will remain;
Gates of hell can never
'Gainst that Church prevail;
We have Christ's own promise,
And that cannot fail.

5 Onward, then, ye people!
Join our happy throng;
Blend with ours your voices
In the triumph song:
'Glory, laud, and honour
Unto Christ the King!'
This, through countless ages,
Men and angels sing.

SABINE BARING-GOULD, 1834–1924.

536 GRACE DIEU. (98. 98.)

SAMUEL SEBASTIAN WESLEY, 1810–76.

Doh = B♭. *In moderate time.*

```
:s, |d   :m    |r   :s,    |d   :-.r  |r   :d   || s, |s,  :-.s,
:m, |d,  :s,   |s,  :s,    |s,  :f,   |f,  :m,  || m, |r,  :r,
:s, |s,  :d    |t,  :d.t,  |l,  :-.t, |t,  :d   || s, |t,  :t,
:d, |m,  :d,   |s,  :m,    |l,  :-.s, |d,  :d,  || d, |s,  :f,

|d   :t,   |l,  :f,.m, |r,  || s, |l,  :d   |f   :-.m |r   :l,.d
|d,  :m,   |m,  :r,.d, |t,, || s, |d,  :s,  |f,  :l,  |l,  :l,
|s,  :se,  |l,  :l,    |t,  || d  |d   :s,  |l,  :de  |r   :re
|m,  :r,   |de, :r,    |s,  || m, |f,  :m,  |r,  :m,  |f,  :f,

|d   :t,  || t,  |m   :t,  |d     :m.r   |d   :t,  |d   || d  |d  ||
|l,  :se, || se, |m,  :m,  |m,    :s,.f, |m,  :r,  |m,  || f, |m, ||
|m   :m   || m   |t,  :se, |l,    :l,    |s,  :s,  |s,  || l, |s, ||
|m,  :m,  || m,  |se, :m,  |l,.s, :f,    |s,  :s,, |d,  || f, |d, ||
                                                            A-men.
```

SAY not, 'The struggle nought availeth;
The labour and the wounds are vain;
The enemy faints not nor faileth,
And as things have been they remain.'

2 If hopes were dupes, fears may be liars:
It may be, in yon smoke concealed,
Your comrades chase even now the fliers,
And, but for you, possess the field.

3 For while the tired waves, vainly breaking,
Seem here no painful inch to gain,
Far back, through creeks and inlets making,
Comes silent, flooding in, the main.

4 And not by eastern windows only,
When daylight comes, comes in the light;
In front the sun climbs slow, how slowly!
But westward, look! the land is bright.

ARTHUR HUGH CLOUGH, 1819–61.

537 CHRISTCHURCH. (66. 66. 88.)

Doh = C. *Moderately fast.* CHARLES STEGGALL, 1826–1905.

d :—	m :s	d' :r'	s :—	d' :—	l :s	s :f	m :—	
s, :—	d :r	m :f	r :—	d :—	d :d	d :t,	d :—	
m :—	s :t	d' :l	t :—	s :—	f :s	l :s	s :—	
d :—	d :t,	l, :f	s :—	m :—	f :m	r :s,	d :—	

G.t. f.C.

r :—	m :s	(l)r :f	m :—	m :—	s :f	r :r	(d)s :—	
r :—	d :t,	(m)l, :l,	se, :—	l, :—	s, :l,	s, :s,	(m)t, :—	
s :—	s :s	(m)l, :r	t, :—	d :—	d :d	d :t,	(d)s :—	
t, :—	d :m	(d)f, :r,	m, :—	l, :—	m, :f,	s, :s,	(d,)s, :—	

s :—	d' :l	s :m	d :r	m :—	m :—	d' :r'	s :l	r :r	d :— (fermata)		f	m	
s :—	d' :l	s :m	d :r	m :—	r :—	d :f	m :d	d :t,	d :—		d	d	
s :—	d' :l	s :m	d :r	m :—	se :—	l :r'	d' :l	s :s	m :—		l	s	
s :—	d' :l	s :m	d :r	m :—	m :—	l, :t,	d :f,	s, :s,	d :—		f,	d	

A-men.

MARCH on, my soul, with strength,
March forward, void of fear ;
He who hath led will lead,
While year succeedeth year ;
And as thou goest on thy way,
His hand shall hold thee day by day.

2 March on, my soul, with strength,
In ease thou dar'st not dwell ;
High duty calls thee forth ;
Then up, and quit thee well !
Take up thy cross, take up thy sword,
And fight the battles of thy Lord !

3 March on, my soul, with strength,
With strength, but not thine own ;
The conquest thou shalt gain,
Through Christ thy Lord alone ;
His grace shall nerve thy feeble arm,
His love preserve thee safe from harm.

4 March on, my soul, with strength,
From strength to strength march on ;
Warfare shall end at length,
All foes be overthrown.
Then, O my soul, if faithful now,
The crown of life awaits thy brow.

WILLIAM WRIGHT, 1859–1924.

538 VEXILLUM. (65. 65. D. and refrain.)

Doh = E. *Brightly.* HENRY SMART, 1813–79.

m :f |s :s |d' :— |s :— |m :f |s :r |m :— |— :— ||
d :t, |d :t, |d :m |r :t, |d :d |d :t, |d :— |— :— ||
s :s |s :s |s :— |s :— |s :l |s :s |s :— |— :— ||
d :r |m :f |m :d |t, :s, |d :l, |m, :s, |d :— |— :— ||

B.t. f.E.

d :r |m :s |[d']f :— |m :d |l, :l, |t, :r |[d]s :— |— :— ||
d :t, |d :r |[d]f, :l, |s, :— |f, :f, |f, :f, |[m,]t, :— |— :— ||
s :s |s :r |[m]l, :t, |d :— |d :r |r :t, |[d]s :— |— :— ||
m :r |d :t, |[l]r, :— |m, :— |f, :r, |s, :s, |[d,]s, :— |— :— ||

f.A.

r :r |[m]t, :d |r :— |m :— |d :m |r :t, |d :— |— :— ||
t, :t, |[de]se, :l, |t, :— |t, :— |l, :l, |t, :se, |l, :— |— :— ||
s :s |[s]r :m |f :— |t, :— |m :m |f :m |m :— |— :— ||
s :f |[m]t, :l, |l, :— |se, :— |l, :d, |r, :m, |l, :— |— :— ||

E.t.

d :d |r :r |m :— |s :— |m :r |[d]f :m |r :— |s :— ||
m, :s, |l, :s, |s, :— |s, :— |s, :se, |[l]r :d |d :— |t, :— ||
d :d |d :t, |d :— |r :— |d :t, |[d]f :l |r :— |— :f ||
l, :m, |f, :s, |d, :— |t,, :— |d, :m, |[l,]r :f, |s, :— |— :— ||

s :s |s :s |d' :— |s :— |m :f |s :r |m :— |— :— ||
d :d |r :t, |d :m |r :t, |d :d |d :t, |d :— |— :— ||
m :s |t :r' |s :— |s :— |s :l |s :s |s :— |— :— ||
d :m |s :f |m :d |t, :s, |d :l, |m, :s, |d :— |— :— ||

m :s |d' :t |l :— |s :— |d :f |m :r |d :— |— :— || d |d ||
d :r |d :d |d :— |t, :— |d :r |d :t, |d :— |— :— || l, |s, ||
s :r |m.f :s |f :— |r :— |d :l |s :f |m :— |— :— || f |m ||
d :t, |l, :m, |f, :— |s, :— |l, :f, |s, :s, |d :— |— :— || f, |d ||

A-men.

BRIGHTLY gleams our banner,
Pointing to the sky,
Waving on Christ's soldiers
To their home on high.
Marching through the desert,
Gladly thus we pray,
Still with hearts united
Singing on our way.
Brightly gleams our banner,
Pointing to the sky,
Waving on Christ's soldiers
To their home on high.

2 Jesus, Lord and Master,
At Thy sacred feet,
Here, with hearts rejoicing,
See Thy children meet.
Often have we left Thee,
Often gone astray;
Keep us, mighty Saviour,
In the narrow way.

3 Pattern of our childhood,
Once Thyself a child,
Make our childhood holy,
Pure, and meek, and mild.
In the hour of danger
Whither can we flee,
Save to Thee, dear Saviour,
Only unto Thee?

4 All our days direct us
In the way we go;
Crown us still victorious
Over every foe;
When the march is over,
Then come rest and peace,
Jesus in His beauty,
Songs that never cease.

THOMAS JOSEPH POTTER, 1827–73, and others.

Also the following:

79 Forty days and forty nights
165 Join all the glorious names
216 Lord of our life, and God of our salvation
217 Fear not, thou faithful Christian flock
403 Lord Jesus, think on me

TRUST AND RESIGNATION

539 WIMBLEDON. (88. 84.)

Doh = E. *In moderate time.* SAMUEL SEBASTIAN WESLEY, 1810–76.

```
:s, |d  :— :r  |f  :— :m  |r  :— :r  |m  :— :f  |s :— :l |s :— :m  |m  :— :re |m  :— ||
:s, |s, :— :s, |d  :— :d  |d  :— :t, |d  :— :t, |d :— :d |d :— :s, |t, :— :t, |t, :— ||
:m  |m  :— :s  |f  :— :s  |l  :— :s  |s  :— :s  |s :— :f |s :— :s  |s  :— :fe |s  :— ||
:d  |d  :— :t, |l, :— :s, |f, :— :s, |d  :— :r  |m :— :f |m :— :d  |t, :— :t, |m  :— ||

:s    |d' :— :t  |l  :— :s     |f    :— :m  |r     :— :d  |d  :— :— |r  :— :— |d :— ||d  |d  ||
:d    |d  :— :d  |d  :— :d.ta, |l,:r    :de |r     :— :l, |s, :— :— |t, :— :— |d :— ||l, |s, ||
:m    |m  :— :m  |f  :— :s     |l    :— :s  |f     :— :m  |m  :— :— |f  :— :— |m :— ||f  |m  ||
:d.t, |l, :— :s, |f, :— :m,    |f,   :— :l, |r,:m,    :f, |s, :— :— |s, :— :— |d :— ||f, |d  ||
```

A-men.

MY God and Father, while I stray
Far from my home in life's rough way,
O teach me from my heart to say,
 'Thy will be done.'

2 Though dark my path and sad my lot,
Let me be still and murmur not,
Or breathe the prayer divinely taught,
 'Thy will be done.'

3 What though in lonely grief I sigh
For friends beloved, no longer nigh,
Submissive still would I reply,
 'Thy will be done.'

4 If Thou shouldst call me to resign
What most I prize, it ne'er was mine,
I only yield Thee what was Thine:
 Thy will be done.

5 Let but my fainting heart be blest
With Thy sweet Spirit for its guest,
My God, to Thee I leave the rest:
 Thy will be done.

6 Renew my will from day to day;
Blend it with Thine; and take away
All that now makes it hard to say,
 'Thy will be done.'

7 Then, when on earth I breathe no more
The prayer oft mixed with tears before,
I'll sing upon a happier shore,
 'Thy will be done.'

CHARLOTTE ELLIOTT, 1789–1871.

540 WAS GOTT THUT (BADEN). (87. 87. 888.)

SEVERUS GASTORIUS, *c.* 1675.

Doh = G. *Moderately slow.*

```
:s, |d  :r  |m :f  |s  :s  |m  :l  |s  :f    |m  :m  |r  :—   |d  ||
:s, |l, :t, |d :d  |d  :t, |d  :d  |d  :—.t, |d  :d  |d  :t,  |d  ||
:m  |m  :s  |s :f  |r  :s  |d  :f  |m  :f    |s  :l  |r  :s.f |m  ||
:d  |l, :s, |d :l, |s, :s, |l, :f, |d, :r,   |m, :f, |s, :—   |d, ||
```

```
:s, |d  :r      |m  :f  |s  :s   |m  :l      |s  :f      |m  :m  |r  :—   |d  ||
:s, |s, :l,.t,  |d  :d  |s, :t,  |d  :d      |t, :l,     |s, :d  |d  :t,  |d  ||
:s, |s  :f      |m  :d  |r  :s   |d  :f      |r  :d.r    |m  :s  |l  :s.f |m  ||
:s, |m  :r      |d  :l, |t, :s,  |l, :f,     |s, :l,.t,  |d  :m, |f, :s,  |d, ||

                                  D.t.                                 f.G.
:s  |l  :l      |r  :r  |s  :s   |d  :(m)l   |s  :f      |m  :m  |r  :r   |(d)s, ||
:d  |d  :d      |d  :t, |d  :d   |l, :(fe)t, |d  :d.r    |d  :d  |d  :t,  |(d)s, ||
:m  |f  :f      |l  :s  |s  :s   |m  :(d)f   |s  :l      |s  :d  |l  :s.f |(m)t, ||
:d  |f, :f,     |f  :f  |m  :m   |l, :(l,)r  |m  :l,.t,  |d  :l, |f, :s,  |(d)s, ||

:s  |l  :s      |f     :m     |r  :r    |d  ||d  |d  ||
:d  |d  :t,     |l,    :s,.d  |d  :t,   |d  ||l, |s, ||
:s  |f  :r      |d.r   :m.f   |s  :-.f  |m  ||f  |m  ||
:m, |f, :s,     |l,.t, :d     |s, :s,   |d, ||f, |d, ||
                                            A-men.
```

Was Gott thut das ist wohlgethan.

WHATE'ER my God ordains is right :
Holy His will abideth ;
I will be still whate'er He doth,
And follow where He guideth :
He is my God ;
Though dark my road,
He holds me that I shall not fall :
Wherefore to Him I leave it all.

2 Whate'er my God ordains is right :
He never will deceive me ;
He leads me by the proper path ;
I know He will not leave me :
I take, content,
What He hath sent ;
His hand can turn my griefs away,
And patiently I wait His day.

3 Whate'er my God ordains is right :
Though now this cup, in drinking,
May bitter seem to my faint heart,
I take it, all unshrinking :
Tears pass away
With dawn of day ;
Sweet comfort yet shall fill my heart,
And pain and sorrow shall depart.

4 Whate'er my God ordains is right :
Here shall my stand be taken ;
Though sorrow, need, or death be mine,
Yet am I not forsaken ;
My Father's care
Is round me there ;
He holds me that I shall not fall :
And so to Him I leave it all.

SAMUEL RODIGAST, 1649–1708 ; *tr.* by CATHERINE WINKWORTH, 1829–78.

541 NEUMARK. (98. 98. 88.)

Georg Neumark, 1621–81.

Lah = G. Doh = B♭. *Moderately slow.*

```
:m,  |l,  :t,  |d   :t,  |l,  :t,  |se,  :m,         |—  :s,  |s,  :f,
:d,  |m,  :m,  |m,  :m,  |f,  :f,  |m,   :m,         |—  :m,  |r,  :r,
:l,  |l,  :se, |l,  :t,  |d   :r   |t,  {:t, / :se,} |—  :d   |t,  :l,
:l2  |d,  :m,  |l,  :s,  |f,  :r,  |m,   :m,         |—  :d,  |s,  :r,

|m,  :l,  |l,  :se, |l,  :—  |—  ||m,    |l,  :t,  |d   :t,  |l,  :t,
|t2  :m,  |f,  :m,  |m,  :—  |—  ||m,    |m,  :m,  |m,  :m,  |f,  :f,
|se, :l,  |r   :t,  |d   :—  |—  ||se,   |l,  :se, |l,  :t,  |d   :r
|m,  :d,  |r,  :m,  |l2  :—  |—  ||m,.r, |d,  :m,  |l,  :s,  |f,  :r,

|se, :m,         |—  :s,  |s,  :f,  |m,  :l,  |l,  :se, |l,  :—  |—  ||t,
|m,  :m,         |—  :m,  |r,  :r,  |t2  :m,  |f,  :m,  |m,  :—  |—  ||m,
|t, {:t, / :se,} |—  :d   |t,  :l,  |se, :l,  |r   :t,  |d   :—  |—  ||se,
|m,  :m,         |—  :d,  |s,  :r,  |m,  :d,  |r,  :m,  |l2  :—  |—  ||m,

|d  :r  |m  :m  |r  :r     |d  :m  |r  :d  |t,     :l,.t, |d  :t,  |l,  ||l,  |l,  ||
|m, :s, |s, :s, |l, :s,.f, |m, :s, |s, :m, |f,.s,  :l,    |l, :se, |l,  ||f,  |m,  ||
|l, :t, |d  :d  |d  :t,    |d  :d  |t, :d  |r      :d.r   |m  :-.r |d   ||r   |de  ||
|l, :s, |d  :m, |f, :s,    |d, :d, |s, :l, |r,.m,  :f,    |m, :m,  |l2  ||r,  |l2  ||
                                                                          A-men.
```

Wer nur den lieben Gott lässt walten.

IF thou but suffer God to guide thee,
And hope in Him through all thy ways,
He'll give thee strength, whate'er betide thee,
And bear thee through the evil days;
Who trusts in God's unchanging love
Builds on the rock that nought can move.

2 What can these anxious cares avail thee,
These never-ceasing moans and sighs?
What can it help if thou bewail thee
O'er each dark moment as it flies?
Our cross and trials do but press
The heavier for our bitterness.

3 Only be still, and wait His leisure
In cheerful hope, with heart content
To take whate'er thy Father's pleasure
And all-discerning love have sent;
Nor doubt our inmost wants are known
To Him who chose us for His own.

4 Sing, pray, and keep His ways unswerving;
So do thine own part faithfully,
And trust His word,—though undeserving,
Thou yet shalt find it true for thee;
God never yet forsook at need
The soul that trusted Him indeed.

GEORG NEUMARK, 1621–81; *tr.* by CATHERINE WINKWORTH, 1829–78.

542 WEM IN LEIDENSTAGEN (FILITZ). (65. 65.)

Doh = G. *Moderately slow.* FRIEDRICH FILITZ, 1804–76.

m :m	r :r	d :—	t_1 :—	d :d	r :r	m :—	— :—
s_1 :d	d :t_1	t_1 :l_1	se_1 :—	l_1 :d	d :t_1	d :—	— :—
d :m	s :s	m :—	m :—	m :m	s :s	s :—	— :—
d :d	s_1 :s_1	l_1 :—	m_1 :—	l_1 :l_1	s_1 :s_1	d :—	— :—

s :s	f :f	m :—	r :—	m :m	r :r	d :—	— :—	d	d
t_1 :d	l_1 :r	r :d	t_1 :—	d :d	d :t_1	d :—	— :—	l_1	s_1
s :m	f :s	s :—	s :—	s :s	l :s.f	m :—	— :—	f	m
m :d	r :t_1	d :—	s_1 :—	d :m_1	f_1 :s_1	d_1 :—	— :—	f_1	d_1

A-men.

Wem in Leidenstagen.

O LET him whose sorrow
No relief can find,
Trust in God, and borrow
Ease for heart and mind.

2 Where the mourner, weeping,
Sheds the secret tear,
God His watch is keeping,
Though none else be near.

3 God will never leave thee;
All thy wants He knows,
Feels the pains that grieve thee,
Sees thy cares and woes.

4 If in grief thou languish,
He will dry the tear,
Who His children's anguish
Soothes with succour near.

5 All thy woe and sadness,
In this world below,
Balance not the gladness
Thou in heaven shalt know,

6 When thy gracious Saviour,
In the realms above,
Crowns thee with His favour,
Fills thee with His love.

HEINRICH SIEGMUND OSWALD, 1751–1834; *tr.* by FRANCES ELIZABETH COX, 1812–97.

543 PSALM 6. (886. 886.)

French Psalter, 1542.
Composed or arranged by LOUIS BOURGEOIS, 1510– ?.
Adapted from the *Scottish Psalter*, 1564,
by JAMES SMITH ANDERSON, 1853– .

Lah = F. Doh = A♭. *Moderately slow. In free rhythm.*

|l, :— |l, :l, |s, :— :l, |d :— |— :t, |d :— ||m :— |m :s
|m, :— |m, :m, |m, :— :d, |s, :— |s, :— |s, :— ||d :— |d :t,
|d :— |d :d |t, :— :l, |m :— |r :— |m :— ||s :— |m :r
|l, :— |l, :l, |m, :— :f, |d, :s, |— :s, |d :— ||d, :— |d :s,

f :m	r :r	d :—		s, :—	l, :d	t, :l,	m :—	
d.r :d	d :t,	d :—		d, :—	d, :s,	s, :m,.l,	se, :—	
l :s	f :s	m :—		m :—	f :m	r :d	t, :—	
l,.t, :d	r :s,	d :—		d, :—	f, :d,	s, :l,	m, :—	

|s :— |s :f |m :r |d :d |l, :— ||r :— |r :d |t, :l,
|s, :— |d :l, |l, :l, |l, :m, |fe, :— ||f, :— |l, :l, |s, :f,
|m :— |m :r |d :f |m :d |r :— ||l, :— |f :f |r :r
|d, :— |d :r |l, :f, |l, :l, |r, :— ||r, :— |r, :f, |s, :r,

d :d	s, :—		l, :—	m :m	r :—	t, :—	l, :—		l,	l,	
s, :l,	m, :—		l, :—	d :d	t, :l,	— :se,	l, :—		f,	m,	
m :m	d :—		d :—	s :s	f :—	m :—	de :—		r	de	
d, :l,,	d, :—		f, :—	m, :d,	r, :—	m, :—	l, (l,,) :—		r,	l, (l,,)	

A-men.

MAGDALEN COLLEGE. (886. 886.)

Doh = C. *In moderate time.* WILLIAM HAYES, 1706–77.

|d :— |m :s |d' :— |— :l |f :-.f |m :— ||r :— |m :f
|d :— |m :r |d :— |— :d |d :t, |d :— ||t, :— |d :t,
|d' :— |d' :r' |m' :— |— :l |l :f |s :— ||s :— |s :f
|d :— |d' :t |l :— |— :f |r :-.r |d :— ||s, :— |d :r

s :l	t :d'	r' :—	—		s	d' :t.d'	l :-.l	s :—	—	
d :d	f :m	r :—	—		r	m.fe :s	s :fe	s :—	—	
m :l	f :s	t :—	—		r'	d' :r'	r' :-.r'	t :—	—	
m :f	r :d	s :—	—		t,	l, :s,	r :-.r	s, :—	—	

:t |t :t |d' :-.d' |d' :ta |l :— ||— :l |l :l |r' :-.d'
:r |r :r |d :m |f :s |f :— ||— :d |d :r |f :-.m
:s |s :s |s :d' |d' :d' |d' :— ||— :l |l :f |s :-.s
:s |s :f |m :d |r :m |f :— ||— :f |f :r.d |t, :-.d

t :d'	t :—	—		d'	f :m.f	m :r	d :—	— :—		f	m	
r :m	r :—	—		d	d.t, :d	d :t,	d :—	— :—		d	d	
s :s	s :—	—		s	f :s	s :-.f	m :—	— :—		l	s	
s :d	s :—	—		m	r :d	s :s,	d :—	— :—		f,	d	

A-men.

O LORD, how happy should we be
If we could cast our care on Thee,
If we from self could rest,
And feel at heart that One above,
In perfect wisdom, perfect love,
Is working for the best ;

2 Could we but kneel, and cast our load,
Even while we pray, upon our God,
Then rise with lightened cheer,
Sure that the Father, who is nigh
To still the famished raven's cry,
Will hear, in that we fear.

3 We cannot trust Him as we should ;
So chafes weak nature's restless mood
To cast its peace away ;
But birds and flowerets round us preach ;
All, all the present evil teach
Sufficient for the day.

4 Lord, make these faithless hearts of ours
Such lessons learn from birds and flowers :
Make them from self to cease,
Leave all things to a Father's will,
And taste, before Him lying still,
Even in affliction, peace.

JOSEPH ANSTICE, 1808–36.

544

TABERNACLE. (10 10. 10 10. 10 10.)

Doh = D. *In moderate time.* EDWARD ARTHUR, 1874–

```
{:d  |m  :— :m  |s  :— :m  |d  :t, :d  |f  :— :f  |m  :— :m  |r  :— :s  }
{:s, |d  :— :d  |m  :— :t, |l, :— :l, |d  :— :d  |d  :— :l, |r  :— :t, }
{:m  |s  :— :l  |t  :— :s  |m  :r  :m  |l  :— :l  |s  :— :fe |s  :— :t  }
{:d  |d  :— :l, |m, :— :s, |l, :— :l, |f, :— :l, |d  :— :d  |t, :— :m  }

{|s  :fe :s  |t  :l  :m  |r  :— :fe |s  :— ||d  |m  :— :m  |s  :— :m  }
{|r  :— :s  |m  :— :m  |r  :— :d  |t, :— ||d  |d  :— :d  |m  :— :t, }
{|t  :l  :r' |r' :d' :l  |t  :— :l  |s  :— ||m  |s  :— :l  |t  :— :s  }
{|r  :d  :t, |d  :— :d  |r  :— :r  |s, :— ||d  |d  :— :l, |m, :— :s, }

                                   A.t.
{|d  :t, :d  |f  :— :f  |m  :— :m  |(s)d  :t, :l, |m   :—  :r  |d  :t,  :l, }
{|l, :— :l, |d  :— :d  |d  :— :d  |(d)f, :— :l, |se, :l,  :t, |l, :se, :l, }
{|m  :r  :m  |l  :— :l  |s  :— :s  |(l)r  :— :l, |t,  :—  :m  |m  :r   :d  }
{|l, :— :l, |f, :— :l, |d  :— :d  |(l)r, :— :f, |m,  :ba, :se,|l, :t,  :d  }

                         f.D
{|t, :— :d   |t,  :— ||t,  |(d)s :l  :t  |d' :— :t  |t  :l :m |s :— :f }
{|l, :— :ba, |se, :— ||se, |(l)m :— :f  |m  :f  :s  |s  :f :d |m :— :r }
{|m  :— :re  |m   :— ||m   |(m)t :d' :r' |s  :— :d' |d' :— :l |l :— :l }
{|t, :— :l,  |m,  :— ||m,  |(l)m :— :r  |d  :r  :m  |f  :— :l |r :— :f }

{|r  :— :— |m  :m :m  |m :r :m |s  :m :d |r :— :r  |m :— ||f    |m ||
{|t, :— :— |s, :d :d  |d :— :d |r  :d :d |d :— :t, |d :— ||d    |d ||
{|s  :— :— |m  :s :d' |t :l :s |s  :— :s |l :— :s  |s :— ||l    |s ||
{|s  :— :— |d  :m :l  |s :f :m |t, :d :m |f :— :s  |d :— ||f f, |d ||
                                                          A - men.
```

[*Copyright*, 1927, *by Edward Arthur*.]

LONG did I toil, and knew no earthly rest,
 Far did I rove, and found no certain home;
At last I sought them in His sheltering breast,
 Who opes His arms, and bids the weary come:
With Him I found a home, a rest divine,
And I since then am His, and He is mine.

2 The good I have is from His stores supplied,
  The ill is only what He deems the best;
He for my Friend, I'm rich with nought beside,
  And poor without Him, though of all possest:
Changes may come—I take, or I resign,
Content, while I am His, while He is mine.

3 Whate'er may change, in Him no change is seen;
  A glorious Sun that wanes not nor declines,
Above the clouds and storms He walks serene,
  And on His people's inward darkness shines:
All may depart—I fret not, nor repine,
While I my Saviour's am, while He is mine.

4 While here, alas! I know but half His love,
  But half discern Him, and but half adore;
But, when I meet Him in the realms above,
  I hope to love Him better, praise Him more,
And feel, and tell, amid the choir divine,
How fully I am His, and He is mine.

JOHN QUARLES, 1624–65; and HENRY FRANCIS LYTE, 1793–1847.

545 SONG 24. (10 10. 10 10.)

ORLANDO GIBBONS, 1583–1625.

Lah = E. Doh = G. *Moderately slow.*

```
                                                          D.t.
 :d  |d  :r  |m  :-.m |r   :d  |t,  :t,  |l,  :—  | :ml  |l  :t
 :l, |l, :t, |d  :-.d |t,  :l, |l,  :se, |l,  :—  | :df  |m  :se
 :m  |m  :s  |s  :-.s |s.f :m  |m   :-.r |d   :—  | :ml  |l  :r'
 :l, |l, :s, |d, :-.d,|s,  :l, |m,  :m,  |l,} :—  | :l,r |d  :t,
                                    f.G.   l2}

|d' :-.d'|t   :l   |l  :se  |l   :— || :mt, |t, :d      |r  :-.t, |d  :d
|l  :-.l |m.r :d.r |m  :m   |m   :— || :ds, |s, :m,.fe, |s, :-.s, |l, :s,
|d' :-.d'|s   :l   |t  :t   |de' :— || :lm  |m  :d      |t, :-.r  |f  :d
|l, :-.l,|m   :f   |m  :m,  |l,  :— || :lm, |m, :l,     |s, :-.s, |f, :m,

|r  :f  |m  :— | :r  |s  :fe     |m  :-.f  |d  :d  |t, :t,  |l, :— || l, |l, ||
|f, :f, |s, :— | :s, |t, :t,.l,  |s, :-.t, |t, :l, |l, :se, |l, :— || f, |m, ||
|d  :t, |d  :— | :t, |t, :r      |m  :-.f  |s  :m  |m  :-.r |d  :— || r  |de ||
|r, :r, |d, :— | :s, |m, :t2     |d, :-.r, |m, :l, |m, :m,  |l, :— || r, |l, ||
                                                                     A-men.
```

O CHRIST, my God, who seest the unseen,
  O Christ, my God, who knowest the unknown,
Thy mighty blood was poured forth to atone
For every sin that can be or hath been.

2 O Thou who seest what I cannot see,
  Thou who didst love us all so long ago,
O Thou who knowest what I must not know;
Remember all my hope, remember me.

CHRISTINA GEORGINA ROSSETTI, 1830–94.

546

NARENZA. (S.M.) *Kirchen Gesäng*, Cologne, 1619.

Doh = B♭. *Moderately slow.* Arranged by WILLIAM HENRY HAVERGAL, 1793–1870.

```
:d  |t,  :s,  |l,  :t,  |d   :—  |— :m   |r   :t,  |d   :l,   |s,  :— |— ‖
:s, |s,  :s,  |d,  :f,  |m,  :—  |— :s,  |fe, :s,  |m,  :r,   |t,, :— |— ‖
:m  |r   :d   |d   :r   |s,  :—  |— :d   |l,  :s,  |s,  :fe,  |s,  :— |— ‖
:d, |s,  :m,  |f,  :r,  |d,  :—  |— :d,  |r,  :m,  |d,  :r,   |s,  :— |— ‖
```

```
:s, |s,   :s,  |l,  :t,  |d   :l,  |t,  :m   |r   :d   |r   :r      |d   :— |— ‖ d  |d
:m, |f,   :m,  |f,  :f,  |m,  :l,  |se, :s,  |s,  :m,  |l,  :s,.f,  |m,  :— |— ‖ f, |m,
:s, |r    :d   |d   :r   |d   :r   |t,  :d   |t,  :d   |d   :t,     |d   :— |— ‖ l, |s,
:d, |t,,  :d,  |f,  :r,  |l,  :f,  |m,  :d,  |s,  :l,  |f,  :s,     |d,  :— |— ‖ f, |d,
```

A-men.

SONG 20. (S.M.)

Lah = B. Doh = D. *Moderately slow.* ORLANDO GIBBONS, 1583–1625.

```
|m  :— |m :ba |se :l  |t :— |— :m  |d' :l  |s  :f |m  :— |— ‖
|l, :— |m :r  |t, :m  |r :— |— :d  |m  :f  |m  :r |t, :— |— ‖
|d' :— |l :l  |m  :m  |f :— |— :m  |l  :d' |d' :l |se :— |— ‖
|l, :— |d :r  |m  :d  |r :— |— :l, |l, :f, |d  :r |m  :— |— ‖
```

```
                      f.G.                D.t.
:s  |s  :fe |s  :(m)t,    |d  :r      |(m)l   :t |m  :l |l  :se   |l  :— ‖ l |l
:r  |m  :r  |t, :(d)s,    |s, :l,.t,  |(d)f   :f |t, :m |m  :-.r  |d  :— ‖ r |de
:s  |d' :l  |s  :(s)r     |s  :f      |(m)l   :l |se :l |t  :t    |l  :— ‖ f |m
:t, |d  :r  |s, :(d)s,.f, |m, :r,     |(d)f,  :r |m  :d |m  :m    |l, :— ‖ r |l,
```

A-men.

Befiehl du deine Wege.

COMMIT thou all thy griefs
And ways into His hands,
To His sure truth and tender care
Who earth and heaven commands.

2 Who points the clouds their course,
Whom winds and seas obey,
He shall direct thy wandering feet,
He shall prepare thy way.

3 Thou on the Lord rely,
So safe shalt thou go on;
Fix on His work thy steadfast eye,
So shall thy work be done.

4 No profit canst thou gain
By self-consuming care;
To Him commend thy cause; His ear
Attends the softest prayer.

5 Thy everlasting truth,
Father, Thy ceaseless love,
Sees all Thy children's wants, and knows
What best for each will prove.

6 Thou everywhere hast sway,
And all things serve Thy might;
Thy every act pure blessing is,
Thy path unsullied light.

PAUL GERHARDT, 1607–76; *tr.* by JOHN WESLEY, 1703–91.

547 ICH HALTE TREULICH STILL. (D.S.M.)

Doh = D. *Brightly.* JOHANN SEBASTIAN BACH, 1685–1750.

```
:s |m  :r.d |s  :l.s |s  :—  |—  :d' |r  :m.s |f.m:r.d  |d  :— |— ||r
:d |s, :l,  |s, :d   |d  :—  |—  :d  |t, :d   |l, :t,.d |d  :— |— ||t,
:m |d  :m   |s  :f   |m  :f  |s  :m.f|s  :s.m |l.s:f    |m  :— |— ||s
:d |d  :l,  |m  :f   |d  :r  |m  :d  |s, :d   |f, :s,   |d  :— |— ||s,

        A.t.                                                   f.D.
|m :r  |m :lr   |t, :d  |r  :s  |m :r.d |r  :d.t, |d  :— |— ||ds  |f  :m
|d :r  |d :ml,  |s, :s, |s, :t, |d :s,  |l, :s,   |s, :— |— ||s,r |d  :t,
|s :s  |s :d'f  |r  :m  |r  :r  |m :s   |f  :r    |m  :— |— ||mt  |l  :t
|d :t, |d :lr,  |s, :d  |t, :s, |d :m,  |f, :s,   |d, :— |— ||ds, |l, :s,

|f  :s  |m :— |— :m  |l  :t |m :se |l  :— |— ||d' |s  :-.l |s  :f
|d  :r  |d :— |— :r  |d  :f |d :r  |d  :r |m ||d  |r  :d   |r  :t,
|l  :s  |s :— |— :se |l  :l |l :t  |l  :— |— ||m  |s  :d   |s  :s
|l, :t, |d :r |d :t, |l, :r |m :m  |l, :t,|d ||l, |t, :l,  |t, :s,

|m :f  |s :d'  |r :m.s |f.m:r.d  |d :— |— ||f  :m |l :— |s  :— ||
|d :t, |d :m   |r :d   |d  :t,.d |d :— |— ||d  :— |— :r |m  :— ||
|s :s  |s :s.l |t :s   |l.s:f    |m :— |— ||f  :s |l :t |d' :— ||
|d :r  |m :d   |s :m   |r  :s,   |d :— |— ||l, :d |f :— |d  :— ||
                                            A    -    -   men.
```

Unison.

PUT thou thy trust in God,
In duty's path go on ;
Walk in His strength with faith and hope,
So shall thy work be done.

Harmony.

2 Give to the winds thy fears ;
Hope, and be undismayed ;
God hears thy sighs and counts thy tears,
God shall lift up thy head.

3 Through waves, and clouds, and storms
He gently clears thy way ;
Wait thou His time ; so shall this night
Soon end in joyous day.

4 Leave to His sovereign sway
To choose and to command ;
So shalt thou, wondering, own His way
How wise, how strong His hand.

5 Thou seest our weakness, Lord ;
Our hearts are known to Thee :
O lift Thou up the sinking hand,
Confirm the feeble knee.

Unison.

6 Let us, in life, in death,
Thy steadfast truth declare,
And publish, with our latest breath,
Thy love and guardian care.

PAUL GERHARDT, 1607–76 ;
tr. by JOHN WESLEY, 1703–91.

[May be sung to NARENZA, No. 546.]

548 MORWELLHAM. (86. 86. 86.)

Doh = F. *In moderate time.* CHARLES STEGGALL, 1826–1905.

```
:m.f |s :l |s :m |d :f |m :l,.t, |d :r |m :f |r :— |— ||
:d.d |d :d |d :t, |l, :d |d :l, |s, :t, |d :d |t, :— |— ||
:d.r |m :f |m :s |m :l |s :f |s :f |s :l |s :— |— ||
:d.d |d :d |d :s, |l, :f, |d :f |m :r |d :f, |s, :— |— ||

:m.r |d :d |d :r |m :fe |s :s.l |t :s |l :-.l |s :— |— ||
:t,.t, |d :l, |s, :t, |d :r |r :d.d |r :t, |m :r |t, :— |— ||
:f.f |m :f |s :f |s :l |s :m.fe |s :s |s :fe |s :— |— ||
:s,.s, |l, :f |m :r |d :d |t, :l,.l, |s, :m |d :r |s, :— |— ||

:s.s |l :t |s :l |f :m.r |s :d.r |m :f |r :-.d |d :— |— || d |d ||
:d.d |d :r |d :m |r :t, |d :d.d |d :d |d :t, |d :— |— || l, |s, ||
:s.s |f :f |s :d' |l :s |s :m.f |s :l |s :f |m :— |— || f |m ||
:m.m |f :r |m :d |r :f |m :l,.l, |s, :f, |s, :s, |d, :— |— || f, |d, ||
```

A-men.

FATHER, I know that all my life
Is portioned out for me;
And the changes that are sure to come
I do not fear to see;
But I ask Thee for a present mind,
Intent on pleasing Thee.

2 I ask Thee for a thoughtful love,
Through constant watching wise,
To meet the glad with joyful smiles,
And to wipe the weeping eyes,
And a heart at leisure from itself,
To soothe and sympathise.

3 I would not have the restless will
That hurries to and fro,
Seeking for some great thing to do,
Or secret thing to know;
I would be treated as a child,
And guided where I go.

4 Wherever in the world I am,
In whatsoe'er estate,
I have a fellowship with hearts
To keep and cultivate,
And a work of lowly love to do,
For the Lord on whom I wait.

5 So I ask Thee for the daily strength
To none that ask denied,
And a mind to blend with outward life
While keeping at Thy side,
Content to fill a little space,
If Thou be glorified.

ANNA LAETITIA WARING, 1820–1910.

549 ST. HUGH. (C.M.)

Doh = E♭. *In moderate time.* EDWARD JOHN HOPKINS, 1818–1901.

```
:d |d :r |m :d |s :r |m :m |f :l |s :d |r :— |— ||
:s, |l, :s, |s, :d |d :-.t, |d :d |d :t, |d :d |t, :— |— ||
:m |f :f |m :m |m :f |m :s |f :f |s :-.fe |s :— |— ||
:d |l, :t, |d :l, |s, :s, |d :ta, |l, :r |m :l, |s, :— |— ||
```

:s |d' :t |l :s |f :m |r :l |s :d |r :-.r |d :— |— ||d |d ||
:t, |d :m |m :d |d :d |d :t, |d :d |d :t, |d :— |— ||l, |s, ||
:f |m :se |l :m |f :s |l :r |s :m |r :f |m :— |— ||f |m ||
:s, |l, :t, |d :ta, |l, :s, |fe, :f, |m, :l, |f, :s, |d :— |— ||f, |d ||

A-men.

SIDON. (C.M.)

Lah = D. Doh = F. *Moderately slow.* WILLIAM CROTCH, 1775–1847.

:m |l :s :f |m :— :l, |r :d :t, |d :— :d
:l, |d :— :l,.t, |d :— :l, |l, :s, :s, |s :— :d
:d |m :— :f .s |l :— :d |f :m :r |m :— :l
:l, |l, :d :r |l, :— :l,.s, |f, :s, :s, |d :— :l,

|s :-.f :m |r :m :f |m :— ||d |l, :— :r |d :t, :m
|d :r :d |d :— :d |t, :— ||l, |l, :— :l, |l, :se, :t,
|s :— :s |l :— :l |se :— ||m |m :d :r |m :— :m
|m :t, :d |f :m :r |m :— ||l, |d :l, :f, |m, :— :se,

d :— :f	m :r :l	se :— :l	r :d :t,	l, :—		r	de	
l, :— :r	d :t, :t,	t, :— :m.d	t, :l, :se,	l, :—		l,	l,	
m :f :l	s :— :r	m :— :m	f :m :m.r	d :—		f	m	
l, :f, :r,	s, :— :f,	m, :m :d	r :m :m,	l, :—		r,	l,	

A-men.

LORD, it belongs not to my care
Whether I die or live;
To love and serve Thee is my share,
And this Thy grace must give.

2 If life be long, I will be glad,
That I may long obey;
If short, yet why should I be sad
To welcome endless day?

3 Christ leads me through no darker rooms
Than He went through before;
He that into God's Kingdom comes
Must enter by this door.

4 Come, Lord, when grace hath made me meet
Thy blessèd face to see;
For, if Thy work on earth be sweet,
What will Thy glory be?

5 My knowledge of that life is small,
The eye of faith is dim;
But 'tis enough that Christ knows all,
And I shall be with Him.

RICHARD BAXTER, 1615–91.

550 HERONGATE. (L.M.)

Doh = E♭. *In moderate time.* English Traditional Melody.

```
:s |s  :— :d |l  :— :s |s  :m  :r  |d :— :s |d' :— :d'
:d |d  :— :d |d  :— :d |t, :—  :t, |d :— :d |d  :— :d
:m |m  :— :s |f  :— :s |s  :—  :f  |m :— :m |s  :— :s
:d |d  :— :m |f  :— :m |s, :—  :s, |d :— :d |m  :— :m

m :— :s |l :s :l  |s  :— ‖ s |l :s :l |d' :t :l  |s :m :r
d :— :d |d :— :d  |t, :— ‖ d |d :— :d |f  :— :t, |d :— :t,
s :— :s |s :— :fe |s  :— ‖ s |f :— :f |l  :— :f  |s :— :f
d :— :m |r :— :r  |s  :— ‖ m |f :— :f |r  :— :r  |m :— :s,

d  :— :d  |m  :— :d  |l  :— :s  |s  :m :r  |d :— ‖ d  |d
d  :— :d  |t, :— :d  |d  :— :d  |t, :— :t, |d :— ‖ l, |s,
m  :— :m  |m  :— :m  |f  :— :s  |s  :— :f  |m :— ‖ f  |m
l, :— :l, |s, :— :l, |f, :— :m, |s, :— :s, |d :— ‖ f, |d
                                                      A-men.
```

GREAT God! and wilt Thou condescend
To be my Father and my Friend?
I a poor child, and Thou so high,
The Lord of earth and air and sky.

2 Art Thou my Father? canst Thou bear
To hear my poor imperfect prayer?
Or wilt Thou listen to the praise
That such a little one can raise?

3 Art Thou my Father? let me be
A meek obedient child to Thee,
And try, in word and deed and thought,
To serve and please Thee as I ought.

HOLLEY. (L.M.)

Doh = E♭. *Moderately slow.*

GEORGE HEWS, 1806–73.

m :re .m	d :m	r .m :f .s	m :—	s :fe .s	m :m .s
d :d .d	d :d	t_1 .d :r .t_1	d :—	d :d .d	d :d .m
s :fe .s	m :s	s :s	s :—	m :re .m	s :s
d :d .d	d :d	s :s_1	d :—	d :d .d	d :d

s .f :f .m	r :—	m :r .r	d :r	m .f :s .l	r :—
m .r :r .d	t_1 :—	d :t_1.t_1	l_1 :t_1	d .t_1 :d	d :t_1
s :s	s :—	s :s .f	m :s	s .f :m .l	s :—
t_1 :d	s_1 :—	d :s_1.se_1	l_1 :s_1	d .r :m .f	s :—

m :s .s	f :– .r	d :t_1	d :—	d	d
d :d .d	d :– .l_1	s_1 :s_1	s_1 :—	l_1	s_1
s :ta.ta	l :– .f	m :r	m :—	f	m
d :m .m	f :– .f_1	s_1 :s_1	d :—	f_1	d

A-men.

4 Art Thou my Father? I'll depend
Upon the care of such a Friend,
And only wish to do and be
Whatever seemeth good to Thee.

5 Art Thou my Father? then at last,
When all my days on earth are past,
Send down and take me in Thy love
To be Thy better child above.

ANN GILBERT, 1782–1866.

551

FRANCONIA. (S.M.)

Doh = E♭. *In moderate time.* *König's Choralbuch*, 1738.

```
:d  |r  :m  |f  :s  |m  :—  |— :s  |l  :d' |f  :m  |r  :— |— ||
:s, |t, :d  |d  :t, |d  :—  |— :d  |d  :d  |t, :d  |t, :— |— ||
:m  |s  :s  |f  :r  |m  :—  |— :m  |f  :s  |f  :s  |s  :— |— ||
:d  |s, :d  |l, :s, |d  :—  |— :d  |f  :m  |r  :d  |s, :— |— ||

:s  |d' :t  |l  :s   |l   :l   |s  :s  |d  :m  |r  :r   |d :— |— || d  |d  ||
:r  |d  :r  |m  :m   |m   :r.d |t, :t, |d  :d  |d  :t,  |d :— |— || l, |s, ||
:t  |s  :s  |d' :t   |l.s :fe  |s  :s  |m  :s  |l  :s.f |m :— |— || f  |m  ||
:s  |m  :s  |d  :m.r |d   :r   |s, :s, |l, :m, |f, :s,  |d :— |— || f, |d  ||
                                                                      A-men.
```

ST. EDMUND. (S.M.)

Doh = G. *In moderate time.* EDMUND GILDING, ? –1782.

```
:d  |d  :— :m  |r  :d  :t, |d  :— :r  |m  :— :s  |f  :— :m
:s, |l, :— :d  |l, :s, :s, |s, :— :s, |s, :— :d  |d  :— :d
:m  |m  :— :s  |f  :m  :r  |m  :— :t, |d  :— :s  |l  :— :s
:d  |l, :— :m, |f, :s, :s, |d, :— :s, |d, :— :m, |f, :— :d

|r  :— ||r  |r  :— :m  |f  :— :m  |r  :— :d  |d  :t, :s,
|t, :— ||s, |l, :— :s, |f, :— :s, |l, :— :m, |s, :— :s,
|s  :— ||t, |r  :— :de |r  :— :d  |f  :— :d  |r  :— :t,
|s, :— ||s, |f, :— :m, |r, :— :m, |f, :— :l, |s, :— :s,

|d  :— :m  |r  :d  :t, |d  :— :— ||d  |d  ||
|s, :— :d  |l, :s, :s, |s, :— :— ||l, |s, ||
|d  :— :s  |f  :m  :r  |m  :— :— ||f  |m  ||
|m, :— :d, |f, :s, :s, |d  :— :— ||f, |d  ||
                                   A-men.
```

MY times are in Thy hand:
My God, I wish them there;
My life, my friends, my soul I leave
Entirely to Thy care.

2 My times are in Thy hand,
Whatever they may be,
Pleasing or painful, dark or bright,
As best may seem to Thee.

3 My times are in Thy hand:
Why should I doubt or fear?
My Father's hand will never cause
His child a needless tear.

4 My times are in Thy hand,
Jesus, the Crucified;
Those hands my cruel sins had pierced
Are now my guard and guide.

5 My times are in Thy hand:
I'll always trust in Thee;
And, after death, at Thy right hand
I shall for ever be.

WILLIAM FREEMAN LLOYD, 1791–1853.

552 GOSHEN. (65. 65. D.)

Doh = B♭. *In moderate time.* *The Bible Class Magazine*, 1860.

```
d  :-.d  |t,  :l,  |s,  :—  |m,  :—  |s,  :m   |r   :d   |r   :—  |—  :—  ||
m, :-.m, |s,  :f,  |m,  :—  |d,  :—  |m,  :s,  |f,  :m,  |s,  :—  |—  :—  ||
s, :-.s, |m,  :f,  |s,  :—  |s,  :—  |d   :s,  |l,  :d   |t,  :—  |—  :—  ||
d, :-.d, |d,  :d,  |d,  :—  |d,  :—  |d,  :d,  |f,  :l,  |s,  :—  |—  :—  ||

d  :-.d  |t,  :l,     |s,  :—  |m,  :—  |s,  :s,  |m   :r   |d   :—  |—  :—  ||
m, :-.m, |f,  :f,     |s,  :—  |d,  :—  |d,  :m,  |s,  :f,  |m,  :—  |—  :—  ||
d  :-.s, |s,  :l,.t,  |d   :—  |d   :—  |d   :s,  |d   :t,  |d   :—  |—  :—  ||
d, :-.d, |r,  :r,     |m,  :—  |l,  :—  |m,  :d,  |s,  :s,  |d,  :—  |—  :—  ||

r  :r    |r   :m   |f   :—  |r   :—  |m   :d    |l,  :r    |s,  :—  |—  :—  ||
s, :s,   |l,  :s,  |f,  :—  |s,  :—  |s,  :s,   |s,  :fe,  |s,  :—  |—  :—  ||
t, :t,   |l,  :de  |r   :—  |t,  :—  |d   :m    |r   :-.d  |t,  :—  |—  :—  ||
s, :s,   |f,  :m,  |r,  :—  |s,  :—  |d,  :l,,  |r,  :r,   |s,  :—  |—  :—  ||

d  :-.d  |t,  :l,  |s,  :—  |m,  :—  |s,  :s,  |m   :r   |d   :—  |—  :—  || d  |d  ||
m, :-.s, |f,  :m,  |r,  :—  |d,  :—  |m,  :d,  |s,  :f,  |m,  :—  |—  :—  || f, |m, ||
d  :-.m  |r   :d   |r   :—  |m   :—  |d   :s,  |d   :t,  |d   :—  |—  :—  || l, |s, ||
d  :-.d  |s,  :l,  |t,  :—  |d   :—  |d,  :m,  |s,  :s,  |d,  :—  |—  :—  || f, |d, ||
                                                                          A-men.
```

JESUS is our Shepherd,
  His the voice we hear ;
Folded in His bosom,
  What have we to fear ?
Only let us follow
  Whither He doth lead,—
To the thirsty desert,
  Or the dewy mead.

2 Jesus is our Shepherd :
  Well we know His voice ;
How its gentlest whisper
  Makes our heart rejoice !
Even when He chideth,
  Tender is its tone ;
None but He shall guide us ;
  We are His alone.

3 Jesus is our Shepherd :
  For the sheep He bled ;
Every lamb is sprinkled
  With the blood He shed ;
Then on each He setteth
  His own secret sign :
'They that have My Spirit,
  These', saith He, 'are Mine.'

4 Jesus is our Shepherd :
  Guarded by His arm,
Though the wolves may raven,
  None can do us harm ;
When we tread death's valley,
  Dark with fearful gloom,
We will fear no evil,
  Victors o'er the tomb.

Hugh Stowell, 1799–1865.

553

LEUCHARS. (66. 66.)

Doh = F. *Moderately slow.* THOMAS LEGERWOOD HATELY, 1815–67.

m :—	m :s	f :m	r :—	m :—	d :d	r :r	m :—	
d :—	d :t,	r :d	t, :—	t, :—	l, :l,	t, :t,	d :—	
s :—	s :s	s :s	s :—	s :—	m :m	s :s	s :—	
d :—	d :s,	t, :d	s, :—	m, :—	l, :l,	s, :s,	d :—	

m :—	f :m	r :d	t, :—	d :—	r :m	r :r	d :—		d	d	
d :—	l, :d	t, :l,	se, :—	l, :—	t, :d	d :t,	d :—		l,	s,	
s :—	f :s	s :m	m :—	m :—	s :s	l :s	m :—		f	m	
d :—	r :d	s, :l,	m, :—	l, :—	s, :m,	f, :s,	d :—		f,	d	

A-men.

THY way, not mine, O Lord,
However dark it be!
Lead me by Thine own hand;
Choose out the path for me.

2 Smooth let it be or rough,
It will be still the best;
Winding or straight, it leads
Right onward to Thy rest.

3 I dare not choose my lot,
I would not if I might:
Choose Thou for me, my God,
So shall I walk aright.

4 The Kingdom that I seek
Is Thine; so let the way
That leads to it be Thine,
Else I must surely stray.

5 Take Thou my cup, and it
With joy or sorrow fill
As best to Thee may seem:
Choose Thou my good and ill;

6 Choose Thou for me my friends,
My sickness or my health;
Choose Thou my cares for me,
My poverty or wealth.

7 Not mine, not mine the choice
In things or great or small;
Be Thou my Guide, my Strength,
My Wisdom, and my All.

HORATIUS BONAR, 1808–89.

554

COLLAUDEMUS. (87. 87. 87.)

Doh = F. *In moderate time.* French Carol.

| d :— :r | d :t, :d | r :— :r | m :— :d | m :f :s | f :m :r
| s, :— :s, | s, :— :s, | t, :— :t, | d :— :s, | d :— :d | t, :d :s,
| m :— :f | m :r :m | f :— :f | s :— :m | s :— :s | s :— :r
| d :— :d | d :— :d | s, :— :s, | d :— :d | d :r :m | r :d :t,

| d :— :r | r :— :— || r :m :f | s :— :s | d :t, :d | r :— :r
| s, :— :fe, | s, :— :— || r :d :t, | d :— :s, | s, :— :fe, | s, :— :s,
| m :— :d | t, :— :— || s :— :s | s :— :d | m :— :d | d :— :t,
| l, :— :l, | s, :— :— || t, :d :r | m :— :m, | l, :— :l, | s, :— :s,

```
| m  :f  :m  | r   :—:r   | d  :l, :t, | d  :—:— || r  :m :f  | s :—:s  |
| s, :l, :s, | fe, :—:fe, | s, :—:f,   | m, :—:— || r  :d :t, | d :—:s, |
| d  :—:d    | d   :—:l,  | m  :d :r   | d  :—:— || s  :—:s   | s :—:d  |
| d  :—:d    | l,  :—:r,  | s, :—:s,   | d, :—:— || t, :d :r  | m :—:m, |

:||:
| d  :t, :d   | r  :—:r  | m  :f  :m  | r   :—:r   | d  :l, :t, | d  :—:— || d  | d  ||
| s, :—:fe,   | s, :—:s, | s, :l, :s, | fe, :—:fe, | s, :—:f,   | m, :—:— || f, | m, ||
| m  :—:d     | d  :—:t, | d  :—:d    | d   :—:l,  | m  :d :r   | d  :—:— || l, | s, ||
| l  :—:l,    | s, :—:s, | d  :—:d    | l,  :—:r,  | s  :—:s,   | d, :—:— || f, | d, ||
                                                                         A-men.
```

SAVIOUR, like a shepherd lead us.
Much we need Thy tender care;
In Thy pleasant pastures feed us;
For our use Thy folds prepare:
Blessèd Jesus! [are.
Thou hast bought us, Thine we

2 We are Thine; do Thou befriend us;
Be the Guardian of our way;
Keep from ill; from sin defend us;
Seek us when we go astray:
Blessèd Jesus!
Hear us children when we pray.

3 Thou hast promised to receive us,
Poor and sinful though we be;
Thou hast mercy to relieve us,
Grace to cleanse, and power to
Blessèd Jesus! [free:
Early let us turn to Thee.

4 Early let us seek Thy favour;
Early let us do Thy will;
Blessèd Lord and only Saviour,
With Thyself our bosoms fill:
Blessèd Jesus!
Thou hast loved us, love us still.

DOROTHY ANN THRUPP'S *Hymns for the Young*, 1836.

555 MISERERE MEI. (48. 84.)

Seven Sobs of a Sorrowful Soul, 1585.

Lah = G. Doh = B♭. *Slow.* G.t. f.B♭.

```
| d   :— | t, :l, | se, :-. || l, | t, :r  | (de)m :d   | r   :r     | d  :— | —:— || (d)  l,  :— |
| l,  :— | f, :f, | m,  :-. || m, | f, :l, | (l,)d :s,  | la, :s,.f, | m, :— | —:— || (ma) d,  :— |
| m   :— | r  :d  | t,  :-. || l, | l, :l, | (m)s  :d   | d   :t,    | d  :— | —:— || (d)  l,  :— |
| l,, :— | r, :r, | m,  :-. || d, | r, :f, | (m)s, :m,  | f,  :s,    | d, :— | —:— || (d)  l,  :— |

| s, :l,      | t, :t, | m  :r.d   | t,  :— || l, :— | r  :— | t,  :— | l,  :— | —:— || l, | l,  ||
| m, :m,.fe,  | s, :s, | d  :t,.l, | se, :— || l, :— | l, :— | se, :— | l,  :— | —:— || f, | m,  ||
| t, :d       | r  :r  | s  :f     | t,  :— || m  :— | f  :— | m   :r | d   :— | —:— || r  | de  ||
| m, :l,      | s, :s, | d, :r,    | m,  :— || d, :— | r, :— | m,  :— | l,, :— | —:— || r, | l,, ||
                                                                                      A-men.
```

HOLD Thou my hands! [fear,
In grief and joy, in hope and
Lord, let me feel that Thou art
Hold Thou my hands! [near:

2 If e'er by doubts
Of Thy good Fatherhood depressed,
I cannot find in Thee my rest,
Hold Thou my hands!

3 Hold Thou my hands,— [smite,
These passionate hands too quick to
These hands so eager for delight:
Hold Thou my hands!

4 And when at length, [cold,
With darkened eyes and fingers
I seek some last loved hand to hold,
Hold Thou my hands!

WILLIAM CANTON, 1845–1926.

556

FINLANDIA. (10. 10. 10. 10. 10. 10.)

Doh = E♭. *Unison.* *Moderately quick.* JEAN SIBELIUS, 1865-

{ :m |r :m |f :— |— :m |r :m |d :-.r|r :m |— :— |— ||

{ :m |r :m |f :— |— :m |r :m |d :-.r|m :— |— :— |— ||

{ :s |s :s |l :— |— :m |m :s |s :-.r|r :f |— :— |— ||

{ :f |m :r |m :— |— :d |d :r |r :-.m|m :— |— :— |— ||

{ :s |s :s |l :— |— :m |m :s |s :-.r|r :f |— :— |— ||

{ :f |m :r |m :— |— :d |d :r |r :-.d|d :— |— :— |— || f |m ||
d |d
l |s
f_1 |d
A-men.

[*Copyright, 1927, by Breitkopf & Härtel, Leipzig.*]

ST. HELEN. (10. 10. 10. 10. 10. 10.)

Doh = E♭. *Moderately quick.* WALTER HATELY, 1843-1907.

:m |f :— |f :— |m :— |— :d' |t :l |s :l |s :— |—
:d |d :— |t_1 :— |d :— |— :m |s :f |f :f |m :— |—
:s |s :— |s :— |s :— |— :d' |d' :d' |t :t |d' :— |—
:d |r :— |s_1 :— |d :— |— :d |m :f |s :s |d :— |—

:m |r :— |r :— |m :— |— :l |s :m |r :m |r :— |— ||
:d |d :— |t_1 :— |d :— |— :d |d :d |d :d |t_1 :— |— ||
:s |l :— |s :— |s :— |— :f |s :s |fe :l |r :— |— ||
:d |f_1 :— |s_1 :— |d :— |— :f |m :d |l_1 :fe_1 |s_1 :— |— ||

:m |f :— |f :— |m :— |— :d' |t :l |s :l |s :— |—
:d |d :— |t_1 :— |d :— |— :m |s :f |f :f |m :— |—
:d |s :— |s :— |s :— |— :d' |d' :d' |t :t |d' :— |—
:d |r :— |s_1 :— |d :— |— :d |m :f |s :s |d :— |—

Bb.t. f.Eb.

```
:^m l, |s, :—  |s, :—  |s, :—  |— :m   |r  :l,  |d  :t,  |^d s  :— |—  ||
:^d f, |m, :—  |r, :—  |m, :—  |— :s,  |l, :l,  |s, :f,  |^m t, :— |—  ||
:^s d  |d  :—  |t, :—  |d  :—  |— :d   |l, :r   |m  :r   |^d s  :— |—  ||
:^d f, |s, :—  |s, :—  |d  :—  |— :d,  |f, :f,  |s, :s,  |^d, s,:— |—  ||

:r  |f  :—  |m  :—  |r  :—  |— :m   |f  :s   |l  :t   |d' :— |—
:t, |d  :—  |t, :—  |l, :—  |— :de  |r  :m   |f  :f   |m  :— |—
:s  |f  :—  |s  :—  |l  :—  |— :l   |l  :d'  |d' :r'  |s  :— |—
:s, |l, :—  |s, :—  |f, :—  |— :l,  |r  :d   |f  :r   |d  :— |—

:t  |l  :—  |m  :—  |l  :—  |— :f   |m  :r   |s  :t,  |d  :— |— || d  |d  ||
:r  |d  :—  |de :—  |r  :—  |— :r   |t, :t,  |t, :s,  |s, :— |— || l, |s, ||
:se |l  :—  |l  :—  |l  :—  |— :l   |s  :f   |r  :f   |m  :— |— || f  |m  ||
:m  |l  :—  |s  :—  |f  :—  |— :r   |s  :s   |s, :s,  |d  :— |— || f, |d  ||
```

A-men.

Stille, mein Wille; dein Jesus hilft siegen.

BE still, my soul: the Lord is on thy side;
  Bear patiently the cross of grief or pain;
Leave to thy God to order and provide;
  In every change He faithful will remain.
Be still, my soul: thy best, thy heavenly Friend
Through thorny ways leads to a joyful end.

2 Be still, my soul: thy God doth undertake
  To guide the future as He has the past.
Thy hope, thy confidence let nothing shake;
  All now mysterious shall be bright at last.
Be still, my soul: the waves and winds still know
His voice who ruled them while He dwelt below.

3 Be still, my soul: when dearest friends depart,
  And all is darkened in the vale of tears,
Then shalt thou better know His love, His heart,
  Who comes to soothe thy sorrow and thy fears.
Be still, my soul: thy Jesus can repay,
From His own fulness, all He takes away.

4 Be still, my soul: the hour is hastening on
  When we shall be forever with the Lord,
When disappointment, grief, and fear are gone,
  Sorrow forgot, love's purest joys restored.
Be still, my soul: when change and tears are past,
All safe and blessèd we shall meet at last.

KATHARINA VON SCHLEGEL, 1697– ?; *tr.* by JANE LAURIE BORTHWICK, 1813–97.

557 ST. HUGH. (C.M.)

Doh = D. *In moderate time.* v. 2. English Traditional Melody.

d' :d'.d'	l :l	s :-.f	m :s	l.l :l	l :l	s :—	—	
d :d.d	t, :t,	d :r	d :d	d.d :d	r :r	r :—	—	
m :m.m	f :f	s :s	s :s	f.f :f	f :f	s :—	—	
d :d.d	r :r	m :t,	d :m	f.f :f.m	r :d	t, :—	—	

:m.f | s :s | m :l | s :s.m | d :d.r | m :m | r :r | d :— | — :— || f | m ||
:d | d :r | d :l, | t, :t, | d :d | d :d | d :t, | d :— | — :— || d | d ||
:s | s :s | s :f | r :s | m :m.f | s :m | l :s | m :— | — :— || l | s ||
:d.r | m :t, | d :f, | s, :s, | l, :l, | s, :l, | f, :s, | d :— | — :— || f, | d ||

A-men.

He that is down needs fear no fall,
He that is low, no pride;
He that is humble ever shall
Have God to be his guide.

2 I am content with what I have,
Little be it or much;
And, Lord, contentment still I crave,
Because Thou savest such.

3 Fulness to such a burden is
That go on pilgrimage;
Here little, and hereafter bliss,
Is best from age to age.

John Bunyan, 1628–88.

558 ST. KILDA. (C.M.)

Lah = E. Doh = G. *Slow.* William Robert Broomfield, 1826–88.

:l, | l, :t, | d :m | r :d | t, :d | l, :t, | d :r | m :— | — ||
:m, | m, :s, | s, :s,.d | t, :l, | se, :l, | m, :se, | l, :t, | d :— | — ||
:d | d :r | m :s | s :m | m :m | d :r | m :s | s :— | — ||
:l, | l, :s, | d, :d | s, :l, | m, :l, | d :t, | l, :s, | d :— | — ||

:m | r :m | s :m | r :d | t, :m | l, :d | t, :t, | l, :— | — || l, | l, ||
:d | t, :d | r :d | t, :l, | se, :se, | l, :l, | l, :se, | l, :— | — || f, | m, ||
:s | s :m | r :s | s :m | m :m | d :m | f :m.r | d :— | — || r | de ||
:d | s, :d | t, :d | s, :l, | m, :m, | f, :d, | r, :m, | l, :— | — || r, | l, ||

A-men.

SONG 67. (ST. MATTHIAS). (C.M.)

Doh = D. *In moderate time.* ORLANDO GIBBONS, 1583–1625.

d :—	s :m	f :s	l :l	s :s	d' :l	t :t	l :—	—	
d :—	r :d	d :m	m :r	m :d	d :m	m :-.r	d :—	—	
m :—	s :s	d' :t	l :t	d' :m	m :l	l :se	l :—	—	
d :—	t, :d	l, :s,	f, :f,	d :d	l, :d	m :m	l, :—	—	

:d' |t :l |s :s |f :m |r :s |s :d |m :r |d :— || d |d ||
:d.r |m :f |m :d |l,.t, :d |t, :t,.d |r :d |d :t, |d :— || l, |s, ||
:m.f |s :l.t |d' :m |f :s |s :s |s.f :m |s :-.f |m :— || f |m ||
:l, |s, :f, |d :m |r :d |s, :s,.l, |t, :d |s, :s, |d :— || f, |d ||

A-men.

WHO fathoms the eternal thought?
Who talks of scheme and plan?
The Lord is God! He needeth not
The poor device of man.

2 Here in the maddening maze of things,
When tossed by storm and flood,
To one fixed ground my spirit clings:
I know that God is good.

3 I long for household voices gone,
For vanished smiles I long;
But God hath led my dear ones on,
And He can do no wrong.

4 I know not what the future hath
Of marvel or surprise,
Assured alone that life and death
His mercy underlies.

5 And if my heart and flesh are weak
To bear an untried pain,
The bruisèd reed He will not break,
But strengthen and sustain.

6 And so beside the silent sea
I wait the muffled oar;
No harm from Him can come to me
On ocean or on shore.

7 I know not where His islands lift
Their fronded palms in air;
I only know I cannot drift
Beyond His love and care.

JOHN GREENLEAF WHITTIER, 1807–92.

[May be sung to FINGAL, No. 141.]

559 ST. SYLVESTER. (D.C.M.)

Doh = D. *In moderate time.* JOSEPH BARNBY, 1838–96.

```
:d  |d  :-.d |r  :m  |m  :-.r |r  :m  |f  :s  |l  :t  |s  :— |—
:d  |s, :-.d |d  :d  |d  :-.d |d  :d  |d  :d  |d  :t, |t, :— |d
:m  |m  :-.m |f  :s  |l  :-.l |l  :s  |l  :s  |f  :f  |f  :— |m
:d  |d  :-.d |d  :d  |f, :-.f,|f  :m  |r  :r  |r  :s, |d  :— |—

:s  |d' :-.t |l  :m  |s  :-.f |f  :m  |d  :-.d |m  :r  |r  :— |—
:r  |d  :-.r |m  :d  |m  :-.r |r  :t, |l, :-.d |d  :d  |t, :— |—
:s  |m  :-.m |m  :l  |l  :-.l |l  :se |m  :l   |s  :fe |s  :— |—
:t, |l, :-.t,|d  :l, |r  :-.r |r  :m  |l, :-.l,|r  :r  |s, :— |—

:r  |f  :-.m |r  :r  |s  :-.f |m  :m  |l  :-.s |f  :m  |f  :—
:r  |d  :-.d |d  :t, |d  :-.t,|d  :r  |de :-.de|de :de |r  :—
:t  |l  :-.s |f  :s  |s  :-.s |s  :s  |s  :m   |l  :s  |f  :—
:s  |s, :-.s,|s, :f  |m  :-.r |d  :ta,|l, :-.l,|l, :l, |r  :—

|s  :— |l  :-.l |t  :t  |d' :de'|r' :l  |t  :l  |f  :-.r |d :— |— ||f  |m ||
|m  :— |f  :-.d |r  :r  |d  :m  |r  :r  |r  :d  |l, :t,  |d :— |— ||d  |d ||
|ta :— |l  :-.l |l  :se |l  :ta |l  :f  |f  :r  |r  :f   |m :— |— ||l  |s ||
|d  :— |f  :-.f |m  :m  |l  :s  |f  :r  |s, :s, |s, :s,  |d :— |— ||f, |d ||
```

A-men.

THIRD MODE MELODY. (D.C.M.)

Doh = C. *Slow.* THOMAS TALLIS, *c.* 1510–85 (*rhythm slightly simplified*).

```
:m |s :s |s :— |— :s |l :l |t  :— |— ||t  |t  :— |— :t  |t  :d'
:m |m :m |m :— |— :m |d :r |t, :— |— ||m  |m  :— |— :re |m  :m
:s |t :t |t :— |— :t |l :l |se :— |— ||se |se :— |— :ba |se :l
:m |m :m |m :— |— :s |f :f |m  :— |— ||m  |m  :— |— :t, |m  :l,

|t  :— |— ||m |t :t |t :— |— :s |l :l |t  :— |— ||t  |t  :— |—
|m  :— |— ||m |m :m |m :— |— :m |m :r |t, :— |— ||m  |m  :— |—
|se :— |— ||s |s :s |s :— |— :t |l :l |se :— |— ||se |se :— |—
|m  :— |— ||m |m :m |m :— |— :s |f :f |m  :— |— ||m  |m  :— |—
```

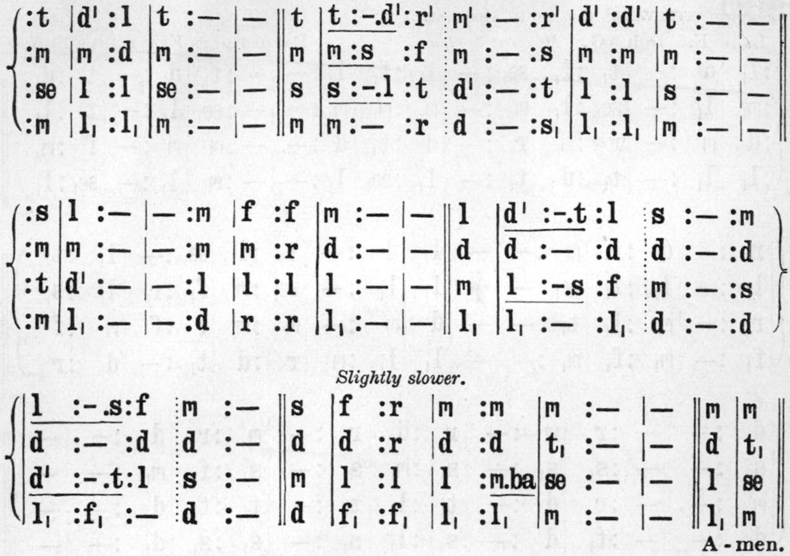

:t |d' :l |t :— |— ||t |t :-.d' :r' ¦m' :— :r' |d' :d' |t :— |— ||
:m |m :d |m :— |— ||m |m :s :f ¦m :— :s |m :m |m :— |— ||
:se |l :l |se :— |— ||s |s :-.l :t ¦d' :— :t |l :l |s :— |— ||
:m |l$_1$:l$_1$ |m :— |— ||m |m :— :r ¦d :— :s$_1$ |l$_1$:l$_1$ |m :— |— ||

:s |l :— |— :m |f :f |m :— |— ||l |d' :-.t :l ¦s :— :m
:m |m :— |— :m |m :r |d :— |— ||d |d :— :d ¦d :— :d
:t |d' :— |— :l |l :l |l :— |— ||m |l :-.s :f ¦m :— :s
:m |l$_1$:— |— :d |r :r |l$_1$:— |— ||l$_1$ |l$_1$:— :l$_1$ ¦d :— :d

Slightly slower.

l :-.s :f ¦m :—		s	f :r	m :m	m :—	—		m	m	
d :— :d ¦d :—		d	d :r	d :d	t$_1$:—	—		d	t$_1$	
d' :-.t :l ¦s :—		m	l :l	l :m.ba	se :—	—		l	se	
l$_1$:f$_1$:— ¦d :—		d	f$_1$:f$_1$	l$_1$:l$_1$	m :—	—		l$_1$	m	

A - men.

'TWIXT gleams of joy and clouds of doubt
Our feelings come and go ;
Our best estate is tossed about
In ceaseless ebb and flow.
No mood of feeling, form of thought,
Is constant for a day ;
But Thou, O Lord, Thou changest not :
The same Thou art alway.

2 I grasp Thy strength, make it mine own,
My heart with peace is blest ;
I lose my hold, and then comes down
Darkness, and cold unrest.
Let me no more my comfort draw
From my frail hold of Thee,
In this alone rejoice with awe—
Thy mighty grasp of me.

3 Out of that weak, unquiet drift
That comes but to depart,
To that pure heaven my spirit lift
Where Thou unchanging art.
Lay hold of me with Thy strong grasp,
Let Thy almighty arm
In its embrace my weakness clasp,
And I shall fear no harm.

4 Thy purpose of eternal good
Let me but surely know ;
On this I'll lean—let changing mood
And feeling come or go—
Glad when Thy sunshine fills my soul,
Not lorn when clouds o'ercast,
Since Thou within Thy sure control
Of love dost hold me fast.

JOHN CAMPBELL SHAIRP, 1819–85.

560 TREWEN. (88. 88. D. Anapaestic.)

Lah = E. Doh = G. *Moderately slow.* DAVID EMLYN EVANS, 1843–1913.

```
:l,  |d  :—  |t,  :l,  |se, :—  |l,  :t,  |l,  :—  |—  :t,  |d  :—  |t,  :d
:m,  |l, :—  |se, :l,  |m,  :—  |m,  :m,  |m,  :—  |—  :se, |l, :—  |t,  :l,
:d   |m  :—  |r   :m   |r   :—  |d   :t,  |d   :—  |—  :m   |m  :—  |f   :m
:l,  |l, :—  |t,  :d   |t,  :—  |l,  :se, |l,  :—  |—  :m,  |l, :—  |se, :l,

|r   :—  |d   :r   |m   :—  |—  :l, ‖ d   :—  |t,  :l,  |se, :—  |l,  :t,
|l,  :—  |l,  :l,  |se, :—  |—  :l, ‖ l,  :—  |se, :m,  |f,  :r,  |l,  :s,
|r   :—  |m   :l,  |t,  :—  |—  :d  ‖ m   :—  |m   :m   |r   :f   |m   :f
|f,  :—  |m,  :f,  |m,  :—  |—  :l, ‖ l,  :m  |r   :d   |t,  :—  |d   :r

|d  :—  |—  :r   |m   :—  |r   :d   |r   :—  |m   :r   |d   :—  |—  ‖
|s  :—  |—  :s,  |s,  :—  |s,  :m,  |s,  :—  |s,  :f,  |m,  :—  |—  ‖
|m  :—  |—  :r   |d   :—  |t,  :l,  |t,  :—  |t,  :t,  |d   :—  |—  ‖
|d  :—  |—  :t,  |d   :—  |s,  :l,  |s,  :—  |s,  :s,  |d,  :—  |—  ‖

:m  |m  :—  |d  :l,  |f   :—  |m   :r   |m   :—  |—  :m  |m  :—  |d  :l,
:m  |m  :—  |d  :l,  |l,  :—  |l,  :l,  |se, :—  |—  :m  |m  :—  |d  :l,
:m  |m  :—  |d  :l,  |r   :—  |d   :r   |t,  :—  |—  :m  |m  :—  |d  :l,
:m  |m  :—  |d  :l,  |r,  :—  |m,  :f,  |m,  :—  |—  :m  |m  :—  |d  :l,

|l   :—     |s   :fe  |s   :—  |—  ‖ f   |m  :—  |r  :d   |t,  :—  |d   :r
|l,  :t,.d  |t,  :l,  |t,  :—  |—  ‖ r   |d  :—  |t, :l,  |se, :—  |l,  :t,
|m   :—     |r   :r   |r   :—  |—  ‖ s   |s  :—  |f  :l   |m   :—  |m   :se
|d   :—     |r   :r,  |s,  :—  |—  ‖ t,  |d  :—  |r  :re  |m   :—  |m,  :m,

|d   :—  |—  :d   |d   :—  |t,  :l,  |se, :—  |l,  :t,  |l,  :—  |—  ‖ l,  |l,  ‖
|l,  :—  |—  :l,  |l,  :—  |f,  :f,  |m,  :—  |m,  :m,  |m,  :—  |—  ‖ f,  |m,  ‖
|l   :—  |—  :m   |f   :—  |f   :t,  |t,  :—  |d   :r   |d   :—  |—  ‖ r   |de  ‖
|f,  :—  |—  :m,  |r,  :—  |r,  :r,  |m,  :—  |m,  :m,  |l,  :—  |—  ‖ r,  |l,  ‖
```

A-men.

A SOVEREIGN Protector I have,
Unseen, yet for ever at hand,
Unchangeably faithful to save,
Almighty to rule and command.
He smiles, and my comforts abound;
His grace as the dew shall descend,
And walls of salvation surround
The soul He delights to defend.

2 Inspirer and Hearer of prayer,
Thou Shepherd and Guardian of Thine,
My all to Thy covenant care
I sleeping and waking resign.
If Thou art my Shield and my Sun,
The night is no darkness to me;
And, fast as my moments roll on,
They bring me but nearer to Thee.

AUGUSTUS MONTAGUE TOPLADY, 1740–78.

561 BUCER. (S.M.)

Doh = A. *In moderate time.* *Cantica Laudis*, 1850.

:s_1 | d :s_1 | l_1 :t_1 | d :— | — :d | f :m | r :d | t_1 :— | — ||
:s_1 | m_1 :s_1 | f_1 :f_1 | s_1 :— | — :s_1 | f_1 :s_1 | l_1 :l_1 | s_1 :— | — ||
:s_1 | s_1 :d | d :r | m :— | — :m | d :d | f :m | r :— | — ||
:s_1 | d_1 :m_1 | f_1 :r_1 | d_1 :— | — :d | l_1 :s_1 | f_1 :fe_1 | s_1 :— | — ||

:t_1 | d :s_1 | l_1 :t_1 | d :-.r | m :s | f :r | d :t_1 | d :— | — || d | d ||
:s_1 | m_1 :s_1 | f_1 :f_1 | s_1 :-.s_1 | s_1 :ta_1 | l_1 :l_1 | s_1 :f_1 | m_1 :— | — || f_1 | m_1 ||
:r | d :d | d :r | d :-.t_1 | d :d | d :f | m :r | d :— | — || l_1 | s_1 ||
:s_1 | d_1 :m_1 | f_1 :r_1 | m_1 :-.s_1 | d :m_1 | f_1 :f_1 | s_1 :s_1 | d_1 :— | — || f_1 | d_1 ||

A-men.

YOUR harps, ye trembling saints,
Down from the willows take:
Loud to the praise of love divine
Bid every string awake.

2 Though in a foreign land,
We are not far from home;
And nearer to our house above
We every moment come.

3 His grace will to the end
Stronger and brighter shine;
Nor present things nor things to come
Shall quench the spark divine.

4 When we in darkness walk,
Nor feel the heavenly flame,
Then is the time to trust our God,
And rest upon His Name.

5 Soon shall our doubts and fears
Subside at His control;
His loving-kindness shall break through
The midnight of the soul.

6 Wait till the shadows flee;
Wait thy appointed hour;
Wait till the Bridegroom of thy soul
Reveals His love with power.

7 Blest is the man, O God,
That stays himself on Thee:
Who wait for Thy salvation, Lord,
Shall Thy salvation see.

AUGUSTUS MONTAGUE TOPLADY, 1740–78.

Also the following:

30 Though troubles assail and dangers affright
31 God moves in a mysterious way
33 God is love; His mercy brightens
143 O Love Divine! that stooped to share
148 There is no sorrow, Lord, too light
424 O Love that wilt not let me go
438–48 *Hymns of Peace and Joy*
695 I am trusting Thee, Lord Jesus
696 Jesus, I will trust Thee
697 My hope is built on nothing less

PILGRIMAGE AND REST

562

SALZBURG. (C.M.)

Doh = E♭. *Moderately slow.* JOHANN MICHAEL HAYDN, 1737–1806.

:d | m :— :s | s :f :m | m :— :r | d :— :d | d :t, :d
:s, | d :— :d | r :— :d | d :— :t, | d :— :l, | s, :— :s,
:m | s :— :s | s :— :s | s :— :f | m :— :f | s :f :m
:d | d :— :m | t, :— :d | s, :— :se, | l, :— :f | m :r :d

| s :f :m | m :r || d | d :— :l | s :m :d | d :— :l
| s, :r :d | d :t, || s, | d :— :d | d :— :s, | d :— :d
| r :s :s | s :— || m | f :— :f | m :s :m | f :— :f
| t, :— :d | s, :— || d.ta, | l, :— :f, | d :— :d.ta, | l, :— :f,

s :— :d'	d' :l :f	m :f :r	d :—		d	d	
d :— :d	d :— :d	d :t, :t,	d :—		l,	s,	
m :— :s	l :f :l	s :r :f	m :—		f	m	
d :— :m,	f, :— :f,	s, :— :s,	d :—		f,	d	

A-men.

FRENCH. (C.M.)

Doh = E♭. *Moderately slow.* *Scottish Psalter*, 1615.

d :—	m :f	s :d	r :m	f :—		m :—	r :d	d :t,	d :—	
s, :—	d :d	d :l,	t, :d	d :—		d :—	t, :l,	l, :s,	s, :—	
m :—	s :l	s :m	s :s	l :—		s :—	s :m	f :r	m :—	
d :—	d :f,	m, :l,	s, :d	f, :—		d :—	s, :l,	f, :s,	d :—	

s :—	d' :t	l :s	s :fe	s :—		m :—	r :d	d :t,	d :—		d	d	
d :—	m :r	d :t,	l, :l,	t, :—		s, :—	l, :m,.f,	s, :s,	s, :—		l,	s,	
m :—	s :s	m :r	m :r	r :—		m :—	f :d	r :r	m :—		f	m	
d :—	d :s,	l, :t,	d :r	s, :—		d :—	f, :l,	s, :s,	d :—		f,	d	

A-men.

From Genesis xxviii. 20–22.

O GOD of Bethel! by whose hand
Thy people still are fed;
Who through this weary pilgrimage
Hast all our fathers led:

2 Our vows, our prayers, we now present
Before Thy throne of grace:
God of our fathers! be the God
Of their succeeding race.

3 Through each perplexing path of life
Our wandering footsteps guide ;
Give us each day our daily bread,
And raiment fit provide.

4 O spread Thy covering wings around,
Till all our wanderings cease,
And at our Father's loved abode
Our souls arrive in peace.

5 Such blessings from Thy gracious hand
Our humble prayers implore ;
And Thou shalt be our chosen God,
And portion evermore.

PHILIP DODDRIDGE, 1702–51 ; and JOHN LOGAN, 1748–88 ;
as in *Scottish Paraphrases*, 1781.

563

CORINTH. (87. 87. 87.)

Doh = A. *Moderately slow.* *Essay on the Church Plain Chant*, 1782.

d :r |m :f |s :f |m :r |d :d |d :f |m :r |d :— ||
s, :s, |s, :d |d :l, |s, :s, |s, :m, |f, :f, |s, :s, |m, :— ||
m :r |d :-.r |m :d |d :t, |d :d.t, |l, :d |d :t, |d :— ||
d :t, |d :l, |m, :f, |s, :s, |m, :d, |f, :l, |s, :s, |d, :— ||

E.t.

l, :l, |s, :s, |d :d |d :t, |(r)s :d' |t.l :s.f |m :r |d :— ||
f, :f, |m, :s, |l, :s,.l, |s, :s, |(s,)d :d |d :r |d :t, |d :— ||
d :d |d :r |m :d |m :r |(r)s :m |f :l |s :s |m :— ||
f, :l, |d :t, |l, :m,.f, |s, :s, |(t,)m :d |f :r |s :s, |d :— ||

f.A.

(m)t, :t, |d :s, |l, :t, |d :r |m.r :d.t, |l, :f |m :r |d :— ||d |d ||
(d)s, :s, |s, :m, |f, :f, |m, :s, |s, :s, |f, :l, |s, :-.f, |m, :— ||f, |m, ||
(s)r :r |d :d |d :r |d :t, |d :d |d :d |d :t, |d :— ||l, |s, ||
(d)s, :f, |m, :d, |f, :r, |l, :s, |d :m, |f, :r, |m,.f, :s, |d, :— ||f, |d, ||

A-men.

LEAD us, heavenly Father, lead us
O'er the world's tempestuous sea ;
Guard us, guide us, keep us, feed us,
For we have no help but Thee ;
Yet possessing every blessing
If our God our Father be.

2 Saviour, breathe forgiveness o'er us ;
All our weakness Thou dost know ;
Thou didst tread this earth before us,
Thou didst feel its keenest woe ;
Lone and dreary, faint and weary,
Through the desert Thou didst go.

3 Spirit of our God, descending,
Fill our hearts with heavenly joy,
Love with every passion blending
Pleasure that can never cloy ;
Thus provided, pardoned, guided,
Nothing can our peace destroy.

JAMES EDMESTON, 1791–1867.

564 MANNHEIM. (87. 87. 87.)

Doh = E. *In moderate time.* FRIEDRICH FILITZ, 1804–76.

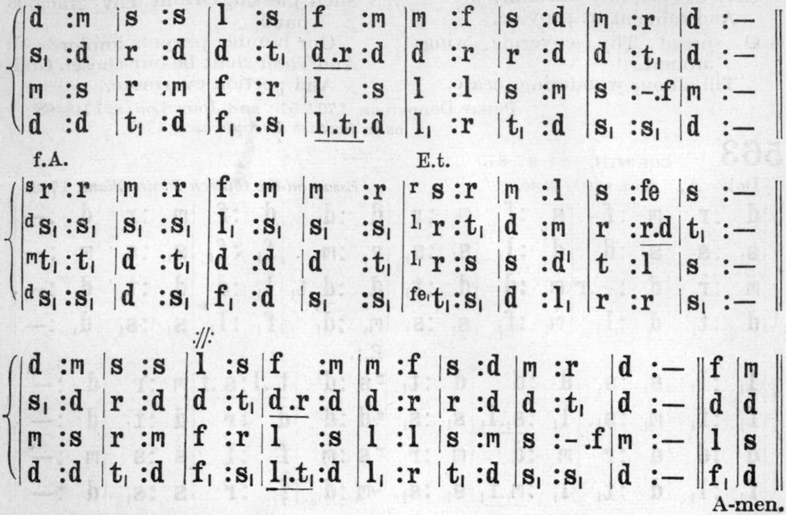

```
d  :m  |s  :s  |l  :s  |f   :m |m  :f |s  :d |m  :r   |d :— ||
s, :d  |r  :d  |d  :t, |d.r :d |d  :r |r  :d |d  :t,  |d :— ||
m  :s  |r  :m  |f  :r  |l   :s |l  :l |s  :m |s  :-.f |m :— ||
d  :d  |t, :d  |f, :s, |l,.t, :d |l, :r |t, :d |s, :s, |d :— ||
```

f.A. E.t.

```
(s)r  :r  |m  :r  |f  :m  |m  :r  |(r)s  :r  |m :l  |s :fe  |s  :— ||
(d)s, :s, |s, :s, |l, :s, |s, :s, |(l,)r :t, |d :m  |r :r.d |t, :— ||
(m)t, :t, |d  :t, |d  :d  |d  :t, |(l,)r :s  |s :d' |t :l   |s  :— ||
(d)s, :s, |d  :s, |f, :d  |s, :s, |(fe)t, :s, |d :l, |r :r  |s, :— ||
```

```
              :||:
d  :m |s  :s |l  :s  |f   :m |m  :f |s  :d |m  :r   |d :— || f  |m ||
s, :d |r  :d |d  :t, |d.r :d |d  :r |r  :d |d  :t,  |d :— || d  |d ||
m  :s |r  :m |f  :r  |l   :s |l  :l |s  :m |s  :-.f |m :— || l  |s ||
d  :d |t, :d |f, :s, |l,.t, :d |l, :r |t, :d |s, :s, |d :— || f, |d ||
```

A-men.

CAERSALEM. (87. 87. 87.)

Doh = G. *In moderate time.* ROBERT EDWARDS, 1797–1862.

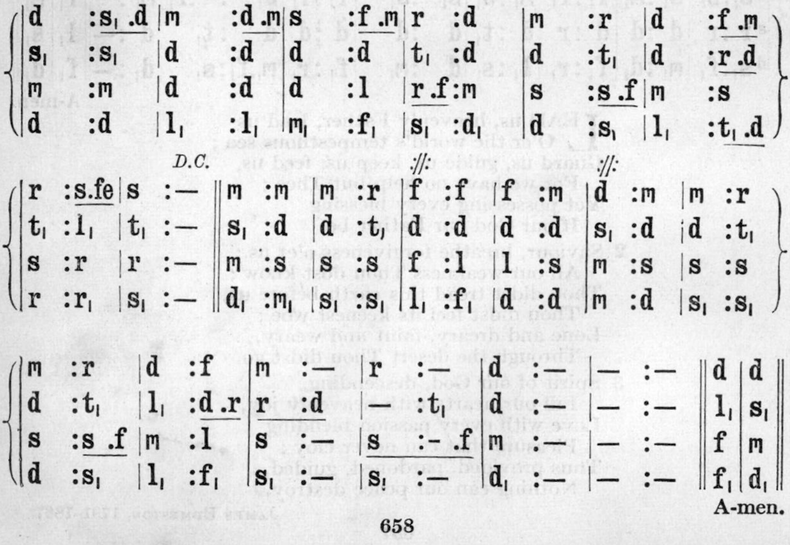

```
d  :s,.d |m  :d.m |s  :f.m |r   :d  |m :r   |d  :f.m
s, :s,   |d  :d   |d  :d   |t,  :d  |d :t,  |d  :r.d
m  :m    |d  :d   |d  :l   |r.f :m  |s :s.f |m  :s
d  :d    |l, :l,  |m, :f,  |s,  :d, |d :s,  |l, :t,.d
```

```
             D.C.           :||:               :||:
r  :s.fe |s  :— || m  :m  |m  :r  |f  :f  |f :m |d  :m |m  :r
t, :l,   |t, :— || s, :d  |d  :t, |d  :d  |d :d |s, :d |d  :t,
s  :r    |r  :— || m  :s  |s  :s  |f  :l  |l :s |m  :s |s  :s
r  :r,   |s, :— || d, :m, |s, :s, |l, :f, |d :d |m  :d |s, :s,
```

```
m :r   |d  :f   |m  :— |r  :—   |d  :— |— :— || d  |d  ||
d :t,  |l, :d.r |r  :d |—  :t,  |d  :— |— :— || l, |s, ||
s :s.f |m  :l   |s  :— |s  :-.f |m  :— |— :— || f  |m  ||
d :s,  |l, :f,  |s, :— |s, :—   |d, :— |— :— || f, |d, ||
```

A-men.

Arglwydd, arwain trwy'r anialwch.

GUIDE me, O Thou great Jehovah,
Pilgrim through this barren land;
I am weak, but Thou art mighty;
Hold me with Thy powerful hand:
Bread of heaven,
Feed me till my want is o'er.

2 Open now the crystal fountain,
Whence the healing stream doth flow;
Let the fire and cloudy pillar
Lead me all my journey through:
Strong Deliverer,
Be Thou still my strength and shield.

3 When I tread the verge of Jordan,
Bid my anxious fears subside!
Death of death, and hell's Destruction,
Land me safe on Canaan's side!
Songs of praises
I will ever give to Thee.

WILLIAM WILLIAMS, 1717–91; *tr.* by PETER WILLIAMS, 1727–96.

565 LYNE. (77. 77.)

Doh = E♭. *In moderate time.* *Magdalen Chapel Hymns, c.* 1760.

d :— :r	m :-.r :d	m :— :fe	s :— :—	s :— :l
d :— :s_1	s_1 :— :s_1	d :— :d	r :— :—	d :— :t_1
m :— :s	s :— :m	s :— :l	t :— :—	s :— :f
d :— :t_1	d :— :m	d :t_1 :l_1	s_1 :s :f	m :— :r

s :— :f	m :-.f :r	d :— :—	s :-.f :m	s :— :d	m :-.f :m
d :— :r	d :— :t_1	d :— :—	r :— :d	d :— :d	d :-.r :d
s :— :l	s :— :f	m :— :—	s :— :s	s :— :s	l :— :s
m :— :f	s :— :s_1	d :— :—	t_1 :— :d	m :— :m	l_1 :— :d

r :— :—	m :-.f :s	d' :s :f	m :f :r	d :— :—	d	d
t_1 :— :—	d :— :t_1	d :— :d	d :r :t_1	d :— :—	l_1	s_1
s :— :—	s :— :f	m :s :l	s :— :f	m :— :—	f	m
s_1 :— :—	d :— :r	m :— :f	s :— :s_1	d :— :—	f_1	d

A-men.

FATHER, lead me, day by day,
Ever in Thine own sweet way;
Teach me to be pure and true;
Show me what I ought to do.

2 When in danger, make me brave;
Make me know that Thou canst save;
Keep me safe by Thy dear side;
Let me in Thy love abide.

3 When I'm tempted to do wrong,
Make me steadfast, wise, and strong;
And, when all alone I stand,
Shield me with Thy mighty hand.

4 When my heart is full of glee,
Help me to remember Thee,
Happy most of all to know
That my Father loves me so.

5 May I do the good I know,
Be Thy loving child below,
Then at last go home to Thee,
Evermore Thy child to be.

JOHN PAGE HOPPS, 1834–1912.

566

LONGWOOD. (10 10. 10 10.)

Doh = E. *In moderate time.* JOSEPH BARNBY, 1838–96.

```
m  :—  |m  :f  |s  :m  |r  :d  |d  :—  |t,  :—  |d  :—  |—  :—
s, :—  |d  :d  |d  :t, |l, :l, |s, :—  |s,  :—  |s, :—  |—  :—
d  :—  |d  :r  |m  :s  |f  :m  |r  :—  |r   :—  |m  :—  |—  :—
d  :—  |l, :l, |m, :m, |f, :f, |s, :—  |s,  :—  |d  :—  |—  :—

        B.t.                                    f.E.
m  :—  |(m)l, :t, |d  :m  |r  :l, |d  :—  |t,  :—  |(d)s   :—  |— :—  ||
d  :—  |(m)l, :l, |l, :s, |f, :l, |s, :—  |f,  :—  |(m)t,  :—  |— :—  ||
s  :—  |(d)f  :f  |m  :d  |l, :f  |m  :—  |r   :—  |(d)s   :—  |— :—  ||
d  :—  |(l)r, :r, |l, :l, |r, :r, |s, :—  |s,  :—  |(d)s,  :—  |— :—  ||

r  :—  |d  :d  |f  :—  |m  :—  |s   :s   |f  :s  |l  :—  |— :—
t, :—  |d  :s, |l, :t, |d  :—  |d   :d   |d  :m  |f  :—  |— :—
s  :—  |s  :m  |f  :—  |s  :—  |m   :m   |f  :ta |l  :—  |— :—
f  :—  |m  :m  |r  :—  |d  :—  |ta, :ta, |l, :s, |f, :—  |— :—

t  :—  |d' :s  |f  :f  |m  :s   |d  :—  |—  :r  |m  :—  |— :—  || f  |m  ||
r  :—  |d  :d  |d  :r  |s, :ta, |l, :—  |l, :—  |s, :—  |— :—  || d  |d  ||
s  :—  |s  :s  |l  :t  |d' :s   |s  :—  |f  :—  |m  :—  |— :—  || l  |s  ||
f  :—  |m  :m  |r  :s, |d  :m,  |f, :—  |f, :—  |d  :—  |— :—  || f, |d  ||
                                                                   A-men.
```

[*By permission of Novello & Co., Ltd.*]

LEAD us, O Father, in the paths of peace :
  Without Thy guiding hand we go astray,
And doubts appal, and sorrows still increase ;
  Lead us through Christ, the true and living Way.

2 Lead us, O Father, in the paths of truth :
  Unhelped by Thee, in error's maze we grope,
While passion stains and folly dims our youth,
  And age comes on uncheered by faith or hope.

3 Lead us, O Father, in the paths of right :
  Blindly we stumble when we walk alone,
Involved in shadows of a darkening night ;
  Only with Thee we journey safely on.

4 Lead us, O Father, to Thy heavenly rest,
  However rough and steep the pathway be,
Through joy or sorrow, as Thou deemest best,
  Until our lives are perfected in Thee.

WILLIAM HENRY BURLEIGH, 1812–71.

[May be sung to SONG 22, No. 195.]

567 SEELENBRÄUTIGAM (ARNSTADT). (55. 88. 55.)

Doh = G. *Slow.* ADAM DRESE, 1620–1701.

```
d .d  :t,  :d     |r    :—   :—  ||d .r  :m     :r    |d   :—  :—  ||
s,.s, :s,  :s,.l, |t,   :—   :—  ||l,.t, :d     :t,   |d   :—  :—  ||
m .m  :r   :d     |s    :—   :—  ||m .s  :s     :s .f |m   :—  :—  ||
d .d  :s,  :m,    |s,   :—   :—  ||l,.s, :m,.f, :s,   |d,  :—  :—  ||

m .f  :s   :f     |m .r :m     :r  ||d .r  :m  :r   |d .t,  :d      :t,  ||
d .d  :d   :l,    |d .t,:s,.l, :t, ||l,.t, :d  :t,  |l,.se, :m,.ba,  :se, ||
s .f  :d   :d     |m .s :s     :s  ||m .s  :s  :s   |m .m   :m      :m   ||
d .l, :m,  :f,    |d .s,:d     :s, ||l,.s, :d, :s,  |l,.m,  :l,     :m,  ||

d .d    :t,  :d     |r   :—  :—  ||d .r  :m  :r     |d   :—  :—  ||d  |d  ||
m,.fe,  :s,  :s,.l, |t,  :—  :—  ||s,.l, :s, :s,.f, |m,  :—  :—  ||f, |m, ||
d .d    :r   :d     |s   :—  :—  ||d .d  :d  :t,    |d   :—  :—  ||l, |s, ||
l,.l,   :s,  :m,    |s,  :—  :—  ||m,.f, :s, :s,    |d,  :—  :—  ||f, |d, ||
                                                                  A - men.
```

Jesu, geh' voran.

JESUS, still lead on,
Till our rest be won,
And, although the way be cheerless,
We will follow, calm and fearless;
Guide us by Thy hand
To our fatherland.

2 If the way be drear,
If the foe be near,
Let not faithless fears o'ertake us,
Let not faith and hope forsake us;
For, through many a foe,
To our home we go.

3 When we seek relief
From a long-felt grief,
When oppressed by new temptations,
Lord, increase and perfect patience;
Show us that bright shore
Where we weep no more.

4 Jesus, still lead on,
Till our rest be won;
Heavenly Leader, still direct us,
Still support, console, protect us,
Till we safely stand
In our fatherland.

NICOLAUS LUDWIG VON ZINZENDORF, 1700–60;
tr. by JANE LAURIE BORTHWICK, 1813–97.

FIRST TUNE

568

BONIFACIO. (104. 104. 1010.)

Lah = D. Doh = F. *Moderately slow.* DAVID EVANS, 1874-

```
| d  :—  | m  :l  | s  :—  | —  :m  | d  :r  | m  :d  | l, :—  | t, :—  |
| l, :—  | l, :d  | t, :—  | —  :t, | l, :l, | s, :s, | f, :—  | l, :—  |
| m  :—  | d  :m  | s  :—  | —  :s  | s  :f  | m  :r  | d  :—  | f  :—  |
| l, :—  | d  :l, | m  :—  | —  :m, | l, :t, | d  :m, | f, :—  | m, :r, |

| d  :—  | l, :—  | m   :— | — :— | — || d  | m  :l  | s  :—  | — :m  |
| l, :—  | l, :—  | se, :— | — :— | — || m, | l, :t, | d  :—  | — :t, |
| m  :d  | r  :l, | t,  :— | — :— | — || d  | d  :r  | m  :s  | — :s  |
| l, :—  | s, :f, | m,  :— | — :— | — || l, | s, :f, | m, :—  | — :s, |

| d  :r  | m  :d  | l, :—  | t,  :—  | d  :—  | r  :—  | d      :— | — :— ||
| l, :l, | t, :m, | f, :—  | l,  :se,| l, :d  | —  :t, | d      :— | — :— ||
| s  :f  | m  :s  | d  :—  | r   :m  | d  :m  | l  :s  | m      :— | — :— ||
| l, :l, | s, :s, | f, :—  | f,  :m, | l, :s, | f, :s, | d (d,) :— | — :— ||

  C.t.                                                                f. F.
|  :[t]m | l  :t  | d' :l  | r' :d' | t  :—  | m  :—  | l  :—  | — :[l]m    |
|  :[t]m | m  :r  | d  :m  | l  :s  | f  :—  | m  :r  | de :—  | — :[r]l,   |
|  :[t]m | ba :se | l  :d' | t  :d' | r' :l  | —  :se | l  :—  | — :[fe]de  |
|  :[t]m | d  :m  | l  :s  | f  :m  | r  :—  | m  :—  | l, :—  | — :[r]l,   |

| f  :—  | m   :—   | r  :f   | m  :t, | d  :—  | t, :—   | l, :— | — :— ||
| l, :—  | —   :m,  | l, :se, | l, :t, | t, :l, | —  :se, | l, :— | — :— ||
| r  :—  | d   :t,  | f  :r   | m  :f  | m  :—  | m  :r   | d  :— | — :— ||
| r, :m, | ba, :se, | l, :t,  | d  :r  | m  :—  | m, :    | l, :— | — :— ||

                  rall. . . . .
| t, :d  | r  :m  | f  :—  | m  :r  | m  :— | — :— ||
| l, :—  | t, :d  | r  :—  | d  :t, | de :— | — :— ||
| f  :—  | —  :m  | r  :m  | f  :s  | l  :— | — :— ||
| r  :—  | —  :d  | t, :d  | r  :—  | l, :— | — :— ||
  A     -        -        -        men.
```

[*Copyright*, 1927, *by David Evans.*]

SECOND TUNE.

PATMOS. (104. 104. 1010.)

Doh = F. *Slow.*

SAMUEL SEBASTIAN WESLEY, 1810–76.

:s, |m :m |m :-.m |m :-.m |r :l |l :-.l |s :f |m :— |— ||

:s, |s, :s, |se, :-.se, |l, :-.l, |l, :d |t, :-.t, |t, :t, |s, :— |— ||

:s |d :d |d :-.d |d :-.de |r :r |f :-.f |m :r |m :— |— ||

:s, |d :d |d :-.d |f, :-.f, |f, :f, |s, :-.s, |s, :s, |d :— |— ||

C.t.

:m |s :-.r |m :^{s}d' |t :-.l |s :f |m :m |f :r |d :— |— ||

:s, |s, :-.s, |s, :^{s}d |r :-.d |de :r |t, :d |r :t, |d :— |— ||

:m |r :-.r |d :^{r}s |se :-.l |ta :l |se :l |l :f |m :— |— ||

:d |t, :-.t, |d :^{t}m |f :-.f |r :r |m :l, |f, :s, |d :— |— ||

f.F.

:^{d}s, |d :r |s, :m |d :f |f :m |r :— |l :—

:^{d}s, |s, :l, |s, :t, |d :d |r :d |t, :— |t, :—

:^{m}t, |d :l, |t, :m |m :d |s :s |s :— |r :—

:^{ta}f, |m, :f, |s, :s, |l, :l, |t, :d |s, :— |f, :—

|s :-.f |m :r |d :r |m :r |d :— |— || d |d ||

|d :-.d |d :t, |d :d |d :t, |d :— |— || l, |s, ||

|s :-.l |s :f |m :fe |s :f |m :— |— || f |m ||

|m, :-.f, |s, :se, |l, :l, |s, :s, |d :— |— || f, |d ||

A-men.

LEAD, kindly Light, amid the encircling gloom,
Lead Thou me on;
The night is dark, and I am far from home;
Lead Thou me on.
Keep Thou my feet; I do not ask to see
The distant scene,—one step enough for me.

2 I was not ever thus, nor prayed that Thou
Shouldst lead me on;
I loved to choose and see my path, but now
Lead Thou me on;
I loved the garish day, and, spite of fears,
Pride ruled my will: remember not past years.

3 So long Thy power hath blest me, sure it still
Will lead me on,
O'er moor and fen, o'er crag and torrent, till
The night is gone,
And with the morn those angel faces smile,
Which I have loved long since, and lost awhile.

JOHN HENRY NEWMAN, 1801–90.

THIRD TUNE.

568 *(continued)*

LUX BENIGNA. (10 4. 10 4. 10 10.)

Doh = A♭. *Slow.* JOHN BACCHUS DYKES, 1823–76.

```
.s, :d .r   | m .,m :r .d :l, .d      | l, :s, :—  | d  :t, :d      | r  :- .
.s, :s, .s, | s, .,m, :f, .s, :s, .f, | f, :s, :—  | s, :s, :s, .m, | f, :- .
.m  :m .f   | m .,d :d .d :d .d       | d  :m  :f  | s  :f  :m .d   | d  :t, .
.d  :d .d   | d .,d, :r, .m, :f, .l,  | d  :— :r   | m  :r  :d      | s, :- .
```

```
.s, :d .r   | m .,m :r .d :l, .d      | l, :s, :— | s, :d  :-.t, | t, :d  :—
.s, :s, .s, | s, .,m, :f, .s, :s, .f, | f, :m, :— | m, :s, :-.f, | s, :— :—
.f  :f .f   | m .,d :d .d :d .d       | d  :— :—  | d  :m  :-.r  | f  :m  :—
.s, :l, .t, | d .,d, :r, .m, :f, .l,  | d  :d, :m, | s, :s, :-.s, | s, :d  :—
```

E♭.t. f.A♭.

```
[r]s  :s  :s     | s  :— :s | s .l   :s .f :m .r | [d]s,  :—  :—
[s,]d :t, :d     | r  :— :d | d .d   :t,   :t,   | [d]s,  :m, :f,
[r]s  :f  :m .l  | s  :f :m | m .m   :f    :f    | [m]t,  :d  :r
[t,]m :r  :d     | t, :— :d | s, .s, :s,   :s,   | [d]s,  :—  :—
```

```
m  :r      :d        | d  :-.d  :t, .l, | s, :d  :-.t, | t, :d  . || d  | d  ||
m, :f,     :s, .se,  | l, :-.l, :s, .f, | m, :s, :-.f, | f, :m, . || f, | m, ||
d  :l, .t, :d        | d  :-.l, :t, .d  | d  :m  :-.r  | r  :d  . || l, | d  ||
d, :r,     :m,       | f, :-.f, :f, .f, | s, :—  :s,   | s, :d, . || f, | d, ||
```

A-men.

FOURTH TUNE.

SANDON. (10 4. 10 4. 10 10.)

Doh = G. *Slow.* CHARLES HENRY PURDAY, 1799–1885.

```
m :m .m | f :- .m | m .r :d .r       | m :- .d  | r  :t, | d  :— ||
d :d .d | d :- .d | t, .t, :d .t,    | d :- .m, | l, :s, | s, :— ||
s :s .s | l :- .s | f .f :m .r       | d :- .d  | f  :f  | m  :— ||
d :d .d | d :- .d | s, .s, :s, .s,   | d :- .l, | f, :s, | d  :— ||
```

```
| m   :m .m   | f  :- .m  | m .r  :d .r   | m :- .d  | r  :t,  | d  :—  ||
| d   :d .d   | d  :- .d  | t, .t, :d .t, | d :- .m, | l, :s,  | s, :—  ||
| s   :s .s   | l  :- .s  | f .f  :m .r   | d :- .d  | f  :f   | m  :—  ||
| d   :d .d   | d  :- .d  | s, .s, :s, .s,| d :- .l, | f, :s,  | d  :—  ||

| r   :r .m   | f  :r   | s .f  :m .r   | m :- . || s | l :s |
| t,  :t, .d  | t, :t,  | d .t, :d .t,  | d :- . || d | d :d |
| f   :f .m   | r  :s   | s .s  :s .s   | s :- . || s | f :s |
| s,  :s, .s, | s, :s,  | m .r  :d .s,  | d :- . || m | f :m |

| f   :- .m  | s .f  :m .r    | d :—  || d  | d  ||
| t,  :- .d  | d .r  :d .t,   | d :—  || l, | s, ||
| s   :- .s  | l .l  :s .f    | m :—  || f  | m  ||
| r   :- .d  | f, .f, :s, .s, | d :—  || f, | d  ||
                                        A-men.
```

LEAD, kindly Light, amid the encircling gloom,
Lead Thou me on;
The night is dark, and I am far from home;
Lead Thou me on.
Keep Thou my feet; I do not ask to see
The distant scene,—one step enough for me.

2 I was not ever thus, nor prayed that Thou
Shouldst lead me on;
I loved to choose and see my path, but now
Lead Thou me on;
I loved the garish day, and, spite of fears,
Pride ruled my will: remember not past years.

3 So long Thy power hath blest me, sure it still
Will lead me on,
O'er moor and fen, o'er crag and torrent, till
The night is gone,
And with the morn those angel faces smile,
Which I have loved long since, and lost awhile.

JOHN HENRY NEWMAN, 1801–90.

569

MAMRE. (76. 76.)

Doh = C. *In moderate time.* FRIEDRICH KARL LUDWIG SCHOLINUS, 1772–1816.

:s | l :s | l :t | d' :— | s :d' | t :r' | d' :m' | r' :— | — ||
:m | f :m | f :f | m :— | m :s | s :s | s :s | s :— | — ||
:d' | d' :d' | d' :r' | s :— | d' :d' | r' :t | d' :d' | t :— | — ||
:d | f :d | f :r | d :— | d :m | s :f | m :d | s :— | — ||

:s | m' :r' | d' :t | l :— | s :s | l :r' | d' :t | d' :— | — || d' | d' ||
:s | s :f | m :s | f :— | m :d | d :f | m :r | m :— | — || f | m ||
:t | d' :t | d' :d' | d' :— | d' :s | f :l | s :s | s :— | — || l | s ||
:s | d' :s | l :m | f :— | d :m | f :r | s :s_1 | d :— | — || f | d ||

A-men.

Στομίον πώλων ἀδαῶν.

LEAD, holy Shepherd, lead us,
Thy feeble flock, we pray;
Thou King of little pilgrims,
Safe lead us all the way.

2 In Thy blest footprints guide us
Along the heavenward road;
Thine age fills all the ages,
Undying Word of God.

3 That life, O Christ, is noblest
Which praises God the best,
A life celestial, nourished
At wisdom's holy breast.

4 By her good nurture let us,
Thy little ones, be fed,
And by her guidance gentle
Our wandering steps be led.

5 O fill us with Thy Spirit,
Like morning dew shed down,
And with our praises loyal
King Jesus we shall crown.

6 O be our lives our tribute,
The meed of praise we bring,
When thus we join to honour
Our Teacher and our King.

CLEMENT OF ALEXANDRIA, *c.* 170–220;
tr. by HAMILTON MONTGOMERIE MACGILL, 1807–80.

[May be sung to KNECHT, No. 577.]

570 KILLIN. (76. 76. D.)

Gaelic Melody. Harmonized by
THOMAS CUTHBERTSON LEITHEAD PRITCHARD, 1885–

Lah = D. Doh = F. *Unison.* *In moderate time.*

{ :l, | d :-.t, | m :d | t, :— | l, :t, | d :-.t, | l, :d.t, | l, :— | — ||

{ :l, | d :-.t, | m :d | t, :— | l, :t, | d :-.t, | l, :d.t, | l, :— | — ||

{ :l,.t, | d :-.r | m :m | s :— | m :m | s :-.s | l :s.l | t :— | — ||

{ :t.l | s :-.l | s :m.r | d :— | m :m.r | d :-.t, | l, :d.t, | l, :— | — || l, | l, ||
f, | m,
r | de
r, | l,
A-men.

[*Copyright*, 1927, *by Oxford University Press.*]

A Shlanuighear ro ghlòrmhor.

O LORD, I sing Thy praises
  Who art my strength and stay,
My leader through life's mazes,
  To bring me to Thy way;
Thou didst not leave me straying
  When I afar would go,
With heedless footsteps, playing
  Upon the brink of woe.

2 For Thou, Thy glory showing,
  Mad'st me Thy beauty see;
Thy love has been bestowing
  New life and joy on me.
Thou grace and glory givest,
  Thou art a Sun and Shield,
Thou only ever livest,
  Thy words salvation yield.

3 O Lord, do not forsake me,
  But guide me as a friend;
And strong in heart still make me
  For what Thy love may send.
Through death's dark vale victorious,
  O let me lean on Thee,
And let me see Thee glorious,
  Through all eternity.

PETER GRANT, 1783–1867; *tr.* by LACHLAN MACBEAN, 1853–

571 LEONI. (66. 84. D.)

Lah = F#. Doh = A. *With vigour.* Hebrew Melody.

```
S  :m,  |l,   :t,   |d    :r    |m    :—    |—    :d    |r    :m    |f    :s
A  :m,  |m,   :m,   |m,   :l,   |se,  :—    |—    :m,   |s,   :s,   |l,   :s,
T  :m,  |l,   :se,  |l,   :l,   |t,   :—    |—    :d    |t,   :d    |d    :r
B  :m,  |d,   :m,   |l,   :f,   |m,   :—    |—    :l,   |s,   :d    |l,   :t,

S  |m    :—   |—   ||t,  |d    :r    |m    :f    |s    :t,   |d    :f
A  |s,   :—   |—   ||s,  |s,   :s,   |s,   :d    |t,   :s,   |s,   :f,
T  |d    :—   |—   ||r   |d    :t,   |d    :d    |r    :r    |m    :d
B  |d    :—   |—   ||s,  |m,   :s,   |d    :l,   |s,   :f,   |m,   :l,

S  |m   :—  |r   :—   |d   :—  |—  ||d   |m  :m   |m   :m   |r   :—  |—
A  |s,  :—  |s,  :—   |m,  :—  |—  ||s,  |d  :s,  |s,  :l,  |t,  :—  |—
T  |d   :—  |d   :t,  |d   :—  |—  ||m   |s  :m   |d   :d   |t,  :—  |—
B  |s,  :—  |s,  :—   |d,  :—  |—  ||d,  |d  :d,  |m,  :f,  |s,  :—  |—

S  :d .t,  |l,.t,  :d .r   |m    :l,  |se,  :—  |—  ||m,  |l,  :t,   |d    :r
A  :s,     |l,     :f,     |m,   :f,  |m,   :—  |—  ||m,  |m,  :se,  |l,   :l,
T  :d      |d      :-.t,   |d    :d   |t,   :—  |—  ||m,  |m   :r    |m    :l,.t,
B  :m,     |f,     :r,     |d,   :r,  |m,   :—  |—  ||m,  |d   :t,   |l,   :f,

S  |m    :r .m    |f    :m .r  |d    :—    |t,   :—    |l,    :—  |—  ||l,  |l,  ||
A  |m,   :l,      |f,   :l,    |l,   :—    |l,   :se,  |l,    :—  |—  ||f,  |m,  ||
T  |d    :r .d    |l,   :f     |m    :f    |t,   :m    |d     :—  |—  ||r   |de  ||
B  |d,   :f,.m,   |r,   :r,    |m,   :r,   |m,   :—    |l,    :—  |—  ||r,  |l,, ||
                                                        |l,,   :—  |—  ||  A-men.
```

THE God of Abraham praise,
Who reigns enthroned above,
Ancient of everlasting days,
And God of love.
Jehovah, Great I AM!
By earth and heaven confessed,
I bow, and bless the sacred Name
For ever blest.

2 The God of Abraham praise,
At whose supreme command
From earth I rise, and seek the joys
At His right hand.
I all on earth forsake—
Its wisdom, fame, and power—
And Him my only portion make,
My shield and tower.

3 He by Himself hath sworn,
I on His oath depend:
I shall, on eagle's wings upborne,
To heaven ascend;
I shall behold His face,
I shall His power adore,
And sing the wonders of His grace
For evermore.

4 There dwells the Lord our King,
The Lord our Righteousness;
Triumphant o'er the world and sin,
The Prince of Peace;
On Zion's sacred height
His Kingdom He maintains,
And glorious with His saints in light
For ever reigns.

5 The whole triumphant host
Give thanks to God on high;
'Hail, Father, Son, and Holy Ghost!'
They ever cry.
Hail, Abraham's God, and mine!—
I join the heavenly lays,—
All might and majesty are Thine,
And endless praise.

THOMAS OLIVERS, 1725–99.

572 MOAB. (6 5. 6 5. 6 6. 6 5.)

Lah = E. Doh = G. *Slow.* JOHN ROBERTS (IEUAN GWYLLT), 1822–77.

```
:l, |l, :d  |t, :l, |s, :— |— :l, |d  :d  |t,  :—    |t,  :— |— ||
:m, |m, :l, |s, :f, |m, :— |— :f, |l, :l, |l,  :—    |se, :— |— ||
:d  |d  :m  |r  :d  |d  :— |— :d  |m  :m  |f   :—    |m   :— |— ||
:l, |l, :l, |m, :f, |d, :— |— :f, |m, :m, |m,  :re,  |m,  :— |— ||

:d  |d  :l, |t, :d  |r  :— |— :t,  |d  :m  |r  :—     |m   :— |— ||
:l, |l, :l, |se,:l, |l, :— |— :se, |l, :t, |d  :t,.l, |t,  :— |— ||
:m  |m  :m  |r  :m  |f  :— |— :m   |m  :m  |l  :—     |se  :— |— ||
:l, |l, :d  |t, :l, |r, :— |— :m,  |l, :s, |f, :—     |m,  :— |— ||

:s  |m  :f  |r  :t, |d  :— |— :r  |m  :s  |s  :fe  |m  :— |— ||
:d  |d  :d  |t, :s, |s, :— |— :s, |d  :t, |t, :l,  |s, :— |— ||
:m  |s  :l  |s  :r  |m  :— |— :s  |s  :m  |m  :re  |m  :— |— ||
:d  |d  :f, |s, :s, |d  :— |— :t, |d  :m  |t, :t,  |m  :— |— ||

:m   |l  :l  |s  :m  |s  :— |— :m  |d  :r  |t, :—   |l, :— |— || l, |l,  ||
:se, |l, :d  |s, :s, |t, :— |— :l, |m, :l, |l, :se, |l, :— |— || f, |m,  ||
:m   |m  :m  |r  :m  |r  :— |— :d  |l, :f  |m  :r   |d  :— |— || r  |de  ||
:r   |d  :l, |t, :d  |s, :— |— :l, |l, :r, |m, :—   |l, :— |— || r, |l,  ||
                                                                  A-men.
```

FAR off I see the goal—
  O Saviour, guide me ;
I feel my strength is small—
  Be Thou beside me ;
With vision ever clear,
With love that conquers fear,
And grace to persevere,
  O Lord, provide me.

2 Whene'er Thy way seems strange,
  Go Thou before me ;
And, lest my heart should change,
  O Lord, watch o'er me ;
But, should my faith prove frail,
And I through blindness fail,
O let Thy grace prevail,
  And still restore me.

3 Should earthly pleasures wane,
  And joy forsake me,
And lonely hours of pain
  At length o'ertake me,—
My hand in Thine hold fast
Till sorrow be o'er-past,
And gentle death at last
  For heaven awake me.

4 There, with the ransomed throng
  Who praise for ever
The love that made them strong
  To serve for ever,
I, too, would see Thy face,
Thy finished work re-trace,
And magnify Thy grace,
  Redeemed for ever.

ROBERT ROWLAND ROBERTS, 1865–

573 WILDERSMOUTH. (87. 87. 47.)

Doh = E. *In moderate time.* EDWARD JOHN HOPKINS, 1818–1901.

```
:d .r  |m  :- .m :r .m  |s  :f  :m .r   |d   :- .d  :r .r   |m  :— ||
:s,.s, |d  :- .d :d .d  |d  :d  :l,.l,  |s,  :- .d  :d .t,  |d  :— ||
:m .f  |s  :- .s :f .s  |l  :l  :s .f   |m   :- .m  :r .s   |s  :— ||
:d .d  |d  :- .d :d .d  |f, :f, :f,.f,  |s,  :- .s, :s,.s,  |d  :— ||

:m .l  |s  :- .f  :m .r   |r  :d  :m .m   |r .m  :fe :l   |s  :— ||
:d .d  |t, :- .t, :t,.t,  |t, :d  :l,.l,  |t,.r  :d  :d   |t, :— ||
:s .m  |r  :- .l  :s .f   |f  :m  :m .fe  |s .t  :l  :fe  |s  :— ||
:d .d  |s, :- .s, :s,.s,  |l, :l, :d .d   |r .r  :r  :r   |s, :— ||

:s .s   |d' :— :s   |d .r  :m  :m   |f  :— :r   |d :— ||d  |d  ||
:t,.t,  |d  :— :t,  |d .s, :d  :l,  |l, :r  :t, |d :— ||l, |s, ||
:s .s   |s  :l :f   |m .r  :d  :de  |r  :l  :f  |m :— ||f  |m  ||
:s .f   |m  :— :r   |d .t, :l, :s,  |f, :r, :s, |d :— ||f, |d  ||
                                                          A-men.
```

WHEN from Egypt's house of bondage
Israel marched, a mighty band,
Little children numbered with them
Journeyed to the promised land;
Little children
Trod the desert's trackless sand.

2 Little children crossed the Jordan,
Landed on fair Canaan's shore;
'Neath the sheltering vine they rested,
Homeless wanderers now no more;
Little children
Sang sweet praise for perils o'er.

3 Saviour, like those Hebrew children,
Youthful pilgrims we would be;
From the chains of sin and Satan
Thou hast died to set us free;
We would traverse
All the wilderness with Thee.

4 Guide our feeble, erring footsteps;
Shade us from the heat by day;
Be our light from shadowy nightfall
Till the darkness pass away;
Jesus, guard us
From the dangers of the way.

5 When we reach the cold, dark river,
Bid us tremble not nor fear;
Be Thou with us in the waters—
We are safe if Thou art near;
Through the billows
Let the emerald bow appear.

6 Then, our pilgrim journey ended,
All Thy glory we shall see,
Dwell with saints and holy angels,
Rest beneath life's healing tree,—
Happy children,
Praising, blessing, loving Thee.

JENNETTE THRELFALL, 1821–80.

574

DA CHRISTUS GEBOREN WAR. (77. 77.)

JOHANN FRIEDRICH DOLES, 1715–97.

Doh = D. *In moderate time.*

```
                                              A.t.
d.r:m.f |s  :l    |f  :s.f |m  :— |(d)f :m   |r  :d.r   |m  :r   |d  :— ||
d  :d   |d.t,:l,  |l, :t,  |d  :— |(d)f,:s,  |l,.t,:d   |d  :t,  |d  :— ||
m  :l   |s  :f    |f  :r   |m  :— |(l)r :d   |f  :m.f   |s  :-.f |m  :— ||
d  :l,  |m  :f    |r  :s,  |d  :— |(l)r,:m,  |f,.s,:l,  |s, :s,  |d  :— ||
```

```
d.f.G.                               D.t.
(f)s :r  |m :f     |m :r  |d  :—  |(r)s   :r     |m :f  |m  :r   |d :— ||d  |d  ||
(d)r :t, |d :l,.t, |d :s, |d  :t, |(l,)r  :d.t,  |d :d  |d  :t,  |d :— ||l, |s, ||
(f)s :s  |s :f     |s :s  |m  :—  |(l,)r  :s     |s :l  |s  :-.f |m :— ||f  |m  ||
(l,)t,:f |m :r     |d :t, |l, :s, |(fe,)t,:l,.s, |d :f, |s, :s,  |d :— ||f, |d  ||
                                                                        A-men.
```

INNOCENTS. (77. 77.)

Doh = E♭. *Moderately fast.*

? JOSEPH SMITH, 1800–73.

```
m  :-.f  |s :d'  |t   :l   |s  :— |d  :-.r  |m :s  |f     :m |r  :— ||
d  :-.t, |d :m   |r   :d.r |m  :— |d  :-.t, |d :s, |l,.t, :d |t, :— ||
s  :-.f  |m :s   |f.s :l.t |d' :— |m  :-.s  |s :m  |f     :s |s  :— ||
d  :-.r  |m :d   |r.m :f   |d  :— |l, :-.s, |d :m  |r     :d |s, :— ||
```

```
m :-.f  |s :d'   |t    :l   |s  :— |d :-.r  |m :f  |m  :r  |d :— ||d  |d  ||
d :-.t, |d :m    |r    :r.d |t, :— |d :-.t, |d :r  |d  :t, |d :— ||l, |s, ||
s :-.f  |m :m.fe |s    :fe  |s  :— |s :-.f  |s :l  |s  :f  |m :— ||f  |m  ||
d :-.r  |m :l,   |t,.d :r   |s  :f |m :-.r  |d :f, |s, :s, |d :— ||f, |d  ||
                                                                    A-men.
```

CHILDREN of the heavenly King,
As ye journey, sweetly sing ;
Sing your Saviour's worthy praise,
Glorious in His works and ways.

2 We are travelling home to God,
In the way the fathers trod ;
They are happy now, and we
Soon their happiness shall see.

3 Lift your eyes, you sons of light ;
Zion's city is in sight ;
There our endless home shall be,
There our Lord we soon shall see.

4 Fear not, brethren ; joyful stand
On the borders of your land ;
Jesus Christ, your Father's Son,
Bids you undismayed go on.

5 Lord, obediently we go,
Gladly leaving all below ;
Only Thou our Leader be,
And we still will follow Thee.

JOHN CENNICK, 1718–55.

575 PORTHKERRY. (76. 76. 76. 73.)

Doh = E. *Brightly.* JOHN MORGAN LLOYD, 1880–

:s_1 |d :m |s :l |s :-.m |d :m |r :-.r |l :r |r :— |—
:s_1 |d :m |s :l |s :-.m |d :d |d :-.d |d :d |t_1 :— |—
:s_1 |d :m |s :l |s :-.m |d :s |l :-.l |l :l |s :— |—
:s_1 |d :m |s :l |s :-.m |d :d |f :-.f |fe :fe |s :— |—

B.t.

:s_1 |d :m |s :d' |^{t}m :-.r |d :r |m :-.s_1 |l_1 :s_1 |d :— |—
:s_1 |d :s_1 |d :m |$^{re}se_1$:t_1 |l_1 :fe_1 |s_1 :-.s_1 |f_1 :f_1 |m_1 :— |—
:s_1 |d :s |m :l |$^{fe}t_1$:— |d :d |d :-.m |r :t_1 |d :— |—
:s_1 |d :d |t_1 :l_1 |$^{t_1}m_1$:$ba_1.se_1$ |l_1 :l_1 |s_1 :-.s_1 |s_1 :s_1 |d_1 :— |—

f.E.

:^{s_1}r |r :m |f :l |se :-.l |t :m |d' :-.l |f :m |r :— |—
:$^{m_1}t_1$ |t_1 :de |r :m |r :d |t_1 :r |d :-.m |r :d |t_1 :— |—
:^{d}s |s :s |f :m |m :— |m :m |m :-.m |f :s.l |t :— |—
:^{d}s |f :m |r :d |t_1 :l_1 |se_1 :$ba_1.se_1$ |l_1 :t_1.d |r :m.f |s :— |—

:s_1 |d :m |s :l |s :-.m |d :— |r :— |r :— |d :— |— || f |m
:s_1 |d :m |s :l |s :-.m |d :— |d :— |t_1 :— |d :— |— || d |d
:s_1 |d :m |s :l |s :-.m |d :— |l :— |s :f |m :— |— || l |s
:s_1 |d :m |s :l |s :-.m |d :— |f_1 :— |s_1 :— |d :— |— || f_1 |d

A-men.

[*Copyright*, 1927, *by Oxford University Press.*]

THE world looks very beautiful
And full of joy to me;
The sun shines out in glory
On everything I see;
I know I shall be happy
While in the world I stay,
For I will follow Jesus
All the way.

2 I'm but a little pilgrim,
My journey 's just begun;
They say I shall meet sorrow
Before my journey 's done;
'The world is full of sorrow
And suffering,' they say;
But I will follow Jesus
All the way.

3 Then, like a little pilgrim,
Whatever I may meet,
I'll take it, joy or sorrow,
To lay at Jesus' feet.
He'll comfort me in trouble;
He'll wipe my tears away;
With joy I'll follow Jesus
All the way.

4 Then trials cannot vex me,
And pain I need not fear,
For, when I'm close by Jesus,
Grief cannot come too near;
Not even death can harm me,
When death I meet one day;
To heaven I'll follow Jesus
All the way.

ANNA BARTLETT WARNER, 1820–1915.

576 MONKS GATE. (65. 65. 6665.)

Doh = E♭. *Brightly.* English Traditional Melody.

d :-.r	m :d	m.f :s	l :—	s :—	s :d	t_1 :d	— :—	
s_1 :—	d :s_1	d :t_1	l_1 :—	t_1 :—	d :s_1	s_1 :s_1	— :—	
m :-.f	s :m	d :r	f :—	s :—	s :s	f :m	— :—	
d :—	d :d	l_1 :s_1	f_1 :—	f :—	m :m	r :d	— :—	

d :-.r	m :d	m.f :s	l :—	s :—	s :d	t_1 :d	— :—	
s_1 :—	d :s_1	d :t_1	l_1 :—	t_1 :—	d :s_1	s_1 :s_1	— :—	
m :-.f	s :m	d :r	f :—	s :—	s :s	f :m	— :—	
d :—	d :d	l_1 :s_1	f_1 :—	f :—	m :m	r :d	— :—	

s :—	d^1 :l	t :d^1.t	l :—	— :s	m.r :d	m :f	s :—	—	
d :-.r	m :m	f :m.r	d :—	— :r	d :s_1	d :d	t_1 :—	—	
m :—	l :l	l :se	l :—	f :r	s :s	m :d	r :—	s	
d :-.t_1	l_1 :d	r :m	f :—	l_1 :t_1	d :m	d :l_1	s_1 :s	f	

:d^1 |s :- .s |l .s :f .m |r :l |s :d |t_1 :d || d |d ||
:d |t_1 :d |d :d |r :t_1 |d :l_1 |s_1 :s_1 || l_1 |s_1 ||
:s |f :m |f :l |t :t |s :f |f :m || f |m ||
:m |r :d |f :r |s :f |m :r |s_1 :d || f_1 |d ||

A-men.

LEITHEAD. (65. 65. 6665.)

Doh = C. *Brightly.* THOMAS CUTHBERTSON LEITHEAD PRITCHARD, 1885–

:m.f |s :d^1 |d^1 :t.l |s :— |— :m |s :d |r :d || :m.f
:d |t_1 :d |f :f |r :t_1 |d :d |r :d |t_1 :d || :d
:s |f :s |l :f |s :f |m :s |r :m |s :m || :s
:d |r :m |f.m :r.d |t_1 :s_1 |d :d |t_1 :l_1 |s_1 :d || :d.r

```
                                                      G.t.
s  :d'  |d'  :t.l |s   :—   |—  :m.f |s  :f.m |r  :d  ||  :d f  |m  :d
d  :d   |m   :r.d |t,  :r   |d  :d   |d  :d   |t, :d  ||  :m l, |l, :l,
s  :l   |s   :fe  |s   :f   |m  :s   |s  :l   |f  :m  ||  :l r  |d  :m
m  :l,  |r   :r   |s,  :—   |d  :d   |m  :f   |s  :d  ||  :l r, |l, :l,

                                                             f.C.
r    :m.f |m  :— |—  :d.r  |m     :f.s    |l  :s  |d  :—   |— ||l m.f |s  :d'
l,   :s,  |s, :— |—  :s,   |d     :d      |d  :t, |s, :—   |— ||f d   |t, :d
r.d  :t,  |d  :— |—  :m    |d     :l.s    |f  :f  |f  :m.r |m ||d s   |f  :s
f,   :s,  |d, :— |—  :d.t, |l,.s, :f,.m,  |r, :s, |d  :—   |— ||f d   |r  :m

d'  :l  |s    :—   |—  :m.f |s  :d  |r  :d |— ||d   |r  :— |d :— |—
d   :f  |f.m  :r.f |m  :d   |t, :d  |t, :d |— ||d   |—  :t,|d :— |—
l   :d' |d'   :s   |—  :s   |s  :m  |s  :m |— ||l   |—  :s |s :— |—
                                                              m
f   :f  |d    :t,  |d  :d   |m  :l, |s, :d |— ||l.s |f  :s |d :— |—
                                                 A      -    men.
```

[*Copyright*, 1927, *by Oxford University Press.*]

WHO would true valour see,
  Let him come hither;
One here will constant be,
  Come wind, come weather;
There 's no discouragement
Shall make him once relent
His first avowed intent
  To be a pilgrim.

2 Whoso beset him round
  With dismal stories,
Do but themselves confound;
  His strength the more is.
No lion can him fright,
He'll with a giant fight,
But he will have a right
  To be a pilgrim.

3 Hobgoblin nor foul fiend
  Can daunt his spirit;
He knows he at the end
  Shall life inherit.
Then fancies fly away;
He'll fear not what men say;
He'll labour night and day
  To be a pilgrim.

JOHN BUNYAN, 1628–88.

577 KNECHT. (76. 76.)

Doh = F. *Brightly.* JUSTIN HEINRICH KNECHT, 1752–1817.

:d |d :t,.d |r :r |r :d |— :m |m :r.m |f :r |t, :— |— ||
:s, |s, :s, |s, :t, |t, :l, |— :d.t, |l, :r.de |r :l, |s, :— |— ||
:m |s :f.m |r :f |f :m |— :m |l :l.s |f :f |r :— |— ||
:d |m :r.d |t, :s, |l, :l, |— :l,.s, |f, :f.m |r :f, |s, :— |— ||

:d |d :r |r :m |f :l |— :l |s :m |r :r |d :— |— ||d |d ||
:s, |l, :l, |t, :t, |d :d |— :d |d :d |d :t, |d :— |— ||l, |s, ||
:d |f :r |s :m |d :f |— :f |s :l |l :s.f |m :— |— ||f |m ||
:m, |f, :f, |s, :s, |l, :f, |— :f, |m, :l, |f, :s, |d, :— |— ||f, |d, ||

A-men.

Unison.

O HAPPY band of pilgrims,
If onward ye will tread,
With Jesus as your Fellow,
To Jesus as your Head!

Harmony.

2 O happy if ye labour
As Jesus did for men;
O happy if ye hunger
As Jesus hungered then!

3 The Cross that Jesus carried,
He carried as your due;
The crown that Jesus weareth,
He weareth it for you.

4 The faith by which ye see Him,
The hope in which ye yearn,
The love that through all troubles
To Him alone will turn,—

5 What are they but vaunt-couriers
To lead you to His sight?
What are they save the effluence
Of uncreated light?

6 The trials that beset you,
The sorrows ye endure,
The manifold temptations
That death alone can cure,—

7 What are they but His jewels
Of right celestial worth?
What are they but the ladder
Set up to heaven on earth?

Unison.

8 O happy band of pilgrims,
Look upward to the skies,
Where such a light affliction
Shall win you such a prize.

JOHN MASON NEALE, 1818–66; based on JOSEPH the Hymnographer, 9th century.

578 PILGRIM BAND. (87. 87. 887.)

Doh = G. Tenors and Basses. *In moderate time.* JOHN STAINER, 1840–1901.

|m :-.r |d :s, |l, :r |t, :s, |d :-.t, |l, :t, |d :m |r :

m :-.r |d :s, |l, :r |t, :s, |d :-.t, |l, :t, |d :m/:d |r/t, :
s, :-.f, |m, :— |f, :— |r, :— |s, :— |f, :— |s, :— |— :
d, :-.r, |m, :d, |f, :r, |s, :-.f, |m, :— |f, :r, |m, :d, |s, :

All voices (or children alone).

```
                D.t.                                                        f.G.
| m  :-.r  | d  :(s)d | r  :s   | m  :d   | d'  :t.l  | s   :l     | r  :t  | (d')s  :  ||
| s, :-.s, | s, :(s)d | d  :t,  | d  :d   | d   :f    | s   :f.m   | r  :f  | (m)t,  :  ||
| s  :-.f  | m  :(r)s | l  :s   | s  :m   | s   :d'   | d'  :d'    | t  :r' | (d')s  :  ||
| d  :-.d  | d  :(t)m | f  :s   | d  :d.r | m   :f    | m   :f     | s  :s, | (d)s,  :  ||

| s   :m   | f  :r    | m  :t,  | d  :r   | m   :m.f  | m    :r.d    | t, :m   | d  :l,  |
| ta, :l,  | l, :l,   | t, :t,  | l, :se, | l,  :se,  | l,.d :t,.l,  | l, :se, | l, :l,  |
| r   :de  | r  :l    | se :m   | m  :r   | d   :r    | m    :f.l    | m  :m   | m  :d   |
| m,  :l,  | r, :f,   | m, :se, | l, :t,  | d   :t,   | d    :r      | m  :m,  | l, :l,  |

| m  :s   | r.m :f   | m  :r   | d  :—  || d  | d  ||
| d  :s,  | l,  :r   | d  :t,  | d  :—  || l, | s, ||
| d  :d   | f   :l   | s  :s.f | m  :—  || f  | m  ||
| l, :m,  | f,  :r,  | s, :s,  | d, :—  || f, | d, ||
                                          A-men.
```

[*By permission of Novello & Co., Ltd.*]

WHITHER, pilgrims, are you going,
Going each with staff in hand ?
'We are going on a journey,
Going at our King's command ;
Over hills and plains and valleys,
We are going to His palace,
Going to the better land.'

2 Fear ye not the way so lonely,
You a little, feeble band ?
'No ; for friends unseen are near us,
Holy angels round us stand ;
Christ, our Leader, walks beside us ;
He will guard, and He will guide us,
Guide us to the better land.'

3 Tell us, pilgrims, what you hope for
In that far-off better land ?
'Spotless robes and crowns of glory,
From a Saviour's loving hand ;
We shall drink of life's clear river,
We shall dwell with God for ever,
In that bright and better land.'

4 Pilgrims, may we travel with you
To that bright and better land ?
'Come and welcome, come and welcome,
Welcome to our pilgrim band.
Come, O come, and do not leave us ;
Christ is waiting to receive us
In that bright and better land.'

Golden Chain, 1861.

579

SMART. (65. 65. 65. D.)

Doh = G. *With vigour.* HENRY SMART, 1813–79.

```
s   .s   :m   .r    | d        :s,  | d    .d   :r   .s,  | m    :—
d   .d   :d   .s,   | s,       :s,  | m,   .s,  :l,  .s,  | s,   :—
m   .m   :s   .f    | m        :r   | d    .d   :d   .t,  | d    :—
d   .d   :d   .d    | d        :t,  | l,   .m,  :f,  .s,  | d,   :—
```

```
s   .s   :m   .r    | d        :t,  | l,   .d   :t,  .l,  | s,   :—
s,  .t,  :s,  .f,   | m,  .fe, :s,  | s,   .s,  :s,  .fe, | s,   :—
r   .r   :m   .t,   | d        :r   | m    .m   :r   .d   | t,   :—
t,  .s,  :d   .s,   | l,       :t,  | d    .l,  :r   .r,  | s,   :—
```

```
                                      D.t.                   f.G.
r   .r   :m   .d    | f        :r   | ^{m}l  .l  :t  .m    | ^{d'}s   :—
s,  .s,  :s,  .l,   | l,       :s,  | ^{s}d  .d  :f  .m    | ^{m}t,   :—
t,  .t,  :d   .m    | r        :t,  | ^{m}l  .l  :l  .se   | ^{l}m    :—
s,  .f,  :m,  .l,   | r,       :s,  | ^{d}f  .m  :r  .m    | ^{l}m,   :—
```

```
l   .s   :f   .m    | r        :l,  | f    .m   :r   .d   | s    :—
l,  .l,  :l,  .l,   | l,       :l,  | l,   .l,  :l,  .l,  | t,   :—
m   .de  :r   .de   | r        :de  | r    .s   :f   .m   | r    :—
de  .l,  :r   .l,,s, | f,      :l,  | r,   .m,  :f,  .f,  | s,   :—
```

```
                                 f.C.                        G.t.
s   .s   :m   .r    | d   :^{s}r    | s    .d'  :r'  .s   | ^{m'}l   :—
t,  .t,  :s,  .f,   | m,  :^{m,}t,  | d    .s   :f   .f   | ^{m}l,   :—
m   .m   :t,  .t,   | d   :^{d}s    | s    .s   :l   .t   | ^{d}f    :—
m,  .m,  :s,  .s,   | l,  :^{ta,}f  | m    .m   :r   .s   | ^{d}f,   :—
```

l .s :f .s	m .t_1 :d .r	m .d :f .r	d :—	d	d
d .d :d .s_1	s_1 :d	d .d :t_1 .t_1	d :—	l_1	s_1
f .m :f .r	m .f :s .l	s .m :r .f	m :—	f	m
f_1 .s_1 :l_1 .t_1	d .r :m .f	s .s_1 :s_1 .s_1	d_1 :—	f_1	d_1

A-men.

[*By permission of Novello & Co., Ltd.*]

'FORWARD!' be our watch-
word,
Steps and voices joined;
Seek the things before us,
Not a look behind;
Burns the fiery pillar
At our army's head;
Who shall dream of shrinking,
By Jehovah led?
Forward through the desert,
Through the toil and fight;
Jordan flows before us,
Zion beams with light.

2 Glories upon glories
Hath our God prepared,
By the souls that love Him
One day to be shared;
Eye hath not beheld them,
Ear hath never heard,
Nor of these hath uttered
Thought or speech a word.
Forward, marching forward,
Where the heaven is bright,
Till the veil be lifted,
Till our faith be sight.

3 Far o'er yon horizon
Rise the city towers,
Where our God abideth;
That fair home is ours:
Flash the streets with jasper,
Shine the gates with gold,
Flows the gladdening river,
Shedding joys untold.
Thither, onward thither,
In Jehovah's might;
Pilgrims to your country,
Forward into light!

4 To the Father's glory
Loudest anthems raise,
To the Son and Spirit
Echo songs of praise;
To the Lord Jehovah,
Blessèd Three in One,
Be by men and angels
Endless honour done.
Weak are earthly praises,
Dull the songs of night;
Forward into triumph,
Forward into light!

HENRY ALFORD, 1810–71.

580

PILGRIMS. (11 10. 11 10. 9 11.)

Doh = E. *Moderately fast.* Henry Smart, 1813–79.

| m :— | s :f | m :— | — :r | d :r | m :f | m :— | r :— ||

| d :— | r :r | d :— | t_1 :— | d :t_1 | d :r | d :— | t_1 :— ||

| s :— | s :s | s :— | — :f | m :m | l :l | s :— | s :— ||

| d :— | t_1 :t_1 | d :— | s_1 :— | l_1 :l_1 | l_1 :f_1 | s_1 :— | s_1 :— ||

| s :— | d' :t | l :— | — :s | f :r | m :f | r :— | — :— ||

| d :— | d :d | d :— | — :d | t_1 :r | d :r | t_1 :— | — :— ||

| s :— | m :s | f :— | — :s | s :s | s :l | s :— | — :— ||

| m :— | d :m | f :— | — :m | r :t_1 | d :f_1 | s_1 :— | — :— ||

B.t.

| m :— | s :f | m :— | — :r | d :r | $^{m}l_1$:t_1 | r :— | d :— ||

| d :— | d :r | d :— | t_1 :— | d :t_1 | $^{d}f_1$:f_1 | s_1 :— | s_1 :— ||

| s :— | s :l | s :— | f :— | m :m | ^{l}r :r | s_1 :— | d :— ||

| d :— | m_1 :f_1 | s_1 :— | — :se_1 | l_1 :l_1 | $^{l}r_1$:r_1 | m_1 :— | m_1 :— ||

f.E.

| f :— | m :r | d :s_1 | l_1 :r | d :— | t_1 :— | ^{d}s :— | — :— ||

| f_1 :— | s_1 :s_1 | s_1 :s_1 | f_1 :l_1 | s_1 :— | — :f_1 | $^{m}t_1$:— | — :— ||

| d :— | d :t_1 | d :d | d :f | m :— | r :— | ^{d}s :— | — :— ||

| l_1 :— | s_1 :f_1 | m_1 :m_1 | f_1 :r_1 | s_1 :— | s_1 :— | $^{d}s_1$:— | — :— ||

| r :— | m :f | s :— | d :— | l :— | s :f | m :— | — :— ||

| t_1 :— | t_1 :t_1 | d :— | d :— | d :— | t_1 :t_1 | d :— | — :— ||

| s :— | s :s | s :— | s :— | f :m | r :r | d :— | — :— ||

| f :— | f :f | m :— | m_1 :— | f_1 :— | s_1 :s_1 | l_1 :— | — :— ||

d' :—	t :l	s :m	d :f	m :m	f :r	d :—	— :—	d	d
d :—	r :r	m :s_1	l_1 :r	d :d	t_1 :t_1	d :—	— :—	l_1	s_1
f :l	s :f	m :—	f :l	s :s	r :f	m :—	— :—	f	m
l_1 :—	t_1 :t_1	d :—	f :r	s :s	s_1 :s_1	d :—	— :—	f_1	d

A-men.

HARK, hark, my soul! angelic songs are swelling
O'er earth's green fields and ocean's wave-beat shore:
How sweet the truth those blessèd strains are telling
Of that new life when sin shall be no more.
Angels of Jesus, angels of light,
Singing to welcome the pilgrims of the night!

2 Onward we go, for still we hear them singing,
'Come, weary souls, for Jesus bids you come';
And through the dark, its echoes sweetly ringing,
The music of the Gospel leads us home.

3 Far, far away, like bells at evening pealing,
The voice of Jesus sounds o'er land and sea,
And laden souls, by thousands meekly stealing,
Kind Shepherd, turn their weary steps to Thee.

4 Rest comes at length; though life be long and dreary,
The day must dawn, and darksome night be past;
Faith's journey ends in welcomes to the weary,
And heaven, the heart's true home, will come at last.

5 Angels, sing on, your faithful watches keeping,
Sing us sweet fragments of the songs above,
Till morning's joy shall end the night of weeping,
And life's long shadows break in cloudless love.

FREDERICK WILLIAM FABER, 1814–63.

581

RUTHERFORD. (76. 76. 76. 75.)

Doh = F. *In moderate time.* CHRÉTIEN URHAN, 1790–1845.

```
:m  |m  :m   |r  :-.r  |d  :—   |d   :d    |f  :-.f  |m  :f  |r  :— |— ||
:d  |d  :d   |t, :-.t, |l, :—   |l,  :l,   |d  :-.d  |d  :d  |t, :— |— ||
:s  |s  :s   |f  :-.f  |m  :—   |m   :m    |l  :-.l  |s  :l  |s  :— |— ||
:d  |d  :d   |s, :-.s, |l, :—   |l,  :l,.s,|f, :-.f, |d  :f, |s, :— |— ||

:r  |s  :-.s |f  :f    |m  :—   |r    :r     |d  :d     |t,.d :r.t, |d  :— |— ||
:t, |d  :-.d |d  :t,   |d  :—   |l,   :l,    |l, :m,.f, |s,   :s,   |s, :— |— ||
:s  |s  :-.s |s  :s    |s  :—   |f    :f     |m  :d     |r.m  :f.r  |m  :— |— ||
:f  |m  :-.m |r  :s,   |d  :d,  |r,.m,:f,.s, |l, :l,    |s,   :s,   |d  :— |— ||

:d  |d  :-.d  |d  :r   |m  :—   |m  :d   |d  :-.d  |d  :r   |m  :— |— ||
:s, |l, :-.l, |d  :d   |d  :—   |s, :d   |l, :-.d  |l, :t,  |d  :— |— ||
:m  |f  :-.f  |f  :l   |s  :—   |d  :m   |l  :-.s  |l  :s.f |s  :— |— ||
:d  |f, :-.f, |l, :f,  |d  :—   |d  :d   |f  :-.m  |f  :m.r |d  :— |— ||

:m.f  |s :s  |l :-.s |s :—  |f  :—  |m :m  |r  :-.d  |d  :— |— || d  |d  ||
:d.t, |d :d  |d :-.d |d :—  |t, :—  |d :d  |t, :-.d  |s, :— |— || l, |s, ||
:s    |s :m  |f :-.s |s :—  |s  :—  |s :s  |f  :-.m  |m  :— |— || f  |m  ||
:d.r  |m :d  |f :-.m |m :—  |r  :s, |d :m, |s, :-.d, |d, :— |— || f, |d, ||
```

A-men.

THE sands of time are sinking;
The dawn of heaven breaks;
The summer morn I've sighed for,
The fair, sweet morn, awakes.
Dark, dark hath been the midnight,
But dayspring is at hand,
And glory, glory dwelleth
In Immanuel's land.

2 O Christ! He is the fountain,
The deep, sweet well of love;
The streams on earth I've tasted
More deep I'll drink above:
There to an ocean fulness
His mercy doth expand,
And glory, glory dwelleth
In Immanuel's land.

3 With mercy and with judgment
My web of time He wove,
And aye the dews of sorrow
Were lustred by His love;
I'll bless the hand that guided,
I'll bless the heart that planned,
When throned where glory dwelleth
In Immanuel's land.

4 I've wrestled on towards heaven,
'Gainst storm and wind and tide;
Now, like a weary traveller
That leaneth on his guide,
Amid the shades of evening,
While sinks life's lingering sand,
I hail the glory dawning
In Immanuel's land.

ANNE ROSS COUSIN, 1824–1906.

582 MOUNT ZION. (77. 77. 77.)

Doh = D. *In moderate time.* ARTHUR SEYMOUR SULLIVAN, 1842-1900.

```
m  :f  |s  :l  |d' :t  |d' :— |s  :m  |l  :l  |l  :r  |r  :—
d  :d  |d  :d  |d  :f  |m  :— |r  :d  |m  :de |r  :d  |t, :—
s  :f  |m  :r  |m  :s  |s  :— |s  :s  |l  :s  |f  :fe |s  :—
d  :l, |s, :f, |s, :s, |d  :— |t, :d  |de :l, |r  :r  |s, :—

r  :m  |f  :f  |f  :-.s|f  :m  |d' :t  |l  :s  |s  :fe |s  :—
t, :d  |r  :r  |r  :-.m|r  :d  |d  :r  |m  :m  |r  :r  |r  :—
s  :s  |t  :l  |s  :s  |s  :— |l  :se |l  :d' |t  :d' |t  :—
f  :m  |r  :d  |t, :t, |d  :— |l, :t, |d  :l, |r  :r  |s, :—

s  :m  |r  :m  |f  :f  |f  :— |m  :f  |s  :l  |d  :r  |d  :— ||d  |d
m  :de |t, :de |r  :r  |r  :— |d  :d  |d  :d  |s, :t, |d  :— ||l, |s,
ta :l  |l  :l  |l  :l  |s  :— |s  :f  |m  :r  |m  :f  |m  :— ||f  |m
s, :s  |f  :m  |r  :d  |t, :— |d  :l, |s, :f, |s, :s, |d  :— ||f, |d
                                                              A-men.
```

WHEN this passing world is done,
When has sunk yon glaring sun,
When we stand with Christ in glory,
Looking o'er life's finished story,
Then, Lord, shall I fully know,
Not till then, how much I owe.

2 When I stand before the throne,
Dressed in beauty not my own,
When I see Thee as Thou art,
Love Thee with unsinning heart,
Then, Lord, shall I fully know,
Not till then, how much I owe.

3 When the praise of heaven I hear,
Loud as thunders to the ear,
Loud as many waters' noise,
Sweet as harp's melodious voice,
Then, Lord, shall I fully know,
Not till then, how much I owe.

4 Even on earth, as through a glass,
Darkly, let Thy glory pass;
Make forgiveness feel so sweet;
Make Thy Spirit's help so meet;
Even on earth, Lord, make me know
Something of how much I owe.

ROBERT MURRAY McCHEYNE, 1813-43.

583 MONTGOMERY. (D.S.M.)

Doh = A♭. *In moderate time.* ISAAC BAKER WOODBURY, 1819–58.

```
:s,  |s,  :s,  |m   :-.r  |d   :-   |-  :d   |r    :-.r  |d   :r   |m   :-  |-  ||
:m,  |m,  :s,  |s,  :f,   |m,  :-   |-  :s,  |s,   :t,   |l,  :s,  |s,  :-  |-  ||
:d   |d   :d   |d   :t,   |d   :-   |-  :d   |t,   :f    |m   :r   |d   :-  |-  ||
:d,  |d,  :m,  |s,  :s,   |d,  :-   |-  :m,  |s,   :-.s, |l,  :t,  |d   :-  |-  ||

:m   |f   :-.f  |f   :r   |m   :-.m  |m  :d   |r    :r    |m   :r   |d   :-  |-  ||
:s,  |l,  :-.l, |l,  :s,  |s,  :-.d  |d  :s,  |l,   :l,   |s,  :f,  |m,  :-  |-  ||
:d   |d   :-.d  |d   :f   |m   :-.s  |s  :d   |f.m  :r.d  |d   :t,  |d   :-  |-  ||
:d   |l,  :-.l, |l,  :t,  |d   :-.d  |d  :m,  |f,   :f,   |s,  :s,  |d,  :-  |-  ||

                                    v. 2.
:d   |r   :-.r  |d   :r   |m   :-   |- (:m)  |m   :m.m   |r   :m   |f   :-  |-  ||
:d   |t,  :-.t, |l,  :t,  |d   :-   |- (:d)  |d   :d.d   |l,  :l,  |l,  :-  |-  ||
:m   |s   :-.r  |m   :s   |s   :-   |- (:s)  |d   :d.m   |l   :s   |f   :-  |-  ||
:d   |s,  :-.s, |s,  :s,  |d   :-   |- (:d)  |l,  :l,.s, |f,  :m,  |r,  :-  |r  ||

:f   |m   :s   |s   :m   |m   :d   |d   :l,  |s,  :d   |m   :-.r |d   :-  |-  ||d   |d   ||
:l,  |s,  :t,  |d   :s,  |l,  :s,  |l,  :f,  |m,  :s,  |d   :t,  |d   :-  |-  ||l,  |s,  ||
:r   |m   :f   |s   :d   |d   :d   |d   :d   |d   :m   |s   :f   |m   :-  |-  ||f   |m   ||
:t,  |d   :r   |m   :d   |l,  :m,  |f,  :f,  |s,  :s,  |s,  :s,  |d,  :-  |-  ||f,  |d,  ||
                                                                              A-men.
```

FOR ever with the Lord !
Amen, so let it be :
Life from the dead is in that word,
'Tis immortality.
Here in the body pent,
Absent from Him I roam,
Yet nightly pitch my moving tent
A day's march nearer home.

2 My Father's house on high,
Home of my soul, how near
At times, to faith's foreseeing eye,
Thy golden gates appear !
Ah ! then my spirit faints
To reach the land I love,
The bright inheritance of saints,
Jerusalem above.

OLD 25TH. (D.S.M.)

Doh = G. *In moderate time.* *Anglo-Genevan Psalter*, 1558.

```
|d  :—  |m  :r  |m  :f  |s  :—  ||m  :—  |m  :d    |f  :r   |d  :—  ||
|s, :—  |d  :r  |d  :d  |t, :—  ||s, :—  |l, :d    |d  :t,  |d  :—  ||
|m  :—  |s  :s  |m  :d  |r  :—  ||d  :—  |d  :m    |l  :s.f |m  :—  ||
|d  :—  |d  :t, |l, :l, |s, :—  ||d  :—  |l, :-.s, |f, :s,  |d, :—  ||

                                         f.C.
|m  :—  |r  :d    |s  :f  |m  :r  |m  :—  ||^l m  :—  |l    :s  |d' :t     |l  :—  ||
|s, :—  |s, :l,   |t, :r  |d  :t, |d  :—  ||^l m  :—  |m.fe :s  |l  :se    |l  :—  ||
|d  :—  |r  :m.f  |s  :l  |s  :s  |s  :—  ||^f d' :—  |l    :r' |m' :-.r'  |d' :—  ||
|d  :—  |t, :l,   |s, :r, |m, :s, |d, :—  ||^f d  :—  |d    :t, |l, :m     |l, :—  ||

G.t.
|^t m  :—  |m  :f  |s  :f  |m  :—  ||d  :—  |l, :t,     |d  :r  |m   :—  ||
|^s d  :—  |d  :d  |d  :l, |s, :—  ||s, :—  |f, :f,.s,  |l, :l, |se, :—  ||
|^t m  :—  |m  :l  |s  :d  |d  :—  ||d  :—  |d  :r      |m  :r  |t,  :—  ||
|^m l, :—  |l, :f, |m, :f, |d  :—  ||m, :—  |f, :r,     |l, :f, |m,  :—  ||

|d  :—  |m  :m  |l  :s    |f     :m   |r  :—  |d  :—  |s  :m  |f  :r   |d  :—  ||d  |d  ||
|m, :—  |d  :t, |l, :t,   |l,.s, :d   |t, :—  |l, :—  |t, :d  |d  :t,  |d  :—  ||l, |s, ||
|l, :—  |m  :m  |f  :m.r  |d.r   :m.f |s  :—  |m  :—  |m  :d  |l  :s.f |m  :—  ||f  |m  ||
|l, :—  |l, :s, |f, :s,   |l,.t, :d   |s, :—  |l, :—  |m, :l, |f, :s,  |d, :—  ||f, |d, ||
                                                                            A-men.
```

3 For ever with the Lord!
Father, if 'tis Thy will,
The promise of that faithful word
Even here to me fulfil.
Be Thou at my right hand,
Then can I never fail;
Uphold Thou me, and I shall stand;
Fight, and I must prevail.

4 So, when my latest breath
Shall rend the veil in twain,
By death I shall escape from death,
And life eternal gain.
Knowing as I am known,
How shall I love that word,
And oft repeat before the throne,
'For ever with the Lord!'

JAMES MONTGOMERY, 1771–1854.

584 IRENE. (77. 75.)

Doh = A♭. *Moderately slow.* CLEMENT COTTERILL SCHOLEFIELD, 1839–1904.

s, :s,	l, :s,	d :d	t, :—	r :r	m :f	t, :d	r :—
m, :s,	f, :f,	m, :fe,	s, :—	s, :l,	s, :f,	s, :s,	s, :—
d :d	d :t,	d :d	r :—	t, :l,	de :r	f :m	r :—
d, :m,	f, :s,	l, :l,	s, :—	s, :f,	m, :r,	s, :l,	t, :—

m :m	s :f	m :r	d :—	l, :d	d :t,	d :—	— :—	d	d
s, :s,	s, :t,	d :t,	d :s,	s, :f,.m,	f, :f,	m, :—	— :—	f,	m,
d :m	r :s	s :f	m :d	d :r	r :r	d :—	— :—	l,	s,
d :d	t, :s,	d :s,	l, :m,	f, :r,	s, :s,	d, :—	— :—	f,	d,

A-men.

WHEN the day of toil is done,
When the race of life is run,
Father, grant Thy wearied one
Rest for evermore.

2 When the strife of sin is stilled,
When the foe within is killed,
Be Thy gracious word fulfilled,
'Peace for evermore.'

3 When the darkness melts away
At the breaking of Thy day,
Bid us hail the cheering ray,
Light for evermore.

4 When the heart by sorrow tried
Feels at length its throbs subside,
Bring us, where all tears are dried,
Joy for evermore.

5 When for vanished days we yearn,
Days that never can return,
Teach us in Thy love to learn
Love for evermore.

6 When the breath of life is flown,
When the grave must claim its own,
Lord of life, be ours Thy crown—
Life for evermore.

JOHN ELLERTON, 1826–93.

Also the following :

147 Thou who didst stoop below
176 O Jesus, ever present
212 For the might of Thine arm we bless Thee
214 Through the night of doubt and sorrow

585 ST. SYLVESTER. (8 7. 8 7.)

Doh = F. *Moderately slow.* JOHN BACCHUS DYKES, 1823–76.

```
m .,m :m .m :r .m | f .s :m :— | m .,m :m .m :m .r | r :— :—
d .,d :d .d :t, .d | d .t, :d :— | d .,d :d .d :d .d | t, :— :—
s .,s :s .m :f .m | r :m :s | l .,l :l .s :fe .fe | s :r :f
d .,d :d .d :r .d | s, :d :— | l, .,l, :l, .l, :r .r | s, :— :—

d .,d :d .d :m .s | s .f :m :— | r .,r :r .r :m .r | d :— :— || d | d
d .,l, :s, .d :d .d | d :d :— | d .,d :d .d :t, .t, | d :— :— || l, | s,
m .,f :m .m :s .ta | l :s :m | fe .,fe :fe .fe :s .f | m :— :— || f | m
d .,d :d .d :d .d | f, :d :— | r .,r :r .l, :s, .s, | d :— :— || f, | d
```

A-men.

DAYS and moments quickly flying
  Blend the living with the dead :
Soon our bodies will be lying
  Each within its narrow bed.

2 Jesus, infinite Redeemer,
  Maker of this mighty frame,
Teach, O teach us to remember
  What we are, and whence we came.

3 As a shadow life is fleeting ;
  As a vapour, so it flies ;
For the bygone years retreating,
  Pardon grant, and make us wise,—

4 Wise that we our days may number,
  Strive and wrestle with our sin,
Stay not in our work, nor slumber,
  Till Thy holy rest we win.

5 Jesus, merciful Redeemer,
  Rouse dead souls to hear Thy voice ;
Wake, O wake each idle dreamer
  Now to make the eternal choice.

6 Soon before the Judge all glorious
  We with all the dead shall stand ;
Saviour, over death victorious,
  Place us then at Thy right hand.

EDWARD CASWALL, 1814–78, and others.

586

ULTIMA. (86.)

Doh = F. *Moderately slow.* JAMES MOFFATT, 1870–

vv. 1 and 3. vv. 2, 4, and 5.

m :d.r	m :d	l, :t,	d :-.r	m :d	d :r	d :—		m :d.r	m :d
d :d.d	d :s,	f, :f,	m, :-.s,	s, :s,	l, :t,	d :—		s, :l,.l,	se, :s,
s :l.l	s :d	d :r	d :-.t,	t, :d	f :f	m :—		m :m.r	t, :d
d :d.d	d :m,	f, :r,	l, :-.s,	m, :m,	r, :s,	d :—		d :l,.f,	m, :m,

l, :t,	d :-.r	m :d	d :r	d :—		d :r	d :t,	d :—	
l,.s, :f,	f, :m,.s,	s, :s,	l, :t,	d :—		d :l,	s, :—	s, :—	
f.m :r	d :-.t,	t, :d	m :s	m :—		m :f	r :—	m :—	
r, :s,	l, :-.s,	m, :m,	l, :s,	d :—		l, :f,	s, :—	d :—	

A - men.

[*Copyright*, 1927, *by Oxford University Press.*]

OLD 18TH. (86. 86. 86. 86. 86.) *English Psalter*, 1561.

Arranged by JAMES SMITH ANDERSON, 1853–

Lah = G. Doh = B♭. *Moderately slow.* *D.C.*

l, :—	l, :se,	l, :d	t, :t,	m, :m,	l, :d	t, :t,	l, :—	
m, :—	m, :m,	d, :m,	m, :re,	m, :d,	m, :m,	m, :m,	d, :—	
d :—	d :t,	l, :l,	fe, :t,	s, :l,	l, :l,	l, :se,	l, :—	
l, :—	l, :m,	f, :l,,	t,, :t,,	d, :l,,	d, :l,,	m, :m,	l,, :—	

m :—	r :d	t, :d	t, :l,	se, :d	t, :l,	l, :se,	l, :—	
s, :—	s, :m,	se, :l,	m, :d,	m, :m,	m, :d,	m, :m,	d, :—	
s, :—	t, :d	m :m	s, :l,	t, :l,	se, :l,	t, :t,	l, :—	
d, :—	s, :l,	m, :l,	s, :f,	m, :d,	m, :f,	m, :m,	l,, :—	

l, :—	d :t,	l, :m	m :re	m :—	m :—	r :d	t, :l,	se, :—	
m, :—	l, :se,	l, :l,	ba, :ba,	se, :—	s, :—	s, :m,	se, :m,	m, :—	
d :—	m :m	d :d	t, :t,	t, :—	d :—	t, :d	m :d	t, :—	
l, :—	l, :m,	l, :l,	t, :t,	m, :—	d, :—	s, :l,	m, :l,,	m, :—	

d :—	s, :l,	t, :d	r :d	t, :—	d :—	t, :—:l,	l, :—:se,	l, :—		l,	l,	
s, :—	s, :m,	se, :l,	l, :l,	se, :—	l, :—	m, :—:m,	m, :—:m,	de, :—		r,	de,	
m :—	m :d	m :m	f :m	m :—	m :—	t, :—:d	t, :—:t,	l, :—		f,	m,	
d, :—	d, :l,,	m, :l,	r, :l,	m, :—	l, :—	se, :—:l,	m, :—:m,	l,, :—		r,	l,,	

A-men.

SOONER or later: yet at last
The Jordan must be past.

2 Sooner or later: yet one day
We all must pass that way.

3 When mysteries shall be revealed,
All secrets be unsealed:

4 Jesus, most merciful of men,
Show mercy on us then;

5 Lord God of mercy and of men,
Show mercy on us then.

CHRISTINA GEORGINA ROSSETTI, 1830–94.

587 HAPPY LAND. (64. 64. 67. 64.)

Doh = E♭. *Brightly.* *Select Melodies*, 1827.

m :m .r	m .s :s	m :m .r	d :—	m :m .r	m .s :s
d :d .r	d .t, :d	d :d .t,	d :—	d :d .r	d .t, :d
s :s .s	s .f :m	s :s .f	m :—	s :s .s	s .f :m .s
d :d .t,	d .r :m .d	s, :s, .s,	d :—	d :s .f	m .r :d .m

m :m .r	d :—	d' :d' .l	l .s :s	m .,r :m .s	l .s :s
d :d .t,	d :—	d :m .d	t, .d :d	d .,t, :d .d	d .t, :d
s :s .f	m :—	s :s .f	f .s :m .s	s .,s :s .d'	f .f :s .m
s :s, .s,	d :—	m :d .f	r .m :d .m	s .,s :d .m	f .r :m .d

d' :d' .l	l .s :s	m :m .r	d :—	d	d
m :s .f	f .m :m .d	d :d .t,	d :—	l,	s,
l :s .d'	t .d' :s	s :s .f	m :—	f	m
l :m .f	r .m :d .m	s :s, .s,	d :—	f,	d

A-men.

THERE is a happy land,
Far, far away,
Where saints in glory stand,
Bright, bright as day.
O how they sweetly sing,
'Worthy is our Saviour King!'
Loud let His praises ring,
Praise, praise for aye.

2 Come to this happy land,
Come, come away;
Why will ye doubting stand?
Why still delay?
O we shall happy be
When, from sin and sorrow free,
Lord, we shall live with Thee,
Blest, blest for aye.

3 Bright in that happy land
Beams every eye;
Kept by a Father's hand,
Love cannot die:
On then to glory run;
Be a crown and kingdom won;
And, bright above the sun,
Reign, reign for aye.

ANDREW YOUNG, 1807–89.

588 CROSSING THE BAR.

Doh = C. *mp* *Slow.* JOSEPH BARNBY, 1838–96.

|m :m .m |s :- .s |d :— |— :d |f :f |l :- .l

|d :d .d |t, :- .t, |d :— |— :d |l, :l, |d :- .d

1. Sun-set and eve - ning star, And one clear call for

|s :s .s |f :- .f |m :— |— :m |f :f |r :- .r

|d :d .d |s, :- .s, |l, :— |— :l, |r :r |f, :- .f,

|r :— | .r :m .f |s :d' |d' :t |t :- .l |l :r

|t, :— | .t, :t, .t, |d :d |r :r |r :- .d |d :d

me! And may there be no moan - ing of the bar, When

|s :— | .s :s .s |s :s |se :se |se :- .l |l :l

|s, :— | .s :s .f |m :m |m :m |f :- .f |f :f

|f :- .f |m :r |d :— |- .m :m .m |m :m |m .m :f .m

|d :- .d |t, :t, |d :— |- .d :d .d |r :r |r .r :r .r

I put out to sea, But such a tide as, mov-ing, seems a-

|l :- .l |s :f |m :— |- .s :s .s |se :se |se .se :se .se

|r :- .r |s, :s, |d :— |- .d :d .d |t, :t, |m .m :m .m

|m :— |— :l |d' :- .d' |t :l |se :— |s .s :l .s

|d :— |— :m |m :- .m |re :re |m :— |f .f :f .f

-sleep, Too full for sound and foam, When that which

|l :— |— :d' |l :- .l |t :t |t :— |- .t :t .t

|l :— |— :s |fe :- .fe |t :t |m :— |r .r :s .s

rall.

|m' :- .r' |d' :t |l :- .s |f :r |s :- .d |r :m

|m :- .f |s :se |l :m |r :l, |d :- .s, |l, :t,

drew from out the bound - less deep Turns a - gain

|s :- .t |d' :r' |de' :l |l :f |m :- .m |f :—

|d :- .r |m :m |l :de |r :f, |s, :- .s, |s, :—

a tempo. *dim.*

| d :— |— :— | f :f .f | m :- .m | r :— |— :r
| d :— |— :— | d :d .d | d :- .d | d :— |— :d
home. 2. Twi - light and eve - ning bell, And
| m :— |— :— | l :l .l | s :- .s | f :— |— :f
| d :— | d :— | — :— | d :d | d :- .d | d :d
Twi - - - light and eve - ning bell;

mp.

| s :- .s | f :f | m :— | .m :f .s | l :l | ta :l
| d :- .d | d :d | d :— | .d :d .d | d :d | de :de
af - ter that the dark! And may there be no sad - ness
| ta :- .ta | l :l | s :— | .d' :d'.ta | l :l | s :l
| d :- .d | d :d | d :— | .d :r .m | f :f | m :m

| s :- .f | f :s | m :— | fe :— | s :— | — :s
| r :- .r | r :r | d :— | r :— | s :— | — :s_1
of fare-well, When I em - - bark; For,
| ta :- .l | l :s | s :— | d' :— | t :— | — :s
| r :- .r | r :t_1 | d :— | l_1 :— | s_1 :— | — :s

cres - - - cen - - - do.

| s :s | s :s | s :t | l :s | s :d' | t :l
| t_1 :d | r :m | f :f | f :f | m :m | m :m
though from out our bourne of time and place The flood may
| s :l | t :d' | r' :t | d' :r' | s :l | s :l
| f :m | r :d | t_1 :s_1 | l_1 :t_1 | d :l_1 | t_1 :d

rit. *Slower.*

| s :— | fe :— | s :— | — :s | f' :m' | r' :d' | t :l | s :f
| m :— | re :— | m :— | f :s | l :s | f :s | s :f | m :r
bear me far, I hope to see my Pi - lot face to
| t :— | t :— | t :s | l :t | d' :s | t :d' | d' :d' | ta :l
| t_1 :— | t_1 :— | m :— | r :r | d :d | r :m | f :f | de :r

| m :s | f :l_1 | d :— | r :— | d :— | — :— || d | d
| d :de | l_1 :l_1 | s_1 :— | t_1 :— | d :— | — :— || l_1 | s_1
face When I have crost the bar. A - men.
| s :m | f :f | m :— | f :— | m :— | — :— || f | m
| s_1 :l_1 | r :f_1 | s_1 :— | s_1 :— | d :— | — :— || f_1 | d

[*By permission of Novello & Co., Ltd.*]

 ALFRED TENNYSON, 1809–92.

589 GIFFORD. (11 10. 11 6.)

Doh = D. *In moderate time.*

THOMAS CUTHBERTSON LEITHEAD PRITCHARD, 1885–

𝄋

:m |d :r |m :s |l :d' |s :m |r :— |r :m |d :r |m :s |l :d'
:t, |l, :t, |d :r |d :d |d :d |d :— |t, :t, |d :d |d :t, |d :s
:s |m :f |s :r |m :l |s :s |f :— |s :s |s :f |s :s |s :l
:s, |s, :s, |d :t, |l, :f, |m, :d |l, :— |s, :f, |m, :l, |s, :f |m :l,

|t :s |m :— |— ‖ f |s :-.d |d :m |f :s |l :d' |r' :— |d'
|f :r |d :t, |l, ‖ d |d :d |d :d |d :d |d :m |f :r |m
|t :l |se :— |l ‖ l |s :l |s :s |f :m |f :s |l :f |s
|r :t, |m :r |d ‖ l, |m :f |m :d |l, :d |f :m |r :— |s

vv. 1–6. *D.S.* *Last verse ends thus—*

:t |d' :s |l :m |f :— |— : | : | :m ‖ t |d' :s |l :m
:r |d :t, |d :d |r :— |— : | : | :t, ‖ r |d :t, |d :d
The life for which I
:s |s :f |m :s |f :— |— : | : | :s ‖ s |s :f |m :s
:f |m :r |d :l, |r :— |— : | : | :s, ‖ f |m :r |d :l,

|f :— |— :r |s :d |d :r |d :— |— :— ‖ d :— |— :— |d :— |— :— ‖
|d :— |l, :t, |t, :d |l, :t, |d :— |— :— ‖ d :t, |l, :— |s, :— |— :— ‖
long, The life for which I long. A - - men.
|f :— |— :s |s :s |f :f |m :— |— :— ‖ m :— |f :r |m :— |— :— ‖
|r :— |— :s |f :m |r :s, |d :— |— :— ‖ l, :s, |f, :— |d :— |— :— ‖

[*Copyright*, 1927, *by Oxford University Press.*]

WHEN on my day of life the night is falling,
And in the winds, from unsunned spaces blown,
I hear far voices out of darkness calling
My feet to paths unknown,

2 Thou who hast made my home of life so pleasant,
Leave not its tenant when its walls decay;
O Love Divine, O Helper ever present,
Be Thou my strength and stay.

3 Be near me when all else is from me drifting,—
Earth, sky, home's pictures, days of shade and shine,
And kindly faces, to my own uplifting
The love which answers mine.

4 I have but Thee, my Father ; let Thy Spirit
Be with me then to comfort and uphold ;
No gate of pearl, no branch of palm I merit,
Nor street of shining gold.

5 Suffice it if—my good and ill unreckoned,
And both forgiven through Thy abounding grace—
I find myself by hands familiar beckoned
Unto my fitting place,

6 Some humble door among Thy many mansions,
Some sheltering shade where sin and striving cease,
And flows for ever, through heaven's green expansions,
The river of Thy peace.

7 There, from the music round about me stealing,
I fain would learn the new and holy song,
And find at last, beneath Thy trees of healing,
The life for which I long.

John Greenleaf Whittier, 1807–92.

590 ST. OLAVE (ST. GEORGE). (S.M.)

Doh=C. *In moderate time.* Henry John Gauntlett, 1805–76.

```
:m |f  :l  |s :f  |m  :—  |— :m' |r' :d' |d' :t  |d' :— |— ||
:d |d  :d  |d :t, |d  :—  |— :s  |s  :m  |s  :s  |m  :— |— ||
:s |l  :f  |s :s  |s  :—  |— :d' |t  :d' |r' :r' |d' :— |— ||
:d |f  :f  |m :r  |d  :—  |— :d' |s  :l  |s  :s  |d  :— |— ||

:s |l  :fe |s :t  |r' :-.r' |d' :l  |s :m |r  :m.f |m :— |— ||f  |m ||
:m |m  :r  |r :s  |s  :-.s  |s  :d  |d :d |d  :t,  |d :— |— ||d  |d ||
:t |d' :l  |t :r' |t  :-.t  |d' :d' |s :s |s  :s   |s :— |— ||l  |s ||
:m |d  :r  |s :s  |f  :-.f  |m  :f  |m :d |s, :s,  |d :— |— ||f, |d ||
```

A-men.

THERE is no night in heaven :
In that blest world above,
Work never can bring weariness,
For work itself is love.

2 There is no grief in heaven :
For all is perfect day ;
And tears are of those former things
Which all have passed away.

3 There is no sin in heaven,
Amid that blessèd throng ;
All holy is their spotless robe,
All holy is their song.

4 There is no death in heaven :
For they who gain that shore
Have won their immortality,
And they can die no more.

5 Lord Jesus, be our Guide ;
O lead us safely on,
Till night and grief and sin and death
Are past, and heaven is won.

Francis Minden Knollis, 1815–63.

591 ETERNITY. (75. 75. 77.)

Doh = A♭. *In moderate time.* LAURA JOSEPHINE HUTTON, 1852–88.

```
m  :-.m |r  :d  |t, :l,    |s, :—  |s,   :s, |l, :r  |d  :— |t, :— ||
s, :-.s,|s, :s, |s, :f,    |m, :—  |r,   :s, |f, :l, |s, :— |—  :— ||
d  :-.m |f  :m  |d  :d     |d  :—  |t,   :d  |d  :f  |m  :— |r  :— ||
d  :-.d |t, :d  |f, :l,    |d  :—  |s,.f,:m, |f, :r, |s, :— |—  :— ||

s, :s,  |l, :l, |t, :l,.t, |d  :—  |l,   :-.l,|s, :s, |s, :— |— :— ||
s, :m,  |f, :f, |f, :f,    |m, :—  |f,   :-.f,|m, :f, |m, :— |— :— ||
d  :d   |d  :r  |r  :r     |d  :—  |d    :-.d |d  :t, |d  :— |— :— ||
m, :d,  |f, :r, |s, :s,    |l, :—  |f,   :-.f,|s, :s, |d, :— |— :— ||

s  :-.s |f  :m  |r  :l,    |t, :—  |d  :d  |r  :f  |m  :r  |d :— || d  |d  ||
d  :-.d |t, :d  |l, :f,    |s, :f, |m, :s, |l, :l, |d  :t, |d :— || l, |s, ||
m  :-.s |s  :s  |f  :f     |r  :—  |d  :d  |f  :f  |s  :f  |m :— || f  |m  ||
m  :-.m |r  :d  |f, :r,    |s, :—  |l, :m, |f, :r, |s, :s, |d :— || f, |d  ||
```

A-men.

EVERY morning the red sun
Rises warm and bright;
But the evening cometh on,
And the dark, cold night:
There 's a bright land far away,
Where 'tis never-ending day.

2 Every spring the sweet young flowers
Open bright and gay,
Till the chilly autumn hours
Wither them away:
There 's a land we have not seen,
Where the trees are always green.

3 Little birds sing songs of praise
All the summer long,
But in colder, shorter days
They forget their song:
There 's a place where angels sing
Ceaseless praises to their King.

4 Christ our Lord is ever near
Those who follow Him;
But we cannot see Him here,
For our eyes are dim:
There is a most happy place,
Where men always see His face.

5 Who shall go to that bright land?
All who love the right:
Holy children there shall stand
In their robes of white;
For that heaven, so bright and blest,
Is our everlasting rest.

CECIL FRANCES ALEXANDER, 1823–95.

592 MENDIP. (C.M.)

Doh = E♭. *In moderate time.* English Traditional Melody.

```
:s |s :f      |m :s  |d' :t  |l  :l  |s :m |d  :d  |r  :— |— ||
:d |d :l,.t,  |d :r  |d  :d  |d  :t, |d :d |d  :d  |t, :— |— ||
:m |m :f      |s :s  |l  :s  |f  :f  |s :s |s  :fe |s  :— |— ||
:d |m :r      |d :t, |l, :m, |f, :r  |m :d |l, :l, |s, :— |— ||
```

:d.r | m :m | r :d | s :s | f :f.s | l :f | r :r | d :— | — || d | d ||
:s, | d :d | t, :l, | d :ta, | l, :f | f :d | d :t, | d :— | — || l, | s, ||
:m.f | s :s | f :m | d :d | d :l | l :l | s :s.f | m :— | — || f | m ||
:d | d :d | s, :l, | m, :m, | f, :f.m | r :f | s :s, | d :— | — || f, | d ||

A - men.

BEATITUDO. (C.M.)

Doh = A♭. *In moderate time.* JOHN BACCHUS DYKES, 1823–76.

d :r :m	s :— :m	d :— :f	m :— :—	l, :t, :d
m, :s, :s,	s, :— :s,	f, :m, :l,	s, :— :—	s, :s, :s,
s :f :m	d :— :d	d :— :d	d :— :—	m :m :m
d :d :d	m, :— :s,	l, :s, :f,	d, :— :—	d :t, :l,

m :— :r	r :— :—		r :s :f	m :— :d	m :— :r
{d :— :d / fe, :— :fe,}	{t, / s,} :— :—		{t, :d :r / s, :s, :s,}	s, :— :l,	se, :— :se,
d :— :l,	t, :— :—		f :m :r	d :— :d	t, :— :t,
r, :— :r,	s, :— :—		s, :l, :t,	d :— :l,	m, :— :m,

d :— :r	m :— :m	f :— :t,	d :— :—		d	d	
l, :— :l,	s, :— :ta,	t, :— :s,	s, :— :—		l,	s,	
d :— :d	d :— :de	r :— :f	m :— :—		f	m	
l, :— :f,	s, :— :s,	s, :— :s,	d, :— :—		f,	d,	

A-men.

THERE is a land of pure delight,
Where saints immortal reign ;
Infinite day excludes the night,
And pleasures banish pain ;

2 There everlasting spring abides,
And never-withering flowers :
Death, like a narrow sea, divides
This heavenly land from ours.

3 Sweet fields beyond the swelling flood
Stand dressed in living green ;
So to the Jews old Canaan stood,
While Jordan rolled between.

4 But timorous mortals start and shrink
To cross this narrow sea,
And linger, shivering on the brink,
And fear to launch away.

5 O could we make our doubts remove—
Those gloomy doubts that rise—
And see the Canaan that we love,
With unbeclouded eyes ;

6 Could we but climb where Moses stood,
And view the landscape o'er,
Not Jordan's stream, nor death's cold flood,
Should fright us from the shore.

ISAAC WATTS, 1674–1748.

593 IN MEMORIAM. (86. 76. 76. 76.)

Doh = E♭. *In moderate time.* JOHN STAINER, 1840–1901.

```
|m  :— :m  |f  :— :m  |r  :— :m  |d  :— :—  |d  :— :r
|d  :— :d  |d  :— :t, |l, :— :t, |d  :— :—  |d  :— :t,
|s  :— :s  |f  :— :s  |l  :— :f  |m  :— :l  |s  :— :f
|d  :— :t, |l, :— :s, |f, :— :s, |d  :— :f  |m  :— :r

|m :— :f  |s :m :l  |s :— :— |— :— ||s  |d' :— :t |l :— :t
|d :— :t, |d :— :d  |d :— :— |— :— ||t, |d  :— :d |d :— :r
|s :— :s  |s :— :f  |m :— :— |— :— ||f  |s  :— :s |l :— :s
|d :— :r  |m :— :f  |d :— :— |— :— ||r  |m  :— :m |f :— :f

|d' :— :— |s :— :s |l :— :s |s  :f :m |r  :— :— |— :— ||
|d  :— :— |d :— :d |d :— :d |r  :— :d |t, :— :— |— :— ||
|s  :— :— |s :— :s |f :— :s |s  :— :s |s  :— :— |— :— ||
|m  :— :— |m :— :m |f :— :m |t, :— :d |s, :— :— |— :— ||

:r  |r  :— :de |r  :— :m  |f :— :— |f :— :d
:t, |l, :— :l, |t, :— :de |r :— :— |r :— :d
:s  |l  :— :l  |l  :— :s  |l :— :— |l :— :l
:s  |f  :— :s  |f  :— :m  |r :— :— |r :— :f

|d :— :t, |d  :— :r  |m :— :— |— :— ||s  |d' :— :d' |t  :— :t
|d :— :s, |l, :— :t, |d :— :— |— :— ||r  |d  :— :d  |d  :— :d
|s :— :s  |s  :— :f  |m :— :— |— :— ||r  |m  :— :m  |m  :— :m
|m :— :f  |m  :— :r  |d :— :— |— :— ||t, |l, :— :l, |s, :— :s,

|l  :— :— |s :— :f  |m :f :s  |m  :— :r  |d :— :— ||f  |m ||
|d  :— :— |d :— :t, |d :r :m  |d  :— :t, |d :— :— ||d  |d ||
|f  :— :— |s :— :s  |s :— :s  |s  :— :f  |m :— :— ||l  |s ||
|f, :— :f |m :— :r  |d :— :m, |s, :— :s, |d :— :— ||f, |d ||
```

A-men.

THERE 's a Friend for little children,
Above the bright blue sky,
A Friend that never changes,
Whose love will never die.
Unlike our friends by nature,
Who change with changing years,
This Friend is always worthy
The precious name He bears.

2 There 's a home for little children
Above the bright blue sky,
Where Jesus reigns in glory,
A home of peace and joy.
No home on earth is like it,
Or can with it compare,
For every one is happy,
Nor could be happier, there.

3 There 's a crown for little children
Above the bright blue sky,
And all who look to Jesus
Shall wear it by and by,—
A crown of brightest glory,
Which He will then bestow
On all who love the Saviour,
And walk with Him below.

4 There 's a song for little children
Above the bright blue sky,
And a harp of sweetest music
And a palm of victory;
All, all above is pleasure,
And found in Christ alone;
O come, dear little children,
That all may be your own!

ALBERT MIDLANE, 1825–1909.

594

ANNUE CHRISTE. (12 12 12 12.)

Doh = G. *Unison. In free rhythm.* *La Feillée's Méthode du Plain-Chant*, 1808.

:d :d :r :m :m :m :r :m :f :m :—:r :-.d:d :—‖m :m :f

:s :s :d :l, :t, :d :t, :—:l, :-.s,:s, :—‖d :l, :t, :d :d

:r :d :r :m :f :—:m :-.r:r :—‖s :m :d :f :m :d :r

:m :f :m :—:r :-.d:d :—‖d :—:r :—:d :—:t, :—:d :—:—:—‖

A - - men.

THERE is a blessèd home
 Beyond this land of woe,
Where trials never come,
 Nor tears of sorrow flow;
Where faith is lost in sight,
 And patient hope is crowned,
And everlasting light
 Its glory throws around.

2 There is a land of peace;
 Good angels know it well;
Glad songs that never cease
 Within its portals swell;
Around its glorious throne
 Ten thousand saints adore
Christ, with the Father one
 And Spirit, evermore.

3 O joy all joys beyond!
 To see the Lamb who died,
For ever there enthroned,
 For ever glorified;
To give to Him the praise
 Of every triumph won,
And sing, through endless days,
 The great things He hath done.

4 Look up, ye saints of God!
 Nor fear to tread below,
The path your Saviour trod
 Of daily toil and woe;
Wait but a little while
 In uncomplaining love,
His own most gracious smile
 Shall welcome you above.

HENRY WILLIAMS BAKER, 1821–77.

595

THIS ENDRIS NYGHT. (C.M.)

Doh = D. *Moderately slow.* English Carol. 15th cent.

:d |m :— :f |s :— :s |l :t :l |s :— :s |d' :— :t |l.,s:l :f
:d |d :— :d |t, :— :d |d :— :f |r :— :r |d :— :m |f :— :l,
:m |s :— :f |r :— :m |f :s :l |t :— :t |s :— :s |l :— :r'
:d |d :— :l, |s, :— :d |f :— :f, |s, :— :f |m :— :d |f :— :r

|m :— :— |— :— ||m |l :— :l |s :— :s |f :— :f
|l, :— :— |— :— ||l, |l, :— :t, |d :— :m |r :— :d
|d' :— :— |— :— ||d' |d' :— :f |s :— :l |l :t :l
|l, :— :— |— :— ||l |f :— :r |m :— :d |r :— :r

m :— :m	s :— :m	f :r :—	d :— :—	— :—		d	d	
t, :— :d	d :— :d	d :t, :—	d :— :—	— :—		l,	s,	
se :— :l	s :— :l	l :s :f	m :— :—	— :—		f	m	
m :— :l,	m, :— :l,	f, :s, :—	d :— :—	— :—		f,	d	

A-men.

JERUSALEM, my happy home,
When shall I come to thee?
When shall my sorrows have an end?
Thy joys when shall I see?

2 O happy harbour of the saints!
O sweet and pleasant soil!
In thee no sorrow may be found,
No grief, no care, no toil.

3 Thy walls are made of precious stones,
Thy bulwarks diamonds square;
Thy gates are of right orient pearl,
Exceeding rich and rare;

4 Thy gardens and thy gallant walks
Continually are green;
There grow such sweet and pleasant flowers
As nowhere else are seen.

5 Quite through the streets, with silver sound,
The flood of life doth flow,
Upon whose banks on every side
The wood of life doth grow.

6 Our sweet is mixed with bitter gall,
Our pleasure is but pain,
Our joys scarce last the looking on,
Our sorrows still remain.

7 But there they live in such delight,
Such pleasure and such play,
As that to them a thousand years
Doth seem as yesterday.

8 Jerusalem, my happy home,
Would God I were in thee!
Would God my woes were at an end,
Thy joys that I might see!

F. B. P.; probably 16th century.

596

CRUGYBAR. (98. 98. D.)

Doh = E♭. *In moderate time.* Welsh Hymn Melody.

:d |m :— |m :m |m :s |— :m |d :r |— :d
:s, |d :— |s, :d |d :r |— :d |d :t, |— :d
:m |s :— |m :s |l :s |— :s |s .fe:s |— :m
:d |d :— |d :d |l, :t, |— :d |l, :s, |— :l,

|s :l |— :s .l |s :m |— :r |d :— |— ||d |m :—
|d :d |— :d |d :d |— :t, |d :— |— ||s, |d :—
|d :f |— :s .f |m :s |— :f |m :— |— ||m |s :—
|m, :f, |— :m,.f, |s, :s, |— :s, |d :— |— ||d |d :—

|m :m |m :s |— :m |d :r |— :d |s :l |— :s .l
|s, :d |d :r |— :d |d :t, |— :d |d :d |— :d
|m :s |l :s |— :s |s.fe:s |— :m |d :f |— :s .f
|d :d |l, :t, |— :d |l, :s, |— :l, |m, :f, |— :m,.f,

|s :m |— :r |d :— |— |s |s :— |f :m |l :—
|d :d |— :t, |d :— |— |d |r :d |l,.t, :d |d :—
|m :s |— :f |m :— |— |m |r :m |f :s |l :s
|s, :s, |— :s, |d :— |— |d |t, :d |r :d |f :m

|l :d' |l :s |— :f |m :s |— :l |l :— |s :m
|f :m .r |d .r :m |— :l,.t, |d :r |— :d |d :-.r |s, :d
|f :s |l .t :d' |— :f |s :s |— :m |f.s :l.t |d' :s
|r :m |f :d |— :r |d :t, |— :l,.s, |f, :f |m :d

|r :— |— ||d |m :— |m :m |m :s |— :m |d :r |— :d
|t, :— |— ||s, |d :— |s, :d |d :r |— :d |d :t, |— :d
|s :— |— ||m |s :— |m :s |l :s |— :s |s :s |— :s.f
|s, :— |— ||d |d :— |d :d |l, :t, |— :d |m :s |— :m.r

s	:l	—	:s .l	s	:m	—	:r	d	:—	—		f	m
d	:d	—	:d	m	:d	—	:t_1	d	:—	—		d	d
m	:f	—	:d'	d'	:s	—	:f	m	:—	—		l	s
d	:f	—	:m .f	s	:s_1	—	:s_1	d	:—	—		f_1	d

A-men.

The Saints at Rest.

O fryniau Caersalem ceir gweled.

FROM heavenly Jerusalem's towers
The path through the desert they trace;
And every affliction they suffered
Redounds to the glory of grace;
Their look they cast back on the tempests,
On fears, on grim death and the grave,
Rejoicing that now they're in safety,
Through Him that is mighty to save.

2 And we, from the wilds of the desert,
Shall flee to the land of the blest;
Life's tears shall be changed to rejoicing,
Its labours and toil into rest:
There we shall find refuge eternal,
From sin, from affliction, from pain,
And in the sweet love of the Saviour,
A joy without end shall attain.

DAVID CHARLES, 1762–1834; *tr.* by LEWIS EDWARDS, 1809–87.

597 ST. ALPHEGE. (76. 76.)

Doh = F. *Moderately slow.* HENRY JOHN GAUNTLETT, 1805–76.

:d |m :f |s :d |t, :— |d :d |t, :d |f :m |r :— |— ||
:s, |d :l, |s, :f, |f, :— |m, :s, |s, :s, |r :d |t, :— |— ||
:m |d :d |d :d |r :— |d :s |f :m |s :s |s :— |— ||
:d |l, :f, |m, :l, |s, :— |d :m |r :d |t, :d |s, :— |— ||

:d |m :f |s :s |l :— |s :d |d :r |m :r |d :— |— ||d |d ||
:d |d :d |t, :d |d :t, |d :s, |d :d |d :t, |d :— |— ||l, |s, ||
:m |s :d |r :m |f :r |m :m |m :l |s :-.f |m :— |— ||f |m ||
:d |d :l, |s, :d |f, :— |d :m, |l, :f, |s, :s, |d :— |— ||f, |d, ||

A-men.

JABEZ. (76. 76. D.)

Welsh Hymn Melody.

Lah = G. Doh = B♭. *Moderately slow.*

:l,.se, |l, :— :t, |d :— :t, |d :t, :d.r |m :— :r
:m, |m, :— :m, |m, :— :m, |m, :m, :m, |l, :— :f,
:d.t, |l, :— :l,.se, |l, :— :r |d.l, :se, :m |d :— :l,
:l,,.t,, |d, :— :m, |l, :— :l,.se, |l, :m, :l,,.t,, |d, :— :r,

D.C.

|d :— :t, |l, :— ||t, |d :— :r |m :—:r |m.d :t, :d.t,
|m, :— :r, |d, :— ||m, |m, :— :s, |s, :—:s, |s, :s, :se,
|l, :— :se, |l, :— ||se, |l, :— :t, |d :—:t, |d :r :m.r
|m, :— :m, |l,, :— ||m, |l, :— :s, |d :—:s, |m, :s, :m,

|l, :— :t,.l, |s, :l, :fe, |m, :— ||l,.se, |l, :— :t, |d :— :t,
|l, :— :f, |m, :— :m,.re, |m, :— ||m, |m, :— :m, |m, :— :m,
|d :— :r.d |t, :d :t, |s, :— ||d.t, |l, :— :l,.se, |l, :— :r
|f, :— :r, |m, :l,, :t,, |m, :— ||m,.r, |d, :— :m, |l, :— :l,.se,

d :t,	:d .r	m :— :r	d :— :t,	l, :—	l,	l,
m, :m,	:m,	l, :— :f,	m, :— :r,	d, :—	r,	de,
d .l, :se,	:l, .t,	d :— :l,	l, :— :se,	l, :—	f,	m,
l, :m,	:l,	l, :— :r,	m, :— :m,	l_2 :—	r,	l_2

A-men.

Hic breve vivitur, hic breve plangitur.

BRIEF life is here our portion,
Brief sorrow, short-lived care ;
The life that knows no ending,
The tearless life, is there.

2 O happy retribution !
Short toil, eternal rest ;
For mortals and for sinners
A mansion with the blest !

3 There grief is turned to pleasure,
Such pleasure as below
No human voice can utter,
No human heart can know.

4 And now we fight the battle,
But then shall wear the crown
Of full and everlasting
And passionless renown.

5 And now we watch and struggle,
And now we live in hope,
And Zion, in her anguish,
With Babylon must cope ;

6 But He whom now we trust in
Shall then be seen and known,
And they that know and see Him
Shall have Him for their own.

7 The morning shall awaken,
The shadows shall decay,
And each true-hearted servant
Shall shine as doth the day.

8 Yes ! God, our King and Portion,
In fulness of His grace,
We then shall see for ever,
And worship face to face.

9 O sweet and blessèd country,
The home of God's elect !
O sweet and blessèd country,
That eager hearts expect !

10 Jesus, in mercy bring us
To that dear land of rest,
Who art, with God the Father
And Spirit, ever blest.

BERNARD OF CLUNY, 12th cent. ; *tr.* by JOHN MASON NEALE, 1818–66.

598 MEIRIONYDD. (7 6. 7 6. D.)

Doh = E♭. *In moderate time.* WILLIAM LLOYD, 1786–1852.

s :- .f	m :m .r	d :r	m :—	m :s	f :m
d :—	d :t_1	l_1 :t_1	d :—	d :d	l_1 .t_1 :d
m :- .l	s :s .f	m :s	s :—	s :m	f :s
d :—	d :s_1	l_1 :s_1	d :—	d :m	r :d

f .m :r	d :—		s :- .f	m :m .r	d :r	m :—
d :t_1	d :—		r :—	d :t_1	d :d	d :—
l :r .f	m :—		s :—	s :s .f	m :l	l :—
f_1 :s_1	d :—		t_1 :—	d :s_1	l_1 :f_1	m_1 :—

m :s	f :m	f .m :r	d :—		s :—	l :s
t_1 :d	d :d	d :t_1	d :—		d :—	d :d
se :s	f :s	l :r .f	m :—		m :—	m :m
m_1 :m	l_1 :d	f_1 :s_1	d :—		d :—	l_1 :d

l :t	d' :—	s :m	s :l	s :m	r :—		m :- .r
d :r	d :—	r :d	d :d	r :s_1 .l_1	t_1 :—		t_1 :—
f :f	m :fe	s :s	s :m	r :m .fe	s :—		s :—
f :r	l_1 :—	t_1 :d	m :l_1	t_1 :d	s_1 :—		m_1 :—

d :d .r	m :m .r	m :fe	s :d	m :s	f .m :r	d :—		d	d	
l_1 :l_1	t_1 :l_1 .se_1	l_1 :d	t_1 :s_1	d :d	d :t_1	d :—		l_1	s_1	
m :l	se :l .t	d' :l	s :m	d :d	l :r .f	m :—		f	m	
l_1 :f	m .r :d .t_1	l_1 :r	s_1 :d	l_1 :m_1	f_1 :s_1	d :—		f_1	d	

A-men.

O bona patria, lumina sobria.

FOR thee, O dear, dear country,
  Mine eyes their vigils keep;
For very love, beholding
  Thy happy name, they weep;
The mention of thy glory
  Is unction to the breast,
And medicine in sickness,
  And love, and life, and rest.

2 With jaspers glow thy bulwarks;
  Thy streets with emeralds blaze;
The sardius and the topaz
  Unite in thee their rays;
Thine ageless walls are bonded
  With amethyst unpriced;
Thy saints build up its fabric,
  And the corner-stone is Christ.

3 The Cross is all thy splendour,
  The Crucified thy praise;
His laud and benediction
  Thy ransomed people raise.
Upon the Rock of Ages
  They build thy holy tower;
Thine is the victor's laurel,
  And thine the golden dower.

4 O sweet and blessèd country,
  The home of God's elect!
O sweet and blessèd country,
  That eager hearts expect!
Jesus, in mercy bring us
  To that dear land of rest,
Who art, with God the Father
  And Spirit, ever blest.

BERNARD OF CLUNY, 12th cent.; *tr.* by JOHN MASON NEALE, 1818-66.

599

EWING. (76. 76. D.)

Doh = D♭. *In moderate time.* ALEXANDER EWING, 1830–95.

```
:d  |r  :d  |f  :m   |r  :—  |d  :m |s  :d'   |t  :se  |l  :— |—
:s, |s, :s, |d  :d   |t, :—  |d  :d |d  :m    |m  :r   |d  :— |—
:m  |f  :m  |l  :s   |f  :—  |m  :s |m  :l    |se :t   |l  :— |—
:d  |d  :d  |d  :d   |s, :—  |d  :d |d  :l,   |m  :m   |l, :— |—

:l  |s  :m  |m  :r   |d  :—  |r  :m |m  :m    |r  :d   |r  :— |—
:f  |m  :d  |t, :se, |l, :—  |t, :d |d  :d    |l, :d   |t, :— |—
:d' |d' :s  |se :m   |m  :—  |s  :s |s  :s    |f  :m   |s  :— |—
:f, |d  :d  |m  :m,  |l, :—  |s, :d |d  :d    |f, :l,  |s, :— |—

:r  |f  :m  |l  :t   |d' :—  |r' :s |m' :-.m' |r' :d'  |t  :— |—
:t, |d  :d  |d  :m   |m  :—  |s  :s |s  :s    |l  :fe  |s  :— |—
:s  |l  :s  |l  :se  |l  :—  |t  :t |d' :d'   |l  :d'  |r' :— |—
:s, |f, :d  |f  :m   |l  :—  |s  :s |d  :m    |f  :l   |s  :— |—

:l  |s  :m  |m  :r   |d  :—  |r  :m |m  :m    |r  :-.d |d  :— |— ||f  |m ||
:r  |s  :d  |t, :se, |l, :—  |t, :d |d  :d    |t, :-.d |d  :— |— ||d  |d ||
:t  |d' :s  |se :m   |m  :—  |s  :s |s  :s    |f  :-.m |m  :— |— ||l  |s ||
:f  |m  :d  |m  :m,  |l, :—  |s, :d |d  :m,   |s, :-.d |d  :— |— ||f, |d ||
                                                                   A-men.
```

Urbs Sion aurea, patria lactea.

JERUSALEM the golden,
With milk and honey blest,
Beneath thy contemplation
Sink heart and voice oppressed:
I know not, O I know not
What social joys are there,
What radiancy of glory,
What light beyond compare.

2 They stand, those halls of Zion,
Conjubilant with song,
And bright with many an angel,
And all the martyr throng:
The Prince is ever in them;
The daylight is serene;
The pastures of the blessèd
Are decked in glorious sheen.

3 There is the throne of David,
And there, from care released,
The shout of them that triumph,
The song of them that feast;
And they who, with their Leader,
Have conquered in the fight,
For ever and for ever
Are clad in robes of white.

4 O sweet and blessèd country,
The home of God's elect!
O sweet and blessèd country,
That eager hearts expect!
Jesus, in mercy bring us
To that dear land of rest,
Who art, with God the Father
And Spirit, ever blest.

BERNARD OF CLUNY, 12th cent.; *tr.* by JOHN MASON NEALE, 1818–66.

600 GLORY. (C.M. and refrain.)

Doh = C. *Brightly.* *Tune Book for Sunday Schools,* 1842.

```
:d   |d  :m.f |s  :s   |l    :l   |s  :d'  |l    :r'   |s :l.t |d' :— |— ||
:d   |d  :d   |r  :d   |d.t, :d.r |m  :s   |l    :l    |s :f   |m  :— |— ||
:s.f |m  :l   |s  :m   |f.s  :l.t |d' :d'  |d'   :f'   |m':r'  |d' :— |— ||
:m.r |d  :l,  |t, :d   |f,   :f   |d  :m   |f    :r    |s :s,  |d  :— |— ||

:d'  |l  :f   |s  :m   |l.s  :l.t |d' :l   |s.l  :s.f  |m :r   |d  :— |— ||
:s   |f  :d   |d  :m.r |d    :f   |m  :d.r |m.f  :m.r  |d :t,  |d  :— |— ||
:m'  |d' :l   |s  :s   |l    :f.s |l  :l.t |d'.t :d'.l |s :s.f |m  :— |— ||
:d   |f  :f   |m  :d   |f    :r   |l, :f   |m.r  :m.f  |s :s,  |d  :— |— ||
```

REFRAIN.

```
:m.f |s  :s  |l    :l   |s  :— |s  :d'.r' |m' :d' |r' :t  |d' :— |d' ||d' d' ||
:d.r |m  :m  |f    :d.r |m  :— |m  :s.s   |s  :l  |l  :s  |s  :— |m  ||f  m  ||
:s.s |d' :d' |d'.t :l.t |d' :— |d' :d'.t  |d' :m' |f' :r' |m' :— |d' ||l  s  ||
:d.d |d  :d  |f    :f   |d  :— |d  :m.s   |d' :l  |f  :s  |d  :— |d  ||f, d  ||
                                                                        A-men.
```

AROUND the throne of God in heaven
  Thousands of children stand,
Children whose sins are all forgiven,
  A holy, happy band,
    Singing, 'Glory, glory, glory!'

2 What brought them to that world above,
  That heaven so bright and fair,
Where all is peace and joy and love?
  How came those children there,
    Singing, 'Glory, glory, glory'?

3 Because the Saviour shed His blood
  To wash away their sin;
Bathed in that pure and precious flood,
  Behold them white and clean,
    Singing, 'Glory, glory, glory!'

4 On earth they sought the Saviour's grace,
  On earth they loved His Name;
So now they see His blessèd face,
  And stand before the Lamb,
    Singing, 'Glory, glory, glory!'

ANNE SHEPHERD, 1809–57.

Also the following:

137 Blest be the everlasting God
205–27 *Hymns on the Communion of Saints*
286 Abide with me! fast falls the eventide
328–32 *Hymns on the Burial of the Dead*
480 There is a city bright
582 When this passing world is done

New Year and Anniversaries (601–607).

601 ST. ANNE. (C.M.)

Doh = C. *Slow and dignified.* WILLIAM CROFT, 1678–1727.

```
s :— | m :l   | s :d' | d' :t  | d' || s | d' :s  | l :fe | s :—
d :— | d :d.r | m :m  | r :r   | m  || m | m :m   | m :r  | r :—
m :— | s :l.t | d' :d'| l :s   | s  || d'| d' :t  | l :l  | t :—
d :— | d :f   | m :l  | f :s   | d  || d | l, :m  | d :r  | s :—

t :— | d' :l  | r' :t | d' :l  | t  || s | l :d'  | r' :t | d' :— || d' | d'
r :— | m :d   | f :r  | m :-.r | t, || d | f :m   | r :r  | m :—  || f  | m
s :— | s :l   | l :s  | s :l   | se || s | f :s   | l :s  | s :—  || l  | s
s :— | d :f   | r :s  | d :f   | m  || m | r :d   | f :s  | d :—  || f, | d
                                                                      A-men.
```

FAUX-BOURDON SETTING.

Doh = C. MARTIN SHAW, 1876–

```
  :s | d' :d' | d' :m'| r' :r' | m' || r'| d' :t  | m :r  | r :—
d :— | s :f   | s :m  | l :s   | s  || s | m :-.r | d :l, | t, :—
s :— | m :l   | s :d' | d' :t  | d' || s | d' :s  | l :fe | s :—
d :— | d :f   | m :l  | f :s   | d  || t,| l, :s, | d :r | s, :—

r' :— | d' :d' | t :t  | l :-.l | se || t | d' :-.d' | f' :r' | m' :—
   :r | s :f   | f :m  | m :r   | m  || r | l :s     | f :s   | s :—
t :—  | d' :l  | r' :t | d' :l  | t  || s | l :d'    | r' :t  | d' :—
s :—  | m :f   | r :s  | f :f   | m  || s | f :m     | r :s   | d :—
```

[*Copyright*, 1915, *by J. Curwen & Sons, Ltd.*]

From Psalm xc.

Unison.

O GOD, our help in ages past,
  Our hope for years to come,
Our shelter from the stormy blast,
  And our eternal home!

Harmony.

2 Under the shadow of Thy throne
  Thy saints have dwelt secure;
Sufficient is Thine arm alone,
  And our defence is sure.

Unison.

3 Before the hills in order stood,
  Or earth received her frame,
From everlasting Thou art God,
  To endless years the same.

Harmony.

4 A thousand ages in Thy sight
  Are like an evening gone;
Short as the watch that ends the night
  Before the rising sun.

5 Time, like an ever-rolling stream,
  Bears all its sons away;
They fly forgotten, as a dream
  Dies at the opening day.

Unison.

6 O God, our help in ages past,
  Our hope for years to come,
Be Thou our guard while troubles last,
  And our eternal home.

ISAAC WATTS, 1674–1748.

602 WELLESLEY. (76. 76. D.)

Doh = E♭. *In moderate time.* GEORGE JOB ELVEY, 1816–93.

```
:d  |r  :m  |f  :m  |m  :r  |d  :l   |l  :s  |s  :r  |m  :— |—
:d  |d  :d  |d  :d  |t, :—  |d  :d   |r  :r  |t, :t, |d  :— |—
:m  |f  :s  |l  :s  |s  :f  |m  :f   |r  :r  |s  :s  |s  :— |—
:d  |d  :d  |d  :d  |s, :—  |d  :l,  |t, :t, |s, :s, |d  :— |—

       B♭.t.
:d' |d'  :[d]f  |f  :m  |m  :r  |d  :r   |m  :d  |l, :t, |d  :— |—
:m  |m   :[m]l, |s, :s, |s, :f, |m, :l,  |s, :m, |f, :f, |m, :— |—
:l  |l   :[l]r  |r  :d  |t, :—  |d  :d   |d  :d  |r  :r  |d  :— |—
:l, |l   :[s]d  |t, :d  |s, :—  |l, :fe, |s, :s, |s, :s, |d, :— |—

     d.f.A♭.                                 E♭.t.
:d  |[d]r      :f   |m   :r   |d  :—  |t,  :t,  |[d]f  :l  |s  :f  |m  :— |—
:m, |[l,]t,    :se, |l,  :t,  |l, :—  |se, :se, |[l,]r :r  |r  :t, |d  :— |—
:l, |[l,]t,    :r   |d   :t,  |m  :—  |m   :m   |[m]l  :f  |r  :s  |s  :— |—
:l, |[fe,]se,  :m,  |ba, :se, |l, :d  |m   :m,  |[l,]r :d  |t, :s, |d  :— |—

:m   |f  :f  |m  :r  |s  :—  |s  :l  |s  :d  |m  :r  |d  :— |— || f  |m
:d   |d  :d  |d  :t, |d  :t, |d  :d  |d  :d  |d  :t, |d  :— |— || d  |d
:s   |f  :l  |d' :s  |s  :f  |m  :f  |s  :m  |s  :f  |m  :— |— || l  |s
:ta, |l, :l  |s  :f  |m  :r  |d  :f, |m, :l, |s, :s, |d  :— |— || f, |d
                                                                A-men.
```

STILL on the homeward journey
  Across the desert plain,
Beside another landmark,
  We pilgrims meet again.
We meet, in cloud and sunshine,
  Beneath a changeful sky,
With calm and storm before us,
  As in the days gone by.

2 We meet with loving greetings,
  Fond wishes from the heart,
As brothers often parted,
  And soon again to part.
With tender recollections,
  With many a gentle tear
We meet, for some are wanting;
  All loved ones are not here.

3 Safe in the home of Jesus,
  With Him for ever blest,
How glorious is their portion,
  How undisturbed their rest!
How gladly will they greet us,
  When, all our journey past,
We reach the better country,
  The Father's house, at last!

4 Thus round the silent landmark,
  Here on the desert plain,
We pilgrims meet together,
  With loving hearts, again.
The storm may gather round us,
  But Christ has gone before;
We follow in His footsteps,
  And doubt and fear no more.

JANE LAURIE BORTHWICK, 1813–97.

[May be sung to AURELIA, No. 205.]

603

BETHANY (CRUCIFER). (87. 87. D.)

Doh = E. *In moderate time.*

HENRY SMART, 1813–79.

```
|m  :l  |s  :m  |d  :-.r|d  :t, |l, :s, |d  :m  |s  :f.m|r  :— ||
|d  :d  |d  :t, |d  :l, |s, :s, |l, :s, |s, :d  |d  :r.d|t, :— ||
|s  :f  |s  :s  |m  :f  |m  :r  |t, :t, |d  :s  |s  :l  |r  :s ||
|d  :f  |m  :s, |l, :f, |s, :s, |f, :f, |m, :d  |m, :f, |s, :— ||

|m  :l  |s  :m  |d  :-.r|d  :t, |l, :s, |d  :f  |m  :r  |d  :— ||
|s, :d  |r  :t, |l, :fe,|s, :s, |l, :s, |s, :d  |d  :t, |d  :— ||
|m  :m  |r  :s  |m  :r  |r  :r  |t, :t, |d  :d  |s  :s.f|m  :— ||
|d  :l, |t, :s, |l, :r  |s, :s, |f, :f, |m, :l, |s, :s, |d  :— ||

B.t.                                                        f.E.
|(r)s, :d  |d  :t, |l, :l, |l, :s, |s, :m  |r  :l, |d  :t, |(d)s  :— ||
|(t)m, :s, |s, :s, |f, :f, |f, :m, |s, :s, |f, :r, |m, :f, |(m)t, :— ||
|(s)d  :d  |r  :r  |d  :r  |d  :d  |d  :ta,|l, :l, |s, :r  |(d)s  :— ||
|(s)d, :m, |s, :s, |l, :t, |d  :d, |m, :d, |f, :f, |s, :s, |(d)s, :— ||

|t  :s  |d' :s  |f  :-.s|f  :m  |l  :s  |f  :m  |r  :r  |d  :— || d  | d  ||
|r  :t, |d  :d  |d  :r  |d  :d  |d  :de |r  :d  |d  :t, |d  :— || l, | s, ||
|s  :s  |s  :m  |l  :s  |s  :s  |f  :m  |f  :s  |l  :s.f|m  :— || f  | m  ||
|s  :f  |m  :d  |l, :t, |d  :d  |f, :l, |r  :m  |f  :s  |d  :— || f, | d  ||
                                                              A-men.
```

HEAVENLY Father, Thou hast brought us
Safely to the present day,
Gently leading on our footsteps;
Watching o'er us all the way.
Friend and Guide through life's long journey,
Grateful hearts to Thee we bring;
But for love so true and changeless
How shall we fit praises sing?

2 Mercies new and never-failing
Brightly shine through all the past,
Watchful care and loving-kindness,
Always near from first to last,
Tender love, divine protection
Ever with us day and night;
Blessings more than we can number
Strew the path with golden light.

3 Shadows deep have crossed our pathway;
We have trembled in the storm;
Clouds have gathered round so darkly
That we could not see Thy form;
Yet Thy love hath never left us
In our griefs alone to be,
And the help each gave the other
Was the strength that came from Thee.

4 Many that we loved have left us,
Reaching first their journey's end;
Now they wait to give us welcome—
Brother, sister, child, and friend.
When at last our journey's over,
And we pass away from sight,
Father, take us through the darkness
Into everlasting light.

HESTER PERIAM HAWKINS, 1885.

604

SONG 13. (77. 77.)

ORLANDO GIBBONS, 1583–1625.

Doh = E♭. *In moderate time.*

```
                                                   B♭.t.
:m  |— :f  |s  :l    |r  :-.r |m :—  || :(s)d  |— :r
:s, |— :d  |t, :d    |d  :t,  |d :—  || :(d)f, |— :f,
:d  |— :d  |r  :f.m  |r  :s   |s :—  || :(m)l, |— :t,
:d  |— :l, |s, :f,   |s, :s,  |d :—  || :(d)f, |— :r,

                       d.f.A♭.                                   E♭.t.
m  :f  |r  :r    |d  :—  || :(l)t, |— :d  |r      :m  |d      :t,      |(l)r   :— ||
m, :l, |s, :-.f, |m, :—  || :(f)s, |— :s, |f,     :m, |f,.m,  :r,.m,   |(fe)t, :— ||
d  :d  |d  :t,   |d  :—  || :(d)r  |— :s, |l,.t,  :d  |l,     :t,.d    |(r)s   :— ||
d, :f, |s, :s,   |d, :—  || :(f)s, |— :m, |r,     :d, |f,     :s,      |(r,)s, :— ||

:s  |— :f.m |r  :d.r,m |r  :r    |d :—  || d  |d  ||
:d  |— :d   |t, :d     |d  :t,   |d :—  || l, |s, ||
:s  |— :l   |r  :s     |s  :-.f  |m :—  || f  |m  ||
:m, |— :f,  |s, :m,    |s, :s,   |d :—  || f, |d  ||
```

Amen.

FOR Thy mercy and Thy grace,
Faithful through another year,
Hear our song of thankfulness;
Jesus, our Redeemer, hear.

2 Lo! our sins on Thee we cast,
Thee, our perfect sacrifice,
And, forgetting all the past,
Press towards our glorious prize.

3 Dark the future; let Thy light
Guide us, Bright and Morning Star;
Fierce our foes, and hard the fight;
Arm us, Saviour, for the war.

4 In our weakness and distress,
Rock of strength, be Thou our stay;
In the pathless wilderness
Be our true and living way.

Unison.

5 Keep us faithful, keep us pure,
Keep us evermore Thine own;
Help, O help us to endure;
Fit us for the promised crown.

HENRY DOWNTON, 1818–85.

605 DEERHURST. (8 7. 8 7. D.)

Doh = E♭. *In moderate time.* JAMES LANGRAN, 1835-1909.

m :s	m :d	t_1 :d	r :m	f :m	r :s	t :l	s :—
d :r	d :s_1	s_1 :s_1	s_1 :s_1	d :d.t_1	l_1 :r	r :d	t_1 :—
s :s	s :s	f :m	r :d	l :s	fe :s	s :fe	s :—
d :t_1	d :m	r :d	t_1 :d	d :d	d :t_1	r :r	s_1 :—

m :s	m :d	t_1 :d	r :m	f :m	l :s	m :r	d :—
d :r	d :s_1	s_1 :s_1	s_1 :s_1	d :d	d :d	d :t_1	d :—
s :s	s :s	f :m	r :d	d :m	f :s	s :f	m :—
d :t_1	d :m	r :d	t_1 :d	l_1 :s_1	f_1 :m_1	s_1 :s_1	d :—

m :s	d' :l	s :d	f :m	r :m	s :f	d :r	m :—
d :t_1	d :d	d :d	t_1 :d	r :de	r :r	d :l_1	t_1 :—
s :s	s :f	s :s	s :s	l :l	l :l	l :l	se :—
d :r	m :f	m :m	r :d	f :m	r :r	f :f	m :—

m :s	d' :l	s :d	f :m	r :m	s :f	l_1 :t_1	d :—	d	d
d :r	d :d	d :d	t_1 :d	r :de	r :l_1	l_1 :s_1	s_1 :—	l_1	s_1
l :s.f	m :f	s :s	s :s	l :l	l :r	r :f	m :—	f	m
l_1 :t_1	d :f	m :m	r :d	f :m	r :r_1.m_1	f_1 :s_1	d/d_1 :—	f_1	d

A-men.

[*By permission of Novello & Co., Ltd.*]

AT Thy feet, our God and Father,
Who hast blessed us all our days,
We with grateful hearts would gather,
To begin the year with praise,—
Praise for light so brightly shining
On our steps from heaven above,
Praise for mercies daily twining
Round us golden cords of love.

2 Jesus, for Thy love most tender,
On the Cross for sinners shown,
We would praise Thee, and surrender
All our hearts to be Thine own.
With so blest a Friend provided,
We upon our way would go,
Sure of being safely guided,
Guarded well from every foe.

3 Every day will be the brighter
When Thy gracious face we see;
Every burden will be lighter
When we know it comes from Thee.
Spread Thy love's broad banner o'er us;
Give us strength to serve and wait,
Till the glory breaks before us,
Through the city's open gate.

JAMES DRUMMOND BURNS, 1823-64.

606 ST. IGNATIUS. (75. 75. D.)

Doh = E. *Moderately slow.* JOSEPH BARNBY, 1838–96.

```
:d .d  | r .d  :m .f   | s  :m .r   | d  :d  | d  || d .d  | r .d  :m .f
:s,.s, | s,.s, :d .d   | r  :d .t,  | d  :l, | s, || s,.s, | s,.s, :s,.l,
:m .m  | r .m  :s .l   | s  :s .s   | m  :f  | m  || m .m  | r .m  :m .d
:d .d  | t,.d  :d .l,  | t, :d .s,  | l, :f, | d  || d .d  | t,.d  :d .l,

                            B.t.
| s  :m .r   | d  :r  | m  || m l,.t,  | d .l,  :d .r   | m  :r .l,   | d
| s, :t,.t,  | d  :l, | t, || d f,.f,  | m,.m,  :m,.l,  | s, :f,.f,   | m,
| r  :s .f   | m  :l  | se || l r .r   | d .d   :d .l,  | d  :l,.l,   | s,
| t, :s,.s,  | l, :f, | m, || l r,.r,  | l,.l,  :l,.f,  | d, :f,.f,   | s,

      f.E.
:t, | d s  || d'.t   | l .s  :m .f   | s  .t,  :m .r    | d  :r  | d || d  | d  ||
:f, | m t, || d .d   | d .t, :d .d   | d  .t,  :l,.l,   | s, :t, | d || l, | s, ||
:r  | d s  || s .s   | f .r  :d .r   | m  .s   :s .f    | m  :f  | m || f  | m  ||
:s, | d s, || m,.m,  | f,.s, :l,.l,  | m,       :f,.f,   | s, :s, | d || f, | d  ||
                                                                          A-men.
```

[*By permission of Novello & Co., Ltd.*]

FATHER, let me dedicate
 All my times to Thee,
In whatever worldly state
 Thou wilt have me be;
Not from sorrow, pain, or care
 Freedom dare I claim;
This alone shall be my prayer,
 'Glorify Thy Name!'

2 Can a child presume to choose
 Where or how to live?
Can a father's love refuse
 All the best to give?
More Thou givest every day
 Than the best can claim,
Nor withholdest aught that may
 Glorify Thy Name.

3 If Thou callest to the cross,
 And its shadow come,
Turning all my gain to loss,
 Shrouding heart and home,
Let me think how Thy dear Son
 To His glory came,
And in deepest woe pray on,
 'Glorify Thy Name.'

4 If in mercy Thou wilt spare
 Joys that yet are mine,
If on life, serene and fair,
 Brighter rays may shine,
Let my glad heart, while it sings,
 Thee in all proclaim,
And, whate'er the future brings,
 Glorify Thy Name.

LAWRENCE TUTTIETT, 1825–97.

607

WAREHAM. (L.M.)

Doh = B♭. *In moderate time.* WILLIAM KNAPP, 1698–1768.

```
:d  |d  :t,  :l,  |s,  :—  :d  |r  :d  :t,  |d  :—  :r  |m  :r  :d
:m, |m, :—   :f,  |s,  :—  :m, |l, :s, :s,  |s, :—  :s, |s, :—  :s,.fe,
:s, |d  :—   :d   |d   :—  :d  |f  :m  :r   |m  :—  :t, |d  :r  :m.d
:d, |d, :—   :f,  |m,  :—  :l, |f, :s, :s,  |d, :—  :s, |d  :t, :l,

t,  :d  :r   |d  :t, :l,  |s, :—  ||s, |l, :s, :l,.t, |d  :—  :t, |d  :—  :r
s,  :—  :s,  |l, :s, :fe, |s, :—  ||s, |f, :s, :f,    |s, :—  :s, |m, :—  :l,
r   :d  :t,  |m  :r  :d   |t, :—  ||d  |d  :—  :f     |m  :d  :r  |d  :t, :l,
s,  :m, :t,, |d, :r, :r,  |s, :—  ||m, |f, :m, :r,    |d, :m, :s, |l, :s, :f,

m   :—  :r.m    |f  :m  :r   |d  :t, :d  |r  :d  :t, |d  :—  ||d  |d
se, :—  :l,.s,  |f, :s, :l,  |s, :f, :m, |l, :s, :s, |s, :—  ||f, |m,
t,  :—  :l,     |t, :d  :f   |m  :r  :d  |f  :m  :r  |m  :—  ||l, |s,
m,  :—  :f,.m,  |r, :m, :f,  |s, :—  :l, |f, :s, :s, |d, :—  ||f, |d,
```

A-men.

GREAT God, we sing that mighty hand
By which supported still we stand;
The opening year Thy mercy shows,
And mercy crowns its lingering close.

2 By day, by night, at home, abroad,
Still are we guarded by our God,
By His incessant bounty fed,
By His unerring counsel led.

3 With grateful hearts the past we own;
The future, all to us unknown,
We to Thy guardian care commit,
And peaceful leave before Thy feet.

4 In scenes exalted or depressed
Thou art our joy, and Thou our rest;
Thy goodness all our hopes shall raise,
Adored through all our changing days.

5 When death shall interrupt these songs,
And seal in silence mortal tongues,
Our Helper God, in whom we trust,
Shall keep our souls and guard our dust.

PHILIP DODDRIDGE, 1702–51.

Also the following:

29 Now thank we all our God
211 We come unto our fathers' God
215 Thy hand, O God, has guided
537 March on, my soul, with strength
562–84 *Hymns on Pilgrimage and Rest*
649 Thou gracious Power, whose mercy lends

Spring (608–611).

608 KING'S LANGLEY. (C.M.)

Doh = D. *In moderate time.* English Traditional May-Day Carol.

:m .f |s :s |m :m |f :f .m |r :r |m :m .f |s :d' |s :— |— ||

:d |d :d |d :d |r :d |t, :t, |d :d .t, |d :d |d :t, |d ||

:s |s :s |s :s |s :s |s :s |s :s |s :l |s :f |m ||

:d .r |m :m |d :d |t, :d |s, :s |d :d .r |m :f |m :r |d ||

:l |s :f |m :r |d :d |d' :d' |s :s.f |m :r |d :— |— || d |d ||

:d |r :d .r |m :t, |d :d |d :f |s :d |d :t, |d :— |— || l, |s, ||

:m |s :s |s :f |s :f.s |l :l |d' :l |s :f |m :— |— || f |m ||

:l, |t, :l,.t, |d :r |m :r.m |f :r |m :f |s :s, |d :— |— || f, |d ||

A-men.

THE glory of the spring how sweet !
The new-born life how glad !
What joy the happy earth to greet,
In new, bright raiment clad !

2 Divine Renewer, Thee I bless ;
I greet Thy going forth ;
I love Thee in the loveliness
Of Thy renewèd earth.

3 But O these wonders of Thy grace,
These nobler works of Thine,
These marvels sweeter far to trace,
These new births more divine,

4 This new-born glow of faith so strong,
This bloom of love so fair,
This new-born ecstasy of song,
And fragrancy of prayer !

5 Creator Spirit, work in me
These wonders sweet of Thine ;
Divine Renewer, graciously
Renew this heart of mine.

THOMAS HORNBLOWER GILL, 1819–1906.

609

ADRIAN. (8 7. 8 7. D.)

Doh = G. *In moderate time.*

ROBERT PRESCOTT STEWART, 1825–94.

s :-.m	r :d	m :d	l_1 :s_1	d :t_1	r :d	s :f	r :—
s_1 :-.d	t_1 :d	s_1 :s_1	f_1 :m_1	s_1 :s_1	t_1 :d	s_1 :d	t_1 :—
m :-.s	f :m	d :d	d :d	s :s	s :s	d :l	s :—
d :-.d	d :d	d_1 :m_1	f_1 :d	m :r	f :m	m_1 :f_1	s_1 :—

	D.t.						f.G.
m :-.r	^{d}f :f	r^1 :d^1	t :l	s :d^1	m :s	r :-.m	$^{d}s_1$:—
t_1 :-.t_1	^{l}r :r	f :f	f :r	s :d	d :d	t_1 :-.t_1	$^{s}r_1$:—
m :-.m	^{m}l :l	s :d^1	r^1 :t	d^1 :s	s :s	f :-.s	$^{m}t_1$:—
se_1 :-.se_1	^{l}r :d	t_1 :l_1	s_1 :f	m :m	d :m_1	s_1 :-.s_1	$^{d}s_1$:—

			f.C.				G.t.
l_1 :t_1	d :s_1	r :s_1	m :^{d}s	l :t	d^1 :s	r^1 :s	$^{m^1}l$:—
f_1 :s_1	s_1 :s_1	f_1 :f_1	m_1 :^{s_1}r	r :s	s :s	f :f	$^{m}l_1$:—
d :r	d :d	t_1 :r	d :^{m}t	l :r^1	d^1 :d^1	t :t	$^{d^1}f$:—
f_1 :f_1	m_1 :m_1	r_1 :t_1	d :^{d}s	f :f	m :m	r :r	$^{d}f_1$:—

r :r	m :f	l :s	m :d	s_1 :d	s :f	m :r	d :—	d	d
t_1 :t_1	t_1 :t_1	d :d	s_1 :l_1	s_1 :l_1	s_1 :l_1	t_1 :t_1	s_1 :—	l_1	s_1
s :s	s :f	f :m	d :ma	m :f	d :d	s :f	m :—	f	m
f :f	m :r	d :d	m_1 :fe_1	s_1 :f_1	m_1 :f_1	s_1 :s_1	d_1 :—	f_1	d_1

A-men.

EVERTON. (8 7. 8 7. D.)

HENRY SMART, 1813–79.

Doh = E♭. *Brightly.*

D.C.

m :f	s :d^1	l :t	d^1 :s	f :s	m :d	r :r	r :—
d :t_1	d :m	d :f	m :d	d :r	d :s_1	l_1 :t_1.d	t_1 :—
s :s	s :s	l :f	s :s	l :r	s :s	s :fe	s :—
d :r	m :d	f :r	d :m	l_1 :t_1	d :m	r :r_1	s_1 :—

SPRING

Bb.t.

r s, :s,	l, :d	d :t,	d :m	m :m	r :l,.t,	d :t,	l, :—	
t m, :s,	f, :f,	s, :s,	s, :s,	l, :l,	l, :l,	l, :se,	l, :—	
s d :d	d :d	r :r	d :d	d :m	f :r	m :r	d :—	
s d, :m,	f, :l,	s, :s,.f,	m, :d,	d :d,	r, :f,	m, :m,	l, :—	

f.Eb.

d s :s	s :d'	f :l	l :s	d :r	m :s	f :r	d :—		d	d	
m t, :t,	d :d	d :d	d :d	d :t,	d :d	d :t,	d :—		l,	s,	
d s :f	m :m	f :f	f :m	m :s	s :s	l :s.f	m :—		f	m	
l m :r	d :ta,	l, :f,	d :d	l, :s,	d :m,	f, :s,	d :—		f,	d	

A-men.

ALL is bright and cheerful round us;
  All above is soft and blue;
Spring at last hath come and found us,
  Spring and all its pleasures too.
Every flower is full of gladness;
  Dew is bright, and buds are gay;
Earth, with all its sin and sadness,
  Seems a happy place to-day.

2 If the flowers that fade so quickly,
  If a day that ends in night,
If the skies that clouds so thickly
  Often cover from our sight—
If they all have so much beauty,
  What must be God's land of rest,
Where His sons that do their duty,
  After many toils are blest?

3 There are leaves that never wither;
  There are flowers that ne'er decay;
Nothing evil goeth thither;
  Nothing good is kept away.
They that came from tribulation,
  Washed their robes and made them white,
Out of every tongue and nation,
  Now have rest, and peace, and light.

JOHN MASON NEALE, 1818–66.

610

NEW GRANGE. (Irr.)

Doh = A♭. *In moderate time.* Robert Alexander Stewart Macalister, 1870–

|m :m |r :d .d |t, :l,.l, |l, :-.s, |s, :m .m |r :d .d |t, :l,

|s, :s, |s, :s,.s, |s, :f,.f, |f, :f, |m, :s,.s, |l, :l,.l, |f, :f,

1. For all Thy love and good - ness, so boun-ti - ful and

|d :d |s, :d .d |d :d .d |t, :r |m :m .m |m :m .m |r :t,

|d, :d, |m, :m,.m, |f, :f,.f, |s, :t, |d :d .d |l, :l,.l, |r, :r,

Lord, be a - dored!

|s, :— |— :s, |d :— |l, :— |— :— |r :r |t, :—

|d, :— |s, :— |s, :— |s, :— |f, :— |l, :— |s, :—

free, Thy Name, Lord, be a - dored!

|d :— |t, :— |d :— |de :— |r :— |r :— |r :—

|m, :— |f, :— |m, :— |m, :— |r, :— |f, :— |s, :—

E♭.t.

|f :f |m :r |d :t,.t, |t, :-.l, |l, :ˢd'.d' |t :l |s :m

|l, :l, |l, :l, |l, :se,.se, |se, :m, |m, :ˢd .d |s :f |m :t,

On the wings of joy - ous praise our hearts soar up to

|t, :t, |d :r |m :f .f |m :m |m :ʳs .s |l :l |t :s

|r, :r, |m, :m, |m, :r .r |d :d |d :ᵗm .m |f :f |s :s,

f.A♭.

Glo - ry to the Lord!

ᵈs, :— |— :— |d :— |f :— |— :— |m :r |d :—

ᵈs, :— |— :— |s, :— |l, :— |s, :— |— :f, |m, :—

Thee: Glo - ry to the Lord!

ᵐt, :— |r :— |d :— |d :— |t, :— |t, :— |d :—

ˡm, :— |f, :— |m, :— |r, :— |s, :— |s, :— |d, :—

Last verse.

|d :— |— :— |— :— |r :-.r |m :— |— :fe

Lord! Hal - - le- lu - - jah!

|m, :— |fe, :-.fe, |s, :— |l, :— |s, :— |d :—

Lord! Hal - le - lu jah! A - - -

|d :— |— :— |— :— |d :-.d |d :— |— :r

Lord! Hal - le- lu - - jah!

|l, :— |r, :-.r, |m, :— |fe, :— |s, :— |l, :—

Hal - le - lu - jah! A - -

*

s :— |— :— |d :— |f :— |m :— |— :— |— :— |—

s :— |— :— |l :— |— :— |s :— |— :— |— :— |—

A - - - - - - men.

— :— |d :— |l_1 :— |— :t_1 |d :— |— :— |— :— |—

- - men, A - - - men.

m :— |r :d |— :— |r :— |m :— |— :— |— :— |—

A - - - - - - men.

s_1 :— |f_1 :m_1 |f_1 :— |— :— |d :— |— :— |— :— |—

d_1 :— |— :— |— :— |—

- - - - - - - - men.

* Alternative line for Soprano.

[*Copyright*, 1927, *by Oxford University Press.*]

2 The springtime breaks all round about, waking from winter's night :
Thy Name, Lord, be adored !
The sunshine, like God's love, pours down in floods of golden light :
Glory to the Lord !

3 A voice of joy is in all the earth, a voice is in all the air :
Thy Name, Lord, be adored !
All nature singeth aloud to God ; there is gladness everywhere :
Glory to the Lord !

4 The flowers are strown in field and copse, on the hill and on the plain :
Thy Name, Lord, be adored !
The soft air stirs in the tender leaves that clothe the trees again :
Glory to the Lord !

5 The works of Thy hands are very fair ; and for all Thy bounteous love
Thy Name, Lord, be adored !
But what, if this world is so fair, is the better land above ?
Glory to the Lord !

6 O to awake from death's short sleep, like the flowers from their wintry grave—
Thy Name, Lord, be adored !—
And to rise all glorious in the day when Christ shall come to save !
Glory to the Lord !

7 O to dwell in that happy land where the heart cannot choose but sing !—
Thy Name, Lord, be adored !—
And where the life of the blessèd ones is a beautiful endless spring !
Glory to the Lord ! Hallelujah !

WILLIAM WALSHAM HOW, 1823–97.

611 GORDON. (C.M.)

Doh=E♭. *In moderate time.* HENRY SMART, 1813–79.

:s | s :s | d' :m | f :l | s :d | r :f | m :r | m :— | — ||
:d | d :r | s, :d | d :d | d :d | d :d | d :t, | d :— | — ||
:m | s :t | d' :s | f :f | m :m | l :l | s :s | s :— | — ||
:d | m :s.f | m :d | l, :f, | d :l, | f :r | s :s, | d :— | — ||

:s | m :d' | t :l | s :fe | s :r.m | f :m | r :r | d :— | — || d | d ||
:r | m :m.fe | s :m | r :-.d | t, :t, | l,.t, :d | d :t, | d :— | — || l, | s, ||
:s | s :l | r' :d' | t :l | s :s | f :s | l :s.f | m :— | — || f | m ||
:t, | d :l, | t, :d | r :r | s, :s (:s,) | r (r,) :m (:m,) | f (f,) :s, | d :— | — || f, | d ||

A-men.

LORD, in Thy Name Thy servants plead,
And Thou hast sworn to hear;
Thine is the harvest, Thine the seed,
The fresh and fading year.

2 Our hope, when autumn winds blew wild,
We trusted, Lord, with Thee;
And now, when spring has on us smiled,
We wait on Thy decree.

3 The former and the latter rain,
The summer sun and air,
The green ear and the golden grain,
All Thine, are ours by prayer;

4 Thine too by right, and ours by grace,
The wondrous growth unseen,
The hopes that soothe, the fears that brace,
The love that shines serene.

5 So grant the precious things brought forth
By sun and moon below,
That Thee in Thy new heaven and earth
We never may forgo.

JOHN KEBLE, 1792–1866.

Also the following:

17 For the beauty of the earth
18 All things bright and beautiful
19 O Lord of heaven and earth and sea
20 God, who made the earth

Summer (612-613).

612 FOREST GREEN. (D.C.M.)

English Traditional Melody.

Doh = F. *In moderate time.* *D.C.*

```
:s, |d  :d  |d  :r     |m.r:m.f |s  :m  |f  :m.d   |r  :r      |d  :— |— ||
:s, |s, :l, |s, :l,.t, |d  :d   |t, :l, |l, :d     |d  :t,     |d  :— |— ||
:r  |m  :f  |s  :f     |s  :d   |r  :d  |f  :s     |l  :s.f    |m  :— |— ||
:t, |d  :f  |m  :r     |d  :l,  |s, :l, |r, :m,    |f, :s,     |s  :— |— ||

:d.m |s  :-.l  |s.f:m.r  |d.r:m.f |s  :s,    |d  :m  |r  :d       |s, :— ||
:d   |t, :-.l, |t, :s,   |s, :d   |t, :s,    |s, :s, |f, :m,.f,   |s, :— ||
:m   |m  :-.d  |s  :s.f  |m  :d   |r  :t,    |d  :d  |l,.t, :d    |t, :— ||
:l,  |m, :-.f, |s, :l,.t,|d  :l,  |s, :s,.f, |m, :d, |f, :l,      |s, :— ||

|s, :— |d :d   |d :r      |m.r:m.f |s :m   |f :m.d     |r :r    |d   :— |— ||d  |d  ||
|s, :— |s,:l,  |s,:l,.t,  |d  :d   |t,:l,  |l,:d       |d :t,   |d   :— |— ||l, |s, ||
|d  :r |m :f   |s :f      |s  :d   |r :d   |f :s.m     |s :s.f  |m   :— |— ||f  |m  ||
|l, :t,|d :f   |m :r      |d  :l,  |s,:l,  |r,:m,.l,   |s,:s,   |d d,:— |— ||f, |d, ||
                                                                              A-men.
```

THE summer days are come again;
Once more the glad earth yields
Her golden wealth of ripening grain,
And breath of clover fields,
And deepening shade of summer woods,
And glow of summer air,
And winging thoughts, and happy moods
Of love and joy and prayer.

2 The summer days are come again;
The birds are on the wing;
God's praises, in their loving strain,
Unconsciously they sing.
We know who giveth all the good
That doth our cup o'erbrim;
For summer joy in field and wood,
We lift our song to Him.

SAMUEL LONGFELLOW, 1819-92.

613 RUTH. (65. 65. D.)

Doh = E♭. *In moderate time.* SAMUEL SMITH, 1821–1917.

```
|d   :-.d  |d   :r   |m   :—   |s   :—   |f   :-.f  |f   :l   |
|s,  :-.s, |s,  :t,  |d   :—   |d   :—   |d   :-.d  |d   :f   |
|m   :-.m  |m   :f   |s   :—   |ta  :—   |l   :-.l  |l   :l   |
|d   :-.d  |d   :d   |d   :—   |d   :—   |d   :-.d  |d   :d   |

|d'  :—    |—   :—   ||d'  :-.d' |t   :l   |s   :—   |m   :—   |
|m   :—    |—   :—   ||d   :-.d  |r   :r   |m   :—   |d   :—   |
|s   :—    |—   :—   ||l   :-.l  |s   :f   |m   :—   |s   :—   |
|d   :—    |—   :—   ||l,  :-.l, |t,  :t,  |d   :—   |d   :—   |

|r   :-.r  |r   :m   |r   :—   |—   :—   ||f   :-.f  |m   :r   |m   :—   |
|d   :-.d  |d   :d   |t,  :—   |—   :—   ||t,  :-.t, |d   :s,  |s,  :—   |
|l   :-.l  |l   :l   |r   :—   |—   :—   ||s   :-.s  |s   :f   |m   :—   |
|f,  :-.f, |fe, :fe, |s,  :—   |—   :—   ||s,  :-.s, |l,  :t,  |d   :—   |

|s   :—    |ta  :-.ta |l   :s   |l   :—   |—   :—   ||t   :-.t  |l   :t   |
|d   :r    |m   :-.m  |f   :d   |d   :—   |—   :—   ||r   :-.r  |d   :r   |
|m   :s    |d'  :-.d' |d'  :ta  |l   :—   |—   :—   ||s   :-.s  |l   :s   |
|d   :—    |d   :-.d  |r   :m   |f   :—   |—   :—   ||f   :-.f  |f   :f   |

|d'  :—    |m   :—   |r   :-.r  |m   :r   |d   :—   |—   :—   ||d  |d  ||
|d   :—    |d   :—   |d   :-.d  |d   :t,  |d   :—   |—   :—   ||l, |s, ||
|s   :—    |d'  :—   |l   :-.l  |s   :f   |m   :—   |—   :—   ||f  |m  ||
|m   :—    |l   :—   |f   :-.f  |s   :s,  |d   :—   |—   :—   ||f, |d  ||
                                                                 A-men.
```

[*By permission of Novello & Co., Ltd.*]

SUMMER suns are glowing
  Over land and sea ;
Happy light is flowing,
  Bountiful and free.
Everything rejoices
  In the mellow rays ;
All earth's thousand voices
  Swell the psalm of praise.

2 God's free mercy streameth
  Over all the world,
And His banner gleameth,
  Everywhere unfurled.
Broad and deep and glorious,
  As the heaven above,
Shines in might victorious
  His eternal love.

3 Lord, upon our blindness
  Thy pure radiance pour ;
For Thy loving-kindness
  Make us love Thee more.
And, when clouds are drifting
  Dark across our sky,
Then, the veil uplifting,
  Father, be Thou nigh.

4 We will never doubt Thee,
  Though Thou veil Thy light ;
Life is dark without Thee ;
  Death with Thee is bright.
Light of light, shine o'er us
  On our pilgrim way ;
Go Thou still before us,
  To the endless day.

William Walsham How, 1823–97.

Also the following :

18 All things bright and beautiful

Harvest (614–620).

614

ST. SULIEN. (98. 98. Dactylic.)

Doh = G. *Brightly.* EDWARD ARTHUR, 1874–

```
:s, | m  :m  :d  | r  :d  :r  | m  :d  :s, | r  :t, :s, | m  :d  :m  | r  :—  ||
:m, | s, :s, :d  | t, :l, :t, | d  :s, :s, | s, :r, :s, | s, :l, :d  | t, :—  ||
:d  | d  :m  :s  | s  :m  :s  | s  :m  :m  | r  :s  :r  | d  :m  :s  | s  :—  ||
:d, | d  :d  :m, | s, :l, :s, | d  :d, :d  | t, :s, :t, | d  :l, :m, | s, :—  ||

:r  | f  :m  :r  | s  :m  :d  | l, :s, :s,    | d  :m  :d  | f  :m  :r   | d  :— || d  | d  ||
:t, | d  :s, :s, | s, :d  :s, | f, :r, :r,    | s, :s, :d  | d  :d  .t,  | d  :— || l, | s, ||
:s  | d  :d  :t, | d  :s  :m  | d  :t, :t,    | d  :d  :s  | l  :s  :f   | m  :— || f  | m  ||
:s, | l, :s, :f, | m, :d, :m, | f, :s, :s,.f, | m, :d, :m, | r, :s, :s,  | {d
                                                                          d,} :— || f, | d, ||
                                                                                    A-men.
```

[*Copyright*, 1927, *by Edward Arthur*.]

NOW sing we a song for the harvest :
  Thanksgiving and honour and praise
For all that the bountiful Giver
  Hath given to gladden our days,

2 For grasses of upland and lowland,
  For fruits of the garden and field,
For gold which the mine and the furrow
  To delver and husbandman yield ;

3 And thanks for the harvest of beauty
  For that which the hands cannot hold,
The harvest eyes only can gather,
  And only our hearts can enfold.

4 We reap it on mountain and moorland ;
  We glean it from meadow and lea ;
We garner it in from the cloudland ;
  We bind it in sheaves from the sea.

5 But the song it goes deeper and higher ;
  There are harvests that eye cannot see ;
They ripen on mountains of duty,
  Are reaped by the brave and the free.

6 And these have been gathered and garnered,
  Some golden with honour and gain,
And some as with heart's blood are ruddy,
  The harvests of sorrow and pain.

7 O Thou who art Lord of the harvest,
  The Giver who gladdens our days,
Our hearts are for ever repeating
  Thanksgiving and honour and praise.

JOHN WHITE CHADWICK, 1840–1904.

615 SURREY. (88. 88. 88.)

Doh = F. *Moderately slow.* HENRY CAREY, 1692–1743.

```
:s  |f  :m  :l   |d  :t, :d   |f  :m  :r   |m  :—  :m  |r  :—  :fe
:d  |d  :—  :l,  |s, :—  :m,  |l, :s, :s,  |s, :—  :d  |r  :—  :d
:m  |l  :s  :f   |m  :r  :d   |d  :—  :t,  |d  :—  :s  |s  :—  :d
:d  |d  :—  :f,  |s, :—  :l,  |f, :s, :s,  |d, :—  :d  |t, :—  :l,

                                D.C.
s   :—   :s,  |d  :t, :l,  |s, :—  ‖ s |l :— :s.f |s :— :f.m
t,  :—   :s,  |l, :s, :fe, |s, :—  ‖ d |d :— :d   |d :— :r.d
r   :—   :r   |m  :r  :r.d |t, :—  ‖ s |f :— :s.l |s :— :l
s,  :-.l,:t,  |d  :r  :r,  |s, :—  ‖ m |f :— :m.r |m :— :l,

f :— :m.r  |m :— :m  |r  :— :f   |m  :r   :d   |r  :d  :t,  |d  :— ‖ d  |d  ‖
r :l,:d.t, |d :— :d  |d  :t,:r   |d  :t,  :d   |l, :s, :s,  |s, :— ‖ l, |s, ‖
l :f :s    |s :— :s  |s  :— :l   |s  :-.f :m   |f  :m  :r   |m  :— ‖ f  |m  ‖
r :— :s,   |d :— :d, |s, :— :r,  |m, :s,  :l,  |f, :s, :s,  |d  :— ‖ f, |d  ‖
                                                                     A-men.
```

LORD of the harvest, once again
We thank Thee for the ripened grain;
For crops safe carried, sent to cheer
Thy servants through another year:
For all sweet holy thoughts, supplied
By seed-time, and by harvest-tide.

2 The bare dead grain, in autumn sown,
Its robe of vernal green puts on;
Glad from its wintry grave it springs,
Fresh garnished by the King of kings:
So, Lord, to those who sleep in Thee
Shall new and glorious bodies be.

3 Daily, O Lord, our prayers be said,
As Thou hast taught, for daily bread;
But not alone our bodies feed,—
Supply our fainting spirits' need.
O Bread of life, from day to day
Be Thou their comfort, food and stay!

JOSEPH ANSTICE, 1808–36.

616 GOLDEN SHEAVES. (8 7. 8 7. D.)

Doh = G. *In moderate time.* ARTHUR SEYMOUR SULLIVAN, 1842–1900.

```
:s, |m  :s  |s  :f  |m  :r  |d  :d    |r   :m    |f   :l,  |t,  :— |d  ||
:s, |d  :t, |d  :r  |d  :t, |d  :s,   |l,  :s,   |f,  :f,  |f,  :— |m, ||
:s, |s  :s  |s  :s  |s  :f  |m  :d    |l,  :-.l, |l,  :r   |r   :— |d  ||
:s, |d  :r  |m  :t, |d  :s, |l, :m,   |f,  :m,   |r,  :r,  |s,  :— |d, ||

                                D.t.                                     f.G.
:s, |m  :s  |s  :f  |m  :r  |d  :(m)l   |l   :s    |l   :t   |r'  :— |(d)s  ||
:s, |d  :t, |d  :r  |d  :t, |d  :(d)f   |f   :f    |f   :f   |f   :— |(m)t, ||
:s, |s  :s  |s  :s  |s  :f  |m  :(s)d'  |t   :t    |d'  :r'  |t   :— |(d)s  ||
:s, |d  :r  |m  :t, |d  :s, |l, :(l,)r  |s,  :s,   |s   :s   |s   :— |(d)s, ||

                            f.C.
:r  |r  :-.r  |s  :m  |(r)l  :se    |t  :m  |d' :d' |r' :d'.r' |m' :— |m' ||
:t, |t, :-.t, |t, :t, |(l,)m :m     |m  :m  |m  :m  |s  :s     |s  :— |s  ||
:s  |s  :-.s  |s  :s  |(m)t  :-.l   |se :se |l  :l  |t  :l.t   |d' :— |d' ||
:s, |s, :-.s, |m, :s, |(l,)m :-.ba  |se :m  |l  :l  |s  :s     |d' :— |d  ||

      G.t.
:d'.r' |(m')l :l  |s  :d   |f  :f  |m  :d  |r  :m    |f  :l, |t, :— |d  || d  |d  ||
:m     |(s)d  :r  |r  :d   |d  :t, |d  :s, |l, :s,   |f, :l, |s, :— |s, || l, |s, ||
:d'    |(d')f :f  |m  :f.s |l  :s  |d  :d  |l, :-.l, |l, :f  |f  :— |m  || f  |m  ||
:d     |(d')f :t, |m  :m   |r  :s, |l, :m, |f, :m,   |r, :r, |s, :— |d, || f, |d, ||
                                                                        A-men.
```

[*By permission of Novello & Co., Ltd.*]

TO Thee, O Lord, our hearts we raise
In hymns of adoration,
To Thee bring sacrifice of praise,
With shouts of exultation.
Bright robes of gold the fields adorn,
The hills with joy are ringing,
The valleys stand so thick with corn
That even they are singing.

2 And now, on this our festal day,
Thy bounteous hand confessing,
Before Thee thankfully we lay
The first-fruits of Thy blessing.
By Thee the souls of men are fed
With gifts of grace supernal;
Thou who dost give us earthly bread,
Give us the Bread eternal.

3 We bear the burden of the day,
And often toil seems dreary;
But labour ends with sunset ray,
And rest comes for the weary.
May we, the angel-reaping o'er,
Stand at the last accepted,
Christ's golden sheaves, for ever-more
To garners bright elected.

4 O blessèd is that land of God
Where saints abide for ever,
Where golden fields spread far and broad,
Where flows the crystal river.
The strains of all its holy throng
With ours to-day are blending;
Thrice blessèd is that harvest song
Which never hath an ending.

William Chatterton Dix, 1837–98.

617 NATIVITY. (C.M.)

Doh = B♭. *In moderate time.* Henry Lahee, 1826–1912.

m, :m,.m,	s, :s,	d :d	m :-.r	d :l,	l, :r	d :—	t,	
d, :d,.d,	r, :r,	m, :m,	m, :-.m,	m, :m,	f, :l,	s, :—	—	
s, :s,.s,	s, :r	d :d	t, :-.t,	d :d	d :f	m :—	r	
d, :d,.d,	t_2 :t,	l, :l,	se, :-.se,	l, :l,	f, :f,	s, :—	—	

:s, |l, :t, |d :s, |l, :t, |d :r |m :m |r :r |d :— |— :— ||d |d ||
:s, |f, :f, |s, :s, |s, :f, |m, :s, |s, :s, |l, :s,.f, |m, :— |— :— ||f, |m, ||
:d |d :r |s, :m |d :r |d :t, |d :d |d :t, |d :— |— :— ||l, |s, ||
:m, |f, :r, |m, :d, |f, :r, |l, :s, |d :m, |f, :s, |d, :— |— :— ||f, |d, ||

A-men.

FOUNTAIN of mercy, God of love,
How rich Thy bounties are!
The rolling seasons, as they move,
Proclaim Thy constant care.

2 When in the bosom of the earth
The sower hid the grain,
Thy goodness marked its secret birth,
And sent the early rain.

3 The spring's sweet influence was Thine;
The plants in beauty grew;
Thou gav'st refulgent suns to shine,
And mild refreshing dew.

4 These various mercies from above
Matured the swelling grain;
A yellow harvest crowns Thy love,
And plenty fills the plain.

5 Seed-time and harvest, Lord, alone
Thou dost on man bestow;
Let him not then forget to own
From whom his blessings flow.

6 Fountain of love, our praise is Thine;
To Thee our songs we'll raise,
And all created nature join
In sweet harmonious praise.

Alice Flowerdew, 1759–1830.

618 WIR PFLÜGEN (DRESDEN). (76. 76. D. and refrain.)

Doh = B♭. *In moderate time.* JOHANN ABRAHAM PETER SCHULZ, 1747–1800.

:s, |d :d |s, :s, |m :— |d :s, |f, :m, |r, :d, |s, :— |— ||
:s, |d :d |s, :s, |m :— |d :s, |f, :m, |r, :d, |s, :— |— ||
:s, |d :d |s, :s, |m :— |d :s, |f, :m, |r, :d, |s, :— |— ||
:s, |d :d |s, :s, |m :— |d :s, |f, :m, |r, :d, |s, :— |— ||

F.t.

:d f |m :r |d :l |s :f |m :d |r :l |s :t, |d :— |— ||
:s, d |d :t, |d :d |d :t, |d :d |d :d |t, :s, |s, :— |— ||
:d f |s :s |s :f |m :r |d :s |l :f |r :f |m :— |— ||
:m, l, |s, :f, |m, :f, |s, :— |l, :m, |f, :r, |s, :s, |d :— |— ||

f.B♭.

:d s, |r :r |m :m |f :— |r :r |s :s |f :m |r :— |— ||
:d s, |s, :s, |s, :s, |l, :— |s, :t, |d :s, |t, :d |t, :— |— ||
:d s, |t, :t, |d :d |d :— |t, :s |s :m |f :s |s :— |— ||
:d s, |f, :f, |m, :m, |r, :— |s, :f, |m, :m |r :d |s, :— |— ||

:s, |d :d |s, :s, |l, :— |m, :m, |f, :-.r, |s, :t, |d :— |— :— ||
:s, |d :d |s, :s, |l, :— |m, :m, |f, :-.r, |s, :f, |m, :— |— :— ||
:s, |d :d |s, :s, |l, :— |m, :m, |f, :-.r, |s, :r |d :— |— :— ||
:s, |d :d |s, :s, |l, :— |m, :m, |f, :-.r, |s, :s, |d, :— |— :— ||

REFRAIN.

d :d	d :d	r :—	r :r	m :-.s	f :m	r :—	—	
m, :m,	s, :m,	s, :—	s, :t,	d :-.s,	t, :d	t, :—	—	
s, :s,	d :d	t, :d	r :s	s :-.m	f :s	s :—	—	
d, :s,	m, :d,	s, :l,	t, :s,	d :-.m	r :d	s, :—	—	

HARVEST

:r	m :r	m :-.r	d :t_1	d :-.s_1	l_1 :r	d :t_1	d :—	—	d	d
:s_1	s_1 :t_1	d :-.t_1	l_1 :se_1	l_1 :-.s_1	f_1 :l_1	s_1 :—	s_1 :—	—	f_1	m_1
:r	d :s	s :-.s	m :m	m :-.d	d :f	m :r	m :—	—	l_1	s_1
:t_1	d :s_1	d :-.s_1	l_1 :m_1	l_1 :-.m_1	f_1 :r_1	s_1 :—	d_1 :—	—	f_1	d_1
									A -	men.

Wir pflügen und wir streuen.

WE plough the fields, and scatter
The good seed on the land,
But it is fed and watered
By God's almighty hand;
He sends the snow in winter,
The warmth to swell the grain,
The breezes and the sunshine
And soft refreshing rain.
All good gifts around us
Are sent from heaven above;
Then thank the Lord, O thank the Lord,
For all His love.

2 He only is the Maker
Of all things near and far;
He paints the wayside flower,
He lights the evening star;
The winds and waves obey Him,
By Him the birds are fed;
Much more to us, His children,
He gives our daily bread.

3 We thank Thee then, O Father,
For all things bright and good,
The seed-time and the harvest,
Our life, our health, our food.
Accept the gifts we offer
For all Thy love imparts,
And, what Thou most desirest,
Our humble, thankful hearts.

MATTHIAS CLAUDIUS, 1740–1815; *tr.* by JANE MONTGOMERY CAMPBELL, 1817-78.

619 ST. GEORGE'S, WINDSOR. (77. 77. D.)

Doh = G. *Brightly.* GEORGE JOB ELVEY, 1816–93.

```
| m :-.m | s :m | d :r | m :— | m :-.m | s :m | d :r | m :— ||
| s, :-.s, | s, :s, | l, :t, | d :— | s, :-.s, | s, :s, | l, :l, | se, :— ||
| d :-.d | r :m | m :s | s :— | d :-.d | r :d | m :f | t, :— ||
| d :-.d | t, :d | l, :s, | d :— | d :-.d | t, :d | l, :f, | m, :— ||

                                   D.t.                          f.G.
| m :-.m | f :f | r :-.r | m :— | {m}l :t | d' :f | m :r | {d}s, :— ||
| l, :-.l, | l, :l, | s, :s, | s, :— | {s}d :r | d :r | d :t, | {d}s, :— ||
| d :-.d | r :r | t, :t, | d :— | {d}f :f | s :l | s :-.f | {m}t, :— ||
| l, :-.l, | r, :r, | s, :s, | d, :— | {d}f :r | m :f | s :s, | {d}s, :— ||

                                   f.C.
| t, :-.t, | r :t, | d :r | m :— | {m}t :-.t | r' :t | d' :r' | m' :— ||
| s, :-.s, | s, :s, | s, :f, | m, :— | {s}r :-.r | s :s | s :f | m :— ||
| r :r | t, :r | d :-.t, | d :— | {d}s :-.s | t :r' | d' :-.t | d' :— ||
| s, :-.s, | s, :f, | m, :r, | d, :— | {d}s :-.s | s :f | m :r | d :— ||

            G.t.
| m' :-.m' | {d'}f :r | s :-.s | m :— | f :l | s :d | m :r | d :— || d | d ||
| m :se | {l}r :l, | s, :t, | d :— | d :d | d :d | d :t, | d :— || l, | s, ||
| t :m' | {m'}l :f | r :s | s :— | f :f | s :m | s :-.f | m :— || f | m ||
| se :m | {l}r :-.r | t, :s, | d :— | l, :f, | m, :l, | s, :s, | d, :— || f, | d, ||
                                                                     A-men.
```

COME, ye thankful people, come,
Raise the song of harvest-home:
All is safely gathered in,
Ere the winter storms begin;
God, our Maker, doth provide
For our wants to be supplied:
Come to God's own temple, come,
Raise the song of harvest-home.

2 All this world is God's own field,
Fruit unto His praise to yield;
Wheat and tares together sown,
Unto joy or sorrow grown;
First the blade, and then the ear,
Then the full corn shall appear:
Lord of harvest, grant that we
Wholesome grain and pure may be.

3 For the Lord our God shall come,
And shall take His harvest home;
From His field shall in that day
All offences purge away;
Give His angels charge at last
In the fire the tares to cast;
But the fruitful ears to store
In His garner evermore.

4 Even so, Lord, quickly come;
Bring Thy final harvest home:
Gather Thou Thy people in,
Free from sorrow, free from sin;
There, for ever purified,
In Thy garner to abide:
Come, with all Thine angels, come,
Raise the glorious harvest-home.

HENRY ALFORD, 1810–71.

620 MONKLAND. (77. 77.)

Original unknown; arranged by John Bernard Wilkes, 1785-1869.

Doh = C. *In moderate time.*

```
d  :m  |s  :m  |f.s :l.t |d'  :—  |m'  :m'  |r' :d' |t  :l    |s  :—
d  :d  |r  :d  |d   :f   |m   :—  |s   :s   |s  :s  |s  :fe   |s  :—
m  :l  |t  :s  |l   :f   |s   :—  |d'  :d'  |t  :d' |r' :-.d' |t  :—
d  :l, |s, :d  |f   :r   |d   :—  |d.r :m.f |s  :m  |r  :r    |s, :—

r' :r'.d' |t :s   |d' :m' |r' :—  |m' :r'.d' |t  :d' |d' :t  |d' :— ‖ d' |d'
s  :r     |r :s   |s  :s  |s  :—  |s  :s     |s  :s  |s  :r  |m  :— ‖ f  |m
t  :l     |s :t   |d' :d' |t  :—  |d' :t.d'  |r' :d' |r' :s  |s  :— ‖ l  |s
s  :fe    |s :s.f |m  :d  |s  :—  |d  :r.m   |f  :m  |s  :s, |d  :— ‖ f  |d
                                                                        A-men.
```

PRAISE, O praise our God and King;
Hymns of adoration sing;
For His mercies still endure,
Ever faithful, ever sure.

2 Praise Him that He made the sun
Day by day his course to run;—
For His mercies still endure,
Ever faithful, ever sure;—

3 And the silver moon, by night
Shining with her gentle light;
For His mercies still endure,
Ever faithful, ever sure.

4 Praise Him that He gave the rain
To mature the swelling grain;—
For His mercies still endure,
Ever faithful, ever sure;—

5 And hath bid the fruitful field
Crops of precious increase yield;
For His mercies still endure,
Ever faithful, ever sure.

6 Praise Him for our harvest-store;
He hath filled the garner floor;—
For His mercies still endure,
Ever faithful, ever sure;—

7 And for richer food than this,
Pledge of everlasting bliss;
For His mercies still endure,
Ever faithful, ever sure.

8 Glory to our bounteous King!
Glory let creation sing,
Glory to the Father, Son,
And blest Spirit, Three in One!

Henry Williams Baker, 1821-77.

Also the following:

494 Fair waved the golden corn

Autumn.

621 DEVONSHIRE. (76. 76.)

Doh = F. *In moderate time.* English Traditional Melody.

```
:d  | m .m :m  :- .m   | m .r :d  :- .r  | m .s :s  :f .m | r  :— ||
:s, | d .d :d  :- .d   | d .t,:l, :- .s, | d .t,:l, :l,   | t, :— ||
:m  | s .s :m  :- .f   | s .f :m  :- .s  | s .s :d  :f    | s  :— ||
:d  | d .d :d  :t,.l,  | s,   :l, :- .t, | d .m,:f, :r,   | s, :— ||

:r  | m .f :s  :- .l   | s .m :d  :- .d   | d .m :f  :-.m.r   | d    :— || d  | d  ||
:s, | s,.d :d  :- .d   | t,   :d  :- .s,  | l,.d :d  :-.l,.t, | d    :— || l, | s, ||
:f  | m .d :d  :- .d   | m .s :s  :f .m   | f .s :l  :f       | m    :— || f  | m  ||
:t, | d .l,:m, :- .f,  | s,   :l, :- .s,  | f,.m,:r, :s,      | d/d, :— || f, | d, ||
```

A-men.

THE year is swiftly waning,
The summer days are past;
And life, brief life, is speeding;
The end is nearing fast.

2 The ever-changing seasons
In silence come and go;
But Thou, eternal Father,
No time or change canst know.

3 O pour Thy grace upon us,
That we may worthier be,
Each year that passes o'er us,
To dwell in heaven with Thee.

4 Behold, the bending orchards
With bounteous fruit are crowned;
Lord, in our hearts more richly
Let heavenly fruits abound.

5 O by each mercy sent us,
And by each grief and pain,
By blessings like the sunshine,
And sorrows like the rain,

6 Our barren hearts make fruitful
With every goodly grace,
That we Thy Name may hallow,
And see at last Thy face.

WILLIAM WALSHAM HOW, 1823-97.

Winter (622–623).

622 CLARENCE. (77. 77.)

Arranged by ARTHUR SEYMOUR SULLIVAN, 1842–1900.

Lah = E. Doh = G. *In moderate time.*

l, :-.l,	l, :t,	d :t,	l, :—	t, :-.t,	t, :d	r :d	t, :—	
l, :-.l,	l, :t,	d :t,	l, :—	se, :-.se,	se, :l,	t, :l,	se, :—	
l, :-.l,	l, :t,	d :t,	l, :—	m :-.m	m :m	m :m	m :—	
l, :-.l,	l, :t,	d :t,	l, :—	m, :-.m,	m, :l,	se, :l,	m, :—	

d :f	f :m	l, :r	r :d	t, :t,	d :t,.l,	l, :se,	l, :—	
l, :l,	t, :t,	l, :l,	l, :—	l, :l,	l, :m,	m, :m,	m, :—	
m :d	t, :m	d :l,	m :—	f :f	m :r.d	t, :t,	d :—	
l, :l,	s, :s,	f, :f,	m, :—	r, :r,	m, :m,	m, :m,	l, :—	

v.v. 5 & 6.
E.t.m.l.

(m)s :-.s	s :s	d' :s	s :m	r :-.r	r :m	f :m	r :—	
(l)d :-.d	d :r	m :r	d :—	t, :-.t,	t, :d	r :d	t, :—	
(de)m :-.m	m :f	s :f	m :—	s :-.s	s :s	s :s	s :—	
(l)d :-.d	d :d	d :d	d :—	s, :-.s,	s, :d	t, :d	s, :—	

m :l	l :s	d :f	f :m	r :l	t :d'	s :t,	d :—		d	d	
d :d	r :r	d :d	de :—	r :r	r :r	d :s,	s, :—		l,	s,	
s :m	r :s	l :l	ta :—	l :l	s :f	m :f	m :—		f	m	
d :d	t, :t,	l, :l,	s, :—	f, :f	m :r	s, :s,	d :—		f,	d	

A-men.

[*By permission of Novello & Co., Ltd.*]

WINTER reigneth o'er the land,
Freezing with its icy breath;
Dead and bare the tall trees stand;
All is chill and drear as death.

2 Yet it seemeth but a day
Since the summer flowers were here,
Since they stacked the balmy hay,
Since they reaped the golden ear.

3 Sunny days are past and gone;
So the years go, speeding fast,
Onward ever, each new one
Swifter speeding than the last.

4 Life is waning; life is brief;
Death, like winter, standeth nigh:
Each one, like the falling leaf,
Soon shall fade, and fall, and die.

5 But the sleeping earth shall wake;
New-born flowers shall burst in bloom,
And all nature, rising, break
Glorious from its wintry tomb.

6 So the saints, from slumber blest
Rising, shall awake and sing,
And our flesh in hope shall rest,
Till there breaks the endless spring.

WILLIAM WALSHAM HOW, 1823–97.

623 BRYNTEG. (L. M.)

Lah = E. Doh = G. *Moderately slow.* JOHN AMBROSE LLOYD, 1815–74.

:l, |d :r |m :l,.t, |d :t, |l, :d |r :m |f :m |m :r |m
:l, |l, :l, |se, :l, |l, :se, |l, :l, |l, :l, |l, :se, |l, :l, |se,
:d |m :r |r :d.r |m :r |d :m |r :d |r :t, |l,.d :t,.l, |t,
:l, |l, :f, |m, :f, |d, :m, |l, :l, |f, :l, |r, :m, |f, :f, |m,

:m |m :fe |s :m |l :d.r |m :d |r :f |m :l,.t, |d :t, |l, || r |de
:s, |t, :t, |t, :t, |l, :l, |se, :l, |l, :l, |se, :l, |l, :se, |l, || l, |l,
:t,.m |m :re |m :s |m :m |m :m |r :r |r :d.r |m :r |d || f |m
:m, |s, :t, |m :m |d :l, |m, :l, |f, :r, |m, :f, |m, :m, |l, || r, |l,

A-men.

DANBY. (L.M.)

Doh = G. *In moderate time.* English Traditional Melody.

:s, |d :t, |d :— |— :s, |ta, :l, |s, :— |— :s, |d :t,
:m, |s, :s, |s, :— |— :m, |s, :f, |f, :— |m, :f, |s, :s,
:d |d :r |m :— |— :d |d :d |d :— |— :t, |d :r
:d, |m, :s, |d :— |— :d,.r, |m, :f, |d, :— |— :r, |m, :s,

|d :— |— :r.m |f :m |r :— |— || d |r :s |s :— |f :m
|m, :— |— :s, |l, :s, |s, :— |— || s, |l, :t, |d :— |s, :s,
|d :— |— :t, |d :d |d :— |t, || d |f :m.r |d :— |r :m
|l, :— |— :s, |f, :d |s, :— |— || m, |f, :s, |l, :— |t, :d

|r :s, |d :— |— :d |r :m |r :— |— :l, |s, :s, |s, :— |— || l, |s,
|l, :s, |s, :— |— :m, |s, :s, |l, :— |— :f,.m, |r,.m, :f, |f, :— |m, || f, |m,
|f :m.r |d :— |— :d |s :s |f :m |r :d |d :t, |d :— |— || d |d
|f, :f, |m, :— |— :l, |t, :d |f, :— |— :f, |s, :s, |d, :— |— || f, |d,

A-men.

'TIS winter now ; the fallen snow
Has left the heavens all coldly clear ;
Through leafless boughs the sharp winds blow,
And all the earth lies dead and drear.

2 And yet God's love is not withdrawn ;
His life within the keen air breathes ;
His beauty paints the crimson dawn,
And clothes the boughs with glittering wreaths.

3 And though abroad the sharp winds blow,
And skies are chill, and frosts are keen,
Home closer draws her circle now,
And warmer glows her light within.

4 O God ! who giv'st the winter's cold,
As well as summer's joyous rays,
Us warmly in Thy love enfold,
And keep us through life's wintry days.

SAMUEL LONGFELLOW, 1819–92.

TRAVELLERS AND THE ABSENT

624

RANDOLPH. (98. 89.)

Doh = D. *In moderate time.* RALPH VAUGHAN WILLIAMS, 1872–

```
| m :s | l.s:f.m | r :-.d | d :— | m :fe | s :-.s | l :t.d' | d' :t ||
| m :s | l.s:f.m | r :-.d | d :— | d :r  | r :t,  | m :r    | r :r  ||
| m :s | l.s:f.m | r :-.d | d :— | s :l  | s :s   | s :fe   | s :s  ||
| m :s | l.s:f.m | r :-.d | d :— | d :d  | t, :m  | d :r    | s :s.f ||

| d' :-.t | l :s | f :s.l | s :f   | m :s | l.s:f.m | r :-.d | d :— || d  | d  ||
| d :-.d  | d :d | r :r   | r :t,  | m :s | l.s:f.m | r :-.d | d :— || l, | s, ||
| s :-.s  | l :l | l :f   | s :s   | m :s | l.s:f.m | r :-.d | d :— || f  | m  ||
| m :-.m  | f :m | r :d   | t, :s, | m :s | l.s:f.m | r :-.d | d :— || f, | d  ||
                                                                         A-men.
```

GOD be with you till we meet again,
By His counsels guide, uphold you,
With His sheep securely fold you :
God be with you till we meet again.

2 God be with you till we meet again,
'Neath His wings protecting hide you,
Daily manna still divide you :
God be with you till we meet again.

3 God be with you till we meet again,
When life's perils thick confound you,
Put His arms unfailing round you :
God be with you till we meet again.

4 God be with you till we meet again,
Keep love's banner floating o'er you,
Smite death's threatening wave before you :
God be with you till we meet again.

JEREMIAH EAMES RANKIN, 1828–1904.

Seafarers (625–627).

625

FARRANT. (C.M.) Adaptation from a Melody attributed to RICHARD FARRANT, *c.* 1530–80.

Doh = G. *Moderately slow.*

d :—	d :-.r	m :r	d :f	r :r	m.fe :s	s :fe	s :—	
s, :—	l, :-.t,	d :t,	l, :d	t, :t,	d :t,.d	r :r.d	t, :—	
m :—	m :-.s	s :s	m :l	s :s	s :s	l :l	s :—	
d :—	l, :-.s,	d :s,	l, :f,	s, :s,	d :m	r :r	s, :—	

d :—	f :f	m :r	d :r	t, :m	l,.t, :d	d :t,	d :—		d	d	
d :—	r :r	d :t,	l, :l,	s, :s,	f, :m,.f,	s, :s,	s, :—		l,	s,	
m :—	l :s	s :s	m :f	r :d	d :d	r :r	m :—		f	m	
d :—	d :t,	d :s,	l, :r,	s, :d,	f, :l,	s, :s,	d, :—		f,	d,	

A-men.

O LORD, be with us when we sail
  Upon the lonely deep,
Our Guard when on the silent deck
  The midnight watch we keep.

2 We need not fear, though all around,
  'Mid rising winds, we hear
The multitude of waters surge ;
  For Thou, O God, art near.

3 The calm, the breeze, the gale, the storm,
  That pass from land to land,
All, all are Thine—are held within
  The hollow of Thy hand.

4 As when on blue Gennesaret
  Rose high the angry wave,
And Thy disciples quailed in dread,
  One word of Thine could save,

5 So when the fiercer storms arise
  From man's unbridled will,
Be Thou, Lord, present in our hearts,
  To whisper, ' Peace, be still ! '

6 Across this troubled tide of life
  Thyself our Pilot be,
Until we reach that better land,
  The land that knows no sea.

7 To Thee the Father, Thee the Son,
  Whom earth and sky adore,
And Spirit, moving o'er the deep,
  Be praise for evermore.

EDWIN ARTHUR DAYMAN, 1807–90.

626

MELITA. (88. 88. 88.)

JOHN BACCHUS DYKES, 1823–76.

Doh = C. *Moderately slow.* G.t.

```
:d  |m  :-.m  |s  :s  |l   :l    |s  :(s)d |f  :s    |m  :d     |d  :t,  |d  ||
:d  |d  :-.d  |m  :m  |f   :f    |m  :(s)d |d  :-.t, |d  :-.l,  |s, :s,  |s, ||
:m  |s  :-.s  |d' :-.t|l.t :d'.r'|m' :(r')s|f  :r    |m  :s.f   |r  :r   |m  ||
:d  |d  :-.d  |d  :d  |f.s :l.t  |d' :(t)m |r  :s,   |d  :m,.f, |s, :s,  |d  ||
```

f.C.

```
:s, |ta, :-.ta, |l, :l, |d   :-.d   |t, :m   |d  :t,   |l, :r   |d  :t,  |(l)m ||
:m, |s,  :-.s,  |f, :f, |l,  :-.l,  |s, :t,  |l, :-.se,|l, :-.t,|l, :se, |(l)m ||
:d  |d   :-.d   |d  :d  |r   :-.r   |r  :m   |m  :r    |m  :f   |m  :m   |(d)s ||
:d  |m,  :-.m,  |f, :f, |fe, :-.fe, |s, :se, |l, :t,   |d  :r   |m  :m   |(l)m ||
```

```
:m  |m   :-.m   |f  :f  |fe :-.fe |s  :s  |s  :l   |s  :m  |r  :-.d |d || f  |m ||
:t, |ta, :-.ta, |l, :d  |d  :-.d  |t, :f  |m  :r   |m  :d  |t, :-.d |d || d  |d ||
:s  |s   :-.s   |f  :l  |l  :-.l  |s  :r' |d' :d'  |d' :s  |f  :-.m |m || l  |s ||
:m  |d   :-.d   |f  :f  |r  :-.r  |s  :t, |d  :fe, |s, :s, |s, :-.d |d || f, |d ||
```

A-men.

ETERNAL Father, strong to save,
Whose arm hath bound the restless wave,
Who bidd'st the mighty ocean deep
Its own appointed limits keep:
O hear us when we cry to Thee
For those in peril on the sea.

2 O Christ, whose voice the waters heard,
And hushed their raging at Thy word,
Who walkedst on the foaming deep,
And calm amid the storm didst sleep:
O hear us when we cry to Thee
For those in peril on the sea.

3 O Holy Spirit, who didst brood
Upon the waters dark and rude,
And bid their angry tumult cease,
And give, for wild confusion, peace:
O hear us when we cry to Thee
For those in peril on the sea.

4 O Trinity of love and power,
Our brethren shield in danger's hour;
From rock and tempest, fire and foe,
Protect them wheresoe'er they go:
Thus evermore shall rise to Thee
Glad hymns of praise from land and sea.

WILLIAM WHITING, 1825–78.

627

STAR OF PEACE. (87. 84.)

Doh = D. *Moderately slow.* LOWELL MASON, 1792–1872.

```
d  :-.d  |d   :d  |r  :r  |m  :r  |m  :-.m |m  :fe |s  :l  |t  :—  ||
s, :-.s, |l,  :d  |d  :t, |d  :t, |d  :-.d |d  :d  |r  :r  |r  :—  ||
m  :-.m  |l   :s  |f  :s  |s  :s  |s  :-.s |l  :l  |s  :fe |s  :—  ||
d  :-.d  |f   :m  |r  :s, |d  :s  |m  :-.d |l, :l, |t, :r  |s  :—  ||

d' :-.d' |r'.d' :t.l |s  :-.m |m  :r  |d  :—  |r  :-.r  |m :— |— :— ||
d  :-.m  |f.m   :r.d |r  :-.d |d  :t, |l, :—  |t, :-.t, |d :— |— :— ||
s  :-.s  |l     :m   |s  :-.s |s  :f  |m  :—  |s  :-.s  |s :— |— :— ||
m  :-.d  |f     :l,  |t, :-.d |s, :s, |l, :—  |s, :-.s, |d :— |— :— ||

://:
d' :-.d' |r'.d' :t.l |s  :-.m |m  :r  |d  :—  |m  :-.r  |d :— |— :— || d  |d  ||
d  :-.m  |f.m   :r.d |r  :-.d |d  :t, |l, :—  |t, :-.t, |d :— |— :— || l, |s, ||
s  :-.s  |l     :m   |s  :-.s |s  :f  |m  :—  |s  :-.f  |m :— |— :— || f  |m  ||
m  :-.d  |f     :l,  |t, :-.d |s  :s, |l, :—  |s, :-.s, |d :— |— :— || f, |d  ||
                                                                        A-men.
```

STAR of peace to wanderers weary,
Bright the beams that smile on me;
Cheer the pilot's vision dreary,
Far, far at sea.

2 Star of hope, gleam on the billow;
Bless the soul that sighs for Thee;
Bless the sailor's lonely pillow,
Far, far at sea.

3 Star of faith, when winds are mocking
All his toil, he flies to Thee;
Save him on the billows rocking,
Far, far at sea.

4 Star Divine, O safely guide him;
Bring the wanderer home to Thee;
Sore temptations long have tried him,
Far, far at sea.

JANE CROSS SIMPSON, 1811–86.

628 BRISTOL. (L.M.)

SAMUEL WESLEY, 1766–1837.

Doh = E♭. *In moderate time.* B♭.t. f.E♭.

```
:m |m  :— :f  |m  :r  :d  |f  :m  :r  |m  :— :(s)d  |f  :— :m
:d |d  :— :r  |d  :t, :d  |r  :d  :t, |d  :— :(m)l, |l, :— :se,
:s |s  :— :l  |s  :f  :m  |l  :s  :s  |s  :— :(s)d  |t, :— :d
:d |d  :— :f, |s, :— :l,  |f, :s, :—  |d  :— :(d)f, |r, :— :m,

r   :—  :d  |t, :l, :se,   |l, :— ||(d)s  s  :— :f |f  :m :— |r  :d   :-.r
l,  :m, :m, |f, :m, :m,.r, |d, :— ||(l)m  m  :— :r |r  :d :— |l, :fe, :—
d   :t, :l, |r  :d  :t,    |l, :— ||(m)t  l  :— :l |s  :s :— |f  :r   :—
ba, :se,:l, |r, :m, :—     |l, :— ||(s)r  de :— :r |t, :d :— |f, :l,  :—

d  :t, :s  |d' :— :l |f  :—  :m  |m.r :d  :t, |d  :— ||d  |d  ||
s, :— :t,  |m  :— :m |m  :r  :d  |l,  :s, :s, |s, :— ||l, |s, ||
r  :— :s   |l  :— :l |l  :-.t:s  |s.f :m  :r  |m  :— ||f  |m  ||
s, :— :m   |l, :— :d |r  :r, :m, |f,  :s, :—  |d  :— ||f, |d  ||
                                                          A-men.
```

WHOM oceans part, O Lord, unite
To love Thy Name, and seek Thy light:
Though from each other far we be,
Let none, O Christ, be far from Thee.

2 On many a distant island shore
Still let men see heaven's opened door;
'Mid silent hills, beneath fresh skies,
Let Bethel's shining ladder rise.

3 Bring thoughts of home and Christian ways
To those who miss sweet Sabbath days;
The long-forgotten prayer recall
To those who sin, and mourn their fall.

4 Our sons and daughters guide in truth;
Take for Thyself the flower of youth;
Afar from home, through gain or loss,
Keep them true-hearted to Thy Cross.

5 Whom oceans part, O Lord, unite—
One commonwealth for God and right,
A ransomed people, strong and free,
To bring the whole wide world to Thee!

HOWELL ELVET LEWIS, 1860-

629 MINTO. (85.83.)

Doh = F. *Moderately slow.* WILLIAM HENRY MONK, 1823–89.

```
m  :m   |s  :s    |d  :d   |m  :m   |l, :l,.t, |d    :r  |m  :—  |—   :— ||
d  :d   |d  :t,   |t, :l,  |l, :se, |l, :l,    |l,   :l, |l, :—  |se, :— ||
s  :d   |r  :f    |m  :l,  |t, :r   |d  :m     |m    :l, |t, :—  |—   :— ||
d  :l,  |s, :s,   |l, :f,  |m, :m,  |l, :d.t,  |l,.s,:f, |m, :—  |—   :— ||

m  :s   |f  :m    |f  :s   |l    :s  |m  :—  |—  :r  |d :—  |— :— ||d  |d  ||
s, :s,  |d  :d    |d  :ta, |l,.t,:d  |d  :—  |—  :t, |d :—  |— :— ||l, |s, ||
m  :r.m |f  :s    |f  :m   |f    :d  |d  :s  |l  :f  |m :—  |— :— ||f  |m  ||
d  :t,  |l, :d.ta,|l, :d   |f,   :m, |l, :m, |f, :s, |d :—  |— :— ||f, |d, ||
                                                                  A-men.
```

HOLY Father, in Thy mercy,
Hear our anxious prayer;
Keep our loved ones, now far distant,
'Neath Thy care.

2 Jesus, Saviour, let Thy presence
Be their light and guide;
Keep, O keep them, in their weakness,
At Thy side.

3 When in sorrow, when in danger,
When in loneliness,
In Thy love look down and comfort
Their distress.

4 May the joy of Thy salvation
Be their strength and stay;
May they love and may they praise Thee
Day by day.

5 Holy Spirit, let Thy teaching
Sanctify their life;
Send Thy grace that they may conquer
In the strife.

6 Father, Son, and Holy Spirit,
God the One in Three,
Bless them, guide them, save them, keep them
Near to Thee.

ISABEL STEPHANA STEVENSON, 1843–90.

630 RALEIGH. (66. 66. 88.)

Doh = E. *In moderate time.* EBENEZER PROUT, 1835–1909.

```
:m |r  :m |l  :-.l |s  :— |— :d  |t, :d |f  :f  |m :— |— ||s
:d |t, :d |d  :-.r |m  :— |— :d  |s, :d |d  :t, |d :— |— ||m
:s |s  :s |l  :-.t |d' :— |— :s  |f  :m |r  :s  |s :— |— ||s
:d |s, :d |f  :-.f |m  :— |— :m  |r  :d |s, :s, |d :— |— ||d
```

B.t. f.E.

```
|d' :t  |[l]r  :d   |t, :d  |m  :r  |d  :— |— :t, |[d]s   :— |— ||s |l :s
|m  :r  |[m]l, :l,  |s, :m, |f, :l, |s, :— |f, :— |[m]t,  :— |— ||r |r :m
|l  :se |[l]r  :r   |r  :d  |l, :f  |m  :— |r  :— |[d]s   :— |— ||t |t :d'
|l, :t, |[d]f, :fe, |s, :l, |r, :r, |s, :— |— :s, |[d]s,  :— |— ||s |f :m
```

```
|f  :m |s  :-.f  |m   :r   |d  :m  |r  :d  |d  :— |— :t, |d  :— |— ||d  |d
|t, :d |r  :-.d  |t,  :se, |l, :l, |l, :l, |s, :— |— :s, |s, :— |— ||l, |s,
|f  :s |s  :-.l  |t   :m   |m  :d  |f  :m  |r  :m |f :—  |m  :— |— ||f  |m
|r  :d |t, :-.l, |se, :m,  |l, :l, |r, :r, |s, :— |— :s, |d  :— |— ||f, |d
```

A-men.

[*By permission of the Congregational Union of England and Wales.*]

FATHER, who art alone
Our helper and our stay,
O hear us, as we plead
For loved ones far away,
And shield with Thine almighty hand
Our wanderers by sea and land.

2 For Thou, our Father God,
Art present everywhere,
And bendest low Thine ear
To catch the faintest prayer,
Waiting rich blessings to bestow
On all Thy children here below.

3 O compass with Thy love
The daily path they tread;
And may Thy light and truth
Upon their hearts be shed,
That, one in all things with Thy will,
Heaven's peace and joy their souls may fill.

4 Guard them from every harm
When dangers shall assail,
And teach them that Thy power
Can never, never fail;
We cannot with our loved ones be,
But trust them, Father, unto Thee.

5 We all are travellers here
Along life's various road,
Meeting and parting oft
Till we shall mount to God,—
At home at last, with those we love,
Within the fatherland above.

EDITH JONES.

Also the following:

276 As darker, darker, fall around

631 NATIONAL ANTHEM. (664. 6664.)

Doh = G. *In moderate time.*

d :d :r | t, :-.d :r | m :m :f | m :-.r :d | r :d :t,
s, :s, :l, | s, :-.fe, :s, | d :d :r | d :-.t, :d | l, :s, :s,
m :d :f | r :-.r :r | s :l :l | s :-.f :m | f :m :r
d :m, :f, | s, :-.l, :t, | d :l, :f, | s, :-.se, :l, | f, :s, :s,

d :— :— || s :s :s | s :-.f :m | f :f :f | f :-.m :r
s, :— :— || d :d :t, | d :-.t, :d | t, :r :t, | t, :-.d :t,
m :— :— || m :s :f | m :-.r :d | s :s :s | s :-.s :s
d, :— :— || d :m :r | d :-.s, :d | s, :t, :r | s, :-.d :s,

m :f .m :r .d | m :-.f :s | l .f :m :r | d :— :— || d | d ||
d :t,.d :s, | d :-.t, :d | d .r :d :t, | d :— :— || l, | s, ||
s :s :s | s :-.f :m | f .l :s :s .f | m :— :— || f | m ||
d :r .d :t,.l, | s,.f, :m,.r, :d, | f, :s, :s, | d, :— :— || f, | d, ||

A-men.

GOD save our gracious Queen,
Long live our noble Queen;
God save the Queen;
Send her victorious,
Happy and glorious,
Long to reign over us:
God save the Queen!

2 Thy choicest gifts in store
On her be pleased to pour;
Long may she reign;
May she defend our laws,
And ever give us cause
To sing with heart and voice,
'God save the Queen!'

632

MOSCOW. (664. 6664.)

Doh = G. *In moderate time.* Felice de Giardini, 1716–96.

s :m :d	r :—:t,	d :—:—	d :r :m	f :—:m	r :—:—
d :t, :d	l, :—:s,	s, :—:—	l, :t, :d	d :—:d	t, :—:—
m :s :m	f :—:r	m :—:—	m :s :s	l :—:s	s :—:—
d :s, :l,	f, :—:s,	d, :—:—	l, :s, :d	f, :—:d	s, :—:—

s :m :d	s, :—:—	r :m :f	m :-.r :d	r :m :f	m :-.r :d
s, :m :d	s, :—:—	t, :d :r	d :-.s, :s,	l,.t, :de :r	d :-.t, :l,
s :m :d	s, :—:—	s :s :s	s :-.f :m	l :s :f	s :-.f :m
s :m :d	s, :—:—	s, :d :t,	d :-.d :d	f :m :r	s, :-.s, :l,

d :d :d	s :-.f :m	r :d :t,	d :—:—	d	d
d :t, :l,	s, :l,.t, :d	l, :s, :s,	s, :—:—	l,	s,
m :m :f	d :-.r :m	f :m :r	m :—:—	f	m
l, :s, :f,	m, :-.r, :d,	f, :s, :s,	d, :—:—	f,	d,

A - men.

GOD bless our native land;
God's all-protecting hand
Still guard our shore:
May peace her sway extend,
Foe be transformed to friend,
And Britain's power depend
On war no more.

2 Lord God, our monarch bless;
Girded with righteousness,
Long may she reign!
Her heart inspire and move
With wisdom from above;
Throned on a nation's love,
Her power maintain.

3 Break, Lord, all lawless might;
Founded in truth and right,
Stablish our laws;
God of all equity,
Set Thou the captive free;
Give the poor liberty,
Judge Thou his cause.

4 Nor on this land alone,
But be Thy mercies known
From shore to shore.
Lord, make the nations see
All men should brothers be,
One league, one family,
One, the world o'er.

William Edward Hickson, 1803–70.

633 ST. LAWRENCE. (C.M.)

Doh = E♭. *In moderate time.* ROBERT ARCHIBALD SMITH, 1780–1829.

:d | m :m.f | s :-.l | m :r | d :s | l :d' | s.f :f.m | m :r | — ‖
:s, | d :d | d :m.d | d :t, | d :d | d.r :m.d | t, :d | d :t, | — ‖
:m | s :l | s :d'.l | s :s.f | m :d'.t | l :s | s :s | s :— | — ‖
:d | d :l, | m :-.f | s :s, | d :m | f :m | r :d | s, :— | — ‖

:s | d :r | m.f :s | l.s :f.m | l :d' | s :-.l | m :r | d :— | — ‖ d | d ‖
:t, | d.s, :l,.t, | d :r.s, | d.m :r.d | d :d.r | m.f :m.r | d :t, | d :— | — ‖ l, | s, ‖
:s | s :s.f | m :r | m :s | f :l.t | d'.t :d'.l | s :s.f | m :— | — ‖ f | m ‖
:s.f | m :r | d :t, | l, :t,.d | f, :f | m.r :m.f | s :s, | d :— | — ‖ f, | d ‖

A-men.

LORD, while for all mankind we pray,
Of every clime and coast,
O hear us for our native land,
The land we love the most.

2 Our fathers' sepulchres are here,
And here our kindred dwell,
Our children too; how should we love
Another land so well?

3 O guard our shores from every foe;
With peace our borders bless;
With prosperous times our cities crown,
Our fields with plenteousness.

4 Unite us in the sacred love
Of knowledge, truth, and Thee;
And let our hills and valleys shout
The songs of liberty.

5 Lord of the nations, thus to Thee
Our country we commend;
Be Thou her refuge and her trust,
Her everlasting Friend.

JOHN REYNELL WREFORD, 1800–81.

[May be sung to DUNFERMLINE, No. 295.]

634 AGINCOURT SONG. (L.M.)

Ray = D. *Unison.* *Moderately slow.* English Melody, 15th cent.

| r' :r' :d' | r' :— :d' | d' :t :— | l :— ‖ r' | r' :d' :l | s :l :s.r |

| f :m :— | r :— ‖ l | d' :— :d' | r' :d' :t | l :s :— | f :— ‖

:f | l :— :l | s :— :f | f :m :— | r :— ‖ f :r :m | r :— :— ‖

A - men.

LLEDROD (LLANGOLLEN). (L.M.)

Doh = A. *With vigour.* Welsh Hymn Melody.

```
| d  :—  | d  :r     | d  :—  | s, :—  | m, :s, | d  :—  || m  :—  | r  :r   | r  :—  |
| s, :—  | s, :s,.f, | m, :—  | s, :—  | d, :r, | m, :—  || s, :—  | s, :fe, | s, :—  |
| m  :—  | d  :t,    | d  :—  | d  :t, | l, :t, | d  :—  || d  :—  | r  :d   | t, :—  |
| d, :—  | m, :s,    | d  :—  | m, :—  | l, :s, | d, :—  || d  :—  | t, :l,  | s, :—  |

| s,  :—    | d  :l,  | s, :—  || d  :—  | d  :r  | m  :-.r  | d  :d  | r  :m  |
| s,  :—    | s, :fe, | s, :—  || s, :—  | l, :t, | d  :-.t, | d  :l, | l, :l, |
| d   :-.r  | m  :r.d | t, :—  || m  :—  | m  :s  | s  :-.f  | m  :m  | r  :de |
| m,  :-.r, | d, :r,  | s, :—  || d, :—  | l, :s, | d  :-.r  | m  :l, | f, :l, |

| f  :-.m | r  :—  || s  :-.f | m  :r     | d  :—  | s, :—  | m, :s, | d  :—  || d  | d  ||
| l, :—   | —  :—  || s, :—   | s, :s,.f, | m, :—  | m, :r, | d, :r, | m, :—  || f, | m, ||
| r  :-.m | f  :—  || r  :—   | d  :t,    | d  :—  | d  :t, | l, :t, | d  :—  || l, | s, ||
| r  :—   | —  :d  || t, :—   | d  :s,    | l, :—  | m, :—  | l, :s, | d, :—  || f, | d, ||
                                                                                A-men.
```

PRAISE to our God, whose bounteous hand
Prepared of old our glorious land,
A garden fenced with silver sea,
A people prosperous, strong, and free!

2 Praise to our God! through all our past
His mighty arm hath held us fast,
Till wars and perils, toils and tears,
Have brought the rich and peaceful years!

3 Praise to our God! the vine He set
Within our coasts is fruitful yet;
On many a shore her seedlings grow;
'Neath many a sun her clusters glow.

4 Praise to our God! His power alone
Can keep unmoved our ancient throne,
Sustained by counsels wise and just,
And guarded by a people's trust.

5 Praise to our God! though chastenings stern
Our evil dross should throughly burn,
His rod and staff, from age to age,
Shall rule and guide His heritage.

JOHN ELLERTON, 1826–93.

v. 1, line 2, should commence:

```
:m  | r  :r
:s, | s, :fe,
:d  | r  :d
:d  | t, :l,
```

Pre-pared of, &c.

v. 1, line 3, thus:

```
:d  | d  :r
:s, | l, :t,
:m  | m  :s
:d, | l, :s,
```

A gar-den, &c.

635

BEVAN. (66. 66. and refrain.)

Doh = E♭. *In moderate time.* JOHN GOSS, 1800–80.

:d |d :r |m :f |s :— |— :s |s :s |f :m
:s$_1$ |s$_1$:t$_1$ |d :d |t$_1$:— |— :d |r :d |d :d
:m |s :f |m :d |r :— |— :m |r :m |l :s
:d |m :r |d :l$_1$ |s$_1$:— |— :d |t$_1$:d |l$_1$.t$_1$:d

|r :— |— ||r |m :f |s :l.t |d' :— |— :t |l :s
|t$_1$:— |— ||t$_1$ |d :d |d :f |m :— |— :r |d :t$_1$
|s :— |— ||s |s :l |s :f |s :— |— :s |m.fe :s
|s$_1$:— |— ||s$_1$ |d :f |m :r |d :— |— :s$_1$ |l$_1$:t$_1$

REFRAIN.

|s :fe |s :— |— ||s |l :d' |t :l |s :f |m :d
|m :r |r :— |— ||m |d :d |r :m |r :t$_1$ |d :d
|l :l |t :— |— ||d'.t |l :s |f :m.f |s :r |m :m
|d :r |s$_1$:— |— ||d |f :m |r :d |t$_1$:s$_1$ |d :ta$_1$

f :l	s :f	m :—	r :—	d :—	—		d	d	
d :d	d :r	d :—	t$_1$:—	d :—	—		l$_1$	s$_1$	
f :f	s :l	s :—	— :f	m :—	—		f	m	
l$_1$:f$_1$	m$_1$:f$_1$	s$_1$:—	s$_1$:—	d :—	—		f$_1$	d	

A-men.

TO Thee our God we fly
For mercy and for grace;
O hear our lowly cry,
And hide not Thou Thy face.
O Lord, stretch forth Thy mighty hand,
And guard and bless our fatherland.

2 Arise, O Lord of hosts!
Be jealous for Thy Name,
And drive from out our coasts
The sins that put to shame.

3 Give peace, Lord, in our time;
O let no foe draw nigh,
Nor lawless deed of crime
Insult Thy majesty.

4 The powers ordained by Thee
   With heavenly wisdom bless ;
May they Thy servants be,
   And rule in righteousness.

5 The Church of Thy dear Son
   Inflame with love's pure fire ;
Bind her once more in one,
   And life and truth inspire.

6 Thy best gifts from on high
   In rich abundance pour,
That we may magnify
   And praise Thee more and more.

William Walsham How, 1823–97.

636 PICARDY. (87. 87. 87.)

Lah = D. Doh = F. *Unison.* *Slow.* French Traditional Carol.

| l, .t, :d .r | m :m .r | m :m || m .m :f .s | f :m .r | m :— ||

| l, .t, :d .r | m :m .r | m :m || m .m :f .s | f :m .r | m :— ||

| m .m :l .m | r :-.d | l, .d :m .d | t, :— || m .m :l .m | r :t, .d | l, :— || l, f, r r, | l, m, de l, ||

A-men.

JUDGE Eternal, throned in splendour,
   Lord of lords and King of kings,
With Thy living fire of judgment
   Purge this land of bitter things ;
Solace all its wide dominion
   With the healing of Thy wings.

2 Still the weary folk are pining
   For the hour that brings release ;
And the city's crowded clangour
   Cries aloud for sin to cease ;
And the homesteads and the woodlands
   Plead in silence for their peace.

3 Crown, O God, Thine own endeavour ;
   Cleave our darkness with Thy sword ;
Feed the faint and hungry heathen
   With the richness of Thy word ;
Cleanse the body of this Empire
   Through the glory of the Lord.

Henry Scott Holland, 1847–1918.

637 RECESSIONAL. (88. 88. 88.)

Lah = C. Doh = E♭. *Moderately slow, dignified.* CHARLES WOOD, 1866–1926.

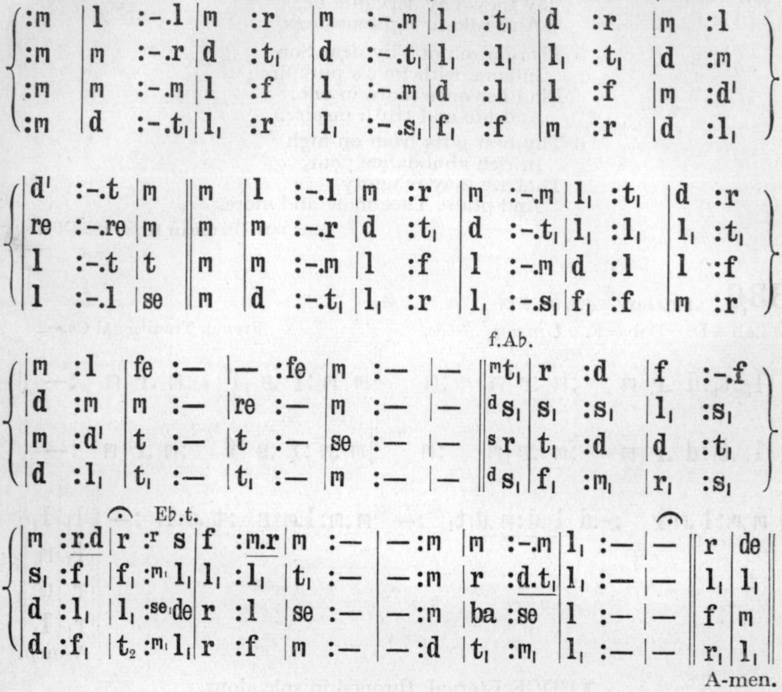

```
:m  |l    :-.l  |m   :r   |m   :-.m   |l_1 :t_1 |d   :r   |m :l
:m  |m    :-.r  |d   :t_1 |d   :-.t_1 |l_1 :l_1 |l_1 :t_1 |d :m
:m  |m    :-.m  |l   :f   |l   :-.m   |d   :l   |l   :f   |m :d'
:m  |d    :-.t_1|l_1 :r   |l_1 :-.s_1 |f_1 :f   |m   :r   |d :l_1
```

```
|d'  :-.t  |m  ||m |l  :-.l   |m   :r   |m   :-.m   |l_1 :t_1 |d   :r
|re  :-.re |m  ||m |m  :-.r   |d   :t_1 |d   :-.t_1 |l_1 :l_1 |l_1 :t_1
|l   :-.t  |t  ||m |m  :-.m   |l   :f   |l   :-.m   |d   :l   |l   :f
|l   :-.l  |se ||m |d  :-.t_1 |l_1 :r   |l_1 :-.s_1 |f_1 :f   |m   :r
```

```
                                              f.A♭.
|m :l   |fe  :— |—   :fe |m  :— |— ||^m t_1 |r   :d   |f   :-.f
|d :m   |m   :— |re  :—  |m  :— |— ||^d s_1 |s_1 :s_1 |l_1 :s_1
|m :d'  |t   :— |t   :—  |se :— |— ||^s r   |t_1 :d   |d   :t_1
|d :l_1 |t_1 :— |t_1 :—  |m  :— |— ||^d s_1 |f_1 :m_1 |r_1 :s_1
```

```
          (fermata) E♭.t.                                  (fermata)
|m   :r.d |r   :^r s     |f   :m.r |m   :— |— :m |m   :-.m  |l_1 :— |— ||r   |de ||
|s_1 :f_1 |f_1 :^m l_1   |l_1 :l_1 |t_1 :— |— :m |r   :d.t_1|l_1 :— |— ||l_1 |l_1
|d   :l_1 |l_1 :^se de   |r   :l   |se  :— |— :m |ba  :se   |l   :— |— ||f   |m
|d_1 :f_1 |t_2 :^m l_1   |r   :f   |m   :— |— :d |t_1 :m_1  |l_1 :— |— ||r_1 |l_1
                                                                    A-men.
```

FOLKINGHAM. (88. 88. 88.)

Supplement to the New Version, 1708.

Lah = C. Doh = E♭. *Moderately slow, dignified.*

```
|m   :— |l_1 :t_1  |d   :l_1 |l   :f     |m   :— ||d   :— |f   :m |r   :d
|l_1 :— |l_1 :t_1  |d   :l_1 |d   :-.t_1 |d   :— ||s_1 :— |r   :d |t_1 :l_1
|d   :— |d   :m    |m   :d   |d   :r     |m   :— ||m   :— |s   :s |m   :m
|l_1 :— |l_1 :se_1 |l_1 :l_1 |f_1 :r_1   |l_1 :— ||d   :— |t_1 :d |se_1 :l_1
```

```
                           B♭.t.                                             f.E♭.
|r   :t_1  |l_1 :— |— ||m   |^s d   :t_1 |m   :l_1 |l_1 :se_1 |l_1 :— |— :^d s
|l_1 :se_1 |l_1 :— |— ||d   |^r s_1 :t_1 |l_1 :f_1 |m_1 :m_1  |m_1 :— |— :^f d
|f   :m    |d   :— |— ||l   |^s d   :f   |m   :r.d |t_1 :t_1  |d   :— |— :^d s
|r   :m    |l_1 :— |— ||l_1 |^t m_1 :r_1 |d_1 :r_1 |m_1 :m_1  |l_1 :— |— :^l m
```

```
| r  :m  | f    :m | r  :r   | d :— || r  :— | m :d  | s  :s    | s  :fe |
| d  :d  | d.t, :d | d  :t,  | d :— || t, :— | d :s, | r  :m.r  | d  :r  |
| l  :s  | f    :s | s  :-.f | m :— || s  :— | s :m  | r  :s    | d' :l  |
| f  :m  | r    :d | s, :s,  | d :— || s, :— | d :d  | t, :d.t, | l, :r  |

| s  :— || m :— | l :t | se :l  | l  :se | l  :— || l     | l  ||
| r  :— || d :— | d :r | t, :d  | t, :t, | d  :— || r     | de ||
| t  :— || s :— | f :f | m  :m  | m  :m  | m  :— || f     | m  ||
| s, :— || d :— | f :r | m  :l, | m  :m, | l, :— || r  r, | l, ||
                                                      A  -  men.
```

Recessional.

GOD of our fathers, known of old,
Lord of our far-flung battle-line,
Beneath whose awful hand we hold
Dominion over palm and pine—
Lord God of hosts, be with us yet,
Lest we forget—lest we forget!

2 The tumult and the shouting dies;
The captains and the kings depart:
Still stands Thine ancient sacrifice,
An humble and a contrite heart.
Lord God of hosts, be with us yet,
Lest we forget—lest we forget!

3 Far-called, our navies melt away;
On dune and headland sinks the fire:
Lo, all our pomp of yesterday
Is one with Nineveh and Tyre!
Judge of the nations, spare us yet,
Lest we forget—lest we forget!

4 If, drunk with sight of power, we loose
Wild tongues that have not Thee in awe,
Such boastings as the Gentiles use,
Or lesser breeds without the law—
Lord God of hosts, be with us yet,
Lest we forget—lest we forget!

5 For heathen heart that puts her trust
In reeking tube and iron shard,
All valiant dust that builds on dust,
And, guarding, calls not Thee to guard,
For frantic boast and foolish word—
Thy mercy on Thy people, Lord!

RUDYARD KIPLING, 1865–

vv. 2 & 5. 1st line.

```
| :m  | l, :t,  | d  :l, | l  :f   | m  :— || — :d  | f  :m |
| :l, | l, :t,  | d  :l, | d  :-.t,| d  :— || — :s, | r  :d |
| :d  | d  :m   | m  :d  | d  :r   | m  :— || — :m  | s  :s |
| :l, | l, :se, | l, :l, | f, :r,  | l, :— || — :d  | t, :d |
```

638 MONTAGUE. (76. 76. D.)

Doh = C. *Unison.* *Moderately slow.* ARCHIE FAIRBAIRN BARNES, 1878–

v. 3.

: | m :m.m | | | | | | l :— | — :—
:m | m :-.m | m :m | m :— | m :m | l :-.l | l :l | l :— | — :l

1. O God of earth and al - tar, Bow down and hear our cry; Our
2. From all that ter - ror teach - es, From lies of tongue and pen, From
3. Tie in a liv - ing teth - er The prince and priest and thrall;

v. 3.

s :s.s | s :s | s :— | s : | t :t.t | t :t | t :— | — ||
s :-.s | s :s | s :— | s :s | t :-.t | t :t | t :— | — ||

earth - ly ru - lers fal - ter, Our peo - ple drift and die;
all the ea - sy speech - es That com - fort cru - el men,
Bind all our lives to - geth - er, Smite us and save us all;

Harmony.

:s | d' :-.d' | r' :d' | t :l | s :s | d' :-.d' | r' :d' | t :— | — :—
:r | d :-.s | fe :fe | r :— | r :f | m :-.l | l :s.l | s :— | — :—

The walls of gold en - tomb us, The swords of scorn di - vide,
From sale and pro - fa - na - tion Of hon - our and the sword,
In ire and ex - ul - ta - tion, A - flame with faith, and free,

:t | d' :-.l | t :l | s :l | t :r' | d' :-.m' | r' :r' | r' :— | — :—
:f | m :-.m | r :r | s :— | s :t | l :-.s | fe :m.fe | s :— | — :—

r' :r'.r' | m' :r' | d' :— | t :l | s :-.l | d' :r' | d' :— | — :—
l :l.l | se :m | l :— | s :f | m :-.s | f :f | m :— | — :—

Take not Thy thun - der from us, But take a - way our pride.
From sleep and from dam - na - tion, De - liv - er us, good Lord!
Lift up a liv - ing na - tion, A sin - gle sword to Thee.

t :r'.r' | d' :t | d' :— | r' :d' | d' :-.m' | m' :t | d' :— | — :—
f :t,.t, | m :se | l :— | m :f | s :-.s | s :s | d :— | — :—

GILBERT KEITH CHESTERTON, 1874–

| d' | m' ||
| f | s ||
A - men.
| l | d' ||
| f | d ||

[*Copyright*, 1927, *by Oxford University Press.*]

639 DOVERSDALE. (L.M.)

SAMUEL STANLEY, 1767–1822.

Doh = D. *Brightly.* A.t.

:d | s.,f:m :r | d :— :s | s :l :t | d' :— :d'f | f :— :f
:d | d.,r:d :t_1 | d :— :r | d :— :f | m :— :ml_1 | l_1 :— :s_1
:d | s.,l:s :s | m :— :r | m :f :f | s :— :sd | f :-.m:r
:d | m.,f:s :s_1 | l_1 :— :t_1 | d :f :r | d :— :df_1 | r :-.d:t_1

f.D.

m :-.r:d | r :d :t_1 | d :— ds | s :l.s:f.m | f :—:f | f :s.f:m.r
s_1 :— :m_1 | l_1 :s_1 :s_1 | s_1 :— mt_1 | m :— :r.de | r :—:r | r :t_1 :d.r
d :t_1 :d | f :m :r | m :— ds | l :— :l | l :—:l | s :— :s
d :s_1 :l_1 | f_1 :s_1 :s_1 | d_1 :— lm | de :— :l_1 | r :—:d | t_1:s_1 :l_1.t_1

m :— :s | s :l :t | d' :— :s | s.f:m :r | d :— :— || d | d
d :— :t_1 | d :— :f | m :— :d.m | m.r:d :t_1 | d :— :— || l_1 | s_1
s :— :f | s :f :f | l :— :s | l :s :s | m :— :— || f | m
d :— :r | m :f :r | l_1 :— :m | f :s :s_1 | d :— :— || f_1 | d

A-men.

THESE things shall be: a loftier race
Than e'er the world hath known, shall rise,
With flame of freedom in their souls
And light of knowledge in their eyes.

2 They shall be gentle, brave, and strong,
To spill no drop of blood, but dare
All that may plant man's lordship firm
On earth, and fire, and sea, and air.

3 Nation with nation, land with land,
Inarmed shall live as comrades free;
In every heart and brain shall throb
The pulse of one fraternity.

4 Man shall love man, with heart as pure
And fervent as the young-eyed throng
Who chant their heavenly psalms before
God's face with undiscordant song.

5 New arts shall bloom of loftier mould,
And mightier music thrill the skies,
And every life shall be a song,
When all the earth is paradise.

6 There shall be no more sin, nor shame,
Though pain and passion may not die;
For man shall be at one with God
In bonds of firm necessity.

JOHN ADDINGTON SYMONDS, 1840–93.

640

JERUSALEM. (D.L.M.)

Slow, but with animation.

CHARLES HUBERT HASTINGS PARRY, 1848–1918.

Doh = D. *Unison.*

Three measures instrumental. *mf.* : .d :m .s | l :- .d' :l .s ,f | s :— :l .s ,f
1. And did those feet in an-cient time Walk up-on

s .m :r :d | l, *p* :- .d :m .s | l :- .d' :t .l ,s
Eng-land's moun - tains green? And was the Ho - ly Lamb of

l :- .(A.t.) r :m .l, | d .t, :l, :s, | d *mf* (d.f.G.) :- s l, :l, .t,
God On Eng-land's plea-sant pas - tures seen? And did the

d :- .m :r .,l, | d :- .l, *poco cres.* :d .r | m :- .s :f .r
coun - te-nance di - vine Shine forth up - on our cloud-ed

m *f* :- .d :m .s | (D.t.) r' .,d' :t :t .,l
hills? And was Je - ru - sa - lem build-ed

s :- *poco rit.* .s :d' .l | s .,l :m :r | d :— : ||
here A-mong these dark sa - tan - ic mills?

Two measures instrumental. *mf* :d :m .s | l :- .d' :l .s,f | s :— :l .s ,f
2. Bring me my bow of burn-ing gold! Bring me my

s .m :r :d | l, :- .d :m .s | l :d' :t .l,s
ar-rows of de - sire! Bring me my spear! O clouds, un -

l :- .(A.t.) r :m .l, | d .,t, :l, :s, | d *p* (d.f.G.) :- .s l, :l, .t,
- fold! Bring me my cha-ri - ot of fire! I will not

d :- .m :r .,l, | d :- .l, :d .r | m :s :f .r
cease from men-tal fight, Nor shall my sword sleep in my

Allargando.
m :- .d :m .s | *ff* (D.t.) r' :- .d' :t .,l | s *rit.* :- .s :d' .l
hand, Till we have built Je - ru - sa-lem In Eng-land's

s .l :m :r | d :— :— | — : : | : : ||
green and plea - sant land.

WILLIAM BLAKE, 1757–1827.

[*Copyright*, 1916, *by C. Hubert H. Parry.*]

641 RUSSIA. (11 10. 11 9.)

Doh = E♭. *With dignity.* ALEXIS FEODOROVITCH LVOV, 1799–1871.

```
s  :—  |l  :l  |s  :-.m |d  :d  |d' :—  |t  :l   |s  :— |l  :—
d  :—  |d  :d  |m  :-.d |s, :s, |d  :—  |s  :f   |m  :— |d  :—
m  :—  |f  :l  |d' :-.s |m  :m  |s  :—  |d' :d'  |d' :— |m  :—
d  :—  |f  :f  |d  :-.d |d  :d  |m  :—  |f  :f   |d  :— |l, :—

f  :—  |s  :s  |m  :—   |m  :fe |s  :—  |fe :-.m |m  :— |—  :—
l, :—  |r  :t, |d  :—   |m  :m  |m  :—  |re :-.m |t, :— |—  :—
f  :—  |r  :s  |s  :—   |s  :d' |t  :—  |l  :-.s |s  :— |—  :—
r  :—  |t, :s, |d  :—   |d  :l, |t, :—  |t, :-.m |m  :— |—  :—

f  :—  |m  :r  |m  :-.r  |m  :s  |d' :t |l  :se |l  :— |s  :—
r  :—  |d  :t, |d  :-.t, |d  :r  |d  :f |m  :r  |d  :— |f  :—
l  :—  |s  :s  |s  :—    |s  :s  |l  :t |d' :t  |l  :— |t  :—
r  :—  |s, :s, |d  :—    |d  :t, |l, :r |m  :m  |f  :— |r  :—

d' :—  |t  :l  |s  :—   |s  :f  |m  :—  |r  :-.d |d  :— |—  :— || d  | d
m  :—  |r  :t, |d  :—   |d  :r  |d  :—  |t, :-.d |d  :— |—  :— || l, | s,
d' :m  |f  :f  |s  :—   |l  :l  |s  :—  |f  :-.m |m  :— |—  :— || f  | m
d  :—  |r  :r  |m  :m,  |f, :f, |s, :—  |s, :-.d |d  :— |—  :— || f, | d
                                                                  A-men.
```

Unison. GOD the Omnipotent! King, who ordainest
Great winds Thy clarions, lightnings Thy sword:
Show forth Thy pity on high where Thou reignest;
Give to us peace in our time, O Lord.

Harmony. 2 God the All-merciful! earth hath forsaken
Meekness and mercy, and slighted Thy word;
Bid not Thy wrath in its terrors awaken;
Give to us peace in our time, O Lord.

3 God the All-righteous One! man hath defied Thee;
Yet to eternity standeth Thy word;
Falsehood and wrong shall not tarry beside Thee;
Give to us peace in our time, O Lord.

4 God the All-wise! by the fire of Thy chastening,
Earth shall to freedom and truth be restored;
Through the thick darkness Thy Kingdom is hastening;
Thou wilt give peace in Thy time, O Lord.

Unison. 5 So shall Thy children, with thankful devotion,
Praise Him who saved them from peril and sword,
Singing in chorus, from ocean to ocean,
Peace to the nations, and praise to the Lord.

HENRY FOTHERGILL CHORLEY, 1808–72, and JOHN ELLERTON, 1826–93.

642 RUSSIA. (11 10. 11 9.)

Doh = E♭. *With dignity.* ALEXIS FEODOROVITCH LVOV, 1799–1871.

```
s  :—  |l  :l  |s  :-.m |d  :d  |d' :—  |t  :l
d  :—  |d  :d  |m  :-.d |s, :s, |d  :—  |s  :f
m  :—  |f  :l  |d' :-.s |m  :m  |s  :—  |d' :d'
d  :—  |f  :f  |d  :-.d |d  :d  |m  :—  |f  :f

s  :—  |l  :—  |f  :—  |s  :s  |m  :—  |m  :fe
m  :—  |d  :—  |l, :—  |r  :t, |d  :—  |m  :m
d' :—  |m  :—  |f  :—  |r  :s  |s  :—  |s  :d'
d  :—  |l, :—  |r  :—  |t, :s, |d  :—  |d  :l,

s  :—  |fe :-.m |m  :—  |—  :—  ‖f  :—  |m  :r  |m  :-.r  |m  :s
m  :—  |re :-.m |t, :—  |—  :—  ‖r  :—  |d  :t, |d  :-.t, |d  :r
t  :—  |l  :-.s |s  :—  |—  :—  ‖l  :—  |s  :s  |s  :—   |s  :s
t, :—  |t, :-.m |m  :—  |—  :—  ‖r  :—  |s, :s, |d  :—   |d  :t,

d' :t  |l  :se |l  :—  |s  :—  |d' :—  |t  :l
d  :f  |m  :r  |d  :—  |f  :—  |m  :—  |r  :t,
l  :t  |d' :t  |l  :—  |t  :—  |d' :m  |f  :f
l, :r  |m  :m  |f  :—  |r  :—  |d  :—  |r  :r

s  :—  |s  :f  |m  :—  |r  :-.d |d  :—  |—  :—  ‖d  |d  ‖
d  :—  |d  :r  |d  :—  |t, :-.d |d  :—  |—  :—  ‖l, |s, ‖
s  :—  |l  :l  |s  :—  |f  :-.m |m  :—  |—  :—  ‖f  |m  ‖
m  :m, |f, :f, |s, :—  |s, :-.d |d  :—  |—  :—  ‖f, |d  ‖
                                                  A-men.
```

For use overseas.

GOD of Eternity, Lord of the Ages,
Father and Spirit and Saviour of men!
Thine is the glory of time's numbered pages;
Thine is the power to revive us again.

2 Thankful, we come to Thee, Lord of the nations,
Praising Thy faithfulness, mercy, and grace,
Shown to our fathers in past generations,
Pledge of Thy love to our people and race.

3 Far from our ancient home, sundered by oceans,
Zion is builded, and God is adored:
Lift we our hearts in united devotions!
Ends of the earth, join in praise to the Lord!

4 Beauteous this land of ours, bountiful Giver!
Brightly the heavens Thy glory declare;
Streameth the sunlight on hill, plain, and river,
Shineth Thy Cross over fields rich and fair.

5 Pardon our sinfulness, God of all pity,
Call to remembrance Thy mercies of old;
Strengthen Thy Church to abide as a city
Set on a hill for a light to Thy fold.

6 Head of the Church on earth, risen, ascended!
Thine is the honour that dwells in this place:
As Thou hast blessed us through years that have ended,
Still lift upon us the light of Thy face.

ERNEST NORTHCROFT MERRINGTON, 1876–

643 OLD 137TH. (D.C.M.)

Doh = G. *Moderately slow.* *Anglo-Genevan Psalter*, 1556.

d :t,.l,	s, :d	m :r	d :—		d :r.m	f :r	m :—	
m, :f,.f,	s, :l,	s, :s,	m, :—		l, :t,.d	d :t,	d :—	
s, :t,.t,	d :m	d :t,	d :—		m :s.s	l :s	s :—	
d, :r,.r,	m, :l,	m,.f, :s,	d, :—		l, :s,.d	f, :s,	d :—	

m :r.d	t, :d	l,.l, :s,	—		s,	d :-.r	m :r	d :—	
d :s,.s,	s, :s,	s,.fe, :s,	—		s,	l, :-.t,	d :t,	d :—	
s :r.m	r :d	m.r :t,	—		d	m :-.s	s :s.f	m :—	
d :t,.d	s, :m,	d,.r, :s,	—		m,	l, :-.s,	m,.f, :s,	d, :—	

s, :—	d :-.r	m :d	f :-.f	m :—		d :l,.t,	d :r	d :—	
m, :—	l, :-.l,	t, :d	r :-.r	de :—		l, :l,.se,	l,.d :-.t,	d :—	
d :—	m :-.l	se :m	l :-.l	l :—		m :m.r	d.m :s	m :—	
d :—	l, :-.f,	m, :l,	r, :-.f,	l, :—		l, :d.t,	l, :s,	d :—	

d :—	m.f :s.s	l :-.l	s :—		m :r.m	f :r	d :—		d	d	
s, :—	d.d :t,.d	d :-.d	d :—		d :t,.d	r.d :-.t,	d :—		l,	s,	
m :—	s.d :r.s	f :-.f	m :—		s :s.s	l :s	m :—		f	m	
d :—	d.l, :s,.m,	f, :-.f,	d :—		d :s,.d	f, :s,	d, :—		f,	d,	

A-men.

GREAT King of nations, hear our prayer,
While at Thy feet we fall,
And humbly with united cry
To Thee for mercy call.
The guilt is ours, but grace is Thine;
O turn us not away,
But hear us from Thy lofty throne,
And help us when we pray.

2 Our fathers' sins were manifold,
And ours no less we own;
Yet wondrously from age to age
Thy goodness hath been shown.
When dangers, like a stormy sea,
Beset our country round,
To Thee we looked, to Thee we cried,
And help in Thee was found.

3 With one consent we meekly bow
Beneath Thy chastening hand,
And, pouring forth confession meet,
Mourn with our mourning land.
With pitying eye behold our need,
As thus we lift our prayer;
Correct us with Thy judgments, Lord,
Then let Thy mercy spare.

JOHN HAMPDEN GURNEY, 1802–62.

644 LEYDEN. (D.C.M.)

Doh = G. *In moderate time.* JAN WILLEM WILMS, 1772–1847.

:s, |d :d |m :r |d :t,.l, |s, :d |t, :d |f :m |r :— |—
:s, |d :s, |s, :s,.f, |m, :f, |s, :s, |s, :s, |l,.t, :d |t, :— |—
:s, |s :m |d :t, |d :d |d :m |r :m |f :s |s :— |—
:s, |m, :d, |d :s, |l, :f, |m, :d, |s, :m, |r, :m,.f, |s, :— |—

D.t.

:s, |d :d |m :r |d :- .t, |l, :m l |s .l :t.d' |m :r |d :— |—
:s, |d :s, |s, :s,.f, |m, :ba,.se, |l, :fe t, |d :f.m |d :t, |d :— |—
:s, |s :m |d :t, |d :- .r |m :d f |s :s |s :s.f |m :— |—
:s, |m, :d, |d :s, |l, :- .t, |d :l r |m :r.d |s :s, |d :— |—

f.G.

:d s, |f :-.m |r :r |m :- .r |d :d .m |s :s |m :d |r :— |—
:d s, |r :-.de |r :l, |s, :l,.t, |d :s,.d |r :t, |m :d |s, :— |—
:d s |l :-.s |f :f |m :- .f |s.f :m |r :r |m :d |t, :— |—
:d s, |r, :-.m, |f,.s, :l,.t, |d :- .r |m.r :d |t, :s, |m :d |s, :— |—

:s, |d :d |m.r :d.t, |l, :l, |f :-.r |d :d |t,.d :r .t, |d :— |— ||d |d
:s, |d :s, |s, :s, |f, :m, |l, :-.l, |s, :l,.s, |s, :f, |m, :— |— ||f, |m,
:s, |s :m |d :m.r |d :d |r :-.r |m :f .m |r .d :t,.r |d :— |— ||l, |d
:s, |m, :d, |d :m, |f, :l, |r, :-.f, |s, :s, |s, :s, |d, :— |— ||f, |d,

A-men.

WHAT service shall we render thee,
O Fatherland we love?
What gift of hand, or heart, or brain
May our devotion prove?
The coming age invokes our aid,
Thy voice of old inspires;
Shall we, thy sons and daughters, be
Less worthy than our sires?

2 The service of the commonwealth
Is not in arms alone;
A nobler chivalry shall rise
Than war has ever known:
Glad rivalries in arts of peace.
True ministries of life,
Shall supersede the arts of war
And calm our feverish strife.

3 Too long the pagan rule of force
Has held the world in thrall;
Too long the clash of arms has drowned
The higher human call.
O comrades, seek a nobler quest!
O keep a worthier tryst!
The laws of hate have had their day;
Proclaim the laws of Christ!

4 Lord of the nations, far and near,
Send forth Thy quickening breath,
Equip us for the tasks of life,
Save us from deeds of death;
Enlist us in Thy ranks to fight
Fair freedom's holy war,
Whose battle-cry is 'Brotherhood',
Far-flung from shore to shore.

ERNEST DODGSHUN, 1876–

645

GREYFRIARS. (11 10. 11 10 10.) *Scottish Psalter*, 1635.

Arranged by JAMES SMITH ANDERSON, 1853– .

Lah = E. Doh = G. *Not too slow.*

```
l,  :—  :d   :d   :r   :r   :m   :m   :f   :r   :m   :m   | l,  :—
m,  :—  :l,  :l,  :l,  :l,  :se, :l,  :l,  :s,  :s,  :s,  | m,  :—
d   :—  :m   :m   :f   :l,  :t,  :d   :d   :t,  :d   :d   | d   :—
l,  :—  :l,  :l,  :f,  :f,  :m,  :l,  :f,  :s,  :d   :d   | l,  :—

:d  :d  :r  :r  :m  :m  :f  :r  :m  :—  | m   :m.m:m  :m
:l, :m, :l, :s, :s, :l, :l, :s, :s, :—  | s,  :d.d:d  :d
:m  :d  :d  :t, :d  :d  :d  :t, :d  :—  | d   :s.s:l  :s
:l, :l, :f, :s, :d, :l, :f, :s, :d  :—  | d   :d.d:l, :d

:f  :-.m  :r.t, :d.r :m  :m  | s  :s.f    :m  :r   :d  :t,  :d  :r.d
:l, :-.s, :s,   :s,  :s, :s, | s, :s,.s,  :s, :t,  :l, :se, :l, :t,.l,
:f  :-.s  :t,.r :m.t,:d  :d  | t, :r.r    :m  :s.f :m  :m   :m  :m
:f, :-.d, :s,   :s,  :d  :d  | s, :t,.t,  :d  :s,  :l, :m,  :l, :se,.l,

:t,  :— | d  :d.t,   :d.r  :m  :r   :d.r   :m.r  :t,  :l, :— || l, | l,  ||
:se, :— | l, :l,.se, :l,.t,:d  :t,  :l,.l, :l,   :se, :l, :— || f, | m,  ||
:m   :— | m  :m      :m.s  :s  :s.f :m.r   :d.t, :m.r :d  :— || r  | de  ||
:m,  :— | l, :l,.m,  :l,.s,:d  :s,  :l,.f, :m,   :m,  :l, :— || r, | l,  ||
                                                              A-men.
```

The League of Nations.

FATHER Eternal, Ruler of Creation,
Spirit of Life, which moved ere form was made,
Through the thick darkness covering every nation,
Light to man's blindness, O be Thou our aid!
Thy Kingdom come, O Lord, Thy will be done.

2 Races and peoples, lo! we stand divided,
And, sharing not our griefs, no joy can share;
By wars and tumults Love is mocked, derided,
His conquering Cross no kingdom wills to bear;
Thy Kingdom come, O Lord, Thy will be done.

3 Envious of heart, blind-eyed, with tongues confounded,
Nation by nation still goes unforgiven;
In wrath and fear, by jealousies surrounded,
Building proud towers which shall not reach to heaven.
Thy Kingdom come, O Lord, Thy will be done.

4 Lust of possession worketh desolations ;
  There is no meekness in the sons of earth.
Led by no star, the rulers of the nations
  Still fail to bring us to the blissful birth.
  Thy Kingdom come, O Lord, Thy will be done.

5 How shall we love Thee, holy, hidden Being,
  If we love not the world which Thou hast made ?
O, give us brother-love, for better seeing
  Thy Word made flesh and in a manger laid.
  Thy Kingdom come, O Lord, Thy will be done.

LAURENCE HOUSMAN, 1865–

646 MELCOMBE. (L.M.)

SAMUEL WEBBE, 1740–1816.

Doh = E♭. *Moderately slow.*

```
:s  |s  :f     |m  :r    |d  :l   |s  :s   |d' :t     |l  :s   |s  :fe   |s  ||
:d  |s, :l,.t, |d  :t,   |l, :d   |d  :r   |d  :r     |r  :t,  |m  :r.d  |t, ||
:m  |m  :f     |s  :s.f  |m  :f   |m  :s   |fe :s     |fe :s   |l  :l    |s  ||
:d  |m  :r     |d  :s,   |l, :f,  |d  :t,  |l, :t,.d  |r  :m   |d  :r    |s, ||

:m  |m  :f     |s  :m    |r  :-.m   |f  :f   |m  :r      |s  :f   |m  :r    |d  || f  |m  ||
:d  |d  :t,.l, |s, :d    |t, :-.de  |r  :r   |d  :t,     |d  :d   |d  :t,   |d  || d  |d  ||
:s  |s  :f     |m  :s    |s  :-.s   |l  :s   |s  :s      |s  :l   |s  :s.f  |m  || l  |s  ||
:d  |d  :r     |m  :d    |s  :-.m   |r  :t,  |d  :s,.f,  |m, :f,  |s, :s,   |d  || f, |d  ||
                                                                                   A-men.
```

O GOD of love, O King of peace,
Make wars throughout the world to cease ;
The wrath of sinful man restrain :
Give peace, O God, give peace again.

2 Remember, Lord, Thy works of old,
The wonders that our fathers told ;
Remember not our sin's dark stain :
Give peace, O God, give peace again.

3 Whom shall we trust but Thee, O Lord ?
Where rest but on Thy faithful word ?
None ever called on Thee in vain :
Give peace, O God, give peace again.

4 Where saints and angels dwell above,
All hearts are knit in holy love ;
O bind us in that heavenly chain :
Give peace, O God, give peace again.

HENRY WILLIAMS BAKER, 1821–77.

647 GALILEE. (L.M.)

Doh = E♭. *In moderate time.* PHILIP ARMES, 1836-1908.

s :m :r |d :— :d |l :— :l |s :— :s |d' :— :l |t :-.l :s

d :d :t$_1$ |d :— :t$_1$ |l$_1$:-.t$_1$:d .r |m :d :t$_1$ |d :— :r |r :— :r

m :s :f |m :— :m |f :— :f |m :s :s |s :— :d' |t :— :t

d :d :s$_1$ |l$_1$:— :s$_1$ |f$_1$:-.s$_1$:l$_1$.t$_1$ |d :m :f |m :— :fe |s :— :t$_1$

l :m :fe |s :— :— ‖ s :l :ta |l :— :s |l :s :f |m :r

d :r :d |t$_1$:— :— ‖ d :d :d |d :— :m |f :m :r |d :t$_1$

l :t :l |s :— :— ‖ m :f :s |f :l :d' |d' :— :l |s :—

r :— :r |s$_1$:— :— ‖ d :d :d |f :— :d |f :— :f |s :-.f

:m .f |s :f :m |d' :l :f |m :— :r |d :— :— ‖ d |d ‖

:d .r |m :r :d |d :— :d |d :— :s$_1$ |s$_1$:— :— ‖ l$_1$ |s$_1$ ‖

:s .f |m :f :s |l :f :d |s :d :f |m :— :— ‖ f |m ‖

:m .r |d :— :d |f$_1$:— :l$_1$ |s$_1$:— :s$_1$ |d :— :— ‖ f$_1$ |d ‖

A-men.

TRURO. (L.M.)

Doh = C. *In moderate time.* *Psalmodia Evangelica*, 1789.

d :m.,f |s :-.s |l :t |d' :-.s |d' :s |f .m :r .d

d :d.,t$_1$ |d :-.m |f :f |m :-.t$_1$ |d :d |d :t$_1$ .d

m :s.,s |s :-.d' |d' :f |s :-.s |s :s |d' :s

d :d.,r |m :-.d |f :r |d :-.r |m :m |l .s :f .m

G.t. f.C.

f :m |r :-. ‖ ^{r}s$_1$ |d :r |m :-.f |s .f :m .r |^{d}s :-.s

t$_1$:d |t$_1$:-. ‖ ^{t}m$_1$ |s$_1$:s$_1$ |s$_1$:-.l$_1$ |s$_1$.l$_1$:s$_1$.f$_1$ |^{m}t$_1$:-.t$_1$

s :s |s :-. ‖ ^{s}d |d :t$_1$ |d :-.d |d :d .t$_1$ |^{d}s :-.s

r :d |s$_1$:-. ‖ ^{s}d$_1$ |m$_1$:s$_1$ |d :-.l$_1$ |m$_1$.f$_1$:s$_1$ |^{d}s$_1$:-.f

s :d' |r :f |m :r |d :— ‖ f |m ‖

d :d |d :d |d :t$_1$ |d :— ‖ d |d ‖

s :m |l :l |s :-.f |m :— ‖ l |s ‖

m :d |f :r |s :s$_1$ |d :— ‖ f$_1$ |d ‖

A-men.

Unison. *LAND of our Birth, we pledge to thee*
Our love and toil in the years to be ;
When we are grown and take our place,
As men and women with our race.

Harmony. 2 Father in heaven, who lovest all,
O help Thy children when they call ;
That they may build from age to age,
An undefilèd heritage.

3 Teach us to bear the yoke in youth,
With steadfastness and careful truth ;
That, in our time, Thy grace may give
The truth whereby the nations live.

4 Teach us to rule ourselves alway,
Controlled and cleanly night and day ;
That we may bring, if need arise,
No maimed or worthless sacrifice.

5 Teach us to look, in all our ends,
On Thee for Judge, and not our friends ;
That we, with Thee, may walk uncowed
By fear or favour of the crowd.

6 Teach us the strength that cannot seek,
By deed or thought, to hurt the weak ;
That, under Thee, we may possess
Man's strength to succour man's distress.

7 Teach us delight in simple things,
And mirth that has no bitter springs ;
Forgiveness free of evil done,
And love to all men 'neath the sun !

Unison. 8 *Land of our Birth, our faith, our pride,*
For whose dear sake our fathers died ;
O Motherland, we pledge to thee,
Head, heart, and hand through the years to be !

RUDYARD KIPLING, 1865–

Also the following :

215 Thy hand, O God, has guided
489 Eternal Ruler of the ceaseless round
503 Almighty Father of all things that be
562 O God of Bethel ! by whose hand
601 O God, our help in ages past
628 Whom oceans part, O Lord, unite

Family Life (648–50).

648

WELWYN. (11 10. 11 10.)

Doh = F. *Moderately slow.* ALFRED SCOTT-GATTY, 1847–1918.

A-men.

O selig Haus, wo man dich aufgenommen.

O HAPPY home, where Thou art loved the dearest,
Thou loving Friend, and Saviour of our race,
And where among the guests there never cometh
One who can hold such high and honoured place!

2 O happy home, where two in heart united
In holy faith and blessèd hope are one,
Whom death a little while alone divideth,
And cannot end the union here begun!

3 O happy home, whose little ones are given
Early to Thee, in humble faith and prayer,—
To Thee, their Friend, who from the heights of heaven
Dost guide and guard with more than mother's care!

4 O happy home, where each one serves Thee, lowly,
Whatever his appointed work may be,
Till every common task seems great and holy,
When it is done, O Lord, as unto Thee!

5 O happy home, where Thou art not forgotten
When joy is overflowing, full and free:
O happy home, where every wounded spirit
Is brought, Physician, Comforter, to Thee:

6 Until at last, when earth's day's-work is ended,
All meet Thee in the blessèd home above,
From whence Thou camest, where Thou hast ascended,
Thy everlasting home of peace and love!

KARL JOHANN PHILIPP SPITTA, 1801–59; *tr.* by SARAH LAURIE FINDLATER, 1823–1907.

649 UFFINGHAM. (L.M.)

Lah = F. Doh = A♭. *Slow.* JEREMIAH CLARK, 1670–1707.

l, :l,.s, :f,	m, :— :t,	d :t, :l,	se, :— :—	m :m :m	r :— :d
m, :m, :r,	d, :— :m,	m, :— :m,.r,	m, :— :—	m, :s, :s,	s, :f, :m,
d :l, :l,	d :— :t,	l, :t, :d .l,	t, :— :—	d :d :d	t, :— :d
l, :d, :r,	l, :— :se,	l, :s, :f,	m, :— :—	d, :m, :d,	s, :— :l,

r :t, :—	d :— :—	s :s :f	m :— :m	m :r :d
f, :r, :—	m, :— :—	d :d :t,	d :— :s,	s, :— :s,.fe,
l, :s, :—	s, :— :—	m :d :r	m :— :m	d :r :m.d
f, :s, :—	d, :— :—	d / d, :m, :s,	d :— :d	d :t, :l,

t, :— :t,	d :t, :l,	se, :— :m	d :— :t,.l,	l, :— :—	l,	l,
s, :— :se,	l, :m, :-.r,	m, :— :m,	m, :— :se,.l,	m, :— :—	f,	m,
r :— :m	m :— :l,	t, :— :l,	l, :— :t,	d :— :—	r	de
s, :— :m,	l, :s, :f,	m, :— :d,	m, :— :m,	l, / l_2 :— :—	r,	l_2

A-men.

THOU gracious Power, whose mercy lends
The light of home, the smile of friends,
Our gathered flock Thine arms enfold,
As in the peaceful days of old.

2 Wilt Thou not hear us while we raise,
In sweet accord of solemn praise,
The voices that have mingled long
In joyous flow of mirth and song?

3 For all the blessings life has brought,
For all its sorrowing hours have taught,
For all we mourn, for all we keep,
The hands we clasp, the loved that sleep,

4 The noontide sunshine of the past,
These brief, bright moments fading fast,
The stars that gild our darkening years,
The twilight ray from holier spheres,

5 We thank Thee, Father; let Thy grace
Our loving circle still embrace,
Thy mercy shed its heavenly store,
Thy peace be with us evermore.

OLIVER WENDELL HOLMES, 1809–94.

[May be sung to MELCOMBE, No. 646.]

650

PRO NOSTRIS LIBERIS. (6 10. 10 10.)

Doh = C. *Slowly and devotionally.* JOHN MORGAN LLOYD, 1880-

d' :t .s :m .s	l :s	s .d' :t .l	r' .,t :s .l	s :- .	
m :m .m :d .r	f :r	s .s :s .m	s .,s :m .fe	s :- .	
s :s .t :d' .t	l :t	r' .d' :s .l	r .m :t .d'	t :- .	
d :m .s :l .s	f :f	m .m :r .d	t, .d :r .r	s :- .	

.s | r' :m' | r' .d' :s .l | d' :t | l :s .m | d .r :m
.s | s :s | s .s :s .s | f :f | f .m :r .d | l, .t, :d
.s | l :t | t .d' :r' .d' | s :s | d' .d :r .m | l :s
.s | f :f | m .m :ma .ma | r :s, | l, :t, .d | f :m

f .l :s .m	d :r	d :—		f	m	
r .d :t, .t,	d :d .t,	d :—		d	d	
l .r :m .f	f .m :l .s	m :—		l	s	
r .r :s, .s,	l, :f .s	d :—		f,	d	

A-men.

[*Copyright*, 1927, *by Oxford University Press.*]

FATHER, our children keep;
We know not what is coming on the earth;
Beneath the shadow of Thy heavenly wing
O keep them, keep them, Thou who gav'st them birth.

2 Father, draw nearer us;
Draw firmer round us Thy protecting arm;
O clasp our children closer to Thy side,
Uninjured in the day of earth's alarm.

3 Them in Thy chambers hide;
O hide them and preserve them calm and safe,
When sin abounds, and error flows abroad,
And Satan tempts, and human passions chafe.

4 O keep them undefiled,
Unspotted from a tempting world of sin,
That, clothed in white, through the bright city-gates,
They may with us in triumph enter in.

HORATIUS BONAR, 1808-89.

651 SONG 34 (ANGELS' SONG). (L.M.)

Doh = F. *Moderately slow.* ORLANDO GIBBONS, 1583–1625.

```
|d  :—  |d  :d  |r  :—  |m  :—  |f  :r  |s  :—  ||d  :m  :f  |s  :—  :r
|s, :—  |s, :d  |t, :—  |d  :—  |l, :t, |d  :—  ||s, :d  :d  |r  :—  :t,
|m  :—  |m  :m  |s  :—  |s  :—  |f  :f  |m  :—  ||m  :s  :f  |r  :—  :s
|d  :—  |d  :d  |s  :—  |m  :—  |r  :r  |d  :—  ||d  :d  :l, |t, :—  :s,

|s  :—  :fe |s  :—  :—  ||m  :f  :s   |l  :—  :s  |f  :—  :m
|d  :r  :—  |t, :—  :—  ||d  :d  :r.m |f  :m  :r  |d  :r  :d
|s  :l  :—  |s  :—  :—  ||s  :d' :ta  |l  :—  :t  |d' :s  :s
|m  :r  :—  |s, :—  :—  ||d  :l, :s,  |f, :—  :s, |l, :t, :d

|r  :—  :—  ||s  :f  :m  |r  :—  :d  |m  :r  :—  |d  :—  :—  ||d  |d
|t, :—  :—  ||d  :d  :d  |d  :t, :l, |d  :d  :t, |d  :—  :—  ||l, |s,
|s  :—  :—  ||s  :l  :s  |s  :—.f:m  |s  :s  :—  |m  :—  :—  ||f  |m
|s, :—  :—  ||m, :f, :d  |s, :—  :l, |m, :s, :—  |d  :—  :—  ||f, |d
                                                              A-men.
```

Daily Work.

FORTH in Thy Name, O Lord, I go,
My daily labour to pursue,
Thee, only Thee, resolved to know
In all I think, or speak, or do.

2 The task Thy wisdom hath assigned
O let me cheerfully fulfil,
In all my works Thy presence find,
And prove Thy good and perfect will.

3 Thee may I set at my right hand,
Whose eyes mine inmost substance see,
And labour on at Thy command,
And offer all my works to Thee.

4 Give me to bear Thy easy yoke,
And every moment watch and pray,
And still to things eternal look,
And hasten to Thy glorious day;

5 For Thee delightfully employ
Whate'er Thy bounteous grace hath given,
And run my course with even joy,
And closely walk with Thee to heaven.

CHARLES WESLEY, 1707–88.

652 CALVARY. (87. 87. 87.)

Doh = A♭. *In moderate time.* SAMUEL STANLEY, 1767-1822.

```
d  :-.r  |m  :-.r  |d.t, :l,.s, |s,.d :d   |r  :m.fe  |s  :-.d  |t, :l,  |s, :—  ||
s, :-.s, |s, :-.f, |m,   :f,    |m,   :s,  |s, :s,.l, |s, :-.l, |s, :fe, |s, :—  ||
m  :-.r  |d  :-.t, |d    :d     |d    :m   |t, :d     |r  :-.m  |r  :-.d |t, :—  ||
d  :-.t, |d  :-.s, |l,   :f,    |d    :d,  |s, :d     |t, :-.d  |r  :r,  |s, :—  ||

r  :-.r  |d.t, :l,.s, |d  :r  |m  :m   |m  :-.m   |r.d  :t,.l,  |s, :fe, |s, :—  ||
s, :-.s, |s,   :r,    |s, :s, |s, :s,  |l, :-.l,  |t,.l, :s,.m, |r, :r,  |r, :—  ||
t, :-.t, |r    :t,    |d  :t, |d  :d   |d  :-.d   |t,.d :r.d    |t, :l,  |t, :—  ||
s, :-.s, |s,   :f,    |m, :s, |d  :d,  |l, :-.fe, |s,   :s,.d,  |r, :r,  |s, :—  ||

d  :-.d  |d.t, :t, |l, :-.l, |l,.s, :s, |m  :-.m   |f  :-.f  |m  :r     |d  :—  ||d  |d  ||
s, :-.s, |s,   :r, |f, :-.f, |f,.m, :m, |s, :-.s,  |f, :-.l, |s, :s,.f, |m, :—  ||f, |m, ||
m  :-.d  |r    :s, |d  :-.d  |d     :d  |d  :-.d   |d  :-.d  |d  :t,    |d  :—  ||l, |s, ||
d, :-.m, |s,   :s, |f, :-.l, |d     :d, |d  :-.ta, |l, :-.f, |s, :s,    |d, :—  ||f, |d, ||
                                                                                 A-men.
```

A Mothers' Prayer.

LORD of Life and King of Glory,
  Who didst deign a child to be,
Cradled on a mother's bosom,
  Throned upon a mother's knee:
For the children Thou hast given
  We must answer unto Thee.

2 Since the day the blessèd mother
  Thee, the world's Redeemer, bore,
Thou hast crowned us with an honour
  Women never knew before;
And, that we may bear it meetly,
  We must seek Thine aid the more.

3 Grant us, then, pure hearts and patient,
  That, in all we do or say,
Little souls our deeds may copy,
  And be never led astray;
Little feet our steps may follow
  In a safe and narrow way.

4 When our growing sons and daughters
  Look on life with eager eyes,
Grant us then a deeper insight,
  And new powers of sacrifice:
Hope to trust them, faith to guide them,
  Love that nothing good denies.

5 May we keep our holy calling
  Stainless in its fair renown,
That, when all the work is over,
  And we lay the burden down,
Then the children Thou hast given
  Still may be our joy and crown.

CHRISTIAN BURKE, 1859-

For Little Children (653–71).

653 SPRING-TIDE HOUR. (4 4 6. D.)

JOSEPH BARNBY, 1838–96.

Doh = G. *In moderate time.* D.t.

```
:s, |s, :— :l, |t, :— :d  |d  :t, :d  |r  :— :f  |ml :— :d'
:s, |s, :— :s, |s, :— :s, |f, :— :f, |f, :— :s, |sd :— :f
:m  |m  :— :m  |m  :— :m  |r  :— :d  |t, :— :r  |df :— :l
:d  |d  :— :d  |d  :— :d  |s, :— :s, |s, :— :t, |df :— :r
```

f.G.

```
|t  :l  :s |ds  :— :— |— :— ||s   |s  :— :f  |d  :— :f  |f   :m  :r
|f  :— :f  |mt, :— :— |— :— ||ta, |l, :— :l, |l, :— :l, |se, :— :m,
|t  :d' :t |ds  :— :— |— :— ||m   |d  :— :d  |d  :— :t, |t,  :— :t,
|s  :— :s  |ds, :— :— |— :— ||d   |f, :— :f, |f, :— :r, |m,  :— :se,
```

```
|d  :t, :l, |s, :d  :f  |m  :— :r  |d  :— :— |— :— ||d  |d
|m, :— :f,  |m, :s, :d  |t, :— :t, |d  :— :— |— :— ||l, |s,
|d  :— :d   |d  :m  :l  |s  :— :f  |m  :— :— |— :— ||f  |m
|l, :— :f,  |s, :— :s,  |s, :— :s, |d, :— :— |— :— ||f, |d,
```

A-men.

THE morning bright,
With rosy light,
Has waked me up from sleep;
Father, I own,
Thy love alone
Thy little one doth keep.

2 All through the day,
I humbly pray,
Be Thou my Guard and Guide;
My sins forgive,
And let me live,
Blest Jesus, near Thy side.

3 O make Thy rest
Within my breast,
Great Spirit of all grace;
Make me like Thee,
Then shall I be
Prepared to see Thy face.

THOMAS OSMOND SUMMERS, 1812–82.

```
|s :— :— |— :— :— ||s :s :f |d :—
```

v. 1, 4th line. sleep; Fa-ther, I own,
v. 3, 4th line. grace; Make me like thee,

654 EVENING PRAYER. (87. 87.)

Doh = F. *Unison. In moderate time.* JOHN STAINER, 1840–1901.

```
|s  :s  |s  :f  |m  :m  |m  :r  |d  :r  |m  :m  |s.f:m  |r  :—  ||
|m  :m  |m  :r  |d  :d  |d  :t, |d  :t, |d  :d  |r  :d  |t, :—  ||
|s  :—  |—  :—  |s  :—  |—  :—  |s  :—  |—  :—  |—  :—  |—  :—  ||
|d  :—  |t, :—  |d  :m  |s  :f  |m  :r  |d  :d  |t, :d  |s  :f  ||

|s  :s  |s  :f  |m  :m  |m  :r  |d  :r  |m  :m  |f  :t, |d  :—  ||d  |d  ||
|d  :—  |r  :t, |d  :—  |—  :t, |d  :—  |—  :—  |t, :s, |s, :—  ||l, |s, ||
|s  :m  |r  :—  |m  :—  |m  :—  |m  :fe |s  :d  |r  :f  |m  :—  ||f  |m  ||
|m  :d  |t, :s, |d  :l, |se,:m, |l, :—  |s, :—  |s, :—  |d  :—  ||f, |d  ||
                                                                    d,
```

[*By permission of Novello & Co., Ltd.*] A-men.

JESUS, tender Shepherd, hear me ;
Bless Thy little lamb to-night ;
Through the darkness be Thou near me ;
Watch my sleep till morning light.

2 All this day Thy hand has led me,
And I thank Thee for Thy care ;
Thou hast clothed me, warmed and fed me ;
Listen to my evening prayer.

3 Let my sins be all forgiven ;
Bless the friends I love so well ;
Take me, when I die, to heaven,
Happy there with Thee to dwell.

MARY LUNDIE DUNCAN, 1814–40.

655 NEWBURY. (C.M.)

Doh = E. *In moderate time.* English Traditional Melody.

```
:d.m |s  :s  |f  :l  |s  :m.r |d  :m  |r  :r.m |f  :m.r |m  :—  |—  ||
:d   |d  :d  |d  :d  |d  :t,  |l, :d  |d  :d   |d  :t,  |d  :—  |—  ||
:d   |m  :m  |f  :f  |s  :s.f |m  :m  |l  :l   |l  :s   |s  :—  |—  ||
:d   |d  :d  |l, :f, |m, :s,  |l, :l, |f, :f.m |r  :s,  |d  :—  |—  ||

:d.m |s  :s.l |f  :r.m |f.m:f.l |s  :d.m |s  :l .s    |m  :r   |d  :—  |—  ||d  |d  ||
:d   |d  :d   |d  :d   |d  :t,  |d  :d   |d  :d       |d  :t,  |d  :—  |—  ||l, |s, ||
:m   |m  :s   |l  :l.s |f  :f   |m  :m   |d  :d       |s  :s.f |m  :—  |—  ||f  |m  ||
:d   |d  :m   |r  :f.m |r  :r   |m  :l,  |m, :f,.m,   |s, :s,  |d  :—  |—  ||f, |d  ||
```

A-men.

LORD, I would own Thy tender care,
And all Thy love to me;
The food I eat, the clothes I wear,
Are all bestowed by Thee.

2 'Tis Thou preservest me from death
And dangers every hour;
I cannot draw another breath
Unless Thou give me power.

3 Kind angels guard me every night,
As round my bed they stay;
Nor am I absent from Thy sight
In darkness or by day.

4 My health and friends and parents dear
To me by God are given;
I have not any blessing here
But what is sent from heaven.

5 Such goodness, Lord, and constant care
A child can ne'er repay;
But may it be my daily prayer
To love Thee and obey.

JANE TAYLOR, 1783-1824.

656 OLD 100TH. (L.M.)

Doh = G. *Slow and dignified.* *French Psalter*, 1551.

```
|d  :—  |d  :t, |l, :s, |d  :—  |r  :—  |m  :—  ‖m  :—  |m  :m  |r  :d
|s, :—  |s, :s, |m, :m, |m, :—  |s, :—  |s, :—  ‖s, :—  |s, :d  |t, :d
|m  :—  |m  :r  |d  :t, |d  :—  |t, :—  |d  :—  ‖d  :—  |m  :s  |s  :m
|d  :—  |d  :s, |l, :m, |l, :—  |s, :—  |d, :—  ‖d  :—  |d  :d  |s, :l,

|f  :—  |m  :—  |r  :—  ‖d  :—  |r  :m  |r  :d  |l, :—  |t, :—  |d  :—  ‖
|d  :—  |d  :—  |t, :—  ‖d  :—  |s, :s, |s, :s, |l, :—  |f, :—  |s, :—  ‖
|l  :—  |s  :—  |s  :—  ‖m  :—  |r  :d  |t, :d  |d  :—  |r  :—  |m  :—  ‖
|f, :—  |d, :—  |s, :—  ‖l, :—  |t, :d  |s, :m, |f, :—  |r, :—  |d, :—  ‖

|s  :—  |m  :d    |r  :f     |m  :—  |r  :—  |d  :—  ‖d  |d  ‖
|s, :—  |s, :d    |t, :l,.t, |d  :—  |t, :—  |s, :—  ‖l, |s, ‖
|r  :—  |d  :m.fe |s  :l     |s  :—  |s  :f  |m  :—  ‖f  |m  ‖
|t, :—  |d  :l,   |s, :r,    |m, :f, |s, :—  |d, :—  ‖f, |d, ‖
                                                      A - men.
```

BE present at our table, Lord,
Be here and everywhere adored;
These mercies bless, and grant that we
May feast in Paradise with Thee.

JOHN CENNICK, 1718-55.

657

CRADLE SONG. (11 11. 11 11.)

Doh = F. *Unison.* *Moderately slow.* WILLIAM JAMES KIRKPATRICK, 1838–1921.

```
:s, |d  :d  :r.m  |d  :d  :m.f   |s   :s   :l  |f  :—  :r.m
:s, |m, :m, :f,.s,|m, :m, :d.r   |m   :m   :d  |r  :—  :t,.d

|f  :f  :s  |m  :m  :d.m   |r   :l,  :d  |t, :—  ||
|r  :r  :t, |d  :s, :l,.s, |fe, :fe, :l, |s, :—  ||

:s, |d  :d  :r.m  |d  :d  :m.f   |s   :s   :l  |f  :—  :r.m
:f, |m, :m, :f,.s,|m, :m, :s,.l, |ta, :ta, :d  |l, :—  :f,.s,

|f  :f  :s  |m :m  :d.m   |r  :l, :t, |d  :— ||d  :l, :d  |m  :— :— ||
|l, :l, :t, |d :s, :l,.s, |f, :f, :f, |m, :— ||l, :f, :l, |s, :— :— ||
                                             A    -        men.
```

[*Copyright*, 1923, *Renewal.* *Hope Publishing Company, owner.*]

AWAY in a manger, no crib for a bed,
The little Lord Jesus laid down His sweet head.
The stars in the bright sky looked down where He lay,
The little Lord Jesus asleep on the hay.

2 The cattle are lowing, the Baby awakes,
But little Lord Jesus no crying He makes.
I love Thee, Lord Jesus! look down from the sky,
And stay by my side until morning is nigh.

3 Be near me, Lord Jesus; I ask Thee to stay
Close by me for ever, and love me, I pray.
Bless all the dear children in Thy tender care,
And fit us for heaven, to live with Thee there.

ANON.

[*The above tune may be sung as a Duet for S.A.*]

658

CHILDREN OF JERUSALEM. (7 7. 7 7. and refrain.)

Doh = E♭. *Brightly.* *Tune Book for Sunday Schools*, 1842.

```
|d :d.m |m.r :f.r |d  :t, |d  :— |m :m.s |s.m  :d'.l |s :fe  |s  :— ||
|d :d   |l,  :l,  |s, :s, |s, :— |d :s,  |r.d  :d.m  |r :r.d |t, :— ||
|m :m   |f   :r.f |m  :r  |m  :— |s :m   |r.m  :m.d' |t :l   |s  :— ||
|d :d   |f,  :f,  |s, :s, |d  :— |d :d   |t,.d :l,.d |r :r   |s, :— ||

|s :r.m  |f :-.s |l   :l   |s  :— |d' :s |l    :s.f |m :r  |d :— ||
|d :t,.d |r :-.d |d   :d.r |m  :— |d  :d |d.t, :d.r |d :t, |d :— ||
|s :s    |l :-.s |f.s :l.t |d' :— |s  :m |f    :s.l |s :f  |m :— ||
|m :s    |r :-.m |f   :f,  |d  :— |m  :d |f.r  :m.f |s :s, |d :— ||
```

REFRAIN.

|d :r |m : .t_1 |d .d :r .r |m :— |m :f
|d :t_1 |d : .s_1 |s_1 .d :d .t_1 |d :— |d :d
Hark, Hark, Hark! while in - fant voi - ces sing, Hark, Hark,
|m :s |s : .s |s .m :f .f |s :— |s :f
|l_1 :s_1 |d : .f |m .m :r .r |d :— |d :l_1

|s : .r |m .m :fe .fe |s :— || d' :— .s |l :s |d' :— .s
|r : .t_1 |d .d :r .r |r :— || d :— .d |d :d |s .m :f .s
Hark! while in-fant voi-ces sing Loud ho - san - nas, Loud ho-
|r : .s |s .s :d' .d' |t :— || s .m :f .s |f :m |d' :— .d'
|t_1 : .s_1 |d .d :l_1 .r |s_1 :— || m .d :r .m |f :d |m .d :r .m

|l :s |d' :s |l :s .f |m :r |d :— || d |d
|f :m |m :r .d |d .t_1 :d .r |d :t_1 |d :— || l_1 |s_1
-san - nas, Loud ho - san - nas to our King. A- men.
|d' :d' |d' :t .d' |f :s .l |s :f |m :— || f |m
|f :d |l .s :f .m |r :m .f |s :s_1 |d :— || f_1 |d

CHILDREN of Jerusalem
Sang the praise of Jesus' name:
Children, too, of modern days
Join to sing the Saviour's praise.
Hark! while infant voices sing
Loud hosannas to our King.

2 We are taught to love the Lord,
We are taught to read His word,
We are taught the way to heaven:
Praise for all to God be given.

3 Parents, teachers, old and young,
All unite to swell the song,
Higher and yet higher rise,
Till hosannas reach the skies.

JOHN HENLEY, 1800–42.

659

ATHLONE. (Irr.)

Doh = C. *In moderate time.* ROBERT NEWTON QUAILE, 1867–

```
:s  |s   :—  |f   :f  |m   :—  |s   :s  |d'  :d' |r'  :d' |d'  :—  |t  ||
:m  |m   :—  |r   :r  |d   :—  |r   :s  |s   :m  |f   :f  |s   :—  |s  ||
:d' |d'  :s  |l   :t  |d'  :—  |s   :t  |d'  :d' |l   :r' |m'  :—  |r' ||
:d  |d   :—  |d   :d  |d   :—  |t,  :f  |m   :l  |f   :r  |s   :—  |s  ||

:t  |d'  :t  |l   :s  |s   :f  |m   :s  |s   :l  |t   :l  |s   :—  |—  ||
:s  |s   :s  |f   :d  |d   :r  |d   :d  |d   :d  |r   :d  |t,  :—  |—  ||
:r' |d'  :d' |d'  :s  |l   :t  |s   :s  |s   :s  |fe  :fe |s   :—  |—  ||
:f  |m   :m  |f   :m  |r   :s, |d   :m  |ma  :ma |r   :r  |s,  :—  |—  ||

:s  |r'  :d' |t   :l  |s   :-.f |m  :m  |d'  :t  |l   :m  |s   :-.f |m  :—  ||
:s  |f   :f  |f   :f  |m   :r   |d  :r  |d   :r  |m   :d  |m   :r   |t, :—  ||
:t  |t   :d' |r'  :t  |d'  :s   |s  :se |l   :se |l   :l  |l   :l   |se :—  ||
:s  |s   :s  |s   :s, |l,  :t,  |d  :t, |l,  :t, |d   :l, |r   :r   |m  :—  ||

|r   :-.r  |m   :f  |s   :—  |d   :r  |m   :—  |m   :r  |d   :—  |—  || d  |d  ||
|t,  :-.t, |t,  :t, |d   :—  |d   :d  |d   :—  |l,  :t, |d   :—  |—  || l, |s, ||
|s   :-.s  |s   :s  |s   :—  |m   :fe |s   :m  |f   :f  |m   :—  |—  || f  |m  ||
|f   :-.f  |f   :f  |m   :—  |l,  :l, |s,  :—  |s,  :s, |d   :—  |—  || f, |d  ||
                                                                         A-men.
```

WHEN mothers of Salem
Their children brought to Jesus,
The stern disciples drove them
back and bade them depart;
But Jesus saw them ere they fled,
And sweetly smiled, and kindly said,
'Suffer little children
To come unto Me.

2 'For I will receive them
And fold them to My bosom;
I'll be a Shepherd to these lambs,
O drive them not away;
For, if their hearts to Me they give,
They shall with Me in glory live:
Suffer little children
To come unto Me.'

3 How kind was our Saviour
To bid these children welcome!
But there are many thousands
who have never learned His Name;
The Bible they have never read;
They know not that the Saviour said,
'Suffer little children
To come unto Me.'

4 O soon may the heathen,
Of every tribe and nation,
Fulfil Thy blessèd word, and cast
their idols all away;
O shine upon them from above,
And show Thyself a God of love;
Teach the little children
To come unto Thee.

WILLIAM MEDLEN HUTCHINGS, 1827–76.

660 JESUS LOVES ME. (77. 77. and refrain.)

Doh = E♭. *In moderate time.* WILLIAM BATCHELDER BRADBURY, 1816–68.

```
s  .m  :m  .r  | m  .s  :s  | l  .l  :d'  .l  | l  .s  :s  ||
m  .d  :d  .t, | d  .m  :m  | d  .d  :d   .d  | d  .d  :d  ||
s  .s  :s  .s  | s  .s  :s  | f  .f  :l   .f  | f  .m  :m  ||
d  .d  :s, .s, | d  .d  :d  | f  .f  :f,  .l, | d  .d  :d  ||

s  .m  :m  .r  | m  .s  :s  | l  .l  :s   .d  | m  .r  :d  ||
m  .d  :d  .t, | d  .m  :m  | d  .d  :d   .d  | d  .t, :d  ||
s  .s  :s  .s  | s  .s  :s  | f  .f  :m   .s  | s  .f  :m  ||
d  .d  :s, .s, | d  .d  :d  | f, .l, :d   .m  | s  .s, :d  ||
```

REFRAIN.

```
s     :m   .s   | l     .d'  :—   | s     :m   .d   | m     .r   :—  ||
m     :d   .m   | f     .l   :—   | d     :d   .d   | d     .t,  :—  ||
Yes!   Je - sus   loves  me!        Yes!   Je - sus   loves  me!
s     :s   .d'  | d'    .d'  :—   | d'    :s   .s   | s     .s   :—  ||
d     :d   .d   | f     .f   :—   | m     :d   .m   | s     .s   :—  ||

s     :m   .s   | l     .d'  :-  .l   | s    .d    :m    .r   | d    :—  || d   | d    ||
d     :d   .m   | f     .l   :-  .f   | m    .d    :d    .t,  | d    :—  || l,  | s,   ||
Yes!   Je - sus   loves  me!      The   Bi - ble    tells  me   so.       A-    men.
s     :s   .d'  | d'    .d'  :-  .d'  | d'   .s    :s    .f   | m    :—  || f   | m    ||
m     :d   .d   | f     .f   :-  .f   | d    .m    :s    .s,  | d    :—  || f,  | d    ||
```

JESUS loves me! this I know,
For the Bible tells me so;
Little ones to Him belong;
They are weak, but He is strong.
Yes! Jesus loves me!
The Bible tells me so.

2 Jesus loves me! He who died
Heaven's gate to open wide;
He will wash away my sin,
Let His little child come in.

3 Jesus loves me! He will stay
Close beside me all the way;
Then His little child will take
Up to heaven, for His dear sake.

ANNA BARTLETT WARNER, 1820–1915.

661

ROUSSEAU. (87. 87. D.)

Doh = E. *In moderate time.* JEAN JACQUES ROUSSEAU, 1712–78.

m :m.r	d :d	r :r	m :d	s :s.f	m :m	r .d:r .m	d :—
d :d.t_1	d :s_1	t_1 :t_1	d :s_1	r :d.t_1	d :d	d :t_1	d :—
s :m.f	s :m	s :s	s :m	r :m.f	s :s	s :f	m :—
d :d.r	m :d	s :s_1	d :d	t_1 :d.r	m :d	s :s_1	d :—

m :m.r	d :d	r :r	m :d	s :s.f	m :m	r .d:r .m	d :—
d :t_1	d :d	d :t_1	d :s_1	d :r	d :s_1	l_1 :t_1	d :—
s :s .f	m :s	l :s	s :m	m :s	s :d	m :f	m :—
d :s_1	l_1 :m_1	f_1 :s_1	d :d	m :t_1	d :m_1	l_1 :s_1	d :—

m :m .f	s :s	l :l	s :m	m :m .f	s :s	l :d^1.l	s :—
d :d	r :d	d :d	d :d	d :l_1	t_1 :d	d :d	d :—
s :s .f	r :m	f :f	m :s	l :d	r :m	f :l .f	m :—
d :l_1	t_1 :d	f_1 :l_1	d :d	l_1 :l_1	s_1 :d	f :f_1	d :—

m :m.r	d :d	r :r	m :d	s :s .f	m :m	r .d:r .m	d :—	d	d
d :t_1	d :d	d :t_1	d :s_1	d :r	d :s_1	l_1 :t_1	d :—	l_1	s_1
s :s .f	m :s	l :s	s :m	m :s	s :d	m :f	m :—	f	m
d :s_1	l_1 :m_1	f_1 :s_1	d :d	m :t_1	d :m_1	l_1 :s_1	d :—	f_1	d

A-men.

LORD, a little band and lowly,
We are come to sing to Thee;
Thou art great and high and holy;
O how solemn we should be!
Fill our hearts with thoughts of Jesus,
And of heaven, where He is gone;
And let nothing ever please us
He would grieve to look upon.

2 For we know the Lord of glory
Always sees what children do,
And is writing now the story
Of our thoughts and actions too.
Let our sins be all forgiven;
Make us fear whate'er is wrong;
Lead us on our way to heaven,
There to sing a nobler song.

MARTHA EVANS SHELLY, 1812– ? .

662 GENTLE JESUS. (77. 77.)

Doh = F. *In moderate time.* MARTIN SHAW, 1876–

m .f :s :m | f .m :r :— | m .f :s :d | m .r :d :— ||
d .d :d :d | t, .d :t, :— | d .d :d :d | d .t, :d :— ||
s .s :s :s | s .s :s :— | s .s :s :fe | s .r :m :— ||
d .r :m :d | r .d :s, :— | d .r :m :l, | s, .s, :d :— ||

d .t, :l, :d | f .m :r :— | m .f :s :d | m .r :d :— || d | d ||
s, .s, :f, :f, | l, .l, :t, :— | d .d :d :d | d .t, :d :— || l, | s, ||
m .m :d :l, | r .d :t, :r | s .f :m :l | s .r :m :— || f | m ||
m, .m, :f, :-.m, | r, .r, :s, :— | ta, .l, :s, :f, | s, .s, :d :— || f, | d (d,) ||

A - men.

[Copyright, 1915, by J. Curwen & Sons, Ltd.]

SIMPLICITY. (77. 77.)

Doh = E♭. *In moderate time.* JOHN STAINER, 1840–1901.

s :-.l | s :m | f :s | m :— | m :-.r | d :d | s .f :m | r :— ||
d :-.d | d :d | d :t, | d :— | t, :-.t, | d :d | r :d | t, :— ||
m :-.f | s :d' | l :s | s :— | s :-.f | m :m | r :s | s :— ||
d :-.f | m :d | r :s, | d :— | s, :-.s, | l, :l, | t, :d | s .f ||

s :-.l | s :m | f :s | m :— | m :m .r | d :s .f | m :r | d :— || f | m ||
d :-.d | d :d | d :t, | d :— | s, :se, | l, :m .r | d :t, | d :— || d | d ||
s :-.f | s :d' | l :s | s :— | m :m | m :l | s :s .f | m :— || l | s ||
m :-.f | m :d | r :s, | d :— | d :t, | l, (:f / :f,) | s (s,) :s, | d :— || f, | d ||

A-men.

[By permission of Novello & Co., Ltd.]

GENTLE Jesus, meek and mild,
Look upon a little child,
Pity my simplicity,
Suffer me to come to Thee.

2 Lamb of God, I look to Thee ;
Thou shalt my example be ;
Thou art gentle, meek, and mild ;
Thou wast once a little child.

3 Fain I would be as Thou art ;
Give me Thy obedient heart ;
Thou art pitiful and kind ;
Let me have Thy loving mind.

4 Loving Jesus, gentle Lamb,
In Thy gracious hands I am ;
Make me, Saviour, what Thou art ;
Live Thyself within my heart.

5 I shall then show forth Thy praise,
Serve Thee all my happy days ;
Then the world shall always see
Christ, the Holy Child, in me.

CHARLES WESLEY, 1707–88.

663 GLENFINLAS. (65. 65.)

Doh = G. *Unison.* *In moderate time.* KENNETH GEORGE FINLAY, 1882-

```
| s, :d | r :m | r :-.d | l, :— | s, :d | r :m | s :— | — :— ‖
| s :l | s :m | r :d | m :d | l, :— | s, :l, | d :— | — :— ‖ d  | d  ‖
                                                          l, | s, 
                                                          f  | m  
                                                          f, | d, 
```

A-men.

DO no sinful action;
Speak no angry word;
Ye belong to Jesus,
Children of the Lord.

2 Christ is kind and gentle,
Christ is pure and true,
And His little children
Must be holy too.

3 There 's a wicked spirit
Watching round you still,
And he tries to tempt you
To all harm and ill.

4 But ye must not hear him,
Though 'tis hard for you
To resist the evil,
And the good to do.

5 Christ is your own Master;
He is good and true,
And His little children
Must be holy too.

CECIL FRANCES ALEXANDER, 1823–95.

664 ST. CYRIL. (65. 75.)

Doh = B♭. *In moderate time.* PHILIPP BLISS, 1838–76.

```
| s, :d  | t, :l, | s, :— | m, :— | f, :l, | s, :f, | m, :— | — :— ‖
| m, :m, | s, :f, | m, :— | d, :— | d, :f, | m, :r, | d, :— | — :— ‖
| d :d   | d :d   | d :—  | s, :— | l, :d  | t, :t, | d :—  | — :— ‖
| d, :d, | m, :f, | d, :— | d, :— | f, :f, | s, :s, | d, :— | — :— ‖

| s, :s, | d :d   | r :r   | m :—  | l, :r  | d :t,  | d :—  | — :— ‖ d  | d  ‖
| m, :m, | s, :s, | s, :s, | s, :— | f, :f, | m, :r, | m, :— | — :— ‖ f, | m, ‖
| d :d   | d :d   | t, :t, | d :—  | d :l,  | s, :s, | s, :— | — :— ‖ l, | s, ‖
| d, :d, | m, :m, | s, :s, | d :—  | f, :f, | s, :s, | d, :— | — :— ‖ f, | d, ‖
```

A-men.

GOD is always near me,
Hearing what I say,
Knowing all my thoughts and deeds,
All my work and play.

2 God is always near me;
In the darkest night
He can see me just the same
As by mid-day light.

3 God is always near me,
Though so young and small;
Not a look or word or thought,
But God knows it all.

PHILIPP BLISS, 1838–76.

665 FERRIER. (77.77.)

Doh = D. *In moderate time.* JOHN BACCHUS DYKES, 1823–76.

m :m	m :d	s :l	s :—	s :l.t	d' :t	l :t.l	s :—	
m :d	d :d	m :d.r	m :—	t, :d.r	m :r	d :r.d	t, :—	
d' :s	m :s	d' :l.t	d' :—	s :fe	s :s	fe :fe	s :—	
d :d	d :m	d :f	d :—	m :r	d :s,	r :r	s, :—	

m :m	m :d	s :l.t	d' :—	d' :l	s :m	r :m.r	d :—		f	m	
d :d	d :d	m :r	m :—	l :f	m :d	d :t,	d :—		d	d	
s :s	s :s	s :r'	d' :—	d' :d'	d' :s	s :f	m :—		l	s	
d :s,	d :m	d :t,	l, :—	f, :l,	d :m	s :s,	d :—		f,	d	

A - men.

JESUS, holy, undefiled,
Listen to a little child.
Thou hast sent the glorious light,
Chasing far the silent night.

2 Thou hast sent the sun to shine
O'er this glorious world of Thine,
Warmth to give, and pleasant glow,
On each tender flower below.

3 Now the little birds arise,
Chirping gaily in the skies;
Thee their tiny voices praise
In the early songs they raise.

4 Thou by whom the birds are fed,
Give to me my daily bread;
And Thy Holy Spirit give,
Without whom I cannot live.

5 Make me, Lord, obedient, mild,
As becomes a little child;
All day long, in every way,
Teach me what to do and say.

6 Make me, Lord, in work and play,
Thine more truly every day;
And, when Thou at last shalt come,
Take me to Thy heavenly home.

EMILY MARY SHAPCOTE, 1828– ? .

666

GOTT EIN VATER. (6 5. 6 5.) FRIEDRICH SILCHER, 1789–1860.

Doh = E♭. *Unison. Brightly.* Arranged by WILHELM TSCHIRSCH, 1818–92.

s :-.l | s :f | m :— | r :— | d :r.m | f :m | r :— | — :—

m :s | l :s | d' :— | t :l | s :f.m | f :s | m :— | — :— || f d l f, | m d s d ||

A-men.

JESUS, high in glory,
Lend a listening ear ;
When we bow before Thee,
Children's praises hear.

2 Though Thou art so holy,
Heaven's almighty King,
Thou wilt stoop to listen
When Thy praise we sing.

3 We are little children,
Weak and apt to stray ;
Saviour, guide and keep us
In the heavenly way.

4 Save us, Lord, from sinning ;
Watch us day by day ;
Help us now to love Thee ;
Take our sins away.

5 Then, when Thou shalt call us
To our heavenly home,
We will gladly answer,
'Saviour, Lord, we come.'

HARRIET BURN MCKEEVER, 1807–86.

667

CUTTLE MILLS. (8 5. 8 3.)

Doh = D. *In moderate time.* WILLIAM GRIFFITH, 1867– .

m :m | r :m | f :l | s :f | m :d' | l :f | r :— | — :—
d :d | d :d | d :t, | d :r | d :d | d :d | d :— | t, :—
s :s | l :s | l :f | m :s | s :s | f :l | s :— | — :—
d :m | f :m | r :s, | l, :t, | d :m | f :r | s :— | — :f

s :d' | t :d' | s :f | m :l | m :— | r :— | d :— | — :— || d | d
d :d | f :m | r :r | d :d | d :— | t, :— | d :— | — :— || l, | s,
s :s | s :s | s :s | s :r | m :— | f :— | m :— | — :— || f | m
m :m | r :d | t, :t, | d :f, | s, :— | s, :— | d :— | — :— || f, | d

A-men.

JESUS, Friend of little children,
Be a friend to me ;
Take my hand and ever keep me
Close to Thee.

2 Teach me how to grow in goodness
Daily as I grow ;
Thou hast been a child, and surely
Thou dost know.

3 Never leave me nor forsake me,
Ever be my Friend ;
For I need Thee from life's dawning
To its end.

WALTER JOHN MATHAMS, 1853–

668 BATTISHILL. (77. 77.)

Doh = G. *In moderate time.* JONATHAN BATTISHILL, 1738–1801.

s :m |r :d |r :r |m :— |f :m |l :s |f :m |r :— ||
d :d |t_1 :d |d :t_1 |d :— |d :d |d :d |t_1 :d |t_1 :— ||
m :s |s :m |l :s |s :— |d :d |f :s |s :s |s :— ||
d :d |s_1 :l_1 |f_1 :s_1 |d :— |l_1 :s_1 |f_1 :m_1 |r_1 :d_1 |s_1 :— ||

s :m |r :d |r :m |f :— |l :s |t_1 :d |m :r |d :— ||d |d ||
d :d |t_1 :l_1 |l_1 :l_1 |l_1 :— |t_1 :d |s_1.f_1 :m_1 |s_1 :-.f_1 |m_1 :— ||f_1 |m_1 ||
s :s |s.f :m |r :de |r :— |r :m |r :d |d :t_1 |d :— ||l_1 |d ||
m_1 :d_1 |s_1 :l_1 |f_1 :l_1 |r_1 :— |f_1 :m_1 |s_1 :l_1 |s_1 :s_1 |d_1 :— ||f_1 |d_1 ||

A-men.

LOVING Shepherd of Thy sheep,
Keep me, Lord, in safety keep ;
Nothing can Thy power withstand ;
None can pluck me from Thy hand.

2 Loving Shepherd, Thou didst give
Thine own life that I might live ;
May I love Thee day by day,
Gladly Thy sweet will obey.

3 Loving Shepherd, ever near,
Teach me still Thy voice to hear ;
Suffer not my feet to stray
From the straight and narrow way.

4 Where Thou leadest may I go,
Walking in Thy steps below ;
Then, before Thy Father's throne,
Jesus, claim me for Thine own.

JANE ELIZA LEESON, 1807–82.

669

WOODBROOK. (65. 65. and refrain.)

Doh = E. *In moderate time.* JOHN ADCOCK, 1838–1919.

m .m :s .d	r :d	l .l :d^1 .l	s :—		f .l :s .f	m .s :f .m
d .d :r .d	d .t_1 :l_1	d .d :d .d	d :—		d .d :r .r	d .s_1 :r .d
s .s :r .m	f :m	f .f :l .f	m :—		f .d :s .s	s .d^1 :l .s
d .d :t_1 .d	s_1 :l_1 .s_1	f_1 .f_1 :f .f	d :—		l_1 .l_1 :t_1 .t_1	d .m_1 :f_1 .s_1

r :r	r :—		m .m :s .d	r :d	l .l :d^1 .l	s :—	
d :d	t_1 :—		d .d :t_1 .d	d .t_1 :d	d .d :d .r	m :—	
s :fe	s :—		s .s :s .s	f :m	f .f :l .t	d^1 :—	
l_1 :r_1	s_1 :—		d .d :m_1 .m	r .s_1 :l_1 .s_1	f_1 .f_1 :f .f	d :—	

f .l :s .f	m .s :f .m	r :r	d :—		d	d	
d .d :r .r	d .s_1 :r .d	d :t_1	d :—		l_1	s_1	
f .d :s .s	s .d^1 :l .s	s :s .f	m :—		f	m	
l_1 .l_1 :t_1 .t_1	d .m_1 :f_1 .d	s_1 :s_1	d :—		f_1	d	

A-men.

IF I come to Jesus,
He will make me glad;
He will give me pleasure
When my heart is sad.
If I come to Jesus,
Happy shall I be;
He is gently calling
Little ones like me.

2 If I come to Jesus,
He will hear my prayer;
He will love me dearly;
He my sins did bear.

3 If I come to Jesus,
He will take my hand,
He will kindly lead me
To a better land.

4 There with happy children,
Robed in snowy white,
I shall see my Saviour
In that world so bright.

FRANCES JANE VAN ALSTYNE, 1820–1915.

670

CHILD SERVICE. (76. 887.)

Doh = G. *In moderate time.* HENRY ELLIOT BUTTON, 1861–1925.

:m	m :— :m	s :f :m	m :— :—	r :— :m	f :— :f
:d	d :— :d	m :r :d	d :— :—	t_1 :— :d	r :— :r
:s	s :— :s	s :— :s	s :— :—	s :— :s	l :— :l
:d	d :— :d	d :— :m	s :— :—	f :— :m	r :— :d

l :s :f | m :— :— | — :— || m | r :— :m | d :— :r
f :m :r | d :— :— | — :— || d | t, :— :t, | l, :— :l,
r :— :s | s :— :— | — :— || s | s :f :m | m :— :r
t, :— :t, | d :— :— | — :— || d | s, :— :se, | l, :s, :fe,

t, :— :d | l, :— :l, | s, :l, :t, | d :r :m | r :m :f
s, :— :s, | f, :— :m, | r, :— :s, | s, :t, :d | t, :d :r
r :— :d | d :r :d | t, :d :r | m :f :s | s :— :s
s, :f, :m, | f, :— :f, | s, :— :s, | s, :— :s, | s, :— :s,

m :— :s | m :r :d | d :— :t, | d :— :— | — :— || d | d
d :— :r | d :t, :l, | l, :— :s,.f, | m, :— :— | — :— || f, | m,
s :— :s | s :f :m | r :— :r | d :— :— | — :— || l, | d
d :— :t, | d :s, :l, | f, :— :s, | d, :— :— | — :— || f, | d,

A-men.

[*By permission of Novello & Co., Ltd.*]

O WHAT can little hands do
To please the King of heaven?
The little hands some work may try,
To help the poor in misery:
Such grace to mine be given.

2 O what can little lips do
To please the King of heaven?
The little lips can praise and pray,
And gentle words of kindness say:
Such grace to mine be given.

3 O what can little eyes do
To please the King of heaven?
The little eyes can upward look,
Can learn to read God's holy book:
Such grace to mine be given.

4 O what can little hearts do
To please the King of heaven?
Young hearts, if God His Spirit send,
Can love their Maker, Saviour, Friend:
Such grace to mine be given.

ANON.

671 LUMETTO. (55. 65. 64. 64.)

Doh = F. *Unison.* *In moderate time.* EDWARD ARTHUR, 1874-

| m .d :r .m | l_1 :d .m | s :m | s :— || s_1.s_1 :l_1.d | m .m :r .d |

| l_1 :d | d :— || m .m :s .m | r :m .m | d :m | l :— ||

| l_1.l_1 :d .l_1 | s_1 .d :— .d | m :r | d :— || d | d ||

A - men.

[*Copyright*, 1927, *by Edward Arthur.*]

JESUS bids us shine
With a pure, clear light,
Like a little candle
Burning in the night.
In this world is darkness;
So let us shine,
You in your small corner,
And I in mine.

2 Jesus bids us shine,
First of all for Him;
Well He sees and knows it,
If our light grows dim:
He looks down from heaven
To see us shine,
You in your small corner,
And I in mine.

3 Jesus bids us shine,
Then, for all around;
Many kinds of darkness
In the world are found—
Sin, and want, and sorrow;
So we must shine,
You in your small corner,
And I in mine.

SUSAN WARNER, 1819–85.

672 ST. BARTHOLOMEW. (L.M.)

Doh = B♭. *In moderate time.* F.t. HENRY DUNCALF, 18th century.

:s_1 | d :— :s_1 | r :— :^{s}d | l :s :f | s :— :d | f :— :m

:s_1 | s_1 :— :m_1 | s_1 :— :^{s}d | d :— :t_1 | d :— :d | d :t_1 :d

:s_1 | m :— :d | r :— :^{r}s | f :d' :f | m :— :s | l :f :s

:s_1 | d_1 :— :d | t_1 :— :^{t}m | f :m :r | d :— :m_1 | r_1 :— :m_1

f.B♭.

| r :— :d | r :d :t_1 | d :— || $^m t_1$ | d :—.t_1 :l_1 | m :— :m_1 | f_1 :—.m_1 :f_1

| l_1 :t_1 :d | l_1 :s_1 :s_1 | s_1 :— || $^l m_1$ | m_1 :— :m_1 | m_1 :— :d_1 | d_1 :— :t_2

| f :— :s | f :m :r | m :— || $^{de}se_1$ | l_1 :—.t_1 :d | t_1 :— :l_1 | l_1 :— :s_1

| f_1 :— :m_1 | f_1 :s_1 :s_1 | d :— || $^l m_1$ | l_1 :— :l_1 | se_1 :— :l_1 | r_1 :— :s_1

| m_1 :— :s_1 | d :s_1 :l_1 | s_1 :f_1 :m_1 | r :d :t_1 | d :— || d | d ||

| d_1 :— :r_1 | s_1 :— :d_1 | d_1 :t_2 :d_1 | l_1.s_1,f_1 :m_1 :r_1 | d_1 :— || l_1 | s_1 ||

| s_1 :— :t_1 | d :— :d | d :r :s_1 | l_1 :s_1 :s .f | m :— || f | m ||

| d_1 :— :s_1.f_1 | m_1 :— :f_1 | m_1 :r_1 :d_1 | f_1 :s_1 :s_1 | d_1 :— || f_1 | d_1 ||

A-men.

Facing the World.

GO forth to life, O child of earth,
Still mindful of thy heavenly birth:
Thou art not here for ease or sin,
But manhood's noble crown to win.

2 Though passion fires are in thy soul,
Through Christ thou canst their flames control:
Though tempters strong beset thy way,
Through Christ thou art more strong than they.

3 Go on from innocence of youth
To manly pureness, manly truth:
God's angels still are near to save,
And God Himself doth help the brave.

4 Then forth to life, O child of earth;
Be worthy of thy heavenly birth:
For noble service thou art here;
Thy neighbour help, thy God revere.

SAMUEL LONGFELLOW, 1819–92.

673 ORISONS. (66. 66. D.)

A Boy's Prayer.

Doh = G. *Unison.* *In moderate time.* DAVID EVANS, 1874–

| s_1 :— | d :m | m :-.r | s :— | s_1 :— | d :m | m :-.r |

1. God, who cre - a - ted me Nim - ble and light of
2. Je - sus, King and Lord, Whose are my foes to
3. Spi - rit of love and truth, Breath - ing, in gross - er

| s :— | -.s :f | — :m | l_1.l_1 :t_1 | d :r | m :r.d | r :r.r |

limb, In three el - e - ments free, To run, to ride, to
fight, Gird me with Thy sword, Swift and sharp and
clay, The light and flame of youth, De - light of men in the

| s_1 :— | : | f.C. ds :s | f :m | l :l.l | se :m | d' :d'.d' |

swim; Not when the sense is dim, But now from the
bright. Thee would I serve if I might, And con - quer
fray, Wis - dom in strength's de - cay; From pain, strife,

| t :m.m | l :— | G.t. $^ml_1$:— | — :t_1.d | r :t_1 | m :— |

heart of joy, I would re - mem - ber Him:
if I can: From day - dawn till night,
wrong to be free, This best gift I pray—

| d :— | — :l_1 | r :d.t_1 | vv. 1 & 2. d :— | : || v. 3. d :— | — :— || d | d ||

Take the thanks of a boy.
Take the strength of a man.
Take my spi - rit to Thee. A-men.

[*Copyright*, 1927, *by David Evans.*]

HENRY CHARLES BEECHING, 1859–1919.

674 EXCELSIOR. (76. 76. Trochaic.)

Doh = G. *In moderate time.* JOSIAH BOOTH, 1852–

m :f	s :t,	d :r	m :—	m :t,	d :f	m :—	r :—	
d :d	s, :s,	s, :t,	d :—	se, :se,	l, :l,	s, :d	t, :—	
s :f	m :r	s :f	m :—	m :m	d :d	d :m	s :—	
d :l,	s, :f,	m, :r,	d, :—	m, :m,	l, :f,	s, :—	s, :—	

m :fe	s :s	l :s	f :—	m :t,	d :f	r :—	d :—		d	d	
s, :t,	t, :t,	l, :l,	l, :—	se, :m,	m, :l,	s, :f,	m, :—		f,	m,	
m :re	m :m	m :de	r :d	t, :m	d :d	d :t,	d :—		l,	s,	
d :t,	m :r	de :l,	r, :—	m, :se,	l, :f,	s, :—	d, :—		f,	d,	

A-men.

LOOKING upward every day,
Sunshine on our faces;
Pressing onward every day
Toward the heavenly places;

2 Growing every day in awe,
For Thy Name is holy;
Learning every day to love
With a love more lowly;

3 Walking every day more close
To our Elder Brother;
Growing every day more true
Unto one another;

4 Leaving every day behind
Something which might hinder;
Running swifter every day;
Growing purer, kinder,—

5 Lord, so pray we every day:
Hear us in Thy pity,
That we enter in at last
To the holy city.

MARY BUTLER, 1841–1916.

675 ST. FULBERT. (C.M.)

Doh = E♭. *Moderately slow.* HENRY JOHN GAUNTLETT, 1805–76.

:s |s :d |r :l |s :f |m :s |m :s |l :d' |t :— |— ||
:r |d :d |d :t, |d :r |d :r |d :d |l, :l, |r :— |— ||
:s |m :s |l :r' |s :s |s :s |s :s |s :fe |s :— |— ||
:t, |d :m |f :f |m :t, |d :t, |d :m |r :r |s, :— |— ||

:d' |s :l |s :d |f :f |m :m |r :m |f :r |d :— |— || f |m ||
:m |d :d |d :d |d :t, |d :d |d :d |d :t, |d :— |— || d |d ||
:s |s :f |s :s |l :s |s :l |l :s |l :f |m :— |— || l |s ||
:d |m :f |m :m |r :s, |d :l, |f, :m, |r, :s, |d :— |— || f, |d ||

A-men.

A School Hymn.

O JESUS, strong and pure and true,
Before Thy feet we bow;
The grace of earlier years renew,
And lead us onward now.

2 The joyous life that year by year
Within these walls is stored,
The golden hope, the gladsome cheer,
We bring to Thee, O Lord.

3 Our faith endow with keener powers,
With warmer glow our love;
And draw these halting hearts of ours
From earth to things above.

4 In paths our bravest ones have trod,
O make us strong to go,
That we may give our lives to God,
In serving man below.

5 Scorn we the selfish aim or choice,
And love's high precept keep,
'Rejoice with those that do rejoice,
And weep with those that weep.'

6 So hence shall flow fresh strength and grace,
As from a full-fed spring,
To make the world a better place,
And life a worthier thing.

WILLIAM WALSHAM HOW, 1823–97.

676

BEDE. (11 10. 11 10. Dactylic.)

Doh = A♭. *Moderately slow and dignified.* Adapted by JOHN GOSS, 1800–80.

d :t, :d | s :f :m | r :d.t, :d.r | d :— :t,
s, :s, :s, | s, :t, :d | l, :s, :fe, | s, :— :s,
m :f :m | r :r :m | f :m :r | r :— :r
d :r :d | t, :s, :d | f, :s, :l, | s, :— :s,

d :t, :d | r :m :d | t,.l, :l, :-.s, | s, :— :—
s, :s, :s, | s, :s, :s, | s, :s, :fe, | s, :— :—
m :f :m | r :t, :d | m :l,.t, :d | t, :— :—
m :r :d | t, :s, :m, | d, :r, :r, | s, :— :—

s :l, :t,.d | t, :-.l, :s, | s :l, :t,.d | t, :-.l, :s,
s, :l, :f, | r, :r, :s, | s, :l, :f, | r, :— :s,
d :d :r | r :s,.l, :t, | d :d :r | r :-.d :t,
m, :f, :r, | s, :s, :f, | m, :f, :r, | s, :— :s,

d :t, :d | r :m :f | m.r :r :-.d | d :— :— || d | d ||
s, :s, :s, | s, :s, :f, | l, :r,.m, :f, | m :— :— || f, | m, ||
m :f :m | r :t, :d | d :d :t, | d :— :— || l, | s, ||
m :r :d | t, :s, :l, | f, :s, :s, | d, :— :— || f, | d, ||

A-men.

Commemoration.

PRAISE to our God, who with love never swerving
Guides our endeavours, enfolds us from harm,
Peace and prosperity, past our deserving,
Showering upon us with bountiful arm.

2 Gone are the labours, the joy, and the sorrow;
Lo, at the end we draw near to adore,
Ere our full life is begun on the morrow,
Childhood behind us and manhood before.

3 Shepherd of souls, O Door of salvation,
Keep Thou Thy flock in Thine infinite care,
Fold them as one in their last adoration,
Ere in the distance divided they fare.

4 Though nevermore in one place all may gather,
Though in life's battle we struggle apart,
One be our Saviour, and One be our Father,
Bind us together in faith and in heart.

HERBERT BRANSTON GRAY, 1851–

677 LEWES. (87. 87. 87.)

Doh = F. *In moderate time.* JOHN RANDALL, 1715–99.

m :-.f |r :s |d :r |t, :d |f :m |l :s |f :m.f |m :r

d :-.d |r :t, |d :l, |s, :s, |d :d |d :d |d.r :d |d :t,

s :-.l |s :f |m :f |r :m |l :s |f :s |l :s |s :—

d :-.d |t, :s, |l, :f, |s, :d |l, :d |f :m |l,.t, :d |s, :—

m :-.f |r :s |d :r |t, :d |f :m |r.fe:s.l |s :fe |s :—

d :-.d |r :t, |d :l, |s, :s, |d :d |s,.d :r.d |t, :l, |t, :—

s :-.l |s :f |m :f |r :m |f :s |r :r.m |r :r |r :—

d :-.d |t, :s, |l, :f, |s, :d |l, :d |t,.l, :t,.d |r :r, |s, :—

://:

m :-.f |r.d :r |f :-.s |m.r :m |s :-.l |s :f.m |m :r |d :— || d |d

d :-.d |t,.l, :t, |l, :-.r |d.t, :d |d :-.d |r :d |d :t, |d :— || l, |s,

d :-.l |s :s |l :-.s |s :s |s :-.m |s :s |s :f |m :— || f |m

d :-.f, |s, :s, |r :-.t, |d :d |m :-.l, |t, :d |s, :s, |d, :— || f, |d,

A-men.

Beginning of Term.

LORD, behold us with Thy blessing,
Once again assembled here ;
Onward be our footsteps pressing,
In Thy love, and faith, and fear ;
Still protect us
By Thy presence ever near.

2 For Thy mercy we adore Thee,
For this rest upon our way ;
Lord, again we bow before Thee,
Speed our labours day by day ;
Mind and spirit
With Thy choicest gifts array.

3 Keep the spell of home affection
Still alive in every heart ;
May its power, with mild direction,
Draw our love from self apart,
Till Thy children
Feel that Thou their Father art.

4 Break temptation's fatal power,
Shielding all with guardian care,
Safe in every careless hour,
Safe from sloth and sensual snare ;
Thou, our Saviour,
Still our failing strength repair.

HENRY JAMES BUCKOLL, 1803–71.

678

DISMISSAL. (87. 87. 87.)

Doh = A. *In moderate time.* WILLIAM LETTON VINER, 1790–1867.

```
|d  :t,.l, |s, :m, |l, :d.l, |s, :m, |m  :r.d  |l, :r  |d  :t, |d  :— ||
|m, :s,.f, |m, :m, |f, :l,.f, |m, :d, |s, :s,   |f, :l, |s, :s, |s, :— ||
|s, :s,    |d  :d  |d  :l,    |d  :s, |d  :t,.d |d  :f  |m  :r  |m  :— ||
|d, :d,    |d, :d, |f, :f,    |d, :d, |d, :r,.m,|f, :r, |s, :s, |d, :— ||

|m  :m.f |s  :m  |f  :r  |m  :d  |m  :m.f |s  :m  |f     :m     |r  :— ||
|s, :d   |d  :d  |l, :s, |s, :m, |s, :d   |d  :d  |l,.t, :d     |t, :— ||
|d  :d.r |m  :d  |r  :t, |d  :s, |d  :d.r |m  :d  |f     :s     |s  :— ||
|d  :l,  |m, :l, |f, :s, |d  :d, |d  :l,  |m, :l, |r,    :m,.f, |s, :— ||

//:
|d  :t,.l, |s, :m, |l, :d.l, |s, :m, |m  :r.d   |l, :r  |d  :t, |d  :— ||d  |d  ||
|m, :s,.f, |m, :m, |f, :l,.f, |m, :d, |s, :s,    |f, :l, |s, :f, |m, :— ||f, |m, ||
|s, :s,    |d  :d  |d  :l,    |d  :s, |d  :t,.d  |d  :f  |m  :r  |d  :— ||l, |s, ||
|d, :d,    |d, :d, |f, :f,    |d, :d, |d, :r,.m, |f, :r, |s, :s, |d, :— ||f, |d, ||
                                                                         A-men.
```

End of Term.

LORD, dismiss us with Thy bless-
ing,
Thanks for mercies past receive;
Pardon all, their faults confessing;
Time that 's lost may all retrieve;
May Thy children
Ne'er again Thy Spirit grieve.

2 Bless Thou all our days of leisure;
Help us selfish lures to flee;
Sanctify our every pleasure;
Pure and blameless may it be;
May our gladness
Draw us evermore to Thee.

3 By Thy kindly influence cherish
All the good we here have gained;
May all taint of evil perish,
By Thy mightier power re-
strained;
Seek we ever
Knowledge pure and love un-
feigned.

4 Let Thy Father-hand be shielding
All who here shall meet no more;
May their seed-time past be yielding
Year by year a richer store;
Those returning
Make more faithful than before.

HENRY JAMES BUCKOLL, 1803–71.

Also the following:

146 O Son of Man, our Hero strong and tender
621–47 *National Hymns*
Hymns for the Young (see Index)

679

CAMBERWELL. (S.M.)

Doh = A♭. *In moderate time.* *European Psalmist*, 1872.

```
:d   |m  :r.d |r  :d.t, |d  :— |— :r  |m :s  |f     :m   |r  :— |— ||
:s,  |d  :s,  |l, :s,   |s, :— |— :t, |d :s, |l,.t, :d   |t, :— |— ||
:m   |s  :f.m |f  :m.r  |m  :— |— :s  |s :d  |d.r   :m.f |s  :— |— ||
:d,  |d  :d   |f, :s,   |d  :— |— :s, |d :m, |f,    :d,  |s, :— |— ||

:s,    |d  :d.t, |l, :l,     |r  :r.d |t, :s, |l, :f     |m  :r  |d  :— |— ||d  |d  ||
:s,    |s, :s,   |f, :f,     |l, :l,  |s, :s, |s, :f,.l, |d  :t, |d  :— |— ||l, |s, ||
:t,    |d  :m.r  |d  :d      |f  :f.m |r  :d  |d  :l     |s  :f  |m  :— |— ||f  |m  ||
:s,.f, |m, :d,   |f, :f,.m,  |r, :r,  |s, :m, |f, :r,    |s, :s, |d, :— |— ||f, |d, ||
                                                                              A-men.
```

DOANE. (S.M.)

Doh = G. *Moderately fast.* William Howard Doane, 1832–1916.

```
:d.r |m :r.d |l, :s, |m, :— |— :d |r   :r     |r  :m    |r  :— |— ||
:s,  |d :s,  |f, :f, |m, :— |— :d |d   :t,.l, |s, :s,.d |t, :— |— ||
:m.f |s :f.m |d  :t, |d  :— |— :s |l.s :f.m   |r  :d.m  |s  :— |— ||
:d   |d :d,  |f, :s, |l, :— |— :m |f.m :r.d   |t, :d    |s, :— |— ||

:d.r   |m :r.d |l, :l,.t, |d  :t,.l, |s, :d  |r  :-.d  |m  :r   |d      :— |— ||d  |d  ||
:d.t,  |d :s,  |l, :f,    |m, :s,.f, |m, :s, |l, :-.d  |d  :t,  |d      :— |— ||l, |s, ||
:s     |s :-.m |d  :r     |d  :d     |d  :m  |f  :-.m  |s  :s.f |m      :— |— ||f  |m  ||
:m,.s, |d :m,  |f, :r,    |l, :f,    |d, :d  |f, :-.l, |s, :s,  |d {d,} :— |— ||f, |d, ||
                                                                                 A-men
```

REVIVE Thy work, O Lord :
Thy mighty arm make bare ;
Speak with the voice which wakes the dead,
And make Thy people hear.

2 Revive Thy work, O Lord :
Create soul-thirst for Thee ;
And hungering for the Bread of Life
O may our spirits be.

3 Revive Thy work, O Lord :
Exalt Thy precious Name ;
And, by the Holy Ghost, our love
For Thee and Thine inflame.

4 Revive Thy work, O Lord :
Give power unto Thy word ;
Grant that Thy blessèd Gospel may
In living faith be heard.

5 Revive Thy work, O Lord :
And give refreshing showers :
The glory shall be all Thine own,
The blessing, Lord, be ours.

Albert Midlane, 1825–1909.

680

LIMPSFIELD. (73. 73. 77. 73.)

Doh = D. *In moderate time.* JOSIAH BOOTH, 1852–

```
|s  :—  :s  |s  :—  :l  |r  :m  :f  |m  :—  :—  |d  :—  :—
|d  :—  :t, |d  :—  :d  |d  :—  :t, |d  :—  :—  |d  :—  :—
|m  :—  :f  |s  :—  :d' |s  :—  :s  |s  :—  :—  |l  :—  :—
|d  :—  :r  |m  :—  :f  |s  :—  :s, |d  :—  :—  |f  :—  :—

|f  :—  :—  |r  :—  :—  |—  :—  :—  ||s  :—  :s  |s  :—  :l
|r  :—  :—  |t, :—  :—  |—  :—  :—  ||d  :—  :t, |d  :—  :d
|l  :—  :—  |s  :—  :—  |—  :—  :—  ||m  :—  :f  |s  :—  :d'
|r  :—  :—  |s  :—  :—  |—  :—  :—  ||d  :—  :r  |m  :—  :f

|r  :m  :f  |m  :—  :—  |l  :—  :—  |fe :—  :—  |s  :—  :—  |—  :—  :—  ||
|d  :—  :t, |d  :—  :—  |m  :—  :—  |r  :—  :—  |r  :—  :—  |—  :—  :—  ||
|s  :—  :s  |s  :—  :—  |d' :—  :—  |l  :—  :—  |t  :—  :—  |—  :—  :—  ||
|s  :—  :s, |d  :—  :—  |l, :—  :—  |r  :—  :—  |s, :—  :—  |—  :—  :—  ||

                                     *m :—  :s
|t  :—  :t  |d' :—  :s  |f  :—  :s  |m  :—  :—  |t  :—  :t
                                     d  :—  :d
|r  :—  :r  |d  :—  :d  |r  :d  :t, |d  :—  :—  |r  :—  :r
                                     s  :—  :s
|s  :—  :s  |s  :—  :s  |l  :—  :s  |s  :—  :—  |s  :—  :s
                                     d  :—  :m
|f  :—  :f  |m  :—  :m  |r  :—  :s, |d  :—  :—  |f  :—  :f

|d' :—  :m  |s  :f  :m  |r  :—  :—  ||d  :—  :l  |s  :—  :s
|d  :—  :d  |r  :—  :d  |t, :—  :—  ||d  :—  :d  |d  :—  :t,
|s  :—  :s  |s  :—  :s  |s  :—  :—  ||m  :—  :f  |m  :—  :f
|m  :—  :d  |t, :—  :d  |s, :—  :—  ||l, :—  :f, |d  :—  :r

|s  :—  :d' |l  :—  :—  |r' :—  :—  |t  :—  :—  |d' :—  :—  |—  :—  :—  ||d' |d' ||
|d  :r  :m  |d  :—  :—  |f  :—  :—  |f  :—  :—  |m  :—  :—  |—  :—  :—  ||f  |m  ||
|s  :—  :s  |l  :—  :—  |l  :—  :—  |s  :—  :—  |s  :—  :—  |—  :—  :—  ||l  |s  ||
|m  :r  :d  |f  :—  :—  |r  :—  :—  |s  :—  :—  |d  :—  :—  |—  :—  :—  ||f  |d  ||
                                                                         A-men.
```

* Small notes for last verse.

WE have heard a joyful sound,—
'Jesus saves!'
Spread the gladness all around:
'Jesus saves!'
Bear the news to every land,
Climb the steeps and cross the waves;
Onward!—'tis our Lord's command.
Jesus saves!

2 Waft it on the rolling tide:
'Jesus saves!'
Tell to sinners far and wide,
'Jesus saves!'
Sing, ye islands of the sea;
Echo back, ye ocean caves;
Earth shall keep her jubilee:
Jesus saves!

3 Sing above the battle's strife
'Jesus saves!
By His death and endless life
Jesus saves!'
Sing it softly through the gloom,
When the heart for mercy craves;
Sing in triumph o'er the tomb,
'Jesus saves!'

4 Give the winds a mighty voice
'Jesus saves!'
Let the nations now rejoice:
Jesus saves!
Shout salvation full and free
To every strand that ocean laves,—
This our song of victory,
'Jesus saves!'

PRISCILLA JANE OWENS, 1829- ?.

681

COMFORT. (11 10. 11 10. and refrain, Dactylic.)

Doh = D. *In moderate time.* CHARLES A. GARRATT, 19th cent.

```
m  :r  :d  | s  :-.f  :m  | r  :d  :r  | r  :—  :m
d  :t  :d  | r  :-.r  :d  | l, :s, :t, | t, :—  :d
s  :f  :m  | s  :-.s  :s  | f  :m  :f  | f  :—  :m
d  :d  :d  | t, :-.t, :d  | f, :s, :s, | s, :—  :d
                                              D.C.

m  :f  :s  | l  :-.t  :d' | t  :l  :fe | s  :—  :—
d  :t, :d  | d  :-.r  :d  | r  :m  :d  | t, :—  :—
s  :s  :d' | l  :-.s  :s  | s  :d' :l  | s  :—  :—
d  :r  :m  | f  :-.f  :m  | r  :d  :r  | s, :—  :—
```

REFRAIN.

```
s  :l  :s  | d' :-.t  :l  | s  :f  :m  | m  :-.r :d
t, :t, :t, | d  :-.d  :d  | d  :r  :d  | t, :—   :d
s  :s  :s  | s  :-.s  :f  | s  :s  :s  | se :—   :l
s  :f  :f  | m  :-.m  :f  | m  :t, :d  | m, :—   :l,

d  :r   :d   | s  :-.f  :m  | r  :d  :r  | d  :—  :—  || d  | d
l, :ta, :ta, | l, :-.d  :l, | l, :s, :t, | d  :—  :—  || l, | s,
m  :m   :m   | f  :-.l  :s  | f  :m  :f  | m  :—  :—  || f  | m
l, :s,  :s,  | f, :-.f, :f, | f, :s, :s, | d  :—  :—  || f, | d
                                                        A-men.
```

RESCUE the perishing, care for the dying;
Snatch them in pity from sin and the grave;
Weep o'er the erring one, lift up the fallen;
Tell them of Jesus, the mighty to save.
Rescue the perishing, care for the dying;
Jesus is merciful, Jesus will save.

2 Though they are slighting Him, still He is waiting,
Waiting the penitent child to receive;
Plead with them earnestly, plead with them gently;
He will forgive, if they only believe.

3 Down in the human heart, crushed by the tempter,
Feelings lie buried that grace can restore;
Touched by a loving hand, wakened by kindness,
Chords that were broken will vibrate once more.

4 Rescue the perishing—duty demands it;
Strength for thy labour the Lord will provide;
Back to the narrow way patiently win them;
Tell the poor wanderer a Saviour has died.

FRANCES JANE VAN ALSTYNE, 1820–1915.

682 REMEMBRANCE. (76. 76.)

Doh = A♭. *In moderate time.* JOSIAH BOOTH, 1852–

```
s, :l,.t, |d  :r  |d  :t, |— :d  |l, :f  |m  :r  |m  :— |—
m, :m,.m, |m, :m, |f, :f, |— :s, |l, :f, |s, :s, |s, :— |—
s, :l,.t, |d  :r  |d  :t, |— :s, |d  :d  |d  :t, |d  :— |—
d, :d,.d, |d, :d, |r, :r, |— :m, |f, :l, |s, :s, |d, :— |—

:m  |s  :m  |m  :-.r  |r  :d  |—:r   |m  :s, |l, :t, |d  :— |—:— ||f, |d
:s, |s, :s, |t, :-.t, |t, :l, |—:fe, |s, :s, |s, :f, |m, :— |—:— ||f, |m,
:m  |r  :d  |s  :-.f  |f  :m  |—:d   |d  :m  |m  :r  |d  :— |—:— ||l, |s,
:d  |t, :d  |s, :-.s, |se,:l, |—:l,  |s, :s, |s, :s, |d, :— |—:— ||f, |d,
                                                                    A-men.
```

TELL me the old, old story
Of unseen things above,
Of Jesus and His glory,
Of Jesus and His love.

2 Tell me the story simply,
As to a little child;
For I am weak and weary,
And helpless, and defiled.

3 Tell me the story slowly,
That I may take it in,—
That wonderful redemption,
God's remedy for sin.

4 Tell me the story often,
For I forget so soon;
The early dew of morning
Has passed away at noon.

5 Tell me the story softly,
With earnest tones and grave;
Remember, I'm the sinner
Whom Jesus came to save.

6 Tell me the story always,
If you would really be,
In any time of trouble,
A comforter to me.

7 Tell me the same old story
When you have cause to fear
That this world's empty glory
Is costing me too dear.

8 Yes, and, when that world's glory
Shall dawn upon my soul,
Tell me the old, old story,
'Christ Jesus makes thee whole.'

KATE HANKEY, 1834–1911.

683

HYFRYDOL. (8 7. 8 7. and refrain.)

Doh = G. *Moderately slow.* ROWLAND HUGH PRICHARD, 1811–87.

d :— :r | d :r :m | f :— :m | r :d :r | s :— :f | m :— :m
s, :— :t, | d :t, :d | d :r :d | t, :l, :t, | d :s, :l,.t, | d :— :d
m :— :s | s :f :m | l :— :s | s :— :s | d :m :f | s :— :s
d :— :s, | m :r :d | l, :t, :d | s, :— :f, | m, :m :r | d :— :m,

D.C. REFRAIN.

r :d :r | d :— :— || s :— :s | s :f :m | f :— :f | f :m :r
l, :— :t, | d :— :— || t, :— :d | d :— :d | d :t, :l, | t, :d :s,
f :m :s | m :— :— || s :— :m | d :r :m | r :— :r | r :s :f
f, :l, :s, | d :— :— || m :— :d | l, :— :l, | r :— :r | s, :l, :t,

m :— :m | m :f :s | s :f :m | r :— :— || s :m :s | f :r :f
s, :— :d | t, :l, :d | d :r :d | t, :— :— || d :— :d | d :r :t,
m :r :d | d :— .r:m | m :r :m.fe | s :— :— || s :— :s | l :s :r
d :t, :l, | s, :f, :m, | l, :t, :d | s, :— :— || m :d :m | r :t, :s,

m :d :m | r.m:f.m:r | s :— :s | l :s :f | m :— :r | d :— :— || d | d
d :s, :d | t,.d:r.d:t, | d :t, :d | l,.t,:d :r | d :— :t, | d :— :— || l, | s,
m :— :s | s :— :s | d :r :m | f :s :l | s :— :f | m :— :— || f | m
d :m :d | s, :— :f, | m, :s, :d | f :m :r | s :— :s, | d :— :— || f, | d

A-men.

I WILL sing the wondrous story
Of the Christ who died for me,—
How He left the realms of glory
For the Cross on Calvary.
Yes, I'll sing the wondrous story
Of the Christ who died for me,—
Sing it with His saints in glory,
Gathered by the crystal sea.

2 I was lost: but Jesus found me,
Found the sheep that went astray,
Raised me up and gently led me
Back into the narrow way.

3 Faint was I, and fears possessed me,
Bruised was I from many a fall;
Hope was gone, and shame distressed me:
But His love has pardoned all.

4 Days of darkness still may meet me,
Sorrow's paths I oft may tread;
But His presence still is with me,
By His guiding hand I'm led.

5 He will keep me till the river
Rolls its waters at my feet:
Then He'll bear me safely over,
Made by grace for glory meet.

FRANCIS HAROLD ROWLEY, 1854–

684 PENLAN. (76. 76. D.)

Doh = E♭. *In moderate time.* DAVID JENKINS, 1849–1915.

```
:m |s  :— :f  |m  :— :r   |d  :t, :d     |r  :— :m  |s   :— :f   |m  :— ||
:d |d  :— :t, |d  :— :l,  |s, :s, :d     |t, :— :d  |t,  :— :t,  |d  :— ||
:s |s  :— :s  |s  :— :f   |m  :r  :s     |s  :— :s  |s   :— :s   |s  :— ||
:d |m  :— :r  |d  :— :f,  |s, :s, :m     |f  :— :m  |r   :— :s,  |d  :— ||

                          B♭.t.
:m |s  :— :f  |m  :— :r   |d  :t, :(t)m, |l, :— :d  |t,  :— :m,  |l,  :— ||
:d |d  :— :d  |d  :— :t,  |l, :s, :(s)d, |d, :— :m, |r,  :— :r,  |d,  :— ||
:s |s  :— :l  |s  :— :f   |m  :m  :(m)l, |l, :— :l, |se, :— :se, |l,  :— ||
:d |m, :— :f, |s, :— :se, |l, :t, :(t)m, |m, :— :m, |m,  :— :m,  |l,2 :— ||

f.E♭.
:(l)m  |s :—:s |l  :—:m |s  :s  :m  |s :—:s |l  :—:m |s  :—:— |—:— ||
:(m)t, |d :—:d |d  :—:d |t, :t, :t, |d :—:d |d  :—:d |t, :—:— |—:— ||
:(d)s  |m :—:m |m  :—:l |s  :s  :s  |m :—:m |m  :—:l |s  :—:— |—:— ||
:(l)m  |d :—:d |l, :—:d |m  :m  :m  |d :—:d |l, :—:d |m  :—:— |—:— ||

:s |d' :—:t  |l :—:s  |f  :m :m |r :m  :f |r  :—:d  |d  :— ||d  |d  ||
:m |m  :—:r  |d :r :m |t, :d :d |r :de :r |t, :—:s, |s, :— ||l, |s, ||
:s |l  :—:se |l :t :d'|s  :s :s |l :s  :f |f  :—:m  |m  :— ||f  |m  ||
:m |l  :—:m  |f :—:m  |r  :d :d |f :m  :r |s, :—:d  |d  :— ||f, |d  ||
                                                              A-men.
```

TO-DAY Thy mercy calls us
To wash away our sin,
However great our trespass,
Whatever we have been;
However long from mercy
We may have turned away,
Thy blood, O Christ, can cleanse us,
And make us white to-day.

2 To-day Thy gate is open,
And all who enter in
Shall find a Father's welcome,
And pardon for their sin;
The past shall be forgotten,
A present joy be given,
A future grace be promised,
A glorious crown in heaven.

3 O all-embracing Mercy,
Thou ever-open Door,
What should we do without Thee
When heart and eyes run o'er?
When all things seem against us,
To drive us to despair,
We know one gate is open,
One ear will hear our prayer.

OSWALD ALLEN, 1816–78.

685

THE NINETY AND NINE. (97. 97. 99. Irr.)

Doh = F. *Unison.* *Moderately fast.*

IRA DAVID SANKEY, 1840–1908.

:s$_1$ .s$_1$ |d :-.d:d |d :— :d |t$_1$:— :t$_1$ |d :— :d .d

1. There were nine - ty and nine that safe - ly lay In the

|m :— :m |d :— :d |r :— :— | : ||s$_1$.s$_1$|d :— :d

shel - ter of the fold; But one was

|d :— :d .d |m :— :m |d :— :d.d |r :— :r .r |t$_1$:— :t$_1$

out on the hills a - way, Far off from the gates of

|d :— :— | : ||d .d |m :-.m:m |d :— :d |m :— :m

gold; A - way on the moun - tains wild and

|d :— :s* |s :-.s:s |s :m :d |r :d :r |m :— :s

bare, A - way from the ten - der Shep - herd's care, A -

|s :-.s:l |s :m :d |r :m :r |d :— ||d |d ||

-way from the ten - der Shep - - herd's care. A - men.

|s :— :s |s :m :d |r :d :r |m :— :— ||

* v. 3, l. 6. Sick and help - less and rea - dy to die.

BRYANT. (97. 97. 99. Irr.)

Doh = G. *In moderate time.*

WALTER GALPIN ALCOCK, 1861–

:s$_1$.s$_1$|s$_1$:d .d |r :m |m .m :r |r :r .r |t$_1$:d .d |m :r
:s$_1$ |s$_1$:s$_1$ |s$_1$:d |d :d |t$_1$:s$_1$ |s$_1$:s$_1$ |l$_1$:t$_1$
:s$_1$ |m :m |f :s |s :fe |s :t$_1$ |r :d |d :f
:s$_1$ |d :d |d :d |l$_1$:r |s$_1$:s$_1$ |f$_1$:m$_1$ |f$_1$:s$_1$

D.t.

|d :— |— ||^{m}l .l |s. s :l .l |t :d^1.d^1 |r^1 :s |s :d^1.d^1
|d :— |— ||^{d}f |r :m |f :f |f :f |m :d
|m :— |— ||^{s}d^1 |t :d^1 |r^1 :l |s :r^1 |d^1 :m
|d$_1$:— |— ||^{d}f |f :m |r :d |t$_1$:t$_1$ |d :l$_1$

```
                    f.G.                                    f.C.
d'  :m .m |s  :f .f |(m)t, :— |— ||s,.s, |l,  :t,.t, |d .d :(d)s
d   :d    |d  :t,   |(d)s, :— |— ||s,    |s,  :s,    |s,   :(s)r
m   :s    |l  :s    |(s)r  :— |— ||s     |s   :s     |s    :(m)t
s,  :s,   |s, :s,   |(d)s, :— |— ||s     |s   :f     |m    :(d)s
```

v. 3.
heard its cry, Sick and help-less and read-y to die.

```
                    G.t.
l   :t    |d'  :r' .r' |(m')l :l .l |s .s :d  |m .m :r  |d  ||d  |d  ||
f   :s    |s   :s      |(m)l, :t,   |d    :d  |d    :t, |d  ||l, |s, ||
d'  :r'   |d'  :t      |(t)m  :r    |s    :fe |s    :f  |m  ||f  |m  ||
f   :f    |m   :r      |(d)f, :f,   |m,   :l, |s,   :s, |d, ||f, |d, ||
                                                            A-men.
```

THERE were ninety and nine that safely lay
  In the shelter of the fold;
But one was out on the hills away,
  Far off from the gates of gold;
Away on the mountains wild and bare,
Away from the tender Shepherd's care.

2 'Lord, Thou hast here Thy ninety and nine;
  Are they not enough for Thee?'
But the Shepherd made answer, 'This of Mine
  Has wandered away from Me;
And although the road be rough and steep,
I go to the desert to find My sheep.'

3 But none of the ransomed ever knew
  How deep were the waters crossed,
Nor how dark was the night that the Lord passed through,
  Ere He found His sheep that was lost.
Out in the desert He heard its cry,
Sick and helpless and ready to die.

4 'Lord, whence are those blood-drops all the way,
  That mark out the mountain's track?'
'They were shed for one who had gone astray,
  Ere the Shepherd could bring him back.'
'Lord, whence are Thy hands so rent and torn?'
'They are pierced to-night by many a thorn.'

5 And all through the mountains, thunder-riven,
  And up from the rocky steep,
There rose a cry to the gate of heaven,
  'Rejoice, I have found My sheep.'
And the angels echoed around the throne,
'Rejoice, for the Lord brings back His own.'

ELIZABETH CECILIA CLEPHANE, 1830-69.

686 NAIN. (64. 64.)

Doh = F. *In moderate time.* LOWELL MASON, 1792–1872.

```
:s |s :m |m :d   |r  :— |— :s  |l :— |fe :— |s  :— |— ||
:d |d :d |d :d   |t, :— |— :t, |d :— |d  :— |t, :— |— ||
:m |m :s |s :s   |s  :— |— :s  |m :— |l  :— |s  :— |— ||
:d |d :m |s :m.d |s, :— |— :m  |d :— |r  :— |s, :— |— ||

:s |s :m   |f  :s  |l  :— |— :r  |m  :— |r  :— |d :— |— || d  |d  ||
:d |d :d   |d  :d  |d  :— |— :d  |d  :— |t, :— |d :— |— || l, |s, ||
:m |m :s   |f  :m  |f  :— |— :l  |s  :— |f  :— |m :— |— || f  |m  ||
:d |d :ta, |l, :s, |f, :— |— :f, |s, :— |s, :— |d :— |— || f, |d  ||
                                                              A-men.
```

TO-DAY the Saviour calls :
Ye wanderers, come ;
O, ye benighted souls,
Why longer roam ?

2 To-day the Saviour calls :
O hear Him now ;
Within these sacred walls
To Jesus bow.

3 The Spirit calls to-day :
Yield to His power ;
O grieve Him not away ;
'Tis mercy's hour.

SAMUEL FRANCIS SMITH, 1808–95.

687 RHEIDOL. (87. 87. 337.)

Lah = F♯. Doh = A. *Moderately slow.*

JOHN ROBERTS (IEUAN GWYLLT), 1822–77.

```
|l,  :se, |l,  :t, |d  :r  |t,  :l, |m  :f  |m  :d  |r   :d  |t,  :— ||
|m,  :m,  |m,  :s, |s, :l, |se, :l, |l, :l, |l, :l, |t,  :l, |se, :— ||
|d   :t,  |d   :r  |m  :f  |m   :d  |m  :r  |m  :m  |f   :m  |m   :— ||
|l,  :m,  |l,  :s, |m, :r, |m,  :l, |d  :r  |d  :l, |se, :l, |m,  :— ||
```

l, :se,	l, :t,	d :r	t, :l,	d :t,	l, :t,	d :r	m :—
m, :m,	m, :s,	s, :l,	se, :l,	m, :se,	l, :se,	l, :l,	se, :—
l, :t,	d :r	d :f	m :d	d :r	m :m	m :l,	t, :—
d, :m,	l, :s,	m, :r,	m, :l,	l, :t,	d :t,	l, :f,	m, :—

		://:		://:					
m :f	r :—	r :m	d :—	t, :m	m :l,.t,	d :t,	l, :—	l,	l,
l, :l,	s, :—	s, :s,	l, :—	l, :se,	l, :l,	l, :se,	l, :—	f,	m,
d :r	t, :—	t, :d	l, :—	f :t,	m :d.r	m :r	d :—	r	de
l, :r,	s, :—	s, :d,	f, :—	r, :r,	d, :f,	m, :m,	l, :—	r,	l,

A-men.

LORD, I hear of showers of blessing
  Thou art scattering, full and free,—
Showers, the thirsty land refreshing;
  Let some drops descend on me,
      Even me.

2 Pass me not, O gracious Father,
  Sinful though my heart may be!
Thou might'st leave me, but the rather
  Let Thy mercy light on me,
      Even me.

3 Pass me not, O tender Saviour!
  Let me love and cling to Thee;
I am longing for Thy favour;
  When Thou comest, call for me,
      Even me.

4 Pass me not, O mighty Spirit!
  Thou canst make the blind to see;
Witnesser of Jesus' merit,
  Speak the word of power to me,
      Even me.

5 Have I long in sin been sleeping,
  Long been slighting, grieving Thee?
Has the world my heart been keeping?
  O forgive and rescue me,
      Even me.

6 Love of God, so pure and changeless,
  Blood of Christ, so rich and free,
Grace of God, so strong and boundless,—
  Magnify them all in me,
      Even me.

Elizabeth Codner, 1824–1919.

688

ALMA REDEMPTORIS. (11 10. 11 10. Dactylic.)

Doh=C. *Not too slow.* SAMUEL WEBBE, 1740–1816

```
s  :—  |m  :d   |l  :-.s |s  :—  |f  :-.m |f.s:l.t |d' :—  |s  :—
d  :—  |d  :d   |d  :-.d |d  :—  |d  :—   |d  :f   |m  :—  |d  :—
m  :—  |s  :m   |f  :-.s |s  :—  |l  :-.s |l  :f   |s  :—  |m  :—
d  :—  |d  :d   |f  :-.m |m  :—  |l, :-.d |f  :r   |d  :—  |d  :—

m  :—  |m  :m    |f  :l  |d' :l  |s  :—  |fe :fe  |s  :—  |—  :—
d  :—  |d  :d    |d  :d  |s  :m  |r  :—  |r  :r   |r  :—  |—  :—
s  :—  |s  :s    |f  :f  |s  :d' |t  :—  |l  :l   |t  :—  |—  :—
d  :—  |d  :-.t, |l, :f  |m  :d  |r  :—  |r  :r   |s  :—  |—  :—

d' :—  |t  :l   |s  :-.f |m  :s  |d' :—  |t  :l   |s  :-.f |m  :—
m  :—  |s  :f   |m  :-.r |d  :m  |m  :—  |s  :f   |m  :-.r |d  :—
d' :—  |s  :l.t |d' :-.s |s  :—  |s  :—  |s  :l.t |d' :-.s |s  :—
d  :—  |d  :d   |d  :-.d |d  :—  |d  :—  |d  :d   |d  :—   |d  :—

s  :m' |m' :d' |d' :l  |l  :f  |m  :—  |r  :-.d |d  :—  |—  :—  ||f  |m
m  :s  |s  :s  |d  :f  |f  :r  |d  :—  |t, :-.d |d  :—  |—  :—  ||d  |d
d' :—  |d' :s  |l  :d' |d' :l  |s  :—  |f  :-.m |m  :—  |—  :—  ||l  |s
d' :—  |d  :m  |f  :—  |f  :f  |s  :—  |s, :-.d |d  :—  |—  :—  ||f, |d
                                                                   A-men.
```

COME, ye disconsolate, where'er ye languish,
Come to the mercy-seat, fervently kneel;
Here bring your wounded hearts, here tell your anguish;
Earth has no sorrows that heaven cannot heal.

2 Joy of the desolate, Light of the straying,
Hope of the penitent, fadeless and pure!
Here speaks the Comforter, tenderly saying,
Earth has no sorrows that heaven cannot cure.

3 Here see the Bread of Life; see waters flowing
Forth from the throne of God, pure from above:
Come to the feast of love; come, ever knowing
Earth has no sorrows but heaven can remove.

THOMAS MOORE, 1779–1852, and THOMAS HASTINGS, 1784–1872.

689 WELCOME VOICE. (S.M. and refrain.)

Doh = E♭. *In moderate time.* LEWIS HARTSOUGH, 1828–72.

```
:d .m | s   :-.m :r .d  | d     :—  :d    | r   :-.f :l .s   | m  :—
:d    | m   :-.d :t, .d | d     :—  :d    | d   :-.d :t, .t, | d  :—
:m .s | d'  :-.s :f .m  | m     :—  :s    | l   :-.f :r .s   | s  :—
:d    | d   :-.d :s, .d | d     :—  :m    | f   :-.r :s, .s, | d  :—

:s    | d'  :-.t :l .s  | l .s  :m  :d    | r   :-.d :m .r   | d  :— :—
:m    | d   :-.d :d .d  | d .d  :s, :d .t,| l,  :-.d :d .t,  | d  :— :—
:s    | s   :-.s :f .m  | f .s  :d' :s    | f   :-.m :s .f   | m  :— :—
:d    | m   :-.m :f .d  | f .m  :d  :m,   | f,  :-.l, :s, .s,| d  :— :—
```

REFRAIN.

```
d'  :-.t :l .s  | l   :—  :—  | s   :-.m :r .d   | r   :— :—
m   :-.d :d .m  | f   :—  :—  | m   :-.d :s, .d  | t,  :— :—
s   :-.s :l .d' | d'  :—  :—  | d'  :-.s :s .fe  | s   :— :—
d   :-.m :f .d  | f   :—  :—  | d   :-.d :t, .l, | s,  :— :—

s   :l   :m .r    | d .r   :m  :d     | r   :-.d :m .r    | d  :— || d  | d
d   :d   :d .t,   | l, .l, :t, :d .t, | l,  :-.d :d .t,   | d  :— || l, | s,
s   :d   :s .f    | m .l   :se :m     | f   :-.m :s .f    | m  :— || f  | m
m,  :f,  :s, .s,  | l, .f, :m, :l,    | f,  :-.l, :s, .s, | d  :— || f, | d
                                                                    A-men.
```

I HEAR Thy welcome voice
That calls me, Lord, to Thee,
For cleansing in Thy precious blood
That flowed on Calvary.
I am coming, Lord,
Coming now to Thee ;
Wash me, cleanse me in the blood
That flowed on Calvary.

2 'Tis Jesus calls me on
To perfect faith and love,
To perfect hope and peace and trust,
For earth and heaven above.

3 'Tis Jesus who confirms
The blessèd work within,
By adding grace to welcomed grace,
Where reigned the power of sin.

4 All hail, atoning blood !
All hail, redeeming grace !
All hail, the gift of Christ our Lord,
Our Strength and Righteousness !

LEWIS HARTSOUGH, 1828–72.

690 ST. AGATHA. (77. 75.)

Doh = F. *Moderately slow.* FREDERIC SOUTHGATE, 1824–85.

d :r	m :f	m :r	m :—	f :f	m :s	s :fe	s :—
s_1 :t_1	d :d	d :t_1	d :—	d :r	d :t_1.d	r :r.d	t_1 :—
m :s	s :l	s :s	s :—	l :s	s :s	l :l	s :—
d :s_1	d :f_1	s_1 :s_1	d :—	l_1 :t_1	d :m	r :r	s_1 :—

d :r	m :l	s :f	m :—	r :d	d :t_1	d :—	— :—	d	d
s_1.l_1 :t_1	d :m	r :d.t_1	t_1 :—	l_1 :l_1	s_1 :s_1	s_1 :—	— :—	l_1	s_1
m :f	s :d'	t :l	se :—	l :f	r.m :f	m :—	— :—	f	m
m :r	d :l_1	r :r_1	m_1 :—	f_1 :r_1	s_1 :s_1	d_1 :—	— :—	f_1	d_1

A-men.

THOU who didst on Calvary bleed,
Thou who dost for sinners plead,
Help me in my time of need ;
Jesus, hear my cry.

2 In my darkness and my grief,
With my heart of unbelief,
I, who am of sinners chief,
Lift to Thee mine eye.

3 Foes without and fears within,
With no plea Thy grace to win
But that Thou canst save from sin,
To Thy Cross I fly.

4 Others, long in fetters bound,
There deliverance sought and found,
Heard the voice of mercy sound ;
Surely so may I.

5 There on Thee I cast my care ;
There to Thee I raise my prayer ;
Jesus, save me from despair,—
Save me, or I die.

6 When the storms of trial lower,
When I feel temptation's power,
In the last and darkest hour,
Jesus, be Thou nigh.

JAMES DRUMMOND BURNS, 1823–64.

691 ST. CHRISTOPHER. (76. 86. 86. 86.)

Doh = D♭. *In moderate time.* FREDERICK CHARLES MAKER, 1844–1927.

:s |s :-.s |fe :l |s :— |m :d |r :-.m |f :f |m :— |— ||
:m |m :-.m |re :re |m :— |d :d |t, :-.d |d :t, |d :— |— ||
:s |s :-.s |l :fe |s :— |s :s |s :-.s |l :s |s :— |— ||
:d |d :-.d |d :d |d :— |d :m |f :-.m |r :s, |d :— |— ||

:m |d' :-.d' |d' :t |l :s |f :m |r :-.r |re :re |m :— |— ||
:r |d :-.d |d :r |m :m |r :d |d :-.d |d :l, |t, :— |— ||
:se |l :-.l |l :se |l :l |l :l |l :-.l |l :l |se :— |— ||
:t, |l, :-.l, |l, :t, |d :de |r :m |f :-.f |f :f |m :— |— ||

:m |m :-.r |d :r |m :f |s :s |l :-.l |l :m |f :— |— ||
:d |d :-.t, |d :d |d :d |d :d |d :-.d |de :de |r :— |— ||
:s |s :-.f |m :f |s :l |ta :ta |l :-.l |l :l |l :— |— ||
:d |d :-.d |d :d |d :d |d :m |f :-.f |m :l, |r :— |— ||

:f |t :-.l |s :f |m :m |s :f |m :-.d |m :r |d :— |— || d |d ||
:r |f :-.f |f :t, |d :d |d :d |d :-.d |t, :t, |d :— |— || l, |s, ||
:l |r' :-.d' |t :s |s :s |ta :l |s :-.m |s :f |m :— |— || f |m ||
:r |s, :-.s, |s, :s, |d :d |m, :f, |s, :-.s, |s, :s, |d :— |— || f, |d ||

A-men.

[*By permission of the Psalms and Hymns Trust.*]

BENEATH the Cross of Jesus
I fain would take my stand—
The shadow of a mighty rock
Within a weary land;
A home within a wilderness,
A rest upon the way,
From the burning of the noontide heat
And the burden of the day.

2 O safe and happy shelter,
O refuge tried and sweet,
O trysting-place where heaven's love
And heaven's justice meet!
As to the exiled patriarch
That wondrous dream was given,
So seems my Saviour's Cross to me—
A ladder up to heaven.

3 Upon that Cross of Jesus,
Mine eye at times can see
The very dying form of One
Who suffered there for me;
And from my smitten heart, with tears,
Two wonders I confess—
The wonder of His glorious love,
And my own worthlessness.

4 I take, O Cross, thy shadow
For my abiding-place;
I ask no other sunshine than
The sunshine of His face:
Content to let the world go by,
To know no gain nor loss—
My sinful self my only shame,
My glory all, the Cross.

ELIZABETH CECILIA CLEPHANE, 1830–69.

692 EVAN. (C.M.)

Doh = A♭. *In moderate time.* WILLIAM HENRY HAVERGAL, 1793–1870.

:s, |s, :d |m :r |d :l, |s, :s, |s, :d |m :d |r :— |— ||
:m, |s, :s, |s, :f, |m, :f, |m, :m, |s, :s, |s, :l, |t, :— |— ||
:s, |d :m |d :t, |d :d |d :s, |d :m |d :m |s :— |— ||
:d, |m, :d, |d :s, |l, :f, |d, :d, |m, :d, |d :l, |s, :— |— ||

:f |m :r |d :r |m :d |l, :s, |s, :d |m :r |d :— |— ||d |d ||
:d |d :t, |l, :t, |d :s, |f, :r, |s, :l, |d :t, |d :— |— ||l, |s, ||
:l |s :s |m :s |s :d |d :t, |d :m |s :s.f |m :— |— ||f |m ||
:f, |d :s, |l, :s, |d, :m, |f, :s, |m, :l, |s, :s, |d, :— |— ||f, |d, ||

A-men.

THERE is a fountain filled with blood
Drawn from Immanuel's veins;
And sinners, plunged beneath that flood,
Lose all their guilty stains.

2 The dying thief rejoiced to see
That fountain in his day;
And there have I, as vile as he,
Washed all my sins away.

3 Dear dying Lamb, Thy precious blood
Shall never lose its power
Till all the ransomed Church of God
Be saved, to sin no more.

4 E'er since, by faith, I saw the stream
Thy flowing wounds supply,
Redeeming love has been my theme,
And shall be till I die.

5 Then, in a nobler, sweeter song,
I'll sing Thy power to save,
When this poor lisping, stammering tongue
Lies silent in the grave.

6 Lord, I believe Thou hast prepared,
Unworthy though I be,
For me a blood-bought free reward,
A golden harp for me;

7 'Tis strung and tuned for endless years,
And formed, by power divine,
To sound in God the Father's ears
No other name but Thine.

WILLIAM COWPER, 1731–1800.

693 MAN OF SORROWS. (77. 78.)

Doh = C. *Slow.* PHILIPP BLISS, 1838–76.

s :s	s :m	d' :d'	t :—	l :l	s :d'	t :l	s :—	
m :m	r :d	m :m	m :r	d :r	s :s	fe :fe	s :—	
d' :d'	s :s	l :l	se :—	l :t	d' :m'	r' :-.d'	t :—	
d :d	t, :d	l, :l	m :—	f :f	m :d	r :r	s :—	

s :s	s :m	d' :d'	d' :d'.r'	m' :—	r' :d'.l	l :—	s :—		s	s	
m :r	d :d	m :-.f	s :m.s	s :—	s :m.m	f :—	m :—		r	m	
d' :t	d' :s	d' :t.l	s :d'.t	d' :—	t :d'.d'	d' :—	d' :—		t	d'	
d :f	m :d	l,.l :s.f	m :l.s	d' :—	s :l.l	f :—	d :—		s	d	

A-men.

MAN of Sorrows ! wondrous Name
For the Son of God, who came
Ruined sinners to reclaim !
Hallelujah ! what a Saviour !

2 Bearing shame and scoffing rude,
In my place condemned He stood,
Sealed my pardon with His blood :
Hallelujah ! what a Saviour !

3 Guilty, vile, and helpless we ;
Spotless Lamb of God was He :
Full atonement,—can it be ?
Hallelujah ! what a Saviour !

4 Lifted up was He to die,
' It is finished ' was His cry ;
Now in heaven exalted high :
Hallelujah ! what a Saviour !

5 When He comes, our glorious King,
All His ransomed home to bring,
Then anew this song we'll sing,
' Hallelujah ! what a Saviour ! '

PHILIPP BLISS, 1838–76.

694 MUNICH. (76. 76. D.)

Doh = E♭. *Moderately slow.* *Meiningen Gesangbuch*, 1693.

```
:d.r |m :l |s :f |m :— |m ||m |s :f.m |r :r |d :— |— ||
:d |d :d |t, :r |d :— |d ||d |d :d |d :t, |d :— |— ||
:m.f |s :f.m |r :s |s :— |s ||s |s :l |r.m :f |m :— |— ||
:d |d :f, |s, :t, |d :— |d ||d |m, :f, |s, :s, |d :— |— ||

:d.r |m :l |s :f |m :— |m ||m |s :f.m |r :r |d :— |— |
:d |d :d |t, :r |d :— |d ||d |d :d |d :t, |d :— |— |
:m.f |s :f.m |r :s |s :— |s ||s |s :l |r.m :f |m :— |— |
:d |d :f, |s, :t, |d :— |d ||d |m, :f, |s, :s, |d :— |— |

:r |r :m |f :f |m :— |m ||l |d' :l |m :fe |s :— |— ||
:t, |t, :de |r :r |d :— |d ||m |d :m |m :r.d |t, :— |— ||
:s |s :s |l :l |l :— |l ||m |m :d'.t |l :l |s :— |— ||
:s, |f :m |r :r |l, :— |l, ||d |l, :l,.t, |d :r |s, :— |— ||

:s |s :m |f :s |l :— |l ||s |f :m |r :r |d :— |— ||d |d ||
:r |d :d |d :r.m |f :— |f ||d |d :d |d :t, |d :— |— ||l, |s, ||
:f |m :s |d' :ta |l :— |d' ||d' |f :l |r :f |m :— |— ||f |m ||
:t, |d :ta, |l, :s, |f, :— |f, ||m, |l, :f, |s, :s, |d :— |— ||f, |d ||
                                                          A-men.
```

I LAY my sins on Jesus,
The spotless Lamb of God ;
He bears them all, and frees us
From the accursèd load.
I bring my guilt to Jesus,
To wash my crimson stains
White in His blood most precious,
Till not a spot remains.

2 I lay my wants on Jesus ;
All fulness dwells in Him ;
He heals all my diseases,
He doth my soul redeem.
I lay my griefs on Jesus,
My burdens, and my cares ;
He from them all releases,
He all my sorrows shares.

3 I rest my soul on Jesus,
This weary soul of mine ;
His right hand me embraces,
I on His breast recline.
I love the Name of Jesus,
Immanuel, Christ, the Lord ;
Like fragrance on the breezes,
His Name abroad is poured.

4 I long to be like Jesus,
Meek, loving, lowly, mild ;
I long to be, like Jesus,
The Father's holy child.
I long to be with Jesus,
Amid the heavenly throng,
To sing with saints His praises,
To learn the angels' song.

HORATIUS BONAR, 1808–89.

695 ST. HELEN'S. (85. 83.)

Doh = E. *In moderate time.* ROBERT PRESCOTT STEWART, 1825–94.

m :r	f :m	l :s	s :f	m :r	d :—	r :—	m :—
d :d	d :d	m :m	d :d	l_1 :l_1	s_1 :—	t_1 :—	d :—
s :f	l :s	d' :ta	l :l	f :f	m :—	s :—	s :—
d :d	d :d	d :d	f :f	f_1 :f_1	s_1 :—	s_1 :—	d :—

m :m	r :d'	t :l	s :—	d :—	r :—	— :m	d :—	d	d
d :d	d :m	r :d	t_1 :—	d :—	d :—	t_1 :—	d :—	l_1	s_1
s :s	fe :fe	fe :fe	s :f	m :—	l :—	s :f	m :—	f	m
l_1 :l_1	r :r	r :r	s_1 :—	l_1 :—	f_1 :—	s_1 :—	d :—	f_1	d

A-men.

I AM trusting Thee, Lord Jesus,
Trusting only Thee,
Trusting Thee for full salvation,
Great and free.

2 I am trusting Thee for pardon:
At Thy feet I bow,
For Thy grace and tender mercy
Trusting now.

3 I am trusting Thee to guide me;
Thou alone shalt lead,
Every day and hour supplying
All my need.

4 I am trusting Thee for power:
Thine can never fail;
Words which Thou Thyself shalt give me
Must prevail.

5 I am trusting Thee, Lord Jesus;
Never let me fall;
I am trusting Thee for ever,
And for all.

FRANCES RIDLEY HAVERGAL, 1836–79.

696

URSWICKE. (65. 65. D.)

Doh = A♭. *In moderate time.* GEORGE JOB ELVEY, 1816–93.

d :m	m :r	d :—	s, :—	l, :t,	d :r
s, :s,	s, :f,	m, :—	s, :—	f, :s,	s, :s,
m :d	t, :t,	d :—	d :—	d :r	d :t,
d :d	s, :s,	l, :—	m, :—	f, :f,	m, :s,

E♭.t.

m :—	— :—	^{m}l :s	l :t	d' :—	s :—	f :m
s, :—	— :—	^{s_1}d :d	d :r	d :—	d :—	d :d
d :—	— :—	^{d}f :s	f :f	s :—	m :—	l :l
d :—	— :—	^{d}f :m	f :r	m :—	d :—	f, :f,

f.A♭.

m :r	^{d}s, :—	— :—	s, :l,	t, :d	r :—	d :—
t, :t,	^{d}s, :—	— :—	s, :s,	s, :s,	l, :—	s, :—
s :f	^{m}t, :—	— :—	t, :d	r :d	f :—	m :—
s, :s,	^{d}s, :—	— :—	s, :s,	f, :m,	r, :—	m, :f,

t, :d	r :m	f :—	— :—	m :m	m :t,
s, :s,	s, :s,	s, :—	— :—	s, :l,	t, :m,
r :s	f :m	r :—	— :—	m :m	m :m
s, :l,	t, :d	t, :—	— :—	d :d	se, :se,

d :—	l, :—	s, :d	d :t,	d :—	— :—	d	d
m, :—	f, :—	s, :fe,	s, :s,	s, :—	— :—	l,	s,
d :—	d :—	d :d	m :r	m :—	— :—	f	m
l, :—	f, :—	m, :l,	s, :s,	d, :—	— :—	f,	d,

A-men.

JESUS, I will trust Thee,—
Trust Thee with my soul;
Guilty, lost, and helpless,
Thou canst make me whole.
There is none in heaven
Or on earth like Thee;
Thou hast died for sinners—
Therefore, Lord, for me.

2 Jesus, I will trust Thee;
Name of matchless worth,
Spoken by the angel
At Thy wondrous birth,
Written, and for ever,
On Thy Cross of shame:
Sinners read and worship,
Trusting in that Name.

3 Jesus, I will trust Thee,
Pondering Thy ways
Full of love and mercy
All Thine earthly days.
Sinners gathered round Thee,
Lepers sought Thy face,
None too vile or loathsome
For a Saviour's grace.

4 Jesus, I will trust Thee,
Trust without a doubt;
Whosoever cometh
Thou wilt not cast out.
Faithful is Thy promise;
Precious is Thy blood;
These my soul's salvation,
Thou my Saviour God!

MARY JANE WALKER, ? –1878.

697

TYNEMOUTH (ST. CATHERINE). (L.M. and refrain.)

Doh = G. *In moderate time.* *Hemy's Crown of Jesus Music*, 1864.

```
m  :r  :d       | d  :t,   :d  | r  :l,  :t,  | d  :—  :—  | d  :t,      :l,
s, :s, :s,      | s, :—    :s, | l, :—   :s,  | s, :—  :—  | l, :s,      :f,
s  :f  :m       | m  :r    :d  | f  :—   :r   | m  :—  :—  | d  :d       :f
d, :r, :m,.f,   | s, :—.f, :m, | f, :—   :s,  | d, :—  :—  | f, :f,.s,   :l,.t,

s, :—  :d       | d   :t,  :d   | r  :—  :—  || m  :r  :d      | d  :t,   :d
s, :—  :s,      | fe, :—   :fe, | s, :—  :—  || s, :s, :s,     | s, :—    :s,
m  :—  :m       | r   :—   :r   | t, :—  :—  || s  :f  :m      | m  :r    :d
d  :—  :l,      | r   :—   :r,  | s, :—  :—  || d, :r, :m,.f,  | s, :—.f, :m,

r  :l, :t,      | d  :—  :—  | d  :t,     :l,     | s, :—  :m   | r  :m  :r
l, :—  :s,      | m, :—  :—  | l, :s,     :f,     | s, :—  :d   | d  :—  :t,
f  :—  :r       | d  :—  :—  | d  :d      :f      | m  :—  :s   | f  :—  :f
r, :—  :s,      | l, :—  :—  | f, :f,.s,  :l,.t,  | d  :—  :d,  | r, :—  :s,
```

Refrain.

```
d  :—  :—  || f  :f  :f   | m  :—  :m   | r  :—  :r   | m  :—  :—
d  :—  :—  || d  :d  :d   | d  :—  :d   | d  :—  :t,  | d  :—  :—
m  :—  :—  || f  :l  :f   | s  :—  :s   | s  :—  :s   | s  :—  :—
d, :—  :—  || l, :f, :l,  | d  :—  :d   | s, :—  :s,  | d  :—  :—

m  :r  :d   | l, :—  :d   | r  :—  :r   | d  :—  :—  || d  | d
s, :s, :s,  | l, :—  :l,  | t, :—  :t,  | d  :—  :—  || l, | s,
s  :f  :m   | d  :f  :m   | s  :—  :f   | m  :—  :—  || f  | m
d, :r, :m,  | f, :—  :l,  | s, :—  :s,  | d, :—  :—  || f, | d,
                                                        A-men.
```

MY hope is built on nothing less
Than Jesus' blood and righteousness;
I dare not trust my sweetest frame,
But wholly lean on Jesus' Name.
On Christ, the solid rock, I stand;
All other ground is sinking sand.

2 When darkness seems to veil His face,
I rest on His unchanging grace;
In every high and stormy gale,
My anchor holds within the veil.

3 His oath, His covenant, and blood,
Support me in the whelming flood;
When all around my soul gives way,
He then is all my hope and stay.

EDWARD MOTE, 1797–1874.

698

ACH GOTT UND HERR. (88. 87.) *Neu Leipziger Gesangbuch*, 1682.

Doh = B♭. *Slow and dignified.* Arranged by JOHANN SEBASTIAN BACH, 1685–1750.

```
:d  |t, :l,   |s, :s,    |l,    :t, |d  ||r      |d      :t,     |l, :t,.d |l, :l,   |s, ||
:s, |s, :fe,  |r, :m,.r, |d,    :r, |m, ||s,     |s,.fe, :s,     |fe, :s,  |s, :fe,  |s, ||
:m  |r  :-.d  |t, :d .t, |l,.s, :f, |s, ||t,     |d      :r      |r  :r    |m  :r.d  |t, ||
:d, |s, :r,   |s, :d,    |f,.m, :r, |d, ||s,(s,,)|l,,    :t,,.d, |r, :s,   |d, :r,   |s, ||
```

```
:d  |t, :d  |r  :r  |m    :r.d |r  ||s, |l,  :t,  |d.r     :m.f  |r  :—    |d  ||d  |d  ||
:s, |f, :s, |s, :s, |s,   :fe, |s, ||s, |r,  :r,  |d,(d)   :-.l, |s, :-.f, |m, ||f, |m, ||
:d  |r  :m  |t, :t, |d    :d   |t, ||d  |d   :t,  |m.f     :s .d |d  :t,   |s, ||l, |s, ||
:m, |r, :d, |s, :s, |d.t, :l,  |s, ||m, |ba, :se, |l,      :s,.f,|s, :—    |d, ||f, |d, ||
                                                                          A-men.
```

I AM not skilled to understand
What God hath willed, what God hath planned;
I only know at His right hand
Stands One who is my Saviour.

2 I take God at His word and deed:
'Christ died to save me', this I read;
And in my heart I find a need
Of Him to be my Saviour.

3 And was there then no other way
For God to take?—I cannot say;
I only bless Him, day by day,
Who saved me through my Saviour.

4 That He should leave His place on high
And come for sinful man to die,
You count it strange?—so do not I,
Since I have known my Saviour.

5 And O that He fulfilled may see
The travail of His soul in me,
And with His work contented be,
As I with my dear Saviour!

6 Yea, living, dying, let me bring
My strength, my solace, from this spring,
That He who lives to be my King
Once died to be my Saviour.

DORA GREENWELL, 1821–82.

699 NONE BUT CHRIST. (C.M. and refrain.)

Doh = F. *In moderate time.* JAMES McGRANAHAN, 1840–1907.

REFRAIN.

Now none but Christ can sa - tis - fy, None oth - er Name for me! There's love, and life, and last - ing joy, Lord Je - sus, found in Thee. A - men.

O CHRIST, in Thee my soul hath found,
And found in Thee alone,
The peace, the joy, I sought so long,
The bliss till now unknown.
Now none but Christ can satisfy,
None other Name for me!
There 's love, and life, and lasting joy,
Lord Jesus, found in Thee.

2 I sighed for rest and happiness,
I yearned for them, not Thee;
But, while I passed my Saviour by,
His love laid hold on me.

3 I tried the broken cisterns, Lord,
But, ah, the waters failed:
Even as I stooped to drink they fled,
And mocked me as I wailed.

4 The pleasures lost I sadly mourned,
But never wept for Thee,
Till grace the sightless eyes received,
Thy loveliness to see.

B. E.

700 I NEED THEE. (64. 64. and refrain.)

Doh = A♭. *In moderate time.* ROBERT LOWRY, 1826–99.

```
:d  |m  :-.r  :d .t, |d  :—  :d  |d  :-.r  :d .l,  |s, :— ||
:m, |s, :-.f, :m,.r, |m, :—  :m, |f, :—    :f,     |m, :— ||
:s, |d  :-.l, :s,.s, |s, :—  :s, |l, :—    :l,.d   |d  :— ||
:d, |d, :-.f, :s,.s, |d, :—  :d, |f, :—    :f,     |d, :— ||

:s, |r  :-.m  :r .s, |m  :—  :d  |t, :-.d  :t,.l,  |s, :— ||
:s, |s, :-.s, :s,.s, |s, :—  :s, |s, :-.l, :s,.fe, |s, :— ||
:t, |t, :-.d  :t,.t, |d  :—  :m  |r  :—    :r .d   |t, :— ||
:s, |s, :-.s, :s,.s, |d  :—  :d, |r, :—    :r,     |s, :— ||
```

REFRAIN.

```
:m  |m    :-.d  :f .m    |m    :r  :—   |r  :-.d  :m .r      |r    :d     ||
:s, |s,   :-.s, :d .d    |d    :t, :—   |s, :-.s, :s, .s,    |s,   :s,    ||
 I  |need   Thee, O  I   |need  Thee;   |Ev - ery hour I     |need  Thee; 
:d  |d    :-.m  :l .s    |s    :s  :—   |f  :-.m  :s .f      |f    :m     ||
:d  |d    :-.d  :d .d    |s,   :s, :—   |s, :-.s, :s, .s,    |d,   :d,    ||

:d  |d    :-.r  :d .l,   |s,  :d  :r    |m    :-.d  :r  |d     :—  ||d  |d   ||
:s, |l,   :-l,  :l, .f,  |m,  :s, :l,   |s,   :-.m, :f, |m,    :—  ||f, |m,  ||
 O  |bless  me  now, my  |Sa - viour; I |come       to  |Thee.     ||A -|men.
:d  |d    :-.d  :d .d    |d   :d  :d    |d    :—    :t, |d     :—  ||l, |s,  ||
:m, |f,   :-.f, :f, .f,  |d,  :m, :f,   |s,   :—    :s, |d,    :—  ||f, |d,  ||
```

I NEED Thee every hour,
Most gracious Lord;
No tender voice but Thine
Can peace afford.
I need Thee, O I need Thee;
Every hour I need Thee;
O bless me now, my Saviour;
I come to Thee.

2 I need Thee every hour;
Stay Thou near by;
Temptations lose their power
When Thou art nigh.

3 I need Thee every hour,
In joy or pain;
Come quickly and abide,
Or life is vain.

4 I need Thee every hour;
Teach me Thy will;
And Thy rich promises
In me fulfil.

ANNIE SHERWOOD HAWKS, 1835–1918. Refrain added.

701 EBENEZER. (87. 87. D.)

[*This tune may be sung in Unison.*]

Lah = F. Doh = A♭. *Slow.* THOMAS JOHN WILLIAMS, 1869–

l_1 :l_1,t_1,d |t_1 :l_1 |t_1 :t_1,d,r |d.,t_1 :l_1 |m :r,m,f |m.,r :d
m_1 :m_1 |se_1 :l_1 |l_1 :se_1 |l_1 :m_1 |m_1 :s_1,–,l_1 |t_1 :l_1
d :m |m :d |f :m |m.,r :d |s :r,–,d |m :m
l_2 :d_1 |m_1 :f_1 |r_1 :m_1 |l_1 :l_1 |d :t_1,–,l_1 |se_1 :l_1

D.C.

r.,d :t_1 |l_1 :— ‖ m :d,r,m |r :r |d :l_1,t_1,d |t_1 :t_1
l_1 :se_1 |l_1 :— ‖ s_1 :s_1 |s_1 :s_1 |m_1 :l_1 |l_1 :se_1
f.,m :r |d :— ‖ d :d |d :t_1 |d :m |m :m
r_1 :m_1 |l_1 :— ‖ d_1 :m_1 |s_1 :s_1 |l_1 :d_1 |m_1 :m_1

l_1 :l_1,t_1,d |r :r |d :r,d,r |m :— ‖ l_1 :l_1,t_1,d |t_1 :l_1
l_1 :m_1 |l_1 :s_1 |m_1 :l_1 |se_1 :— ‖ d_1 :l_1 |se_1 :l_1
l_1 :d |d :t_1 |d :l_1 |t_1 :— ‖ l_1 :m |m :d
l_1 :s_1 |f_1 :s_1 |l_1.s_1 :f_1 |m_1 :— ‖ f_1 :d_1 |m_1 :f_1

t_1 :t_1,d,r |d.,t_1 :l_1 |m :r,m,f |m.,r :d |r.,d :t_1 |l_1 :— ‖ l_1 |l_1 ‖
l_1 :se_1 |l_1 :l_1 |s_1 :s_1 |s_1 :l_1 |l_1 :se_1 |l_1 :— ‖ f_1 |m_1 ‖
f :m |m.,r :d |d :t_1,d,r |d.,t_1 :l_1 |f.,m :r |d :— ‖ r |de ‖
r_1 :m_1 |l_1 :l_1 |d :s_1 |d_1 :f_1 |r_1 :m_1 |l_1 :— ‖ r_1 |l_1 ‖

A-men.

[*By permission of W. Gwenlyn Evans & Son, Carnarvon.*]

CONVERSE. (87. 87. D.)

Doh = F. *In moderate time.* CHARLES CROZAT CONVERSE, 1832–1918.

s :–.s |l.s :m.d |d :— |l_1 :— |s_1 :–.d |m.d :s.m
d :–.d |d.d :s_1.s_1 |l_1 :— |f_1 :— |m_1 :–.s_1 |d.d :d.d
m :–.m |f.m :d.d |d :— |d :— |d :–.m |s.m :m.s
d :–.d |d.d :d.m_1 |f_1 :— |f_1 :— |d :–.d |d.d :d.m

r :— |— :— ‖ s :–.s |l.s :m.d |d :— |l_1 :—
t_1 :— |— :— ‖ d :–.d |d.d :s_1.s_1 |l_1 :— |f_1 :—
s :— |— :— ‖ m :–.m |f.m :d.d |d :— |d :—
s :— |— :— ‖ d :–.d |d.d :d.m_1 |f_1 :— |f_1 :—

s, :-.d |m.r :d.t, |d :— |— :— || r :-.de |r.m :f.r
m, :-.s, |s,.s, :s,.s, |s, :— |— :— || t, :-.le, |t,.d :r.t,
d :-.m |s.f :m.r |m :— |— :— || s :-.s |s.s :s.s
s, :-.s, |s,.s, :s,.s, |d :— |— :— || s, :-.s, |s,.s, :s,.s,

m :— |s :— |l :-.l |s.m :f.m |r :— |— :— || s :-.s |l.s :m.d
d :— |d :— |d :-.d |d.d :r.d |t, :— |— :— || d :-.d |d.d :s,.s,
s :— |m :— |f :-.f |s.s :s.s |s :— |— :— || m :-.m |f.m :d.d
d :— |d :— |f, :-.f |m.d :t,.d |s :— |— :— || d :-.d |d.d :d.m,

d :— |l, :— |s, :-.d |m.r :d.t, |d :— |— :— || d |d ||
l, :— |f, :— |m, :-.s, |s,.s, :s,.s, |s, :— |— :— || l, |s, ||
d :— |d :— |d :-.m |s.f :m.r |m :— |— :— || f |m ||
f, :— |f, :— |s, :-.s, |s,.s, :s,.s, |d :— |— :— || f, |d ||

A-men.

WHAT a Friend we have in Jesus,
All our sins and griefs to bear!
What a privilege to carry
Everything to God in prayer!
O what peace we often forfeit,
O what needless pain we bear,
All because we do not carry
Everything to God in prayer!

2 Have we trials and temptations?
Is there trouble anywhere?
We should never be discouraged:
Take it to the Lord in prayer.
Can we find a friend so faithful,
Who will all our sorrows share?
Jesus knows our every weakness:
Take it to the Lord in prayer.

3 Are we weak and heavy-laden,
Cumbered with a load of care?
Jesus only is our refuge:
Take it to the Lord in prayer.
Do thy friends despise, forsake thee?
Take it to the Lord in prayer;
In His arms He'll take and shield thee;
Thou wilt find a solace there.

JOSEPH SCRIVEN, 1820–86

702

NUTFIELD. (84. 84. 8884.)

Doh = D. *In moderate time.* WILLIAM HENRY MONK, 1823–89.

|m :m |f :s |l :t |d' :s |s :— |r :s
|d :d |d :d |d :f |m :d |d :— |d :t,
|s :s |l :d' |f :f |s :s |s :— |s :s
|d :d |f :m |f :r |d :m |m :-.f |s :s,

|m :— |— :— ||m :m |f :s |l :t |d' :s |s :—
|d :— |— :— ||d :d |d :d |d :f |m :d |d :—
|s :— |— :— ||s :s |l :d' |f :f |s :s |s :—
|d :— |— :— ||d :d |f :m |f :r |d :m |m :-.f

|r :s |m :— |— :— ||d :d |r :m |f :m |r :d
|d :t, |d :— |— :— ||d :d |t, :d |d :d |t, :d
|s :s |s :— |— :— ||m :m |s :s |l :s |f :m
|s :s, |d :— |— :— ||d :l, |s, :d |l, :d |s, :d

|m :m |f :s |l :s |f :m ||f :s |l :t
|d :d |d :ta, |l, :t, |d :d ||d :d |d :f
|s :s |f :f.m |f :r |l :s ||f :m |f :f
|d :ta, |l, :s, |f, :s, |l,.t, :d ||l, :d |f :r

d' :s	f :m	s :—	r :m	d :—	— :—		f	m	
m :d	r :d	d :—	d :t,	d :—	— :—		d	d	
s :s	s :s	s :—	s :s	m :—	— :—		l	s	
d :m	t, :d	m :-.f	s :s,	d :—	— :—		f,	d	

A-men.

THROUGH the love of God our Saviour
All will be well.
Free and changeless is His favour;
All, all is well.
Precious is the blood that healed us,
Perfect is the grace that sealed us,
Strong the hand stretched forth to shield us;
All must be well.

2 Though we pass through tribulation,
All will be well.
Ours is such a full salvation,
All, all is well.
Happy, still in God confiding,
Fruitful, if in Christ abiding,
Holy, through the Spirit's guiding;
All must be well.

3 We expect a bright to-morrow;
All will be well.
Faith can sing through days of sorrow,
'All, all is well.'
On our Father's love relying,
Jesus every need supplying,
Or in living or in dying,
All must be well.

MARY PETERS, 1813-56.

703

LLANGRISTIOLUS. (88. 88. D. Anapaestic.)

Lah = G. Doh = B♭. *Moderately slow.* JOSEPH PARRY, 1841–1903.

:l,	m	:d	:l,	t,	:l,	:se,	l,	:—	:l,	d	:t,	:l,
:l,	m	:d	:l,	f,	:m,	:m,	m,	:—	:l,	l,	:se,	:l,
:l,	m	:d	:l,	r	:d	:t,	d	:—	:l,	m	:m	:m
:l,	m	:d	:l,	r,	:m,	:m,	l,	:—	:l,	m	:r	:d

m	:r	:d	t,	:—	‖ l,	m	:d	:l,	d .t,	:l,	:se,
l,	:se,	:l,	se,	:—	‖ l,	m	:d	:l,	f,	:m,	:m,
m	:m	:m	m	:—	‖ l,	m	:d	:l,	r	:d	:t, .r
d	:t,	:l,	m,	:—	‖ l,	m	:d	:l,	r,	:m,	:m,

F.t.

l,	:—	:^{d}f	m	:l	:f	m .l,	:d	:t,	l,	:—	‖
m,	:—	:^{l}r	t,	:l,	:r	d	:l	:se,	l,	:—	‖
d	:—	:^{m}l	se	:l	:l	l	:m	:r	d	:—	‖
l, / l_2	:—	:^{l}r	r	:d	:r	m	:m,	:m,	l,	:—	‖

f.B♭.

:^{l}m,	l,	:l,	:t,	d	:d	:r	m	:—	:se,	l,	:l,	:m,
:^{l}m,	m,	:l,	:se,	l,	:l,	:l,	l,	:se,	:m,	m,	:m,	:m,
:^{l}m	m	:m	:m	m	:m	:l, .t,	d	:t,	:r	d	:d	:t,
:^{l}m, .r	d	:d	:t,	l,	:s,	:f,	m,	:—	:m, .t,	l,	:l,	:s,

l,	:l,	:t,	d	:—	‖ l,	f	:m	:t,	r	:r	:d
d,	:s,	:f,	f,	:m,	‖ l,	l,	:se,	:se,	t,	:t,	:l,
d	:d	:f, .s,	l,	:s,	‖ l,	r .d	:t,	:m	f	:m	:m .re
f,	:m,	:r,	d,	:—	‖ l,	r,	:m,	:m,	se,	:se,	:l,

t,	:—	:m,	l,	:l,	:t,	d	:l,	:t,	l,	:—	l,	l,
se,	:—	:m,	r,	:d,	:f,	m,	:l,	:se,	l,	:—	f,	m,
m	:—	:m,	l,	:l,	:l,	l,	:d	:r	d	:—	r	de
m,	:—	:m,	f,	:m,	:r,	d, .r,	:m,	:m,	l, l_2	:—	r,	l, l_2

A-men.

A DEBTOR to mercy alone,
Of covenant mercy I sing;
Nor fear, with Thy righteousness on,
My person and offering to bring.
The terrors of law and of God
With me can have nothing to do;
My Saviour's obedience and blood
Hide all my transgressions from view.

2 The work which His goodness began,
The arm of His strength will complete;
His promise is Yea and Amen,
And never was forfeited yet.
Things future, nor things that are now,
Nor all things below or above,
Can make Him His purpose forgo,
Or sever my soul from His love.

3 My name from the palms of His hands
Eternity will not erase;
Impressed on His heart it remains,
In marks of indelible grace.
Yes, I to the end shall endure,
As sure as the earnest is given;
More happy, but not more secure,
The glorified spirits in heaven.

AUGUSTUS MONTAGUE TOPLADY, 1740–78

[May be sung to TREWEN, No. 560.]

704

FORTITUDE. (11 11. 11 12. and refrain.)

Doh = A♭. *In moderate time.* Horatio Richmond Palmer, 1834–1907.

m :— :— |m :f :m |r :— :— |r :— :— |d :— :— |d :r :d
s, :— :— |s, :s, :s, |s, :— :— |f, :— :— |m, :— :— |m, :m, :m,
d :— :— |d :r :d |t, :— :— |t, :— :— |l, :— :— |l, :t, :l,
d :— :— |d, :d, :d, |s, :— :— |s, :— :— |l, :— :— |l,, :l,, :l,,

t, :— :— |— :— :— |l, :— :— |l, :t, :d |s, :— :— |d :— :—
m, :— :— |— :— :— |d, :— :— |f, :s, :l, |s, :— :— |m, :— :—
se, :— :— |— :— :— |l, :— :— |d :d :d |d :— :— |d :— :—
m, :— :— |— :— :— |f, :— :— |f, :f, :f, |m, :— :— |l, :— :—

r :— :— |r :d :r |m :— :— |— :— :— ||m :— :— |m :f :m
s, :— :— |s, :s, :s, |s, :— :— |— :— :— ||s, :— :— |s, :s, :s,
t, :— :— |t, :l, :t, |d :— :— |— :— :— ||d :— :— |d :r :d
s, :— :— |s, :s, :s, |d, :— :— |— :— :— ||d :— :— |d, :d, :d,

r :— :— |r :— :— |d :— :— |d :r :d |t, :— :— |— :— :—
s, :— :— |f, :— :— |m, :— :— |m, :m, :m, |m, :— :— |— :— :—
t, :— :— |t, :— :— |l, :— :— |l, :t, :l, |se, :— :— |— :— :—
s, :— :— |s, :— :— |l, :— :— |l,, :l,, :l,, |m, :— :— |— :— :—

l, :— :— |l, :t, :d |s, :— :— |d :— :— |m :— :m |r :d :r
d, :— :— |f, :s, :l, |s, :— :— |m, :— :— |s, :— :s, |f, :f, :f,
l, :— :— |d :d :d |d :— :— |d :— :— |d :— :d |t, :l, :t,
f, :— :— |f, :f, :f, |m, :— :— |l, :— :— |s, :— :s, |s, :s, :s,

REFRAIN.

```
d  :—:— |—:—:— || s, :— :s, | s, :l, :s, | s, :— :— | d  :— :—
m, :—:— |—:—:— || m, :— :m, | m, :f, :m, | m, :— :— | m, :— :—
                   Ask         the Sa - viour to help      you,
d  :—:— |—:—:— || d  :— :d  | d  :d  :d  | d  :— :— | d  :— :—
d, :—:— |—:—:— || d, :— :d, | d, :d, :d, | d, :— :— | d, :— :—
```

```
r  :— :r  | r  :d  :r  | m  :—:— | d  :—:— | d  :—:d  | d  :t, :l,
s, :— :s, | s, :s, :s, | s, :—:— | m, :—:— | l, :—:l, | l, :s, :f,
Com - fort, streng-then, and keep      you;      He   is   will - ing to
t, :— :t, | t, :l, :t, | d  :—:— | d  :—:— | d  :—:d  | d  :d  :d
s, :— :s, | s, :s, :s, | d  :—:— | d, :—:— | f, :—:f, | f, :f, :f,
```

```
s, :—:— | d  :—:— | m  :—:m  | r  :d  :r  | d  :—:— | —:—:— || d  | d  ||
s, :—:— | m, :—:— | s, :—:s, | f, :f, :f, | m, :—:— | —:—:— || f, | m, ||
aid       you;      He         will car - ry you through.        A -  men.
d  :—:— | d  :—:— | d  :—:d  | t, :l, :t, | d  :—:— | —:—:— || l, | s, ||
m, :—:— | l, :—:— | s, :—:s, | s, :s, :s, | d, :—:— | —:—:— || f, | d, ||
```

YIELD not to temptation, for yielding is sin;
Each victory will help you some other to win;
Fight manfully onward; dark passions subdue;
Look ever to Jesus, He will carry you through.
Ask the Saviour to help you,
Comfort, strengthen, and keep you;
He is willing to aid you;
He will carry you through.

2 Shun evil companions; bad language disdain;
God's Name hold in reverence, nor take it in vain;
Be thoughtful and earnest, kind-hearted and true;
Look ever to Jesus, He will carry you through.

3 To him that o'ercometh God giveth a crown;
Through faith we shall conquer, though often cast down;
He who is our Saviour our strength will renew;
Look ever to Jesus, He will carry you through.

HORATIO RICHMOND PALMER, 1834–1907.

705 HIS FOR EVER. (87. 87. D.)

Doh = G. *In moderate time.* JOSEPH BARNBY, 1838–96.

```
:s, |s,  :-.s, |d   :t,  |r   :-.d  |d   :d     |d   :f   |m   :r   |s   :—  |m
:s, |s,  :-.s, |s,  :s,  |s,  :-.s, |s,  :d     |d   :d   |d   :t,  |d   :—  |d
:m  |m   :-.m  |m   :r   |f   :-.m  |m   :m     |f   :d   |s   :s   |s   :—  |s
:d  |d   :-.d  |d   :d   |d   :-.d  |d   :d     |l,  :l,  |s,  :f,  |m,  :—  |d,

                                     D.t.                                      f.G.
:m  |r   :-.m  |d   :d   |t,  :-.d  |l,  :(m)l  |s   :d   |m   :r.m |r   :—  |(d)s,
:d  |d   :t,   |l,  :l,  |l,  :se,  |l,  :(fe)t,|d   :d   |d   :t,  |t,  :—  |(d)s,
:s  |f   :-.s  |m   :m   |r   :-.m  |d   :(d)f  |s   :l   |s   :f.s |f   :—  |(m)t,
:m, |s,  :-.s, |l,  :d,  |m,  :-.m, |l,  :(l,)r |m   :f   |s   :s,  |s,  :—  |(d)s,

:s, |s,  :d    |d   :t,  |t,  :-.l, |l,  :l,    |l,  :m   |r   :d   |d   :—  |t,
:s, |s,  :m,   |f,  :s,  |s,  :-.f, |f,  :m,    |f,  :s,  |l,  :l,  |s,  :—  |s,
:t, |d   :d    |d   :d   |d   :-.d  |d   :de    |r   :de  |r   :f   |m   :—  |r
:f, |m,  :d,   |r,  :m,  |f,  :-.f, |f,  :l,    |r,  :m,  |f,  :r,  |s,  :—  |s,

:s, |d   :r    |m   :d   |f   :s    |l   :l     |s   :d   |m   :r.m |r   :—  |d   || d  |d
:s, |s,  :s,   |s,  :d   |d   :d    |d   :d     |d   :d   |d   :t,  |t,  :—  |d   || l, |s,
:t, |d   :t,   |d   :m   |f   :m    |r   :r     |m   :f   |s   :f.s |f   :—  |m   || f  |m
:f, |m,  :s,   |d   :ta, |l,  :s,   |f,  :fe,   |s,  :l,  |s,  :s,  |s,  :—  |d,  || f, |d,
                                                                               A-men.
```

[By permission of Novello & Co., Ltd.]

I'VE found a Friend; O such a Friend!
He loved me ere I knew Him;
He drew me with the cords of love,
And thus He bound me to Him;
And round my heart still closely twine
Those ties which nought can sever,
For I am His, and He is mine,
For ever and for ever.

2 I've found a Friend; O such a Friend!
He bled, He died to save me;
And not alone the gift of life,
But His own self He gave me.
Nought that I have mine own I'll call,
I'll hold it for the Giver;
My heart, my strength, my life, my all,
Are His, and His for ever.

3 I've found a Friend; O such a Friend!
All power to Him is given,
To guard me on my onward course,
And bring me safe to heaven.
The eternal glories gleam afar,
To nerve my faint endeavour;
So now to watch, to work, to war,
And then to rest for ever.

4 I've found a Friend; O such a Friend,
So kind, and true, and tender!
So wise a Counsellor and Guide,
So mighty a Defender!
From Him who loves me now so well
What power my soul shall sever?
Shall life or death, shall earth or hell?
No! I am His for ever.

JAMES GRINDLAY SMALL, 1817–88.

706 VOLLER WUNDER. (77. 77. 77.)

Doh = B♭. *In moderate time.*

JOHANN GEORG EBELING, 1637–76.

d :— :s,	l, :— :d	d :— :t,	d :— :—	t, :— :d
m, :— :s,	f, :— :m,	s, :— :s,	s, :— :—	s, :— :s,
d :— :d	d :— :d	r :— :r	m :— :—	m :— :m
d, :— :m,	f, :— :l,	s, :— :s,	d, :— :—	m, :— :d,

D.C.

r :— :s,	l, :t, :l,	s, :— :—		s, :— :l,	d :— :l,	t, :— :d
s, :— :s,	s, :— :fe,	s, :— :—		r, :— :f,	s, :— :f,	f, :— :s,
r :— :t,	m :— :l,	t, :— :—		t, :— :d	d :— :d	r :— :m
t_2 :— :m,	d, :— :r,	s, :— :—		s, :— :f,	m, :— :f,	r, :— :d,

r :— :—	d :— :r	m :— :d	d :— :t,	d :— :—		d	d	
s, :— :—	m, :— :l,	se, :— :m,	s, :— :s,	s, :— :—		l,	s,	
t, :— :—	d :— :l,	t, :— :d	r :— :r	m :— :—		f	m	
s, :— :—	l, :— :f,	m, :— :l,	s, :— :s,	d, :— :—		f,	d,	

A-men.

JESUS, Saviour, pilot me
Over life's tempestuous sea;
Unknown waves before me roll,
Hiding rock and treacherous shoal;
Chart and compass come from Thee:
Jesus, Saviour, pilot me.

2 As a mother stills her child,
Thou canst hush the ocean wild;
Boisterous waves obey Thy will,
When Thou say'st to them, 'Be still!'.
Wondrous Sovereign of the sea,
Jesus, Saviour, pilot me.

3 When at last I near the shore,
And the fearful breakers roar
'Twixt me and the peaceful rest,
Then, while leaning on Thy breast,
May I hear Thee say to me,
'Fear not, I will pilot thee.'

EDWARD HOPPER, 1818–88.

707 REFUGE. (76. 76. D. and refrain.)

Doh = G. *In moderate time.* WILLIAM HOWARD DOANE, 1832–1916.

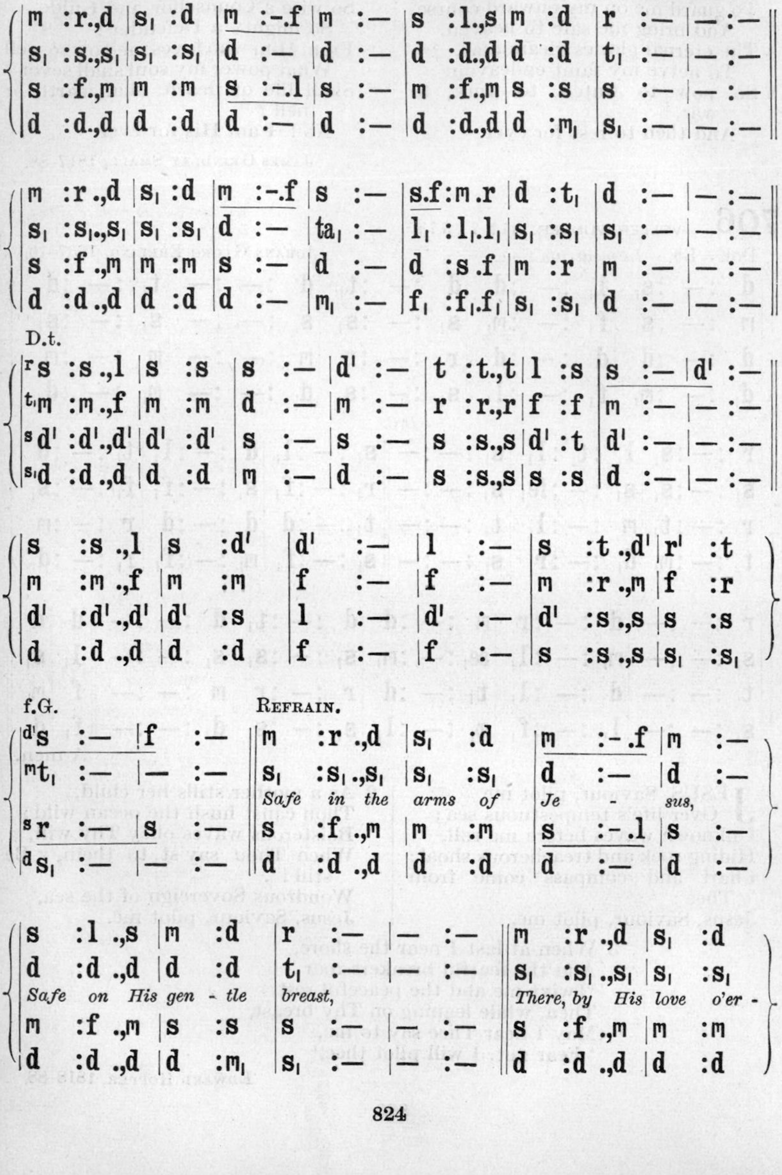

m :r.,d |s, :d |m :-.f |m :— |s :l.,s |m :d |r :— |— :—
s, :s.,s, |s, :s, |d :— |d :— |d :d.,d |d :d |t, :— |— :—
s :f.,m |m :m |s :-.l |s :— |m :f.,m |s :s |s :— |— :—
d :d.,d |d :d |d :— |d :— |d :d.,d |d :m, |s, :— |— :—

m :r.,d |s, :d |m :-.f |s :— |s.f :m.r |d :t, |d :— |— :—
s, :s,.,s, |s, :s, |d :— |ta, :— |l, :l,.l, |s, :s, |s, :— |— :—
s :f.,m |m :m |s :— |d :— |d :s.f |m :r |m :— |— :—
d :d.,d |d :d |d :— |m, :— |f, :f,.f, |s, :s, |d :— |— :—

D.t.
r s :s.,l |s :s |s :— |d' :— |t :t.,t |l :s |s :— |d' :—
t, m :m.,f |m :m |d :— |m :— |r :r.,r |f :f |m :— |— :—
s d' :d'.,d' |d' :d' |s :— |s :— |s :s.,s |d' :t |d' :— |— :—
s, d :d.,d |d :d |m :— |d :— |s :s.,s |s :s |d :— |— :—

s :s.,l |s :d' |d' :— |l :— |s :t.,d' |r' :t
m :m.,f |m :m |f :— |f :— |m :r.,m |f :r
d' :d'.,d' |d' :s |l :— |d' :— |d' :s.,s |s :s
d :d.,d |d :d |f :— |f :— |s :s.,s |s, :s,

f.G. REFRAIN.
d s :— |f :— || m :r.,d |s, :d |m :-.f |m :—
m t, :— |— :— || s, :s,.,s, |s, :s, |d :— |d :—
Safe in the arms of Je - sus,
s r :— |s :— || s :f.,m |m :m |s :-.l |s :—
d s, :— |— :— || d :d.,d |d :d |d :— |d :—

s :l.,s |m :d |r :— |— :— || m :r.,d |s, :d
d :d.,d |d :d |t, :— |— :— || s, :s,.,s, |s, :s,
Safe on His gen - tle breast, There, by His love o'er -
m :f.,m |s :s |s :— |— :— || s :f.,m |m :m
d :d.,d |d :m, |s, :— |— :— || d :d.,d |d :d

m :- .f	s :—	s .f :m .r	d :t_1	d :—	— :—	d	d
d :—	ta_1 :—	l_1 :l_1 .l_1	s_1 :s_1	s_1 :—	— :—	l_1	s_1
sha -	*ded,*	*Sweet - ly my*	*soul shall*	*rest.*		A -	men.
s :—	d :—	d :s .f	m :r	m :—	— :—	f	m
d :—	m_1 :—	f_1 :f_1 .f_1	s_1 :s_1	d :—	— :—	f_1	d

SAFE in the arms of Jesus,
Safe on His gentle breast,
There, by His love o'ershaded,
Sweetly my soul shall rest.
Hark ! 'tis the voice of angels,
Borne in a song to me,
Over the fields of glory,
Over the crystal sea !
Safe in the arms of Jesus,
Safe on His gentle breast,
There, by His love o'ershaded,
Sweetly my soul shall rest.

2 Safe in the arms of Jesus,
Safe from corroding care,
Safe from the world's temptations,
Sin cannot harm me there,—
Free from the blight of sorrow,
Free from my doubts and fears,
Only a few more trials,
Only a few more tears.

3 Jesus, my heart's dear refuge,
Jesus has died for me ;
Firm on the Rock of Ages
Ever my trust shall be.
Here let me wait with patience,
Wait till the night is o'er,
Wait till I see the morning
Break on the golden shore.

FRANCES JANE VAN ALSTYNE, 1820–1915.

Also the following :

708

TRIUMPH. (87. 87. 447.)

Doh = B♭. *In moderate time.* HENRY JOHN GAUNTLETT, 1805–76.

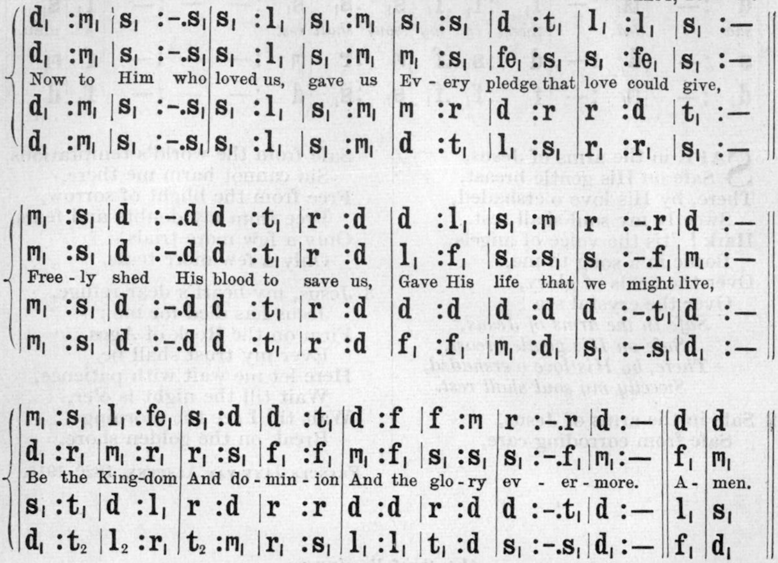

```
d, :m, |s, :-.s, |s, :l, |s, :m, |s, :s, |d  :t, |l, :l, |s, :-
d, :m, |s, :-.s, |s, :l, |s, :m, |m, :s, |fe,:s, |s, :fe,|s, :-
Now to  Him  who  loved us, gave us  Ev - ery pledge that love could give,
d, :m, |s, :-.s, |s, :l, |s, :m, |m  :r  |d  :r  |r  :d  |t, :-
d, :m, |s, :-.s, |s, :l, |s, :m, |d  :t, |l, :s, |r, :r, |s, :-
```

```
m, :s, |d :-.d |d :t, |r :d |d  :l, |s, :m  |r  :-.r |d  :-
m, :s, |d :-.d |d :t, |r :d |l, :f, |s, :s, |s, :-.f,|m, :-
Free - ly shed His blood to save us, Gave His life that we might live,
m, :s, |d :-.d |d :t, |r :d |d  :d  |d  :d  |d  :-.t,|d  :-
m, :s, |d :-.d |d :t, |r :d |f, :f, |m, :d, |s, :-.s,|d, :-
```

```
m, :s,  |l,  :fe, |s,  :d  |d  :t, |d  :f  |f  :m  |r  :-.r  |d  :- || d  |d
d, :r,  |m,  :r,  |r,  :s, |f, :f, |m, :f, |s, :s, |s, :-.f, |m, :- || f, |m,
Be the King-dom And do - min - ion And the glo - ry ev - er - more. A - men.
s, :t,  |d   :l,  |r   :d  |r  :r  |d  :d  |r  :d  |d  :-.t, |d  :- || l, |s,
d, :t,, |l,, :r,  |t,, :m, |r, :s, |l, :l, |t, :d  |s, :-.s, |d, :- || f, |d,
```

SAMUEL MILLER WARING, 1792–1827.

709

OLD 100TH. (L.M.)

Doh = G. *Slow and dignified.* *French Psalter*, 1551.

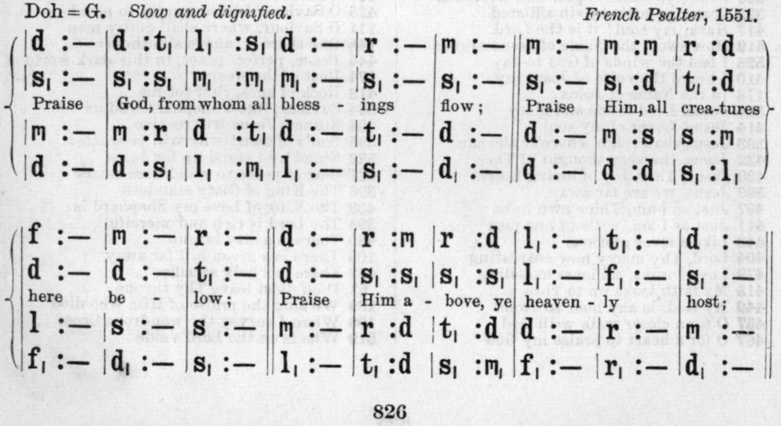

```
d  :- |d  :t, |l, :s, |d  :- |r  :- |m  :- || m  :- |m  :m  |r  :d
s, :- |s, :s, |m, :m, |m, :- |s, :- |s, :- || s, :- |s, :d  |t, :d
Praise  God, from whom all bless - ings flow;   Praise  Him, all crea-tures
m  :- |m  :r  |d  :t, |d  :- |t, :- |d  :- || d  :- |m  :s  |s  :m
d  :- |d  :s, |l, :m, |l, :- |s, :- |d, :- || d  :- |d  :d  |s, :l,
```

```
f  :- |m  :- |r  :- || d  :- |r  :m |r  :d  |l, :- |t, :- |d  :-
d  :- |d  :- |t, :- || d  :- |s, :s,|s, :s, |l, :- |f, :- |s, :-
here   be  -  low;     Praise  Him a - bove, ye heaven - ly host;
l  :- |s  :- |s  :- || m  :- |r  :d |t, :d  |d  :- |r  :- |m  :-
f, :- |d, :- |s, :- || l, :- |t, :d |s, :m, |f, :- |r, :- |d, :-
```

s :— |m :d |r :f |m :— |r :— |d :— ||d |d
s, :— |s, :d |t, :l,.t, |d :— |t, :— |s, :— ||l, |s,
Praise Fa - ther, Son, and Ho - ly Ghost. A- men.
r :— |d :m.fe |s :l |s :— |s :f |m :— ||f |m
t, :— |d :l, |s, :r, |m, :f, |s, :— |d, :— ||f, |d,

THOMAS KEN, 1637–1711.

710 ST. JOHN. (66. 66. 88.)

Doh = D. *With vigour.* *Parish Choir*, 1851.

:d |m :m |s :s |d' :— |— :d' |t :l |s :fe
:d |d :m |r :r |d :— |— :d |r :m |r :r
Now to the King of heaven Your cheer-ful voi - ces
:m |s :s |s :s |m :— |— :m |s :d' |t :l
:d |d :d |t, :t, |l, :— |— :l, |t, :d |r :r

s :— |— ||s |l :t |d' :l |s :— |— :s |f :m |r :r
r :— |— ||m |f :f |s :f |m :— |— :d |d :d |d :t,
raise; To Him be glo - ry given, Power, ma - jes - ty, and
t :— |— ||d' |d' :r' |d' :d' |d' :— |— :s |l :s |s :f
s, :— |— ||d |f :r |m :f |d :— |— :m |l, :d |s, :s,

d :— |— ||d |d :r |m :d |m :f |s :s
d :— |— ||d |d :t, |d :d |d :d |r :m
praise; Wide as He reigns His Name be sung By
m :— |— ||m |m :s |s :s |s :l |t :d'
d :— |— ||d |l, :s, |d :m |d :l, |s, :d

l :t |d' :d' |r' :— |t :— |d' :— |— ||d' |d'
f :f |s :m |f :— |r :— |m :— |— ||f |m
ev - ery tongue In end - less strains. A - men.
d' :r' |d' :d' |l :— |s :— |s :— |— ||l |s
f :r |m :l |f :— |s :— |d :— |— ||f |d

PHILIP DODDRIDGE, 1702–51, and ISAAC WATTS, 1674–1748.

711 ST. MAGNUS (NOTTINGHAM). (C.M.)

Doh = G. *Moderately slow.* JEREMIAH CLARK, 1670–1707.

:s,	d :r	t, :s,	d :r	m :r	m :d
:s,	l, :l,	s, :s,	s, :l, .t,	d :t,	d :s,
To	Him who	sits up -	on the	throne, The	God whom
:m	m :f	r :t,	d :f	m :s	s :s .f
:d	l, :f,	s, :s, .f,	m, :r,	d, :s,	d :m .r

m :fe	s :—	—	r	m :r	d :t,	l, :r
s, :d	t, :—	—	t,	d :t,	l, :s,	f, :l,
we a -	dore,		And	to the	Lamb that	once was
m .r :d	r :—	—	s	s :s	m :m .r	d :f
d .t, :l,	s, :—	—	s,	d :s,	l, :m,	f, :r,

t, :s,	s :s .f	m :r	d :—	—	d	d
s, :s,	d :d	d :t,	d :—	—	l,	s,
slain, Be	glo - ry	ev - er -	more.		A -	men.
r :t,	d :l	s :- .f	m :—	—	f	m
s, :s, .f,	m, :f,	s, :s,	d :—	—	f,	d

ISAAC WATTS, 1674–1748.

712 GLORIA.

Doh = D. *In free rhythm.* *Parisian Tone.*

d :m :s :s :s :s :s	d' :t :l :s	m :— :f :m
d :d :m :m :m :m :m	s :s :fe :s	d :— :d :t,
Glo - ry be to the Fa - ther,	and to the Son,	and to the
m :s :d' :d' :d' :d' :d'	d' :r' :d' :t	s :— :f :s
d :d :d :d :d :d :d	m :s :r :s,	d :ta, :l, :s,

r :- .d :d :—	:d :m		Soh
l, :t, :d :—	:d :d		Me
Ho - ly Ghost :	As it	was in the beginning, is now, and	
l :s :m :—	:m :s		Doh'
f, :s, :d :—	:d :d		Doh

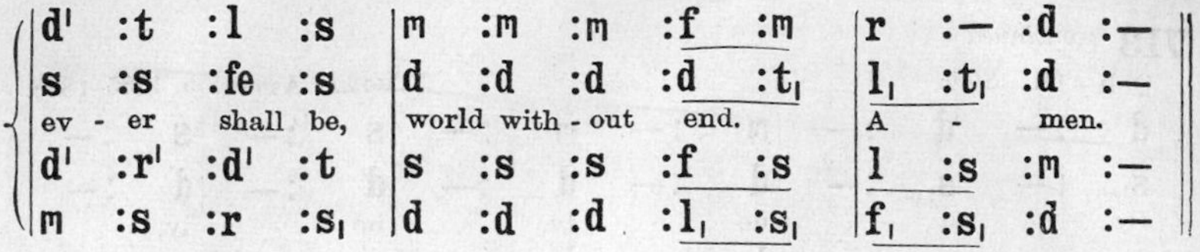

d' :t :l :s |m :m :m :f :m |r :— :d :—
s :s :fe :s |d :d :d :d :t, |l, :t, :d :—
ev - er shall be, world with - out end. A - men.
d' :r' :d' :t |s :s :s :f :s |l :s :m :—
m :s :r :s, |d :d :d :l, :s, |f, :s, :d :—

RESPONSIVE SETTING.

Minister. Glory be to the Father, and to the Son, and to the Holy Ghost,

Congregation.

Doh = C. THOMAS TALLIS, *c.* 1510–85.

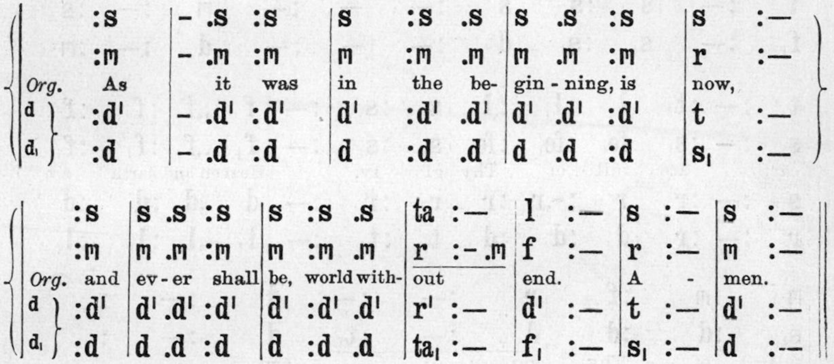

:s |— .s :s |s :s .s |s .s :s |s :—
:m |— .m :m |m :m .m |m .m :m |r :—
Org. As it was in the be- gin - ning, is now,
d :d' |— .d' :d' |d' :d' .d' |d' .d' :d' |t :—
d, :d |— .d :d |d :d .d |d .d :d |s, :—

:s |s .s :s |s :s .s |ta :— |l :— |s :— |s :—
:m |m .m :m |m :m .m |r :— .m |f :— |r :— |m :—
Org. and ev - er shall be, world with- out end. A - men.
d :d' |d' .d' :d' |d' :d' .d' |r' :— |d' :— |t :— |d' :—
d, :d |d .d :d |d :d .d |ta, :— |f, :— |s, :— |d :—

713

Lah = E. Doh = G. *Unison.* *Slow.* JOHN MERBECKE, 1523–*c.* 1585.

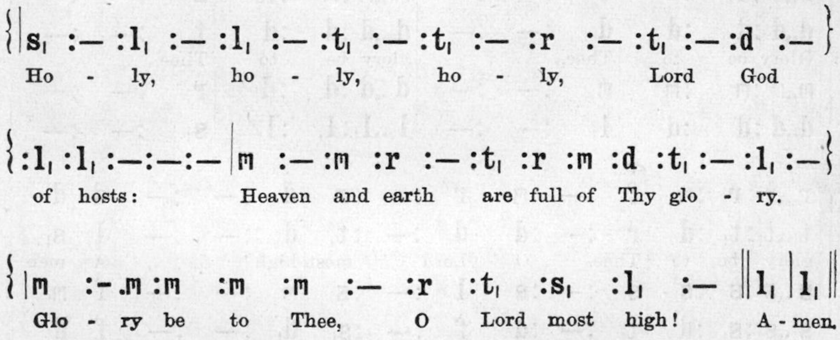

|s, :— :l, :— :l, :— :t, :— :t, :— :r :— :t, :— :d :—
Ho - ly, ho - ly, ho - ly, Lord God

:l, :l, :—:—:— |m :— :m :r :— :t, :r :m :d :t, :— :l, :—
of hosts: Heaven and earth are full of Thy glo - ry.

|m :- .m :m :m :m :— :r :t, :s, :l, :— || l, | l, ||
Glo - ry be to Thee, O Lord most high! A - men.

713 *(continued)*

Doh = G. *Slow.* THOMAS ATTWOOD, 1765–1838.

| d :— | d :— | m :— | m :— | s :— | s :— |
| s, :— | s, :— | d :— | d :— | d :— | d :— |
Ho - ly, ho - ly, ho - ly,
| m :— | m :— | l :— | l :— | s :— | s :— |
| d :— | d :— | l, :— | l, :— | m, :— | m, :— |

Quicker.

| r :— | r :r | m :— | — :— || d :— :d |
| d :— | t, :t, | d :— | — :— || s, :— :s, |
Lord God of hosts: Heaven and
| l :— | s :s | s :— | — :— || m :— :s |
| f, :— | s, :s, | d :— | — :— || d :— :m |

| t, :— :t, | l, :l, :l, | s, :s, :— | f .,f :f :f |
| s, :— :s, | fe, :fe, :fe, | s, :s, :— | f, .,f, :f, :f, |
earth are full of Thy glo - ry, Heaven and earth are
| s :— :r | r :-.r :r | r :r :— | d .,d :d :d |
| r :— :r | d :d :d | t, :t, :— | l, .,l, :l, :l, |

| m :m :f | r :— :— | d :— : ||
| s, :d :d | d :— :t, | d :— : ||
full of Thy glo - - ry.
| d :d :d | l :— :s | m :— : ||
| s, :s, :l, | f, :— :s, | d, :— : ||

| s.,s :s :s | l :— :— | m .,m :m :fe | s :— :— |
| d.,d :d :d | d :— :— | d .,d :d :d | t, :— :— |
Glory be to Thee, glory be to Thee,
| m.,m :m :m | m :— :— | d .,d :d :d | r :— :— |
| d.,d :d :d | l, :— :— | l,.,l, :l, :l, | s, :— :— |

| r .,r :r :m | f :— :m | r :— :r | d :— :— || d | d ||
| t,.,t, :t, :d | r :— :d | d :— :t, | d :— :— || l, | s, ||
glory be to Thee, O Lord most high! A - men.
| s .,s :s :s | s :— :s | l :— :s | m :— :— || f | m ||
| s,.,s, :s, :d | t, :— :d | f, :— :s, | d, :— :— || f, | d, ||

DOXOLOGIES

Doh = G. *Slow.* STEPHEN ELVEY, 1805–60.

```
d  :d  :   | m  :m  :   | f  :f  :   | m  :r   :d    | s  :— :—
s, :s, :   | l, :l, :   | l, :l, :   | s, :s,  :d    | t, :— :—
Ho - ly,   | ho - ly,   | ho - ly,   | Lord God of   | hosts:
m  :m  :   | d  :d  :   | d  :d  :   | d  :r.m :fe   | s  :— :—
d  :d  :   | l, :l, :   | f, :f, :   | d  :t,  :l,   | s, :— :—
```

```
s  :f  :m  | m  :r  :d  | s  :f  :m  | m  :r  :—     | m   :— :r
d  :t, :d  | d  :t, :d  | d  :t, :d  | d  :t, :—     | t,  :— :t,
Heaven and | earth   are | full of Thy| glo - ry.     | Glo  -  ry
m  :f  :s  | s  :—  :s  | m  :f  :s  | s  :s  :—     | m   :— :m
m  :r  :d  | s  :f  :m  | m  :r  :d  | s, :s, :—     | se, :— :se,
```

```
d  :—   :d      | f  :—  :m  | r  :d  :t,     | d  :— :—  | m  :— :r
l, :—   :l,     | l, :t, :d  | l, :s, :s,.f,  | m, :— :—  | s, :— :s,
be      to      | Thee,   O  | Lord    most   | high!     | Glo  -  ry
m  :—   :f.s    | l  :—  :s  | f  :m  :r      | d  :— :—  | d  :— :t,
l, :-.s,:f,.m,  | r, :—  :m, | f, :s, :s,     | d, :— :—  | d  :— :s,
```

```
d  :—   :d      | f  :—  :m  | r  :d  :t,     | d  :— :—  || d  | d
m, :—   :l,.s,  | f, :s, :s, | l, :s, :s,.f,  | m, :— :—  || f, | m,
be      to      | Thee,   O  | Lord    most   | high!     || A- | men.
d  :—   :d      | l, :t, :d  | f  :m  :r      | d  :— :—  || l, | s,
l, :-.s,:f,.m,  | r, :—  :m, | f, :s, :s,     | d, :— :—  || f, | d,
```

Also the following:

7 Glory be to God the Father
29, v. 3 All praise and thanks to God
34 Praise ye Jehovah, praise the Lord most holy
35 Praise the Lord! ye heavens, adore Him
116, v. 6 To Father, Son, and Holy Ghost
126, v. 3 Hallelujah! hallelujah!
179, v. 4 All glory to the Father
207, v. 4 Laud and honour to the Father
228 From all that dwell below the skies
252, v. 4 Honour, glory, might, and merit

714

BENEDICTUS

Doh = G. SAMUEL WESLEY, 1766–1837.

```
| m  :—  | r  :d  | f  :—  || m  :—  | r  :t,  | d  :r   | t, :— ||
| d  :—  | t, :d  | l, :—  || d  :—  | l, :s,  | s, :fe, | s, :— ||
| s  :—  | f  :m  | r  :—  || s  :—  | f  :m   | m  :r   | r  :— ||
| d  :—  | s, :l, | r, :—  || m, :—  | f, :s,  | l, :r,  | s, :— ||

| r  :—  | m  :f  | s  :—  || f  :—    | m  :r  | d  :t,  | d  :— ||
| s, :—  | s, :f, | l, :—  || l, :-.t, | d  :l, | s, :s,  | s, :— ||
| t, :—  | de :r  | m  :—  || f  :—    | s  :f  | m  :r   | m  :— ||
| f, :—  | m, :r, | de, :— || r, :—    | m, :f, | s, :s,  | d, :— ||
```

St. Luke i. 68–79. FIRST FORM.

BLESSÈD be the | Lord · God of | Isra-el : || for He hath | visited · and re- | deemed His | people ; ||

2 And hath raised up an horn of sal- | vation | for us || in the | house of His | servant | David ; ||

3 As He spake by the mouth of His | holy | prophets : || which have | been · since the | world be- | gan ; ||

4 That we should be | saved · from our | ene-mies : || and from the | hand of | all that | hate us ; ||

5 To perform the mercy promised to our fathers * and to remember His | holy | cove-nant ; ||

6 The oath which He sware to our father | Abra-ham that | He would · grant | unto · us, ||

7 That we, being delivered out of the hand of our enemies, might | serve Him with-out | fear ; ||

8 In holiness and righteousness before Him, | all the | days of our | life. ||

9 And thou, child, shalt be called the | prophet · of the | Highest : || for thou shalt go before the face of the | Lord · to pre- | pare His | ways ; ||

10 To give knowledge of salvation | unto His | people || †by ⁝ the re- | mission · of their | sins, ||

11 Through the tender | mercy · of our | God : || whereby the | dayspring · from on | high hath | visited · us, ||

12 To give light to them that sit in darkness and in the | shadow of | death : || to guide our | feet in-to the | way of | peace. ||

Glory | be · to the | Father, || and to the Son, | and · to the | Holy | Ghost ; ||

As it | was in · the be- | ginning, || is now, and ever shall be : | world with-out | end. A- | men. ||

```
† | f  3 m  :r  | d  .d  :t,  .t,  | d  :— ||
   by   the re - mis - sion ' of their sins,
```

[May also be sung to Gregorian Chant, on p. 834.]

BENEDICTUS

Doh = E♭. JOHN ROBINSON, 1682–1762.

s :—	d' :l	s :—	m :—	fe :s	s :fe	s :—
d :—	d :d	d :—	d :—	d :t_1	l_1 :l_1	t_1 :—
m :—	s :f	m :—	s :—	l :r	r :r	r :—
d :—	m :f	d :—	d :—	l_1 :s_1	r :r	s_1 :—

s :—	f :m	l :—	s :—	r :m	r :r	d :—
d :—	t_1 :d	d :—	d :—	r :d	d :t_1	d :—
m :—	f :s	f :—	s :—	s :s	s :-.f	m :—
d :—	r :m	f :—	m :—	t_1 :d	s_1 :s_1	d :—

SECOND FORM.

BLESSÈD be the | Lord · God of | Isra-el : || for He hath | visited · and re- | deemed His | people ; ||

2 And hath raised up a mighty sal- | vation | for us || in the | house of His | servant | David ; ||

3 As He spake by the mouth of His | holy | prophets : || which have | been · since the | world be- | gan ; ||

4 That we should be | saved · from our | ene-mies, || and from the | hands of | all that | hate us ; ||

5 To perform the mercy promised to our forefathers * and to remember His | holy | cove-nant ; ||

6 To perform the oath which He sware to our forefather | Abra-ham that | He would | give us, ||

7 That we, being delivered out of the hands of our enemies, might | serve Him with-out | fear ; ||

8 In holiness and righteousness before Him, | all the | days of our | life. ||

9 And thou, child, shalt be called the | prophet · of the | Highest : || for thou shalt go before the face of the | Lord · to pre- | pare His | ways ; ||

10 To give knowledge of salvation | unto His | people : || † for $\overset{3}{}$ the re- | mission · of their | sins, ||

11 Through the tender | mercy · of our | God : || whereby the | dayspring · from on | high hath | visited · us, ||

12 To give light to them that sit in darkness and in the | shadow of | death : || and to guide our | feet in-to the | way of | peace. ||

Glory | be · to the | Father, || and to the Son, | and · to the | Holy | Ghost ; ||

As it | was in · the be- | ginning, || is now, and ever shall be : | world with-out | end. A- | men. ||

† See p. 832.

714 (*continued*)

Doh = A. BENE-

{| s, l, DOH r (d) d (d) t, d }

St. Luke i. 68–79. FIRST

1. Bless - ed be the Lord God of Is - ra - el:
2. And hath raised up an horn of sal - va - tion for us:
3. As He spake by the mouth of His ho - ly pro-phets:
4. That we should be saved from our en - e - mies:
5. To per - form the mercy promised to our fa - thers:
6. The oath which He sware to our fa - ther A - bra- ham:
7. That we being delivered out of the hand of our en - e - mies:
8. In ho - liness and righteous - ness be - fore Him:
9. And thou, child, shalt be called the prophet of the High - est:
10. To give knowledge of salvation un - to His peo - ple:
11. Through the tender mer - cy of our God:
12. To give light to them that sit in darkness and in the sha - dow of death:

Glo - ry be to the Fa - ther and to the Son:
As it was in the beginning, is now, and ev - er shall be:

[May also be sung to Chant on p. 832.]

715 MAGNI-

Doh = G.

{| t, d RAY f (f) m (m) r (r) m }

St. Luke i. 46–55. FIRST

1. My soul doth mag ni - fy the Lord:
2. For He hath re - gard - ed:
3. For, be- hold, from hence - forth:
4. For He that is mighty hath done to me great things:
5. And His mercy is on them that fear Him:
6. He hath shewed strength with His arm:
7. He hath put down the might-y from their seats:
8. He hath filled the hun - gry with good things:
9. He hath holpen His ser - vant Is - ra - el:
10. As He spake to our fa - thers:

Glo - ry be to the Fa - ther, and to the Son:
As it was in the beginning, is now, and ev - er shall be:

[May also be sung to Chant on p. 836.]

DICTUS

Tone iii. Ending ii.

DOH	**d** $t_{|}$	$l_{|}$ $t_{|}$	$l_{|}$	($s_{|}$) $s_{|}$
FORM.				
(1.) for He hath visited and re -	deemed	His	peo -	ple,
(2.) in the house of His	ser -	vant	Da -	vid;
(3.) which have been	since	the	world be -	gan;
(4.) and from the hand of	all	that	hate	us;
(5.) and to remember His	ho -	ly	co - ve-	nant;
(6.) that He would	grant	un -	to	us,
(7.) might serve	Him	with -	out	fear,
(8.) all the	days	of	our	life.
(9.) for thou shalt go before the face of the Lord	to	pre -	pare His	ways;
(10.) by the remis - - - -	sion	of	their	sins,
(11.) whereby the dayspring from on high hath	vi -	sit -	ed	us,
(12.) to guide our feet in - - -	to	the	way of	peace.
and	*to*	*the*	*Ho - ly*	*Ghost;*
world with- - - - -	*out*	*end.*	*A*	*men.*

SECOND FORM on p. 833.

FICAT

Tone vii. Ending i.

RAY	**m**	**r**	**d**	(d) $t_{|}$ $l_{|}$
FORM.				
(1.) and my spirit hath rejoiced in	God	my	Sa -	viour.
(2.) the low estate of	His	hand-	maid -	en;
(3.) all generations shall	call	me	bless -	ed.
(4.) and	ho -	ly	is His	Name.
(5.) from generation to	ge -	ne -	ra -	tion.
(6.) He hath scattered the proud in the imagi -	na -	tion	of their	hearts.
(7.) and exalted	them	of	low de -	gree.
(8.) and the rich He hath sent	emp -	ty	a -	way.
(9.) in remembrance	of	His	mer -	cy;
(10.) to Abraham and to his	seed	for	ev -	er.
and	*to*	*the*	*Ho - ly*	*Ghost;*
world with - - - - -	*out*	*end.*	*A* -	*men.*

SECOND FORM on p. 837.

715 *(continued)* MAGNIFICAT

Doh = B♭. RICHARD WOODWARD, 1744–77.

s, :—	l, :t,	d :—	r :—	m :r.d	d :t,	d :—
m, :—	f, :f,	m, :—	s, :—	s, :f,	m, :r,	m, :—
d :—	d :r	d :—	t, :—	d :l,	s, :s,	s, :—
d, :—	f, :r,	l, :—	s, :—	d :f,	s, :s,	d, :—

Doh = E. JOHN GOSS, 1800–80.

m :—	s :f	m :—	r :–.d	t, :d	f :m	r :—
s, :—	s, :l,.t,	d :—	l, :—	s, :s,	t, :d	t, :—
d' :—	t :l	s :—	f :–.m	r :s	s :s	s :—
d :—	d :d	d :—	f, :—	f :m	r :d	s, :—

s :—	d' :t	l :—	r :—	s :m	r :r	d :—
t, :—	d :d	f :m	r :—	s, :d	d :t,	d :—
s :—	m :m	f :s	l :–.t	d' :s	s :–.f	m :—
m :—	l, :l,	r :m	f :—	m :d	s, :s,	d :—

St. Luke i. 46–55. FIRST FORM.

MY soul doth magnify the Lord,* and my spirit hath rejoiced in | God my | Saviour. ||

2 For He hath regarded the | low es-tate | of His | hand-maiden : ||

3 For, be- | hold, from | henceforth || all gener- | ations · shall | call me | blessèd. ||

4 For He that is mighty hath | done to me | great things ; || and | holy | is His | Name. ||

5 And His mercy is on | them that | fear Him || from gener- | ation to | gener- | ation. ||

6 He hath shewed | strength · with His | arm ; || He hath scattered the proud in the imagi- | nation | of their | hearts. ||

7 He hath put down the | mighty · from their | seats, || and ex- | alted · them of | low de- | gree. ||

8 He hath filled the | hungry with | good things ; || and the | rich He · hath sent | empty a- | way. ||

9 He hath holpen His servant Israel in re- | membrance · of His | mercy ; ||

10 As He spake to our fathers, to | Abraham · and to his | seed for | ever. ||

Glory | be · to the | Father, || and to the Son, | and · to the | Holy | Ghost ; ||

As it | was in · the be- | ginning, || is now, and ever shall be : | world with-out | end. A- | men. ||

[May also be sung to Gregorian Chant, on p. 834.]

MAGNIFICAT

Doh = A♭. JAMES NARES, 1715–83.

m :—	f :r	t, :— ‖	d :—	l, :f	m :r	d :— ‖
s, :—	f, :l,	s, :— ‖	s, :—	f, :l,	s, :-.f,	m, :— ‖
d :—	d :f	r :— ‖	d :—	d :d	d :t,	d :— ‖
d :—	l, :f,	s, :— ‖	m, :—	f, :r,	s, :s,	d, :— ‖

Doh = A. THOMAS SANDERS DUPUIS, 1730–96.

d :—	t, :d	l, :— ‖	f :—	m :r.d	t, :d	r :— ‖
s, :—	f, :s,	l, :— ‖	f, :—	s, :s,	f, :m,	r, :— ‖
m :—	r :d	d :— ‖	t, :—	d :d	r :m.d	t, :— ‖
d, :—	r, :m,	f, :— ‖	r, :—	d, :m,	r, :d,	s, :— ‖

r :—	r :m	f :— ‖	r :—	m :r.d	d :t,	d :— ‖
s, :—	s, :s,	l, :— ‖	s, :—	s, :l,	s, :s,	s, :— ‖
t, :—	t, :de	r :— ‖	t, :—	d :f	m :r	m :— ‖
s, :—	f, :m,	r, :— ‖	s, :—	d :f,	s, :s,	d, :— ‖

SECOND FORM.

MY soul doth magnify the Lord,* and my spirit hath rejoiced in | God my | Saviour. ||

2 For He hath regarded the | lowliness | of His | hand-maiden. ||

3 For be- | hold from | henceforth || all gener- | ations · shall | call me | blessèd. ||

4 For He that is | mighty · hath | magnified · me ; || and | holy | is His | Name. ||

5 And His mercy is on | them that | fear Him || through- | out all | gener- | ations. ||

6 He hath shewed | strength · with His | arm ; || He hath scattered the proud in the imagi- | nation | of their | hearts. ||

7 He hath put down the | mighty · from their | seat, || and hath ex- | alted the | humble and | meek. ||

8 He hath filled the | hungry with | good things ; || and the | rich He · hath sent | empty a- | way. ||

9 He remembering His mercy hath holpen His | servant | Isra-el : || as He promised to our forefathers, | Abraham · and his | seed for | ever. ||

Glory | be · to the | Father, || and to the Son, | and · to the | Holy | Ghost ; ||

As it | was in · the be- | ginning, || is now, and ever shall be : | world with-out | end. A- | men. ||

716

NUNC DIMITTIS

St. Luke ii. 29–32. FIRST FORM.

Doh = F. Tone i. Ending iv.

| d :r :m :m :m :m :m :m :m :m :r :m
Lord, now let - test Thou Thy ser - vant de - part in peace :

| m :m :r :d :r :m || d :r :m :r :m
ac - cord - ing to Thy word; For mine eyes have seen:

| r :d :r :m || d :r :m :m :r :m
Thy sal - va - tion, Which Thou hast pre - pa - red:

| m :m :m :m :r :d :r :m || d :r :m :m
be - fore the face of all peo - ple; A light to ligh -

:m :m :r :m | m :m :m :m :m :m :r :d :r :r :m ||
- ten the Gen - tiles and the glo - ry of Thy peo - ple Is - ra - el.

| d :r :m :m :m :m :m :m :m :r :m
Glo - ry be to the Fa - ther, and to the Son:

| m :r :d :r :r :m | d :r :m :m :m :m :m :m
and to the Ho - ly Ghost, As it was in the be - gin - ning,

:m :m :m :m :m :r :m | m :m :r :d :r :— :m :— ||
is now, and ev - er shall be: world with - out end. A - men.

716 *(continued)*

NUNC DIMITTIS

Lah = E. Doh = G. *Unison.* Adapted from the *Tonus Peregrinus.*

m :-.r	f :m	r :d	r :—	r :l_1	d :t_1	l_1 :—

St. Luke ii. 29–32.

First Form.

LORD, now lettest Thou Thy servant depart in peace,* ac- | cording · to Thy | word : ||
2 For mine | eyes have | seen Thy sal- | vation, ||
3 Which Thou hast prepared before the | face of · all | people ; ||
4 A light to lighten the Gentiles, and the | glory · of Thy | people | Isra-el. ||
Glory | be · to the | Father, || and to the Son, | and · to the | Holy | Ghost ; ||
As it | was in · the be- | ginning, || is now, and ever shall be : | world with-out | end. A- | men. ||

Lah = C. Doh = E♭. William Felton, 1715–69.

m :—	m :m	m :—	m :—	f :l	s :-.f	m :—
d :—	r :d	t_1 :—	d :—	d :d	d :t_1	d :—
l :—	t :l	se :—	s :—	f :f	m :r.s	s :—
l_1 :—	se_1 :l_1	m_1 :—	d :—	l_1 :f_1	s_1 :s_1	d :—

Doh = F. Richard Farrant (?), 1530–80.

d :—	d :r	m :—	s :—	f :m	r :r	d :—
s_1 :—	l_1 :t_1	d :—	d :—	d :d	d :t_1	d :—
m :—	m :s	s :—	s :—	l :s	s :s	m :—
d :—	l_1 :s_1	d :—	m_1 :—	f_1 :d	s_1 :s_1	d :—

Doh = E. Benjamin Vine Westbrook, 1859–

m :—	m :f	m :r	s :—	s :l	f :f	m :—
d :—	d :r	d :t_1	r :—	d :d	d :t_1	d :—
s :—	l :l	s :—	t :—	d^1 :m	l :s	s :—
d :—	l_1 :f_1	s_1 :—	s :—	m :d	r :s_1	d :—

[By permission of the Congregational Union of England and Wales.]

Second Form.

LORD, now lettest Thou Thy servant depart in peace,* ac- | cording · to Thy | word. ||
2 For mine | eyes have | seen Thy sal- | vation, ||
3 Which Thou hast prepared before the | face of · all | people ; ||
4 To be a light to lighten the Gentiles, and to be the | glory · of Thy | people | Isra-el. ||
Glory | be · to the | Father, || and to the Son, | and · to the | Holy | Ghost ; ||
As it | was in · the be- | ginning, || is now, and ever shall be : | world with-out | end. A- | men. ||

717

GLORIA IN EXCELSIS

1 *A.* vv. 1–4; 11–12.

Doh = B♭. JOHN ALCOCK, 1718–1806.

```
{ f  d  :—  | l, :r  | t, :— || m  :— | d  :r  | d  :t, | d  :— || d  | d  ||
{ l, m, :—  | d, :f, | r, :— || s, :— | m, :l, | s, :s, | s, :— || f, | m, ||
{ d  s, :—  | l, :l, | t, :— || t, :— | d  :f  | m  :r  | m  :— || l, | s, ||
{ f, d, :—  | f, :r, | s, :— || m, :— | l, :f, | s, :s, | d, :— || f, | d, ||
                                                                  A-men.
```

2 *A.* vv. 1–4; 11–12.

Doh = A. JONATHAN BATTISHILL, 1738–1801.

```
{ l   d  :— | s, :m  | r  :— || f  :—   | m  :d  | r  :t, | d  :— || d  | d  ||
{ m   s, :— | s, :d  | t, :— || l, :-.t,| d  :d  | l, :s, | s, :— || l, | s, ||
{ de' m  :— | d  :s  | s  :— || f  :—   | s  :m  | f  :r  | m  :— || f  | m  ||
{ l,  d, :— | m, :d, | s, :— || r, :—   | m, :l, | f, :s, | d, :— || f, | d, ||
                                                                    A-men.
```

GLORY be to | God on | high, ‖ and in earth | peace, good- | will · towards | men. ‖

2 We | praise Thee · we | bless Thee, ‖ we | worship · Thee, we | glorify | Thee, ‖

3 We give thanks to Thee for | Thy great | glory, ‖
4 O Lord God, heavenly King, | God the | Father Al- | mighty. ‖

1 *B.* vv. 5–10.

Lah = D. Doh = F. WILLIAM CROTCH, 1775–1847.

```
{ t, m  :— | r  :m   | d  :— || r  :— | r   :d  | t, :t,  | l, :— ||
{ s, d  :— | t, :t,  | l, :— || l, :— | se, :l, | l, :se, | l, :— ||
{ t, m  :— | f  :m   | m  :— || r  :— | m   :m  | m  :-.r | d  :— ||
{ m, l, :— | l, :se, | l, :— || f, :— | m,  :l, | m, :m,  | l, :— ||
```

2 *B.* vv. 5–10.

Lah = A. Doh = C. WILLIAM CROFT, 1678–1727.

```
{ d  l  :— | s  :f  | m  :— || d' :— | t  :l  | l  :se | l  :— ||
{ s, m  :— | r  :r  | d  :— || s  :— | f  :f  | m  :m  | m  :— ||
{ ma d' :— | s  :s  | s  :— || m' :— | r' :d' | d' :t  | d' :— ||
{ d, l, :— | t, :t, | d  :— || d  :— | r  :r  | m  :m  | l, :— ||
```

5 O Lord, the only begotten Son, | Jesus | Christ; ‖
6 O Lord God, | Lamb of · God, | Son of the | Father, ‖

7 That takest away the sins of the world, have | mer-cy up- | on us. ‖
8 Thou that takest away the sins of the | world, have | mer-cy up- | on us. ‖

9 Thou that takest away the sins of the world, re- | ceive our | prayer. ‖
10 Thou that sittest at the right hand of God the | Father · have | mer-cy up- | on us. ‖

Return to A.

11 For Thou only art holy, Thou only | art the | Lord; ‖
12 Thou only, O Christ, with the Holy Ghost, art most high in the | glory of | God the | Father. ‖

718

TE DEUM LAUDAMUS

The Eighth Tone, arranged by Charles Hylton Stewart, 1884-

All the beats or pulses in the voice parts should be of approximately equal length, and the *tempo* should be that of rather slow reading. A slight break should be made between the halves of each verse.

Doh = A. *Unison* (*may be sung in unison throughout*).

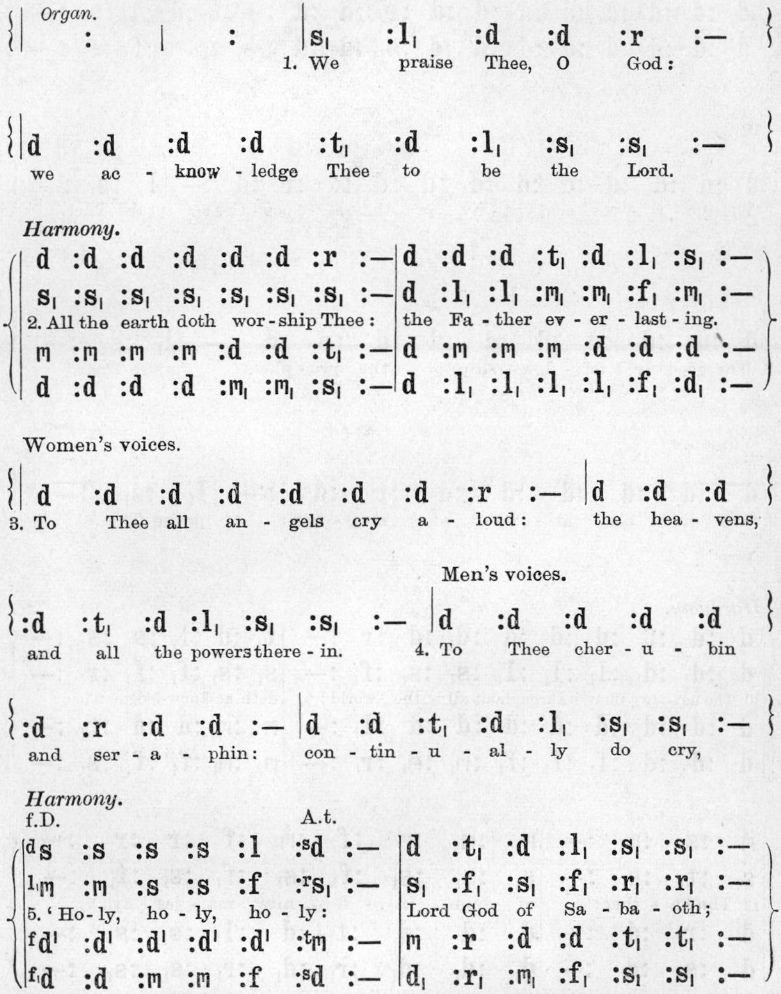

Organ.

: | : | s, :l, :d :d :r :—

1. We praise Thee, O God:

d :d :d :d :t, :d :l, :s, :s, :—

we ac - know - ledge Thee to be the Lord.

Harmony.

d :d :d :d :d :d :r :— | d :d :d :t, :d :l, :s, :—

s, :s, :s, :s, :s, :s, :s, :— | d :l, :l, :m, :m, :f, :m, :—

2. All the earth doth wor - ship Thee: | the Fa - ther ev - er - last - ing.

m :m :m :m :d :d :t, :— | d :m :m :m :d :d :d :—

d :d :d :d :m, :m, :s, :— | d :l, :l, :l, :l, :f, :d, :—

Women's voices.

d :d :d :d :d :d :d :r :— | d :d :d

3. To Thee all an - gels cry a - loud: the hea - vens,

:d :t, :d :l, :s, :s, :— | d :d :d :d :d

and all the powers there - in. | Men's voices. 4. To Thee cher - u - bin

:d :r :d :d :— | d :d :t, :d :l, :s, :s, :—

and ser - a - phin: con - tin - u - al - ly do cry,

Harmony.

f.D. A.t.

ᵈs :s :s :s :l :ˢd :— | d :t, :d :l, :s, :s, :—

ˡm :m :s :s :f :ʳs, :— | s, :f, :s, :f, :r, :r, :—

5. 'Ho - ly, ho - ly, ho - ly: | Lord God of Sa - ba - oth;

ᶠd' :d' :d' :d' :d' :ᵗm :— | m :r :d :d :t, :t, :—

ᶠ,d :d :m :m :f :ˢd :— | d, :r, :m, :f, :s, :s, :—

718 *(continued)*

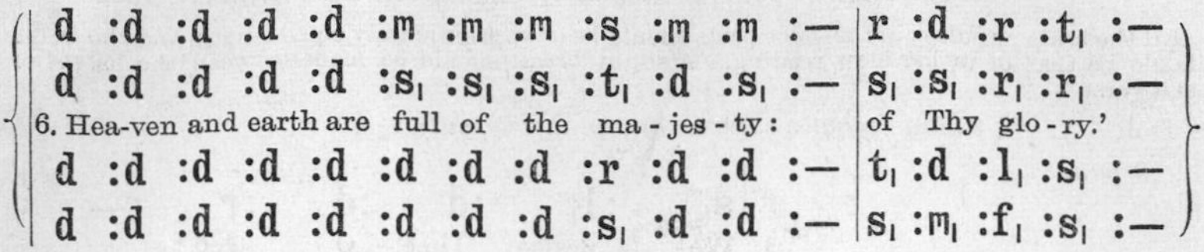

d :d :d :d :d :m :m :m :s :m :m :— | r :d :r :t_1 :—
d :d :d :d :d :s_1 :s_1 :s_1 :t_1 :d :s_1 :— | s_1 :s_1 :r_1 :r_1 :—
6. Hea-ven and earth are full of the ma - jes - ty : | of Thy glo - ry.'
d :d :d :d :d :d :d :d :r :d :d :— | t_1 :d :l_1 :s_1 :—
d :d :d :d :d :d :d :d :s_1 :d :d :— | s_1 :m_1 :f_1 :s_1 :—

Women.

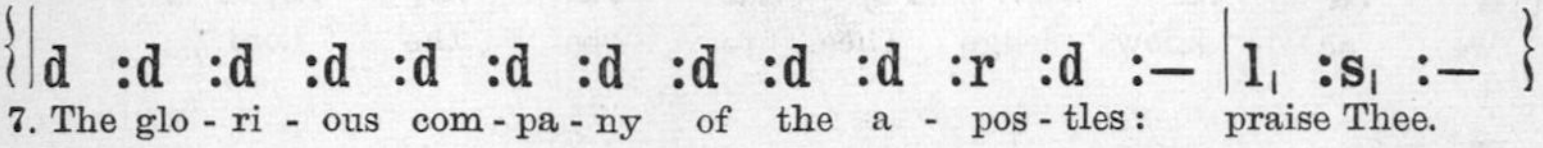

d :d :d :d :d :d :d :d :d :d :r :d :— | l_1 :s_1 :—
7. The glo - ri - ous com - pa - ny of the a - pos - tles : praise Thee.

Men.

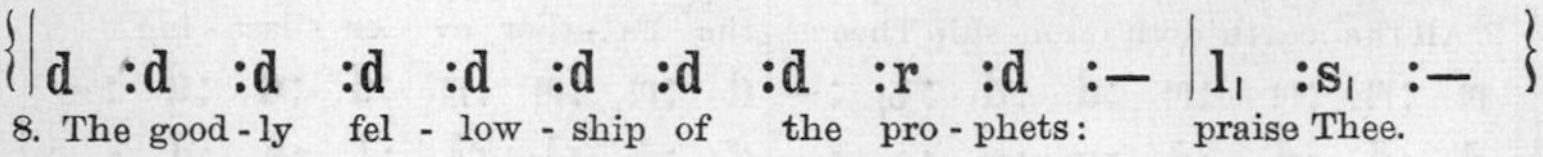

d :d :d :d :d :d :d :d :r :d :— | l_1 :s_1 :—
8. The good - ly fel - low - ship of the pro - phets : praise Thee.

Women.

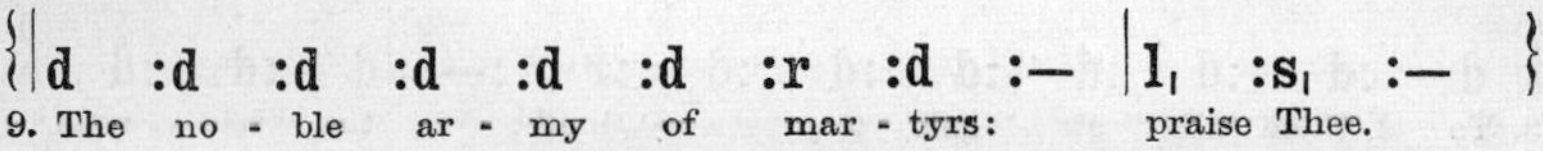

d :d :d :d :d :d :r :d :— | l_1 :s_1 :—
9. The no - ble ar - my of mar - tyrs : praise Thee.

Harmony.

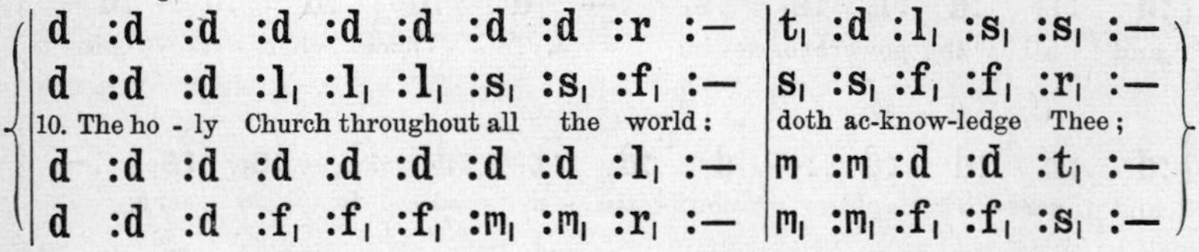

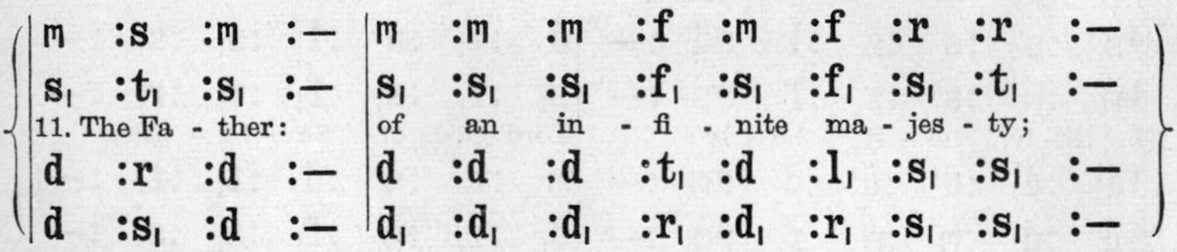

d :d :d :d :d :d :d :d :r :— | t_1 :d :l_1 :s_1 :s_1 :—
d :d :d :l_1 :l_1 :l_1 :s_1 :s_1 :f_1 :— | s_1 :s_1 :f_1 :f_1 :r_1 :—
10. The ho - ly Church throughout all the world : | doth ac-know-ledge Thee ;
d :d :d :d :d :d :d :d :l_1 :— | m :m :d :d :t_1 :—
d :d :d :f_1 :f_1 :f_1 :m_1 :m_1 :r_1 :— | m_1 :m_1 :f_1 :f_1 :s_1 :—

m :s :m :— | m :m :m :f :m :f :r :r :—
s_1 :t_1 :s_1 :— | s_1 :s_1 :s_1 :f_1 :s_1 :f_1 :s_1 :t_1 :—
11. The Fa - ther : | of an in - fi - nite ma - jes - ty ;
d :r :d :— | d :d :d :t_1 :d :l_1 :s_1 :s_1 :—
d :s_1 :d :— | d_1 :d_1 :d_1 :r_1 :d_1 :r_1 :s_1 :s_1 :—

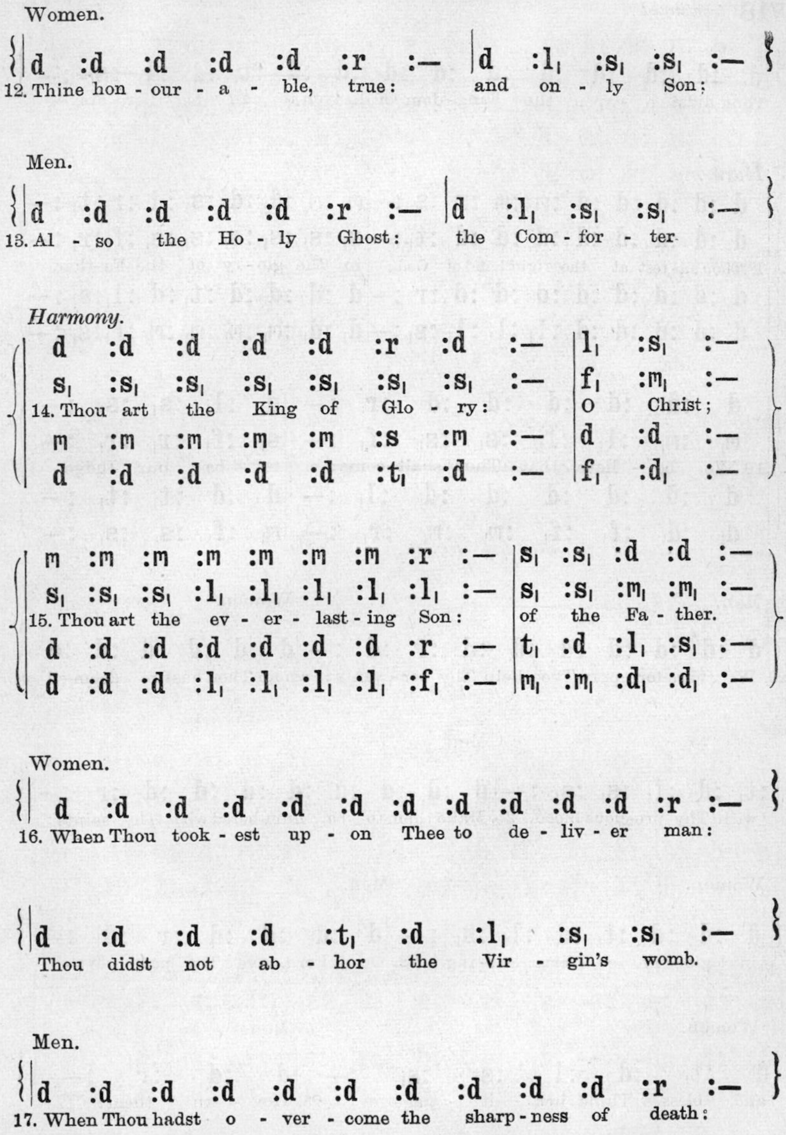

Women.

| d :d :d :d :d :r :— | d :l, :s, :s, :— |

12. Thine hon - our - a - ble, true: and on - ly Son:

Men.

| d :d :d :d :d :r :— | d :l, :s, :s, :— |

13. Al - so the Ho - ly Ghost: the Com - for - ter.

Harmony.

| d :d :d :d :d :r :d :— | l, :s, :— |
| s, :s, :s, :s, :s, :s, :s, :— | f, :m, :— |

14. Thou art the King of Glo - ry: O Christ;

| m :m :m :m :m :s :m :— | d :d :— |
| d :d :d :d :d :t, :d :— | f, :d, :— |

| m :m :m :m :m :m :m :r :— | s, :s, :d :d :— |
| s, :s, :s, :l, :l, :l, :l, :l, :— | s, :s, :m, :m, :— |

15. Thou art the ev - er - last - ing Son: of the Fa - ther.

| d :d :d :d :d :d :d :r :— | t, :d :l, :s, :— |
| d :d :d :l, :l, :l, :l, :f, :— | m, :m, :d, :d, :— |

Women.

| d :d :d :d :d :d :d :d :d :d :d :r :— |

16. When Thou took - est up - on Thee to de - liv - er man:

| d :d :d :d :t, :d :l, :s, :s, :— |

Thou didst not ab - hor the Vir - gin's womb.

Men.

| d :d :d :d :d :d :d :d :d :d :r :— |

17. When Thou hadst o - ver - come the sharp - ness of death:

718 (*continued*)

| d :d :d :d :d :d :d :d :d :d :t, :d :l, :s, :—

Thou didst o - pen the King - dom of heaven to all be - liev - ers.

Harmony.

d :d :d :d :d :m :m :m :s :— | m :m :d :d :s, :d :r :t, :—
d :d :d :d :d :d :d :d :t, :— | s, :s, :s, :s, :s, :s, :f, :r, :—
18. Thou sit - test at the right hand of God: | in the glo - ry of the Fa - ther.
d :d :d :d :d :d :d :d :r :— | d :d :d :d :t, :d :l, :s, :—
d :d :d :d :d :l, :l, :l, :s, :— | d, :d, :m, :m, :m, :m, :f, :s, :—

d :d :d :d :d :d :r :— | d :l, :s, :s, :—
m, :m, :l, :l, :s, :s, :f, :— | s, :f, :r, :r, :—
19. We be - lieve that Thou shalt come: | to be our Judge.
d :d :d :d :d :d :l, :— | d :d :t, :t, :—
d, :d, :f, :f, :m, :m, :r, :— | m, :f, :s, :s, :—

Men. | Women.

| d :d :d :d :d :d :d :r :d :— | d :d :d :d :d :d

20. We there - fore pray Thee, help Thy ser - vants: whom Thou hast re - deem - ed

Men.

:t, :d :l, :s, :s, :— | d :d :d :d :d :d :d :d :r :—

with Thy pre - cious blood. 21. Make them to be num - bered with Thy saints:

Women. | Men.

| d :d :d :t, :d :l, :s, :— | d :d :d :d :r :d :—

in glo - ry ev - er - last - ing. 22. O Lord, save Thy peo - ple:

Women. | Men.

d :t, :d :l, :s, :s, :— | d :d :r :—

and bless Thine her - it - age. 23. Gov - ern them:

Women. Men.

| d :d :d :t_1 :d :l_1 :s_1 :— | d :d :r :— |

and lift them up for ev - er. 24. Day by day:

Women. Men.

| d :t_1 :d :l_1 :s_1 :— | d :d :d :d :d :r :— |

we mag - ni - fy Thee; 25. And we wor - ship Thy Name

Women. Men.

| d :d :t_1 :d :l_1 s_1 :— | d :d :d :r :— |

ev - er world with - out end. 26. Vouch - safe, O Lord:

Women. Men.

| d :d :d :d :t_1 :d :l_1 :s_1 :— | d :d :d :d :d :d :d :r :— |

to keep us this day with-out sin. 27. O Lord, have mer-cy up - on us:

Women. Men.

| d :d :t_1 :d :l_1 s_1 :— | d :d :d :d :d :d |

have mer - cy up - on us. 28. O Lord, let Thy mer - cy

Women.

:d :d :d :d :r :— | d :d :t_1 :d :l_1 :s_1 :— |

light - en up - on us: as our trust is in Thee.

Unison.

| d :d :d :d :d :d :r :d :— |

29. O Lord, in Thee have I trust - ed:

| d :d :d :d :t_1 :d :l_1 :s_1 :— ||

let me nev - er be con - found - ed:

[*By permission of the Composer and the S.P.C.K.*]

718 (*continued*)

TE DEUM LAUDAMUS

First and Second Set of Chants.

1 *A.* vv. 1–13 and 22–29.

Doh = A♭. George Alexander Macfarren, 1813–87.

^{f}d :—	r :m	f :— ‖	l_1 :—	t_1 :d	d :t_1	d :— ‖
$^{d}s_1$:—	s_1 :s_1	f_1 :— ‖	f_1 :—	f_1 :s_1	l_1 :s_1.f_1	m_1 :— ‖
^{l}m :—	r :d	d :— ‖	d :—	f :m	r :r	d :— ‖
^{f}d :—	t_1 :d	l_1 :— ‖	f_1 :—	r_1 :m_1	f_1 :s_1	d_1 :— ‖

2 *A.* vv. 1–13 and 22–29.

Doh = D. Richard Woodward, 1744–77.

^{r}s :—	s :s	d^1 :— ‖	m :—	l :s	f :m	r :— ‖
^{t_1}m :—	m :r	m :— ‖	d :—	d :d	t_1 :d	t_1 :— ‖
$^{s}d^1$:—	d^1 :r^1	d^1 :— ‖	d^1 :—	d^1 :s	s :s	s :— ‖
^{s_1}d :—	d^1 :t	l :— ‖	l :-.s	f :m	r :d	s_1 :— ‖

s :-.f	m :d^1	t :— ‖	d^1 :—	d :r	m :r	d :— ‖
r :—	d :r	r :— ‖	d :—	d :d	d :t_1	d :— ‖
t :—	d^1 :l	s :— ‖	s :—	l :l	s :-.f	m :— ‖
s :—	l :fe	s :— ‖	m :—	l :f	s :s_1	d :— ‖

WE praise | Thee, O | God; ‖ we ac- | knowledge · Thee to | be the | Lord. ‖

2 All the | earth doth | worship · Thee, ‖ the | Father | ever- | lasting. ‖

3 To Thee all angels | cry a- | loud ; ‖ the | heavens · and | all the | powers there-in. ‖

4 To Thee | cheru-bin and | seraph-in ‖ con- | tinu-al- | ly do | cry, ‖

5 ' Holy, holy, holy ; Lord | God of Sa- | baoth ; ‖
6 Heaven and earth are full of the | majesty | of Thy | glory.' ‖

7 The glorious company of the a- | postles | praise Thee. ‖
8 The goodly | fellowship · of the | prophets | praise Thee. ‖

9 The noble army of | martyrs | praise Thee. ‖
10 The holy Church throughout | all the | world · doth ac- | knowledge · Thee ; ‖

11 The Father of an | infinite | majes-ty ; ‖
12 Thine honourable, true, and only Son ; *(13) Also the | Holy | Ghost the | Comfort-er. ‖

1 *B.* vv. 14–21.

Doh = E♭. JOHN HENRY ROBERTS, 1848–1924.

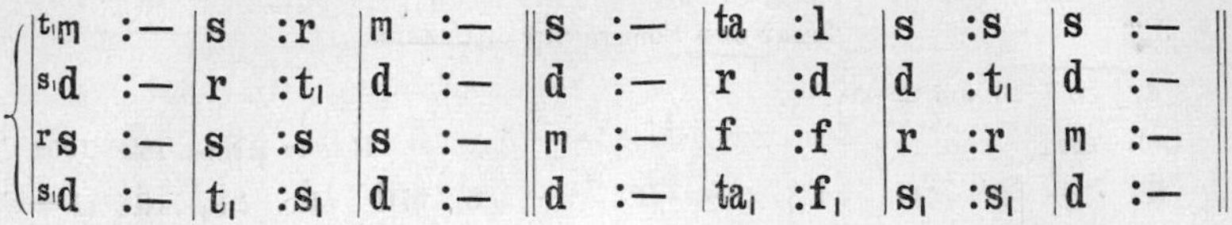

t m :—	s :r	m :— ‖	s :—	ta :l	s :s	s :— ‖
s, d :—	r :t,	d :— ‖	d :—	r :d	d :t,	d :— ‖
r s :—	s :s	s :— ‖	m :—	f :f	r :r	m :— ‖
s, d :—	t, :s,	d :— ‖	d :—	ta, :f,	s, :s,	d :— ‖

2 *B.* vv. 14–21.

Doh = G. HENRY SMART, 1813–79.

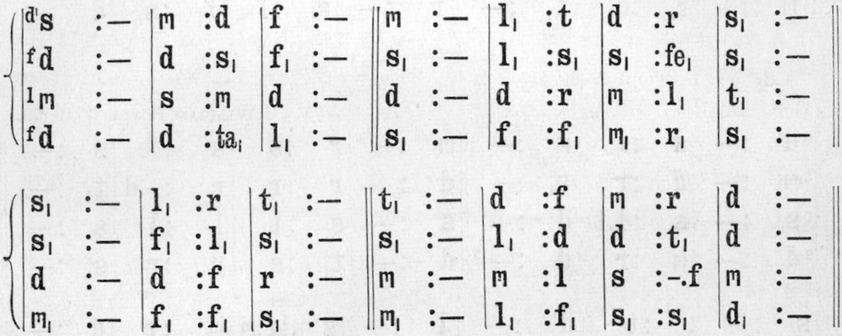

d' s :—	m :d	f :— ‖	m :—	l, :t	d :r	s, :— ‖
f d :—	d :s,	f, :— ‖	s, :—	l, :s,	s, :fe,	s, :— ‖
l m :—	s :m	d :— ‖	d :—	d :r	m :l,	t, :— ‖
f d :—	d :ta,	l, :— ‖	s, :—	f, :f,	m, :r,	s, :— ‖

s, :—	l, :r	t, :— ‖	t, :—	d :f	m :r	d :— ‖
s, :—	f, :l,	s, :— ‖	s, :—	l, :d	d :t,	d :— ‖
d :—	d :f	r :— ‖	m :—	m :l	s :-.f	m :— ‖
m, :—	f, :f,	s, :— ‖	m, :—	l, :f,	s, :s,	d, :— ‖

[*By permission of Novello & Co., Ltd.*]

Chant B.

14 Thou art the King of | Glory · O | Christ ; ‖
15 Thou art the ever- | lasting | Son · of the | Father. ‖

16 When Thou tookest upon Thee to de- | liver | man, ‖ Thou didst not ab- | hor the | Virgin's | womb. ‖

17 When Thou hadst overcome the | sharpness of | death, ‖ Thou didst open the Kingdom of | heaven to | all be- | lievers. ‖

18 Thou sittest at the | right · hand of | God, ‖ in the | glory | of the | Father. ‖

19 We believe that Thou shalt | come to · be our | Judge. ‖
20 We therefore pray Thee, help Thy servants, whom Thou hast re- | deemed · with Thy | precious | blood. ‖

21 Make them to be | numbered · with Thy | saints ‖ in | glory | ever- | lasting. ‖

Return to A.

22 O Lord, save Thy people, and | bless Thine | herit-age. ‖
23 Govern them and | lift them | up for | ever. ‖

24 Day by | day we | magnify · Thee ; ‖
25 And we worship Thy | Name · ever | world with-out | end. ‖

26 Vouchsafe, O Lord, to keep us this | day with-out | sin. ‖
27 O Lord, have mercy up- | on us · have | mer-cy up- | on us. ‖

28 O Lord, let Thy mercy lighten upon us, as our | trust · is in | Thee. ‖
29 O Lord, in Thee have I trusted ; let me | never | be con- | founded. ‖

718 *(continued)* TE DEUM LAUDAMUS

THIRD AND FOURTH SET OF CHANTS.

3 *A.* vv. 1–13 and 22–29.

Doh = B♭. HENRY HILES, 1826–1904.

^{f}d :—	r :m	l_1 :—	r :—	s_1 :d	d :t_1	d :—
$^{d}s_1$:—	s_1 :s_1	f_1 :—	f_1 :—	f_1 :m_1	l_1 :s_1	s_1 :—
^{f}d :—	t_1 :d	d :—	r :—	t_1 :d	r :r	m :—
$^{l}m_1$:—	r_1 :d_1	f_1 :—	r_1 :—	s_1 :l_1	f_1 :s_1	d_1 :—

4 *A.* vv. 1–13 and 22–29.

Doh = D. WILLIAM BOYCE, 1710–79.

$^{s}d^1$:—	s :f	m :—	m :—	r :s	s :fe	s :—
^{t_1}m :—	d :r	s_1 :—	d :—	r :r	r :-.d	t_1 :—
^{r}s :—	s :l.t	d^1 :—	s :—	s :t	l :l	s :—
^{s_1}d :—	m :r	d :—	d :—	t_1 :s_1	r :r	s_1 :—

s :—	l :t	d^1 :—	l :—	s :f.m	m :r	d :—
d :—	d :f	m :—	f :—	d :r.d	d :t_1	d :—
s :—	f :r^1	d^1 :—	d^1 :—	s :l	s :-.f	m :—
m :—	f :r	l :—	f :—	m :f	s :s_1	d :—

WE praise | Thee, O | God; || we ac- | knowledge · Thee to | be the | Lord. ||

2 All the | earth doth | worship · Thee, || the | Father | ever- | lasting. ||

3 To Thee all angels | cry a- | loud; || the | heavens · and | all the | powers there-in. ||

4 To Thee | cheru-bin and | seraph-in || con- | tinu-al- | ly do | cry, ||

5 'Holy, holy, holy; Lord | God of Sa- | baoth; ||
6 Heaven and earth are full of the | majesty | of Thy | glory.' ||

7 The glorious company of the a- | postles | praise Thee. ||
8 The goodly | fellowship · of the | prophets | praise Thee. ||

9 The noble army of | martyrs | praise Thee. ||
10 The holy Church throughout | all the | world · doth ac- | knowledge · Thee; ||

11 The Father of an | infinite | majes-ty; ||
12 Thine honourable, true, and only Son; *(13) Also the | Holy | Ghost the | Comfort-er. ||

3 *B.* vv. 14–21.

Doh = F. WILLIAM RUSSELL, 1777–1813.

^{t_1}m :—	f :r	s :— ‖	d :—	f :m	r :r	d :— ‖
^{s_1}d :—	d :t_1	d :— ‖	d :—	s_1 :d	d :t_1	d :— ‖
^{r}s :—	f :f	s :— ‖	m :—	r :s	s :-.f	m :— ‖
^{s_1}d :—	r :r	m :— ‖	l_1 :—	t_1 :d	s_1 :s_1	d :— ‖

4 *B.* vv. 14–21.

Doh = G. ROBERT COOKE, 1768-1814.

^{l}m :—	f :s	l :— ‖	s :—	f :m	r :d	t_1 :— ‖
$^{d}s_1$:—	f_1 :ta_1	l_1 :— ‖	d :—	l_1.t_1 :d	f_1 :m_1.fe_1	s_1 :— ‖
^{f}d :—	d :m	f :— ‖	s :—	r :s	l :l	r :— ‖
^{f}d :-.ta_1	l_1 :s_1	f_1 :— ‖	m_1 :—	r_1 :d_1	f_1.s_1 :l_1	s_1 :— ‖

d :—	r :m	f :— ‖	m :—	r :d	d :t_1	d :— ‖
s_1 :—	s_1 :d	d :— ‖	t_1 :—	l_1.t_1 :d	s_1 :s_1	s_1 :— ‖
s :—	s :s	f :— ‖	s :—	r :s.l	r :r	m :— ‖
m :—	t_1 :d	l_1 :— ‖	s_1 :—	f_1 :m_1.f_1	s_1 :s_1	d_1 :— ‖

Chant B.

14 Thou art the King of | Glory · O | Christ ; ‖
15 Thou art the ever- | lasting | Son · of the | Father. ‖

16 When Thou tookest upon Thee to de- | liver | man, ‖ Thou didst not ab- | hor the | Virgin's | womb. ‖

17 When Thou hadst overcome the | sharpness of | death, ‖ Thou didst open the Kingdom of | heaven to | all be- | lievers. ‖

18 Thou sittest at the | right · hand of | God, ‖ in the | glory | of the | Father. ‖

19 We believe that Thou shalt | come to · be our | Judge. ‖
20 We therefore pray Thee, help Thy servants, whom Thou hast re- | deemed · with Thy | precious | blood. ‖

21 Make them to be | numbered · with Thy | saints ‖ in | glory | ever- | lasting. ‖

Return to A.

22 O Lord, save Thy people, and | bless Thine | herit-age. ‖
23 Govern them and | lift them | up for | ever. ‖

24 Day by | day we | magnify · Thee ; ‖
25 And we worship Thy | Name · ever | world with-out | end. ‖

26 Vouchsafe, O Lord, to keep us this | day with-out | sin. ‖
27 O Lord, have mercy up- | on us · have | mer-cy up- | on us. ‖

28 O Lord, let Thy mercy lighten upon us, as our | trust · is in | Thee. ‖
29 O Lord, in Thee have I trusted ; let me | never | be con- | founded. ‖

719 BENEDICITE,

Daniel iii. (Greek Version.)

Doh = D. A.t.

m :— :—	s :s :f	m :— :—		ʳs, :l, :t,	d :-.r :m	r :d :t,	t, :d :—	
d :— :—	m :m :r	d :— :—		ᵈf, :m, :r,	s, :-.s, :s,	l, :s, :s,	s, :s, :—	
s :— :—	s :s :s	s :— :—		ᶠᵉt, :d :r	d :-.t, :m	f :m {:f / :r}	{f :m / r :d} :—	
d :— :—	s, :s, :s,	d :— :—		ʳs, :s, :f,	m, :-.r, :d,	f, :s, :s,	d, :d, :—	

1. O all ye works of the Lord, bless ye the Lord: Praise Him, and mag-ni-fy Him for ev-er.

3 O ye heavens, | bless ye the | Lord : ||
Praise Him, and | magnify | Him for | ever. ||

5 O all ye powers of the Lord, | bless ye the | Lord : ||
Praise Him, and | magnify | Him for | ever. ||

7 O ye stars of heaven, | bless ye the | Lord : ||
Praise Him, and | magnify | Him for | ever. ||

9 O ye winds of God, | bless ye the | Lord : ||
Praise Him, and | magnify | Him for | ever. ||

11 O ye winter and summer, | bless ye the | Lord : ||
Praise Him, and | magnify | Him for | ever. ||

13 O ye frost and cold, | bless ye the | Lord : ||
Praise Him, and | magnify | Him for | ever. ||

15 O ye nights and days, | bless ye the | Lord : ||
Praise Him, and | magnify | Him for | ever. ||

17 O ye lightnings and clouds, | bless ye the | Lord : ||
Praise Him, and | magnify | Him for | ever. ||

19 O ye mountains and hills, | bless ye the | Lord : ||
Praise Him, and | magnify | Him for | ever. ||

21 O ye wells, | bless ye the | Lord : ||
Praise Him, and | magnify | Him for | ever. ||

23 O ye whales, and all that move in the waters, | bless ye the | Lord : ||
Praise Him, and | magnify | Him for | ever. ||

25 O all ye beasts and cattle, | bless ye the | Lord : ||
Praise Him, and | magnify | Him for | ever. ||

27 O let Israel | bless the | Lord : ||
Praise Him, and | magnify | Him for | ever. ||

29 O ye servants of the Lord, | bless ye the | Lord : ||
Praise Him, and | magnify | Him for | ever. ||

31 O ye holy and humble men of heart, | bless ye the | Lord : ||
Praise Him, and | magnify | Him for | ever. ||

m :— :—	s :s :f	m :— :—		d' :t :l	s :— :fe	s :— :—	
d :— :—	d :d :t,	d :— :—		m :m :m	r :— :r	r :— :—	
s :— :—	s :s :s	s :— :—		l {:r' :d' / :se :l}	t :— :l [d']	s [t] :— :—	
d :— :—	m :m :r	d :— :—		l, :t, :d	r :— :r	s, :— :—	

Glory be to the Father, and to the Son: and to the Ho - ly Ghost;

OMNIA OPERA

SAMUEL SEBASTIAN WESLEY, 1810–76.

f.D.

| ¹ₗm :— :— | s :f :m | r :— :— ‖ s :l :t | d' :-.d' :r' | r' :d' :t | t :d' :— ‖
| ᶠd :— :— | d :t, :d | t, :— :— ‖ t, :m :m | m :-.m :r | m :— :r | r :d :— ‖
| (upper: :s | s :s :—)
| ᵈs :— :— | s :s :s | s :— :— ‖ s :s :se | l :-.l :l | s :— :f | f :m :— ‖
| ᶠd :— :— | m :r :d | f :— :— ‖ m :d :t, | l, :-.l, :f, | s, :— :s, | d :d :— ‖

2. O ye angels of the Lord, bless ye the Lord : Praise Him, and mag - ni - fy Him for ev - er.

4 O ye waters that be above the firmament, | bless ye the | Lord : ||
Praise Him, and | magnify | Him for | ever. ||
6 O ye sun and moon, | bless ye the | Lord : ||
Praise Him, and | magnify | Him for | ever. ||
8 O ye showers and dew, | bless ye the | Lord : ||
Praise Him, and | magnify | Him for | ever. ||
10 O ye fire and heat, | bless ye the | Lord : ||
Praise Him, and | magnify | Him for | ever. ||
12 O ye dews and frosts, | bless ye the | Lord : ||
Praise Him, and | magnify | Him for | ever. ||
14 O ye ice and snow, | bless ye the | Lord : ||
Praise Him, and | magnify | Him for | ever. ||
16 O ye light and darkness, | bless ye the | Lord : ||
Praise Him, and | magnify | Him for | ever. ||
18 O let the earth | bless the | Lord : ||
Yea, let it praise Him, and | magnify | Him for | ever. ||
20 O all ye green things upon the earth, | bless ye the | Lord : ||
Praise Him, and | magnify | Him for | ever. ||
22 O ye seas and floods, | bless ye the | Lord : ||
Praise Him, and | magnify | Him for | ever. ||
24 O all ye fowls of the air, | bless ye the | Lord : ||
Praise Him, and | magnify | Him for | ever. ||
26 O ye children of men, | bless ye the | Lord : ||
Praise Him, and | magnify | Him for | ever. ||
28 O ye priests of the Lord, | bless ye the | Lord : ||
Praise Him, and | magnify | Him for | ever. ||
30 O ye spirits and souls of the righteous, | bless ye the | Lord : ||
Praise Him, and | magnify | Him for | ever. ||
32 O Ananias, Azarias, and Misael, | bless ye the | Lord : ||
Praise Him, and | magnify | Him for | ever. ||

| s :— :— | l :-.l :t.t | d' :d :— ‖ d :r :m | f :d :— | d :— :— ‖
| r :— :— | m :-.m :r.r | d :d :— ‖ d :d :d | d :ta, :l, | s, :— :— ‖
| t :— :— | d' :-.d' :s.s | s :s :— ‖ m :f :s | f :m :f | m :— :— ‖
| s :— :— | s :-.s :f.f | m :m :— ‖ d :d :ta, | l, :s, :f, | d :— :— ‖

As it was in the beginning, is now, and ev-er shall be : world with-out end. A - men.

720 THE TEN COMMANDMENTS

Exodus xx.

GOD spake all these words, saying, I am the Lord Thy God, which have brought thee out of the land of Egypt, out of the house of bondage. Thou shalt have no other gods before Me.

Doh = F. *Softly and lightly.* JOHN MERBECKE, 1523–85.

d	r	m	r	m	r	d	r	r	f	f	f	f	m	r	m
Lord,	*have*	*mer-*	*cy*	*up-*	*on*	*us,*	*and*	*in-*	*cline*	*our*	*hearts*	*to*	*keep*	*this*	*law.*

Thou shalt not make unto thee any graven image, or any likeness of any thing that is in heaven above, or that is in the earth beneath, or that is in the water under the earth : thou shalt not bow down thyself to them, nor serve them : for I the Lord thy God am a jealous God, visiting the iniquity of the fathers upon the children unto the third and fourth generation of them that hate Me ; and shewing mercy unto thousands of them that love Me, and keep My commandments.

Lord, have mercy upon us, and incline our hearts to keep this law.

Thou shalt not take the Name of the Lord thy God in vain ; for the Lord will not hold him guiltless that taketh His Name in vain.

Lord, have mercy upon us, and incline our hearts to keep this law.

Remember the sabbath day, to keep it holy. Six days shalt thou labour, and do all thy work : but the seventh day is the sabbath of the Lord thy God : in it thou shalt not do any work, thou, nor thy son, nor thy daughter, thy manservant, nor thy maidservant, nor thy cattle, nor thy stranger that is within thy gates : for in six days the Lord made heaven and earth, the sea, and all that in them is, and rested the seventh day : wherefore the Lord blessed the sabbath day, and hallowed it.

Lord, have mercy upon us, and incline our hearts to keep this law.

Honour thy father and thy mother : that thy days may be long upon the land which the Lord thy God giveth thee.

Lord, have mercy upon us, and incline our hearts to keep this law.

Thou shalt not kill.

Lord, have mercy upon us, and incline our hearts to keep this law.

Thou shalt not commit adultery.

Lord, have mercy upon us, and incline our hearts to keep this law.

Thou shalt not steal.

Lord, have mercy upon us, and incline our hearts to keep this law.

Thou shalt not bear false witness against thy neighbour.

Lord, have mercy upon us, and incline our hearts to keep this law.

Thou shalt not covet thy neighbour's house, thou shalt not covet thy neighbour's wife, nor his manservant, nor his maidservant, nor his ox, nor his ass, nor any thing that is thy neighbour's.

d	r	m	r	m	r	d	r	f	f	f	f	f	f	f	m	r	m	r	d
Lord,	*have*	*mer-*	*cy*	*up-*	*on*	*us,*	*and*	*write*	*all*	*these*	*Thy*	*laws*	*in*	*our*	*hearts,*	*we*	*be-*	*seech*	*Thee.*

721 THE COMMANDMENTS OF THE LORD JESUS

St. Matthew xxii ; *St. Mark* xii ; *St. John* xiii.

JESUS said : The first of all the commandments is : The Lord our God is one Lord : and thou shalt love the Lord thy God with all thy heart, and with all thy soul, and with all thy mind, and with all thy strength. This is the first and great commandment.

WILLIAM BYRD, 1538-1623.

Lah = D. Doh = F.

m :— |— :m |s :— |f :m |— .r :d |t_1 :— |t_1 :t_1
d :— |— :d |t_1 :— |d :d |— .t_1 :l_1 |se_1 :— |s_1 :r
Lord, have mer - cy up - on us, and in -
m :— |— :m |m :— |d :m |— :m |m :— |r :r
l_1 :— |— :l_1 |m :— |l_1 :d |— .s_1 :l_1 |m_1 :— |s_1 :s_1

-cline our hearts to keep this law.
m :— |r :d |— .t_1 :l_1 |— :se_1 |l_1 :— |— :—
d :— .t_1 |l_1 :— .s_1 |f_1 :m_1 |— :m_1 |m_1 :— |— :—
-cline our hearts to keep this law.
-cline our hearts to keep this law.
m .f :s |f :m |— .r :d |t_1 :t_1 |l_1 :— |— :—
d :— |f_1 :l_1 |— :l_1 |m_1 :m_1 |l_1 :— |— :—

And the second is like unto it, namely this : Thou shalt love thy neighbour as thyself.

Lord, have mercy upon us, and incline our hearts to keep this law.

A new commandment I give unto you, That ye love one another ; as I have loved you, that ye also love one another.

m :— |— :m |s :— |f :m |— .f :r |m :m |r :d |t_1 :— .t_1
d :— |— :d |t_1 :— |d :d |— .t_1,l_1 :t_1 |d :d |t_1 :l_1 |l_1 :se_1
Lord, have mer - cy up - on us, and write all these Thy
m :— |— :l |s :m |l :m |f :r |s :s |s :m |m :— .m
l_1 :— |— :l_1 |m :— |l_1 :l_1 |r :— |d :d |s_1 :l_1 |m_1 :— .m_1

we be - seech
l_1 :d .d |t_1 :l_1 |— .l_1 :se_1 |l_1 :f |— :m |r :— |de :—
l_1 :s_1 .s_1 |s_1 :m_1 .f_1 |m_1 :— |m_1 :l_1 |— :l_1 |l_1 :— |l_1 :—
laws in our hearts, we be - seech Thee, we be - seech Thee.
m :m .m |r :d .t_1 |t_1 :— |de :r |— :m |f :r |m :—
l_1 :m_1 .m_1 |s_1 :d_1 .r_1 |m_1 :— |l_1 :r_1 |— :de_1 |r_1 :— |l_1 :—

722

St. Matthew v.

BLESSED are the poor in spirit : for theirs is the Kingdom of heaven.

Doh = G.

```
p                                  pp                      Ancient Tone.
d  :—  |d  :d  |r  :—  |  :d .d   |d  :—  |l, :t, |d  :—  ||
s, :—  |s, :s, |s, :—  |  :s, .s, |s, :—  |l, :s, |s, :—  ||
Grant   us  this grace,    we be-  seech   Thee, O  Lord.
m  :—  |m  :m  |t, :—  |  :d .d   |d  :—  |f  :r  |m  :—  ||
d  :—  |d  :d  |s, :—  |  :m, .m, |m, :—  |f, :s, |d, :—  ||
```

Blessed are they that mourn : for they shall be comforted.

Grant us this grace, we beseech Thee, O Lord.

Blessed are the meek : for they shall inherit the earth.

Grant us this grace, we beseech Thee, O Lord.

Blessed are they which do hunger and thirst after righteousness : for they shall be filled.

Grant us this grace, we beseech Thee, O Lord.

Blessed are the merciful : for they shall obtain mercy.

Grant us this grace, we beseech Thee, O Lord.

Blessed are the pure in heart : for they shall see God.

Grant us this grace, we beseech Thee, O Lord.

Blessed are the peacemakers : for they shall be called the children of God.

Grant us this grace, we beseech Thee, O Lord.

Blessed are they which are persecuted for righteousness' sake : for theirs is the Kingdom of heaven.

```
p                                         pp rall.
d  :d  |d  :d .d   |r  :—   |  :d .d   |d  :—  |l, :t, |d  :—  ||
s, :s, |s, :s, .s, |s, :—   |  :s, .s, |s, :—  |l, :s, |s, :—  ||
Write these words in our hearts,  we be-  seech   Thee, O  Lord.
m  :m  |m  :m .m   |t, :—   |  :d .d   |d  :—  |f  :r  |m  :—  ||
d  :d  |d  :d .d   |s, :—   |  :m, .m, |m, :—  |f, :s, |d, :—  ||
```

723

FIRST FORM.

St. Matthew vi. 9–13.

Doh = G.

Org. d :—	*p* Doh	Doh	*cres.* Doh	Doh
	Our Fáther which art in heáven,	Hallowed be Thy Náme.	Thy Kingdom come.	Thy will be done in eárth,

Doh	Doh	Doh
as it is in heáven.	Give us this day our daily breád.	And forgive us our débts,

Doh	*pp* Doh	(cres.) Doh
As wé forgive our débtors.	And leád us not into temptation,	but deliver us from évil:

mf Doh	*f* Doh	Doh	Doh	Doh
For Thine is the Kingdom,	and the pówer, and the glóry,	for éver.	A	- men.

SECOND FORM.

Doh = F. JOHN MERBECKE, 1523–*c.* 1585.

m :— | m m m | m m m f f | m m r m r d

Our Fa - ther, which art in hea - ven, Hal - low - ed be thy Name.

| r d r m | m f r m r d | r r d r m m

Thy King-dom come. Thy will be done in earth as it is in hea - ven,

| m r m f m m r r | r r r d r m r r

Give us this day our dai - ly bread. And for - give us our tres - pass - es,

| r r r r d r m r d r r | l, d r r r m r r d

as we for-give them that tres-pass a-gainst us. And lead us not in - to temp-ta-tion,

| d r r r d r r d | l, d r r m r

but de - liv - er us from e - vil: For Thine is the King-dom,

| r r r d r r d | d r d r r d || d r —

the pow - er, and the glo - ry, for ev - er and ev - er. A - men.

724 THE APOSTLES' CREED

Doh = G.

Org. d :—	Doh	Doh	Doh
	I belíeve	in Gód the Father Almíghty,	Maker of heáven and éarth;

Doh	Doh
And in Jésus Christ His only Són our Lórd,	Who was concéived by the Holy Ghóst,

Doh	Doh	Doh
Bórn of the Virgin Máry,	Súffered under Pontius Pilate,	Was crúcified, deád, and búried;

Doh	Doh
He descénded into héll;	The thírd day He róse again from the déad;

Doh	Doh
He ascénded into héaven,	And sítteth on the ríght hand of Gód the Fáther Almíghty;

Doh	Doh
From thénce He shall cóme	to júdge the qúick and the déad.

Doh	Doh	Doh
I belìeve in the Holy Ghóst;	The hóly Catholic Chúrch;	The Commúnion of Sáints;

Doh	Doh	Doh	Doh	Doh
The Forgíveness of sins;	The Resurréction of the body;	And the Life everlásting.	A -	men.

725 THE NICENE CREED.

Lah = D. Doh = F. *In free rhythm.* JOHN MERBECKE, 1523–*c.* 1585.

| l, l, d r r m | m m m f s m
I be - lieve in one God the Fa - ther Al - migh - ty,

| r d r m m d t, | l, t, d r r t, t,
Mak - er of hea - ven and earth, And of all things vi - si - ble

d t, l, l, l, | d d r m f r m
and in - vi - si - ble: And in one Lord Je - sus Christ,

| m m m f s m l l s | m m m d r
the on - ly - be - got - ten Son of God, Be - got - ten of His

m l, t, d l, l, | m r m | m r m
Fa - ther be - fore all worlds, God of God, Light of Light,

| d r m s f f m | d r r t, d
Ve - ry God of Ve - ry God, Be - got - ten, not made,

| l, l, t, d r l, r d t, l, | m r d s f m
Be - ing of one sub-stance with the Fa - ther, By whom all things were made:

| d r m d l, d r t, d l, | m m r m m
Who for us men, and for our sal - va - tion, came down from hea - ven,

| l, t, d r r r r m f s m m r d f m
And was in - car - nate by the Ho - ly Ghost of the Vir - gin Ma - ry,

| d r m d | l, d r r t, r d l, l, m m
And was made man, And was cru - ci - fied al - so for us un - der

m m r m d | r m m m m r m m l,
Pon - ti - us Pi - late. He suf - fer - ed and was bu - ri - ed,

THE NICENE CREED

l_1 t_1 d r r s f m r d l_1 d t_1 l_1 l_1
And the third day He rose a - gain ac - cord -ing to the Scrip-tures,

m f s m f s l l | s m m m r
And as - cend - ed in - to hea - ven, And sit - teth on the

m d r d t_1 l_1 | m m m d r m r s m
right hand of the Fa - ther. And He shall come a - gain with glo - ry

m m r t_1 d t_1 l_1 l_1 | d r r t_1 d t_1 l_1
to judge both the quick and the dead : Whose King-dom shall have no end.

m m r m d r m m m | r m f s s m m
And I be - lieve in the Ho - ly Ghost, the Lord and Giv-er of Life,

l_1 t_1 d r m f s m l l s | m m m
Who pro - ceed - eth from the Fa - ther and the Son, Who with the

s f m r m f m m d r r t_1 d t_1 l_1 l_1
Fa - ther and the Son to - ge - ther is wor - ship - ped and glo - ri - fied,

d r m f r d | m l l s m
Who spake by the Pro - phets. And I be - lieve one

f f f r r d r m m m m
Ho - ly Ca - tho - lic and A - pos - to - lic Church.

d d r d r m m l_1 d t_1 d l_1 t_1 l_1
I ac - know-ledge one Bap - tism for the re - mis - sion of sins.

d r m r r m f s m r r d
And I look for the Re - sur - rec - tion of the dead,

m m s m r d t_1 l_1 || s_1 | l_1 ||
And the Life of the world to come. A - men.

COUNCIL OF NICÆA, A.D. 325.

726

Doh = B♭.

Henry Lawes, 1596–1662.

s_1 :— | m :r | d :— || s_1 :— | l_1 :s_1 | f_1 :f_1 | m_1 :— ||
m_1 :— | s_1 :f_1 | m_1 :— || d_1 :— | d_1 :d_1 | d_1 :t_2 | d_1 :— ||
d :— | d :t_1 | d :— || d :— | f_1 :s_1 | l_1 :f_1 | s_1 :— ||
d_1 :— | d :s_1 | l_1 :— || m_1 :— | f_1 :m_1 | r_1 :r_1 | d_1 :— ||

s_1 :— | s_1 :fe_1 | s_1 :— || l_1 :— | f :m | r :r | d :— ||
m_1 :— | r_1 :r_1 | r_1 :— || f_1 :— | f_1 :s_1 | s_1 :-.f_1 | m_1 :— ||
d :— | r :d | t_1 :— || d :— | t_1 :d | d :t_1 | d :— ||
d :— | t_1 :l_1 | s_1 :— || f_1 :— | r_1 :d_1 | s_1 :s_1 | d_1 :— ||

Ecclesiasticus xliv. *πατέρων ὕμνος.*

LET us now praise | famous | men : || and our | fathers | that be- | gat us. ||

2 The Lord hath wrought great | glory ✝ by them : || through His great | power | from the be- | ginning. ||

3 Such as did bear rule in their kingdoms, men re- | nowned · for their | power : ||

4 Giving counsel by their under- | standing · and de- | claring | prophe-cies : ||

5 Leaders of the people by their counsels, and by their knowledge of learning | meet for the | people : || wise and | eloquent | in their in- | structions : ||

6 Such as found out | musical | tunes : || and re- | cited | verses in | writing : ||

7 Rich men | furnished · with a- | bility : || living | peaceably | in their · habi- | tations : ||

8 All these were honoured in their generations, and were the | glory · of their | times. ||

9 There be of them that have left a name behind them that their | praises | might be re- | ported : ||

And some there be which | have no me- | morial ; ||

Who are perished, as | though · they had | never | been, ||

2nd part of the Chant. 10 And are become as though they had | never been | born : || and their | children | after | them. ||

11 But these were | merciful | men : || whose righteousness | hath not | been for- | gotten. ||

12 With their seed shall continually remain a | good in- | heritance : || their | children · are with- | in the | cove-nant. ||

13 Their | seed · standeth | fast : || and their | children | for their | sakes. ||

14 Their seed shall re- | main for | ever : || and their | glory shall · not be | blotted | out. ||

15 Their bodies are | buried in | peace : || but their name | liveth for | ever- | more. ||

16 The people will | tell of their | wisdom : || and the congre- | gation · will shew | forth their | praise. ||

727 *Numbers* vi.

Arranged by LOWELL MASON, 1792–1872.

Doh = G. *Moderately slow.*

```
:d  |m  :—  |r  :r .r  |d  :—  |d  :d  |m  :m .m  |m  :d
:m, |s, :—  |s, :s,.f, |m, :l, |s, :m, |s, :s,.s, |s, :s,
The  Lord    bless thee, and keep    thee : the  Lord make His face to
:d  |d  :—  |d  :t,.t, |d  :f  |m  :d  |d  :d .d  |d  :d
:d, |d  :—  |s, :s,.s, |l, :f, |d, :d, |d  :d .d  |d  :m,
```

```
|d  :l, |s, :s, |d  :m  |r  :r     |d  :d  |d  :d
|l, :f, |m, :m, |s, :s, |s, :s,.f, |m, :l, |s, :m,
shine up - on thee, and be  gra - cious un - to thee : the
|d  :d  |d  :d  |d  :d  |d  :t,    |d  :f  |m  :d
|f, :f, |d, :d, |m, :d, |s, :s,    |l, :f, |d, :d,
```

```
|m  :d  |s, :m  |f  .,f  :f  .f  |m  :m  .m
|s, :m, |m, :s, |l, .,l, :l, .s, |s, :l, .l,
Lord lift  up His   coun-te - nance up - on  thee, and
|d  :d  |d  :d  |d  .,d  :d  .r  |d  :d  .d
|d  :d  |d  :d  |l, .,l, :l, .t, |d  :l, .l,
```

```
|r  :r       |d  ||d  |d  ||
|l, :s, .f,  |m, ||f, |m, ||
give thee     peace. A - men.
|d  :t,      |d  ||l, |s, ||
|f, :s,      |d, ||f, |d, ||
```

Unison. With reverence.

Doh = E♭. *mf* JOHN MORGAN LLOYD, 1880–

```
:  .m |m  :m  .m |  .m :m  .m |—  .m
   The Lord bless thee,  and keep thee : the
:f .s |l  :s .f |m  :d |r  :m |l, .l, :  |
Lord    make His face to  shine up - on thee,
```

Harmony.

Bb.t. f.Eb.

```
:m .m  |s d   :t, .l,  |t,    :t,     |l m  :—  |     : .m
:d .d  |t m,  :se, .l, |l,    :se,    |l m  :—  |     : .m
 and be  gra  -  cious   un  -  to      thee:              the
:l .l  |s d   :m       |f     :m .r   |de se :— |     : .m
:l, .l,|m l₂  :d,      |r,    :m,     |l m  :—  |     : .m
```

```
|m    :—   |s    :s .s    |d .,d :d .d      |m .m :   .m
|m    :—   |t,   :t, .t,  |l, .,l, :l, .l,  |s, .s, : .t,
 Lord       lift   up His   coun-te - nance up - on thee,  and
|s    :—   |s    :f .f    |m .,m :m .m      |m .m :   .s
|d    :—   |s,   :s, .s,  |l, .,l, :l, .l,  |m, .m, : .m
```

cres.

```
|r   :m  |f   :m .r  |m   :—  |—   :m  |f   :s
|t,  :d  |r   :l,    |t,  :r  |d   :m  |f   :s
 give         thee     peace.       A  -   -  -  men,
|s   :—  |l   :l     |se  :—  |l   :m  |f   :s
|s   :m  |r   :f     |m   :—  |l,  :m  |f   :s
```

dim. *pp*

```
|l  :s .f |s  :—  |—  :—  |d   :—   |f   :—  |m   :—  ||
|l  :s .f |s  :—  |—  :—  |d   :t,  |l,  :—  |s,  :—  ||
 A  -  -   men,            A  -  -  -  -      men.
|l  :s .f |s  :—  |—  :—  |m   :—   |f   :—  |s   :—  ||
|l  :s .f |s  :—  |—  :—  |l,  :s,  |f,  :—  |d   :—  ||
```

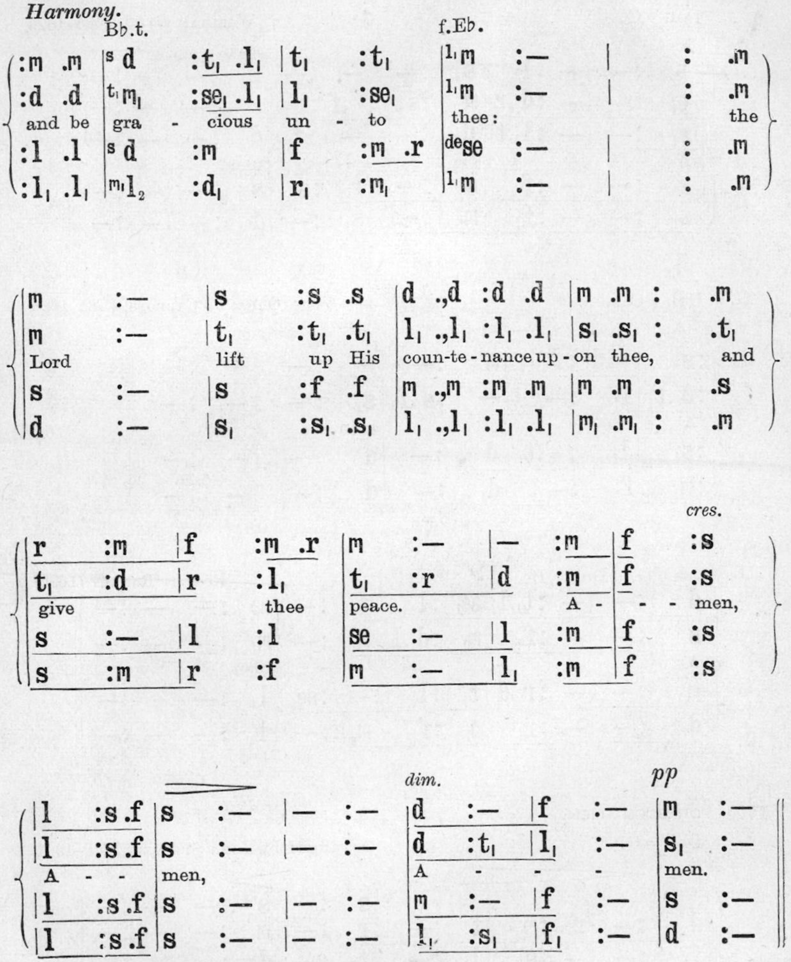

[*Copyright*, 1927, *by Oxford University Press.*]

728

I. Doh = C. WILLIAM BYRD, 1538–1623.

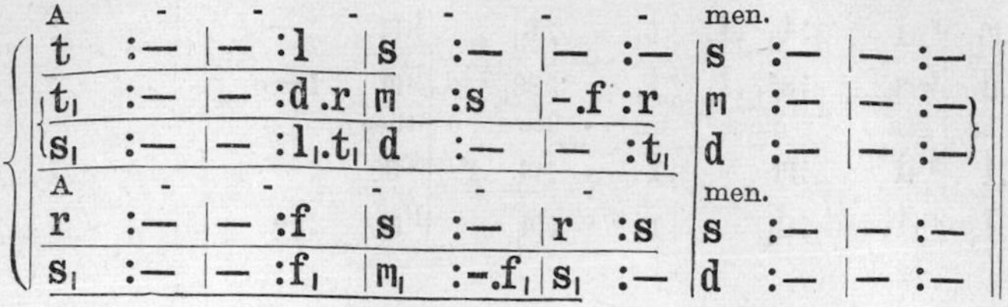

A - - - - - - men.
t :— |— :l |s :— |— :— |s :— |— :—
t_1 :— |— :d .r |m :s |—.f :r |m :— |— :—
s_1 :— |— :l_1.t_1 |d :— |— :t_1 |d :— |— :—
A - - - - - men.
r :— |— :f |s :— |r :s |s :— |— :—
s_1 :— |— :f_1 |m_1 :—.f_1 |s_1 :— |d :— |— :—

II. Doh = G. ORLANDO GIBBONS, 1585–1625.

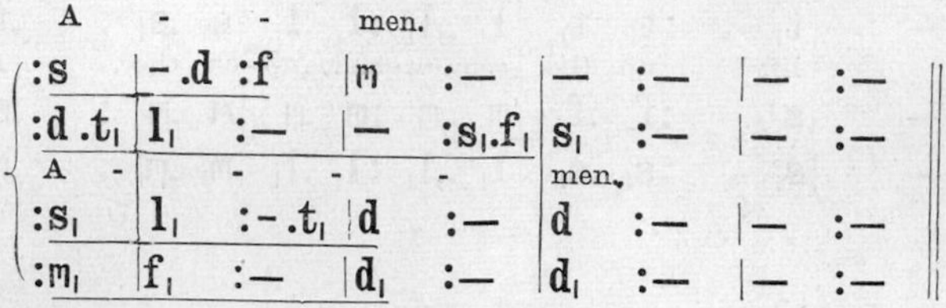

A - - men.
:s |—.d :f |m :— |— :— |— :—
:d .t_1 |l_1 :— |— :s_1.f_1 |s_1 :— |— :—
A - - - - men.
:s_1 |l_1 :—.t_1 |d :— |d :— |— :—
:m_1 |f_1 :— |d_1 :— |d_1 :— |— :—

III. Lah = G. Doh = B♭. ROBERT RAMSEY (1635).

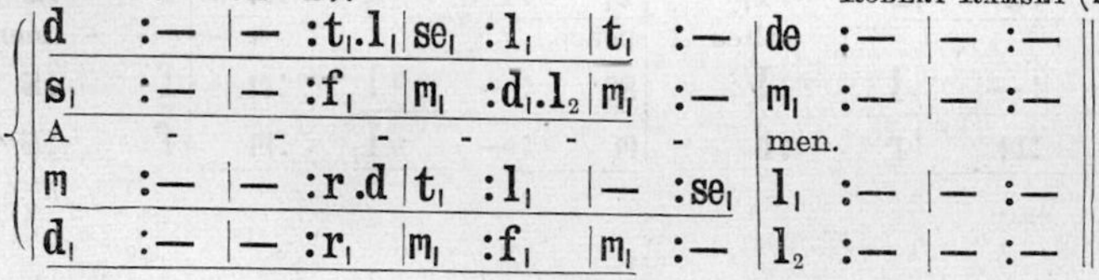

d :— |— :t_1.l_1 |se_1 :l_1 |t_1 :— |de :— |— :—
s_1 :— |— :f_1 |m_1 :d_1.l_2 |m_1 :— |m_1 :— |— :—
A - - - - - - men.
m :— |— :r .d |t_1 :l_1 |— :se_1 |l_1 :— |— :—
d_1 :— |— :r_1 |m_1 :f_1 |m_1 :— |l_2 :— |— :—

IV. DRESDEN AMEN.

Doh = G. Arranged by JOHN STAINER, 1840–1901.

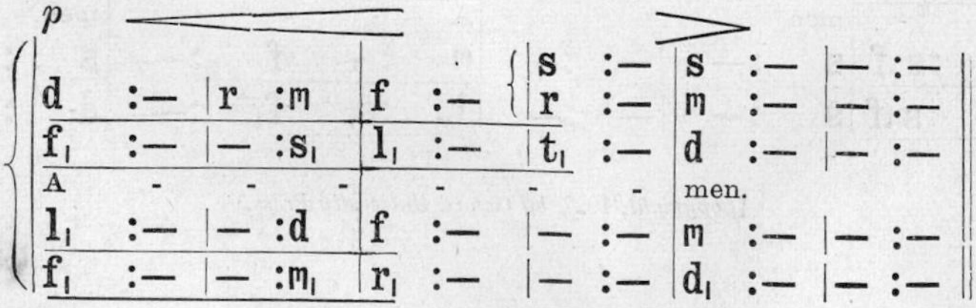

p < >
d :— |r :m |f :— |{s :— / r :—} |s :— / m :— |— :—
f_1 :— |— :s_1 |l_1 :— |t_1 :— |d :— |— :—
A - - - - - - men.
l_1 :— |— :d |f :— |— :— |m :— |— :—
f_1 :— |— :m_1 |r_1 :— |— :— |d_1 :— |— :—

[*By permission of Novello & Co., Ltd.*]

THREEFOLD AMEN.

Doh = A♭. Danish.

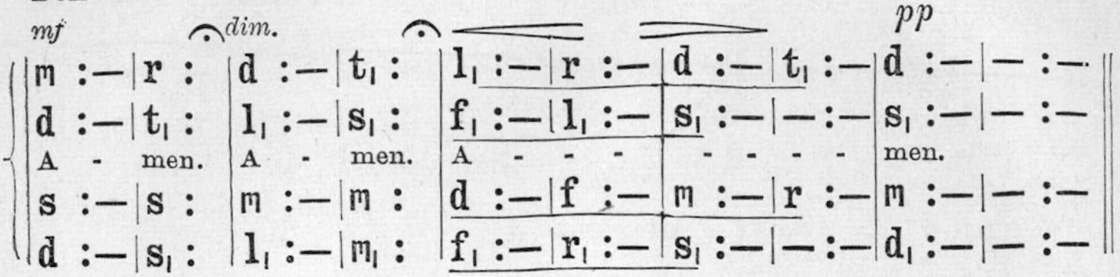

```
mf          dim.                                        pp
| m  :— | r  : | d  :— | t, : | l, :— | r  :— | d  :— | t, :— | d  :— | — :— ||
| d  :— | t, : | l, :— | s, : | f, :— | l, :— | s, :— | —  :— | s, :— | — :— ||
  A  -   men.    A  -   men.    A  -    -  -    -  -    -  -    men.
| s  :— | s  : | m  :— | m  : | d  :— | f  :— | m  :— | r  :— | m  :— | — :— ||
| d  :— | s, : | l, :— | m, : | f, :— | r, :— | s, :— | —  :— | d, :— | — :— ||
```

SEVENFOLD AMEN.

Doh = A. JOHN STAINER, 1840–1901.

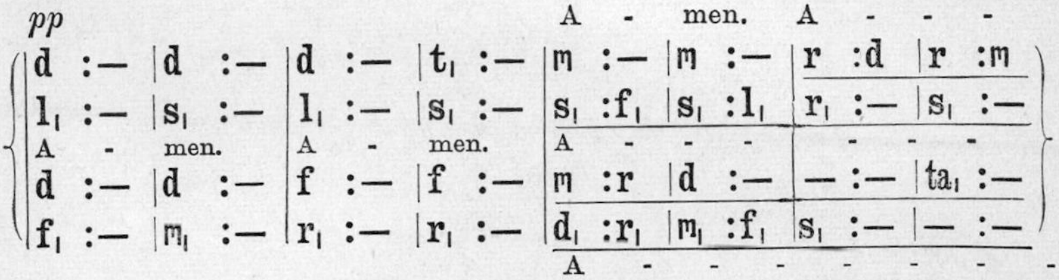

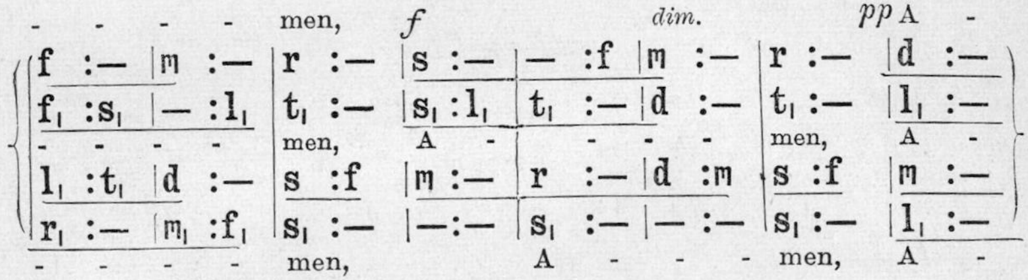

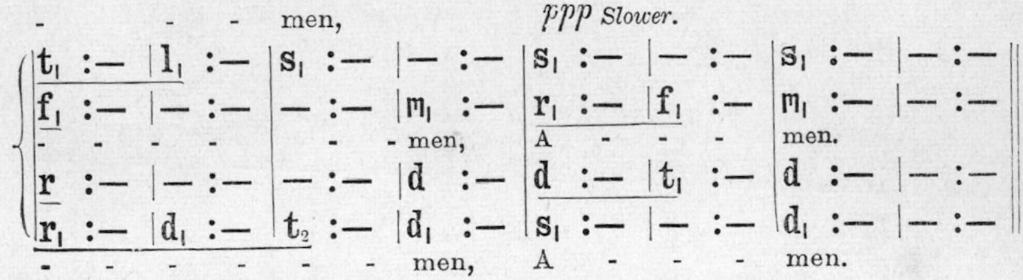

```
pp                                      cres.
                                          A   -   men.    A   -   -   -
| d  :— | d  :— | d  :— | t, :— | m  :—  | m  :—  | r  :d  | r  :m  |
| l, :— | s, :— | l, :— | s, :— | s, :f, | s, :l, | r, :—  | s, :—  |
  A  -   men.    A  -   men.      A  -     -  -     -  -     -  -
| d  :— | d  :— | f  :— | f  :— | m  :r  | d  :—  | —  :—  | ta, :— |
| f, :— | m, :— | r, :— | r, :— | d, :r, | m, :f, | s, :—  | —  :—  |
                                  A  -   -   -   -   -   -   -   -
```

```
  -  -   -  -   men,    f                  dim.              pp A  -
| f  :—  | m  :—  | r  :— | s  :—  | —  :f | m  :—  | r  :— | d  :— |
| f, :s, | —  :l, | t, :— | s, :l, | t, :— | d  :—  | t, :— | l, :— |
  -  -   -  -     men,    A  -      -  -   -  -     men,    A  -
| l, :t, | d  :—  | s  :f | m  :—  | r  :— | d  :m  | s  :f | m  :— |
| r, :—  | m, :f, | s, :— | —  :—  | s, :— | —  :—  | s, :— | l, :— |
  -  -   -  -     men,             A  -   -  -     men,    A  -
```

```
  -  -   -  -   men,             ppp Slower.
| t, :— | l, :— | s,  :— | —  :— | s, :— | —  :— | s, :— | — :— ||
| f, :— | —  :— | —   :— | m, :— | r, :— | f, :— | m, :— | — :— ||
  -  -   -  -    -   -   men,     A  -   -  -     men.
| r  :— | —  :— | —   :— | d  :— | d  :— | t, :— | d  :— | — :— ||
| r, :— | d, :— | t,, :— | d, :— | s, :— | —  :— | d, :— | — :— ||
  -  -   -  -    -   -   men,     A  -   -  -     men.
```

[*By permission of Novello & Co., Ltd.*]

HYMNS FOR THE YOUNG

The following hymns are suggested as suitable for use as Hymns for the Young in Public Worship, and in Sunday Schools, Bible Classes, Guilds, and other meetings for the young. Hymns marked * are more suitable for Children, those marked † for Adolescents.

Ancient Hymns and Canticles

ALPHABETICAL INDEX OF TUNES

* *Denotes that the tune has at the numbers so marked a Faux-bourdon or alternative setting.*

Where the name of a tune appears in alphabetical order in brackets, the tune is indexed elsewhere under another name.

Brackets at a number indicate a hymn at which the tune is referred to by cross-reference.

METRICAL INDEX OF TUNES

The numbers in brackets refer to hymns for which the tune is suggested by cross-reference.
** Denotes that the tune has a Faux-bourdon or alternative setting.*

St. Mary, 401.
(St. Matthias), 433, 558.
St. Paul, 481.
St. Peter, (306), 419.
St. Stephen (Abridge), 483.
Salisbury, 296.
Salzburg, 562.
Sidon, 549.
Song 67 (St. Matthias), 433, 558.
Southwark, 166, (365).
Southwell, 418.
Spohr, 451.
Springtide Hour, 653.
Stracathro, 451, (457).
Tallis, 353.
This endris nyght, 595.
Tiverton, 57.
University, (139), 498.
Walsall, 148.
Warwick, 385.
Westminster, 27.
Wetherby, 513.
Wigtown, 406.
Winchester, (42), 181, *385.
(Windsor), 276.

Double Common Metre (d.c.m.)

Evangel, 42.
First Mode Melody, 433.
Forest Green, 612.
Kingsfold, 74.
Leyden, 644.
Noel, 47.
Northumberland, 531.
Old 22nd, 486.
Old 44th, 530.
Old 81st, 355.
Old 137th, 643.
Pentatone, 446.
Petersham, 398, 528.
Psalm 107, 151.
St. Asaph, 223.
St. Matthew, 86.
St. Sylvester, 559.
St. Ursula, 355.
Third Mode Melody, 559.
Vox dilecti, 410.
Yattendon, 528.

Long Metre (l.m.)

Abends, 292.
Ach bleib bei uns, 278.
Aeterna Christi munera, 4.
Affection, 471.
Agincourt Song, 634.
Alstone, 516.
Andernach, 230.
(Angels' Song), 651.
Angelus, 277.
Babylon's Streams, 366.
Breslau, 501.
Bristol, 472, 628.
Brockham (Confidence), 3, (25).
Bromley, 311.
Brynteg, 623.
Cathcart, 383.
Christe Redemptor omnium, 421.
Church Triumphant, 25.
Commandments, 305.
(Communion), *106, 312.
(Confidence), 3, (25).
Crasselius, 92.
Danby, 623.
Das Leiden des Herrn, 5.
Das walt' Gott Vater, 89.
Deus Tuorum militum, 356.
Doversdale, 639.
Duke Street, 517.
Eisenach, 241, (254).
Ely 334.
Finnart, 491.
Galilee, 647.
Gonfalon Royal, 23, (383).
Heaton Norris, 499.
Herongate, 550.
Herr Gott Vater, 292.
Herr Jesu Christ, 254.
Hesperus, 501.
Hierapolis, 239.
Holley, 550.
Hope, 522.
Hursley, 292.
Hymnus eucharisticus, 471.
Iam lucis, 258.
(Intercession), 305.
Jesu dulcis memoria, 420.
Kent, 225.
Lichfield, 340.
Llandaf, 247.
Lledrod (Llangollen), 634.
Llef, 161.
Ludborough, 188.
Mainzer, 333, 367.
Maryton, 420, (472).
Melcombe, (239), 259, 646, (649).
Morning Hymn, 256.
O amor quam exstaticus, 143.
O grant us light, 466.
O Lux beata Trinitas, 4.
Ober Ammergau, *and refrain*, 92.
Old 100th, *229, 656, 709.
Ombersley, 24.
Pentecost, 517.
Plaistow, 491.
Rivaulx, 5.
Rockingham (Communion), *106, 312.
St. Alkmund (Intercession), 305.
St. Anselm, 386.
St. Bartholomew, 672.
St. Cross, 96.
St. Olave, 257.
St. Venantius, 142.
Sarratt, 436.
Soldau, 140, 185.
Solemnis haec festivitas, 78.
Solothurn, 436.
Song 34 (Angels' Song), 651.
Tallis' Canon, *291.
Thanksgiving, 339.
Truro, 369, 647.
Uffingham, 275, 649.
Veni Creator, 182.
Verbum supernum, 188.
Vom Himmel hoch, 56.
Wainwright, 473.
Walton, 109, (366).
Wareham, (140), 253, 607.
Warrington, 388.
Whitehall, 297.
Winscott, (259), 338, (460).
Woolmer's, 275.

Double Long Metre (d.l.m.)

Cantate Domino, 128.
Firmament, 10.
Jerusalem, 640.
Psalm 86, 460.

FAUX-BOURDONS

ALTERNATIVE VERSIONS

PLAINSONG MELODIES

SPECIAL SETTINGS

INDEX OF COMPOSERS, ARRANGERS AND SOURCES OF TUNES

* *Denotes a Faux-bourdon or arrangement by the person named.*

INDEX OF AUTHORS, TRANSLATORS, AND SOURCES

* *Denotes a translation by the person named.*

INDEX OF AUTHORS, TRANSLATORS, AND SOURCES

GENERAL INDEX

**Denotes a tune with a Faux-bourdon or alternative arrangement.*
Brackets indicate that the first line in some collections begins thus.

GENERAL INDEX

GENERAL INDEX

GENERAL INDEX

GENERAL INDEX

GENERAL INDEX

GENERAL INDEX

GENERAL INDEX

GENERAL INDEX

PRINTED IN
GREAT BRITAIN
AT THE
UNIVERSITY PRESS
OXFORD
BY
CHARLES BATEY
PRINTER
TO THE
UNIVERSITY